THE
ITALIAN
KITCHEN
BIBLE

THE
ITALIAN
KITCHEN
BIBLE

KATE WHITEMAN, JENI WRIGHT
AND ANGELA BOGGIANO

HERMES HOUSE

This edition published published by Hermes House
an imprint of
Anness Publishing Limited
Hermes House
88-89 Blackfriars Road
London SE1 8HA

A CIP catalogue record for this book is available from the British Library.

Publisher: Joanna Lorenz
Senior Editor: Linda Fraser
Designer: Siân Keogh
Photographers: William Adams-Lingwood and Janine Hosegood (cut-outs)
Home Economist: Lucy McKelvie, assisted by Sophie Wheeler
Stylist: Marian Price

Previously published as *The Italian Ingredients Cookbook* and *The Italian Kitchen*

Printed and bound in Singapore

© Anness Publishing Limited 1997, 2000
Updated © 2002
1 3 5 7 9 10 8 6 4 2

NOTES

For all recipes, quantities are given in both metric and imperial measures and, where appropriate,
measures are also given in standard cups and spoons. Follow one set, but not a mixture,
because they are not interchangeable.

Standard spoon and cup measures are level.
1 tsp = 5ml, 1 tbsp = 15ml, 1 cup = 250ml/8fl oz

Australian standard tablespoons are 20ml. Australian readers should use 3 tsp in place of 1 tbsp
for measuring small quantities of gelatine, cornflour, salt, etc.

Medium eggs are used unless otherwise stated.

Contents

Introduction

Italian cookery reflects the fact that the country was unified only in 1861. Until then, each region produced its own characteristic cuisine, relying exclusively on ingredients that could be gathered, cultivated or reared locally. Nowadays, of course, regional produce can be easily transported all over the country, but Italians still prefer to base their cooking on local ingredients, because they regard quality and freshness as more important than diversity and innovation. So the most flavoursome sun–ripened tomatoes, aubergines and peppers are still found in the south, the freshest seafood is on offer along the coast, the finest hams come from the area where the pigs are raised, and so on. *La cucina italiana* remains distinctly regional; northern Italian cooking, for example, incorporates ingredients that are simply never found in the recipes of Sicily and Naples, and vice-versa. In the dairy-farming north, butter is used in place of the olive oil so prevalent in the south; bread and polenta are eaten instead of pasta. The only unifying feature is the insistence on high quality ingredients. Good food has always been essential to the Italian way of life. *La cucina italiana* is one of the oldest cooking cultures in the world, dating back to the ancient Greeks and perhaps even earlier. The Romans adored food and

THIS ITALIAN BUTCHER'S SHOP (BELOW) NOT ONLY SELLS THE LOCAL *CINGHIALE* (WILD BOAR), BUT ALSO CURED MEATS, CHEESES AND OTHER ESSENTIAL COOKING INGREDIENTS.

often ate and drank to excess; it was they who really laid the foundations of Italian and European cuisine. The early Romans were peasant farmers who ate only the simple, rustic foods they could produce, like grain, cheeses and olives. For them, meat was an unheard-of luxury; animals were bred to work in the fields and were too precious to eat. Trading links with other parts of the world, however, encouraged Roman farmers to cultivate new vegetables and fruits and, of course, vines, while their trade in salt and exotic spices enabled them to preserve and pickle all kinds of meat, game and fish. Food became a near-obsession and ever more elaborate dishes were devised to be served at the decadent and orgiastic banquets for which the Romans were famed. The decline and fall of the Roman Empire led inevitably to a deterioration in the quality of cooking and a return to simple, basic foods. For centuries, regional cuisine reverted to its original uncomplicated style. With the Renaissance, however, came great wealth and a new interest in elaborate food. Once again, rich families strove to outdo each other with lavish banquets where courses of rich, extravagant foods were served – truffles, song–birds, game, desserts dripping with honey and spices – all washed down with quantities of wine. The poor, of course, continued to subsist on the simple foods they had

OLIVES (TOP) GROWING IN GROVES ALONG-SIDE GRAPE VINES ON AN UMBRIAN HILLSIDE, AND A SELECTION OF CURED SAUSAGES AND AIR-DRIED *PROSCIUTTO* HANGING IN STORE (ABOVE) ARE JUST TWO OF THE VAST ARRAY OF TRADITIONAL ITALIAN INGREDIENTS THAT ARE NOW EXPORTED AROUND THE WORLD.

ITALIAN COOKS INSIST ON HIGH-QUALITY COOKING INGREDIENTS AND EVEN LOCAL DELICATESSENS (RIGHT) ARE PACKED FULL OF FRESH AND PRESERVED INGREDIENTS AND OTHER FOODS – FRUITY CAKES AND CRISP BISCUITS, SUCH AS *PANFORTE* AND *CANTUCCI*, DRIED *FAGIOLI* (BEANS), FLAVOURFUL OLIVE OILS AND VINEGARS, *PROSCIUTTO CRUDO* (CURED HAMS), TRADITIONAL CHEESES, SUCH AS *PARMIGIANO REGGIANO,* PICKLES AND PRESERVES, MARINATED OLIVES, CANNED TOMATOES AND BOTTLED SAUCES.

THE SUN-DRENCHED SOUTHERN REGIONS OF ITALY PROVIDE ESSENTIAL STORE CUPBOARD INGREDIENTS, SUCH AS FULL-FLAVOURED GREEN AND BLACK OLIVES AND DELICIOUS SUN-DRIED TOMATOES.

always eaten, but the wealthier middle classes developed a taste for fine foods and created their own bourgeois dishes. The finer features of Italian cooking even reached the French, when Catherine de' Medici went to Paris to marry the future Henri II, taking fifty of her own cooks with her. They introduced new ingredients and cooking techniques to France and in return learnt the art of French cuisine. In those regions of Italy which border France, you can still find reciprocal influences of French classical cooking, but, generally speaking, Italians do not like elaborately sauced dishes, preferring to let the natural flavours of their raw ingredients speak for themselves.

The essence of Italian cooking today is simplicity. The Italian way of cooking fish is a good example of this. In coastal areas, freshly caught fish is most often simply chargrilled over hot coals, then served with nothing more than a splash of extra virgin olive oil, a wedge of lemon and freshly ground black pepper. Recipes like *carpaccio di tonno*, in which the fish is so delicious raw that cooking seems unnecessary, and *branzino al forno*, where the delicate flavour of fennel is used to compliment rather than obscure the fresh taste of the fish, are typically simple, as is *grigliata di calamari*, squid chargrilled with chillies to reflect its robust character.

Italians learn to appreciate good food when they are young children, and eating is one of the major pleasures of the day, no matter what the day of the week or time of the year. Witness an Italian family gathered around the Sunday lunch table in a local restaurant, and consider how the Italian menu of *antipasto* followed by pasta, rice or gnocchi, then fish, meat and vegetables served in sequence is devised so that each can be savoured separately – both the food and the occasion are to be enjoyed as long as possible. The first course, or *antipasto*, is a unique feature. In restaurants, this can be a vast array of different dishes, both hot and cold, from which diners can choose as few or as many as they wish. At home with the family, it is more likely to be a slice or two of *salami* or *prosciutto crudo* with fresh figs or melon if these are in season. But no matter how humble or grand the setting or the occasion, the *antipasto* is always visually tempting. Dishes like *bruschetta casalinga* and *peperoni arrostiti con pesto*, which look so attractive, are typical in this way.

The variety and diversity of the Italian ingredients available in supermarkets and delicatessens will surely inspire you to concoct any number of delicious meals, from a simple dish of pasta to a full-blown four-course dinner. A plate of *antipasto* followed by pasta or risotto flavoured with seasonal ingredients, then simply-cooked meat or fish and finally a local cheese and fruit make a veritable feast. You could prepare a different meal along these lines every day of the year and almost never repeat the same combination. If you visit Italy, avail yourself of the wonderful local ingredients to prepare a menu full of the flavours of the region. Every area has its own special delights that make cooking a real pleasure.

FRESH INGREDIENTS ARE HIGHLY PRIZED BY ITALIAN COOKS AND ARE OFTEN SOLD FROM THE LOCAL OUTDOOR MARKETS: DOZENS OF *CARCIOFI* (GLOBE ARTICHOKES) ARE TIED READY FOR TRANSPORT TO A LOCAL MARKET (BELOW), AND AN OUTDOOR STALL IS PILED HIGH WITH A TYPICALLY WIDE SELECTION OF HIGH-QUALITY FRESH HERBS AND SALAD LEAVES, VEGETABLES AND FRUITS (BOTTOM).

The Ingredients

Italian cooks have traditionally relied on local ingredients – whatever could be gathered, cultivated or reared locally. Today, our supermarkets and delicatessens are full of these flavourful, good-quality ingredients. This comprehensive guide provides essential information on the huge range of Italian foods and shows you how to prepare and cook them.

Pasta

If there is one ingredient that sums up the essence of Italian cooking, it must surely be pasta, that wonderfully simple and nutritious staple that can be formed into an almost infinite variety of shapes and sizes. In Italy, pasta is an essential part of every full meal and does not constitute a meal on its own. Il primo, *as the pasta course is known, is eaten between the* antipasto *(appetizer) and* il secondo *(the main course). Sometimes small pasta shapes are served in soup as* pasta in brodo. *There are two basic types of pasta,* pastasciutta *(dried) and* pasta fresca *(fresh).*

Dried pasta is nowadays factory-made. The dough is made from hard durum wheat, which produces an elastic dough, ideal for shaping into literally hundreds of different forms, from long, thin spaghetti to elaborate spirals and frilly, bow-shaped *farfalle*. Basic pasta dough is made only from durum wheat and water, although it is sometimes enriched with eggs (*pasta all'uovo*), which add an attractive yellow tinge, or coloured and flavoured with ingredients like spinach (*pasta verde*) or squid ink (*pasta nera*). These traditional flavourings are more successful than modern gimmicky creations such as chocolate-flavoured pasta. (Most Italians would throw up their hands in horror at this unauthentic folly.) Dried pasta has a nutty flavour and should always retain a firm texture when cooked. It is generally used for thinner-textured, more robust sauces.

Fresh pasta is usually made by hand, using superfine plain white flour enriched with eggs. Unlike dried pasta dough, it can be easily kneaded and is very malleable. Fresh pasta is often wrapped round a stuffing of meat, fish, vegetables or cheese to make ravioli, tortelli or cappelletti, or layered with sauce and meat or vegetables, as in lasagne.

Commercially made fresh pasta is made with durum wheat, water and eggs. The dough is harder than that used for hand-made pasta, but it can be easily kneaded by machine. The flavour and texture of all fresh pasta is very delicate, so it is best suited to more creamy sauces.

HISTORY

The argument about the origins of pasta will probably rage on forever; the Chinese claim that they were the first to discover the art of noodle-making and that pasta was brought to Italy by Marco Polo. The Italians, of course, claim it as their own invention. Historians tell us that the Romans and probably even the ancient Greeks used to eat pasta. Certainly the climate of southern Italy was ideally suited to growing durum wheat, so this theory is quite likely, but the popularity of pasta really spread in the 14th century, when bakeries in southern Italy started to sell pasta as an alternative to bread.

Then, as now, pasta became the traditional *primo* of the south, although in the poorest areas it constituted a complete meal. Its popularity filtered up to the north of Italy and by the 19th century huge factories had been set up to mass-produce vast quantities of pasta, which became an integral part of all Italian cooking.

BUYING AND STORING

Always buy dried pasta made from Italian durum wheat. Even after the packet has been opened, dried pasta will keep for weeks in an airtight container. Hand-made fresh pasta will only keep for a couple of days, but it can be successfully frozen. Machine-made fresh pasta is pasteurized and vacuum-packed, so it will keep in the fridge for up to two weeks and can be frozen for up to six months. When buying coloured and flavoured pasta, make sure that it has been made with natural ingredients.

COOKING PASTA

Allow about 75 g/3 oz pasta per serving as a first course. All pasta must be cooked in a large saucepan filled with plenty of salted, fast-boiling water.

For long shapes like spaghetti, drop one end of the pasta into the water and, as it softens, push it down gently until it bends in the middle and is completely immersed.

Cooking times vary according to the type, size and shape of the pasta, but, as a general rule, filled pasta takes about 12 minutes, dried pasta needs 8–10 minutes and fresh pasta only 2–3 minutes. All pasta should be cooked al dente, so that it is still resistant to the bite. Always test pasta for doneness just before you think it should be ready; it can easily overcook. To stop the cooking, take the pan off the heat and run a little cold water into it, then drain the pasta.

Preparing Fresh Pasta

1 Allow 1 egg to 100 g/3¹⁄₂ oz super-fine plain flour (Italian *tipo 00* is best). Sift the flour and a pinch of salt into a mound on a clean work surface and make a well. Break the eggs into the well and gradually work in the flour until completely amalgamated.

2 Knead the dough with floured hands for at least 15 minutes, until it is very smooth, firm and elastic. (If you are short of time or energy, you can do this in a food processor.)

3 Chill the dough for 20 minutes, then roll it to the required thickness and cut it into your desired shape. (You can buy a specially shaped rolling pin to make the squares for filled pasta.) A pasta machine will make this process much easier. Leave the pasta to dry for at least 1 hour before cooking it.

Pasta Varieties

Pasta shapes can be divided roughly into four categories: long strands and ribbons, flat, short and filled.

The best-known long variety is spaghetti, which comes in a thinner version, spaghettini, and the flatter *linguine*, which means "little tongues". *Bucatini* are thicker and hollow – perfect for trapping sauces in the cavity. Ribbon pasta is wider than the strands: fettuccine, *trenette* and tagliatelle all fall into this category. Dried tagliatelle is usually sold folded into nests, which unravel during cooking. A mixture of white and green noodles is known as *paglia e fieno* (straw and hay). Pappardelle are the widest ribbon pasta; they are often served with s*ugo alla lepre* (hare sauce). The thinnest pasta strands are vermicelli (little worms) and ultra-fine *capelli d'angelo* (angel's hair).

In Italy, flat fresh pasta is often called *maccheroni*, not to be confused with the short tubes with which we are familiar. Lasagne and cannelloni are larger flat rectangles, used for layering or rolling round a filling; dried cannelloni are already formed into wide tubes. Layered pasta dishes like this are cooked *al forno* (baked in the oven). Fillings for fresh pasta squares include meat, pumpkin, artichokes, ricotta and spinach, seafood, chicken and rabbit. There are dozens of names for filled pasta, but the only difference lies in the shape and size. Ravioli are square, tortelli are usually round, while tortellini and *anolini* are ring-shaped.

As for pasta shapes, the list is almost endless and the names wonderfully descriptive. There are *maltagliati* (badly cut), *orecchiette* (little ears) and *cappellacci* (little hats), while from the natural world come penne (quills), *conchiglie* (little shells), *farfalle* (butterflies) and *lumache* (snails).

When choosing the appropriate pasta shape for the sauce, there are no hard and fast rules, but long, thin pasta is best for olive-oil-based and delicate seafood sauces. Short pasta shapes with wide openings (like *conchiglie* and penne) will trap meaty or spicy sauces, as will spirals and curls. Almost any pasta is suitable for tomato sauce.

Tonnarelli al nero
Flavoured and coloured with squid ink

Spinach fettuccine

Plain fettuccine

Bavette
Flavoured with porcini *(ceps)*

Paglia e fieno

Long Pasta

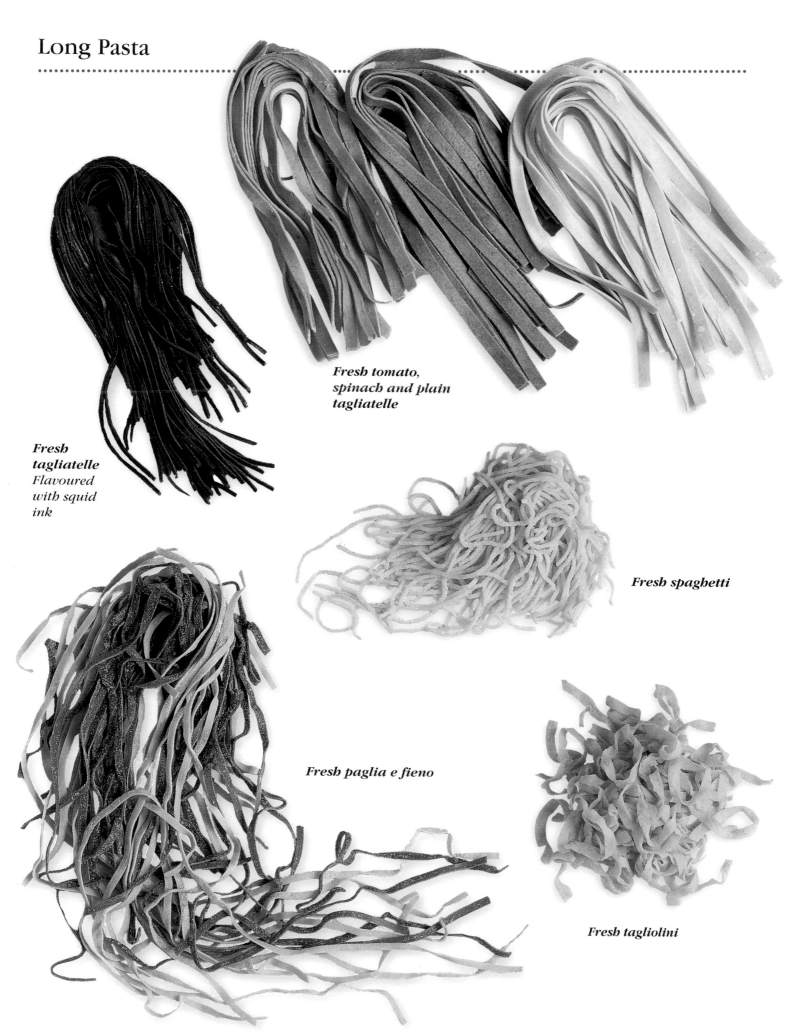

*Fresh tomato,
spinach and plain
tagliatelle*

***Fresh
tagliatelle***
*Flavoured
with squid
ink*

Fresh spaghetti

Fresh paglia e fieno

Fresh tagliolini

Long Pasta

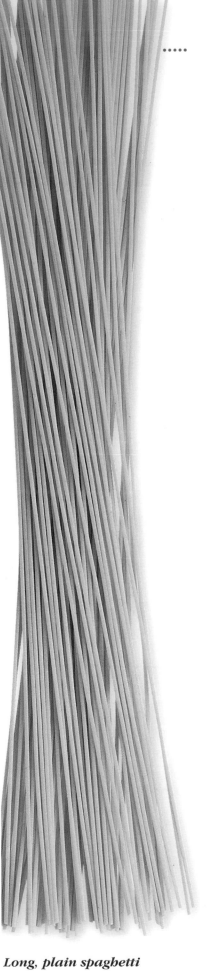

SPAGHETTI

INTEGRALE 100% DI

FARRO

SPECIALITÀ
GASTRONOMICA

CASINO DI CAPRAFICO

AZIENDA AGRICOLA
GIACOMO SANTOLERI

500 g ℮

Wholemeal farro

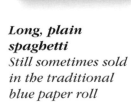

**TRADITIONAL ITALIAN
SPAGHETTI 1 Kg e**
MADE BY:
PASTIFICIO
LUCIO GAROFALO SpA
GRAGNANO (NAPOLI)
ITALIA

Spaghetti tricolore
*Mixed plain, spinach
and tomato spaghetti*

**Long, plain
spaghetti**
*Still sometimes sold
in the traditional
blue paper roll*

Long, plain spaghetti

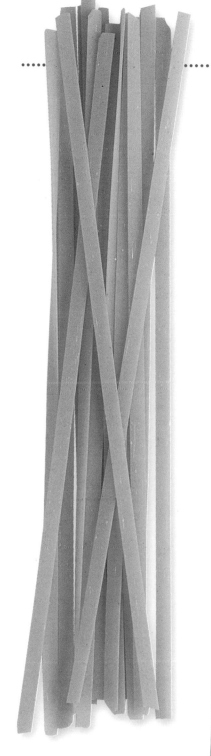

Fettuccelle

Linguine

Linguinette

Plain tagliatelle

Tagliatelle
Flavoured with
squid ink

Mushroom-flavoured
tagliatelle

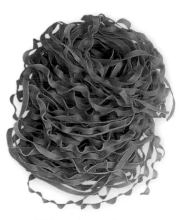

Spinach tagliatelle

Long Pasta

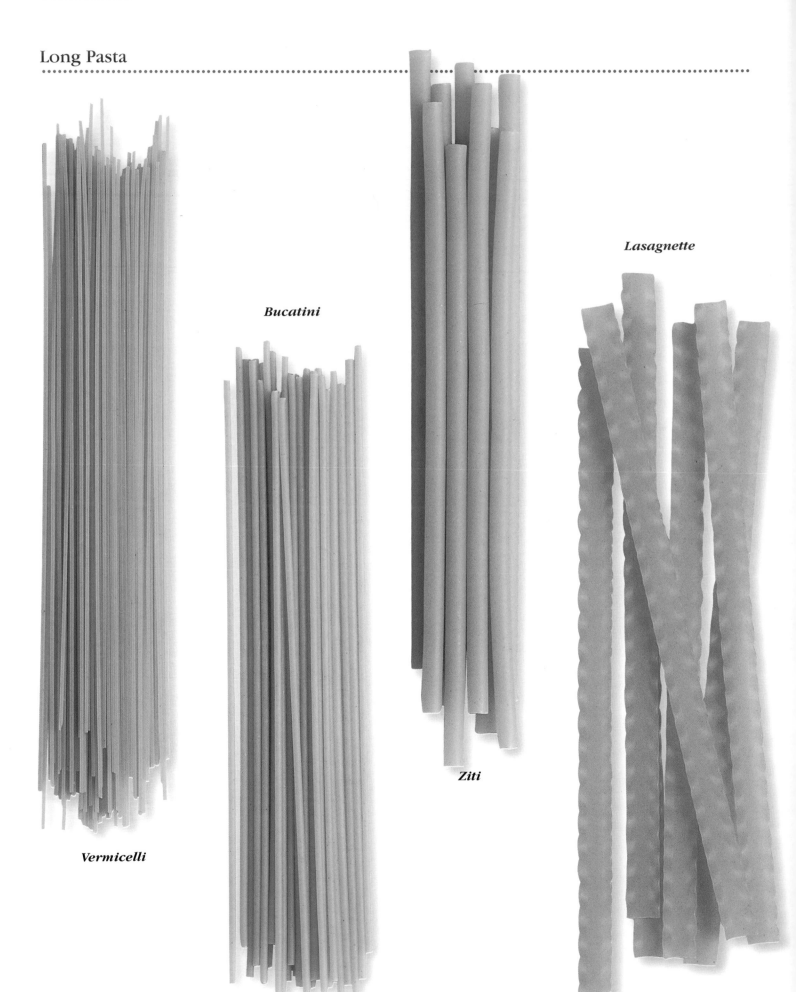

Bucatini

Ziti

Lasagnette

Vermicelli

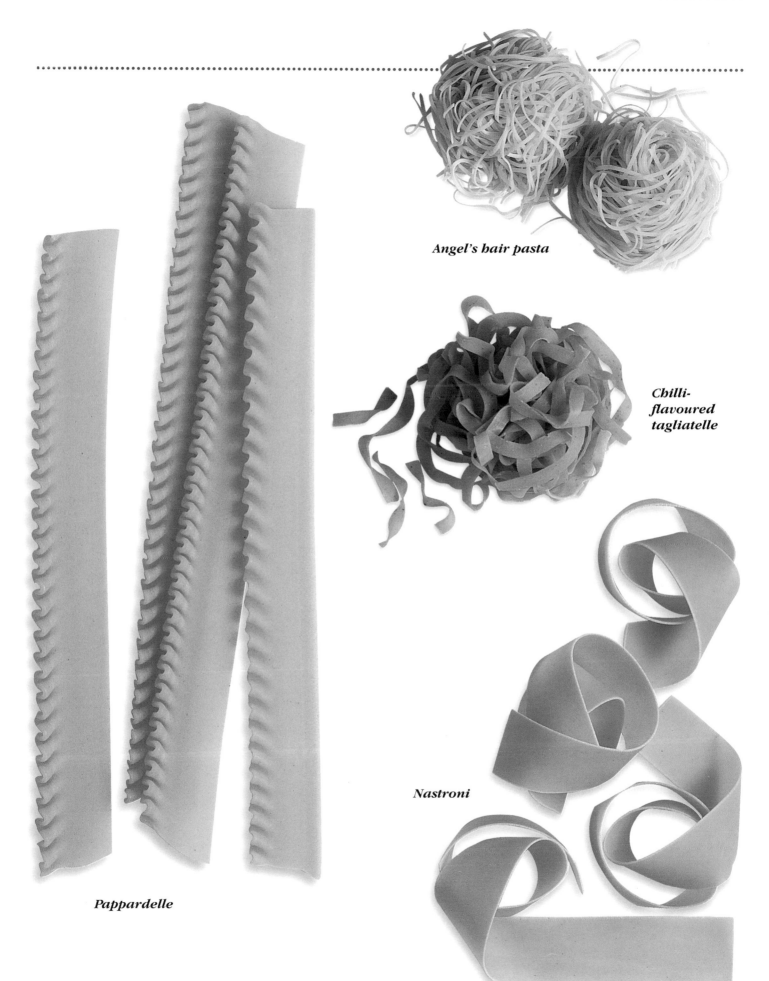

Angel's hair pasta

Chilli-flavoured tagliatelle

Nastroni

Pappardelle

Short Pasta

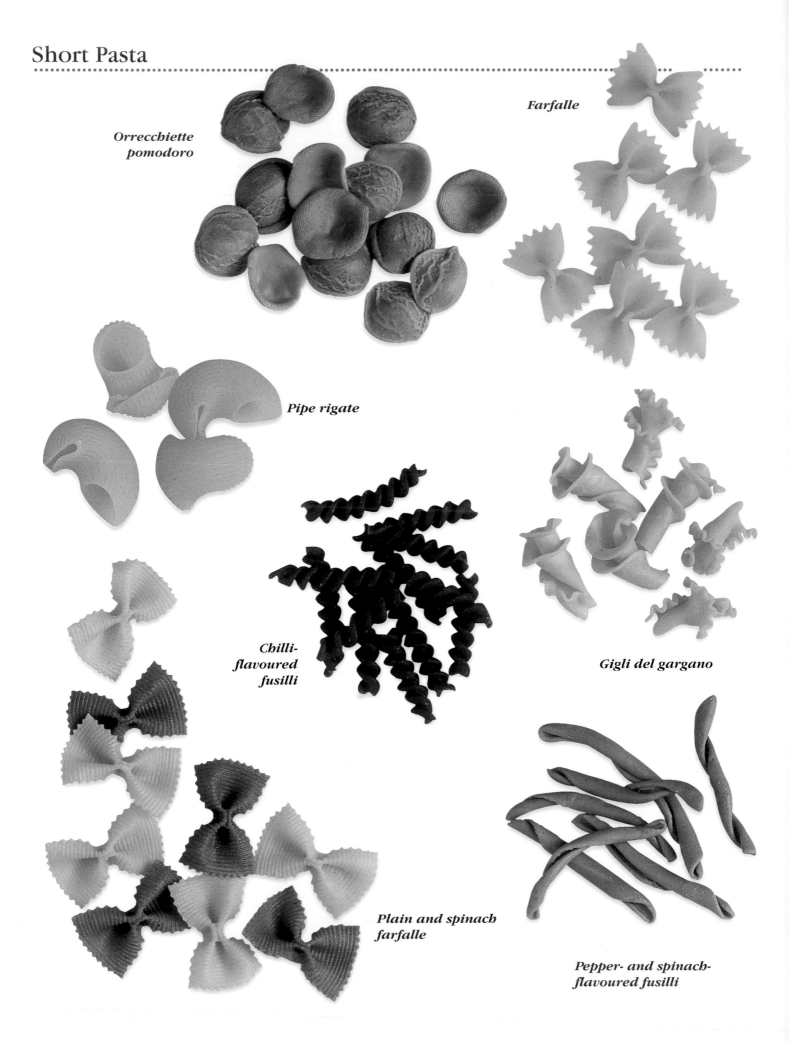

Orrecchiette pomodoro

Farfalle

Pipe rigate

Chilli-flavoured fusilli

Gigli del gargano

Plain and spinach farfalle

Pepper- and spinach-flavoured fusilli

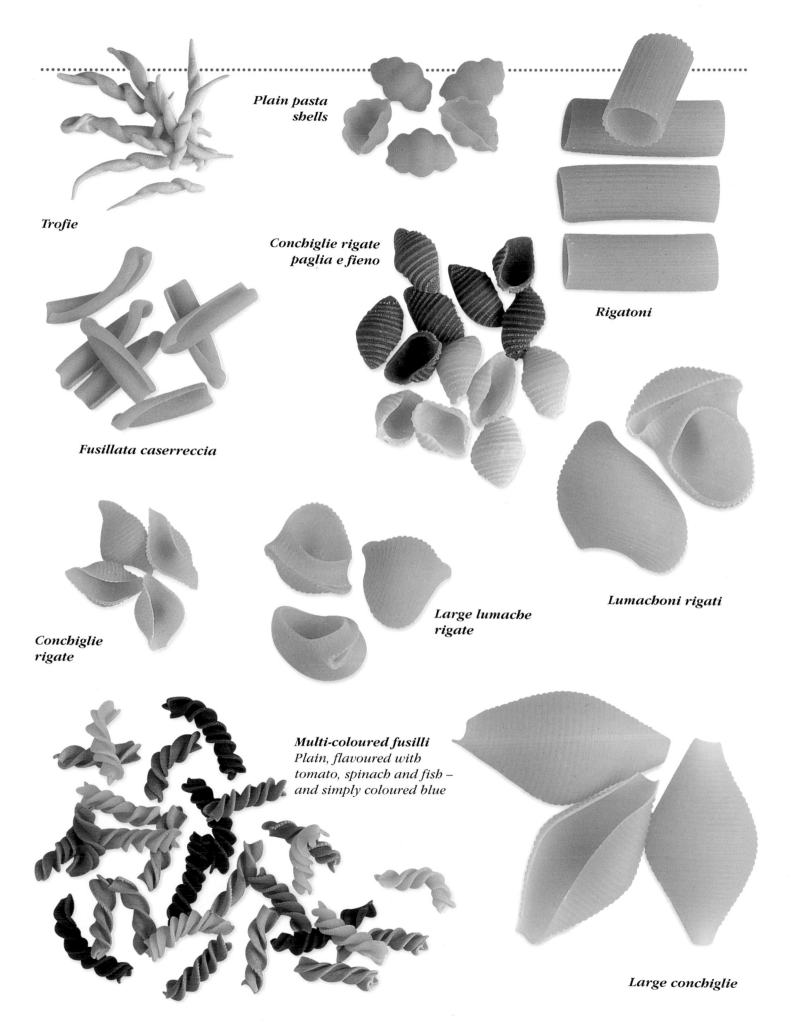

Trofie

Plain pasta shells

Conchiglie rigate paglia e fieno

Rigatoni

Fusillata caserreccia

Lumachoni rigati

Conchiglie rigate

Large lumache rigate

Multi-coloured fusilli
Plain, flavoured with tomato, spinach and fish – and simply coloured blue

Large conchiglie

Short Pasta

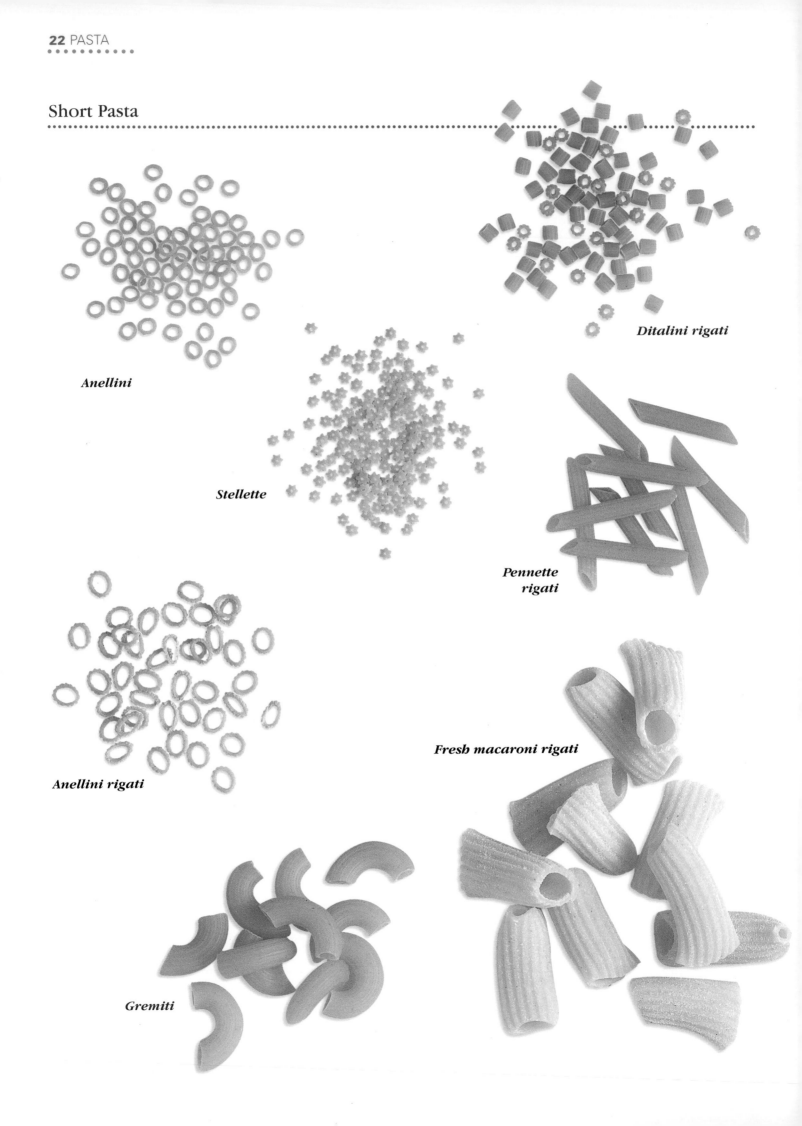

Anellini

Ditalini rigati

Stellette

Pennette rigati

Anellini rigati

Fresh macaroni rigati

Gremiti

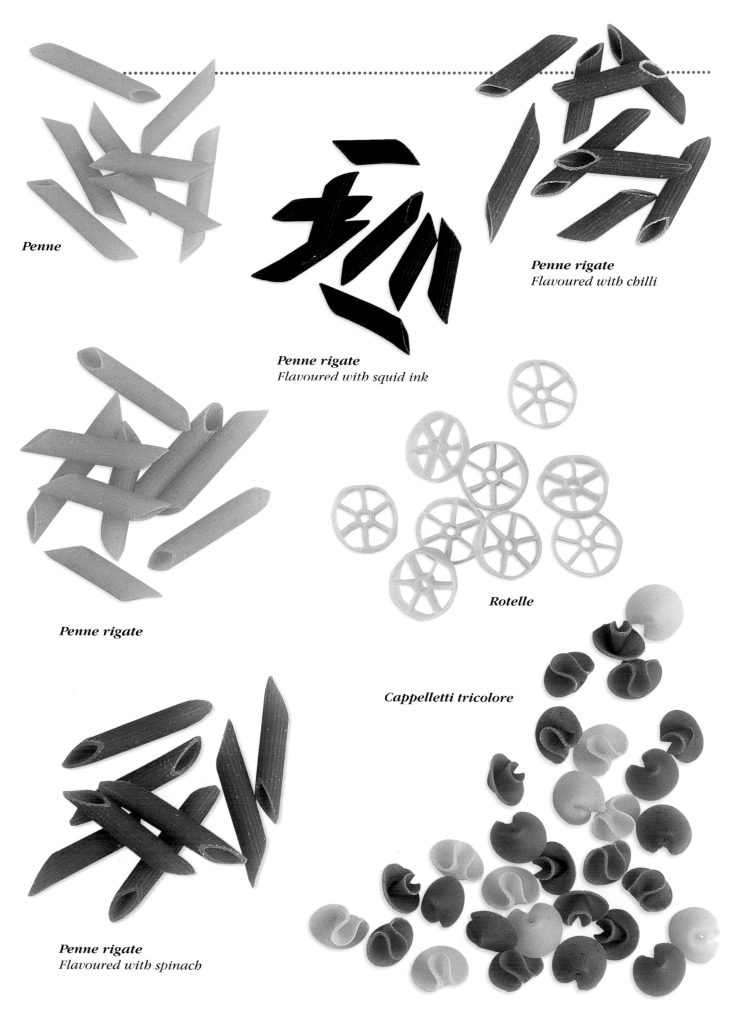

Penne

Penne rigate
Flavoured with squid ink

Penne rigate
Flavoured with chilli

Penne rigate

Rotelle

Cappelletti tricolore

Penne rigate
Flavoured with spinach

Flat Pasta

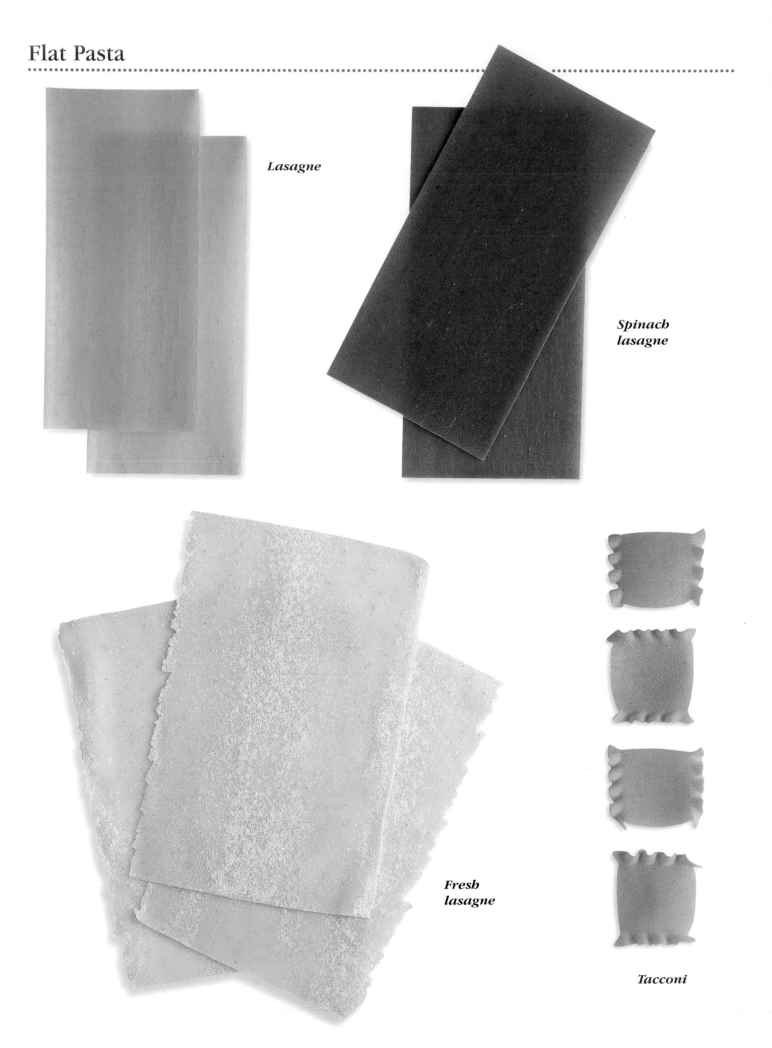

Lasagne

Spinach lasagne

Fresh lasagne

Tacconi

Filled Pasta

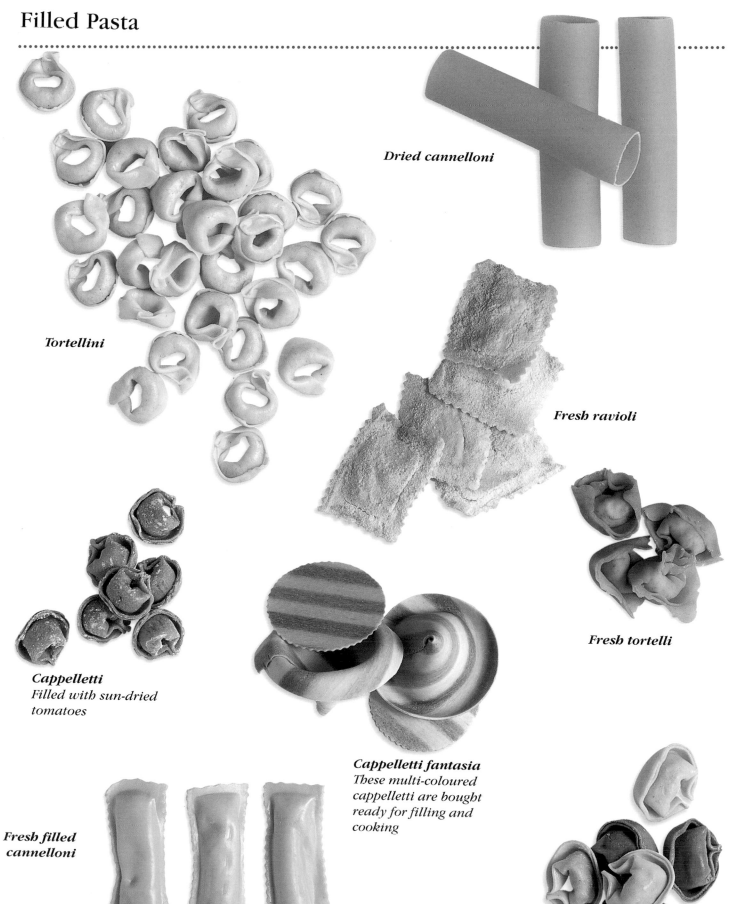

Dried cannelloni

Tortellini

Fresh ravioli

Cappelletti
Filled with sun-dried tomatoes

Fresh tortelli

Cappelletti fantasia
These multi-coloured cappelletti are bought ready for filling and cooking

Fresh filled cannelloni

Tortelli
Plain and flavoured with spinach

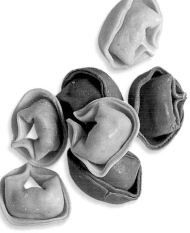

Gnocchi

Gnocchi fall into a different category from other pasta, being more like small dumplings. They can be made with semolina (milled durum wheat), flour, potatoes or ricotta and spinach and may be shaped like elongated shells, ovals, cylinders or flat discs, or roughly shredded into *strozzapreti* (priest-stranglers); at their worst, shop-bought gnocchi resemble large greyish maggots. However they are made, gnocchi should be extremely light and almost melt in the mouth.

CULINARY USES
Gnocchi can be served like any pasta, as a first course, in clear soup or occasionally as an accompaniment to the main course. Almost any pasta sauce is suitable for serving with gnocchi; they are particularly good with a creamy Gorgonzola sauce or they can be served simply, drizzled with olive oil and dredged with freshly grated Parmesan.

BUYING AND STORING
Gnocchi are usually sold loose on delicatessen counters. They are quite filling, so a small portion is enough for a first course; allow 115 g/4 oz per serving. They will keep in a polythene bag in the fridge for two or three days. Home-made gnocchi dough will also keep for a couple of days before cooking.

COOKING GNOCCHI

With the exception of oven-baked gnocchi alla romana, all other types of gnocchi should be poached in a saucepan of lightly salted, barely simmering water.

Drop the gnocchi into the water in batches and cook for about 5 minutes; they will rise to the surface when they are done. Scoop out the cooked gnocchi with a draining spoon and transfer to a plate: keep them warm while you cook the rest.

Fresh plain gnocchi

Gnocchi di patate

The best-known type of gnocchi are those from northern Italy made with potatoes and a little flour. To make 4 servings, peel 500 g/1¼ lb floury potatoes and boil until very tender. Drain and mash until smooth, then mix in 1 large egg and season with salt and pepper. Add 100–115 g/3½ oz–4 oz plain flour, a little at a time, stirring well with a wooden spoon until you have a smooth, sticky dough that forms a ball on the spoon (you may not need all the flour). Turn out the dough on to a floured surface and knead for about 3 minutes, until soft and smooth. Cut the dough into 6 equal pieces and, with floured hands, roll these into sausage shapes about 2 cm/¾ in in diameter. Slice the dough into 2 cm/¾ in discs. Hold a fork in your left hand and press the discs against the tines just hard enough to make ridges, then flip them downwards off the fork so that they curl up into elongated shell shapes. Poach them as above.

Fresh potato gnocchi

*Fresh spinach and
ricotta gnocchi*

*Fresh gnocchi made
with semolina*

Spinach and Parmesan gnocchi

Spinach and ricotta gnocchi

These attractive green gnocchi originated in Tuscany where, confusingly, they were known as ravioli. For 4 servings, you need:

350 g/12 oz cooked spinach, well drained and finely chopped
225 g/8 oz ricotta, mashed until smooth
2 eggs
100 g/3 ½ oz/1 cup freshly grated Parmesan
40 g/1½ oz/3 tbsp plain flour
65 g/2½ oz/5 tbsp butter, melted
salt, pepper and nutmeg

1 Put the spinach, ricotta and seasoning in a saucepan and cook gently, stirring continuously, for 5 minutes. Off the heat, beat in the eggs, 40 g/1½ oz/3 tbsp of the Parmesan and the flour. Chill the mixture for at least 4 hours. Lightly shape into small cylinders and roll them in a very little flour. Poach them as described, left.

2 Preheat the oven to 180°C/350°F/Gas 4. Pour a little melted butter into a serving dish and put in the cooked gnocchi. Sprinkle with some of the remaining Parmesan and place in the oven.

3 Add the rest of the gnocchi as they are cooked and anoint them with melted butter and Parmesan. Replace the dish in the oven for another 5 minutes before serving.

Gnocchi alla romana

These substantial gnocchi from Lazio are made with semolina milled from durum wheat. For 4–6 servings, you need:

1 litre/1¾ pints/4 cups milk
225 g/8 oz semolina
75 g/3 oz freshly grated Parmesan
2 eggs, plus an extra yolk, lightly beaten
60 g/2½ oz/5 tbsp butter
salt, pepper and nutmeg

1 Bring the milk to the boil, season with salt, pepper and nutmeg, then add the semolina in a steady stream, whisking for about 15 minutes, until the mixture is very thick. Off the heat, stir in half the Parmesan and the beaten eggs.

2 Pour the mixture into a greased baking tray to a thickness of about 1 cm/½ in, or spread it over a dampened work surface. Leave to cool completely, then cut out 3 cm/1¼ in discs with a plain or fluted pastry cutter.

3 Preheat the oven to 230°C/350°F/Gas 8. Layer the semolina discs in a buttered baking dish, dotting each layer with flakes of butter and a sprinkling of grated Parmesan, finishing with the cheese. Bake the gnocchi in the hot oven for about 15 minutes, until browned on top.

Rice, Grains & Pulses

Almost as important as pasta in Italian cooking are rice, polenta and pulses, which all appear as primi piatti *(first courses) in various guises. Like all basically agricultural countries, Italy relied heavily on these protein-rich ingredients when luxuries like meat were in short supply, and a host of wholesome and delicious recipes were developed using these modest ingredients.*

Riso (Rice)

Italy produces more rice and a greater variety of rice than anywhere else in Europe. Most of it is grown in the Po Valley in Piedmont, where conditions are perfect for cultivating the short-grain Carnaroli, Arborio and *Vialone Nano* rice, which make the best risotto. Italian rice is classified by size, ranging from the shortest, roundest *ordinario* (used for puddings) to *semifino* (for soups and salads), then *fino* and finally the longer grains of the finest risotto rice, *superfino*. *Superfino* rice swells to at least three times its original size during cooking, enabling it to absorb all the cooking liquid while still retaining its shape and firm *al dente* texture combined with a creamy smoothness.

HISTORY

The Saracens first introduced rice to Italy as long ago as the 11th century (some believe even earlier), but it only became popular in the 16th century, when it began to be cultivated on a large scale in the Po Valley. Traditionally, rice has played a much greater part in the cooking of northern Italy than in the south, particularly in the Veneto, where the famous dish of *risi e bisi* (Venetian dialect for "rice and peas") opened the banquet served every year by the Doges to honour their patron Saint Mark.

Superfino Carnaroli rice (left and above)
This short-grained variety is one of the finest Italian rices. Its ability to absorb liquid and cook to a creamy smoothness while still retaining its shape makes it perfect for risotto

Arborio rice

Superfino Arborio rice

Vialone Nano rice

PREPARING RISOTTO

The most famous of all Italian rice dishes is risotto, which was invented in Milan in the 16th century. A good risotto can be made only with superfine rice. All risotti are basically prepared in the same way, although they can be flavoured with an almost endless variety of ingredients. The rice is coated in butter or oil, then simmering stock is added, one ladleful at a time, and the rice is stirred over a low heat until all the liquid has been completely absorbed.

Only then is more stock added and the risotto is cooked in this way for about 20 minutes until the rice is tender and creamy. The final touch is called mantecatura; *off the heat, a knob of butter or a couple of spoons of olive oil and some freshly grated Parmesan are stirred into the risotto to make it very creamy.*

Leftover cold risotto can be rolled into balls enclosing a piece of mozzarella, coated in fine breadcrumbs and deep-fried to make suppli al teletono *or the Sicilian equivalent,* arancini.

Riso (Rice)

Rice is often used in Italian soups; it combines well with almost all vegetables and makes a substantial addition to minestrone. Baked rice dishes are also popular. Cooked rice is layered in a buttered ovenproof dish with meatballs, vegetables or poultry and cheese, then topped with breadcrumbs and baked in the oven until the top is crispy and brown. The Italians never serve main dishes on a bed of rice, but prefer to serve plain boiled rice on its own with plenty of butter and cheese stirred in.

BUYING AND STORING
Buy only special superfine risotto rice for use in Italian cooking. Shorter grain *semifino* is best for soups, and *ordinario* for puddings (try *riso nero*, a rice pudding topped with melted chocolate). Once you have opened the packet, reseal it tightly; you can then keep the rice in a dry place for several months.

Semifino rice

Brown semifino rice

Supplì al telefono

These rice croquettes contain mozzarella, which, when cooked, melts into strings that resemble "telephone wires". For 4 servings, you will need:
2 eggs, lightly beaten
225 g/8 oz cold, cooked risotto
50 g/2 oz Parma ham, cut into 1 cm/¹⁄₂ in dice
115 g/4 oz Mozzarella, cut into 1 cm/¹⁄₂ in dice
fine dried breadcrumbs, for coating
oil, for deep-frying
salt and freshly ground black pepper

1 Mix the eggs into the cold risotto and season to taste with plenty of salt and pepper.

2 Form the rice mixture into balls about the size of a small orange and make a hollow in each one. Fill this with a cube of ham and one of cheese, then roll each ball in your hand to enclose the ham and cheese completely, adding a little more rice if necessary.

3 Spread out the breadcrumbs in a shallow tray or plate and roll the rice balls in the breadcrumbs to coat them lightly.

4 Heat the oil in a deep, heavy-based pan and deep-fry the rice balls in batches for 3–5 minutes until golden brown. Drain on kitchen paper and keep warm while you cook the remainder. Serve piping hot.

Farro

This is the Tuscan name for spelt, a hard brown wheat with pointed grains, which is very little used in other parts of Italy. Farro is much harder than other wheat and therefore takes longer to process and cook, but it will grow even in poor soil. In Tuscany it is used to make *gran farro*, a delicious and nourishing soup, which is served as a first course instead of pasta.

CULINARY USES
Farro is used mainly as an ingredient for soups, but in remoter country areas of Italy it is sometimes used to make bread.

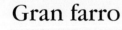

Farro

Ordinario rice

Gran farro

This Tuscan soup is often served as a first course instead of pasta. For 4 servings, you will need:

250 g/8 oz dried borlotti or cannellini beans, soaked overnight, then drained
1 onion, chopped
2 garlic cloves, chopped
100 g/3½ oz finely chopped pancetta
4 sage leaves
a pinch of chopped fresh oregano
45 ml/3 tbsp olive oil
225 g/8 oz chopped fresh tomatoes
150 g/5 oz prepared farro
salt, freshly ground black pepper and grated nutmeg

1 Cook the beans in fresh water until tender (reserve the cooking water). Rub the beans through a vegetable mill. Gently cook the onion, garlic, pancetta and herbs in the olive oil until pale golden brown. Add the tomatoes, season with salt, pepper and nutmeg, then simmer for 10 minutes.

2 Add the bean purée and enough of the cooking water to make a thick soup. Stir in the farro and simmer for 45 minutes, adding more water if the soup becomes too thick. Serve with some extra virgin olive oil to trickle into it.

Polenta

For centuries, polenta has been a staple food of the north of Italy, particularly around Friuli and the Veneto. This grainy yellow flour is a type of cornmeal made from ground maize, which is cooked into a kind of porridge with a wide variety of uses. Polenta is sometimes branded according to the type of maize from which it is made. *Granturco* and *Fioretto* are the two most common types.

In Italy, polenta is available ground to various degrees of coarseness to suit different dishes, but there are two main types – coarse and fine. Coarse polenta has a more interesting texture but takes longer to cook.

HISTORY

The Romans made a savoury porridge they called *puls* using *farro*, a kind of spelt, and the tradition continued in northern Italy, where gruels were prepared from local cereals like buckwheat, barley and oats. Maize or corn was only introduced into Italy from the New World in the 17th century; soon it was being grown in all the north-eastern regions, where cornmeal overtook all other types of grain in popularity, because it combined so well with the local dairy products. Traditionally, polenta was cooked in a *polaio*, a special copper pot which hung in the fireplace; here, it was stirred for at least an hour, to be served for breakfast, lunch or dinner (sometimes all three).

CULINARY USES

Polenta is extraordinarily versatile and can be used for any number of recipes, ranging from rustic to highly sophisticated. Although it is most often served as a first course, it can also be used as a vegetable dish or main course and even made into biscuits and cakes. Plain boiled polenta can be served on its own, or enriched with butter and cheese to make a very satisfying dish. It goes wonderfully well with all meats, sausages and game, helping to cut the richness and mop up the sauce. It can be cooled and cut into squares, then fried, grilled or baked and served with a topping or filling of mushrooms, meat, vegetables or cheese. Fried or grilled squares of polenta form the basis of *crostini*, which are served as an *antipasto*.

GRILLED OR FRIED POLENTA

Pour the cooked polenta on to a wooden board and spread it to a thickness of about 2.5 cm/1 in. Leave it to cool and harden, then cut into squares.

Fry in hot vegetable oil until crunchy and golden, then drain on kitchen paper or grill until golden brown on both sides.

To make a pasticciata *(layered baked dish) of polenta, cut the cold polenta horizontally into 1 cm/¹⁄₂ in slices and layer it in a buttered baking dish with your chosen sauce, mushrooms, cheeses etc. Bake in a hot oven for about 15 minutes, until the top is lightly browned.*

Fine polenta

BUYING AND STORING

It is possible to buy quick-cooking polenta, which can be prepared in only 5 minutes. However, if you can spare the 20 minutes or so that it takes to cook traditional polenta, it is best to buy this for its superior texture and flavour. Whether you choose coarse or fine meal is a matter of personal preference; for soft polenta or sweet dishes, fine-ground is better, while course-ground meal is better for frying. Once you have opened the bag, put the remaining polenta in an airtight container; it will keep for at least a month.

Recipe for Basic Polenta

Coarse polenta

COOK'S TIP

Polenta can be cooked in water, stock or a mixture of water and milk. Whichever liquid you use, cook the polenta very slowly and steadily so that it does not go lumpy. Allow 50–75 g/2–3 oz/ ½ cup polenta meal per person.

To make a basic polenta for 4–6 people, bring to the boil 1.5 litres/2½ pints/6 cups salted water or stock.

Gradually add 300 g/11 oz/2 cups polenta in a steady stream, stirring continuously with a wooden spoon.

Continue cooking, stirring all the time, until the polenta comes away from the sides of the saucepan. This will take 20–30 minutes (5 minutes for quick-cooking polenta).

One alternative, foolproof (though unauthentic) method is to put the polenta meal into a saucepan, add salt, then stir in the cold water, bring the mixture slowly to the boil and simmer gently for about 20 minutes, stirring occasionally.

Another is to cook the polenta for 5 minutes, then finish cooking it in the oven for about an hour.

Pour the cooked polenta into a serving dish, season with pepper and stir in abundant quantities of butter and a strong-flavoured cheese – Parmesan, Fontina, Bel Paese and Gorgonzola are all delicious with piping hot polenta.

Pulses

Fagioli (haricot beans)

Haricot beans are another staple of Tuscan cooking; indeed, the Tuscans are sometimes nicknamed "the bean-eaters", although haricot beans are eaten all over Italy. The most popular varieties include the pretty red-and-cream speckled borlotti, the small white cannellini (a kind of kidney bean), the larger *toscanelli* and *fagioli coll'occhio* (black-eyed beans). All these are eaten as hearty stews, with pasta and in soups, and cannellini are often served as a side dish simply anointed with extra virgin olive oil. *Ceci* (chick-peas) and *fave* (broad beans) are also popular.

HISTORY

Beans were a staple of the Roman and Greek diet, and several recipes for bean stews survive from that period. Many of the beans were brought to Italy from the Middle East, but some, like *fave*, were indigenous and were used as ritual offerings to the dead at Roman funerals. Haricot beans have always been a popular peasant food, but, during the Renaissance, Catherine de Medici attempted to refine Italian cuisine, and beans fell out of favour with the nobility and sophisticated urban dwellers. Thanks to their highly nutritious and economical qualities, however, beans and pulses have once again become an important element in Italian cooking.

CULINARY USES

Haricot beans can be made into any number of nutritious soups and stews, or served as the basis of a substantial salad like *tonno e fagioli* (tuna and beans). A popular Tuscan dish is *fagioli all'uccelletto* (beans cooked like little birds). Cooked cannellini beans are combined with chopped garlic, fresh sage leaves and tomatoes and simmered for about 15 minutes until tender and fragrant. This dish is delicious served with coarse country sausages.

Dried red borlotti beans

Dried cannellini beans

Dried borlotti beans

Dried cannellini beans

BUYING AND STORING

During the summer and early autumn in Italy, you may find fresh haricot beans, sometimes still in the pod. Borlotti beans come in an attractive speckled pod, cannellini in a slim yellowish pod. The pods represent a high proportion of the weight, so allow at least 300 g/11 oz per serving. Most haricot beans, however, are sold dried. Try to buy these from a shop with a quick turnover, or they may become wizened and very hard. Prepacked beans will have a "best before" date on the packet. Loose beans will keep for several weeks in a cool dry place, but are at their best soon after purchase.

If you haven't the time to prepare dried beans, canned varieties make an acceptable substitute, but you cannot control the texture and they are sometimes too mushy. They are, however, fine for recipes that call for puréed beans. Bear in mind, though, that they are an expensive alternative to dried beans.

Canned borlotti beans

Canned haricot beans

Canned cannellini beans

Canned black-eyed beans

COOKING BEANS

All dried beans should be soaked for about 8 hours in cold water or 4 hours in boiling water before cooking (this is not necessary for fresh beans). Discard the soaking water before cooking the beans.

Cook the beans in plenty of unsalted boiling water. Boil briskly for 10 minutes (this is essential to kill off the toxins, which may cause severe stomach upsets), then simmer for 1–2 hours, depending on the size and freshness of the beans.

You can add whatever flavourings you wish to the cooking liquid, but never add salt or any acidic ingredients, such as tomatoes or vinegar, until the beans are cooked, or they will never become tender however long you cook them. To make a hearty stew, after the initial boiling, the beans can be mixed with pancetta, garlic and herbs and cooked very slowly in the oven.

Pulses

Fave (broad beans)

Broad beans are nicest eaten fresh from the fat green pod in late spring and early summer when they are very small and tender with a bittersweet flavour. They are particularly popular in the area around Rome, where they are eaten raw with *prosciutto crudo*, salami or Pecorino. Later in the season, they should be cooked and skinned (hold the hot beans under cold running water; the skin will slip off quite easily). Cooked *fave* have a milder flavour than raw and are excellent with ham and *pancetta*. When buying fresh *fave* in the pod, allow about 350 g/12 oz per person; it may seem a lot, but the pods themselves are comparatively heavy, so a lot goes only a little way. Dried *fave* should be soaked, and the skins removed before cooking. They are used for soups and stews and need about 45 minutes' cooking.

Chick-peas
These round golden pulses can be bought dried (above), or canned and ready to use (left)

Broad beans
Dried fave *need to be soaked overnight before cooking*

Ceci (chick-peas)

These round golden pulses are shaped rather like hazelnuts and have a distinctive, nutty flavour. They are the oldest of all known pulses and, though not indigenous to Italy, have become very popular in Italian country cooking.

CULINARY USES

Chick-peas are cooked and used in the same way as haricot beans and are an essential ingredient of *tuoni e lampo* (thunder and lightning), a sustaining dish of pasta and chick-peas served with tomato sauce and Parmesan. They can also be served cold, dressed with lemon juice, chopped fresh herbs and olive oil, to make a substantial salad.

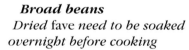

Broad beans
The canned beans (right) are ready to use

COOK'S TIP
Chick-peas can be very hard, so it is best to soak them for at least 12 hours, then cook them in plenty of boiling water for up to 2 hours.

Lenticchie *(lentils)*

Although lentils grow in pods, they are always sold podded and dried. Italian lentils are the small brown variety, which are grown in the area around Umbria; they do not break up during cooking and are often mixed with small pasta shapes or rice for a contrast of flavours and textures. They make the perfect bed for cooked sausage, such as zampone or cotechino, and are delicious served cold dressed with olive oil. The ultimate Italian pulse feast must surely be *imbrecciata*, a nutritious and sustaining soup from Umbria made with chick-peas, haricot beans and lentils.

Brown lentils
These are available in different sizes, large (below) and small (above)

COOK'S TIP
Lentils will absorb the flavours of whatever aromatics they are cooked with, so add any appropriate herbs or spices to the cooking liquid.

Cheeses

Italy has an even greater variety of cheeses than France, ranging from fresh, mild creations like mozzarella to aged, hard cheeses with a very mature flavour, such as Parmesan. All types of milk are used, including ewe's, goat's and buffalo's, which produces the best mozzarella, and some cheeses are made from a mixture of milks. As in France, the Italians eat their cheese after the main course, either accompanied or followed by fresh fruit. You will not, however, find the large selection of cheeses offered on a French menu; Italian restaurants serve only one or two types of cheese and rarely have a cheeseboard.

Many of the cheeses made in Italy are suitable for cooking. What would a pizza be without its delicious, stringy topping of melted mozzarella, or a pasta dish without a grating of fresh Parmesan?

HISTORY
Fresh, rindless cheeses were first introduced to Italy by the ancient Greeks, who taught the Etruscans their cheese-making skills. They in turn refined the craft, developing the first long-matured cheeses with hard rinds, which could last for many months and would travel. Today's Parmesan and Pecorino cheeses are probably very similar to those produced 2,500 years ago.

In ancient days, the milk was left to curdle naturally before being made into cheese. The Romans discovered that rennet would speed up this process. Originally, they probably used rennet made from wild artichokes (this is still used in remoter parts of Italy), but later they began to use animal rennet. The process used to make farmhouse cheeses today has changed very little since Roman times.

Italian cheeses can be divided into four categories: hard, semi-soft, soft and fresh. Some cheeses have an enormously high fat content; others are low in fat and suitable for dieters. Many Italian cheeses are eaten at different stages of maturity; a cheese which has been matured for about a year is known as *vecchio*; after 18 months, it becomes *stravecchio* and tends to have a very powerful flavour. Almost all Italian cheeses can be eaten on their own and used for cooking.

Hard Cheeses

Asiago
This cheese from the Veneto region develops different characteristics as it ages. The large round cheeses with reddish-brown rinds each weigh 10–12 kg/22–55 lb. They are made from partially skimmed cow's milk and have a fat content of only 30 per cent. Asiago starts life as a pale straw-coloured dessert cheese, pitted with tiny holes, with a mild, almost bland flavour. After six months, the semi-matured cheese (*Asiago da taglio*) develops a more piquant, saltier flavour, but can still be eaten on its own. Once it has matured for 12 to 18 months, the *stravecchio* cheese becomes grainy and sharp-tasting, resembling an inferior Grana Padano, and is really only suitable for grating and cooking.

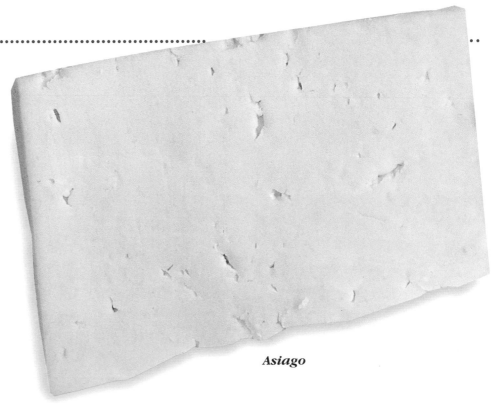

Asiago

Parmesan

Parmesan is by far the best-known and most important of the Italian hard cheeses. There are two basic types – Parmigiano Reggiano and Grana Padano – but the former is infinitely superior.

PARMIGIANO REGGIANO

Parmigiano Reggiano can be made only in a strictly defined zone, which lies between Parma, Modena, Reggio-Emilia, Bologna and Mantua. The farmers of this area claim that the cheese has been made there for over 2,000 years; certainly it appears to be almost identical to that produced by the Etruscans and the methods of production have scarcely changed. The milk comes only from local cows, which graze on the area's rich pastureland.

It takes about 600 litres/132 gallons of milk to make one 30–35 kg/ 70–80 lb wheel of Parmigiano Reggiano. The milk is partially skimmed and some of the whey from the previous day's cheese-making is added, then the mixture is carefully heated before rennet is added to encourage curdling. (The rest of the whey is fed to local pigs destined to become Parma hams.) The curds are poured into wheel-shaped forms and the cheese is

then aged for a minimum of two years; a really fine Parmesan may be aged for up to seven years. During this time, it is nurtured like fine wine, until it becomes pale golden with a slightly granular flaky texture and a nutty, mildly salty flavour. Authentic Parmigiano Reggiano has the word "Reggiano" stamped on the rind.

GRANA PADANO

This cheese is similar to Parmigiano Reggiano, but is inferior in flavour and texture. Although it is made in the same way, the milk used comes from other regions and the cheese is matured for no more than 18 months, so it does not have the crumbly texture of Reggiano and its flavour is sharper and saltier. Its grainy texture (hence the name "grana") makes it fine for grating and it can be used for cooking in the same way as Reggiano.

CULINARY USES

A really good Parmigiano Reggiano can be eaten on its own, cut into chunks or slivers; it is delicious served with ripe pears and a good red wine. But Parmesan, both Reggiano and grana, really comes into its own when used for cooking. Unlike other cheeses, it does not become stringy or rubbery when exposed to heat, so it can be grated over any number of hot dishes, from pasta, polenta and risotto to minestrone, or layered with aubergines or truffles and baked in the oven. Slivers of fresh Parmesan are also excellent with asparagus or in a crisp salad. Don't throw away the rind from Parmesan; use it to add extra flavour to soups and vegetable stocks.

Parmigiano Reggiano

Grana Padano

BUYING AND STORING

If possible, buy Parmigiano Reggiano, which is easilyrecogniz-able by the imprint "Reggiano" in pinpricks on the rind. Whether you buy Reggiano or grana, always buy it in a piece cut from a whole wheel and grate it freshly when you need it; if possible, avoid pre-packed pieces and never buy ready-gratedParmesan, which is tasteless. Tightly wrapped in foil, a hunk of Parmesan will keep in the fridge for at least a month.

Hard Cheeses

Pecorino

All Italian cheeses made from ewe's milk are known as Pecorino, but they vary enormously in texture and flavour, from soft and mild to dry and strong. The best-known hard Pecorino cheeses are *romano* from Lazio and *sardo* from Sardinia; both are medium-fat, salty-tasting cheeses with a sharp flavour, which becomes sharper the longer the cheeses are matured. The milder *sardo* is usually aged for only a few weeks; the *romano* for up to 18 months. Hard Pecorino is a pale, creamy colour with a firm granular texture with tiny holes like Parmesan. Sicilian *Pecorino pepato* is studded with whole black peppercorns, which add a very piquant note.

Fresh Pecorino comes from Tuscany and is sometimes known as *caciotta*. This semi-hard cheese has a delicious mild, creamy flavour, but is not easy to find outside Italy, as it keeps for a very short time.

HISTORY

Pecorino romano is probably the oldest Italian cheese, dating back to Roman times. Then, as now, the cheeses were shaped and laid on *canestri* (rush mats, rather like hammocks) to be air-dried. Sicilian Pecorino is still called *canestro* after these rush mats.

CULINARY USES

Hard Pecorino can be grated and used exactly like Parmesan. It has a more pungent flavour, which is well suited to spicy pasta dishes, such as *penne all'arrabiata*, but it is too strong for more delicate dishes like risotto or creamy chicken dishes. *Caciotta* can be cubed and marinated in olive oil for about 2 hours, then served with a grinding of black pepper to make a delicious and unusual *antipasto*.

BUYING AND STORING

Fresh or semi-hard Pecorino should be eaten the day you buy it, but well-matured Pecorino will keep in the fridge for several weeks wrapped tightly in foil.

Pecorino pepato
This cheese is studded with whole black peppercorns

Pecorino sardo
A milder version that is aged for only a few weeks

Caciotta
A semi-hard cheese with a mild, creamy flavour

Provolone

A southern Italian cheese, straw-white in colour with a smooth, supple texture and an oval or cylindrical shape, Provolone comes in many different sizes (some enormous) and can often be found hanging from the ceiling in Italian delicatessens. Provolone can be made from different types of milk and rennet; the strongest versions use goat rennet, which gives them a distinctively spicy flavour. In the south of Italy, buffalo milk is often used, and the cheeses are sometimes smoked to make *provolone affumicato*. The cheese is made by the *pasta filata* (layering) process, which gives it a smooth, silky texture; the curds are left to solidify, then they are cut into strips before being pressed together into a sausage shape. This is salted in brine for 6 to 12 hours, then the cheese is shaped and left to mature.

Variations on Provolone include *caciocavallo*, a smooth smoky cheese made from a mixture of cow's and goat's or ewe's milk, which develops a sharp flavour that becomes sharper as it matures. It takes its name from the way the oval cheeses are tied up in pairs and hung up to dry over a wooden pole, as though on horseback. (One fallacious theory is that the cheese was originally made from mare's milk; another is that the cheeses were stamped with a horse, which is the symbol of Naples.) In Calabria, a version called *burrino* is made enclosing a lump of unsalted butter in the centre of the cheese, so that when it is sliced, it resembles a hard-boiled egg.

Provolone affumicato

Provolone burrino
There is a lump of butter buried in the centre of this cheese, so that when cut it resembles a hard-boiled egg yolk

CULINARY USES
Milder fresh Provolone can be eaten on its own or in a sandwich with mortadella or ham. Once it becomes strong, it should only be used for cooking; its stringy texture when melted makes it ideal for pizzas and pasta dishes.

BUYING AND STORING
Enclosed in their wax rinds, Provolone and similar cheeses will keep for months. Once they have been opened, they should be eaten within a week. Provolone can be used for cooking in the same way as Parmigiano Reggiano.

Provolone
The stringy texture when melted makes this cheese particularly good for pizzas

Provolone

Semi-hard Cheeses

Bel Paese

This cheese, poetically named "beautiful country", is a baby among Italian cheeses, having been created by the Galbani family from Lombardy early this century. Made from cow's milk, it contains over 50 per cent fat, which makes it very creamy. It is the colour of buttermilk, with a very mild flavour, and is wrapped in pale yellow wax to preserve its freshness. A whole Bel Paese weighs about 2 kg/4¼ lb, but it is often sold ready-packed in wedges.

CULINARY USES

Bel Paese can be eaten on its own; its mild creaminess makes it popular with almost everyone. It is also excellent for cooking, with a good melting quality, and can be used as a substitute for mozzarella, but because it is rather bland it will not add much flavour to a dish.

BUYING AND STORING

Like most cheeses, it is best to buy a wedge of Bel Paese cut from a whole cheese; pre-packed pieces tend to be soggy and tasteless, although they are fine to use in cooking. Use freshly cut cheese as soon as possible after purchase, although wrapped in foil or clear film it will keep in the fridge for two or three days.

Fontina

The only genuine Fontina comes from the Val d'Aosta in the Italian Alps, although there are plenty of poor imitations. True Fontina is made from the rich unpasteurized milk of Valdostana cows and has a fat content of 45 per cent. Although Fontina is nowadays produced on a large scale, the methods are strictly controlled and the cows are grazed only on alpine grass and herbs. Because it is matured for only about four months, the cheese has a mild, almost sweet, nutty flavour and a creamy texture, with tiny holes. Longer-matured Fontina develops a much fuller flavour and is best used for cooking. A whole Fontina weighs about 15–20 kg/33–44 lb; the cheese is pale golden and the soft rind is orangey-brown. The rind of authentic Fontina has the words "Fontina dal Val d'Aosta" inscribed in white writing.

HISTORY

Fontina has been made for at least 500 years; it is mentioned in the "dairy bible"' *La Summa Lacticiniorum* of 1477. Its name probably comes from the mountain peak Fontin.

CULINARY USES

Fontina is delicious eaten on its own, and because it melts beautifully and does not become stringy, it can be used instead of mozzarella in a wide variety of dishes. It is also perfect for making a *fonduta*, the Italian equivalent of a Swiss cheese fondue.

Fontina
The sweet nutty flavour and creamy texture of this cheese makes it delicious to eat on its own

Bel Paese
This creamy, mild-flavoured cheese can also be eaten on its own, and it is excellent for cooking, too

Soft Cheeses

Taleggio

A square creamy cheese from Lombardy with a fat content of almost 50 per cent, Taleggio has a mild, salty-sweet flavour, which can become pungent if it is left to age for too long (it reaches maturity after only six weeks). The cheeses are dipped in brine for about 14 hours before maturing, which gives them a slightly salty tang. Each cheese with its soft edible rind weighs about 2 kg/4¼ lb. If you intend to eat the rind, remove the paper from the top!

CULINARY USES

Taleggio is perfect eaten on its own as a cheese course. Like Fontina, it melts into a velvety smoothness when cooked and does not become stringy, so it can be used in any cooked dish that requires a good melting consistency.

BUYING AND STORING

Both Fontina and Taleggio should be eaten as soon as possible after purchase. If necessary, they can be tightly wrapped in waxed paper or clear film and kept in the fridge for a day or two.

Stracchino

Stracchino is made from very creamy milk and matured for only about ten days, and never longer than two months. The smooth rindless cheese with a fat content of about 50 per cent is reminiscent of Taleggio, but softer-textured and with a sweeter flavour. Robiola is a small, square stracchino weighing about 100 g/ 3½ oz. Because these cheeses are so delicate, they are wrapped in plasticized paper to preserve their freshness.

HISTORY

The name Stracchino comes from the Lombardian dialect word meaning "tired". It does not reflect on the quality of the cheeses, but merely indicates that they were traditionally made in the winter months when the cows were tired from their long trek down from the mountains to their winter quarters on the plain of Lombardy. Some farmhouse-produced Stracchini are still made only in winter, but most are now produced all year round.

CULINARY USES

Stracchino should only be eaten as a dessert cheese; it is not suitable for cooking. On Christmas Eve in Lombardy, Robiola is served as a special delicacy with the spicy candied fruit relish, *mostarda di Cremona*.

Stracchino
A soft-textured cheese with a sweet flavour

Taleggio
Perfect to eat on its own, taleggio has a mild, sweet flavour

Robiola
This is a small square stracchino and is always wrapped in paper to preserve its freshness

Soft Cheeses

Gorgonzola

The proper name for this famous blue-veined cheese is Stracchino Gorgonzola, because it is made from the curds of stracchino. Originally made only in the town of Gorgonzola, the cheese is now produced all over Lombardy.

Gorgonzola is prepared by making alternate layers of hot and cold curds. The difference in temperature causes the layers to separate, leaving air pockets in which the mould (*penicillium glaucum*) will grow. The best Gorgonzola cheeses are left until the mould forms naturally, but more commonly copper wires are inserted into the cheese to encourage the growth. The cheeses are matured from three to five months; the longer the ageing, the stronger the flavour.

Gorgonzola is a very creamy cheese, the colour of buttermilk, with greenish-blue veining and a fat content of 48 per cent. Its flavour can range from very mild (*dolce*) to extremely powerful (*piccante*). The best-known mild version outside Italy is Dolcelatte (sweet milk), which is exceptionally creamy and delicately flavoured. Another version, *torta*, consists of Gorgonzola and mascarpone arranged in alternate layers like a cake.

HISTORY
Gorgonzola has been made in the village of the same name since the 1st century AD, when the cheeses were matured in the chilly caves of the Valsassina.

CULINARY USES
Although it is usually eaten as a cheese course, Gorgonzola is also used in cooking, particularly in creamy sauces for vegetables or pasta or as a filling for pancakes and ravioli. It is delicious stirred into soft polenta, or spread on deep-fried polenta *crostini*. Surprisingly, cooking diminishes the flavour of Gorgonzola, so that it does not dominate a delicate dish.

BUYING AND STORING
Supermarkets sell vacuum-packed portions of Gorgonzola, which are acceptable but not nearly as good as a wedge cut from a whole, foil-wrapped cheese. If you don't like a very strong flavour, be sure to buy Gorgonzola *dolce* or Dolcelatte. Wrapped in clear film, the cheese will keep for several days in the fridge.

Dolcelatte
An exceptionally creamy, delicately flavoured Gorgonzola

Torta
This striped cheese consists of layers of Gorgonzola and mascarpone

Gorgonzola
The greenish-blue veining is typical of this classic cheese

Fresh Cheeses

Caprini

These little disc-shaped goat's cheeses come from southern Italy. They have a pungent flavour, which becomes even stronger as the cheeses mature. Fresh Caprini do not travel well, so you will rarely find them outside Italy, but they are available bottled in olive oil flavoured with herbs and chillies.

CULINARY USES

Fresh goat's cheeses can be fried and served warm with salad leaves as an appetizer, or crumbled over pizzas to make an unusual topping. Bottled Caprini should be drained and eaten as a cheese course. If you like a spicy kick, trickle over some of the oil from the jar, but beware – it will be very piquant.

Caprini
Rarely found fresh outside Italy, these cheeses are usually found bottled in flavoured olive oil

Mascarpone

This delicately flavoured triple cream cheese from Lombardy is too rich to be eaten on its own (it contains 90 per cent fat), but can be used in much the same way as whipped or clotted cream and has a similar texture. Mascarpone is made from the cream of curdled cow's milk. It is mildly acidulated and adds a distinctive richness to risottos and creamy pasta sauces. It takes only 24 hours to produce, so it tastes very fresh, with a unique sweetness that makes it ideal for making desserts. A new lighter version called *fiorello light* is now being produced for the health-conscious. While it is useful for those on a diet, it is nothing like as good as the real thing.

CULINARY USES

In Italy, mascarpone is used for savoury dishes as well as desserts. It makes wonderfully creamy sauces for pasta and combines well with walnuts and artichokes. Mascarpone can also enhance the texture and flavour of risottos or a white bean soup. It is most commonly used in desserts, either served with fresh berries, or as a filling for pastries. It is an essential ingredient of tiramisu and can be churned into a rich, velvety ice cream.

BUYING AND STORING

Delicatessens in Italy serve fresh mascarpone by the *etto* (about 100 g/ 3¹/₂ oz) from large earthenware bowls, but outside Italy it is sold in 250 g/ 9 oz or 500 g/1¹/₄ lb plastic tubs. Although the flavour is not as good, pre-packed cheese will keep for a week in the fridge; fresh mascarpone should be eaten immediately.

> ### COOK'S TIP
> *To lighten the texture of mascarpone and make it less rich, fold in some beaten egg white.*

Mascarpone (above and below)
A triple cream cheese that is too rich to eat on its own, but is ideal for desserts. It is an essential ingredient in tiramisu

Fresh Cheeses

Smoked mozzarella
This cheese has a very smooth texture, a rich golden colour and an interesting smoky flavour

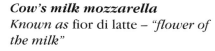

Cow's milk mozzarella
Known as fior di latte – *"flower of the milk"*

Mozzarella
The best is made from buffalo milk

Mozzarella

Italian cooking could hardly exist without mozzarella, the pure white, egg-shaped fresh cheese, whose melting quality makes it perfect for so many dishes. The best mozzarella is made in the area around Naples, using water buffalo's milk. It has a moist, springy texture and a deliciously milky flavour. The cheeses are made by the *pasta filata* (layering) method, where the curds are cut into strips, then covered with boiling water. As they rise to the surface, they are torn into shreds and scrunched into egg-shaped balls each weighing about 200 g/7 oz. These are placed in light brine for 12 hours, then packed in their own whey inside a paper or polythene wrapping to keep them fresh.

Other types of mozzarella include a cow's milk version called *fior di latte* (flower of the milk) and tiny balls of cheese called *bocconcini* (little mouthfuls). Sometimes, the cheese is wound into plaits called *treccie*. All these are fresh cheeses, but mozzarella can also be smoked, which gives it a golden-brown colour and an interesting flavour. You will also find in supermarkets a pale yellow semi-hard mozzarella, which is sometimes sold ready-grated. This is the type used in cheap pizzas; it resembles mozzarella only in name and should be avoided.

HISTORY

No one is quite sure when water buffaloes were brought to Italy from India. They may have been introduced by the Greeks or the early Christians; certainly by the 16th century they had become a feature of southern Italian agricultural life. At this time, farmers began to use the buffalo milk to make mozzarella. Its popularity soon spread to the northern regions, where cheese-makers started to produce inferior versions made from cow's milk.

CULINARY USES

Fresh mozzarella is delicious served in an *insalata tricolore*, a salad in the colours of Italy, with white mozzarella, red tomatoes and fresh green basil. Smoked mozzarella is good in sandwiches or as part of an *antipasto*. When cooked, mozzarella becomes uniquely stringy, so it is perfect for topping pizzas or filling *mozzarella in carrozza* (mozzarella in a carriage), sandwiches dipped in beaten egg and deep-fried. A favourite Roman dish is *supplì al telefono*; mozzarella wrapped inside balls of cooked rice and fried until it melts to resemble telephone wires.

BUYING AND STORING

Cow's milk mozzarella is perfectly adequate for cooking, but for a really fine cheese try to buy *mozzarella di bufala*. Unopened, mozzarella will keep in the fridge for several days, but once the wrapping has been pierced it should be eaten as soon as possible. Opened mozzarella can be kept for a brief time in a covered bowl containing the whey from the bag or, failing that, skimmed milk or lightly salted water.

Mozzarella bocconcini
The name means "little mouthfuls"

Ricotta
Widely used in Italian cooking, ricotta can be combined with spinach for a ravioli filling, or used in desserts, such as cheesecake

Ricotta

Ricotta derives its name (literally "recooked") from the process of reheating the leftover whey from hard cheeses and adding a little fresh milk to make a soft white curd cheese with a rather solid yet granular consistency and a fat content of only about 20 per cent. The freshly made cheeses are traditionally put into baskets to drain and take their hemispherical shape and markings from these c*estelli* (little baskets).

Commercially produced ricotta is made from cow's milk, but in rural areas ewe's or goat's milk is sometimes used.

Ricotta salata is a hard, salted version of the cheese, made from the whey of Pecorino. It has a compact, flaky texture and looks rather like a hard Pecorino.

CULINARY USES
Ricotta is widely used in Italian cooking for both savoury and sweet dishes. It has an excellent texture but very little intrinsic flavour, so it makes a perfect vehicle for seasonings like black pepper and nutmeg or chopped fresh herbs. In its best-known form, it is puréed with cooked spinach to make a classic filling for ravioli, cannelloni or lasagne, or delicious light gnocchi.

It is often used in desserts, such as baked cheesecakes, or it can be sweetened and served with fruit.

Hard *ricotta salata* can be grated and used as a lower-fat substitute for Parmesan or Pecorino.

BUYING AND STORING
Fresh ricotta should always be eaten the day it is bought, as it quickly develops a sour taste. Most supermarkets sell a pre-packed version of the cheese, which has a much longer keeping time.

Ricotta salata is sometimes sold in pre-packed wedges, but for a good flavour and texture you should buy it freshly cut from a whole cheese. Tightly wrapped in foil, it will keep in the fridge for up to a month.

Ricotta salata
This hard, salted version of the cheese has a compact, flaky texture and can be used as a substitute for Parmesan or Pecorino

Cured Meats & Sausages

Every region of Italy has its own special cured meats and sausages, each differing as widely as the regions themselves. Prosciutto crudo *and* salami *appear in every guise and often constitute an* antipasto *(appetizer) on their own.*

HISTORY

Italy was traditionally an agricultural country, so almost every rural family kept a pig and cured every part of it, from snout to tail, to provide food for the family throughout the year. In any Italian larder, a range of home-cured hams, sausages and bacon would be found hanging from the ceiling. Nowadays hundreds of different types of hams, cured meats and sausages are commercially produced, many still using the old artisanal methods. Wherever you travel in Italy, you will find regional variations on the same theme.

Most of these cured meats are served as an *antipasto* before a meal. A Tuscan *antipasto* will consist of a selection of thinly sliced *affettati* (sliced ham and *salami*), and it is sometimes served with pickled vegetables, which are designed to whet the appetite.

Prosciutto crudo

Italy is famous for its *prosciutto crudo*, salted and air-dried ham that requires no cooking. The most famous of these hams, *prosciutto di Parma*, comes from the area around Parma, where Parmesan cheese is also made. The pigs in this region are fed partly on the whey from the cheese-making process, which makes their flesh very mild and sweet. Because they are always reared and kept in sheds and never allowed to roam outdoors, they tend to be rather fatty. Parma hams are made from the pig's hindquarters, which are lightly salted and air-dried for at least one year (and sometimes up to two). The zone of production of Parma ham is restricted by law to the area between the Taro and Baganza rivers, where the air and humidity levels are ideal for drying and curing the hams. In fact, every year thousands of ready-salted hams are sent here from neighbouring regions to be dried and cured in the unique air around Parma.

Prosciutto di Parma
The most famous Italian ham comes from the area around Parma, where Parmesan is also made

Prosciutto cotto
Italy also produces a range of cooked
hams, usually boiled. They can be
flavoured with all sorts of herbs and
spices. Cooked ham is sometimes
served as an *antipasto* together with
raw ham, but it is more often eaten
in sandwiches and snacks.

San Daniele
Some people regard these hams from
the Friuli region as superior even to
Parma ham. San Daniele pigs are
kept outside, so their flesh is leaner,
and their diet of acorns gives it a
distinctive flavour. San Daniele is
produced in much smaller quantities
than Parma ham, which makes it
even more expensive.

Prosciutto cotto
*This cooked ham is sometimes
served with sliced cured hams as
an* antipasto

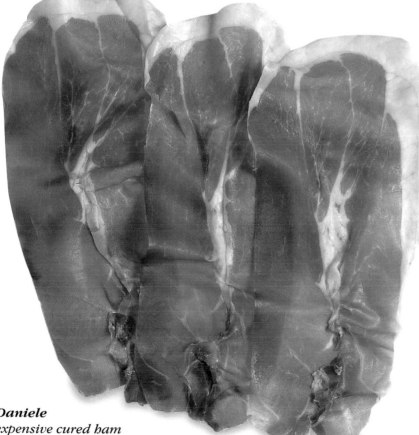

San Daniele
*This expensive cured ham
is considered by some to be
even finer than Parma ham*

CULINARY USES
Wafer-thin slices of *prosciutto crudo*
are delicious served with melon or
fresh figs or, when these are out of
season, with little cubes of unsalted
butter. If you serve bread with this
ham, that too should be unsalted to
counterbalance the salty-sweetness
of the ham. *Prosciutto crudo* can be
rolled up with thin slices of veal and
sage leaves and pan-fried in butter
and white wine or marsala to make
saltimbocca alla romana, finely
chopped and added to risotti and
pasta sauces, or used as a filling
for ravioli.

BUYING AND STORING
The best part of the ham comes from
the centre. Avoid buying the end
pieces, which are very salty and
rather chewy. Because *prosciutto
crudo* should be very thinly sliced,
buy only what you need at any one
time or it may dry out. Ideally you
should eat it on the day it is bought,
although it will keep in the fridge for
up to three days.

Cured Meats

Pancetta and Lardo

Pancetta resembles unsmoked bacon, except that it is not sold sliced, but rolled up into a sausage shape. It is made from pork belly, which is cured in salt and spices, to give it a mild flavour. *Lardo* is very similar (but flat) and less readily available.

CULINARY USES

Pancetta can be eaten raw as an *antipasto* (although it is very fatty), but it is usually cut into strips and cooked like bacon. It is an essential ingredient for *spaghetti alla carbonara*.

Pancetta
These round rolled slices of cured pork belly are the Italian equivalent of unsmoked bacon

Smoked pancetta
The smoked version of pancetta *is sold in thin strips rather than being rolled*

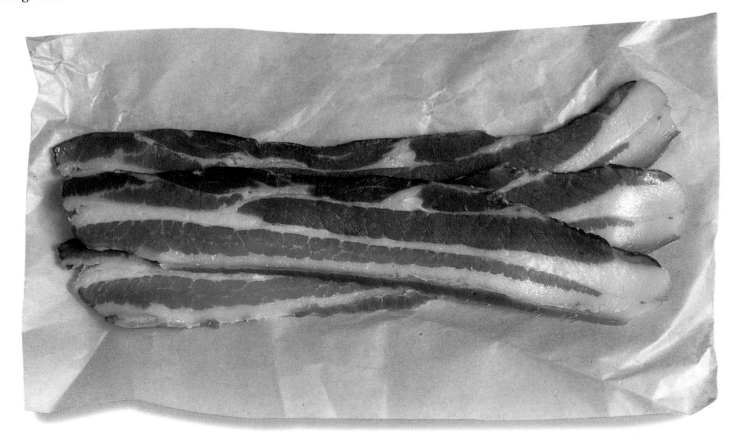

Speck

This fatty bacon is made from pork belly, which is smoke-cured over beechwood with herbs and spices, then air-dried. Sometimes it is covered with peppercorns or dried herbs, which add a distinctive flavour. It comes from the Tyrol, near the Swiss border, which explains its German-sounding name.

CULINARY USES

Speck is too fatty to be eaten raw, but it is used to add flavour to soups, stews and sauces. It is excellent cooked with fresh peas or lentils.

BUYING AND STORING

Italian bacon is sold in the piece, not sliced. Wrapped in clear film, *pancetta*, *lardo* and *speck* will keep in the fridge for up to one month.

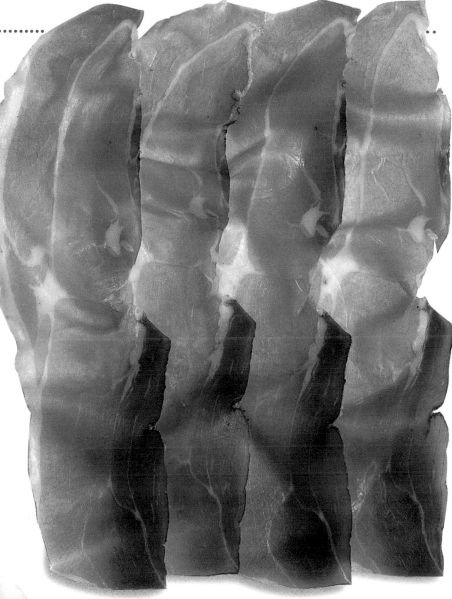

Speck
A fatty ham, smoke-cured over beechwood with herbs and spices, then air-dried

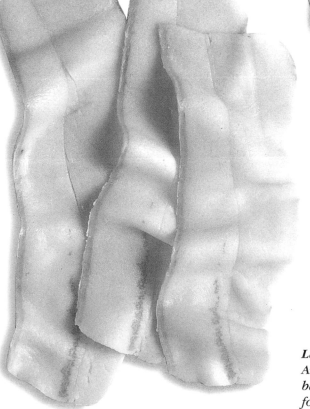

Lardo
An extremely fatty Italian bacon that is always used for cooking

Cured Meats

Bresaola

This cured raw beef is a speciality of Valtellina in Lombardy, but it is eaten and enjoyed all over Italy. It can be made from any cut of beef, but prime fillet produces the best bresaola. It is first cured in salt, then air-dried for many months before being pressed to produce an intensely dark red meat, which resembles *prosciutto crudo* in flavour, but is more delicate and less salty. Like *prosciutto crudo*, it is always sliced wafer-thin and served in small quantities, so you don't need to buy very much. Each bresaola weighs 2–3 kg/4¼–6¼ lb, depending on the size of the original cut of beef.

CULINARY USES

Bresaola is often served as an *antipasto*, sliced very thinly and simply dressed with a drizzle of extra virgin olive oil and a sprinkling of fresh lemon juice. In Lombardy, bresaola is sometimes wrapped around a filling of soft goat's cheese and then rolled up like cannelloni.

BUYING AND STORING

Only buy bresaola made from beef fillet. You can tell the type from the shape; that made from fillet is long with rounded edges, like the original cut of beef, while the cheaper bresaola made from other leg cuts is pressed into an oblong shape. Use it as soon as possible after slicing, preferably the same day, or it will dry out and develop an unpleasantly sharp flavour.

Bresaola
The delicate flavour of this salt-cured beef makes it perfect to serve, thinly sliced, as an antipasto

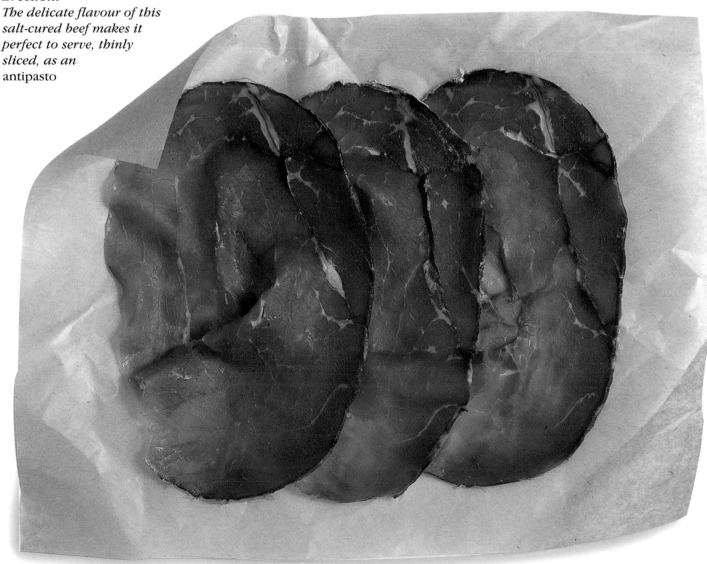

Sausages

Italy boasts almost as many different sausages as there are towns. Practically all are made with pork, although venison and wild boar sausages are popular in country areas. Most sausages and salami are factory-produced nowadays, but many towns in Italy still have *salumerie* (sausage shops) selling home-made sausages flavoured with local produce, such as wild mushrooms or herbs and spices. The most famous sausage-producing town is Bologna. Fresh sausages are made from coarsely chopped pork and contain a high proportion of fat for extra flavour. They are usually sold in links, tied together with string. Most Italian sausages, however, are cured and ready to eat.

Luganega

A speciality of northern Italy, luganega is a mild spiced country sausage made from pork, which often contains Parmesan cheese. Sometimes known as *salsiccia a metro*, because it is sold in a long continuous rope, which is coiled up like a snake, and is sold by the metre or whatever length you require. It can be grilled or pan-fried with white wine and is often served on a bed of lentils or mashed potatoes. Luganega can also be cut into short lengths and stirred into a hearty risotto.

Cotechino

A large fresh pork sausage weighing about 1 kg/2¼ lb, which has been lightly spiced and salted for only a few days. Cotechino is a speciality of Emilia Romagna, Lombardy and the Veneto. It takes its name from *coteca* meaning "skin".

COOKING COTECHINO

Cotechino is boiled and served hot, often as part of a bollito misto *(mixed boiled meats). Pierce the skin in several places and place the sausage in a large saucepan. Cover with cold water and bring slowly to the boil, then simmer slowly for 2–3 hours.*

Slice the cotechino thickly and serve on a bed of cooked lentils, mashed potatoes or cannellini beans.

Luganega
This mildly spiced sausage, which is coiled up like a snake, is sold by the metre, or whatever length you require

Sausages

Coppa

This salted and dried sausage is made from neck or shoulder of pork, and the casing is made from natural skin. *Coppa* has a roughly rectangular shape and a rich deep red colour. It comes from Lombardy and Emilia Romagna, although, confusingly, in Rome you will find a *coppa* that is a sort of pig's head brawn (this variety is never exported).

Zampone

This speciality sausage from Modena is a pig's trotter stuffed with minced pork shoulder and other cuts, including some skin. The stuffing has a creamy texture and the skin of the trotter encloses it to retain its original shape, complete with feet. Each zampone weighs up to 2 kg/4¼ lb.

Coppa
Roughly rectangular in shape, this sausage has a rich, deep red colour

Zampone
A part-cooked zampone needs only to be heated through

COOKING ZAMPONE

A raw zampone needs to be boiled for 2–3 hours, depending on the size, although some vacuum-packed varieties are already part-cooked and need only to be heated through. For a fresh zampone, make a couple of incisions in the skin and cook in the same way as cotechino. Zampone is traditionally sliced into rings and served with lentils or mashed potatoes. A bollito misto *often contains a* zampone.

Mortadella

The most famous of all the sausages from Bologna, mortadella is also the largest, often having a diameter of up to 45 cm/18 in. Nowadays it is cooked in hot-air ovens to a core temperature of 72°C/140°F, which means that it will keep for several weeks. It is considered to be the finest Italian pork sausage, with its wonderfully smooth texture, although it has a rather bland flavour. Apart from its huge size, mortadella is distinctive for its delicate, pale pink colour studded with cubes of creamy white fat and sometimes pale green pistachios. It is the original *bologna* or "boloney" so beloved in America.

BUYING

Authentic Bolognese mortadella is made only from pure pork, but cheaper varieties may contain all sorts of other ingredients, such as beef, tripe, pig's head, soya flour and artificial colourings.

Beware of mortadella that looks too violently pink and, if you are buying it sliced and pre-packed, check the ingredients on the packet before you buy.

CULINARY USES

Mortadella is usually thinly sliced and eaten cold, either in a sandwich or as part of a plate of assorted cold meats as an *antipasto*. It can also be cubed and stirred into risotti or pasta sauces just before the end of cooking, or finely chopped to make an excellent stuffing for poultry or filled pasta.

Mortadella
Considered to be the finest Italian cooked sausage, mortadella has a wonderfully smooth texture, but a rather bland flavour. It is studded with cubes of creamy fat, and often has pale green pistachios peppered through the meat

Salami

Salami

There are dozens of types of *salami*, whose texture and flavour reflect the character and traditions of the different regions of Italy. Essentially, all *salami* are made from pure pork, but the finished product varies according to the kind of meat used, the proportion of lean meat to fat, how finely it is minced, the seasonings and the period of drying and seasoning.

Salame di Felino

This soft, coarse-cut sausage comes from Felino near Parma and is regarded as one of the finest Italian *salami*. It has a very high proportion of lean pork to fat

and is flavoured with peppercorns, a small amount of garlic and the local white wine. Because it is only very lightly cured, it has a very delicate flavour but does not keep well. You may find it in good Italian delicatessens, where it is easily recognizable by its uneven truncheon shape, which makes it look hand-made. Like its neighbour, Parma ham, *salame di Felino* is very expensive, but well worth the cost.

Salame fiorentina

This large coarse-cut pork sausage from Tuscany is often flavoured with fennel seeds and pepper, when it is known as *finocchiona*. The fennel gives it a very distinctive flavour.

Salame di Felino
One of the finest Italian salame
– this lightly cured sausage is
flavoured with peppercorns,
garlic and white wine

Salame fiorentina
This coarse-cut pork sausage from
Tuscany is often flavoured with
fennel seeds and pepper

Salame milano

Probably the most commonly found of all *salami*, this Milanese sausage is made from equal quantities of finely minced pork, fat and beef, seasoned with pepper, garlic and white wine. It is deep red in colour and speckled with grains of fat resembling rice. Also known as *crespone*, it is mass-produced and regarded as inferior to most other *salami*. There is also a small whole *salame milanese*, weighing about 500 g/1¼ lb, called *cacciatoro*, which is cured and matured for a much shorter time and has a more delicate flavour and softer texture.

Salame sardo

This fiery red *salame* from Sardinia is a rustic sausage flavoured with red pepper. A similar sausage is *salame napoletano* from Naples, which uses a mixture of black and red pepper for a powerful kick.

Salame ungharese

Despite its name, this *salame* is manufactured in Italy, using a Hungarian recipe. It is made from very finely minced pure pork or pork and beef, and flavoured with paprika, pepper, garlic and white wine. The fat is evenly spread throughout the sausage, giving it a mottled appearance.

BUYING AND STORING

With the exception of *salame di Felino*, almost all *salami* can be bought ready-sliced and vacuum-packed, but taste much better if they are freshly cut from a whole *salame*. A good delicatessen will slice the *salami* to the thickness you require. Ideally, it should be eaten the same day, but it will keep for three or four days in the fridge.

Salame ungharese
Made in Italy to a Hungarian recipe

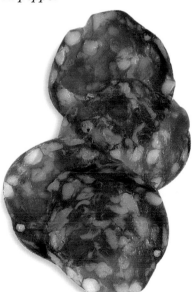

Salame sardo
A fiery salame *flavoured with red pepper*

Salame napoletano
Similar to salame sardo, *this* salame *uses a mix of black and red pepper*

Salame milano

Cacciatoro
This small whole salame milanese *is cured and matured for only a short time*

Meat & Poultry

Until recently, meat did not figure largely in Italian cooking, which relied much more heavily on the peasant staples of pasta, bread, vegetables and, in coastal areas, fish. As the country became more prosperous, however, more people added meat to their daily diet and now animals are farmed all over Italy to provide veal, pork, beef, lamb and kid.

Veal is a favourite meat in Italy and appears in innumerable recipes from every region. The best comes from milk-fed calves that are reared in Piedmont. The area around Rome is famous for its lamb, and spit-roasted suckling lamb and kid are popular specialities of the region. Superb beef cattle are bred in Tuscany, but the beef from other regions comes from working cattle that have reached the end of their useful lives, and is best used for stews and dishes that require long, slow cooking.

Many peasant families in Italy still own a pig, which provides pork as well as a huge variety of hams, sausages and other cured meats. Every part of the pig is eaten in one form or another, from snout to tail. Indeed, Italians never waste any edible part of their meat, so offal of all kinds is used in many dishes. A Tuscan *fritto misto* is composed of a variety of offal ranging from brains to sweetbreads and lungs, while the Milanese version also includes cockscombs – so, unless you are an offal lover, be warned if you see these dishes on a menu!

Poultry is another popular food. Factory farming does exist in Italy, but many flavoursome free-range birds are still available. Chicken, guinea fowl and turkey appear in a huge variety of simple and delicious dishes, usually filleted for quick cooking. Duck and goose make their appearance, too, often cooked with sharp fruits to counteract the richness of the meat. Many recipes use wild duck, shot by the enthusiastic (some say over-enthusiastic) hunters who abound in every region. Mercifully, the Italian habit of shooting every type of wild bird,

whether edible or not, is less prevalent than it was; but hunters are lax about observing a close season for shooting, so game, both feathered and furred, seems to be available almost all year round.

Abbacchio and agnello (lamb)

Lambs are bred mainly in southern Italy, particularly in the area around Rome. They are slaughtered at different ages, resulting in distinctive flavours and texture. The youngest lamb is *abbacchio*, month-old milk-fed lamb from Lazio, whose pale pinkish flesh is meltingly tender. *Abbachio* is usually spit-roasted whole. Spring lamb, aged about four months, is often sold as *abbacchio*. It has darker flesh, which is also very tender and can be used for roasting or grilling. A leg of spring lamb weighs about 1–1.5 kg/ 2¼–3½ lb. Older lamb (*agnello*) has a slightly stronger flavour and is suitable for roasting or stewing.

Lamb cutlets
Allow at least three small, succulent lamb cutlets like these per serving

Leg of lamb
A leg of darker-coloured spring lamb is perfect for roasting whole

COOK'S TIP
A leg of baby abbacchio *is only enough for two people. Roast in a medium oven for about 30 minutes, basting occasionally.*

CHOOSING

Italian lamb tends to be seasonal, so your choice may be restricted according to the time of year. *Abbacchio* should have very pale flesh, almost like veal. A milk-fed lamb will be not much bigger than a rabbit. Spring lamb should have more pinkish flesh and very little fat. Mature lamb should have dark red flesh with a layer of creamy fat on the outside.

CULINARY USES

Lamb is cooked in a variety of ways, from *al forno* (roast) to *costolette alla milanese* (fried breaded cutlets). Roast lamb is the traditional Easter dish. It is not cut into thin slices, but served in large chunks, which should be so tender that they fall off the bone. A favourite recipe for spring lamb is *agnello alla giudea* (Jewish-style lamb), braised in a delicate egg and lemon sauce.

Maiale (pork)

Most Italian pork is transformed into sausages, salami and hams, but fresh meat is enjoyed all over Italy, often combined with local herbs like rosemary, fennel or sage. Different regions eat different parts of the pig; Tuscany is famous for its *arista di maiale alla fiorentina*, (loin of pork roasted with rosemary), while in Naples *il musso* (the snout) is considered a great delicacy.

Pork cutlets
Tender chops or cutlets can be grilled or braised with herbs

CULINARY USES

Pork chops or cutlets can be grilled or braised with herbs or artichokes. Loin of pork is deliciously tender braised in milk (*arrosto di maiale al latte*), or it can be roasted with rosemary or sage.

Meat & Poultry

Manzo (beef)

The quality of Italian beef has an unjustifiably poor reputation. It is true that in agricultural areas, particularly the south, beef can be stringy and tough. This is because the cattle are working animals, not bred for the table, and are only eaten towards the end of their hard-working life. This type of beef is only suitable for long, slow-cooked country stews. In Tuscany, however, superb beef cattle from Val di Chiana produce meat that can rival any other world-renowned beef and which provide the magnificent *bistecche alla fiorentina* (T-bone steaks).

CULINARY USES

Thick-cut T-bone steaks (*bistecche alla fiorentina*) from Val di Chiana cattle are grilled over wood fires until well-browned on the outside and very rare inside. Rump or fillet steaks are also cooked very rare and sliced on the bias as a *tagliata*. A modern creation is *carpaccio*, wafer-thin slices of raw beef marinated in olive oil and aromatics and served as an *antipasto*. Thinly sliced topside is rolled around a stuffing to make *involtini* (beef olives). A favourite Italian family dish is *bollito misto*, a mixture of boiled meats and offal including beef. Leftover boiled beef can be sliced and made into a salad.

Less tender cuts of meat are usually braised, stewed or minced to be used in *ragù* (meat sauce) or *polpettone* (meat balls).

T-bone steak
Italian cooks like to grill these large steaks over wood fires

Beef olives
Thinly sliced topside rolled around a flavourful stuffing

Minced beef
Less tender cuts of beef are minced and used for ragù *(meat sauce) or* polpettone *(meatballs)*

Carpaccio
These wafer-thin slices of raw beef are simply marinated in olive oil and served as an antipasto

Frattaglie (offal)

Nothing is wasted in Italian butchery, so a huge variety of offal is available. Liver is a great favourite; the finest is *fegato di vitello*, tender calf's liver, which is regarded as a luxury. Chicken livers are popular for topping *crostini* or for pasta sauces and pork liver is a speciality of Tuscany. Butchers often sell pig's liver ready-wrapped in natural caul (*rete*), which keeps the liver tender as it cooks. Lamb's and calf's kidneys (*rognoni or rognoncini*), brains (*cervello*) and sweetbreads (*animelle*) are specialities of northern Italy. They are similar in texture and flavour, but sweetbreads are creamier and more delicate. Every region has its own recipes for tripe (*trippa*); this almost always comes from veal calves rather than other cattle, whose tripe has a coarser texture and flavour. All parts of a veal calf are considered great delicacies. The head is used in *bollito misto* (mixed boiled meats), and the trotters give substance to soups and stews. Oxtail (*coda di bue*) comes from older beef cattle.

Oxtail
Nothing is wasted in Italian butchery – the oxtail is used for wonderful slow-cooked stews and soups

Chicken livers
These rich-tasting livers are a popular topping for crostini

Pig's liver
This is a speciality of Tuscany

Calf's liver
Thinly sliced, this is often simply pan-fried with onions

COOKING OFFAL

Most offal will benefit from being soaked in milk before cooking to remove any coarseness of flavour. Some types, like liver and brains, require very little cooking in order to preserve their delicate texture. In Venice, thinly sliced calf's liver is cooked with onions to make *fegato alla veneziana*; this is often served with grilled polenta. The Milanese version is coated in egg and breadcrumbs and fried in butter. The simplest and one of the most delicious ways with liver is to sauté it quickly in butter with fresh sage. Brains and sweetbreads can be blanched, then quickly fried in butter, or pounded to a paste and made into croquettes (*crocchette*). Kidneys should be sautéed in butter, or braised with wine and onions or Marsala (*trifolati*). Pre-prepared (dressed) tripe will have been scrubbed, soaked and boiled by the butcher, but it should still be blanched for 30 minutes before cooking. Tripe can be prepared *alla fiorentina* in tomato sauce flavoured with oregano or marjoram; the version from Parma (*alla parmigiana*) is fried in butter and topped with Parmesan cheese, while in Bologna, eggs are added to the mixture.

Meat & Poultry

Vitello (veal)

Veal is the most popular meat in Italy and appears in hundreds of different recipes. Like lamb, calves are slaughtered at different ages to produce different qualities of meat. The best and most expensive veal is *vitello di latte* from Piedmont and Lombardy. The calves are fed only on milk and are slaughtered at just a few weeks old, producing extremely tender, very pale meat with no fat. Older calves, up to nine months old, are known as *vitello*. Their flesh is still tender, but darker in colour than milk-fed veal. *Vitellone* is somewhere between veal and beef. It comes from bullocks aged between one and three years, which have never worked in the fields and whose flesh is therefore still quite tender and lighter in colour than beef.

CULINARY USES

Young, milk-fed veal is ideal for *scaloppine* (escalopes) and *piccate* (thin escalopes), which need very little cooking. *Vitello* can be served as chops, cutlets or a rolled roast. The shin is cut into *osso buco* (literally "bone with a hole"), complete with bone marrow, or *schinco* (the whole shin), and braised until meltingly tender. An unusual combination which works wonderfully well is *vitello tonnato*, cold roast veal thinly sliced and coated in a rich tuna sauce. *Vitellone* should be treated like tender beef. It can be grilled, roasted or casseroled, but it is not suitable for escalopes or similar cuts.

CHOOSING

Young veal should have very pale, slightly rosy fine-grained flesh with no trace of fat. *Vitellone* should be pinker and paler than beef, with only a faint marbling of fat, and should feel firm, not flabby. Escalopes and *piccate* must be cut only from very young veal. They should be sliced across the grain so that they keep their shape and do not shrivel during cooking. If you are buying boned veal, ask the butcher to give you the bones, which make wonderful stock.

Veal escalopes
These are always sliced very thinly across the grain

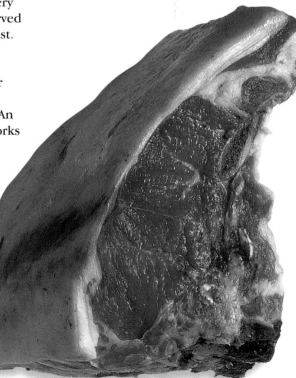

Loin of veal
Usually boned, then roasted with herbs – the bones make the most wonderful stock

COOKING VEAL

Escalopes should be pounded lightly, dusted with flour and fried for just a few moments on each side. The pan juices can be mixed with lemon, white wine or Marsala to make a sauce. Very thin escalopes can be rolled around a stuffing and braised in tomato sauce. Cutlets can be coated with egg and breadcrumbs alla milanese *and fried until golden, or seasoned with herbs and gently cooked with white wine. Costolette alla valdostana are stuffed with Fontina cheese and fried in butter.*
Loin of veal is usually boned and roasted with herbs, or braised in milk. Less tender cuts like shoulder and breast are casseroled or braised.

Cinghiale (wild boar)

Wild boar are the ancestors of the domestic pig, which used to roam in large numbers in the forests of Tuscany and Sardinia, but which are becoming increasingly rare thanks to the predisposition of some Italians to shoot anything that moves. Baby wild boar are an enchanting sight, with light brown fur striped with horizontal black bands. The adults have coarse, brown coats and fierce-looking tusks. The flesh of a young *cinghiale* is as pale and tender as pork; older animals have very dark flesh, which is tougher but full of flavour.

CULINARY USES

Haunches of wild boar are made into hams, which are displayed in butchers' shops. Young animals can be cooked in the same way as pork. Older boar must be marinated for at least 24 hours to tenderize the meat before roasting or casseroling. The classic sweet and sour sauce, (*agrodolce*), sharpened with red wine vinegar, complements the gamey flavour of the meat.

Coniglio (rabbit) and lepre (hare)

Farmed and wild rabbits often replace chicken or veal in Italian cooking. The meat is very pale and lean and the taste is somewhere between that of good-quality farmhouse chicken and veal. Wild rabbit has a stronger flavour, which combines well with robust flavours; farmed rabbit is very tender and much more delicate.

Hare cannot be farmed, so the only animals available come from the wild. Given the Italian obsession with hunting, it is a miracle that the hare population has not been totally decimated. These wily creatures, however, must sometimes escape the gun, as they continue to breed. A hare weighs about twice as much as a rabbit (2 kg/4¼ lb is about average). The flesh is a rich, dark brown and has a strong gamey flavour similar to that of wild rabbit.

Hare
This is always wild – the rich brown flesh has a strong gamey flavour

Rabbit
This can be bought either farmed or wild – wild rabbit has a stronger flavour

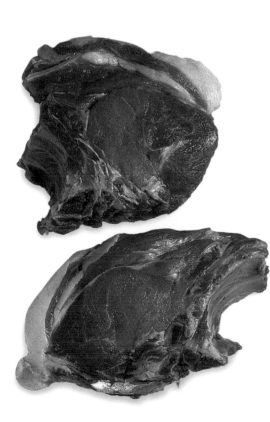

Wild boar
Chops like these can be cooked in the same way as pork

CULINARY USES

Farmed rabbit can replace chicken or turkey in almost any recipe. Wild rabbit can be stewed or braised in white wine or Marsala, or with aubergines, bacon and tomatoes. It can be roasted with root vegetables or fresh herbs. In Sicily, rabbit is often cooked with sultanas and pine nuts in an *agrodolce* (sweet and sour) sauce.

Hare is generally casseroled in red wine or Marsala, cooked *in agrodolce* or made into a rich sauce for pappardelle or other wide noodles. Both rabbit and hare are often served with polenta or fried bread.

COOKING RABBIT AND HARE

Wild rabbit and hare must be cut into six or eight pieces and marinated in red wine and aromatics for 24 hours before cooking. If you like a sweet and sour flavour (game in agrodolce is very popular in Italy), add plenty of red wine vinegar to the marinade. A rabbit weighing about 1 kg/2¼ lb when cleaned will need about 1½ hour's braising or stewing; a hare needs about 2 hours.

Meat & Poultry

Fagiano (pheasant)

Occasionally in the Italian countryside, you may still catch a glimpse of a pheasant with its beautiful plumage and long tail feathers. Cock pheasants have bright, iridescent blue and green feathers, while hens are browner and less dramatic-looking. Pheasant farming is still unknown in Italy, and wild pheasants are something of a rarity, so they are regarded as a luxury. They are not hung, but are eaten almost as soon as they are shot, so their flavour is less gamey than in some other countries. Although pheasants are expensive, they are meaty birds for their size, so a cock pheasant will feed three to four people and a hen pheasant two to three.

CULINARY USES

Hen pheasants are smaller than cocks, but their meat is juicier and the flavour is finer. Young hen pheasants can be roasted with or without a stuffing, but cock birds are more suitable for casseroling. Pheasant breast can tend to be dry, so they should be well barded with bacon or thickly smeared with butter before roasting. A good knob of butter placed inside the cavity will help to keep the flesh moist. For special occasions, pheasants can be stuffed with candied fruits or pomegranate seeds and nuts. Pheasant breasts can be sautéed and served with a wine or balsamic vinegar sauce, but they can sometimes be rather dry.

Pheasant
Usually eaten as soon as they are shot, Italian pheasants are less gamey than in some other countries. Remember that pheasants contain lead shot pellets, so take care not to bite on these!

COOKING QUAIL

Quail should be browned in butter until golden all over, then roasted in a hot oven for about 15 minutes. Their flavour is well complemented by the fruit of the vine, so they are often served with a light sauce containing grapes or raisins soaked in grappa. They can also be wrapped in vine leaves before roasting, which keeps them moist and adds a delicious flavour.

Quaglie (quail)

These small migratory birds are found in Italy throughout the summer months. Wild quails have the reputation of being so stupid that they never run away from hunters, but stay rooted to the spot as sitting targets. As a result, they have become very rare, and most of the birds now available are farmed. They are very small (you need two to serve one person) and have a delicate, subtly gamey flavour. Farmed quails have less flavour than the wild birds and benefit from added flavourings, such as grapes.

COOKING PHEASANTS

Unless you know for sure that a pheasant is very young, it is best to wrap the breast in streaky bacon before roasting to prevent dryness. To roast a pheasant, put a knob of butter inside the cavity, or make a stuffing, drape bacon rashers over the breast and roast at 200 °C/400 °F/Gas 6 for about 40 minutes, until tender. Plain roast pheasant is often served with a risotto. Pheasant can also be pot-roasted or casseroled with wine and herbs. If you are serving cock birds, it is worth removing the lower part of the legs after cooking, as they contain hard sinews that are not pleasant to eat.

Quail
These birds have a very delicate, gamey flavour. They are very small, and so you will need to serve two per person.

Faraona (guinea fowl)

Guinea fowl are extremely decorative birds with luxuriant grey-and-white spotted plumage. They originated in West Africa, but are now farmed all over Europe, so that, although they are technically game, they are classified as poultry. They taste similar to chicken, but have a firmer texture and a more robust flavour.

COOKING GUINEA FOWL

Although their abundant plumage makes them seem larger, guinea fowl are only about the size of a small spring chicken, so one bird will not feed more than three people. To roast guinea fowl, bard the breasts with bacon rashers and roast like chicken, basting frequently. A vegetable stuffing will keep the flesh moist. Guinea fowl can be substituted for chicken or turkey in any recipe.

CULINARY USES

Guinea fowl are hugely popular in Italy, where they are served in much the same ways as chicken. The flesh of an adult guinea fowl is firmer than that of a chicken, so it is best to bard it or cover the breasts with bacon rashers before roasting. The breasts are sometimes sautéed and served with the pan juices mixed with balsamic vinegar, or with a sauce of cream and Marsala. The birds can be roasted or pot-roasted whole, or cut into serving pieces and casseroled with mushrooms (wild mushrooms are especially delicious) or herbs. A favourite autumn dish in Tuscany is guinea fowl braised with chestnuts.

Guinea fowl
These popular birds can be pot-roasted, roasted or casseroled with wild mushrooms

Piccione (pigeon)

Wood pigeons have dark, gamey flesh and a robust flavour, which the Italians love. They are generally too tough to roast, but they make the most delicious casseroles. Domestic pigeons are also reared for food and you will often see large dovecotes in farmyards. Domestic birds are less likely to be tough than wild ones, but their flavour is less robust.

Wild pigeon
Italians love the rich, robust flavour of these small birds; however, they can be very tough, so cook them very slowly, either by braising or casseroling

COOKING PIGEONS

Wild pigeons can be tough, so, unless you are sure that they are young, it is best to casserole them. In Tuscany, they are braised with tomatoes and olives; the classic Venetian way is to stew them with pancetta, ox tongue and fresh green peas. If you desperately want to roast wild pigeons, marinate them in a red wine marinade for three days before cooking, then stuff them with a moist vegetable stuffing. Cover the breasts with streaky bacon and roast in a hot oven for about 20 minutes, basting with the marinade every few minutes.

Fish & Shellfish

Italy's extensive coastal waters once teemed with a huge variety of fish and shellfish, many unique to that part of the Adriatic and Mediterranean. Sadly, pollution and over-fishing have taken their toll, and there is no longer the abundance of seafood there once was, but what remains is of excellent quality. A visit to an Italian fish market will reveal fish and shellfish of every description, some beautiful, some hideous, many unknown outside Italy. Italians like their seafood very fresh and tend to cook it simply, without elaborate sauces. Large fish are usually plainly grilled or baked and dressed with olive oil, or baked in cartoccio (enclosed in a paper bag). Small fry are deep-fried for a crisp fritto misto di mare. Every coastal area has its own version of fish soup, which uses a mixture of local fish and constitutes a meal in itself – cacciucco from Livorno, cold burrida from Sardinia, brodetto from the Adriatic coast – each region claims that its version is the best.

I t is impossible to give a complete list of all the fish that you will find in Italy. Popular favourites include *coda di rospo* (monkfish), *dentice* (dentex – a white-fleshed fish found only in Italy), *sogliola* (sole) and even non-indigenous fish such as salmon.

Freshwater fish – trout, perch, carp and eels – abound in the lakes and rivers and are eaten with gusto. Eels are regarded as a particular delicacy and are cooked in many different ways, from grilling to baking, stewing and frying.

Some fish are dried, salted or preserved in oil. The most popular is tuna, which is packed in olive oil and sold by weight from huge cans. *Baccalà* is salted dried cod, which is creamed to a rich paste or made into soups and stews. Anchovies are salted, or packed in olive oil, or preserved in a sweet and sour marinade. Sardines are also very popular and are used to make a Sicilian pasta sauce.

Anchovies
Canned in olive oil (above) or salted (left) – these tiny, strong-tasting fish are used to add flavour to pasta sauces and salads

Salt cod *(baccalà)*
This dried fish is creamed to a paste or made into soups and stews

CHOOSING FRESH FISH

You can almost guarantee that any fish you buy in an Italian early morning market will be ultra-fresh, but in fishmongers and restaurants you should look for pointers. Fish should have bright, slightly bulging eyes and shiny, faintly slimy skin. Open up the gills to check that they are clear red or dark pink and prod the fish lightly to check that the flesh is springy. All fish should have only a faint, pleasant smell; you can tell a stale fish a mile off by its disagreeable odour.

Orata (gilt-head sea bream)

This Mediterranean fish takes its name from the crescent-shaped golden mark on its domed head and the gold spots on each cheek. It has beautiful silvery scales and slightly coarse but delicious flaky white flesh. Orate usually weigh between 600 g/1 lb 6 oz and 1 kg/2¼ lb; a larger fish will serve two greedy people. Orata is best simply grilled, baked *in cartoccio* or barbecued.

Pesce spada (swordfish)

In Italy, you will occasionally find a whole swordfish on the fishmonger's slab. These huge Mediterranean fish, up to 5 metres/15 feet long and weighing 100–500 kg/220–1200 lb, are immediately recognizable by their long sword-like upper jaw. Because of their size, they are more usually sold cut into steaks. Their firm, close-grained, almost meaty flesh has given them a nickname of "steak of the sea".

COOKING SWORDFISH

Swordfish tends to be dry, so it should be marinated in oil and lemon juice or wine and herbs before cooking. It is excellent grilled or barbecued, or part-cooked in butter or olive oil, then baked in a sauce. Its firm texture makes it ideal for kebabs. It is plentiful in the waters around Sicily, where it is cooked with traditional Mediterranean ingredients like tomatoes, olives, capers, sultanas and pine nuts. Another popular Sicilian dish is bracciole di pesce spada, thin slices of swordfish rolled around a stuffing of breadcrumbs, mozzarella and herbs and grilled. It is also delicious sliced wafer-thin, marinated in olive oil, lemon juice and herbs and served raw.

Swordfish
Often either baked or grilled, this firm-fleshed fish needs to be marinated to keep it moist during cooking

Tuna
Immensely popular throughout Italy, canned tuna in oil is either sold by weight from huge cans or bought in small cans like these

TONNO ALL'OLIO D'OLIVA

NOSTROMO

TONNO DI PRIMA SCELTA

300 g

Fish

Sarde or sardelle (sardines)

Fresh sardines probably take their name from Sardinia, where they were once abundant. These small, silvery fish are still found in Mediterranean waters, where they grow to about 13 cm/5 in. They are at their best in spring. Allow about four larger sardines or six smaller fish per serving. Sardines have very oily flesh and should only be eaten when extremely fresh. They can also be bought preserved in oil or salt.

PREPARING AND COOKING SARDINES

Sardines should be gutted before cooking. If the fishmonger has not already done this, cut the head almost through to the backbone and pull it off; the gut will come away with the head.

Sardines can be barbecued, grilled or baked alla genovese with potatoes, garlic and parsley. Their oily flesh combines well with spices and tart ingredients like capers and olives. In Sicily they are stuffed with breadcrumbs, pine nuts, sultanas and anchovies and fried, then finished in the oven (a beccaficcu). Sardines can also be deep-fried, either plain or stuffed with mushrooms, herbs and cheese (alla ligure) or with chopped spinach and cream (alla romana).

Sardines
These fish are at their best in the spring

Spigola or branzino (sea bass)

The silvery sea bass, which come from Mediterranean waters, are as beautiful to look at as to eat, although their rapacious nature has earned them the nickname of "sea wolf". These slim, elegant fish are almost always sold whole and rarely weigh much more than 1 kg/2¼ lb, so one fish will feed no more than two or three people. Sea bass is prized for its delicate white flesh and lack of irritating small bones. As a result, it is never cheap.

One way of bringing the price down is to farm sea bass, but the flavour of the farmed fish is not so fine as that of wild sea bass, whose predatory habits ensure that their flesh develops a full flavour. So far, farming of these wonderful fish does not seem to have caught on in Italy, where flavour is rarely compromised for cost.

PREPARING AND COOKING SEA BASS

Sea bass should be gutted before cooking. They have quite hard scales, which should be removed before grilling or pan-frying. Scale the fish with a de-scaler or blunt knife, working from the tail towards the head. If you are going to poach or bake sea bass, leave the scales on, as they will hold the fragile flesh together.

Sea bass has rather soft flesh, so it is best grilled, barbecued or pan-fried and dressed with a trickle of olive oil. It can be stuffed with sprigs of fresh herbs (fennel is particularly good) and baked in the oven for 20–30 minutes, depending on the size of the fish. For spigola alla livornese, lay the fish in an ovenproof dish on a layer of rich tomato sauce, sprinkle with seasoned breadcrumbs and olive oil and bake.

Triglia (red mullet)

These small Mediterranean fish rarely weigh more than 1 kg/2¼ lb. They have bright rose-coloured skin and a faint golden streak along their sides. Their flesh is succulent with a distinctive, almost prawn-like flavour, quite unlike any other fish. The liver of red mullet is regarded as a great delicacy and is not removed during cooking, which gives the mullet its nickname of "sea woodcock". Red mullet are extremely perishable and should be eaten the day they are bought. The skin should always look very bright; dullness is a sure indication that the fish is not fresh.

PREPARING AND COOKING RED MULLET

Larger fish should be scaled before cooking, but be warned – this is a delicate operation, as the skin is very fragile. Scaling is worth the effort, however, as it reveals the wonderful red skin in all its glory. Red mullet combines well with traditional Mediterranean flavours of olive oil, black olives, herbs, garlic, saffron and tomatoes. It can be baked, grilled or cooked in cartoccio with powerful herbs like rosemary or fennel. For triglia all'italiana, place whole red mullet on a bed of finely chopped mushrooms and onions that have been sweated until soft and mixed with fresh breadcrumbs, and bake for 20–30 minutes.

Red mullet
The flesh of these pretty fish has a distinctive almost prawn-like flavour

Sea bass
Prized for their delicate white flesh, these slim, elegant fish are almost always sold whole

Shellfish

Italian coastal waters are host to a huge variety of shellfish and crustaceans, many with wonderfully exotic names like *datteri di mare* (sea dates; a kind of mussel), *tartufi di mare* (sea truffles; a type of clam) and *fragolino di mare* (sea strawberry; a tiny octopus that turns bright pink when cooked). Almost all seafood is considered edible, from clams to *cannolichi* (razor-shells), *lumache di mare* (sea snails) and *canestrelli* (small scallops). Shrimps and prawns come in all sizes and colours, from vibrant red to pale grey, while crustaceans range from bright orange crawfish to blue-black lobsters.

COOKING SQUID AND CUTTLEFISH

Small squid and cuttlefish should be cooked only briefly – just until they turn opaque – or they will become rubbery and tough.
Larger specimens need long, slow cooking to make them tender. They can be stuffed with minced fish or meat, anchovies and seasoned breadcrumbs or rice, and baked with tomatoes and wine sauce until tender, or cut into rings and fried in a light batter, or simply dusted with seasoned plain flour and deep-fried.
Squid and cuttlefish are also delicious stewed in their own ink; seal the molluscs in hot oil with some chopped onions and garlic, add finely chopped fresh parsley and seasoning, then cover with dry white wine and a little water and simmer gently for 15 minutes. Crush the ink sacs, mix the inky liquid with a little cold water and 30–45 ml/ 2–3 tbsp plain flour and work to a smooth paste. Add the flour mixture to the pan and cook for another 5–10 minutes.

Squid
Large specimens like this one need long, slow cooking to make them tender – conversely small baby squid should be cooked very quickly or they will become tough

Calamari or totani (squid) *and* seppie (cuttlefish)

Despite their appearance, squid and cuttlefish are actually molluscs, whose shell is located inside the body. They are indistinguishable in taste, but cuttlefish have a larger head and a wider body with stubbier tentacles. The cuttlebone much beloved of budgerigars and parrots is the bone of the cuttlefish inside the body. Once this has been removed, cuttlefish are very tender. The "shell" of a squid is nothing more than a long, thin, transparent quill. Both *seppie* and *calamari* have ten tentacles.

Squid and cuttlefish are immensely popular in Italy, cut into rings and served as part of either an *insalata di mare* (seafood salad) or *fritto misto* (mixed fried fish). Their black ink is used to flavour and colour risotto and fresh pasta.

PREPARING AND COOKING MUSSELS

Scrub the shells under cold running water. Pull away the "beard" protruding from the shell. Give any open mussels a sharp tap; they should close immediately. Discard any which do not, as they are probably dead.
The simplest way to cook mussels is alla marinara. *For 4 people, finely chop 1 large onion, 2 garlic cloves and 15 ml/1 tbsp chopped parsley, put in a large pan with 300 ml/10 fl oz/2¼ cups white wine and simmer for 5 minutes. Add the scrubbed mussels, cover and steam, shaking the pan from time to time, for 5 minutes, or until the shells have opened. Discard any unopened mussels, sprinkle the rest with extra parsley and serve. For a richer sauce, transfer the mussels to a bowl and reduce the sauce over a high heat. Pour over the shellfish and serve.*

PREPARING SQUID

You can usually buy squid ready cleaned, but failing that, it is easy to prepare it yourself. Hold the body in one hand and the head in the other, and pull away the head gently but firmly. The soft entrails will come away cleanly. Cut off the tentacles and remove the dark ink sac from the head.

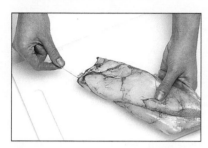

Pull out the transparent quill and rinse the body inside and out. Peel off the purplish membrane. Unless the squid are tiny enough to serve whole, cut the body into 5 mm/¼ in rings and the tentacles into manageable pieces.

Polipi (octopus)

These are much larger than squid and have only eight tentacles. Their ink sac is not located in the head but in their liver, and the ink has a strong, pungent taste. Octopuses look and taste similar to squid, but need a good deal of preparation. They must be pounded (99 times, some say) to tenderize them before they are subjected to very long, slow cooking.

If you can find very small octopuses, they can be cooked in the same way as squid, but otherwise it is less trouble to substitute squid or cuttlefish.

Octopus
When small, these can be cooked like squid

Cozze (mussels)

Mussels, with their smooth texture and sweet flavour, make an attractive addition to many pasta and fish dishes. Pollution in the Mediterranean had threatened the indigenous mussel population, but nowadays most Italian mussels are farmed by the *bouchot* method, on ropes attached to long stakes set in pure seawater, which keeps the molluscs clean and healthy and free from grit and sand. In Italian fish markets on the Adriatic coast, you may find small sweet local mussels with different names like *peoci* or *datteri di mare*. These can be prepared in the same way as other mussels.

CHOOSING

Mussels, are sold by the litre in Italy, and are very inexpensive. Because the shells constitute so much of the weight, allow at least 500 ml/ generous 1 pint/2½ cups mussels per serving. Choose those which feel heavy for their size and discard any with broken shells. Use mussels the day they are gathered or bought.

Mussels
Steamed mussels combine well with black fettuccine or tagliatelle

CULINARY USES

Once mussels have been steamed open, they can be served with a garlicky tomato sauce, or baked on the half shell with garlic butter or a breadcrumb topping. For *cozze gratinate al forno*, lay the mussels on the bottom shells in an ovenproof dish, sprinkle lavishly with breadcrumbs seasoned with garlic and parsley and drizzle with olive oil. Bake in a hot oven for 10 minutes.

Shelled cooked mussels are combined with prawns and squid for an *insalata di mare* (seafood salad), or used as a pizza topping, while mussels in the shell are often mixed with other seafood and pasta for dishes like *spaghetti allo scoglio* ("spaghetti of the rock").

Shellfish

Gamberetti, gamberelli and gamberoni (shrimps, prawns and scampi)

There are so many different varieties of shrimps and prawns in Italian coastal waters that it is almost impossible to recognize them all. The smallest are the *gamberetti*, small pink or brown shrimps which are usually boiled and served simply dressed with olive oil and lemon juice as part of an *antipasto*. Next in size come the *gamberelli*, pink prawns with a delicate flavour. These are the prawns that are most commonly used in a *fritto misto di mare* (mixed fried seafood). *Gamberi rossi* are the larger variety of prawn, which turn bright red when they are cooked. They are highly prized for their fine, strong flavour, and are eaten plainly cooked and dipped into a bowl of *maionese* (mayonnaise). Best (and most expensive) of all are *gamberoni*, large succulent prawns from the Adriatic, which have a superb flavour and texture. Similar to these is the *cicala*, which resembles a small flattish lobster.

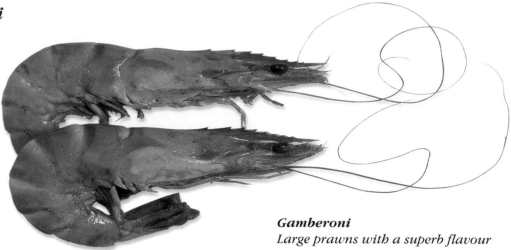

Gamberoni
Large prawns with a superb flavour

COOKING SHRIMPS, PRAWNS AND SCAMPI

Whatever the size, all types of shrimps and prawns can be cooked briefly in boiling salted water (sea water, if possible) until they turn pink. Shrimps will take only 1–2 minutes, large prawns and scampi up to 5 minutes. The robust flavour of prawns makes them ideal for serving in a rich tomato or cream sauce or with rice. Shell them after cooking.
To grill gamberoni, *rub the shells with olive oil and coarse salt and grill over charcoal or on a grilling pan, turning them frequently. When they turn opaque, slit them through the underside and open them out flat like a butterfly. Brush the underside with oil and grill until just cooked. Peeled prawns and scampi can be pan-fried in olive oil flavoured with garlic and/or chilli, parsley and capers; or coated in batter or egg and breadcrumbs and deep-fried.*

Gamberi rossi
These large prawns turn bright red when cooked

PREPARING SHRIMPS, PRAWNS AND SCAMPI

Shrimps, prawns and scampi should be de-veined before or after cooking. Pull off the heads, shell the tails and pick out the black thread-like intestine with a knife tip.

CHOOSING

Almost all the shrimps and prawns you buy in Italy are sold uncooked. They should have bright shells that feel firm; if they look limp or smell of ammonia, do not buy them.

CULINARY USES

Shrimps and prawns are extremely versatile and can be used in a wide variety of dishes. Small shrimps are served as *antipasti*, either on their own, or as a stuffing for tomatoes. They can be added to risotto and pasta dishes or seafood sauces.

Prawns combine well with almost any other seafood. They are usually included in an *insalata di mare* (seafood salad) or *fritto misto di mare* (mixed fried seafood). They make a fine *antipasto* added to an *insalata russa* (Russian salad) or served with haricot beans dressed with extra virgin olive oil. They combine well with a spicy tomato sauce or mushrooms, and can be used for seafood casseroles. Large prawns and scampi can be skewered or split and grilled, or boiled and served with mayonnaise or lemon.

Gamberetti
These small pink shrimps are delicious simply dressed with olive oil and lemon juice

Vongole (clams)

There are almost as many different types of clam as there are regions in Italy, ranging from tiny smooth-shelled *arselle* or *vongole* to long thin razor shells and the large Venus clams with beautiful ridged shells called *tartufi di mare* ("sea truffles"). All have a sweet flavour and a slightly chewy texture. Because they vary so much in size, it is best to ask the fishmonger how many clams you will need for a particular dish.

Clams
These smooth-shelled vongole *are often steamed and served as part of a seafood salad*

PREPARING AND COOKING CLAMS

Their habit of burying themselves in the sand makes clams rather gritty, so they should be left in fresh water for an hour or so to open up and disgorge the sand inside the shells. To open large clams, either use an oyster knife, or put them in a medium oven for a few minutes until they gape open.

Clams can be served raw like oysters, or cooked in exactly the same way as mussels (see page 70). The cooking time depends on the size of the clams; tiny specimens take only a minute or two. Steamed shelled clams are often served as part of an insalata di mare *or in a risotto. Miniature clams in their shells are stewed with olive oil, garlic and parsley and served with their juices (in bianco) or in a tomato sauce (in rosso) for* spaghetti alle vongole, *or served on fried bread as* crostini. *Large varieties can be pan-fried with lemon and parsley, or stuffed with seasoned breadcrumbs and grilled or baked.*

Vegetables

Vegetables have always played a very important role in Italian cooking, particularly in the south of the country, where meat was a luxury that few could afford. They are most often served as dishes in their own right, rather than accompaniments, and the range of imaginative vegetable recipes from all over Italy seems infinite.

One of the great joys of Italy is shopping at the markets, where an astonishing range of seasonal vegetables is on offer, from asparagus, beans and *cavolo nero* from the north to aubergines, peppers and courgettes from Calabria and Sicily. In spring and summer, you will find at least ten different varieties of salad leaves, and you will be overwhelmed by the aroma of freshly picked local tomatoes still on the vine. Italians almost never buy imported or out-of-season vegetables, but prefer to purchase fresh seasonal produce bursting with flavour.

Asparagi *(asparagus)*

Asparagus has been grown commercially in north-eastern Italy for over 300 years and is still highly prized as a luxury vegetable. It has a short growing season from April to early June and is really only worth eating during this period. Both green and white asparagus are cultivated in Italy; the green variety is grown above ground so that the entire spear is bright green. They are harvested when they are about 15 cm/6 in high. The fat white spears with their pale yellow tips are grown under mounds of soil to protect them from the light, and harvested almost as soon as the tips appear above the soil to retain their pale colour. Both varieties have a delicious fresh grassy flavour.

CULINARY USES
In spring, Italians enjoy young asparagus spears simply boiled, steamed or roasted in olive oil and served as a *primo* (first course) with butter and freshly grated Parmesan. For an extra treat, they add a fried egg and dip the asparagus tips into

White asparagus
This variety is grown under mounds of earth to retain the pale colour

the creamy yolk. When served as a vegetable accompaniment, asparagus can be crisply fried in egg and breadcrumbs. The tips also make a luxury addition to risotto.

BUYING AND STORING
Asparagus starts to lose its flavour as soon as it has been cut, so be sure to buy only the freshest spears. The best guide is the tips, which should be

Green asparagus
Enjoyed by Italians, simply boiled or roasted in olive oil

firm and tight. If they are drooping and open, the asparagus is past its best. The stalks should be straight and fresh-looking, not yellowed and wizened or very woody at the base. Allow about eight medium spears per serving as a first course and always buy spears of uniform thickness so that they cook evenly. Asparagus will keep in the vegetable drawer of the fridge for two or three days.

PREPARING AND COOKING ASPARAGUS

Freshly cut garden asparagus needs no trimming, but cut off at least 2 cm/³⁄₄ in from the bottom of the stalks of bought spears until the exposed end looks fresh and moist. Peel the lower half with a potato peeler. (You need not do this for very thin stalks.)

Boiling asparagus can be problematical, since the stalks take longer to cook than the tips. The ideal solution is to use a special asparagus kettle, so as to immerse the stalks in boiling water whilst steaming the tips.

Asparagus can equally well be stood upright in a deep pan of boiling water, tented with foil and cooked for 5–8 minutes, until tender but still al dente. *Alternatively, steam the spears in a vegetable steamer. Serve with a drizzle of extra virgin olive oil or melted butter.*

Asparagus can also be successfully microwaved. Wash the spears and lay them in an oval dish in a single layer with the tips all pointing the same way. You do not need added water. Cover tightly with microwave cling film and cook on full power for 5 minutes per 500 g/1¼ lb. If the spears are not quite done, turn them over and cook for a little longer.

To roast asparagus, heat some olive oil in a roasting pan, turn the spears in the oil, then roast in a hot oven for 5–10 minutes.

To fry, roll the spears in beaten egg and fine dried breadcrumbs, then fry them a few at a time in very hot olive oil until crusty and golden. Drain on absorbent paper and sprinkle with sea salt.

Cardi *(cardoons)*

Cardoons are related to artichokes, but only the leaf-stalks are eaten. They are commercially grown in mounds of soil to keep them creamy white, but in the wild, the stalks are pale green and hairy and can grow to an enormous size. The tough outer stalks are always discarded, and only the inner stalks and hearts are eaten. Cardoons are a popular winter vegetable in Italy and can be found in the markets ready-trimmed.

CULINARY USES

Cardoons can be eaten raw as a salad, or cooked in a variety of ways – fried, puréed or boiled and served with melted butter or a rich cream and Parmesan sauce. They are traditionally used as a vegetable to dip into the hot anchovy and garlic fondue known as *bagna cauda*.

BUYING AND STORING

Cardoons bought in the market will have been trimmed of their outer stalks and are sold with a crown of leaves, rather like large heads of celery. The stalks should be plump and creamy-white and not too hairy. Wrapped in a plastic bag, they will keep in the vegetable drawer of the fridge for two or three days.

PREPARING AND COOKING CARDOONS

Cut off the roots and peel the stalks with a potato peeler to remove the stringy fibres. Cut the stalks into 5 cm/2½ in lengths and the hearts into wedges, and drop into acidulated water to prevent discoloration. Blanch in boiling salted water, then simmer or fry gently in butter until tender. To serve in a sauce, put the blanched cardoons in an ovenproof dish, cover with sauce, sprinkle with grated Parmesan and bake in a very hot oven until browned.

Cardoons
Related to globe artichokes, the tough outer stalks of this vegetable are always discarded

Vegetables

Carciofi (globe artichokes)

As their appearance suggests, artichokes are a type of thistle. Originating from Sicily, where they grow almost wild, they are cultivated throughout Italy and are a particular speciality of Roman cooking. The artichoke itself is actually the flower bud of the large, silvery-leaved plant. There are many different varieties, from tiny purple plants with tapered leaves, which are so tender that they can be eaten raw, to large bright or pale green globes, whose leaves are pulled off one by one and the succulent flesh at the base stripped off with your teeth.

HISTORY

Although artichokes have always grown like weeds in Sicily, they were first cultivated near Naples in the 15th century. Their popularity spread to Florence, where they became a favourite dish of the Medici family. They were believed to have powerful aphrodisiac properties and women were often forbidden to eat them!

CULINARY USES

Tiny tender artichokes can be quartered and eaten raw or braised *alla romana* with olive oil, parsley and garlic. Large specimens can be served boiled with a dressing to dip the leaves into, or stuffed with savoury fillings. They can be cut into wedges, dipped in batter and deep-fried. A favourite Italian dish is the ancient Jewish recipe *carciofi alla giudea*, where the artichokes are flattened out and deep-fried twice, so that the outside is very crisp while the inside remains meltingly moist.

BUYING AND STORING

Artichokes are available almost all year round, but they are at their best in summer. Whichever variety you are buying, look for tightly packed leaves (open leaves indicate that they are too mature) and a very fresh colour. When an artichoke is old, the tips of the leaves will turn brown. If possible, buy artichokes still attached to their stems; they will keep fresher and the

PREPARING AND COOKING GLOBE ARTICHOKES

Tiny tender artichokes can be quartered and eaten raw.

For large artichokes, snap off the stalk and pull off the tough outer leaves. Rub the cut surfaces with lemon juice to prevent discoloration and keep the prepared artichokes in a bowl of acidulated water until ready to cook.

Boil large whole artichokes for about 30 minutes, until the outer leaves can be pulled off easily.

Drain them upside-down, then pull out the centre leaves and scoop out the inedible hairy choke with a spoon before serving. For stuffed artichokes, remove the choke before cooking and fill the cavity with your chosen stuffing. Braise them in olive oil and water, or invert them on to an ovenproof dish, pour over a mixture of olive oil and water, cover with foil and bake in the oven at 190°C/375°F/ Gas 5 for about 1 hour.

Very small artichokes should be quartered and boiled, braised or stewed until tender. The chokes are so soft that the artichokes can be eaten in their entirety.

peeled, cooked stems are often as delicious as the artichoke itself.

Artichokes will keep fresh for several days if you place the stalks in water like a bunch of flowers. If they have no stalks, wrap them in clear film and keep in the vegetable drawer of the fridge for a day or two.

Globe artichokes
These popular vegetables are actually the flower bud of a type of large thistle

Cavolo (cabbage)

Cabbage is an essential ingredient of many Italian hearty winter soups. Three main types are used; *cavolo verza* (curly-leaved savoy cabbage), which is used in Milanese dishes, *cavolo cappuccio* (round white or red cabbage) and the speciality of Tuscany, *cavolo nero*, a tall leafy cabbage whose name means "black cabbage", but which is actually dark purplish green.

CULINARY USES

Italians rarely eat cabbage as a vegetable accompaniment, but prefer to include it in hearty soups, such as *ribollita* or minestrone, or to stuff and braise the outer leaves and serve them as a main course.

BUYING AND STORING

Cabbage heads should be solid and firm, with fresh, unyellowed leaves. It is best to buy them complete with their outer leaves; not only are these tasty for cooking, but they protect the hearts and give a good indication of the freshness of the cabbages. A cabbage will keep in the vegetable drawer of the fridge for up to a week.

Cavolo nero
The name of this tall leafy cabbage means "black cabbage"

PREPARING AND COOKING CABBAGE

Cut off the outer leaves and stalk, cutting out a cone-shaped section of the stalk from the inside of the cabbage. To use the leaves for stuffing, blanch them in boiling water for about 3 minutes, until malleable. For soups and braised dishes, coarsely shred the cabbage and wash it well.

Cabbage can be cooked in a variety of ways. The simplest cooking method is to toss shredded cabbage in butter or olive oil until just tender. Never overcook cabbage; it should still retain some crunch.

Winter cabbages are good shredded and braised with pancetta *and garlic, while* cavolo rosso *(red cabbage) can be spiced with apples, cinnamon and cloves and stewed in a little white wine to cut the richness of pork, duck or roast goose.*

Red and white cabbage
The red variety is often cooked gently with apples and spices to serve with rich meats, while the white variety is added to soups and stews

Savoy cabbage
This curly-leaved cabbage is used in Milanese dishes

Vegetables

Cipolle (onions)

Onions are an essential part of Italian cooking. Many varieties are grown, including mild yellow onions, the stronger-flavoured white onions and their baby version, which is used for pickling and sweet-and-sour onions. The best-known Italian onions are the vibrant deep red variety, which are delicious raw (in a tuna and bean salad, for example, or cooked).

CULINARY USES

The best Italian onions are grown in Piedmont, so many classic Piedmontese recipes include these versatile bulbs. Large onions can be stuffed with Fontina or minced meat and herbs, and baked. Baby white onions are traditionally cooked *in agrodolce*, a sweet-and-sour sauce of sugar and wine vinegar, and served cold as an *antipasto* or hot as a vegetable accompaniment.

BUYING AND STORING

You will often find young fresh onions in Italian markets. These are sold in bunches like large, bulbous spring onions, complete with their leaves. They have a mild flavour and can be used for pickling or in salads. They will keep in the fridge for three or four days; wrap them tightly to stop their smell pervading everything else in the fridge. Older onions have thin, almost papery skins

that should be unblemished. The onions should feel firm and not be sprouting green leaves. They quickly deteriorate once cut, so it is best to buy assorted sizes, then you can use a small onion when the recipe calls for only a small amount. Stored in a dry, airy place, onions will keep for many weeks.

White onion
This variety is very strongly flavoured

Red onion
This vibrant red variety is now widely available – they are delicious raw

Baby white onions
Traditionally cooked in agrodolce, *a classic Italian sweet-and-sour sauce, and served cold as an* antipasto

Yellow onions
These mild onions are best cooked gently in olive oil

PREPARING AND COOKING ONIONS

Some onions are easier to peel than others. The skins of red and yellow onions can be removed without much difficulty, but white onions may need to be plunged into boiling water for about 30 seconds to make peeling easier.

There are all sorts of old wives' remedies to stop your eyes watering when peeling onions. The most effective method is to hold them as far away from you as possible while you peel! For most cooked dishes, onions should be sliced or chopped, but for salads they are sliced into very thin rings.

The flavour of onions will develop in different ways, according to how you cook them. In Italian cooking, they are rarely browned, which gives them a bitter taste, but are generally sweated gently in olive oil to add a mellow flavour to a multitude of dishes.

Finocchio (fennel)

Originally a medicinal remedy for such disagreeable conditions as flatulence, fennel has become one of the most important of all Italian vegetables. Bulb or Florence fennel (so-called to distinguish it from the feathery green herb) resembles a fat white celery root and has a delicate but distinctive flavour of aniseed and a very crisp, refreshing texture.

CULINARY USES

Fennel is delicious eaten raw, dressed with a vinaigrette or as part of a mixed salad. In southern Italy, raw fennel is served with cheese as a dessert instead of fruit – an excellent aid to digesting a meal.

When cooked, the aniseed flavour becomes more subtle and the texture resembles cooked celery. Braised fennel is particularly good with white fish. Fennel can be cooked in all the same ways as celery or cardoons.

BUYING AND STORING

Fennel is available all year round. If possible, buy it with its topknot of feathery green fronds, which you can chop and use as a herb or garnish in any dish where you would use dill. The bulbs should feel firm and the outer layers should be crisp and white, not wizened and yellowish. It should have a delicate, very fresh scent of aniseed and the crisp texture of green celery. Whole fennel bulbs will keep in the fridge for up to a week. Once cut, however, use them immediately, or the cut surfaces will discolour and the texture will soften. Allow a whole bulb per serving.

Fennel
The distinctive aniseed flavour makes this vegetable a perfect partner for white fish

PREPARING AND COOKING FENNEL

If the outer layer of the fennel bulb seems stringy, peel it with a sharp knife. Cut off the round greenish stalks protruding from the top. For salads, cut the bulb vertically into thin slices. For cooked dishes, quarter the bulb. Any trimmings can be chopped and used for soups or sauces for fish.

Fennel can be sautéed, baked or braised. For all cooked fennel recipes, blanch the quartered bulbs in a large saucepan of salted boiling water until it is just tender.

To sauté, heat about 25 g/1 oz butter per bulb with some chopped garlic, drain the fennel and fry it gently in the butter until very tender. To enhance the flavour, add a teaspoon of Pernod or other aniseed-flavoured alcohol.

Braised fennel should be cooked in a little olive oil using a covered frying pan.

To bake fennel, lay the blanched bulbs in a buttered ovenproof dish, season, dot with butter and sprinkle a generous quantity of freshly grated Parmesan over the top. Bake in the oven at 200°C/ 400°F/Gas 6 for 20–30 minutes, or until the top is bubbling and golden brown.

Vegetables

Melanzane (aubergines)

The versatile aubergine plays an important role in the cooking of southern Italy and Sicily, possibly because its dense, satisfying texture makes a good substitute for meat. You will find many different aubergines in Italian markets, the two main types being the familiar deep purple elongated variety and the rotund paler mauve type, which has a thinner skin. Some are small, some huge, but they all taste similar and can be used in the same way for any recipe.

PREPARING AUBERGINES

Some people believe that aubergines should always be sliced and salted for about 30 minutes before cooking to draw out the bitter juices; others deem this unnecessary. Salting does stop the aubergine soaking up large quantities of oil during cooking, so on balance it seems worth doing.

Slice or dice the aubergines, place them in a colander, sprinkle with 15 ml/1 tbsp salt per 1 kg/2¼ lb. Place a dish on the aubergines and weight it down. Leave for 30 minutes. Rinse the aubergines and dry with kitchen paper.

If aubergines have a very tough skin, it is best to peel them (unless you are stuffing them and need the skin as a container). Otherwise, leave the skin on, as its colour will enhance the appearance of the finished dish.

BUYING AND STORING

Shape and size are not important when choosing aubergines; the essentials are tight, glossy skins and a fairly firm texture. Do not buy aubergines with wrinkled or damaged skins. They should feel heavy for their size; a light aubergine will probably be spongy inside and contain a lot of seeds. They will keep in the fridge for up to a week.

HISTORY

Aubergines originated in Asia. They were cultivated in Europe in the Middle Ages, but only very rarely featured in Italian cooking at the time, since they were regarded with suspicion; indeed, the name *melanzane* comes from the Latin *melum insanum* (unhealthy apple). This mistrust had been overcome by the Renaissance, and aubergines began to be grown and used extensively in the south of Italy.

Aubergines
The familiar deep purple variety plays an important role in the cooking of southern Italy

CULINARY USES

Aubergines are extremely versatile vegetables and add a wonderful depth of flavour to any dish in which they appear. They can be grilled, baked, stuffed, stewed and sautéed, on their own or with other ingredients, and the rich colour of their skins enhances the appearance of many different Italian dishes.

The simplest way of cooking aubergines is to slice and fry them in a generous quantity of very hot olive oil.
For a more substantial dish, coat them in light batter, then fine breadcrumbs, and fry until golden brown.
To bake them, halve the aubergines lengthways, removing the calyx and stalk. Make slashes in the flesh and rub it with a cut garlic clove. Drizzle some olive oil over the top, cover with foil and bake in a hot oven for about 1 hour, until very soft. Season with salt and pepper and add lemon juice to taste.
Probably the most famous Italian aubergine dish is melanzane alla parmigiana, *where the aubergines are layered with rich tomato sauce and Parmesan and baked in the oven. A favourite Sicilian dish,* caponata, *combines them with celery and a piquant sweet-and-sour sauce enlivened with olives and sometimes capers.*

Peperoni (sweet peppers)

Generically known as capsicums, the shape of these sweet peppers gives them the alternative name of "bell peppers". Although they come in a range of colours – green (these are unripe red peppers), red, yellow, orange and even purplish-black – all peppers have much the same sweetish flavour and crunchy texture, and are interchangeable in recipes. They are a very healthy food, being rich in vitamin C. The locally grown peppers you will see in the markets in Italy are much larger and more misshapen than the uniformly perfect, hydroponically grown specimens that are usually found in Britain, but their flavour is sweet and delicious.

CULINARY USES

Each region of Italy has its own specialities using peppers. They can be used raw or lightly roasted in salads or as an *antipasto* and can be cooked in a variety of ways – roasted and dressed with olive oil or vinaigrette dressing and capers, stewed (as in *peperonata*), or stuffed and baked. Peppers have a great affinity with other Mediterranean ingredients, such as olives, capers, aubergines, tomatoes and anchovies.

BUYING AND STORING

Choose firm peppers with unwrinkled, shiny skins. Size does not matter unless you plan to stuff the peppers, in which case choose roundish shapes of uniform size. The skin of green peppers may be mottled with patches of orange or red; this indicates that the pepper is ripening, and as long as the pepper is unblemished, there is no reason not to buy it. Peppers can be stored in the fridge for up to two weeks.

COOKING PEPPERS

To make a classic Italian peperonata, *sweat sliced onions and garlic in olive oil, add sliced peppers, cover the pan and cook gently until just tender. Add an equal quantity of peeled, deseeded and chopped tomatoes, a splash of wine vinegar and seasoning and cook, uncovered, until meltingly tender. For* peperonata alla romana, *stir in some capers at the end.*

Peppers
Locally grown Italian peppers are often larger and more misshapen than the uniformly perfect varieties grown in hot-houses

Vegetables

PREPARING AND COOKING PEPPERS

Place the peppers under a very hot grill or hold them over a gas flame and turn them until the skin blackens and blisters. Put them in a plastic bag, seal and leave until the peppers are cool enough to handle. The thin skin will peel off easily.

To slice peppers, halve them lengthways, cut away the calyx and stem and pull out the core, seeds and white membranes. Cut the flesh into strips.

To stuff peppers, cut off the stalk end and remove the seeds and membranes. Fill the pepper with your chosen stuffing (rice, vegetables, meat – what you will) and replace the stalk end. Arrange the peppers in a shallow ovenproof dish, drizzle over some olive oil and pour in enough water to come about 2 cm/³⁄₄ in up the sides of the peppers. Bake at 200ºC/400ºF/Gas 6 for about 1 hour.

For baked peppers alla piemontese, halve the peppers lengthways and fill each with a chopped tomato, a chopped anchovy fillet and a little chopped garlic. Arrange the peppers on a baking tray, rounded side down. Drizzle over some olive oil and bake at 200ºC/400ºF/Gas 6 for about 30 minutes.

Pomodori (tomatoes)

It is impossible to imagine Italian cooking without tomatoes, which seem to be a vital ingredient in almost every recipe. But these "golden apples" were unknown in Italy until the 16th century, when they were brought from Mexico. At first they were grown only in the south, but as their popularity spread, tomatoes were cultivated all over Italy and were incorporated into the cooking of every region. Italians grow an enormous variety of tomatoes, from plum tomatoes (San Marzano are the best) to ridged, pumpkin-shaped, green-tinged salad tomatoes, bright red fruits bursting with aroma and flavour, and tiny *pomodorini* (cherry tomatoes).

CULINARY USES

Tomatoes are used in so many different ways that it is hard to know where to begin. They can be eaten raw, sliced and served with a trickle of extra virgin olive oil and some torn basil leaves (basil and tomatoes have an extraordinary affinity). They are the red component of an *insalata tricolore*, partnering white mozzarella and green basil to make

Cherry tomatoes
Bright red and bursting with flavour, these tiny tomatoes can be used to add colour and flavour to any dish

Plum tomatoes
San Marzano are the best variety of these smooth-skinned tomatoes

up the colours of the Italian flag. Raw ripe tomatoes can be chopped with herbs and garlic to make a fresh-tasting pasta sauce, or made into a topping for *bruschetta*.

Tomatoes can be grilled, fried, baked, stuffed, stewed and made into sauces and soups. They add colour and flavour to almost any savoury dish.

BUYING AND STORING

Tomatoes are at their best in summer, when they have ripened naturally in the sun. Choose your tomatoes according to how you wish to prepare them. Salad tomatoes should be very firm and easy to slice. The best tomatoes for cooking are the plum tomatoes which hold their shape well and should have a fine flavour.

Tomatoes will only ripen properly if left for long enough on the vine, so try to buy "vine-ripened" varieties. If you can find only unripe tomatoes, you can ripen them by putting them in a brown paper bag with a ripe tomato or leaving them in a fruit bowl with a banana; the gases the ripe fruits give off will ripen the tomatoes, but, alas, they cannot improve the flavour.

Try to buy tomatoes loose so that you can smell them. They should have a wonderful aroma. If the flavour is not all it should be, add a good pinch of sugar to enhance it. For cooked recipes, if you cannot find really flavourful tomatoes, use canned instead. The best are San Marzano plum tomatoes which are grown near Salerno. In Italy, you will often find large knobbly green tomatoes, which are sold as *pomodori insalata*. Although you can allow them to ripen in the usual way, Italians prefer to slice these tomatoes thinly and eat them in their unripe state as a crunchy and refreshing salad.

Large tomatoes
Not always as smooth as these, locally grown Italian tomatoes bought from a market can be very ridged and almost pumpkin-shaped

PEELING TOMATOES

It is easy to remove the skin from tomatoes. Prick the tomatoes with the point of a sharp knife, plunge them into a bowl of boiling water for about 30 seconds, then refresh in cold water. Peel away the skins, cut the tomatoes into quarters or halves and remove the seeds using a teaspoon.

Vine-ripened tomatoes
Tomatoes sold on the vine are likely to have a far better flavour than those sold loose

Vegetables

Spinaci (spinach)

Spinach and its close relatives, *bietola* (Swiss chard) and *biete* (spinach beet), are dark green leafy vegetables, rich in minerals (especially iron) and vitamins. Unlike many other vegetables, they are often served in Italy as an accompaniment to a main course, although they appear in numerous composite dishes as well. All spinach, whether flat-leafed or curly-leafed, has a distinctive metallic flavour, which people either love or loathe. The latter should avoid dishes *alla fiorentina*, which use spinach in large quantities.

Curly-leaf spinach is a summer variety with very dark green leaves. Winter spinach has flat, smooth leaves, but tastes very similar. Usually, only the leaves are eaten and the stalks are discarded. Spinach has a delicate, melting quality and should be cooked only very briefly.

The coarser *bietola* contains less iron and has a less pronounced flavour than spinach. The leaves have broad, tender creamy or pale green midribs, and both the leaves and stalks are eaten, but are cooked in different ways. *Bietola* is available all year round, but is particularly popular in autumn and winter, when more delicate spinach is not available. No one is quite sure why it is called Swiss chard; the Swiss certainly eat it, but in much smaller quantities than the French or Italians.

Biete (spinach beet) has a much smaller stalk and more closely resembles spinach. The stalks are usually left attached to the leaves for cooking. The coarser texture of *biete* makes it more suitable than spinach for recipes that require more than the briefest cooking. Balls of ready-cooked *biete* are often sold in Italian delicatessens.

HISTORY

Spinach was originally cultivated in Persia in the 6th century and was brought to Europe by Arab traders some thousand years later. It had become very popular in France, Spain and England by the 16th century, when it was used for both sweet and savoury dishes, but it did not reach Italy until the 18th century.

CULINARY USES

Tender young spinach leaves can be eaten raw in salads or cooked and served cold with a dressing of olive oil and lemon. Cooked spinach is used to make gnocchi and is often combined with ricotta to make fillings for pasta and *crespoline* (pancakes). Florentine-style recipes usually contain spinach, and it is a classic partner for eggs, fish, poultry and white meats. Spinach, *biete* and *bietola* are all used in savoury tarts, such as *torta alla pasqualina*, an Easter speciality. They make excellent soups and soufflés. *Bietola* stalks are delicious sautéed in butter and baked in a white sauce sprinkled with Parmesan.

Spinach
The tender young leaves can be eaten raw; larger leaves need to be cooked

Spinach beet
The coarse texture of biete *makes it more suitable than spinach for slower-cooked recipes*

BUYING AND STORING

All types of spinach should look very fresh and green, with no signs of wilting. The leaves should be unblemished and the stalks crisp. Spinach and spinach beets contain a very high proportion of water and wilt down to about half their weight during cooking, so always buy far more than you think you will need – at least 250 g/9 oz per serving. Loose spinach should be used as soon as possible after buying. Packed loosely into a plastic bag, it will keep in the fridge for a couple of days. Unopened bags of pre-packed spinach will keep for up to a week.

Bietola *(Swiss chard)*

Pull off the green leaves from the stems. Snap the veins and leafstalks and remove the stringy parts (do not cut with a knife, or the strings will not come away). Wash as for spinach and cut the stalks into 6–8 cm/ 2½–3½ in lengths.

Swiss chard
Available all year round, this vegetable is particularly popular in winter when the more tender spinach is not available

PREPARING AND COOKING SPINACH AND SWISS CHARD

Spinach and spinach beet: Carefully pick over the spinach, discarding any withered or damaged leaves and tough stalks. Wash thoroughly in several changes of water until no signs of earth or grit remain. Spinach should be cooked with only the water which clings to the leaves after washing. Sauté it in butter with a clove of chopped garlic for about 5 minutes; overcooked spinach will be unpleasantly watery. To stew spinach, put it in a large saucepan, cover and cook gently until wilted, turning it over halfway through cooking. Drain and gently squeeze out the excess moisture with your hands. Toss in butter or olive oil, season with freshly grated nutmeg or chop finely and use for gnocchi and pasta fillings.

Swiss chard leaves can be cooked exactly like spinach. The prepared stalks should be blanched until tender in salted water or vegetable stock, then baked in a sauce or tart, sautéed in butter or used as a stuffing. A popular bietola *dish is a* sformato, *a savoury, moulded, baked custard.*

Vegetables

Zucca (squash) **and** *zucchini (courgettes)*

Squashes and courgettes are widely used in northern Italian cooking. Both have large, open, deep-yellow flowers, which are considered a great delicacy. Squashes come in a variety of shapes and sizes, from huge orange pumpkins to small, pale butternut squashes and green acorn squashes. They all have dense, sweet-tasting flesh. Courgettes are like small marrows, with shiny green skin and a sweet, delicate flavour. In Italy, tiny specimens are often sold with their flowers attached.

CULINARY USES

The pumpkin is the symbol of Mantua and recipes *alla mantovana* use the flesh a multitude of ways, from *tortelli alla zucca* (pumpkin-filled tortelli) to risotti, soups and sweet dessert tarts. Pumpkin flowers can be coated in batter and deep-fried, stuffed with a filling of ricotta, or chopped and added to risotti for extra colour and flavour.

Courgettes combine well with other Mediterranean vegetables, like tomatoes and aubergines. They can be dipped in batter and deep-fried, made into fritters or served with a white sauce seasoned with Parmesan or nutmeg. Served cold with a mint-flavoured vinaigrette (*zucchini a scapece*) or tomato sauce, they can be part of an *antipasto*. They can be halved and stuffed with a meat or vegetable filling. Young courgettes can also be thinly sliced or grated and eaten raw in a salad.

BUYING AND STORING

Courgettes are available almost all year round, but are at their best in spring and summer. The smaller and skinnier courgettes are, the better they taste. They should have very glossy green skins and feel very firm. Do not buy flabby courgettes or those with blemished skins. Larger specimens are useful for stuffing.

Courgettes
These familiar vegetables combine well with other Mediterranean vegetables

Pumpkins
Italians use the flesh of these large vegetables in a multitude of ways

Small pumpkins
Like their larger cousins, these small pumpkins have dense, sweet-tasting flesh

If you can find them in markets, go for tiny courgettes with their flowers attached. Allow 250 g/9 oz courgettes per serving. They will keep in the vegetable drawer of the fridge for up to a week.

Squashes should feel firm and heavy for their size. It is not worth buying enormous pumpkins (other than for decorative purposes), as their flesh tends to be stringy and flavourless. All whole squashes keep well, but once they are opened, they should be wrapped in clingfilm and kept in the fridge for no more than three days.

If you are lucky enough to find squash or courgette flowers (the best way is to grow your own), they must be cooked straight away, as they are extremely perishable.

PREPARING COURGETTES, SQUASHES AND PUMPKINS

Courgettes should be topped and tailed, then sliced, diced, cut into batons or grated as appropriate. They do not need peeling.

Flowers may contain small insects, so wash them quickly under cold running water and gently pat dry with kitchen paper. Cut off all but 2.5 cm/1 in of the stems. Courgettes are best sautéed in butter or olive oil flavoured with plenty of chopped garlic and parsley. Courgettes deep fried in a light batter are a

favourite accompaniment in Italy. The flowers can be prepared in the same way. To make zucchini a scapece, *slice 1 kg/2¼lb courgettes thickly and brown in hot olive oil. Place in a dish and scatter over about 20 torn mint leaves and 1 finely chopped garlic clove. Season and dress with one part red wine vinegar and two parts olive oil. Mix well and leave the flavours to develop for 2 hours before serving.*

Squashes and pumpkins should be peeled and the seeds and fibrous parts removed. Cut the flesh into chunks or slices. The skin of large pumpkins may be too hard to peel; if so, break open the pumpkin with a hammer or drop it on the floor, and scoop out the flesh, discarding the seeds.

Pumpkin and squash should be blanched in boiling salted water, then sweated in butter until soft and made into soup or stuffing, cooked au gratin or grated raw and added to a risotto. Pumpkin can also be sweetened and used as a pie filling.

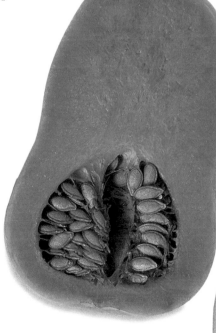

Butternut squash
The brightly coloured flesh of butternut squashes is widely used in northern Italian cooking

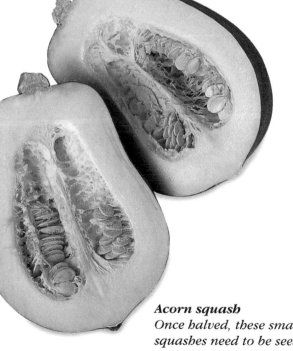

Acorn squash
Once halved, these small squashes need to be seeded and peeled before cooking

Salad Leaves

Italians grow salad leaves in profusion and gather them from the wild to create inventive and interesting combinations, such as *misticanza*, a pot-pourri of wild greens and cultivated leaves. In high season, you will find at least a dozen different salad leaves in an Italian market, ranging from fresh green round garden lettuces to bitter dark green grass-like leaves and purplish-red radicchio. Such salads are served after the main course, simply dressed with olive oil and vinegar to cleanse the palate.

Cicoria di campo or dente di leone (dandelion)

Dandelion leaves are rich in iron and vitamins, and are also reputed to be a powerful diuretic. They have a pungent, peppery taste and long, fresh green indented leaves (hence the name "lion's tooth"). They can be picked from the wild before the plant has flowered, but only the young leaves should be eaten. Cultivated dandelion leaves are available. They are more tender than wild leaves, but have a less intense flavour.

CULINARY USES
Young dandelion leaves are usually served raw in salads together with other leaves; they are particularly good with crisply cooked bacon and hard-boiled eggs. They can also be cooked like spinach.

Radicchio

This variety of red-leafed chicory comes originally from Treviso. *Radicchio di Treviso* has elongated purplish-red leaves with pronounced cream-coloured veins. The more familiar round variety is known as *radicchio di Verona*. Both types of red-leafed chicory have a bitter taste, and for salads are best used in small quantities together with other leaves. They look particularly attractive when combined with frilly-leafed curly endive, pale whitish-green chicory leaves, or the darker cornsalad and rocket.

Dandelion leaves
Pick these peppery-tasting leaves from the wild before the plant has flowered

Radicchio di Verona
The more familiar round red-leafed chicory

Radicchio di Treviso
This elongated variety is delicious grilled with olive oil

CULINARY USES
Radicchio can also be eaten as a hot vegetable, either quartered and grilled with olive oil, or stuffed with a mixture of breadcrumbs, anchovies, capers and olives and baked – but it loses its beautiful colour when cooked. A little radicchio added to a risotto made with red wine will add to the pretty pink colour.

BUYING AND STORING
Radicchio leaves should be fresh-looking with no trace of brown at the edges. *Radicchio di Verona* should be firm with tightly packed leaves. Both types will keep in the fridge for up to a week.

Rucola *(rocket)*

Rocket has dark green elongated, indented leaves and a hot, pungent flavour and aroma. Like dandelions, it grows wild in the Italian countryside, but it is also cultivated commercially. Home-grown rocket has a much better flavour than the immature leaves usually found in supermarkets, but it bolts easily and should be picked as soon as the leaves are large enough.

CULINARY USES

Rocket adds zest to any green salad and can be eaten on its own with a dressing of olive oil and lemon juice or balsamic vinegar. Combined with radicchio, cornsalad and fresh herbs, rocket makes a good substitute for *misticanza*. It can be added to pasta sauces and risotti, or cooked like spinach, but cooking does diminish the pungent flavour.

BUYING AND STORING

In Italy, rocket is always sold in small bunches. The leaves should look very fresh with no sign of wilting. Rocket does not keep well unless it has been pre-packaged. To keep it for a day or two, wrap it in damp newspaper or damp kitchen paper and store in the fridge.

Rocket
This hot, pungent salad leaf grows wild in the Italian countryside, but it is also cultivated commercially

Valeriana *(cornsalad)*

This delicate salad plant, also called lamb's lettuce, has tender green rounded leaves bunched together in a rosette shape. It grows wild in fields in Italy, but is also cultivated and is an essential ingredient of *misticanza*. It has a delicate but distinctive flavour, which adds interest to winter salads.

CULINARY USES

Cornsalad is usually served by itself or in a mixed green salad, but it can also be cooked like spinach. The tender leaves will blacken if damaged, so take care when tossing a salad not to bruise them.

BUYING AND STORING

Cornsalad should look fresh and green, with no withered or drooping leaves. The smaller and rounder the leaves, the better the flavour. It will keep in the salad drawer of the fridge for several days, but take care not to squash it.

Cornsalad
The delicate but distinctive flavour of this salad plant adds interest to winter salads

PREPARING CORNSALAD

Cornsalad is sold with the root attached, so it must be washed thoroughly before use. Dunk it in several changes of cold water to remove all the grit, then dab the leaves dry with kitchen paper, handling them very gently.

Mushrooms

Italian country-dwellers have always been passionate collectors of edible wild mushrooms; in spring and autumn, the woods and fields are alive with furtive fungi hunters in search of these flavourful delicacies. Cultivated button mushrooms are rarely eaten in Italy, even when fresh wild varieties are out of season; Italians prefer to use dried or preserved wild fungi with their robust, earthy taste.

The most highly prized mushroom for use in Italian cooking is the *porcino* (cep). Since these are hugely expensive, they are most often dried and used in small quantities to add flavour to field or other wild mushrooms. Drying actually intensifies the flavour of *porcini*, so they are not regarded as inferior to the fresh mushrooms – quite the reverse. Other popular wild fungi include *gallinacci* (chanterelles), *prataioli* (field mushroooms) and *ovoli* (Caesar's mushrooms).

HISTORY
From earliest times, primitive man gathered and ate wild mushrooms. The Greeks and Romans enjoyed many fungi, including *amanita caesarea* (Caesar's mushroom), which was popular with the Emperor Claudius and ultimately his downfall; his wife Agrippina poisoned him by adding deadly *amanita phalloides* (the aptly named deathcap) to a dish of his favourite fungi. The Romans succeeded in cultivating several types of mushrooms, but cultivation on a large scale really began in the 17th century, when a French botanist discovered how to grow mushrooms in compost all year round.

STORING
Never store mushrooms in a plastic bag, as they will sweat and turn mushy. Put them into a paper bag and keep in the vegetable drawer of the fridge for no more than two days.

PREPARING AND COOKING MUSHROOMS

Mushrooms should never be washed or they will become waterlogged and mushy. To clean them, cut off the earthy base of the stalk and lightly brush the caps with a soft brush or wipe them clean with a slightly damp cloth.

With very few exceptions (including ceps and Caesar's mushrooms, which can be eaten raw), wild mushrooms should be cooked to destroy any mild toxins they may contain. All mushrooms can be sliced and sautéed in hot olive oil or a mixture of butter and olive oil with finely chopped garlic or shallots, a little red chilli and herbs (parsley, marjoram, thyme or mint are particularly good).

Chanterelles
These orangey-yellow mushrooms have a delicious, delicate flavour and a distinct apricot aroma

COOKING CHANTERELLES

Chanterelles have a delicious, delicate flavour and a slightly chewy texture; they should be cooked slowly or they may become hard. Fry them gently in butter with chopped garlic or shallots for about 10 minutes, adding some finely chopped parsley, marjoram or thyme towards the end of the cooking time. Serve them on hot buttered toast, or add to omelettes or scrambled eggs. They are particularly good with poultry, rabbit or veal and can also be dressed with a herb-flavoured vinaigrette and served warm in a salad.

Ovoli (Caesar's mushrooms; Latin name amanita caesarea)

These large mushrooms with an orangey-yellow cap have an excellent flavour and were a favourite of the Roman emperors. They are still found in Italy, but are very rare elsewhere.

CULINARY USES

Ovoli can be thinly sliced and eaten raw in a salad. They combine very well with hazelnuts.

Dried chanterelles
Dried chanterelles can be used to flavour soups, stew and pasta dishes

Mushroom powder

Well-flavoured dried mushrooms can be crushed to a powder and used to flavour sauces, soups and stews. Some Italian delicatessens stock mushroom powder. If you make your own, store it in an airtight container.

RECONSTITUTING DRIED MUSHROOMS

Soak 25 g/1 oz dried mushrooms in 250 ml/8 fl oz/1 cup hot water for about 20 minutes until soft, then drain and use like fresh mushrooms. Keep the soaking water to use in sauces, stocks or soups; it will have an intense mushroom flavour.

DRYING CHANTERELLES

Leave the chanterelles whole, or halve them if they are large.

Lay them on a double thickness of newspaper and leave in a very warm, airy place (above the boiler is ideal), turning them over every few hours until they have become completely dry and brittle. Alternatively, string them like necklaces and hang them up to dry, or place in a very cool fan oven (maximum 130°C/250°F/gas ¹/₂), leaving the door ajar. When the chanterelles are completely dry, store them in jars or paper bags. All mushrooms can be dried in this way; slice them thinly before drying. It is only worth drying perfect specimens.

Mushrooms

Porcini (ceps)

These are the king of mushrooms in Italian cooking. Their Italian name means "little piglets", which aptly describes their bulbous stalks and rounded brown caps. In autumn, they are found in woodlands, where they can grow to an enormous size, weighing more than 500 g/1¼ lb each (although mushroom-hunters rarely leave them for long enough to grow to these proportions). There are many different varities of *porcini*, all of which have a fine flavour and meaty texture.

CULINARY USES

All ceps can be cooked in the same way as other mushrooms. Young ones can be thinly sliced and eaten raw, dressed with extra virgin olive oil. Larger caps are delicious brushed with olive oil, grilled and served with a grinding of salt and pepper. Don't discard the stalks, which have an excellent flavour; chop them and cook with the caps, or use them for sauces, stocks and soups; just trim off the earthy bits from the base.

DRYING

Ceps can be thinly sliced and dried in the same way as *gallinacci*. Dried *porcini* are commercially available. They are very expensive, but a little goes a long way. Just 25 g/1 oz dried porcini, soaked and drained, will enhance the flavour of 500 g/1¼ lb cultivated mushrooms beyond recognition. Don't be tempted to buy cheap packets of dried *porcini*, which may contain a high proportion of inferior dried mushrooms and bits of twig from the forest floor.

STORING

Fresh *porcini* can be kept in the vegetable drawer of the fridge for up to two days. Dried mushrooms will keep in an airtight container for at least a year.

Porcini (ceps)
Italian cooks consider these to be the king of mushrooms

FREEZING

Small *porcini* in perfect condition can be frozen whole. Large or blemished specimens should be sliced and lightly sautéed in butter, then drained and frozen. Do not defrost before use, or they will become mushy. Simply cook the mushrooms from frozen in hot olive oil or butter. Frozen mushrooms will only keep for about one month.

Dried porcini (ceps)
These dried porcini are expensive to buy, but since drying actually accentuates their flavour, a little goes a long way

PICKLING PORCINI

Unblemished fresh porcini *can be preserved by pickling. Choose unblemished funghi (if you haven't enough* porcini, *use a mixture of mushrooms), leaving small ones whole and slicing or quartering large ones.*

1 kg/2¼ lb mushrooms
500 ml/17 fl oz/ generous
    2 cups white wine vinegar
500 ml/17 fl oz/ generous
    2 cups water
10 ml/2 tsp salt
5 ml/1 tsp peppercorns,
    lightly crushed
2 bay leaves
10 ml/2 tsp coriander seeds
2 garlic cloves, peeled
    and halved
4 small dried red chillies
olive oil

1 Put the mushrooms in a saucepan with all the ingredients except the olive oil. Bring to the boil and simmer for 5–10 minutes until the mushrooms are tender but still firm. Drain them, reserving the pickling aromatics, and leave to cool completely.

2 Spoon the mushrooms and aromatics into a sterilized preserving jar and fill up the jar with olive oil. Seal and leave for at least a month. Pickled mushrooms will keep for at least six months.

Black truffles

No one has succeeded in cultivating truffles so they remain rare and expensive – the black variety are more highly prized than the white

White truffles

Found in Piedmont, northern Italy, these delicately flavoured truffles are usually served raw

Chiodini (honey fungus; Latin name armarilla mellea)

No gardener welcomes the sight of honey fungus (the Italian name means "little nails"), as it is a parasitic fungus that destroys the trees on whose roots it grows. However, the caps of these small golden mushrooms are good to eat (the fibrous stalks should be discarded). In their raw state they are mildly toxic, but once they have been blanched in very hot oil or boiling water, then stewed in butter with a little garlic, seasoning and parsley, they make good eating.

CULINARY USES

Honey fungus makes a good filling for a *frittata* (Italian omelette). Allow 150 g/ 5 oz *chiodini* caps and 4 large eggs for two people. Season the eggs and beat them lightly with 25 g/1 oz grated Parmesan. Heat 30 ml/2 tbsp olive oil in a frying pan and sauté the blanched mushroom caps with 1 chopped garlic clove and 15 ml/1 tbsp chopped parsley for about 3 minutes. Season with salt and pepper, pour in the eggs and stir well. Cook the *frittata* until set on the bottom, then sprinkle with a little more Parmesan and place under a hot grill until golden brown. Cut into wedges and serve hot or cold.

Tartufi (truffles)

Truffles grow about 20 cm/8 in underground, usually near oak trees. They are in season from October to late December. Their irregular, knobbly, round shape conceals a pungent, earthy and delicious aroma and flavour. There are two main varieties, black and white. The more highly prized black truffles (*tuber melanosporum*) grow mostly in the Périgord region of France, but they are also found in northern Italy, in Tuscany and Piedmont. The more common Piedmont truffle is the white variety (*tuber magnatum*), which has a more delicate flavour.

No one has yet succeeded in cultivating truffles commercially, so they remain rare and expensive. They are sniffed out by trained pigs or dogs, who can detect their subterranean scent. In order to develop their full aroma and flavour, the truffles must be left to mature, so truffle-hunters often cover up those which the animals have unearthed (praying that nobody else will find their buried treasure) until they reach full maturity.

HISTORY

Truffles have been eaten since ancient times. They were a favourite dish of the ancient Egyptians. The Greeks and Romans believed them to have aphrodisiac properties, but in the Middle Ages they were thought to be manifestations of the devil. Louis XIV of France, however, subscribed to the earlier theory, and from his reign on truffles were enthusiastically consumed by all those rich enough to afford this luxury food.

CULINARY USES

Truffles can be eaten raw or cooked. White Piedmont truffles are usually served raw, shaved very thinly over fresh pasta, a *fonduta* or eggs. They can be heated briefly in butter and seasoned with salt, white pepper and nutmeg. Black or white truffles are delicious with all poultry and white meat. A few slivers of truffle will add a touch of luxury to almost any savoury sauce. A classic rich Italian dish using truffles is *vincigrassi*, sheets of fresh pasta layered with butter, cream, slivers of truffle, ham and chicken livers. It is a speciality of the Marches and the Abruzzi.

BUYING AND STORING

If you are lucky enough to find a fresh truffle, use it as soon as possible, as the flavour is volatile. Brush off the earth from the skin and peel the truffle (keep the peelings to use in a sauce). To give whole fresh eggs the most wonderful flavour, put them in a bowl with the truffle, cover and leave overnight; they will absorb the superb musty aroma.

You are more likely to buy canned or bottled truffles than fresh. Whole ones are extremely expensive, but cheaper pieces and even peelings are available. The most economical way to enjoy the flavour of truffles is to buy Italian oil scented with white truffles. A drop or two of this added to a dish will transform it into something really special.

Truffle oil

The most economical way to enjoy the flavour of truffles – a drop or two of this scented oil will enhance sauces, pastas and salads

Fruit & Nuts

Italians prefer to buy only those fruits and nuts that are in season, and who can blame them? Italy produces an abundance of soft, stone and citrus fruits, all bursting with flavour and often available fresh from the tree. There are apples and pears from the orchards of the northern regions; nuts, peaches, plums and figs from the central plains; while the south and Sicily produce almost every kind of fruit – grapes, cherries, oranges and lemons – as well as pistachio nuts and almonds. Many of these fruits are indigenous to Italy and have been grown there since time immemorial.

After a full meal of *antipasto*, pasta and a *secondo* (main course), it is hardly surprising that Italian desserts very often consist of nothing but a bowl of seasonal fresh fruit served on its own or made into a refreshing *macedonia* (fruit salad). Soft fruits form the basis of ice creams, sorbets, *granite* and *frullati* (fresh fruit milkshakes), while nuts and winter fruits (often dried or candied) are baked into tarts and pastries.

Amarena *(Morello cherry)*

Although Italy does produce sweet dessert cherries, it is best known for the bitter Morello variety, which are preserved in syrup or brandy, or made into ice cream and Maraschino liqueur. These cherries are small, with dark red skins and firm flesh. They are in season from late June to early July, and can be eaten raw, although they have quite a sharp flavour.

CULINARY USES
Morello cherries can be poached in sugar syrup and served whole, or puréed and made into a rich, dark, cherry syrup. Stone the cherries and purée them. Strain the cherries through a fine sieve and leave the juice at room temperature for about 24 hours. Strain through muslin and add 750 g/1 lb 10 oz caster sugar per 500 ml/17 fl oz/generous 2 cups cherry juice. Heat gently. When the sugar has dissolved, bring the cherry syrup to the boil, strain again and pour into airtight bottles or

containers. These cherries also make excellent jam. A popular Venetian dish is Morello cherries poached in a red wine syrup flavoured with cinnamon. Bottled cherries in vinegar can be used in sauces for meat, duck and game.

BUYING AND STORING
Choose fresh cherries with unwrinkled and unblemished skins, which look shiny and feel firm. Stored in a plastic bag, they will keep in the fridge for up to a week.

Morello cherries
These dark red cherries are usually preserved in syrup and used for desserts. Those bottled in vinegar can be used for savoury recipes

Arancia *(orange)*

Many varieties of oranges are grown in Sicily and southern Italy. The best-known Sicilian oranges are the small blood oranges with their bright ruby-red flesh. Other types of sweet oranges include seedless navels, which take their name from the umbilical-like end which contains an embryonic orange, and seeded late oranges, which have paler flesh and are available throughout the winter. Bitter oranges (*arance amare*) are also grown; these rough-skinned varieties are made into preserves (although rarely marmalade in Italy), candied peel and *liquore all'arancia* (orange liqueur).

HISTORY
Oranges originated in China, but bitter oranges may possibly have been known in Ancient Greece; the mythical "golden apples of the Hesperides" are said to have been Seville oranges, although this seems historically far-fetched. They were certainly brought to Italy by Arab traders during the Roman Empire and over the centuries became a symbol of wealth and opulence – so much so that the Medici family incorporated them into their coat of arms as five golden balls. Sweet oranges did not arrive in Italy until the 17th century.

Oranges
Sweet varieties are used for both sweet and savoury recipes – they are a favourite addition to salads

Bitter oranges
This rough-skinned variety can be used to add zest to savoury dishes – it combines well with white fish, liver, duck and game – and is used for preserves

CULINARY USES

A favourite Sicilian recipe is *insalata di arance alla siciliana*, a salad of thinly sliced oranges and red onion rings dressed with black olives and their oil. Oranges also combine well with raw fennel and chicory. They can be sliced and served *alla veneziana*, coated with caramel, or simply macerated in a little lemon juice with a sliver of lemon peel for a refreshing dessert. They can be squeezed for juice, or made into sorbet and *granita*. Bitter oranges combine well with white fish, calf's liver, duck or game, and add zest to a tomato sauce.

BUYING AND STORING

Oranges are available all year round, but are at their best in winter. They should have unblemished shiny skins and feel heavy for their size (this indicates that they contain plenty of juice and that the flesh is not dry). If you intend to candy the peel or incorporate it into a recipe, choose unwaxed oranges. Oranges will keep at room temperature for a week and for at least two weeks in the fridge. Bring them back to room temperature or warm them slightly before eating them.

Preparing Fresh Oranges

1 When peeling an orange it is important to remove all the bitter white pith and membrane. Hold the orange over a bowl to catch the juice and use a very sharp knife to cut off the peel, pith and the membrane enclosing the flesh.

2 To segment the orange, cut down between the membranes of the segments and ease out the flesh. Squeeze the membranes into the bowl to extract the juice.

3 To remove strips of orange rind, run a cannelle knife down the orange, or use a zester for finer shreds. If you cannot find unwaxed fruit, wash the oranges in warm water, rinse and dry well before removing strips of rind.

Fruit

Fico (fig)

Figs are grown all over Italy, but thanks to the hot climate Sicilian figs are perhaps the most luscious of all. During the summer months you will often find Italian farmers at the roadside selling punnets of ripe figs from their own trees. There are two types of Italian figs, green and purple. Both have thin, tender skins and very sweet, succulent, red flesh, and are rich in vitamins A, B and C. They are in season from July to October and are best eaten straight off the tree when they are perfectly ripe.

HISTORY

Figs were said to grow in the Garden of Eden, where Adam and Eve used the leaves to cover their nakedness. In fact they probably originated in Asia Minor, although the oldest fig tree in the world is reputed to be growing in a garden in Palermo in Sicily. The Greeks and Romans certainly enjoyed figs, which are still as highly prized today.

Purple figs
The sweet succulent flesh of this variety makes a perfect partner to nuts of all kinds

CULINARY USES

Fresh figs are delicious served on their own, but they have an affinity with nuts such as walnuts, pistachios and almonds. They can be served raw with Parma ham or salami as an *antipasto*, or stuffed with raspberry coulis or mascarpone as a dessert. Poached in a little water or wine flavoured with cinnamon or nutmeg, they make an excellent accompaniment to duck, game or lamb.

BUYING AND STORING

Ripe figs are extremely delicate and do not travel well, so it is hard to find imported fruit at a perfect stage of maturity. In season in Italy, however, you can find local figs that are just ripe for eating; they should be soft and yielding, but not squashy. Sometimes the skin may have split, revealing the luscious red or pink flesh. As long as you are going to eat the fig immediately, this does not matter. Take great care not to squash the figs on your way home, or you will end up with a squishy, inedible mess.

Under-ripe figs can be kept at room temperature for a day or two until the skin softens, but they will never develop the fine flavour of tree-ripened figs. Ripe figs should be eaten on the day they are bought.

PREPARING AND COOKING FIGS

Wash the figs briefly and gently pat dry. Discard the stalk and peel the figs, if you wish.

To serve as an antipasto or dessert, cut them downwards from the stalk end into quarters, leaving them attached at the base. Open them out like flowers.

Perfectly ripe figs are best eaten raw, but less perfect specimens can be improved by cooking. They can be gently poached in syrup or red wine flavoured with a cinnamon stick or vanilla pod, or rolled in caster sugar and baked in the oven until caramelized. Barely ripe figs also make excellent jam.

Green figs
Delicious served raw with Parma ham or salami as an antipasto

Limone *(lemon)*

Lemons are grown all over Italy, even in the northern regions. Lake Garda even boasts a town called Limone, named for its abundance of lemon trees. But the most famous Italian lemons come from the Amalfi coast, where they grow to an extraordinary size and have such a sweet flavour that they can almost be eaten as a dessert fruit. Their aromatic flavour enhances almost any dish, and they have the added advantage of being rich in vitamin C.

HISTORY

Lemons originated in India or Malaysia and were brought by the Assyrians to Greece, which in turn took them to Italy. The Greeks and Romans greatly appreciated their culinary and medicinal qualities. Later seafarers ate them in large quantities to protect against scurvy, and society ladies used them as a beauty treatment to whiten their skin, bleach their hair and redden their lips.

CULINARY USES

Lemons are extraordinarily versatile. The juice can be squeezed to make a refreshing *spremuta di limone*, or it can be added to other cold drinks or tea. It is an anti-oxidant, which prevents discoloration when applied to other fruits and vegetables. The juice is used for dressings and for flavouring all sorts of drinks and sauces. A squeeze of lemon juice adds a different dimension to intrinsically bland foods, such as fish, poultry, veal or certain vegetables. Its acidity also helps to bring out the flavour of other fruits. The zest makes a wonderfully aromatic flavouring for cakes and pastries, and is an essential ingredient of *gremolata*, a topping of grated zest, garlic and parsley for *osso buco*. Quartered lemons are always served with *fritto misto di mare* (mixed fried fish) and other foods fried in batter.

PREPARING LEMONS

Before squeezing a lemon, warm it gently: either put it in a bowl, pour boiling water over the top and leave to stand for about 5 minutes or, if you prefer, microwave the lemon on full power for about 30 seconds; this will significantly increase the quantity of juice you will obtain.

For sweet dishes, when you want to add the flavour of lemons, but not the grated rind, rub a sugar lump over the skin of the lemon to absorb the oil, then use the sugar as part of the recipe.

To prepare grated lemon rind, thoroughly wash and dry unwaxed lemons. Grate the rind or peel it off with a zester, taking care not to include any white pith.

BUYING AND STORING

Depending on the variety, lemons may have thick indented skin, or be perfectly smooth. Their appearance does not affect the flavour, but they should feel heavy for their size. If you intend to use the zest, buy unwaxed lemons. Lemons will keep in the fridge for up to two weeks.

Lemons
Lemons are grown all over Italy – their aromatic flavour enhances almost any dish

Fruit

Melone (melon)

Many different varieties of sweet, aromatic melons are grown in Italy, and each has its own regional name. *Napoletana* melons have a smooth pale green rind and delicately scented orange flesh. *Cantalupo* (cantaloupe) melons have a warty skin, which is conveniently marked into segments, and highly scented deep yellow flesh. A similar Tuscan melon with grey-green rind and orange flesh is called *popone*. These melons are all perfect for eating with Parma ham or salami as an *antipasto*.

Watermelons (*anguria* or *cocomero*) are grown in Tuscany. These huge green melons with their refreshing bright pink or red flesh and edible brown seeds can be round or sausage-shaped. In Florence, the feast of San Lorenzo, the patron saint of cooks, is celebrated with an orgy of watermelons on August 10th. During this season, roadside stalls groan under the weight of hundreds of these gigantic fruit.

CULINARY USES

Italians eat melon as a starter, usually accompanied by wafer-thin *prosciutto crudo* or cured meats. Melons and watermelons are occasionally served as a dessert fruit on their own, but more often appear in a *macedonia* (fruit salad).

BUYING AND STORING

The best way to tell whether a melon is ripe is to smell it; it should have a mild, sweet scent. If it smells highly perfumed and musky, it will be over-ripe. The fruit should feel heavy for its size and the skin should not be bruised or damaged. Gently press the rind with your thumbs at the stalk end; it should give a little. Melons will ripen quickly at room temperature and should be eaten within two or three days. Wrap cut melon tightly in clear film before storing in the fridge, or its scent may permeate other foods.

PREPARING MELON

For serving as an antipasto, *cut the melon into wedges, scoop out the seeds and run a flexible knife between the rind and flesh. Remove the rind before serving.*

Napoletana melon
The sweet scented flesh of this and the similar cantaloupe melon is perfect for eating with Parma ham as an antipasto

Pesche *(peaches)* and *pesche noci (nectarines)*

Peaches, with their velvety skin and sweet, juicy flesh, are a summer fruit grown in central and southern Italy. The most common variety is the *pesca gialla* (yellow peach), which has succulent, yellow flesh. More highly prized are the *pesche bianche* (white peaches), whose pink-tinted flesh is full of juice and flavour.

Nectarines have smooth plum-like skins and taste very similar to peaches. They also come in yellow and white varieties and, like peaches, the white nectarines have a finer flavour. Some people prefer nectarines as a dessert fruit because they do not require peeling. Peaches and nectarines are interchangeable in cooked dishes.

CULINARY USES

Peaches and nectarines are delicious served as a dessert fruit, but can also be macerated in fortified wine or spirits or poached in white wine and syrup. They have a particular affinity with almonds; a favourite Italian dessert is *pesche ripiene alla piemontese*, halved peaches stuffed with crumbled almond-flavoured amaretti biscuits and baked in white wine. They are also delicious served with raspberries, or made into fruit drinks (the famous Bellini cocktail is made with fresh peach juice) and ice creams and sorbets.

BUYING AND STORING

Peaches are in season from June to September. Make sure they are ripe, but not too soft, with unwrinkled and unblemished skins. They should have a sweet, intense scent. Peaches and nectarines bruise very easily, so try to buy those that have been kept in compartmented trays rather than piled into punnets.

Do not keep peaches and nectarines for more than a day or two. If they are very ripe, store them in the fridge; under-ripe fruit will ripen in a couple of days if kept in a brown paper bag at room temperature.

PREPARING PEACHES

To peel peaches, place them in a heatproof bowl and pour boiling water over them. Leave for 15–30 seconds (depending on how ripe they are), then refresh in very cold water; the skins will slip off easily.

Peaches
This summer fruit is grown in central and southern Italy

Watermelon
Occasionally served on its own in wedges as a dessert fruit, this vibrant red fruit is more usually chopped and added to a fruit salad

Nectarines
These smooth-skinned fruits are delicious served as a dessert fruit

Fruit

Uva (grapes)

Italy is the world's largest producer of grapes of all kinds. Almost every rural property boasts an expanse of vineyards, some producing wine-making grapes intended only for home consumption. Others (particularly in Chianti and the south) are destined for the enormous Italian wine-making industry. But Apulia, Abruzzo and Sicily produce sweet dessert grapes on a vast commercial scale, from large luscious Italia, with their fine muscat flavour, to Cardinal, named for its deep red colour, purple Alphonse Lavallé, and various small seedless varieties.

Despite their high calorific value, grapes are extremely good for you, since they are rich in potassium, iron and vitamins.

HISTORY

Wild grapes grew in the Caucasus as early as the Stone Age, and early man soon discovered the secret of cultivating vineyards and making wine. The Greeks and Romans discovered that drying grapes transformed them into sweet raisins and sultanas. The Gauls invented the wooden wine cask, and from that time wine production became a major industry.

CULINARY USES

Dessert grapes are best eaten on their own or as an accompaniment to cheese, but they can be used in pastries or as a garnish for cooked quails, guinea fowl or other poultry. The seeds are pressed into grapeseed oil, which has a neutral taste and is high in polyunsaturated fatty acids.

BUYING AND STORING

Choosing white, black or red grapes is a matter of preference; beneath the skin, the flesh is always pale green and juicy. Buy bunches of grapes with fruit which is of equal size and not too densely packed on the stalk. Check that none is withered or bad.

The skin should have a delicate bloom and be firm to the touch. Try to eat one grape from a bunch to see how they taste. The flesh should be firm and very juicy and refreshing.

Grapes should be washed immediately after purchase, then placed in a bowl and kept in the fridge for up to three days. Keeping them in a plastic bag causes them to become over-ripe very quickly.

PREPARING GRAPES

Grapes used for cooking should be peeled and deseeded. Put them in a bowl, pour over boiling water and leave for 10–20 seconds, depending on the ripeness of the grapes. Peel off the skin. To remove the seeds, halve the grapes and scoop out the pips with the tip of a pointed knife.

Italia grapes
These luscious red and white grapes have a wonderful Muscat flavour

Nuts

Many different kinds of nuts are grown in Italy – chestnuts and hazelnuts in the north, pine nuts in the coastal regions, and almonds, pistachios and walnuts in the south. They are used in a wide variety of savoury dishes, cakes and pastries, or served as a dessert with a glass of vin santo (sweet white wine).

Castagne (chestnuts)

These are a mainstay of Tuscan and Sardinian cooking, dating back to the days when the peasants could not afford wheat to make flour, so they ground up the chestnuts that grow in abundance throughout the region instead. Most varieties of sweet chestnut contain two or three

Chestnuts
A mainstay of Tuscan and Sardinian cooking

separate nuts inside the spiky green husk, but commercially grown varieties contain a single, large nut, which is easier to peel and better for serving whole.

Chestnuts have shiny, rich reddish-brown shells with a wrinkled, thin skin beneath, which can be very hard to remove. They cannot be eaten raw, but once cooked, the starchy nuts are highly nutritious and very sustaining.

Culinary Uses

Chestnuts roasted over an open fire conjure up the spirit of autumn. Peeled chestnuts can be boiled, poached in red wine or milk or fried in butter as a garnish. They make hearty soups, or can be puréed into

sauces for game. In Piedmont, they are candied to make marrons glacés, and a favourite Italian dessert is *monte bianco*, a rich concoction of puréed chestnuts and cream.

Chestnut flour is still widely used in Tuscany and Liguria, where it is baked into cakes and pastries, such as *castagnaccio*, a confection with pine nuts and herbs.

Buying and Storing

The nicest chestnuts are those you gather yourself, but if you are buying them, look for large, shiny specimens, with no tiny maggot holes in the shells. The chestnuts should feel heavy for their size and not rattle when you shake them. They will keep in a cool place for at least two weeks. If any holes appear in the shells, discard the nut immediately, or you will very soon have an infestation of maggots.

Mandorle (almonds)

Two varieties of almonds are grown in central and southern Italy. *Mandorle dolci* (sweet almonds) are eaten as a dessert or used in cooking and baking, while *mandorle amare* (bitter almonds) are used to flavour liqueurs like amaretto or bittersweet confections such as amaretti biscuits. These almonds are not edible in their raw state; in fact, they are poisonous if consumed in large quantities. Both types of almonds have a velvety pale green outer casing; the hard light brown shell within encloses one or two oval nuts.

Culinary Uses

Early in the season (late May), sweet almonds can be eaten raw as a dessert. They have a delicious fresh flavour and the brown skin is still soft enough to be palatable. Later, dried sweet almonds are blanched, slivered or ground to be used for cakes, pastries and all sorts of confectionery, including *marzapane* (marzipan) and *croccante* (almond brittle). They can be devilled or salted as an appetizing

Preparing Chestnuts

There are three possible ways to peel chestnuts.

Slit the domed side of the shells with a very sharp knife, then drop them into boiling water for 5 minutes, or put them in a roasting pan with a little hot water and cook in a very hot oven for about 10 minutes. Shell and skin the chestnuts as soon as they are cool enough to handle. Alternatively, shell the raw chestnuts and boil them in their skins for about 20 minutes, then peel off the skins.

snack with an *aperitivo*. Toasted almonds are the classic garnish for trout, and go well with chicken or rabbit. Dried bitter almonds are used in small quantities to add a more intense flavour to biscuits and cakes.

Almonds
In Italy in early spring, fresh almonds are eaten raw as a dessert

Nuts

Buying and Storing

Fresh almonds in the shell are available from late May to late June. They are difficult to crack, so you may prefer to buy ready-shelled nuts. They should look plump, and the skins should not feel too dry. Pre-blanched almonds can often be a disappointment; buy the nuts with their skins on and blanch them yourself. Store shelled almonds in an airtight container for no longer than a month.

Nocciole (hazelnuts)

Fresh hazelnuts are harvested in August and September and during these months are always sold in their frilled green husks. The small round nuts have a very sweet flavour and a milky texture when fresh. In Italy, they are generally dried and used in confectionery and cakes.

Culinary Uses

Hazelnuts are used in all sorts of confectionery, including *torrone* (a sort of nougat) and *gianduiotti*, a delicious fondant chocolate from Piedmont. The famous chocolate *baci* ("kisses") from Perugia contain a whole hazelnut in the centre. Hazelnuts are finely ground to make cakes and biscuits, and are excellent in stuffings for poultry and game.

Buying and Storing

If hazelnuts are sold in their fresh green husks, you can be sure they are fresh and juicy. Otherwise, look for shiny shells which are not too thick and unblemished; cracked shells will cause the nut to shrivel and dry out. Shelled hazelnuts should be kept in an airtight container for no longer than one month.

Shelled almonds
These dried almonds are used for cakes, pastries and confectionery

Noci (walnuts)

Walnuts grow in abundance throughout central and southern Italy. The kernels, shaped like the two halves of a brain, grow inside a pale brown, heavily indented shell enclosed by a smooth green fleshy husk or "shuck". Fresh walnuts have a delicious milky sweetness and a soft texture, which hardens as the nuts mature. Walnuts do not need to be skinned before eating.

Walnuts
In Italy, fresh walnuts are very often eaten straight from the shell as a dessert

Shelled hazelnuts
These dried nuts are used for confectionery and cakes

Hazelnuts
When fresh, these small nuts have a very sweet flavour

Preparing Almonds

To blanch almonds, place them in a strainer and plunge into boiling water for a few seconds. As soon as the skin begins to loosen, transfer the almonds to a bowl of cold water and slip off the skins. Dry thoroughly before storing.

CULINARY USES

Fresh walnuts are usually eaten straight from the shell as a dessert. They can be ground or chopped and used in cakes and desserts, or halved and used for decoration. They are used to make savoury sauces for pasta, such as *salsa di noce*, a rich combination of ground walnuts, butter and cream. Walnut oil has a distinctive flavour and, used sparingly, makes an excellent salad dressing. Unripe walnuts can be pickled, and they are used to make sweet, sticky liqueurs.

BUYING AND STORING

Fresh "wet" walnuts are available from late September to late October. They should be kept in a wicker basket and eaten within a week. Dried walnuts should not have cracked or broken shells. They will keep for at least two months. Never store walnuts in the fridge, as the oil they contain will harden and ruin the flavour. Dried walnut kernels will have the flavour and texture of fresh nuts if they are soaked in milk for at least 4 hours.

Pine nuts
The oily, slightly resinous flavour is accentuated by toasting

Pinoli *(pine nuts)*

Pine nuts (more accurately known as pine kernels) are actually the seeds from the stone pine trees that grow in profusion along the Adriatic and Mediterranean coasts of Italy. The small, oblong, cream-coloured seeds grow inside a hard husk and are extracted from between the scales of the pine cones. The soft-textured kernels, which have an oily, slightly resinous flavour, are always sold de-husked. They can be eaten raw, but are usually toasted before use to bring out the flavour.

CULINARY USES

Pine nuts are used in many Italian dishes, both sweet and savoury, but they are best known as an essential ingredient of pesto. They go well with meat and game, and make exceptionally delicious biscuits and tarts.

Pistachio nuts
Grown in southern Italy, these sweet, delicately flavoured nuts are used in mortadella

PREPARING PINE NUTS

For most recipes and when used as a garnish, they should be lightly toasted. Heat a dry, heavy frying pan, put in the pine nuts and toss quickly until they turn pale golden. Do not allow them to brown, or they will taste unpleasant.

BUYING AND STORING

Pine nuts are always sold out of the husk. Because they are very oily, they go rancid quite quickly, so buy only as much as you need at any one time. Store them in an airtight container in the fridge for not more than a week.

Pistacchi *(pistachios)*

Pistachios are native to the Near East, but are grown in southern Italy, particularly Sicily. The small, bright green nut has a yellowish-red skin and is enclosed in a smooth, pale shell. Pistachios have a sweet, delicate flavour, which makes them ideal for desserts, but they are also used to stud mortadella and other pale cooked meat products.

CULINARY USES

Pistachios can be eaten raw or roasted and salted as a snack with an *aperitivo*. Their colour enhances most white meats and poultry. They make deliciously rich ice cream and are used in *cassata gelata*, the famous Sicilian dessert.

BUYING AND STORING

If possible, buy pistachios still in their shells. These will be easier to open if they are already slightly ajar; once open, the nut is very easy to remove. Shelled, blanched pistachios are also available. They are useful for cooking, but lack the fine flavour of whole nuts. Store blanched pistachios in an airtight container for up to two weeks. Whole nuts will keep for well over a month.

Herbs & Seasonings

Herbs are vital to Italian cooking. Their aromatic flavour adds depth and interest to what is essentially plain cooking, based on fine, fresh ingredients. It is impossible to imagine roast chicken or veal without rosemary or sage, or tomatoes or pesto without basil. Many wild herbs grow in the Italian countryside, and these are often incorporated into Italian recipes. One of the most popular is mentuccia, *a wild mint with tiny leaves and the delicate flavour of marjoram. If a recipe specifies* mentuccia *or its close relative* nepitella, *substitute a smaller quantity of mint.*

Always use fresh herbs whenever you can; the dried varieties have a stronger and often quite different taste, and lack the subtlety of fresh herbs. If you must use dried herbs, try to buy them freeze-dried; these taste much closer to the real thing. As a general rule, you will need only about one-third as much dried herb as fresh – in other words, allow about 5 ml/1 tsp dried herbs for every 15 ml/1 tbsp fresh.

Basilico (basil)

Basil, with its intense aroma and fresh, pungently sweet flavour, is associated with Italian cooking more than any other herb. It is an essential ingredient of pesto, but it also finds its way into soups, salads and almost all dishes based on tomatoes, with which it has an extraordinary affinity. There are over 50 varieties of this annual herb, but the one most commonly used in Italy is sweet basil, with its fresh broad green leaves and wonderfully spicy aroma.

CULINARY USES
Basil has a volatile flavour, so it is best added to dishes at the end of cooking. It can be used in any dish that contains tomatoes and is delicious sprinkled on to a pizza. It adds a pungent, sweet note to almost all salads and is particularly good with white fish and seafood. It makes an excellent flavouring for omelettes and is often added to

minestrone. The most famous of all basil dishes is pesto, the fragrant Genoese sauce made by pounding together fresh basil, garlic, Parmesan, pine nuts and olive oil.

BUYING AND STORING
In sunny climates, such as southern Italy, basil grows outdoors all through the summer. In other places it is available cut or growing in pots all year round, so there really is no reason to use dried basil. Look for sweet basil with bright green leaves – the larger the better. If you have grown your own and have a glut, you can freeze basil leaves to preserve the flavour, but they lose their fresh texture and darken in colour. Alternatively, put a bunch of basil in a jar and top up with olive oil for a fragrant flavoured oil for dressings. To store fresh cut basil, wrap it in damp kitchen paper and keep in the vegetable drawer of the fridge for up to two days.

Basil
More than any other, this pungent, intensely flavoured herb is associated with Italian cooking – it is an essential ingredient in many dishes, including pesto

PREPARING BASIL

Basil leaves are tender and bruise easily, so never chop them with a knife, but tear them lightly with your fingers immediately before using.

Pesto

To make enough pesto for 4–6 servings of pasta, put 115 g/4 oz basil leaves in a mortar with 25 g/1 oz pine nuts, 2 fat peeled garlic cloves and a large pinch of coarse salt, and crush to a paste with a pestle. Work in 50 g/2 oz freshly grated Parmesan. Gradually add about 120 ml/4 fl oz extra virgin olive oil, working it in thoroughly with a wooden spoon to make a thick, creamy sauce. Put the pesto in a screwtop jar; it will keep for several weeks in the fridge.

Maggiorana (sweet marjoram) and origano (oregano)

These two highly aromatic herbs are closely related (oregano is the wild variety), but marjoram has a much milder flavour. Marjoram is more commonly used in northern Italy, while oregano is widely used in the south to flavour tomato dishes, vegetables and pizzas. Drying greatly intensifies the flavour of both herbs, so they should be used very sparingly.

CULINARY USES

In northern Italy, sweet marjoram is used to flavour meat, poultry, vegetables and soups; the flavour goes particularly well with carrots and cucumber. Despite its rather pungent aroma, marjoram has a delicate flavour, so it should be added to long-cooked foods towards the end of cooking.

Oregano is used exclusively in southern Italian cooking, especially in tomato-based dishes. It is a classic flavouring for pizza, but should always be used in moderation.

BUYING AND STORING

Marjoram and oregano are in season throughout the summer, but cut fresh herbs are available all year round in supermarkets. The leaves dry out quickly, so store them in plastic bags in the fridge; they will keep for up to a week. Dried oregano should be stored in small airtight jars away from the light. It loses its pungent flavour after a few months, so only buy a little at a time.

Oregano
Widely used in the south of Italy to flavour tomato dishes

Prezzemolo (parsley)

Italian parsley is the flat leaf variety, which has a more robust flavour than curly parsley. It has attractive dark green leaves, which resemble coriander. It is used as a flavouring in innumerable cooked dishes, but rarely as a garnish. If flat leaf parsley is not available, curly parsley makes a perfectly adequate substitute. Parsley is an extremely nutritious herb, rich in iron and potassium and vitamin C.

Marjoram
The aromatic flavour of this herb is very similar to that of oregano, but much milder

Parsley
Italian parsley is the flat leafed variety. It has a strong, robust flavour

Herbs & Seasonings

CULINARY USES

Parsley can be used to flavour innumerable savoury dishes. It adds colour and flavour to sauces, soups and risotti. The stalks can be used to flavour stocks and stews. Chopped parsley can be sprinkled over cooked savoury dishes; whole leaves are rarely used as a garnish in Italy.

BUYING AND STORING

Parsley is available all year round, so it should never be necessary to use the dried variety. A large bunch of parsley will keep for up to a week in the fridge if washed and wrapped in damp kitchen paper. Chopped parsley freezes very well and can be added to cooked dishes straight from the freezer.

Rosmarino (rosemary)

Spiky evergreen rosemary bushes, with their attractive blue flowers, grow wild all over Italy. The herb has a delicious, highly aromatic flavour, which is intensifed when it is dried. The texture of rosemary leaves is quite hard and the flavour very pungent, so it is never used raw, but only in cooking. It can easily overpower a dish, so only a few leaves should be used in a dish.

CULINARY USES

Rosemary combines extremely well with roast or grilled lamb, veal and chicken. A few needles will enhance the flavour of baked fish or any tomato dish, and it adds a wonderful flavour to roast potatoes and onions. Some rosemary branches added to the charcoal on a barbecue impart a superb flavour to whatever is being cooked. Dried rosemary can always be substituted for fresh; it is extremely pungent, so should be used very sparingly.

Salvia (sage)

Wild sage grows in profusion in the Italian countryside. There are several varieties, including the common garden sage, with furry silvery-grey leaves and spiky purple flowers, and clary sage, with hairy curly leaves, which is used to make dry vermouth. All sages have a slightly bitter aromatic flavour, which contrasts well with fatty meats such as pork. In northern Italy, particularly Tuscany, it is used to flavour veal and chicken. It is an excellent medicinal herb (the Latin name means "good health"); an infusion of sage leaves makes a good gargle for a sore throat.

CULINARY USES

Used sparingly, sage combines well with almost all meat and vegetable dishes and is often used in minestrone. It has a particular affinity with veal (such as *osso buco*, *piccata* and, of course, calf's

Sage
Several varieties of this herb grow in profusion in the Italian countryside

liver) and is an essential ingredient of *saltimbocca alla romana*, veal escalopes and *prosciutto crudo* topped with sage leaves and sautéed in butter and white wine. In Tuscany, white haricot beans (*fagioli*) are often flavoured with sage.

BUYING AND STORING

Fresh sage is very easy to grow on a sunny windowsill. It is available in both fresh and dried forms from supermarkets all year round. Dried sage is very strongly flavoured, so should be used in tiny quantities. It starts to taste musty after a few weeks, so replace it fairly frequently. Fresh sage should be stored in a plastic bag in the fridge; it will keep for up to a week.

Rosemary
The highly aromatic flavour of this herb is intensified when it is dried

Aceto (vinegar)

Like all wine-making countries, Italy produces excellent red and white wine vinegar as a by-product. The best vinegar is made from good wines, which are fermented in oak casks to give a depth of flavour. Good vinegar should be clean-tasting and aromatic, with no trace of bitterness and it should be transparent, not cloudy. White wine vinegar is pale golden with a pinkish tinge; red wine vinegar ranges from deep pink to dark red.

Aceto balsamico (balsamic vinegar)

Balsamic vinegar is the king of vinegars. Its name means "balm-like", reflecting its digestive qualities. Indeed, the best has a flavour so mellow and sweet that it can be drunk on its own as a *digestivo*. Balsamic vinegar is made in the area around Modena; the boiled and concentrated juice of local *trebbiano* grapes is aged in a series of barrels of decreasing size and different woods over a very long period – sometimes as long as 50 years – which gives it a slightly syrupy

texture and a rich, deep mahogany colour. Like Parmigiano Reggiano and Parma ham, genuine balsamic vinegar (*aceto balsamico tradizionale di Modena*) is strictly controlled by law; it must have been aged in the wood for at least 12 years. Vinegar aged 20 years or more is called *stravecchio*.

CULINARY USES

Red and white wine vinegars are principally used to make salad dressings and marinades, or to preserve vegetables *sott'aceto* for *antipasti*. They also add the requisite sharpness to sauces like *agrodolce* (sweet and sour). Good balsamic vinegar is also used as a dressing, sometimes on its own. It can be used to finish a delicate sauce for white fish, poultry or calf's liver. A few drops

Balsamic vinegar
This is the king of vinegars and has a wonderfully sweet and mellow flavour

sprinkled over ripe strawberries will enhance their flavour.

BUYING AND STORING

Price is usually an indication of quality where vinegar is concerned, so always buy the best you can afford. Genuine balsamic vinegar must be labelled *aceto balsamico tradizionale di Modena*; products that purport to be the real thing but are not labelled as such have either not been aged for long enough or, worse, are just red wine vinegar coloured and flavoured with caramel. Proper balsamic vinegar is expensive, but the flavour is so concentrated that a little goes a long way, and it is worth paying more for the genuine article. Vinegar will keep in a cool dark place for many months.

Red and white wine vinegars
These vinegars have a sharp flavour and are used principally for salad dressings

Herbs & Seasonings

Aglio (garlic)

Garlic is not, as you might suppose, a type of onion, but is a member of the lily family. The bulb or "head" is a collection of cloves held together by a papery white or purplish skin. When crushed or chopped it releases a pungent, slightly acrid oil with a very distinctive flavour and smell. Freshly picked garlic is milder than older, dried garlic, and the large, mauve-tinged variety has a more delicate flavour than the smaller white variety.

Garlic finds its way into many Italian dishes, but it is generally used with discretion so as not to flavour the food too aggressively. It is indispensable to certain dishes like *bagna cauda* (hot anchovy and garlic dip), *spaghetti all'aglio e olio* (garlic and olive oil) and pesto. In the south, garlic is used to flavour tomato sauces and fish soups.

CULINARY USES

Used in small quantities, garlic enlivens almost any sauce, soup or stew. It can be roasted with lamb and potatoes, or baked in its skin for a mellower flavour. Blanched, crushed garlic will aromatize olive oil to make an excellent dressing for salads or to use in cooking where only a hint of garlic flavour is required. Raw skinned garlic cloves can be rubbed over toasted croutons to make flavourful br*uschetta* bases.

BUYING AND STORING

Garlic sold loose by the head or kilo is usually fresher and better than pre-packaged varieties. The heads should feel firm and the skin should not be too papery. Do not buy garlic that is sprouting green shoots; the cloves will be soft and of no culinary value.

Stored in a cool dry place, garlic will keep for many months. If possible, hang the heads in bunches to keep them aerated. Once garlic has become soft or wizened, it is useless, so throw it away.

Garlic
Italian cooks prefer to use garlic with discretion, but it is indispensable to many dishes. The purple-skinned variety has a more delicate flavour than the white variety

PREPARING AND COOKING GARLIC

To peel garlic, cut off the root end with a small sharp knife and peel the skin upwards.

Alternatively, lay a garlic clove on the work surface, place the flat side of a heavy knife blade on top and bring the side of your fist sharply down on to the blade. This will flatten the garlic and split the skin.

To chop garlic, halve the clove and remove the bitter-tasting green shoot. Chop the garlic as finely as possible.

For very fine garlic, crush it in a garlic press.

Garlic should be softened gently in oil or butter; it will become very bitter if allowed to brown. For a subtle flavour, heat a whole clove of garlic in the oil, then remove it before adding the other ingredients. The flavour of garlic dissipates quite quickly during cooking, so for long-cooked dishes add it towards the end of the cooking time.

Olive (olives)

A wide variety of olives is cultivated all over Italy. Most are destined to be pressed into oil (nearly 20 per cent of their weight is oil), but some are kept as table olives to be salted, pickled or marinated, and served as part of an *antipasto* or used in cooking. There are two main types of olive, green (immature) and black (mature); both are bitter and inedible in their natural state. All olives have a high calorific content and are rich in iron, potassium and vitamins.

Green olives are the unripe fruit, which are picked in October or November. They have a sharper flavour and crunchier texture than black olives, which continue to ripen on the tree and are not harvested until December. Among the best Italian table olives are the small, shiny black Gaeta olives from Liguria. Wrinkled black olives from Lazio have a strong, salty flavour, while Sardinian olives are semi-ripened and are brown or purplish in colour. The largest olives come from Apulia and Sicily, where giant, green specimens are grown. These are sometimes stoned and stuffed with pimento, anchovy or almonds. Cured olives can be flavoured with all sorts of aromatics, such as garlic, local herbs, orange or lemon zest and dried chillies.

HISTORY

Olive trees have been grown in the Mediterranean since biblical times, when they were brought there from the East by the Romans. Ancient civilizations venerated the olive tree; the Egyptians believed that the goddess Isis discovered the secret of extracting oil from the fruit.

CULINARY USES

Olives can be served on their own or as a garnish or topping for pizza. They are used as an ingredient in many Italian recipes, such as *caponata*. Sicilian *caponata* is a dome-shaped salad of fried aubergines with celery, onions, tomatoes, capers and green olives, while the Ligurian dish of the same name consists of stale biscuits or bread soaked in olive oil and topped with a mixture of chopped olives, garlic, anchovies and oregano. Olives combine well with Mediterranean ingredients like tomatoes, aubergines, anchovies and capers and are used in sauces for rabbit, chicken and firm-fleshed fish. Made into a paste with red wine vinegar, garlic and olive oil, they make an excellent topping for *crostini*.

BUYING AND STORING

Cured olives vary enormously in flavour, so ask to taste one before making your selection. Loose olives can be kept in an airtight container in the fridge for up to a week.

Green olives
These unripe olives have a sharper flavour than black olives

Capperi (capers)

Capers are the immature flower buds of a wild Mediterranean shrub. They are pickled in white wine vinegar or preserved in brine which gives them a piquant, peppery flavour. Sicilian capers are packed in whole salt, which should be rinsed off before using the capers. Bottled nasturtium flower buds are sometimes sold as a cheaper alternative to true capers. Caper berries look like large, fat capers on a long stalk, but they are actually the fruit of the caper shrub. They can be served as a cocktail snack or in a salad.

Black olives
Olives are among the oldest fruits known to man. They are grown all over Italy

Caper berries
The pickled fruit of the caper shrub can be served as a cocktail snack

Herbs & Seasonings

CULINARY USES
Capers are mainly used as a condiment or garnish, but they also add zest to seafood and fish dishes, salads, pizzas and pasta sauces like the famous Sicilian *pasta colle sarde*, a mixture of sardines, parsley, tomatoes, pine nuts and raisins.

BUYING AND STORING
Choosing pickled or brined capers is a matter of taste, as is whether or not you should rinse them before use. Large capers are usually cheaper than small ones; there is no difference in flavour, but small capers make a more attractive garnish. Salt-packed capers are always sold loose by the *etto* (100 g/3½ oz); they should be used as soon as possible. Once opened, jars of capers should be kept in the fridge. Make sure any capers left in the jar are covered with the preserving liquid.

Salted capers
These are used to add zest to fish dishes, salads and pasta sauces

Pickled capers
Rinsing these capers before use softens their sharp, piquant flavour

Olio di oliva (olive oil)
Unlike other oils, which are extracted from the seeds or dried fruits of plants, olive oil is pressed from the pulp of ripe olives, which gives it an inimitable richness and flavour. Different regions of Italy produce distinctively different olive oils; Tuscan oil (considered the best) is pungent and peppery, Ligurian oil is lighter and sweeter, while the oils from the south and Sicily are powerful and nutty.

The best olive oil is *extra vergine*, which is strictly controlled and regulated like wine. This is made simply by pressing the olives to extract the oil, with no further processing. Extra virgin olive oil must have an acidity level of less than 1 per cent. The distinctive fruity flavour of this oil makes it ideal for dressings and using raw. Virgin olive oil is pressed in the same way, but has a higher acidity level and a less refined flavour. It, too, can be used as a condiment, but is also suitable for cooking. Unclassified olive oil is refined, then blended with virgin oil to add flavour. It has an undistinguished taste, but is ideal for cooking; it should not be used as a condiment.

BUYING AND STORING
The best olive oil comes from Lucca in Tuscany and is very expensive. It is made with slightly under-ripe olives, which give it a luminous green colour. If your budget does not stretch to this, buy the best extra virgin oil you can afford to use "neat" or in dressings. Experiment with small bottles of different extra virgin oils to see which you prefer. For cooking, pure olive oil is fine. Once opened, olive oil should be kept in a cool place away from the light. The best oil will soon lose its savour, so use it within six months.

Extra virgin olive oil
The distinctive fruity flavour makes this oil ideal for salad dressings

COOKING WITH OLIVE OIL

Olive oil can be heated to very high temperatures without burning or smoking, which makes it ideal for frying, sauce-making and other cooking. Extra virgin olive oil should be saved for dressing fish, vegetables and salads.

Peperoncini (dried red chillies)

Hot flakes of dried chillies are added to many southern Italian dishes, such as *arrabiata* sauce and the famous *pasta all'aglio, olio e peperoncino* (dressed with garlic, oil and chillies). Chillies are unusual in that their "hotness" is usually in inverse proportion to their size, so larger dried varieties are generally milder than the smaller ones. In summer, bunches of tiny fresh red chillies can be bought in Italian markets. These can be used fresh, preserved in olive oil to make a spicy dressing or to drizzle over a pizza, or hung up to dry and crumbled to add "oomph" to a dish. Crushed chilli flakes are available in jars.

CULINARY USES

A small pinch of dried chilli flakes spices up stews and sauces, particularly those made with tomatoes. For a really hot pizza, crumble a few flakes over the top. Dried chillies are extremely fiery and should be used very sparingly.

BUYING AND STORING

Dried chillies will last for years, but they do lose their savour over a period of time, so buy only small quantities. Whole *peperoncini* should be hung up in bunches and crumbled directly into the dish you are cooking.

Zafferano (saffron)

Saffron consists of the dried stigmas of the saffron crocus. It takes about 80,000 crocuses to produce about 500 g/1¼ lb of spice and these have to be hand-picked, so it is hardly surprising that saffron is the world's most expensive spice.

Saffron stigmas or threads are a vivid orangey-red colour with a pungent aroma. They are also sold ground into powder. Saffron has a highly aromatic flavour and will impart a wonderful, rich golden colour to risotti and sauces.

Dried chillies
These are often used in fiery southern Italian dishes, such as arrabbiata *sauce*

Saffron threads
Used to flavour and colour the classic risotto alla milanese

HISTORY

Saffron originated in Asia Minor, where it was used by ancient civilizations as a flavouring, as a dye, in perfumery and for medicinal purposes. Arab traders brought the spice to the Mediterranean in the 10th century; for centuries it was so highly prized that stealing or adulterating it was punishable by death. The best saffron is nowadays cultivated in Spain, but it is also grown in Italy.

CULINARY USES

In Italy, saffron is mainly used to flavour and colour risotti, like the classic *risotto alla milanese*. It is excellent in sauces for fish and poultry and can be used to flavour biscuits and cakes.

BUYING AND STORING

Saffron threads are sold in small boxes or jars containing only a few grams. The wiry threads should be a deep orangey-red in colour; paler yellowish-orange threads are probably the much cheaper and less desirable safflower, which will add colour but not flavour to a dish. Powdered saffron is convenient to use, but less reliable, as it may have been adulterated with safflower. Stored in small, airtight containers, saffron will keep for months.

COOKING WITH SAFFRON

Do not add saffron directly to a dish. Infuse threads in a little hot water for at least 5 minutes before blending into a dish to bring out the flavour and ensure even colouring. Add the soaking water together with the threads. Never fry saffron in hot oil or butter; this will ruin the flavour.

Dried red chilli flakes
Just a small pinch of these fiery flakes spices up stews and sauces

Cakes, Biscuits & Breads

In Italy it is perfectly normal and acceptable for a hostess to buy a dolce *(cake or dessert) to serve at the end of a meal, rather than make it herself. Pastry shops and bakeries sell a wide variety of traditional tarts, spiced yeast cakes and biscuits to be enjoyed with coffee or a glass of vin santo, sweet dessert wine or a liqueur. Some of these, like* panettone *and* pastiera napoletana, *are reserved for special occasions like Christmas and Easter, and almost every town has its own speciality for its local saint's day.*

Amaretti (macaroons)

Amaretti biscuits are made from ground almonds, egg whites and sugar. They have a distinctive flavour, which comes from the addition of bitter almonds. They originated in Venice during the Renaissance and their English name of macaroons comes from the Venetian *macerone*, meaning "fine paste". They come in dozens of different forms, from the famous crunchy sugar-encrusted biscuits wrapped in pairs in twists of crisp white paper to soft-centred macaroons wrapped in brightly-coloured foil. Amaretti are delicious dipped into hot coffee. They can also be crumbled to make a stuffing for baked peaches or apricots.

Panettone
This light-textured yeast cake is a speciality of Milan

Cantucci

These hard, high-baked lozenge-shaped biscuits from Tuscany are designed to be dipped into *espresso* coffee or vin santo. When moistened, they become deliciously soft and crumbly. They are usually studded with almonds or other nuts and flavoured with aniseed or vanilla.

Amaretti
These crunchy sugar-encrusted biscuits are delicious dipped into hot coffee

Cantucci

Panettone

Literally meaning "big bread", *panettone* is a light-textured spiced yeast bread containing sultanas and candied fruit. Originally a speciality of Milan, it is now sold all over Italy as a Christmas delicacy and is traditionally given as a gift. *Panettoni* can vary in size from small to enormous. They are sometimes sold in pastel-coloured dome-shaped boxes, which are often hung from the ceiling of bakeries and delicatessens, and look very festive. At Easter, they are baked into the shape of a lamb (*agnello*) or a dove (*colomba*). *Panettone* is sliced into wedges and eaten like cake.

Crumiri

These sweet elbow-shaped biscuits are a speciality of Piedmont. The rich golden brown dough is made with polenta and honey and piped through a fluted nozzle to give the biscuits their characteristic ridged texture. Although the biscuits seem hard on the outside, the polenta flour gives the *crumiri* a pleasantly crunchy texture. *Crumiri* are good teatime biscuits, but they are also excellent dipped in hot coffee.

Panforte

Somewhat resembling a Christmas pudding in flavour, but shaped like a flat disc, *panforte* is a rich, dark spiced cake crammed with dried fruit and toasted nuts. It is a speciality of Siena and is sold in a colourful glossy wrapping, often depicting Sienese scenes. It is extremely rich, so can only be eaten in small quantities, which is just as well, since it is also quite expensive.

Panettone
The characteristic box often hangs from the ceiling in Italian delicatessens

Panforte
This Italian spice cake is packed full of fruit and nuts

Savoiardi
These soft-textured, Italian sponge finger biscuits are used as a base for tiramisu

Savoiardi (sponge biscuits)

As their name suggests, *savoiardi* come from the Savoy region of Piedmont. They are plumper and wider than sponge fingers and have a softer texture. They are excellent dunked into tea or coffee, and are traditionally served with zabaglione; but they are best of all used as a base for tiramisu, the wickedly rich Italian coffee and mascarpone dessert.

Pane (Bread)

No Italian meal is ever served without bread to accompany the food. Indeed, it often constitutes one of the dishes in a meal in the form of *crostini* and *bruschetta* (toasted canapés), soups like *pancotto*, *panzanella* (bread salad) or pizza. In Tuscany, bread plays a more important part in the food of the region than pasta. A favourite antipasto is *fettunta*, toasted or grilled bread rubbed with garlic, anointed with plenty of olive oil and sprinkled with coarse salt. When a topping is added, it becomes *bruschetta*.

Italians buy or make fresh bread every day, but stale or leftover loaves are never wasted. Instead they are made into breadcrumbs and used for thickening sauces and stews, or for stuffings, salads or wonderfully sustaining soups.

There are hundreds of different types of Italian bread with many regional variations to suit the local food. Traditional Tuscan country bread is made without salt, since it is designed to be served with salty cured meats like salami and *prosciutto crudo*. (If you prefer salted bread, ask for *pane salato*.) Southern Italian breads often contain olive oil, which goes well with tomatoes. *Pane integrale* (wholemeal bread) is traditionally baked in a wood oven. The texture and flavour of the bread depends on the type of flour used and the amount of seasoning, but nearly all Italian breads are firm-textured with substantial crusts. You will never find flabby damp white sandwich loaves in an Italian bakery, although the inside of traditional white *panini* (bread rolls) can sometimes resemble cotton wool.

Ciabatta

These flattish, slipper-shaped loaves with squared or rounded ends are made with olive oil and are often flavoured with fresh or dried herbs, olives or sun-dried tomatoes. They have an airy texture inside and a pale, crisp crust. *Ciabatta* is delicious served warm, and is excellent for sandwiches.

Ciabatta
These popular loaves are available plain or flavoured with olives or sun-dried tomatoes

Wholemeal bread
In Italy this bread is traditionally baked in a wooden oven

Focaccia

A dimpled flat bread similar to pizza dough, *focaccia* is traditionally oiled and baked in a wood oven. A whole *focaccia* from a bakery weighs several kilos and is sold by weight, cut into manageable pieces. A variety of ingredients can be worked into the dough or served as a topping – onions, *pancetta*, rosemary or oregano, ham, cheese or olives. *Focaccine* are small versions, which are split and served with fillings like a sandwich. In Apulia, *focaccia del Venerdi Santo*, with its topping of fennel, chicory, anchovies, olives and capers, is traditionally served on Good Friday.

Focaccia
In Italy these large flat breads are sold by weight, cut into manageable pieces. It can be plain, as here, or flavoured with herbs, sun-dried tomatoes or olives

White bread
Like nearly all Italian breads, this one is firm-textured, with a substantial crust

Grissini
The cover charge in every Italian restaurant invariably includes packets of bread sticks

Grissini

These crisp golden bread sticks originated in Turin, but are now found in almost every Italian restaurant, packed in long envelopes. They range in size from matchstick-thin to hefty, knobbly, home-baked batons. Italian bakers often use up any leftover dough to make *grissini*, which are sold loose by weight. They can be rolled in sesame or poppy seeds for extra flavour.

Store Cupboard

One of the great joys of Italian food is that you can create a delicious meal almost instantly using ingredients from your store cupboard. Rice and pasta can be combined with any number of bottled or tinned vegetables, seafood or sauces to make a speedy and nutritious meal. Unopened jars and cans last for months, if not years, so it is worth keeping a selection in your store cupboard for an impromptu meal that you can rustle up in moments.

Pesto

Although nothing is as good as home-made pesto, there are some excellent bottled varieties of this fragrant green basil sauce. Traditional pesto is made with basil, pine nuts, Parmesan or Pecorino cheese and olive oil, but you may also find a red version based on sweet red peppers.

CULINARY USES
Pesto can be used as an instant dressing for any type of pasta or potato gnocchi. It gives a lift to risotti and tomato sauces, and is delicious stirred into minestrone or tomato-based soups. A spoonful of pesto will add a new dimension to bottled mayonnaise, creating a rich, pungent *maionese verde*. For a quick, attractive cocktail snack, halve some cherry tomatoes, scoop out the seeds and fill the tomatoes with pesto.

Pesto
Both the traditional green version shown here and a red type based on sweet red peppers are used to flavour sauces and pasta

Pomodori secchi (sun-dried tomatoes)

Sun-drying tomatoes intensifies their flavour to an astonishing sweetness and pungency and allows you to enjoy the full savour of tomatoes even in winter. If you are extremely lucky, you may still find in markets in southern Italy locally grown tomatoes that have been spread out to dry in the sun, but the commercially produced "sun-dried" varieties are actually air-dried by machine. Wrinkled red dried tomatoes are available dry in packets or preserved in olive oil. Dry tomatoes are brick-red in colour and have a chewy texture. They can be eaten on their own as a snack, but for cooking they should be soaked in hot water until soft (the tomato-flavoured soaking water can be used for a soup or sauce). Bottled sun-dried tomatoes are sold in chunky pieces or as a paste.

Dried tomatoes
Dried tomatoes should always be softened in water before use

Sun-dried tomatoes
These strong-flavoured tomatoes add extra piquancy to dishes

CULINARY USES
Sun-dried tomatoes add piquancy to vegetable dishes, soups or sauces. They can be chopped and added to a simple *sugo di pomodori* or a meaty *ragù* for extra flavour. They make an excellent *antipasto* combined with sliced fresh tomatoes, mozzarella and basil or with other preserved or pickled vegetables. They go well with fresh Mediterranean vegetables like fennel, aubergines and courgettes, and add a special something to egg dishes, such as *frittata*. Use the oil in which the tomatoes are preserved for salad dressings or for sweating vegetables for a soup or sauce.

The paste can be used in small quantities for sauces and soups, or used on its own or with a little butter as a dressing for pasta.

Passata
This rich tomato pureé varies in fineness from the ultra-smooth to the chunkier sugocasa

Passata *(tomato pulp)*

Rich red passata is simply sieved ripe tomatoes, a wonderfully convenient short-cut wherever tomato pulp is required. Depending on the degree of sieving, it can be perfectly smooth or slightly chunky (*polpa di pomodoro* or *passata rustica*: "rustic passata"). The chunky variety is sold in tall jars, while the smoothest type is available in cartons or jars. More highly concentrated tomato paste or purée (*concentrato di pomodoro*) is packed in small cans or tubes. This product is extremely strong and should only be used in small quantities.

Culinary Uses
Passata can be used as a basis for soups and sauces, and as a substitute for fresh tomatoes in all recipes where they require long cooking. For a very quick pasta sauce, sweat some finely chopped onion and garlic in olive oil, add a jar of passata and bubble the sauce while the pasta is cooking. Flavour with fresh basil, oregano, parsley or some chopped olives, capers and/or anchovies. For more body and depth and a richer colour, stir in a spoonful or two of tomato concentrate.

Black olive paste

Green olive paste

Pasta di olive *(olive paste)*

Green or, more usually, black olives are pounded to a paste with salt and olive oil and packed in small jars. Olive paste tends to be very salty and rich, so a little goes a long way.

Culinary Uses
Olive paste can be spread very thinly over pizza bases, or scraped on to toasted croûtons and topped with tomatoes or mushrooms to make *crostini*. Mixed with olive oil and a little lemon juice, it can be a dip for raw vegetables. For an interesting *antipasto*, mash a little olive paste into the yolks of halved hard-boiled eggs, spoon the mixture back into the cavity and top with a few capers.

A little olive paste adds a rich flavour to a tomato sauce, while a spoonful stirred into a vinaigrette makes a good dressing for a robust salad. If you are a real olive lover, stir a small amount into hot pasta for the simplest of dressings.

Legumi sott'olio *(vegetables preserved in oil)*

Italians produce a wide variety of vegetables preserved in olive or sunflower oil, or a mixture of both. The choicest are often cooked *alla brace* (grilled) before being packed in the best olive oil – tiny *carciofini* (artichokes), *funghi* and *porcini* (button and wild mushrooms), *peperoni* (red and yellow peppers) and *melanzane* (aubergines) – which look as beautiful as they taste. You will sometimes find large bulbous jars containing colourful layers of different vegetables in oil; these are packed by hand and are extremely expensive.

Culinary Uses
A mixture of oil-preserved vegetables combined with a selection of cured meats makes a wonderful *antipasto*. They can also be chopped or sliced and used to dress hot or cold pasta, or stirred into rice for a substantial cold salad. They make a delicious topping for *crostini* or pizza.

Artichoke hearts
These olive oil-packed vegetables are often combined with sliced cured meats to make an antipasto

Store Cupboard

Giardiniera *(pickled vegetables)*

Mixed pickled vegetables are sold packed *in agrodolce* (vinegar and oil). Single varieties like peeled or unpeeled aubergines and courgettes are available, but a mixture of these vegetables along with artichokes, baby onions, carrots, celery and peppers is more colourful. These vegetables are sometimes described as *alla contadina* (peasant-style).

CULINARY USES

Pickled vegctables can be served with salami and ham as an *antipasto*, or drained and mixed with raw vegetables and mayonnaise for a piquant version of *insalata russa* (Russian salad). Their vinegary taste makes an excellent counterpoint to plain cold roast meats or poultry.

Filetti di acciughe *(anchovy fillets)*

Anchovy fillets are available preserved in salt or oil. The salted fillets have a superior flavour, but they are are only available in catering tins to be sold by the *etto* (100 g/ 3½ oz) in delicatessens. You can buy these and soak them for 30 minutes, then dry them thoroughly and pack them in olive oil, but it is more practical to buy ready canned or bottled anchovies.

CULINARY USES

Anchovies can be chopped and added to tomato sauces and salad dressings. They can be stirred into a fish risotto, or mixed with tomatoes and capers for a topping for pizzas or *crostini*. They are best of all made into *bagna cauda*, a delicious and quick hot dip for raw vegetables. For six people, heat 150 ml/5 fl oz/ ⅔ cup olive oil with 50 g/2 oz/4 tbsp unsalted butter. As soon as it begins to foam, add 3 finely chopped garlic cloves and soften but do not brown. Drain and roughly chop a 50 g/2 oz can of anchovy fillets, add to the pan and stir over low heat until they have disintegrated to a paste. Keep the sauce hot and dip in the vegetables.

Bottarga *(salted roe)*

The pressed, salted and dried roe of the grey mullet or tuna, also known as *buttariga, butarega and ovotarica*, is a speciality of Sardinia, Sicily and the Veneto, where it is regarded as a great delicacy. It is usually packed in a sausage shape inside a skin that should be removed before preparing. Wrapped in clear film or polythene, it will keep for several months.

CULINARY USES

Bottarga can be served as an *antipasto* thinly sliced and dressed with a little extra virgin olive oil and lemon juice. In Sicily, it is served with *caponata*, a dome-shaped salad of fried aubergines and celery. It is delicious simply grated over hot pasta with a knob of unsalted butter and a little chopped fresh parsley or dried chilli flakes.

Anchovy fillets
Usually chopped and added to sauces or salads for extra flavour. These are available packed in oil or salt – the salted variety have a better flavour

Peppers
The vinegary flavour of these pickled vegetables goes well with cold roast meats

Baccalà (salted dried cod)

Air-drying is the oldest known method of preserving fish. Before the days of deep-freezing, dried fish was invaluable for people who wished to observe meatless days, but who lived far from the sea, because the salting and drying process ensures that it remains edible for many months. The most popular dried fish in Italy is salt cod, which is traditionally eaten on Good Friday. It is sometimes known confusingly as *stoccafisso* (although true stockfish is unsalted). It looks rather unappealing, like a flat, greyish board, but once it has been soaked and reconstituted it is absolutely delicious. Unlike other store cupboard ingredients, *baccalà* must be prepared a day in advance, but it is worth the effort.

Salt cod
This is the favourite Italian dried fish – it looks unappealing, but once it is soaked and cooked, it is delicious

Clams in brine

Vongole (clams)

Tiny clams are sold packed in brine in glass jars. These miniature golden nuggets need no further cooking and can be simply heated through and tossed into hot pasta or risotto, or combined with tomato sauce. If you have time, drain the clams and reduce the juice in which they are packed with finely chopped garlic and a few dried chilli flakes to make a more intense sauce.

Mostarda di Cremona (mustard fruit chutney)

This sweet crystallized fruit chutney with its piquant undertone of the mustard was first produced over a hundred years ago in Cremona and Venice. Its vibrant multi-colour comes from the assortment of candied fruits from which it is made – cherries, pears, melons, figs, apricots and clementines, infused in mustard seed oil. Also known as *mostarda di frutta*, the chutney is traditionally served with sausages like zampone and cotechino, or roast and boiled beef, veal and pork. For an unusual and delicious dessert, serve the chutney as a topping for creamy mascarpone.

CULINARY USES
Before using *baccalà*, it must be soaked under cold running water for at least 8 hours to rehydrate it and remove the excess salt. Once this has been done, it can be creamed with olive oil, garlic, cream and parsley to make *baccalà mantecato*, a famous Venetian dish, which is served on fried polenta. In the Florentine version, the salt cod is cut into chunks, coated with flour and fried with tomatoes and onions. *Baccalà* combines well with all Mediterranean flavours and can be stewed or baked with red peppers, potatoes, fennel or celery, capers, olives and anchovies. Many recipes also include pine nuts and raisins or sultanas. For a simple pasta sauce, mix some flaked salt cod with cream and chopped herbs and stir it into the hot pasta.

Mustard fruit chutney

Aperitifs & Liqueurs

Behind every bar in Italy is displayed row upon row of bottles containing dozens of different aperitivi *and* digestivi, *many of them never found outside Italy. They are consumed at any hour of the day; a favourite Italian morning drink is* caffè corretto, *espresso coffee laced with grappa or* stock *(Italian brandy). Many of the vermouths and spirits are made from local ingredients, like herbs, nuts, lemons, artichokes or regional wines. The Italians have an unshakeable belief in the digestive properties of such drinks, many of which are so bitter that most non-Italians find them completely unpalatable. At the end of a restaurant meal, you will always find the men clustered around the bar aiding their digestion with a small glass of spirit or liqueur.*

Amaro

A very bitter *aperitivo* much beloved of the Italians, *amaro* is flavoured with gentian, herbs and orange peel and contains quinine and iron. Marginally less bitter than straight *amaro* are the wine-based *amari* like Campari, which is usually mixed with soda water and drunk before a meal to stimulate the appetite and cleanse the palate. Others, like Fernet-Branca, are served as a pick-me-up and cure for stomach upsets. *Amaro* is reputed to have excellent digestive and tonic properties, to cure hangovers and to have aphrodisiac qualities, which probably explains its popularity in Italy.

Campari

A bright crimson *aperitivo* from the *amaro* family, wine-based Campari has a bitter, astringent flavour. It was first produced in the 19th century by the Campari brothers from Milan, and has been produced by the same family ever since. Campari is sold in triangular single-portion bottles ready-mixed with soda (Campari soda). The neat bitters are an essential ingredient of cocktails like *Negroni* and *Americano.*

Amaro

Fernet Branca

Campari soda

Cynar

This dark brown, intensely bitter, aperitif with an alcoholic content of 17 per cent is made from artichokes. Too bitter to swallow on its own, it is usually served as a long drink with ice and soda water.

Punt e Mes

The name of this intensely bitter red *aperitivo* means "point and a half". It is said to have been created by the Carpano distillery when customers ordered their drinks to be mixed according to their own specification. Punt e Mes is usually drunk on its own, but can be served with ice and soda.

Vermouth

All vermouths, both white and red, are made from white wine flavoured with aromatic herbal extracts and spices. The first vermouth was made in Turin in the 18th century, and vermouth is still produced there. Red vermouths, like Cinzano and sweet Martini, are sweetened with sugar and tinted with caramel to give them a deep red colour. These sweet red varieties are generically called "Italian" vermouth – the "it" in gin and it. Dry vermouth is white and contains less sugar. It is known as "French", but is also produced in Italy by companies such as the famous Martini and Rossi. Other well-known brands include Riccadonna and Gancia.

CULINARY USES

Although the Italians tend to use white wine rather than vermouth in their cooking, dry white vermouth can be substituted in sauces and veal, rabbit or poultry dishes. It adds a touch of dryness and intensity.

Cynar

Punt e Mes

Extra-dry white Vermouth

Fortified Wines

Marsala

This rich brown fortified wine has a sweet, musky flavour and an alcoholic content of about 18 per cent. It is made in the west of Sicily, near the town from which it takes its name. The best Marsala (*vergine*) has been matured for at least five years to give an intensity of flavour and colour. Although sweet Marsala is better known, dry varieties (*ambra secco*) are also produced; their flavour is reminiscent of medium sherry. The sweetest version is *Marsala all'uovo*, an intensely rich and sticky dessert wine enriched with egg yolks, which can only be drunk in tiny quantities. Dry Marsala is generally served as an *aperitivo*, while the sweet version is served after a meal, usually with little biscuits to dip into the wine. Unlike sherry, sweet Marsala does not deteriorate once the bottle is opened, so it makes a very useful standby in the kitchen.

Vin santo

This "holy wine" from Tuscany is made from semi-dried grapes with a long slow fermentation, followed by many years ageing to produce a syrupy golden wine. Although not a fortified wine, its intense flavour has some similarity to sherry and it is drunk in much the same way. Vin santo can be dry or sweet, but the sweet version is more common. It is generally served with a plate of *cantucci* or *biscotti di Prato*, hard slipper-shaped biscuits studded with nuts. These are dunked into the wine to make a delicious dessert.

Vin santo

CULINARY USES

Sweet Marsala is probably best known as an essential ingredient of *zabaglione*, a light frothy dessert made from whisked egg yolks, sugar and Marsala. It is used in *zuppa inglese* (trifle) and many other desserts. Dry Marsala is widely used in Italian cooking, particularly in veal dishes like *scaloppine* and *piccata alla Marsala* and sautéed chicken livers. A few spoonfuls of Marsala added to the pan in which veal or poultry has been sautéed will mingle with the pan juices to make a delicious syrupy sauce. It adds extra flavour to wild mushrooms or a mushroom risotto.

Marsala
The sweet variety is used to flavour zabaglione

Dry Marsala
Widely used by Italian cooks for flavouring veal and poultry dishes

Amaretto

This sweet liqueur is made from apricot kernels and flavoured with almonds and aromatic extracts. There are several brands produced, but the best is Disaronno Amaretto, which comes in a distinctive squarish rippled glass bottle with a square cap.

CULINARY USES

The distinctive almond flavour of Amaretto enhances many desserts, such as *macedonia* (fruit salad), *zuppa inglese* (trifle) and *panna* (whipped cream).

Galliano

A bright yellow liqueur from Lombardy, Galliano is flavoured with herbs and spices and tastes a little like a bittersweet Chartreuse. It is occasionally drunk on its own as a *digestivo*, but is best known as an ingredient for cocktails like Harvey Wallbanger or Golden Cadillac.

Galliano

Amaretto

Liqueurs & Digestivi

Grappa

A pungent colourless brandy with an alcoholic content of about 40 per cent, distilled from the pressed skins and pips of the grapes left after wine-making. At its crudest, grappa tastes of raw spirit, but after maturing the taste becomes refined and the best grappa can be as good as a fine French marc. Grappa is made in many regions, usually from local grapes, which lend each variety its characteristic flavour. On the whole, you get what you pay for; cheap grappa is fiery and pungent, while expensive, well-matured varieties can be very smooth. The very best grappa often comes in exquisite hand-blown bottles. The spirit can be flavoured with various aromatics, including rose petals and lemon peel.

CULINARY USES

Grappa is not widely used in Italian cooking, except in *capretto alla piemontese* (braised kid). It can be used for flambéeing and for preserving soft fruits. The spirit takes on the flavour of the fruits and can be drunk as a *digestivo* after the fruits have been eaten.

Liquore al limone or Cedro

This sticky sweet liqueur is made from the peel of the lemons that grow in profusion around the Amalfi coast. Almost every delicatessen in the region sells a home-made version of this opaque yellow drink, whose sweetness is tempered by the tangy citrus fruit. It should be served ice-cold straight from the fridge or freezer and makes a refreshing *aperitivo* or *digestivo*.

Maraschino

This sweet, colourless cherry liqueur is made from fermented bitter Maraschino cherries. It can be drunk on its own as a *digestivo*, but is more commonly used for flavouring cocktails or sweet dishes.

Maraschino

Liquore al limone

Grappa

Nocino

This sticky, dark brown liqueur from Emilia-Romagna is made from unripe green walnuts steeped in spirit. It has an aromatic but bittersweet flavour.

Sambuca

A colourless liqueur with a strong taste of aniseed, although it is actually distilled from witch elder. Traditionally it is served in a schooner-shaped glass, flambéed and with a coffee bean floating on top. The coffee bean is crunched as the Sambuca is drunk, so that its bitterness counteracts the intense sweetness of the liqueur. This method of serving Sambuca is known as *colla mosca* ("with the fly"), the "fly" being the coffee bean.

Strega

A bright yellow liqueur made from herbs and flowers, strega (meaning "witch"), has a bittersweet flavour and is definitely an acquired taste!

Sambuca

Nocino

Strega

The Recipes

....

The recipes in this collection cover a range of styles, from regional specialities to popular modern classics. More unusual, innovative offerings are here too, destined to become future favourites. All of the recipes use ingredients that can be found easily outside Italy, and all are as delicious to eat as they are easy to make.

Buon Appetito.

Antipasti

Antipasto means "before the meal", and no respectable Italian meal would start without it. The recipes in this chapter are typical of Italian antipasti – appetizing and easy on the eye, light and tasty. Vegetables, fish and salads are the mainstay, not only for their lightness and freshness, but also for their colour.

Roast Pepper Terrine

Torta di peperoni al forno

This terrine is perfect for a dinner party because it tastes better if made ahead. Prepare the salsa on the day of serving. Serve with hot Italian bread.

Ingredients

8 peppers (red, yellow and orange)
675 g/1½ lb/3 cups mascarpone cheese
3 eggs, separated
30 ml/2 tbsp each roughly chopped flat
    leaf parsley and shredded basil
2 large garlic cloves, roughly chopped
2 red, yellow or orange peppers, seeded
    and roughly chopped
30 ml/2 tbsp extra virgin olive oil
10 ml/2 tsp balsamic vinegar
a few basil sprigs
pinch of sugar
salt and freshly ground black pepper
serves 8

1 Place the peppers under a hot grill for 8–10 minutes, turning them frequently until the skins are charred and blistered on all sides. Put the hot peppers in polythene bags, seal and leave until cold.

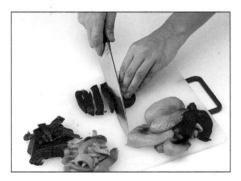

2 ▲ Rub off the pepper skins under cold running water. Break open the flesh and rub out the cores and seeds. Drain the peppers, dry them on kitchen paper, then cut seven of them lengthways into thin, even-size strips. Reserve the remaining pepper for the salsa.

Variation

For a low-fat version of this terrine, use ricotta cheese instead of the mascarpone.

3 Put the mascarpone cheese in a bowl with the egg yolks, herbs and half the garlic. Add salt and pepper to taste. Beat well. In a separate bowl, whisk the egg whites to a soft peak, then fold into the cheese mixture until evenly incorporated.

4 ▲ Preheat the oven to 180°C/ 350°F/ Gas 4. Line the base of a lightly oiled 900 g/2 lb loaf tin. Put one-third of the cheese mixture in the tin and spread level. Arrange half the pepper strips on top in an even layer. Repeat until all the cheese and peppers are used.

5 Cover the tin with foil and place in a roasting tin. Pour in boiling water to come halfway up the sides of the tin. Bake for 1 hour. Leave to cool in the water bath, then lift out and chill overnight.

6 A few hours before serving, make the salsa. Place the remaining roast pepper and fresh peppers in a food processor. Add the remaining garlic, oil and vinegar. Set aside a few basil leaves for garnishing and add the rest to the processor. Process until finely chopped. Tip the mixture into a bowl, add salt and pepper to taste and mix well. Cover and chill until ready to serve.

7 Turn out the terrine, peel off the paper and slice thickly. Garnish with the basil leaves and serve cold, with the sweet pepper salsa.

Pan-fried Chicken Liver Salad

Insalata di fegatini

This Florentine salad uses vin santo, a sweet dessert wine from Tuscany, but this is not essential – any dessert wine will do, or a sweet or cream sherry.

Ingredients

75 g/3 oz fresh baby spinach leaves
75 g/3 oz lollo rosso leaves
75 ml/5 tbsp olive oil
15 ml/1 tbsp butter
225 g/8 oz chicken livers, trimmed and
    thinly sliced
45 ml/3 tbsp vin santo
50–75 g/2–3 oz fresh Parmesan cheese,
    shaved into curls
salt and freshly ground black pepper

serves 4

1 ▲ Wash and dry the spinach and lollo rosso. Tear the leaves into a large bowl, season with salt and pepper to taste and toss gently to mix.

2 ▲ Heat 30 ml/2 tbsp of the oil with the butter in a large heavy-based frying pan. When foaming, add the chicken livers and toss over a medium to high heat for 5 minutes or until the livers are browned on the outside but still pink in the centre. Remove from the heat.

3 ▲ Remove the livers from the pan with a slotted spoon, drain them on kitchen paper, then place on top of the spinach.

4 ▲ Return the pan to a medium heat, add the remaining oil and the vin santo and stir until sizzling.

5 Pour the hot dressing over the spinach and livers and toss to coat. Put the salad in a serving bowl and sprinkle over the Parmesan shavings. Serve at once.

Salad Leaves with Gorgonzola   *Insalata verde con gorgonzola*

Crispy fried pancetta makes tasty croûtons, which contrast well in texture and flavour

with the softness of mixed salad leaves and the sharp taste of Gorgonzola.

Ingredients
225 g/8 oz pancetta rashers, any rinds
    removed, coarsely chopped
2 large garlic cloves, roughly chopped
75 g/3 oz rocket leaves
75 g/3 oz radicchio leaves
50 g/2 oz/½ cup walnuts,
    roughly chopped
115 g/4 oz Gorgonzola cheese
60 ml/4 tbsp olive oil
15 ml/1 tbsp balsamic vinegar
salt and freshly ground black pepper
serves 4

Variation
Use walnut oil instead of olive oil, or
hazelnuts and hazelnut oil instead of
walnuts and olive oil.

1 ▲ Put the chopped pancetta and
garlic in a non-stick or heavy-based
frying pan and heat gently, stirring
constantly, until the pancetta fat
runs. Increase the heat and fry until
the pancetta and garlic are crisp.
Remove with a slotted spoon and
drain on kitchen paper. Leave the
pancetta fat in the pan, off the heat.

2 ▲ Tear the rocket and radicchio
leaves into a salad bowl. Sprinkle over
the walnuts, pancetta and garlic. Add
salt and pepper and toss to mix.
Crumble the Gorgonzola on top.

3 Return the frying pan to a medium
heat and add the oil and balsamic
vinegar to the pancetta fat. Stir until
sizzling, then pour over the salad.
Serve at once, to be tossed at the table.

Tomato and Mozzarella Toasts   *Bruschetta casalinga*

These resemble mini pizzas and are good with drinks before a dinner party. Prepare them

several hours in advance and pop them in the oven just as your guests arrive.

Ingredients
3 *sfilatini* (thin ciabatta)
about 250 ml/8 fl oz/1 cup sun-dried
    tomato paste
3 x 150 g/5 oz packets mozzarella
    cheese, drained
about 10 ml/2 tsp dried oregano or
    mixed herbs
30–45 ml/2–3 tbsp olive oil
freshly ground black pepper
serves 6–8

Variations
Use red or green pesto instead of
the sun-dried tomato paste – a
combination of colours is especially
effective if the toasts are served on a
large platter. Halved olives can be
pressed into the cheese, or criss-
cross strips of anchovy.

1 ▲ Cut each *sfilatino* on the
diagonal into 12–15 slices, discarding
the ends. Toast lightly on both sides.

2 Preheat the oven to 220°C/425°F/
Gas 7. Spread sun-dried tomato paste
on one side of each slice of toast. Cut
the mozzarella into small pieces and
arrange over the tomato paste.

3 ▲ Put the toasts on baking sheets,
sprinkle with herbs and pepper to
taste and drizzle with oil. Bake for
5 minutes or until the mozzarella has
melted and is bubbling. Leave the
toasts to settle for a few minutes
before serving.

Genoese Squid Salad

Calamari in insalata alla genovese

This is a good salad for summer, when French beans and new potatoes are at their best.

Serve it for a first course or light lunch.

Ingredients

450 g/1 lb prepared squid, cut into rings
4 garlic cloves, roughly chopped
300 ml/¹/₂ pint/1¹/₄ cups Italian red wine
450 g/1 lb waxy new potatoes,
    scrubbed clean
225 g/8 oz French beans, trimmed and
    cut into short lengths
2–3 drained sun-dried tomatoes in oil,
    thinly sliced lengthways
60 ml/4 tbsp extra virgin olive oil
15 ml/1 tbsp red wine vinegar
salt and freshly ground black pepper
serves 4–6

Cook's Tips

The French potato called Charlotte is perfect for this type of salad because it retains its shape and does not break up when boiled. Prepared squid can be bought from supermarkets with fresh fish counters, and from fishmongers.

1 ▲ Preheat the oven to 180°C/350°F/ Gas 4. Put the squid rings in an earthenware dish with half the garlic, the wine and pepper to taste. Cover and cook for 45 minutes or until the squid is tender.

2 Put the potatoes in a saucepan, cover with cold water and add a good pinch of salt. Bring to the boil, cover and simmer for 15–20 minutes or until tender. Using a slotted spoon, lift out the potatoes and set aside. Add the beans to the boiling water and cook for 3 minutes. Drain.

3 ▲ When the potatoes are cool enough to handle, slice them thickly on the diagonal and place them in a bowl with the warm beans and sun-dried tomatoes. Whisk the oil, wine vinegar and the remaining garlic in a jug and add salt and pepper to taste. Pour over the potato mixture.

4 Drain the squid and discard the wine and garlic. Add the squid to the potato mixture and fold very gently to mix. Arrange the salad on individual plates and grind pepper liberally all over. Serve warm.

Tuna Carpaccio

Carpaccio di tonno

Fillet of beef is most often used for carpaccio, but meaty fish like tuna – and swordfish – make an unusual change. The secret is to slice the fish wafer thin, made possible by freezing the fish first, a technique used by the Japanese for making sashimi.

Ingredients

2 fresh tuna steaks, about 450 g/1 lb
    total weight
60 ml/4 tbsp extra virgin olive oil
15 ml/1 tbsp balsamic vinegar
5 ml/1 tsp caster sugar
30 ml/2 tbsp drained bottled green
    peppercorns or capers
salt and freshly ground black pepper
lemon wedges and green salad,
    to serve

serves 4

Cook's Tip

Raw fish is safe to eat as long as it is very fresh, so check with your fishmonger before purchase, and make and serve carpaccio on the same day. Do not buy fish that has been frozen and thawed.

1 ▲ Remove the skin from each tuna steak and place each steak between two sheets of clear film or non-stick baking paper. Pound with a rolling pin until flattened slightly.

2 Roll up the tuna as tightly as possible, then wrap tightly in clear film and place in the freezer for 4 hours or until firm.

3 ▲ Unwrap the tuna and cut crossways into the thinnest possible slices. Arrange on individual plates.

4 Whisk together the remaining ingredients, season and pour over the tuna. Cover and allow to come to room temperature for 30 minutes before serving with lemon wedges and green salad.

Marinated Vegetable Antipasto

Verdura marinata per antipasto

Antipasto means "before the meal" and traditionally consists of a selection of marinated vegetable dishes served with good Italian salami and thin slices of Parma ham. Serve in attractive bowls, with plenty of fresh crusty bread.

Ingredients

For the peppers

3 red peppers
3 yellow peppers
4 garlic cloves, sliced
handful fresh basil, plus extra to garnish
extra virgin olive oil
salt and freshly ground black pepper

For the mushrooms

450 g/1 lb open cap mushrooms
60 ml/4 tbsp extra virgin olive oil
1 large garlic clove, crushed
15 ml/1 tbsp chopped fresh rosemary
250 ml/8 fl oz/1 cup dry white wine
fresh rosemary sprigs, to garnish

For the olives

1 dried red chilli, crushed
grated rind of 1 lemon
120 ml/4 fl oz/½ cup extra virgin olive oil
225 g/8 oz/1⅓ cups Italian black olives
30 ml/2 tbsp chopped fresh flat leaf parsley
1 lemon wedge, to serve

serves 4

1 ▲ Place the peppers under a hot grill. Turn occasionally until they are blackened and blistered all over. Remove from the heat and place in a large plastic bag. When cool, remove the skin, halve the peppers and remove the seeds. Cut the flesh into strips lengthways and place them in a bowl with the sliced garlic and basil leaves. Add salt, to taste, cover with oil and marinate for 3–4 hours before serving, tossing occasionally. When serving, garnish with more basil leaves.

2 Thickly slice the mushrooms and place in a large bowl. Heat the oil in a small pan and add the garlic and rosemary. Pour in the wine. Bring the mixture to the boil, then lower the heat and simmer for 3 minutes. Add salt and pepper to taste.

3 ▲ Pour the mixture over the mushrooms. Mix well and leave until cool, stirring occasionally. Cover and marinate overnight. Serve at room temperature, garnished with rosemary sprigs.

4 ▲ Prepare the olives. Place the chilli and lemon rind in a small pan with the oil. Heat gently for about 3 minutes. Add the olives and heat for 1 minute more. Tip into a bowl and leave to cool. Marinate overnight. Sprinkle the parsley over just before serving with the lemon wedge.

Cook's Tip

The pepper antipasto can be stored in the fridge for up to 2 weeks covered in olive oil in a screw-top jar.

Stuffed Roast Peppers with Pesto

Peperoni arrostiti con pesto

Serve these scallop-and-pesto-filled sweet red peppers with Italian bread, such as ciabatta

or focaccia, to mop up the garlicky juices.

Ingredients

4 squat red peppers
2 large garlic cloves, cut into thin slivers
60 ml/4 tbsp olive oil
4 shelled scallops
45 ml/3 tbsp pesto
salt and freshly ground black pepper
freshly grated Parmesan cheese,
    to serve
salad leaves and fresh basil sprigs,
    to garnish

serves 4

Cook's Tip

Scallops are available from most fishmongers and supermarkets with fresh fish counters. Never cook scallops for longer than the time stated in the recipe or they will be tough and rubbery.

1 Preheat the oven to 180°C/350°F/ Gas 4. Cut the peppers in half lengthways, through their stalks. Scrape out and discard the cores and seeds. Wash the pepper shells and pat dry.

2 ▲ Put the peppers, cut-side up, in an oiled roasting tin. Divide the slivers of garlic equally among them and sprinkle with salt and pepper to taste. Spoon the oil into the peppers, then roast for 40 minutes.

3 ▲ Cut each of the shelled scallops in half to make two flat discs. Remove the peppers from the oven and place a scallop half in each pepper half. Top with pesto.

4 Return the tin to the oven and roast for 10 minutes more. Transfer the peppers to individual serving plates, sprinkle with grated Parmesan and garnish each plate with a few salad leaves and fresh basil sprigs. Serve warm.

Mozzarella Skewers

Spiedini alla romana

Stacks of flavour – layers of oven-baked mozzarella, tomatoes, basil and bread.

Ingredients

12 slices white country bread, each
   about 1 cm/½ in thick
45 ml/3 tbsp olive oil
225 g/8 oz mozzarella cheese, cut into
   5 mm/¼ in slices
3 plum tomatoes, cut into 5 mm/
   ¼ in slices
15 g/½ oz/½ cup fresh basil leaves, plus
   extra to garnish
salt and freshly ground black pepper
30 ml/2 tbsp chopped fresh flat
   leaf parsley, to garnish
serves 4

Cook's Tip

If you use wooden skewers, soak
them in water first, to prevent
scorching.

1 ▲ Preheat the oven to 220°C/425°F/
Gas 7. Trim the crusts from the bread
and cut each slice into four equal
squares. Arrange on a baking sheet
and brush on one side (or both
sides) with half the olive oil. Bake for
3–5 minutes until the squares are
pale gold.

2 Remove from the oven and place
the bread squares on a board with
the other ingredients.

3 ▲ Make 16 stacks, each starting
with a square of bread, then a slice of
mozzarella topped with a slice of
tomato and a basil leaf. Sprinkle with
salt and pepper, then repeat, ending
with the bread. Push a skewer
through each stack and place on
the baking sheet. Drizzle with the
remaining oil and bake for
10–15 minutes until the cheese
begins to melt. Garnish with fresh
basil leaves and serve scattered with
chopped fresh flat leaf parsley.

Aubergine Fritters

Frittelle di melanzane

These simply delicious fritters make a superb starter or vegetarian supper dish.

Ingredients

1 large aubergine, about 675 g/1½ lb, cut
   into 1 cm/½ in thick slices
30 ml/2 tbsp olive oil
1 egg, lightly beaten
2 garlic cloves, crushed
60 ml/4 tbsp chopped fresh parsley
130 g/4½ oz/2¼ cups fresh
   white breadcrumbs
90 g/3½ oz/generous 1 cup grated
   Parmesan cheese
90 g/3½ oz/generous 1 cup feta cheese,
   crumbled
45 ml/3 tbsp plain flour
sunflower oil, for shallow frying
salt and freshly ground black pepper

To serve

natural yogurt, flavoured with fried red
   chillies and cumin seeds
lime wedges
serves 4

1 ▲ Preheat the oven to 190°C/375°F/
Gas 5. Brush the aubergine slices
with the olive oil, then place them on
a baking sheet and bake for about
20 minutes until golden and tender.
Chop the slices finely and place them
in a bowl with the egg, garlic, parsley,
breadcrumbs, Parmesan and feta. Add
salt and pepper to taste, and mix well.
Leave the mixture to rest for about
20 minutes. If the mixture looks
very sloppy, add more breadcrumbs.

2 ▲ Divide the mixture into eight
balls and flatten them slightly. Place
the flour on a plate and season with
salt and pepper. Coat the fritters in
the flour, shaking off any excess.

3 Shallow fry the fritters in batches
for 1 minute on each side, until
golden brown. Drain on kitchen
paper and serve with the flavoured
yogurt and lime wedges.

Soups

....

The Italians are great soup eaters, and some of the best soups in the world come from Italy. Clear broth, brodo, *and delicate puréed soups are served as a first course before a main meal. More substantial chunky soups,* minestre, *are often main meals in themselves, usually served in the evening if the main meal of the day has been at lunchtime.*

Onion Soup

La cipollata

This warming winter soup comes from Umbria, where it is sometimes thickened with beaten eggs and lots of grated Parmesan cheese. It is then served on top of hot toasted croûtes – rather like savoury scrambled eggs.

Ingredients

115 g/4 oz pancetta rashers, any rinds
    removed, roughly chopped
30 ml/2 tbsp olive oil
15 g/¹/₂ oz/1 tbsp butter
675 g/1¹/₂ lb onions, thinly sliced
10 ml/2 tsp granulated sugar
about 1.2 litres/2 pints/5 cups
    chicken stock
350 g/12 oz ripe Italian plum tomatoes,
    peeled and roughly chopped
a few basil leaves, shredded
salt and freshly ground black pepper
freshly grated Parmesan cheese,
    to serve

serves 4

1 ▲ Put the chopped pancetta in a large saucepan and heat gently, stirring constantly, until the fat runs. Increase the heat to medium, add the oil, butter, onions and sugar and stir well to mix.

2 ▲ Half cover the pan and cook the onions gently for about 20 minutes until golden. Stir frequently and lower the heat if necessary.

3 ▲ Add the stock, tomatoes and salt and pepper and bring to the boil, stirring. Lower the heat, half cover the pan and simmer, stirring occasionally, for about 30 minutes.

4 Check the consistency of the soup and add a little more stock or water if it is too thick.

5 Just before serving, stir in most of the basil and taste for seasoning. Serve hot, garnished with the remaining shredded basil. Hand round the freshly grated Parmesan separately.

Cook's Tip
Look for Vidalia onions to make this soup. They are available at large supermarkets, and have a very sweet flavour and attractive yellowish flesh.

Cream of Courgette Soup

Vellutata di zucchini

The beauty of this soup is its delicate colour, rich and creamy texture and subtle taste. If you prefer a more pronounced cheese flavour, use Gorgonzola instead of Dolcelatte.

Ingredients

30 ml/2 tbsp olive oil
15 g/½ oz/1 tbsp butter
1 medium onion, roughly chopped
900 g/2 lb courgettes, trimmed
    and sliced
5 ml/1 tsp dried oregano
about 600 ml/1 pint/2½ cups vegetable
    or chicken stock
115 g/4 oz Dolcelatte cheese, rind
    removed, diced
300 ml/½ pint/1¼ cups single cream
salt and freshly ground black pepper
fresh oregano and extra Dolcelatte,
    to garnish

serves 4–6

1 ▲ Heat the oil and butter in a large saucepan until foaming. Add the onion and cook gently for about 5 minutes, stirring frequently, until softened but not brown.

2 ▲ Add the courgettes and oregano, with salt and pepper to taste. Cook over a medium heat for 10 minutes, stirring frequently.

3 ▲ Pour in the stock and bring to the boil, stirring. Lower the heat, half cover the pan and simmer gently, stirring occasionally, for about 30 minutes. Stir in the diced Dolcelatte until melted.

Cook's Tip

To save time, trim off and discard the ends of the courgettes, cut them into thirds, then chop in a food processor fitted with the metal blade.

4 ▲ Process the soup in a blender or food processor until smooth, then press through a sieve into a clean pan.

5 Add two-thirds of the cream and stir over a low heat until hot, but not boiling. Check the consistency and add more stock if the soup is too thick. Taste for seasoning, then pour into heated bowls. Swirl in the remaining cream. Garnish with oregano and extra cheese and serve.

Wild Mushroom Soup

Zuppa di porcini

Wild mushrooms are expensive. Dried porcini have an intense flavour, so only a small quantity is needed. The beef stock may seem unusual in a vegetable soup, but it helps to strengthen the earthy flavour of the mushrooms.

Ingredients

25 g/1 oz/2 cups dried porcini mushrooms
30 ml/2 tbsp olive oil
15 g/¹/₂ oz/1 tbsp butter
2 leeks, thinly sliced
2 shallots, roughly chopped
1 garlic clove, roughly chopped
225 g/8 oz/3 cups fresh wild mushrooms
about 1.2 litres/2 pints/5 cups beef stock
2.5 ml/¹/₂ tsp dried thyme
150 ml/¹/₄ pint/²/₃ cup double cream
salt and freshly ground black pepper
fresh thyme sprigs, to garnish
serves 4

Cook's Tip

Porcini are ceps. Italian cooks would make this soup with a combination of fresh and dried ceps, but if fresh ceps are difficult to obtain, you can use other wild mushrooms, such as chanterelles.

3 ▲ Chop or slice the fresh mushrooms and add to the pan. Stir over a medium heat for a few minutes until they begin to soften. Pour in the stock and bring to the boil. Add the porcini, soaking liquid, dried thyme and salt and pepper. Lower the heat, half cover the pan and simmer gently for 30 minutes, stirring occasionally.

4 ▲ Pour about three-quarters of the soup into a blender or food processor and process until smooth. Return to the soup remaining in the pan, stir in the cream and heat through. Check the consistency and add more stock if the soup is too thick. Taste for seasoning. Serve hot, garnished with thyme sprigs.

1 ▲ Put the dried porcini in a bowl, add 250 ml/8 fl oz/1 cup warm water and leave to soak for 20–30 minutes. Lift out of the liquid and squeeze over the bowl to remove as much of the soaking liquid as possible. Strain all the liquid and reserve to use later. Finely chop the porcini.

2 Heat the oil and butter in a large saucepan until foaming. Add the sliced leeks, chopped shallots and garlic and cook gently for about 5 minutes, stirring frequently, until softened but not coloured.

Tomato and Fresh Basil Soup

Crema di pomodori al basilico

A soup for late summer when fresh tomatoes are at their most flavoursome.

Ingredients

15 ml/1 tbsp olive oil
25 g/1 oz/2 tbsp butter
1 medium onion, finely chopped
900 g/2 lb ripe Italian plum tomatoes,
    roughly chopped
1 garlic clove, roughly chopped
about 750 ml/1¼ pints/3 cups chicken or
    vegetable stock
120 ml/4 fl oz/½ cup dry white wine
30 ml/2 tbsp sun-dried tomato paste
30 ml/2 tbsp shredded fresh basil, plus a
    few whole leaves, to garnish
150 ml/¼ pint/ ⅔ cup double cream
salt and freshly ground black pepper

serves 4–6

1 ▲ Heat the oil and butter in a large saucepan until foaming. Add the onion and cook gently for about 5 minutes, stirring frequently, until softened but not brown.

2 ▲ Stir in the chopped tomatoes and garlic, then add the stock, white wine and sun-dried tomato paste, with salt and pepper to taste. Bring to the boil, then lower the heat, half cover the pan and simmer gently for 20 minutes, stirring occasionally to stop the tomatoes sticking to the base of the pan.

3 ▲ Process the soup with the shredded basil in a blender or food processor, then press through a sieve into a clean pan.

4 ▲ Add the double cream and heat through, stirring. Do not allow the soup to approach boiling point. Check the consistency and add more stock if necessary and then taste for seasoning. Pour into heated bowls and garnish with basil. Serve at once.

Variation

The soup can also be served chilled. Pour it into a container after sieving and chill for at least 4 hours. Serve in chilled bowls.

Minestrone with Pasta and Beans

Minestrone alla milanese

This classic minestrone from Lombardy includes pancetta for a pleasant touch of saltiness.

Milanese cooks vary the recipe according to what is on hand, and you can do the same.

Ingredients

45 ml/3 tbsp olive oil
115 g/4 oz pancetta, any rinds removed,
    roughly chopped
2–3 celery sticks, finely chopped
3 medium carrots, finely chopped
1 medium onion, finely chopped
1–2 garlic cloves, crushed
2 x 400 g/14 oz cans chopped tomatoes
about 1 litre/1¾ pints/4 cups
    chicken stock
400 g/14 oz can cannellini beans, drained
    and rinsed
50 g/2 oz/½ cup short–cut macaroni
30–60 ml/2–4 tbsp chopped flat leaf
    parsley, to taste
salt and freshly ground black pepper
shaved Parmesan cheese, to serve
serves 4

Variation

Use long-grain rice instead of the
pasta, and borlotti beans instead of
cannellini.

1 ▲ Heat the oil in a large saucepan.
Add the pancetta, celery, carrots and
onion and cook over a low heat for
5 minutes, stirring constantly, until
the vegetables are softened.

2 Add the garlic and tomatoes,
breaking them up well with a wooden
spoon. Pour in the stock. Add salt and
pepper to taste and bring to the boil.
Half cover the pan, lower the heat and
simmer gently for about 20 minutes,
until the vegetables are soft.

3 ▲ Drain the beans and add them to
the pan with the macaroni. Bring to
the boil again. Cover, lower the heat
and continue to simmer for about
20 minutes more. Check the
consistency and add more stock if
necessary. Stir in the parsley and taste
for seasoning.

4 Serve hot, sprinkled with plenty of
Parmesan cheese. This makes a meal
in itself if served with chunks of
crusty Italian bread.

Summer Minestrone

Minestrone estivo

This brightly coloured, fresh-tasting soup makes the most of summer vegetables.

Ingredients

45 ml/3 tbsp olive oil
1 large onion, finely chopped
15 ml/1 tbsp sun-dried tomato paste
450 g/1 lb ripe Italian plum tomatoes,
    peeled and finely chopped
225 g/8 oz green courgettes, trimmed
    and roughly chopped
225 g/8 oz yellow courgettes, trimmed
    and roughly chopped
3 waxy new potatoes, diced
2 garlic cloves, crushed
about 1.2 litres/2 pints/5 cups chicken
    stock or water
60 ml/4 tbsp shredded fresh basil
50 g/2 oz/⅔ cup grated Parmesan cheese
salt and freshly ground black pepper
serves 4

1 ▲ Heat the oil in a large saucepan,
add the onion and cook gently for
about 5 minutes, stirring constantly,
until softened. Stir in the sun-dried
tomato paste, chopped tomatoes,
courgettes, diced potatoes and
garlic. Mix well and cook gently for
10 minutes, uncovered, shaking the
pan frequently to stop the vegetables
sticking to the base.

2 ▲ Pour in the stock. Bring to the
boil, lower the heat, half cover the
pan and simmer gently for 15 minutes
or until the vegetables are just tender.
Add more stock if necessary.

3 Remove the pan from the heat and
stir in the basil and half the cheese.
Taste for seasoning. Serve hot,
sprinkled with the remaining cheese.

Clam and Pasta Soup

Zuppa alle vongole

This soup is a play on the pasta dish – spaghetti alle vongole – using store cupboard ingredients. Serve it with hot focaccia or ciabatta for an informal supper with friends.

Ingredients

30 ml/2 tbsp olive oil
1 large onion, finely chopped
2 garlic cloves, crushed
400 g/14 oz can chopped tomatoes
15 ml/1 tbsp sun-dried tomato paste
5 ml/1 tsp granulated sugar
5 ml/1 tsp dried mixed herbs
about 750 ml/1¼ pints/3 cups fish or
    vegetable stock
150 ml/¼ pint/ ⅔ cup red wine
50 g/2 oz/½ cup small pasta shapes
150 g/5 oz jar or can clams in
    natural juice
30 ml/2 tbsp finely chopped flat leaf
    parsley, plus a few whole leaves,
    to garnish
salt and freshly ground black pepper

serves 4

3 ▲ Add the pasta and continue simmering, uncovered, for about 10 minutes or until *al dente*. Stir occasionally, to prevent the pasta shapes from sticking together.

Cook's Tip
This soup has a fuller flavour if it is made the day before and reheated.

4 ▲ Add the clams and their juice to the soup and heat through for 3–4 minutes, adding more stock if required. Do not let it boil or the clams will be tough. Remove from the heat, stir in the parsley and taste the soup for seasoning. Serve hot, sprinkled with coarsely ground black pepper and parsley leaves.

1 ▲ Heat the oil in a large saucepan. Cook the onion gently for 5 minutes, stirring frequently, until softened.

2 ▲ Add the garlic, tomatoes, tomato paste, sugar, herbs, stock and wine, with salt and pepper to taste. Bring to the boil. Lower the heat, half cover the pan and simmer for 10 minutes, stirring occasionally.

Tuscan Bean Soup

Zuppa di fagioli alla toscana

There are lots of versions of this wonderful soup. This one uses cannellini beans, leeks,

cabbage and good olive oil – and tastes even better reheated.

Ingredients

45 ml/3 tbsp extra virgin olive oil
1 onion, roughly chopped
2 leeks, roughly chopped
1 large potato, peeled and diced
2 garlic cloves, finely chopped
1.2 litres/2 pints/5 cups vegetable stock
400 g/14 oz can cannellini beans, drained,
    liquid reserved
175 g/6 oz Savoy cabbage, shredded
45 ml/3 tbsp chopped fresh flat
    leaf parsley
30 ml/2 tbsp chopped fresh oregano
75 g/3 oz/1 cup Parmesan cheese, shaved
salt and freshly ground black pepper

For the garlic toasts

30–45 ml/2–3 tbsp extra virgin olive oil
6 thick slices country bread
1 garlic clove, peeled and bruised
serves 4

3 ▲ Stir in the cabbage and beans, with half the herbs, season and cook for 10 minutes more. Spoon about one-third of the soup into a food processor or blender and process until fairly smooth. Return to the soup in the pan, taste for seasoning and heat through for 5 minutes.

4 ▲ Meanwhile make the garlic toasts. Drizzle a little oil over the slices of bread, then rub both sides of each slice with the garlic. Toast until browned on both sides. Ladle the soup into bowls. Sprinkle with the remaining herbs and the Parmesan shavings. Add a drizzle of olive oil and serve with the toasts.

1 ▲ Heat the oil in a large saucepan and gently cook the onion, leeks, potato and garlic for 4–5 minutes.

2 ▲ Pour on the stock and liquid from the beans. Cover and simmer for 15 minutes.

Lentil Soup with Tomatoes

Minestra di lenticchie

A classic rustic Italian soup flavoured with rosemary, delicious served with garlic bread.

Ingredients

225 g/8 oz/1 cup dried green or
    brown lentils
45 ml/3 tbsp extra virgin olive oil
3 rindless streaky bacon rashers, cut into
    small dice
1 onion, finely chopped
2 celery sticks, finely chopped
2 carrots, finely diced
2 rosemary sprigs, finely chopped
2 bay leaves
400 g/14 oz can chopped plum tomatoes
1.75 litres/3 pints/7½ cups
    vegetable stock
salt and freshly ground black pepper
bay leaves and rosemary sprigs,
    to garnish
serves 4

Cook's Tip

Look out for the small green lentils
in Italian groceries or delicatessens.

1 Place the lentils in a bowl and
cover with cold water. Leave to soak
for 2 hours. Rinse and drain well.

2 ▲ Heat the oil in a large saucepan.
Add the bacon and cook for about
3 minutes, then stir in the onion and
cook for 5 minutes until softened.
Stir in the celery, carrots, rosemary,
bay leaves and lentils. Toss over the
heat for 1 minute until thoroughly
coated in the oil.

3 ▲ Tip in the tomatoes and stock
and bring to the boil. Lower the heat,
half cover the pan, and simmer for
about 1 hour, or until the lentils are
perfectly tender.

4 Remove the bay leaves, add salt
and pepper to taste and serve with a
garnish of fresh bay leaves and
rosemary sprigs.

Spinach and Rice Soup

Minestra di riso e spinaci

Use very fresh, young spinach leaves to prepare this light and fresh-tasting soup.

Ingredients

675 g/1½ lb fresh spinach, washed
45 ml/3 tbsp extra virgin olive oil
1 small onion, finely chopped
2 garlic cloves, finely chopped
1 small fresh red chilli, seeded and
    finely chopped
115 g/4 oz/generous 1 cup risotto rice
1.2 litres/2 pints/5 cups vegetable stock
60 ml/4 tbsp grated Pecorino cheese
salt and freshly ground black pepper
serves 4

1 Place the spinach in a large pan
with just the water that clings to its
leaves after washing. Add a large
pinch of salt. Heat gently until the
spinach has wilted, then remove
from the heat and drain, reserving
any liquid.

2 ▲ Either chop the spinach finely
using a large knife or place in a food
processor and process to a fairly
coarse purée.

3 ▲ Heat the oil in a large saucepan
and gently cook the onion, garlic and
chilli for 4–5 minutes until softened.
Stir in the rice until well coated, then
pour in the stock and reserved
spinach liquid. Bring to the boil,
lower the heat and simmer for
10 minutes. Add the spinach, with
salt and pepper to taste. Cook for
5–7 minutes more, until the rice is
tender. Check the seasoning and
serve with the Pecorino cheese.

Pasta & Gnocchi

In Italy, pasta and gnocchi are traditionally served as first courses after the antipasti *and before the second course of fish or meat. Everyday dishes are often simple, served with nothing more than olive oil or butter, grated Parmesan and basil. Outside of Italy there are no hard-and-fast rules, and nowadays people eat pasta and gnocchi whenever they like.*

Cannelloni with Tuna

Cannelloni sorpresa

Children love this pasta dish. Fontina cheese has a sweet, nutty flavour and very good

melting qualities. Look for it in large supermarkets and Italian delicatessens.

Ingredients

50 g/2 oz/¼ cup butter
50 g/2 oz/½ cup plain flour
about 900 ml/1½ pints/3¾ cups hot milk
2 x 200 g/7 oz cans tuna, drained
115 g/4 oz/1 cup Fontina cheese, grated
1.5 ml/¼ tsp grated nutmeg
12 no-precook cannelloni tubes
50 g/2 oz/⅔ cup grated Parmesan
    cheese
salt and freshly ground black pepper
fresh herbs, to garnish

serves 4–6

1 ▲ Melt the butter in a heavy-based saucepan, add the flour and stir over a low heat for 1–2 minutes. Remove the pan from the heat and gradually add 350 ml/12 fl oz/1½ cups of the milk, beating vigorously after each addition. Return the pan to the heat and whisk for 1–2 minutes until the sauce is very thick and smooth. Remove from the heat.

2 ▲ Mix the drained tuna with about 120 ml/4 fl oz/½ cup of the warm white sauce in a bowl. Add salt and black pepper to taste. Preheat the oven to 180°C/350°F/Gas 4.

3 ▲ Gradually whisk the remaining milk into the rest of the sauce, then return to the heat and simmer, whisking constantly, until thickened. Add the grated Fontina and nutmeg, with salt and pepper to taste. Simmer for a few more minutes, stirring frequently. Pour about one-third of the sauce into a baking dish and spread to the corners.

4 ▲ Fill the cannelloni tubes with the tuna mixture, pushing it in with the handle of a teaspoon. Place the cannelloni in a single layer in the dish. Thin the remaining sauce with a little more milk if necessary, then pour it over the cannelloni. Sprinkle with Parmesan cheese and bake for 30 minutes or until golden. Serve hot, garnished with herbs.

Seafood Lasagne

Lasagne alla marinara

Rich and creamy, this flavoursome lasagne makes a good supper-party dish.

Ingredients

65 g/2 ½ oz/5 tbsp butter
450 g/1 lb monkfish fillets, skinned and diced small
225 g/8 oz fresh prawns, shelled, deveined and roughly chopped
225 g/8 oz/3 cups button mushrooms, chopped
40 g/1½ oz/3 tbsp plain flour
600 ml/1 pint/2 ½ cups hot milk
300 ml/½ pint/1¼ cups double cream
400 g/14 oz can chopped tomatoes
30 ml/2 tbsp shredded fresh basil
8 sheets no-precook lasagne
75 g/3 oz/1 cup grated Parmesan cheese
salt and freshly ground black pepper
fresh herbs, to garnish

serves 6

1 ▲ Melt 15 g/½ oz/1 tbsp of the butter in a large, deep sauté pan, add the monkfish and prawns and sauté over a medium to high heat for 2–3 minutes. As soon as the prawns turn pink, remove them with a slotted spoon and place in a bowl.

2 Add the mushrooms to the pan and sauté for about 5 minutes until the juices run and the mushrooms are soft. Remove with a slotted spoon and add to the fish in the bowl.

3 Melt the remaining butter in a saucepan, add the flour and stir over a low heat for 1–2 minutes. Remove the pan from the heat and gradually whisk in the milk. Return to the heat and bring to the boil, whisking. Lower the heat and simmer for 2–3 minutes, whisking occasionally, until thick. Whisk in the cream and cook over a low heat for 2 minutes more.

4 ▲ Remove the sauce from the heat and stir in the fish and mushroom mixture with all the juices that have collected in the bowl. Add salt to taste, and plenty of pepper. Preheat the oven to 190°C/375°F/Gas 5.

5 Spread half the chopped tomatoes over the bottom of a baking dish. Sprinkle with half the basil and add salt and pepper to taste. Ladle one-third of the sauce over the tomatoes.

6 ▲ Cover the sauce with four lasagne sheets. Spread the remaining tomatoes over the lasagne and sprinkle with the remaining basil and salt and pepper to taste. Ladle half the remaining sauce over. Arrange the remaining lasagne sheets on top, top with the remaining sauce and cover with the cheese. Bake for 30–40 minutes until golden and bubbling. Serve hot, garnished with fresh herbs.

Spaghetti with Clams and White Wine   *Spaghetti alle vongole*

Raid the pantry to make this quick and easy pasta dish with an intense flavour.

Ingredients
30 ml/2 tbsp olive oil
1 onion, very finely chopped
2 garlic cloves, crushed
400 g/14 oz can chopped tomatoes
150 ml/¼ pint/ ⅔ cup dry white wine
150 g/5 oz jar or can clams in natural
   juice, drained with juice reserved
350 g/12 oz dried spaghetti
30 ml/2 tbsp finely chopped fresh flat
   leaf parsley, plus extra
   to garnish
salt and freshly ground black pepper
serves 4

Cook's Tip
The tomato sauce can be made
several days ahead of time and kept
in the fridge. Add the clams and heat
them through at the last minute –
but don't let them boil or they
will toughen.

1 Heat the oil in a saucepan, add the
onion and cook gently, stirring
frequently, for about 5 minutes until
softened, but not brown.

2 ▲ Stir in the garlic, tomatoes, wine
and reserved clam juice, with salt to
taste. Add a generous grinding of
black pepper. Bring to the boil,
stirring, then lower the heat. Cover
the pan and simmer the sauce gently
for about 20 minutes, stirring from
time to time.

3 ▲ Meanwhile, coil the spaghetti
into a large saucepan of rapidly
boiling salted water and cook for
12 minutes or until it is *al dente*.

4 Drain the spaghetti thoroughly.
Add the clams and finely chopped
parsley to the tomato sauce and heat
through, then taste for seasoning.
Tip the drained spaghetti into a
warmed serving bowl, pour over the
tomato sauce and toss to mix. Serve
at once, sprinkled with more parsley.

Pasta with Cream and Parmesan   *Pasta Alfredo*

This popular classic originated in Rome. It is incredibly quick and simple, perfect for a

midweek supper.

Ingredients
350 g/12 oz dried fettuccine
25 g/1 oz/2 tbsp butter
300 ml/½ pint/1¼ cups double cream
50 g/2 oz/ ⅔ cup grated Parmesan
   cheese, plus extra to serve
30 ml/2 tbsp finely chopped fresh flat
   leaf parsley, plus extra
   to garnish
salt and freshly ground black pepper
serves 3–4

Variation
In Rome, fettuccine would
traditionally be served with this
sauce, but tagliatelle can be used if
you prefer. Pasta shapes, such as
penne, rigatoni or farfalle, are also
suitable.

1 Cook the fettuccine in a large pan
of rapidly boiling salted water for
8–10 minutes or until *al dente*.

2 ▲ Meanwhile, melt the butter in a
large flameproof casserole and add
the cream and Parmesan, with salt
and pepper to taste. Stir over a
medium heat until the cheese has
melted and the sauce has thickened.

3 ▲ Drain the fettuccine thoroughly
and add it to the sauce with the
chopped parsley. Fold the pasta and
sauce together over a medium heat
until the strands of pasta are
generously coated. Grind more black
pepper over and garnish with the
extra chopped parsley. Serve at once,
with a bowl of grated Parmesan
handed round separately.

Tagliatelle with Bolognese Sauce   *Tagliatelle alla bolognese*

Most people think of bolognese sauce, the famous ragù from Bologna, as being served with spaghetti. To be absolutely correct, it should be served with tagliatelle.

Ingredients

30 ml/2 tbsp olive oil
1 onion, finely chopped
1 carrot, finely chopped
1 celery stick, finely chopped
1 garlic clove, crushed
350 g/12 oz minced beef
150 ml/¼ pint/⅔ cup red wine
250 ml/8 fl oz/1 cup milk
400 g/14 oz can chopped tomatoes
15 ml/1 tbsp sun-dried tomato paste
350 g/12 oz dried tagliatelle
salt and freshly ground black pepper
shredded fresh basil, to garnish
grated Parmesan cheese, to serve

serves 4

3 ▲ Pour in the wine. Stir frequently until it has evaporated, then add the milk and continue cooking and stirring until this has evaporated, too.

Cook's Tip
Don't skimp on the cooking time – it is essential for a full-flavoured bolognese sauce. Some Italian cooks insist on cooking it for 3–4 hours, so the longer the better.

4 ▲ Stir in the tomatoes and tomato paste, with salt and pepper to taste. Simmer the sauce uncovered, over the lowest possible heat for at least 45 minutes.

5 Cook the tagliatelle in a large pan of rapidly boiling salted water for 8–10 minutes or until *al dente*. Drain thoroughly and tip into a warmed large bowl. Pour over the sauce and toss to combine. Garnish with basil and serve at once, with Parmesan cheese handed separately.

1 ▲ Heat the oil in a large saucepan. Add the onion, carrot, celery and garlic and cook gently, stirring frequently, for about 10 minutes until softened. Do not allow the vegetables to colour.

2 ▲ Add the minced beef to the pan with the vegetables and cook over a medium heat until the meat changes colour, stirring constantly and breaking up any lumps with a wooden spoon.

Penne with Pancetta and Cream

Penne alla carbonara

This makes a gloriously rich supper dish. Follow it with a simple salad.

Ingredients

300 g/11 oz dried penne
30 ml/2 tbsp olive oil
1 small onion, finely chopped
175 g/6 oz pancetta rashers, any rinds
    removed, cut into bite-size strips
1–2 garlic cloves, crushed
5 egg yolks
175 ml/6 fl oz/¾ cup double cream
115 g/4 oz/1⅓ cups grated Parmesan
    cheese, plus extra to serve
salt and freshly ground black pepper

serves 3–4

1 ▲ Cook the penne in a large pan of rapidly boiling salted water for about 10 minutes or until *al dente*.

2 Meanwhile, heat the oil in a large flameproof casserole. Add the onion and cook gently for about 5 minutes, stirring frequently, until softened. Add the pancetta and garlic. Cook over a medium heat until the pancetta is cooked but not crisp. Remove the pan from the heat and set aside.

3 ▲ Put the egg yolks in a jug and add the cream and Parmesan cheese. Grind in plenty of black pepper. Beat well to mix.

4 ▲ Drain the penne thoroughly, tip into the casserole and toss over a medium to high heat until the pancetta mixture is evenly mixed with the pasta.

5 Remove from the heat, pour in the egg yolk mixture and toss well to combine. Spoon into a large shallow serving dish, grind a little black pepper over and sprinkle with some of the extra Parmesan. Serve the rest of the Parmesan separately.

Cook's Tip

Serve this dish the moment it is ready or it will not be hot enough. Having added the egg yolks, don't return the pan to the heat or attempt to reheat the pasta and sauce together or the egg yolks will scramble and give the pasta a curdled appearance.

Farfalle with Mushrooms and Cheese   *Farfalle boscaiole*

Fresh wild mushrooms are very good in this sauce, but they are expensive. To cut the cost, use half wild and half cultivated, or as many wild as you can afford – even a small handful will intensify the mushroom flavour.

Ingredients
15 g/½ oz/1 cup dried porcini
   mushrooms
25 g/1 oz/2 tbsp butter
1 small onion, finely chopped
1 garlic clove, crushed
225 g/8 oz/3 cups fresh mushrooms,
   thinly sliced
a few fresh sage leaves, very
   finely chopped, plus a few whole
   leaves, to garnish
150 ml/¼ pint/ ⅔ cup dry white wine
225 g/8 oz/2 cups dried farfalle
115 g/4 oz/½ cup mascarpone cheese
115 g/4 oz/1 cup Gorgonzola or torta di
   Gorgonzola cheese, crumbled
salt and freshly ground black pepper
serves 4

3 ▲ Cook the farfalle in a large saucepan of rapidly boiling salted water, for about 10 minutes or until *al dente*.

Variation
For a lighter sauce, use crème fraîche instead of mascarpone.

4 ▲ Meanwhile, stir the mascarpone and Gorgonzola into the mushroom sauce. Heat through, stirring, until melted. Taste for seasoning. Drain the pasta thoroughly, add to the sauce and toss to mix. Serve at once, with black pepper ground liberally on top. Garnish with sage leaves.

1 ▲ Put the dried porcini in a small bowl with 250 ml/8 fl oz/1 cup warm water and leave to soak for 20–30 minutes. Remove from the liquid and squeeze the porcini over the bowl to extract as much liquid as possible. Strain the liquid and set it aside. Finely chop the porcini.

2 Melt the butter in a large saucepan, add the onion and chopped porcini and cook gently, stirring for about 3 minutes until the onion is soft. Add the garlic and fresh mushrooms, chopped sage, salt and plenty of black pepper. Cook over a medium heat, stirring frequently, for about 5 minutes or until the mushrooms are soft and juicy. Stir in the soaking liquid and the wine and simmer.

Pasta with Tomato and Chilli Sauce
Pasta all'arrabbiata

This is a speciality of Lazio – the word arrabbiata means rabid or angry, and describes the heat that comes from the chilli. This quick version is made with bottled sugocasa.

Ingredients
500 g/1 lb sugocasa (see Cook's Tip)
2 garlic cloves, crushed
150 ml/¼ pint/ ⅔ cup dry white wine
15 ml/1 tbsp sun-dried tomato purée
1 fresh red chilli
300 g/11 oz penne or tortiglioni
60 ml/4 tbsp finely chopped fresh flat
    leaf parsley
salt and freshly ground black pepper
freshly grated Pecorino cheese, to serve
serves 4

1 ▲ Put the sugocasa, garlic, wine, tomato paste and whole chilli in a saucepan and bring to the boil. Cover and simmer gently.

2 ▲ Drop the pasta into a large saucepan of rapidly boiling salted water and simmer for 10–12 minutes or until *al dente*.

Cook's Tip
Sugocasa is sold in bottles sometimes labelled "crushed Italian tomatoes". It is finer than canned chopped tomatoes and coarser than passata, and so is ideal for pasta sauces, soups and stews.

3 ▲ Remove the chilli from the sauce and add half the parsley. Taste for seasoning. If you prefer a hotter taste, chop some or all of the chilli and return it to the sauce.

4 ▲ Drain the pasta and tip into a warmed large bowl. Pour the sauce over the pasta and toss to mix. Serve at once, sprinkled with grated Pecorino and the remaining parsley.

Three-cheese Lasagne
Lasagne ai tre formaggi

The cheese makes this lasagne quite expensive, so reserve it for a special occasion.

Ingredients
30 ml/2 tbsp olive oil
1 onion, finely chopped
1 carrot, finely chopped
1 celery stick, finely chopped
1 garlic clove, crushed
675 g/1½ lb minced beef
400 g/14 oz can chopped tomatoes
300 ml/½ pint/1¼ cups beef stock
300 ml/½ pint/1¼ cups red wine
30 ml/2 tbsp sun-dried tomato paste
10 ml/2 tsp dried oregano
9 sheets no-precook lasagne
3 x 150 g/5 oz packets mozzarella
    cheese, thinly sliced
450 g/1 lb/2 cups ricotta cheese
115 g/4 oz Parmesan cheese, grated
salt and freshly ground black pepper
serves 6–8

1 Heat the oil and gently cook the onion, carrot, celery and garlic, stirring for 10 minutes until softened.

2 Add the beef and cook until it changes colour, stirring constantly and breaking up the meat.

3 ▲ Add the tomatoes, stock, wine, tomato paste, oregano and salt and pepper and bring to the boil, stirring. Cover, lower the heat and simmer gently for 1 hour, stirring occasionally.

4 ▲ Preheat the oven to 190°C/375°F/ Gas 5. Check for seasoning, then ladle one-third of the meat sauce into a 23 x 33 cm/9 x 13 in baking dish and cover with 3 sheets of lasagne. Arrange one-third of the mozzarella slices over the top, dot with one-third of the ricotta, then sprinkle with one-third of the Parmesan.

5 Repeat these layers twice, then bake for 40 minutes. Leave to cool for 10 minutes before serving.

Tortiglioni with Spicy Sausage Sauce
Tortiglioni alla siciliana

This heady pasta dish is not for the faint-hearted. Serve it with a robust Sicilian red wine.

Ingredients
30 ml/2 tbsp olive oil
1 onion, finely chopped
1 celery stick, finely chopped
2 large garlic cloves, crushed
1 fresh red chilli, seeded and chopped
450 g/1 lb ripe Italian plum tomatoes,
    peeled and finely chopped
30 ml/2 tbsp tomato purée
150 ml/¼ pint/⅔ cup red wine
5 ml/1 tsp sugar
300 g/11 oz dried tortiglioni
175 g/6 oz spicy salami, rind removed
salt and freshly ground black pepper
30 ml/2 tbsp chopped fresh parsley,
    to garnish
grated Parmesan cheese, to serve
serves 4

Cook's Tip
Buy the salami for this dish in one piece so that you can chop it into large chunks.

1 ▲ Heat the oil, then add the onion, celery, garlic and chilli and cook gently, stirring frequently, for about 10 minutes until softened.

2 Add the tomatoes, tomato purée, wine, sugar and salt and pepper to taste and bring to the boil, stirring. Lower the heat, cover and simmer gently, stirring occasionally, for about 20 minutes. Add a few spoonfuls of water from time to time if the sauce becomes too thick.

3 ▲ Meanwhile, drop the pasta into a large saucepan of rapidly boiling salted water and simmer, uncovered, for 10–12 minutes.

4 Chop the salami into bite-size chunks and add to the sauce. Heat through, then taste for seasoning.

5 Drain the pasta, tip it into a large bowl, then pour the sauce over and toss to mix. Scatter over the parsley and serve with grated Parmesan.

Pasta and Bolognese Bake
Pasticcio

Pasticcio is Italian for pie, and in some regions this is made with a pastry topping. This simple version makes a great family supper because it's such a favourite with children.

Ingredients
225 g/8 oz dried conchiglie
1 quantity hot Bolognese Sauce (see
    Tagliatelle with Bolognese Sauce
    page 158)
salt and freshly ground black pepper

For the white sauce
50 g/2 oz/¼ cup butter
50 g/2 oz/½ cup plain flour
750 ml/1¼ pints/3 cups milk
75 g/3 oz/1 cup grated Parmesan cheese
1 egg, beaten
good pinch of grated nutmeg
mixed salad leaves, to serve
serves 4

1 Cook the conchiglie in a large pan of rapidly boiling salted water for 10–12 minutes or until *al dente*.

2 Meanwhile, make the white sauce. Melt the butter in a saucepan until foaming, add the flour and stir over a low heat for 1–2 minutes. Remove the pan from the heat and gradually whisk in the milk. Return the pan to the heat and bring to the boil, whisking all the time. Lower the heat and simmer for 2–3 minutes, whisking occasionally, until the sauce thickens. Remove the pan from the heat.

3 ▲ Preheat the oven to 190°C/375°F/ Gas 5. Drain the pasta thoroughly, tip it into a 20 x 30 cm/8 x 12 in baking dish and mix in the hot bolognese sauce. Level the surface.

4 ▲ Stir about two-thirds of the Parmesan into the white sauce, then stir in the beaten egg and nutmeg, with salt and pepper to taste. Pour over the pasta and sauce and sprinkle with the remaining Parmesan. Bake for 20 minutes or until golden and bubbling. Serve hot, straight from the dish. Add a salad garnish to each plate.

Cook's Tip
This is a good way of using up leftover bolognese sauce and cooked pasta – the quantities do not need to be exact.

Pasta with Aubergines

Pasta alla Norma

This Sicilian recipe is traditionally made from fried aubergines. This version is lighter.

Ingredients

2 medium aubergines, about 225 g/8 oz
　　each, diced small
45 ml/3 tbsp olive oil
275 g/10 oz dried macaroni or fusilli
50 g/2 oz/$\frac{2}{3}$ cup grated Pecorino cheese
salt and freshly ground black pepper
shredded fresh basil leaves, to garnish
crusty bread, to serve

For the tomato sauce

30 ml/2 tbsp olive oil
1 onion, finely chopped
400 g/14 oz can chopped tomatoes or
　　400 g/14 oz passata

serves 4

Cook's Tip

In Sicily, a cheese called ricotta salata is used for this recipe. This is a matured salted ricotta that is grated like Pecorino and Parmesan. It is unlikely that you will find ricotta salata outside Sicily; Pecorino is the best substitute because it tastes slightly saltier than Parmesan.

1 Soak the diced aubergine in a bowl of cold salted water for 30 minutes.

2 Meanwhile, preheat the oven to 220°C/425°F/Gas 7. Make the sauce. Heat the oil in a large saucepan, add the onion and cook gently for about 3 minutes until softened. Add the tomatoes, with salt and pepper to taste. Bring to the boil, lower the heat, cover and simmer for 20 minutes. Stir the sauce and add a few spoonfuls of water from time to time, to prevent it from becoming too thick. Remove from the heat.

3 ▲ Drain the aubergines and pat dry. Spread the pieces out in a roasting tin, add the oil and toss to coat. Bake for 20–25 minutes, turning the aubergines every 4–5 minutes with a fish slice so that they brown evenly.

4 Cook the pasta in a large pan of rapidly boiling salted water for 10–12 minutes or until *al dente*. Reheat the tomato sauce.

5 ▲ Drain the pasta thoroughly and add it to the tomato sauce, with half the roasted aubergines and half the Pecorino. Toss to mix, then taste for seasoning.

6 Spoon the pasta and sauce mixture into a warmed large serving dish and top with the remaining roasted aubergines. Scatter the shredded fresh basil leaves over the top, followed by the remaining Pecorino. Serve at once, with generous chunks of crusty bread.

Spinach and Ricotta Gnocchi

Gnocchi de spinaci e ricotta

The mixture for these tasty little herb dumplings needs to be handled very carefully to achieve light and fluffy results. Serve with a sage butter and grated Parmesan.

Ingredients

6 garlic cloves, unpeeled
25 g/1 oz mixed fresh herbs, such as parsley, basil, thyme, coriander and chives, finely chopped
225 g/8 oz fresh spinach leaves
250 g/9 oz/generous 1 cup ricotta cheese
1 egg yolk
50 g/2 oz/²/₃ cup grated Parmesan cheese
75 g/3 oz/²/₃ cup plain flour
50 g/2 oz/¹/₄ cup butter
30 ml/2 tbsp fresh sage, chopped
salt and freshly ground black pepper

serves 4

1 Cook the garlic cloves in boiling water for 4 minutes. Drain and pop out of the skins. Place in a food processor with the herbs and blend to a purée or mash the garlic with a fork and add the herbs to mix well.

2 ▲ Place the spinach in a large pan with just the water that clings to the leaves and cook gently until wilted. Leave to cool then squeeze out as much liquid as possible. Chop finely.

3 Place the ricotta in a bowl and beat in the egg yolk, spinach, herbs and garlic. Stir in half the Parmesan, sift in the flour and mix well.

Cook's Tip

Squeeze the spinach dry to ensure the gnocchi are not wet and to give a lighter result. The mixture should be fairly soft and will be easier to handle if chilled for an hour before preparing the dumplings.

4 ▲ Using floured hands, break off pieces of the mixture slightly smaller than a walnut and roll into small dumplings.

5 Bring a large pan of salted water to the boil and carefully add the gnocchi. When they rise to the top of the pan they are cooked, this should take about 3 minutes.

6 ▲ The gnocchi should be light and fluffy all the way through. If not, simmer for a further minute. Drain well. Meanwhile, melt the butter in a frying pan and add the sage. Simmer gently for 1 minute. Add the gnocchi to the frying pan and toss in the butter over a gentle heat for 1 minute, then serve sprinkled with the remaining Parmesan.

Gnocchi with Gorgonzola Sauce   *Gnocchi alla gorgonzola*

Gnocchi are prepared all over Italy with different ingredients used in different regions.

These are gnocchi di patate, *potato dumplings.*

Ingredients

450 g/1 lb potatoes, unpeeled
1 large egg
115 g/4 oz/1 cup plain flour
fresh thyme sprigs, to garnish
salt and freshly ground black pepper

For the sauce

115 g/4 oz Gorgonzola cheese
60 ml/4 tbsp double cream
15 ml/1 tbsp fresh thyme, chopped
60 ml/4 tbsp freshly grated
   Parmesan cheese, to serve

serves 4

1 Cook the potatoes in boiling salted water for about 20 minutes until they are tender. Drain and, when cool enough to handle, remove the skins.

2 ▲ Force the potatoes through a sieve, pressing through using the back of a spoon, into a mixing bowl. Add plenty of seasoning and then beat in the egg until completely incorporated. Add the flour a little at a time, stirring well with a wooden spoon after each addition until you have a smooth dough. (You may not need all the flour.)

3 Turn the dough out on to a floured surface and knead for about 3 minutes, adding more flour if necessary, until it is smooth and soft and not sticky to the touch.

Cook's Tips

Choose dry, floury potatoes. Avoid new or red-skinned potatoes which do not have the right dry texture.

4 ▲ Divide the dough into 6 equal pieces. Flour your hands and gently roll each piece between your hands into a log shape measuring 15–20 cm/6–8 in long and 2.5 cm/1 in around. Cut each log into 6–8 pieces, about 2.5 cm/1 in long, then gently roll each piece in the flour. Form into gnocchi by gently pressing each piece on to the floured surface with the tines of a fork to leave ridges in the dough.

5 ▲ To cook, drop the gnocchi into a pan of boiling water about 12 at a time. Once they rise to the surface, after about 2 minutes, cook for 4–5 minutes more. Remove and drain.

6 Place the Gorgonzola, cream and thyme in a large frying pan and heat gently until the cheese melts to form a thick, creamy consistency and heat through. Add the drained gnocchi and toss well to combine. Serve with Parmesan and garnish with thyme.

Rice, Polenta & Pizzas

·······································

In the north of Italy, rice is served as a first course, as creamy risotto, but you can serve it as a main dish, with a salad and Italian bread. Polenta, also from the north of Italy, is most often served with the main course, especially with meaty casseroles. Pizzas hail from the south, where they are eaten at any time of day, the ultimate convenience food.

Risotto with Spring Vegetables   *Risotto primavera*

This is one of the prettiest risottos, especially if you can get yellow courgettes.

Ingredients

150 g/5 oz/1 cup shelled fresh peas
115 g/4 oz/1 cup French beans, cut into
    short lengths
30 ml/2 tbsp olive oil
75 g/3 oz/6 tbsp butter
2 small yellow courgettes, cut
    into matchsticks
1 onion, finely chopped
275 g/10 oz/1½ cups risotto rice
120 ml/4 fl oz/½ cup Italian dry
    white vermouth
about 1 litre/1¾ pints/4 cups boiling
    chicken stock
75 g/3 oz/1 cup grated Parmesan cheese
a small handful of fresh basil leaves,
    finely shredded, plus a few whole
    leaves, to garnish
salt and freshly ground black pepper
serves 4

1 Blanch the peas and beans in a large saucepan of lightly salted boiling water for 2–3 minutes until just tender. Drain, refresh under cold running water, drain again and set aside for later.

2 ▲ Heat the oil and 25 g/1 oz/2 tbsp of the butter in a medium saucepan until foaming. Add the courgettes and cook gently for 2–3 minutes or until just softened. Remove with a slotted spoon and set aside. Add the onion to the pan and cook gently for about 3 minutes, stirring frequently, until softened.

3 ▲ Stir in the rice until the grains start to swell and burst, then add the vermouth. Stir until the vermouth stops sizzling and most of it has been absorbed by the rice, then add a few ladlefuls of the stock, with salt and pepper to taste. Stir over low heat until the stock has been absorbed.

4 Continue cooking and stirring for 20–25 minutes, adding the remaining stock a few ladlefuls at a time. The rice should be *al dente* and the risotto should have a moist and creamy appearance.

5 ▲ Gently stir in the vegetables, the remaining butter and about half the grated Parmesan. Heat through, then stir in the shredded basil and taste for seasoning. Garnish with a few whole basil leaves and serve hot, with the remaining grated Parmesan handed separately.

Variations

Shelled broad beans can be used instead of the peas and asparagus tips instead of the French beans. Use green courgettes if yellow ones are unavailable.

Rice with Peas, Ham and Cheese

Risi e bisi

A classic risotto from the Veneto. Although it is traditionally served as a starter in Italy,

risi e bisi makes an excellent supper dish with hot crusty bread.

Ingredients

75 g/3 oz/6 tbsp butter
1 small onion, finely chopped
about 1 litre/1¾ pints/4 cups boiling
   chicken stock
275 g/10 oz/1½ cups risotto rice
150 ml/¼ pint/⅔ cup dry white wine
225 g/8 oz/2 cups frozen petits
   pois, thawed
115 g/4 oz cooked ham, diced
salt and freshly ground black pepper
50 g/2 oz/⅔ cup Parmesan cheese,
   to serve

serves 4

1 ▲ Melt 50 g/2 oz/4 tbsp of the butter in a saucepan until foaming. Add the onion and cook gently for about 3 minutes, stirring frequently, until softened. Have the hot stock ready in an adjacent pan.

2 ▲ Add the rice to the onion mixture. Stir until the grains start to burst, then pour in the wine. Stir until it stops sizzling and most of it has been absorbed, then pour in a little hot stock, with salt and pepper to taste. Stir over a low heat until the stock has been absorbed.

3 ▲ Add the remaining stock, a little at a time, allowing the rice to absorb all the liquid before adding more, and stirring constantly. Add the peas towards the end. After 20–25 minutes, the rice should be *al dente* and the risotto moist and creamy.

4 ▲ Gently stir in the diced cooked ham and the remaining butter. Heat through until the butter has melted, then taste for seasoning. Transfer to a warmed serving bowl. Grate or shave a little Parmesan over the top and hand the rest separately.

Saffron Risotto

Risotto alla milanese

This classic risotto is always served with osso buco, but makes a delicious first course or

light supper dish in its own right.

Ingredients
about 1.2 litres/2 pints/5 cups beef or
    chicken stock
good pinch of saffron threads or 1 sachet
    of saffron powder
75 g/3 oz/6 tbsp butter
1 onion, finely chopped
275 g/10 oz/1½ cups risotto rice
75 g/3 oz/1 cup grated Parmesan cheese
salt and freshly ground black pepper
serves 4

1 Bring the stock to the boil, then reduce to a low simmer. Ladle a little stock into a small bowl. Add the saffron threads or powder and leave to infuse.

2 Melt 50 g/2 oz/4 tbsp of the butter in a large saucepan until foaming. Add the onion and cook gently for about 3 minutes, stirring frequently, until softened.

3 Add the rice. Stir until the grains start to swell and burst, then add a few ladlefuls of the stock, with the saffron liquid and salt and pepper to taste. Stir over a low heat until the stock is absorbed. Add the remaining stock, a few ladlefuls at a time, allowing the rice to absorb all the liquid before adding more, and stirring constantly. After 20–25 minutes, the rice should be *al dente* and the risotto golden yellow, moist and creamy.

4 ▲ Gently stir in about two-thirds of the grated Parmesan and the remaining butter. Heat through until the butter has melted, then taste for seasoning. Transfer the risotto to a warmed serving bowl or platter and serve hot, with the remaining grated Parmesan sprinkled on top.

Polenta Elisa

Polenta Elisa

This dish comes from the valley around Lake Como. Serve it solo as a starter, or with a

mixed salad and some sliced salami or prosciutto for a midweek supper.

Ingredients
250 ml/8 fl oz/1 cup milk
225 g/8 oz/2 cups pre-cooked polenta
115 g/4 oz/1 cup grated Gruyère cheese
115 g/4 oz/1 cup torta di Dolcelatte
    cheese, crumbled
50 g/2 oz/¼ cup butter
2 garlic cloves, roughly chopped
a few fresh sage leaves, chopped
salt and freshly ground black pepper
prosciutto, to serve
serves 4

1 Preheat the oven to 200°C/400°F/ Gas 6. Lightly butter a 20–25 cm/ 8–10 in baking dish.

Cook's Tip
Pour the polenta into the boiling liquid in a continuous stream, stirring constantly with a wooden spoon or balloon whisk. If using a whisk, change to a wooden spoon once the polenta thickens.

2 ▲ Bring the milk and 750ml/ 1¼ pints/3 cups water to the boil in a large saucepan, add 5 ml/1 tsp salt, then tip in the polenta. Cook for about 8 minutes or according to the instructions on the packet.

3 Spoon half the polenta into the baking dish and level. Cover with half the grated Gruyère and crumbled Dolcelatte. Spoon the remaining polenta evenly over the top and sprinkle with the remaining cheeses.

4 Melt the butter in a small saucepan until foaming, add the garlic and sage and fry, stirring, until the butter turns golden brown.

5 ▲ Drizzle the butter mixture over the polenta and cheese and grind black pepper liberally over the top. Bake for 5 minutes. Serve hot, with slices of prosciutto.

Risotto with Four Cheeses

Risotto ai quattro formaggi

This is a very rich dish. Serve it for a dinner-party first course, with sparkling white wine.

Ingredients

40 g/1½ oz/3 tbsp butter
1 small onion, finely chopped
1 litre/1¾ pints/4 cups boiling
  chicken stock
350 g/12 oz/1¾ cups risotto rice
200 ml/7 fl oz/scant 1 cup sparkling dry
  white wine
50 g/2 oz/½ cup grated Gruyère cheese
50 g/2 oz/½ cup Fontina cheese,
  diced small
50 g/2 oz/½ cup Gorgonzola
  cheese, crumbled
50 g/2 oz/⅔ cup grated
  Parmesan cheese
salt and freshly ground black pepper
fresh flat leaf parsley, to garnish
serves 6

Cook's Tip

If you're feeling extravagant you can use champagne for this risotto, although asti spumante is more often used.

1 Melt the butter in a saucepan until foaming. Add the onion and cook gently, stirring frequently, for about 3 minutes until softened. Have the hot stock ready in an adjacent pan.

2 ▲ Add the rice and stir until the grains start to swell and burst, then add the sparkling wine. Stir until it stops sizzling and most of it has been absorbed by the rice, then pour in a little of the hot stock. Add salt and pepper to taste. Stir over a low heat until the stock has been absorbed.

3 Add more stock, a little at a time, allowing the rice to absorb it before adding more, and stirring constantly. After 20–25 minutes the rice will be *al dente* and the risotto creamy.

4 ▲ Turn off the heat under the pan, then add the Gruyère, Fontina, Gorgonzola and 30 ml/2 tbsp of the Parmesan. Stir gently until the cheeses have melted, then taste for seasoning. Tip into a serving bowl and garnish with parsley. Serve the remaining Parmesan separately.

Polenta with Mushroom Sauce

Polenta con salsa di funghi

Polenta, made from maize flour, fulfils the same function as rice, bread or potatoes in forming the starchy base for a meal. Here, it is cooked until it forms a soft dough, then flavoured with Parmesan. Its subtle taste works well with the rich mushroom sauce.

Ingredients

1.2 litres/2 pints/5 cups vegetable stock
350 g/12 oz/3 cups polenta
50 g/2 oz/²/₃ cup grated Parmesan cheese
salt and freshly ground black pepper

For the sauce

15 g/¹/₂ oz/1 cup dried porcini
    mushrooms
15 ml/1 tbsp olive oil
50 g/2 oz/¹/₄ cup butter
1 onion, finely chopped
1 carrot, finely chopped
1 celery stick, finely chopped
2 garlic cloves, crushed
450 g/1 lb/6 cups mixed chestnut and
    large flat mushrooms, roughly chopped
120 ml/4 fl oz/¹/₂ cup red wine
400 g/14 oz can chopped tomatoes
5 ml/1 tsp tomato purée
15 ml/1 tbsp chopped fresh thyme leaves

serves 4

1 ▲ Make the sauce. Put the dried mushrooms in a bowl, add 150 ml/ ¹/₄ pint/²/₃ cup of hot water and soak for 20 minutes. Drain the mushrooms, reserving the liquid, and chop them roughly.

2 Heat the oil and butter in a saucepan and add the onion, carrot, celery and garlic. Cook over a low heat for about 5 minutes until the vegetables are beginning to soften, then raise the heat and add the fresh and soaked dried mushrooms to the pan of vegetables. Cook for 8–10 minutes until the mushrooms are softened and golden.

3 ▲ Pour in the wine and cook rapidly for 2–3 minutes until reduced, then tip in the tomatoes and reserved mushroom liquid. Stir in the tomato purée with the thyme and plenty of salt and pepper. Lower the heat and simmer for 20 minutes until the sauce is rich and thick.

Cook's Tip

The polenta will spit during cooking, so use a long-handled spoon and wrap a towel around your hand to protect it while stirring.

4 ▲ Meanwhile, heat the stock in a large heavy saucepan. Add a generous pinch of salt. As soon as it simmers, tip in the polenta in a fine stream, whisking until the mixture is smooth. Cook for 30 minutes, stirring constantly, until the polenta comes away from the pan. Remove from the heat and stir in half the Parmesan and some black pepper.

5 Divide among four heated bowls and top each with sauce. Sprinkle with the remaining Parmesan.

Butternut Squash and Sage Pizza

Pizza con zucca e salvia

The combination of the sweet butternut squash, sage and sharp goat's cheese works wonderfully on this pizza. Pumpkin and winter squashes are popular in northern Italy.

Ingredients

15 g/½ oz/1 tbsp butter
30 ml/2 tbsp olive oil
2 shallots, finely chopped
1 butternut squash, peeled, seeded and
    cubed, about 450 g/1 lb
    prepared weight
16 sage leaves
1 quantity risen Pizza Dough
1 quantity Tomato Sauce
115 g/4 oz/1 cup mozzarella cheese, sliced
115 g/4 oz/½ cup firm goat's cheese
salt and freshly ground black pepper

serves 4

3 ▲ Transfer each round to a baking sheet and spread with the tomato sauce, leaving a 1 cm/½ in border all around. Spoon the squash and shallot mixture over the top.

4 ▲ Arrange the slices of mozzarella over the squash mixture and crumble the goat's cheese over. Scatter the remaining sage leaves over and season with plenty of salt and pepper. Bake for 15–20 minutes until the cheese has melted and the crust on each pizza is golden.

1 ▲ Preheat the oven to 200°C/400°F/ Gas 6. Oil four baking sheets. Put the butter and oil in a roasting tin and heat in the oven for a few minutes. Add the shallots, squash and half the sage leaves. Toss to coat. Roast for 15–20 minutes until tender.

2 ▲ Raise the oven temperature to 220°C/425°F/Gas 7. Divide the pizza dough into four equal pieces and roll out each piece on a lightly floured surface to a 25 cm/10 in round.

Ricotta and Fontina Pizza

Pizza con ricotta e fontina

The earthy mixed mushrooms' flavours are delicious with the creamy cheeses.

Ingredients

For the pizza dough

2.5 ml/¹⁄₂ tsp active dried yeast
pinch of granulated sugar
450 g/1 lb/4 cups strong white flour
5 ml/1 tsp salt
30 ml/2 tbsp olive oil

For the tomato sauce

400 g/14 oz can chopped tomatoes
150 ml/¹⁄₄ pint/²⁄₃ cup passata
1 large garlic clove, finely chopped
5 ml/1 tsp dried oregano
1 bay leaf
10 ml/2 tsp malt vinegar
salt and freshly ground black pepper

For the topping

30 ml/2 tbsp olive oil
1 garlic clove, finely chopped
350 g/12 oz/4 cups mixed mushrooms
   (chestnut, flat or button), sliced
30 ml/2 tbsp chopped fresh oregano,
   plus whole leaves, to garnish
250 g/9 oz/generous 1 cup ricotta cheese
225 g/8 oz Fontina cheese, sliced

**makes 4 x 25 cm/10 in thin
   crust pizzas**

1 ▲ Make the dough. Put 300 ml/
¹⁄₂ pint/1¹⁄₄ cups warm water in a
measuring jug. Add the yeast and
sugar and leave for 5–10 minutes
until frothy. Sift the flour and salt
into a large bowl and make a well in
the centre. Gradually pour in the
yeast mixture and the olive oil. Mix
to make a smooth dough. Knead on a
lightly floured surface for about
10 minutes until smooth, springy
and elastic. Place the dough in a
floured bowl, cover and leave to rise
in a warm place for 1¹⁄₂ hours.

2 Meanwhile, make the tomato
sauce. Place all the ingredients in a
saucepan, cover and bring to the
boil. Lower the heat, remove the lid
and simmer for 20 minutes, stirring
occasionally, until reduced.

3 ▲ Make the topping. Heat the oil
in a frying pan. Add the garlic and
mushrooms, with salt and pepper to
taste. Cook, stirring, for about
5 minutes or until the mushrooms
are tender and golden. Set aside.

4 ▲ Preheat the oven to 220°C/425°F/
Gas 7. Brush four baking sheets with
oil. Knead the dough for 2 minutes,
then divide into four equal pieces.
Roll out each piece to a 25 cm/10 in
round and place on a baking sheet.

5 Spoon the tomato sauce over each
dough round. Brush the edge with a
little olive oil. Add the mushrooms,
oregano and cheese. Bake for about
15 minutes until golden brown and
crisp. Scatter the oregano leaves over.

Fried Pizza Pasties

Panzerotti

These tasty little morsels are served all over central and southern Italy as a snack food or as part of a hot antipasti. Although similar to calzone they are fried instead of baked.

Ingredients
½ quantity Pizza Dough
½ quantity Tomato Sauce
225 g/8 oz mozzarella cheese, chopped
115 g/4 oz Italian salami, thinly sliced
handful of fresh basil leaves, roughly torn
sunflower oil, for deep frying
salt and freshly ground black pepper
serves 4

Cook's Tip
To test that the oil is ready, carefully drop a piece of bread into the oil. If it sizzles instantly, the oil is ready.

1 Preheat the oven to 200°C/400°F/ Gas 6. Brush two baking sheets with oil. Divide the dough into 12 and roll out each piece on a lightly floured surface to a 10 cm/4 in round.

2 ▲ Spread the centre of each round with a little of the tomato sauce, leaving sufficient border all round for sealing the pasty, then top with a few pieces of mozzarella and salami slices. Sprinkle with salt and freshly ground black pepper and add a few fresh basil leaves to each round.

3 ▲ Brush the edges of the dough rounds with a little water, then fold over and press together to seal.

4 Heat oil to a depth of about 10 cm/ 4 in in a heavy-based pan. When hot, deep-fry the pasties, a few at a time, for 8–10 minutes until golden. Drain on kitchen paper and serve hot.

Sicilian Pizza

Pizza alla siciliana

This robust-flavoured pizza is topped with mozzarella and Pecorino cheeses.

Ingredients
1 small aubergine, cut into thin rounds
30 ml/2 tbsp olive oil
½ quantity risen Pizza Dough
½ quantity Tomato Sauce
175 g/6 oz mozzarella cheese, sliced
50 g/2 oz/½ cup pitted black olives
15 ml/1 tbsp drained capers
60 ml/4 tbsp grated Pecorino cheese
salt and freshly ground black pepper
serves 2

Cook's Tip
For best results choose olives that have been marinated in extra virgin olive oil and flavoured with herbs and garlic.

1 ▲ Preheat the oven to 200°C/400°F/ Gas 6. Brush one or two baking sheets with oil. Brush the aubergine rounds with olive oil and arrange them on the baking sheet(s). Bake for 10–15 minutes, turning once, until browned and tender. Remove the aubergine slices from the baking sheet(s) and drain on kitchen paper.

2 Raise the oven temperature to 220°C/425°F/Gas 7. Roll out the pizza dough to two 25 cm/10 in rounds. Transfer to baking sheets and spread with the tomato sauce.

3 ▲ Pile the aubergine slices on top of the tomato sauce and cover with the mozzarella. Dot with the black olives and capers. Sprinkle the Pecorino cheese liberally over the top, and season with plenty of salt and pepper. Bake for 15–20 minutes until the crust on each pizza is golden.

Fish & Shellfish

· ·

*Italy has such an extensive coastline – and so many
lakes, rivers and streams – that it is small wonder that
fish and shellfish are so popular. Of course there are
many different types that are unique to the country
itself, but the most common varieties are available
outside Italy. Cooking methods are very simple and
quick, and any accompanying sauces light and fresh.*

Monkfish with Tomato and Olive Sauce
Pesce alla calabrese

This dish comes from the coast of Calabria in southern Italy. Garlic-flavoured mashed

potato is delicious with its robust sauce.

Ingredients

450 g/1 lb fresh mussels, scrubbed
a few fresh basil sprigs
2 garlic cloves, roughly chopped
300 ml/½ pint/1¼ cups dry white wine
30 ml/2 tbsp olive oil
15 g/½ oz/1 tbsp butter
900 g/2 lb monkfish fillets, skinned and
    cut into large chunks
1 onion, finely chopped
500 g/1¼ lb jar sugocasa or passata
15 ml/1 tbsp sun-dried tomato paste
115 g/4 oz/1 cup stoned black olives
salt and freshly ground black pepper
extra fresh basil leaves, to garnish

serves 4

3 ▲ Add the onion to the juices in the casserole and cook gently for about 5 minutes, stirring frequently, until softened. Add the sugocasa or passata, the reserved cooking liquid from the mussels and the tomato paste. Season with salt and pepper to taste. Bring to the boil, stirring, then lower the heat, cover and simmer for 20 minutes, stirring occasionally.

4 ▲ Pull off and discard the top shells from the mussels. Add the monkfish pieces to the tomato sauce and cook gently for 5 minutes. Gently stir in the olives and remaining basil, then taste for seasoning. Place the mussels in their half shells on top of the sauce, cover the pan and heat the mussels through for 1–2 minutes. Serve at once, garnished with basil.

1 ▲ Put the mussels in a flameproof casserole with some basil leaves, the garlic and the wine. Cover and bring to the boil. Lower the heat and simmer for 5 minutes, shaking the pan frequently. Remove the mussels, discarding any that fail to open. Strain the cooking liquid and reserve.

2 ▲ Heat the oil and butter until foaming, add the monkfish pieces and sauté over a medium heat until they just change colour. Remove.

Chargrilled Squid

Grigliata di calamari

If you like your food hot, chop some – or all – of the chilli seeds with the flesh. If not, cut the

chillies in half lengthways, scrape out the seeds and discard them before chopping the flesh.

Ingredients

2 whole prepared squid, with tentacles
75 ml/5 tbsp olive oil
30 ml/2 tbsp balsamic vinegar
2 fresh red chillies, finely chopped
60 ml/4 tbsp dry white wine
salt and freshly ground black pepper
hot cooked risotto rice, to serve
sprigs of fresh parsley, to garnish
serves 2

3 ▲ Cut the squid bodies into diagonal strips. Pile the hot risotto rice in the centre of heated soup plates and top with the strips of squid, arranging them criss-cross fashion. Keep hot.

4 ▲ Add the chopped tentacles and chillies to the pan and toss over a medium heat for 2 minutes. Stir in the wine, then drizzle over the squid and rice. Garnish with the parsley and serve at once.

1 ▲ Make a lengthways cut down the body of each squid, then open out the body flat. Score the flesh on both sides of the bodies in a criss-cross pattern with the tip of a sharp knife. Chop the tentacles. Place all the squid in a china or glass dish. Whisk the oil and vinegar in a small bowl. Add salt and pepper to taste and pour over the squid. Cover and leave to marinate for about 1 hour.

2 ▲ Heat a ridged cast-iron pan until hot. Add the body of one of the squid. Cook over a medium heat for 2–3 minutes, pressing the squid with a fish slice to keep it flat. Repeat on the other side. Cook the other squid body in the same way.

Pan-fried Prawns in their Shells

Gamberi fritti in padella

Although expensive, this is a very quick and simple dish, ideal for an impromptu supper with friends. Serve with hot crusty Italian bread to scoop up the juices.

Ingredients
60 ml/4 tbsp extra virgin olive oil
32 large fresh prawns, in their shells
4 garlic cloves, finely chopped
120 ml/4 fl oz/½ cup Italian dry
    white vermouth
45 ml/3 tbsp passata
salt and freshly ground black pepper
chopped fresh flat leaf parsley, to garnish
crusty bread, to serve
serves 4

Cook's Tip
Prawns in their shells are sweet and juicy, and fun to eat with your fingers. They can be quite messy though, so provide guests with finger bowls and napkins.

1 ▲ Heat the olive oil in a large heavy-based frying pan until just sizzling. Add the prawns and toss over a medium to high heat until their shells just begin to turn pink. Sprinkle the garlic over the prawns in the pan and toss again, then add the vermouth and let it bubble, tossing the prawns constantly so that they cook evenly and absorb the flavours of the garlic and vermouth.

2 ▲ Keeping the pan on the heat, add the passata, with salt and pepper to taste. Stir until the prawns are thoroughly coated in the sauce. Serve at once, sprinkled with the parsley and accompanied by plenty of hot crusty bread.

Grilled Red Mullet with Rosemary

Triglie al rosmarino

This recipe is very simple – the taste of grilled red mullet is so good in itself that it needs very little to bring out the flavour.

Ingredients
4 red mullet, cleaned, about
    275 g/10 oz each
4 garlic cloves, cut lengthways into
    thin slivers
75 ml/5 tbsp olive oil
30 ml/2 tbsp balsamic vinegar
10 ml/2 tsp very finely chopped fresh
    rosemary or 5 ml/1 tsp dried rosemary
freshly ground black pepper
coarse sea salt, to serve
fresh rosemary sprigs and lemon
    wedges, to garnish
serves 4

Variation
Red mullet are extra delicious cooked on the barbecue. If possible, enclose them in a basket grill so that they are easy to turn over.

1 ▲ Cut three diagonal slits in both sides of each fish. Push the garlic slivers into the slits. Place the fish in a single layer in a shallow dish. Whisk the oil, vinegar and rosemary, with ground black pepper to taste.

2 ▲ Pour over the fish, cover with clear film and leave to marinate in a cool place for about 1 hour. Put the fish on the rack of a grill pan and grill for 5–6 minutes on each side, turning once and brushing with the marinade. Serve hot, sprinkled with coarse sea salt and garnished with fresh rosemary sprigs and lemon wedges.

Pan-fried Sole with Lemon

Sogliole al limone

The delicate flavour and texture of sole is brought out in this simple, classic recipe. Lemon sole is used here because it is easier to obtain – and less expensive – than Dover sole.

Ingredients

30–45 ml/2–3 tbsp plain flour
4 lemon sole fillets
45 ml/3 tbsp olive oil
50 g/2 oz/¼ cup butter
60 ml/4 tbsp lemon juice
30 ml/2 tbsp rinsed bottled capers
salt and freshly ground black pepper
fresh flat leaf parsley and lemon wedges,
    to garnish

serves 2

Cook's Tip

It is important to cook the pan juices to the right colour after removing the fish. Too pale, and they will taste insipid, too dark, and they may taste bitter. Take great care not to be distracted at this point so that you can watch the colour of the juices change to a golden brown.

1 ▲ Season the flour with salt and black pepper. Coat the sole fillets evenly on both sides. Heat the oil with half the butter in a large shallow pan until foaming. Add two sole fillets and fry over a medium heat for 2–3 minutes on each side.

2 Lift out the sole fillets with a fish slice and place on a warmed serving platter. Keep hot. Fry the remaining sole fillets.

3 ▲ Remove the pan from the heat and add the lemon juice and remaining butter. Return the pan to a high heat and stir vigorously until the pan juices are sizzling and beginning to turn golden brown. Remove from the heat and stir in the capers.

4 Pour the pan juices over the sole, sprinkle with salt and pepper to taste and garnish with the parsley. Add the lemon wedges and serve at once.

Three-colour Fish Kebabs

Spiedini tricolore

Don't let the fish marinate for more than an hour. The lemon juice will start to break down the fibres of the fish after this time and it will be difficult not to overcook it.

Ingredients

120 ml/4 fl oz/¹/₂ cup olive oil
finely grated rind and juice of
  1 large lemon
5 ml/1 tsp crushed chilli flakes
350 g/12 oz monkfish fillet, cubed
350 g/12 oz swordfish fillet, cubed
350 g/12 oz thick salmon fillet or
  steak, cubed
2 red, yellow or orange peppers, cored,
  seeded and cut into squares
30 ml/2 tbsp finely chopped fresh
  flat leaf parsley
salt and freshly ground black pepper

For the sweet tomato and
chilli salsa

225 g/8 oz ripe tomatoes, finely chopped
1 garlic clove, crushed
1 fresh red chilli, seeded and chopped
45 ml/3 tbsp extra virgin olive oil
15 ml/1 tbsp lemon juice
15 ml/1 tbsp finely chopped fresh
  flat leaf parsley
pinch of sugar
serves 4

1 ▲ Put the oil in a shallow glass or china bowl and add the lemon rind and juice, the chilli flakes and pepper to taste. Whisk to combine, then add the fish chunks. Turn to coat evenly.

2 Add the pepper squares, stir, then cover and marinate in a cool place for 1 hour, turning occasionally.

Variation

Use tuna instead of swordfish. It has a similar meaty texture.

3 ▲ Thread the fish and peppers on to eight oiled metal skewers, reserving the marinade. Barbecue or grill the skewered fish for 5–8 minutes, turning once.

4 Meanwhile, make the salsa by mixing all the ingredients in a bowl, and seasoning to taste with salt and pepper. Heat the reserved marinade in a small pan, remove from the heat and stir in the parsley, with salt and pepper to taste. Serve the kebabs hot, with the marinade spooned over, accompanied by the salsa.

Roast Sea Bass

Branzino al forno

Sea bass has meaty flesh. It is an expensive fish, best cooked as simply as possible. Avoid elaborate sauces, which would mask its delicate flavour.

Ingredients

1 fennel bulb with fronds, about
    275 g/10 oz
2 lemons
120 ml/4 fl oz/$\frac{1}{2}$ cup olive oil
1 small red onion, diced
2 sea bass, about 500 g/1$\frac{1}{4}$ lb each,
    cleaned with heads left on
120 ml/4 fl oz/$\frac{1}{2}$ cup dry white wine
salt and freshly ground black pepper
lemon slices, to garnish

serves 4

1 ▲ Preheat the oven to 190°C/375°F/ Gas 5. Cut the fronds off the top of the fennel and reserve for the garnish. Cut the fennel bulb lengthways into thin wedges, then into dice. Cut one half lemon into four slices. Squeeze the juice from the remaining lemon half and the other lemon.

2 ▲ Heat 30 ml/2 tbsp of the oil in a frying pan, add the diced fennel and onion and cook gently, stirring frequently, for about 5 minutes until softened. Remove from the heat.

3 ▲ Make three diagonal slashes on both sides of each sea bass with a sharp knife. Brush a roasting tin generously with oil, add the fish and tuck two lemon slices in each cavity. Scatter the softened fennel and onion over the fish.

Cook's Tip

Farmed or wild sea bass are available all year round from the fishmonger. They are expensive, but well worth buying for a special main course. Sizes vary from the ones used here, which are a very good size for two servings, to 1.5–1.75 kg/ 3–4$\frac{1}{2}$ lb, which take up to 50 minutes to cook.

4 ▲ Whisk the remaining oil, the lemon juice and salt and pepper to taste and pour over the fish. Cover with foil and roast for 30 minutes or until the flesh flakes, removing the foil for the last 10 minutes. Discard the lemon slices, transfer the fish to a heated serving platter and keep hot.

5 Put the roasting tin on top of the stove. Add the wine and stir over a medium heat to incorporate all the pan juices. Bring to the boil, then spoon the juices over the fish. Garnish with the reserved fennel fronds and lemon slices and serve at once.

Stuffed Swordfish Rolls

Involtini di pesce spada

This is a very tasty dish, with strong flavours from the tomato, olive and caper sauce – and from the salty Pecorino cheese. If you like, substitute Parmesan cheese, which is milder.

Ingredients

30 ml/2 tbsp olive oil
1 small onion, finely chopped
1 celery stick, finely chopped
450 g/1 lb ripe Italian plum
    tomatoes, chopped
115 g/4 oz stoned green olives, half roughly
    chopped, half left whole
45 ml/3 tbsp drained bottled capers
4 large swordfish steaks, each about
    1 cm / ½ in thick and 115 g/4 oz in weight
1 egg
50 g/2 oz/⅔ cup grated Pecorino cheese
25 g/1 oz/½ cup fresh white breadcrumbs
salt and freshly ground black pepper
sprigs of fresh parsley, to garnish

serves 4

Cook's Tip

This dish is not for the inexperienced cook because the pounding, stuffing and rolling of the fish is quite tricky. If you prefer, you can omit the stuffing and simply cook the swordfish steaks in the sauce.

1 ▲ Heat the oil in a large heavy-based frying pan. Add the onion and celery and cook gently for about 3 minutes, stirring frequently. Stir in the tomatoes, olives and capers, with salt and pepper to taste. Bring to the boil, then lower the heat, cover and simmer for about 15 minutes. Stir occasionally and add a little water if the sauce becomes too thick.

2 Remove the fish skin and place each steak between two sheets of clear film. Pound lightly with a rolling pin until each steak is reduced to about 5 mm/¼ in thick.

3 ▲ Beat the egg in a bowl and add the cheese, breadcrumbs and a few spoonfuls of the sauce. Stir well to mix to a moist stuffing. Spread one-quarter of the stuffing over each swordfish steak, then roll up into a sausage shape. Secure with wooden cocktail sticks.

4 ▲ Add the rolls to the sauce in the pan and bring to the boil. Lower the heat, cover and simmer for about 30 minutes, turning once. Add a little water as the sauce reduces.

5 Remove the rolls from the sauce and discard the cocktail sticks. Place on warmed dinner plates and spoon the sauce over and around. Garnish with the parsley and serve hot.

Poultry & Meat

· ·

The Italians eat a wide variety of different meats, and tastes vary according to region. Veal, pork and poultry are popular all over the country, while beef is farmed and eaten more in the north, and lamb is a great Roman speciality. All meats are eaten as a second course – secondo piatto – usually simple and served solo, with vegetables to follow.

Beef Stew with Tomatoes, Wine and Peas *Spezzatino*

It seems there are as many spezzatino recipes as there are Italian cooks. This one is very traditional, perfect for a winter lunch or dinner. Serve it with boiled or mashed potatoes to soak up the deliciously rich sauce.

Ingredients
30 ml/2 tbsp plain flour
10 ml/2 tsp chopped fresh thyme or
    5 ml/1 tsp dried thyme
1 kg/2¼ lb braising or stewing steak, cut
    into large cubes
45 ml/3 tbsp olive oil
1 medium onion, roughly chopped
450 g/1 lb jar sugocasa or passata
250 ml/8 fl oz/1 cup beef stock
250 ml/8 fl oz/1 cup red wine
2 garlic cloves, crushed
30 ml/2 tbsp tomato purée
275 g/10 oz/2 cups shelled fresh peas
5 ml/1 tsp sugar
salt and freshly ground black pepper
fresh thyme, to garnish

serves 4

1 ▲ Preheat the oven to 160°C/325°F/ Gas 3. Put the flour in a shallow dish and season with the thyme and salt and pepper. Add the beef cubes and coat evenly.

2 ▲ Heat the oil in a large flameproof casserole, add the beef and brown on all sides over a medium to high heat. Remove with a slotted spoon and drain on kitchen paper.

3 ▲ Add the onion to the pan, scraping the base of the pan to mix in any sediment. Cook gently for about 3 minutes, stirring frequently, until softened, then stir in the sugocasa or passata, stock, wine, garlic and tomato purée. Bring to the boil, stirring. Return the beef to the pan and stir well to coat with the sauce. Cover and cook in the oven for 1½ hours.

4 ▲ Stir in the peas and sugar. Return the casserole to the oven and cook for 30 minutes more, or until the beef is tender. Taste for seasoning. Garnish with fresh thyme before serving.

Variation
Use thawed frozen peas instead of fresh. Add them 10 minutes before the end of cooking.

Meatballs with Peperonata

Polpette di manzo

These taste very good with creamed potatoes. Use a potato ricer to get them really smooth.

Ingredients

400 g/14 oz minced beef
115 g/4 oz/2 cups fresh
    white breadcrumbs
50 g/2 oz/²/₃ cup grated
    Parmesan cheese
2 eggs, beaten
pinch of paprika
pinch of grated nutmeg
5 ml/1 tsp dried mixed herbs
2 thin slices of mortadella or prosciutto
    (total weight about 50 g/2 oz), chopped
vegetable oil, for shallow frying
salt and freshly ground black pepper
snipped fresh basil leaves, to garnish

For the peperonata

30 ml/2 tbsp olive oil
1 small onion, thinly sliced
2 yellow peppers, cored, seeded and cut
    lengthways into thin strips
2 red peppers, cored, seeded and cut
    lengthways into thin strips
275 g/10 oz/1¼ cups finely chopped
    tomatoes or passata
15 ml/1 tbsp chopped fresh parsley

serves 4

1 ▲ Put the minced beef in a bowl. Add half the breadcrumbs and all the remaining ingredients, including salt and ground black pepper to taste. Mix well with clean wet hands. Divide the mixture into 12 equal portions and roll each into a ball. Flatten the meat balls slightly so they are about 1 cm/½ in thick.

2 Put the remaining breadcrumbs on a plate and roll the meatballs in them, a few at a time, until they are evenly coated. Place on a plate, cover with clear film and chill for about 30 minutes to firm up.

3 ▲ Meanwhile, make the peperonata. Heat the oil in a medium saucepan, add the onion and cook gently for about 3 minutes, stirring frequently, until softened. Add the pepper strips and cook for 3 minutes, stirring constantly. Stir in the tomatoes or passata and parsley, with salt and pepper to taste. Bring to the boil, stirring. Cover and cook for 15 minutes, then remove the lid and continue to cook, stirring frequently, for 10 minutes more, or until reduced and thick. Taste for seasoning. Keep hot.

4 ▲ Pour oil into a frying pan to a depth of about 2.5 cm/1 in. When hot but not smoking, shallow fry the meatballs for 10–12 minutes, turning them 3–4 times and pressing them flat with a fish slice. Remove and drain on kitchen paper. Serve hot, with the peperonata alongside. Garnish with the basil.

Variation

Instead of minced beef, used half minced pork and half minced veal.

Veal Shanks with Tomatoes and White Wine
Osso buco

This famous Milanese dish is rich and hearty. It is traditionally served with risotto alla milanese, but plain boiled rice goes equally well. The lemony gremolata garnish helps to cut the richness of the dish, as does a crisp green salad – serve it after the osso buco and before the dessert, to refresh the palate.

Ingredients

30 ml/2 tbsp plain flour
4 pieces of osso buco
2 small onions
30 ml/2 tbsp olive oil
1 large celery stick, finely chopped
1 medium carrot, finely chopped
2 garlic cloves, finely chopped
400 g/14 oz can chopped tomatoes
300 ml/½ pint/1¼ cups dry white wine
300 ml/½ pint/1¼ cups chicken or
    veal stock
1 strip of thinly pared lemon rind
2 bay leaves, plus extra for
    garnishing (optional)
salt and freshly ground black pepper

For the gremolata

30 ml/2 tbsp finely chopped fresh
    flat leaf parsley
finely grated rind of 1 lemon
1 garlic clove, finely chopped
serves 4

1 ▲ Preheat the oven to 160°C/325°F/ Gas 3. Season the flour with salt and pepper and spread it out in a shallow bowl. Add the pieces of veal and turn them in the flour until evenly coated. Shake off any excess flour.

2 ▲ Slice one of the onions and separate it into rings. Heat the oil in a large flameproof casserole, then add the veal, with the onion rings, and brown the veal on both sides over a medium heat. Remove the veal shanks with tongs and set aside on kitchen paper to drain.

3 ▲ Chop the remaining onion and add it to the pan with the celery, carrot and garlic. Stir the bottom of the pan to incorporate the pan juices and sediment. Cook gently, stirring frequently, for about 5 minutes until the vegetables soften slightly.

4 ▲ Add the chopped tomatoes, wine, stock, lemon rind and bay leaves, then season to taste with salt and pepper. Bring to the boil, stirring. Return the veal to the pan and coat with the sauce. Cover and cook in the oven for 2 hours or until the veal feels tender when pierced with a fork.

5 Meanwhile, make the gremolata. In a small bowl, mix together the chopped parsley, lemon rind and chopped garlic. Remove the casserole from the oven and lift out and discard the strip of lemon rind and the bay leaves. Taste the sauce for seasoning. Serve the osso buco hot, sprinkled with the gremolata and garnished with extra bay leaves, if you like.

Cook's Tip

Osso buco is available from large supermarkets and good butchers. Choose pieces about 2 cm/¾ in thick.

Calf's Liver with Balsamic Vinegar   *Fegato all'aceto balsamico*

This sweet and sour liver dish is a speciality of Venice. Serve it very simply, with green beans sprinkled with browned breadcrumbs.

Ingredients
15 ml/1 tbsp plain flour
2.5 ml/¹⁄₂ tsp finely chopped fresh sage
4 thin slices of calf's liver, cut into
    serving pieces
45 ml/3 tbsp olive oil
25 g/1 oz/2 tbsp butter
2 small red onions, sliced and separated
    into rings
150 ml/¹⁄₄ pint/²⁄₃ cup dry white wine
45 ml/3 tbsp balsamic vinegar
pinch of granulated sugar
salt and freshly ground black pepper
fresh sprigs of sage, to garnish
green beans sprinkled with browned
    breadcrumbs, to serve

serves 2

Cook's Tip
Never overcook calf's liver, because it quickly turns tough. Its delicate flesh is at its most tender when it is served slightly underdone and pink – like a rare steak.

1 ▲ Spread out the flour in a shallow bowl. Season it with the sage and plenty of salt and pepper. Turn the liver in the flour until well coated.

2 Heat 30 ml/2 tbsp of the oil with half of the butter in a wide heavy-based saucepan or frying pan until foaming. Add the onion rings and cook gently, stirring frequently, for about 5 minutes until softened but not coloured. Remove with a fish slice and set aside.

3 ▲ Heat the remaining oil and butter in the pan until foaming, add the liver and cook over medium heat for 2–3 minutes on each side. Transfer to heated dinner plates and keep hot.

4 Add the wine and vinegar to the pan, then stir to mix with the pan juices and any sediment. Add the onions and sugar and heat through, stirring. Spoon the sauce over the liver, garnish with sage sprigs and serve at once with the green beans.

Veal Escalopes with Lemon

Scaloppine al limone

Popular in Italian restaurants, this dish is very easy to make at home.

Ingredients

4 veal escalopes
30–45 ml/2–3 tbsp plain flour
50 g/2 oz/¼ cup butter
60 ml/4 tbsp olive oil
60 ml/4 tbsp Italian dry white vermouth or
    dry white wine
45 ml/3 tbsp lemon juice
salt and freshly ground black pepper
lemon wedges and fresh parsley, to garnish
green beans and Peperonata, to serve

serves 4

1 ▲ Put each escalope between two sheets of clear film and pound until very thin.

2 Cut the pounded escalopes in half or quarters, and coat in the flour, seasoned with salt and pepper.

3 ▲ Melt the butter with half the oil in a large, heavy frying pan until sizzling. Add as many escalopes as the pan will hold. Fry over a medium to high heat for 1–2 minutes on each side until lightly coloured. Remove with a fish slice and keep hot. Add the remaining oil and cook the remaining escalopes in the same way.

4 Remove the pan from the heat and add the vermouth or wine and the lemon juice. Stir vigorously to mix with the pan juices, then return to the heat and return all the veal to the pan. Spoon the sauce over the veal. Shake the pan over a medium heat until all of the escalopes are coated in the sauce and heated through.

5 Serve at once, garnished with lemon wedges and parsley. Lightly cooked green beans and peperonata make a delicious accompaniment.

Variation

Use skinless boneless chicken breasts instead of the veal. If they are thick, cut them in half before pounding.

Roast Lamb with Rosemary

Agnello al rosmarino

In Italy, lamb is traditionally served at Easter. This simple roast with potatoes owes its wonderful flavour to the fresh rosemary and garlic. It makes the perfect Sunday lunch at any time of year, served with one or two lightly cooked fresh vegetables, such as broccoli, spinach or baby carrots.

Ingredients

½ leg of lamb, about 1.4 kg/3 lb
2 garlic cloves, cut lengthways into
    thin slivers
leaves from 4 sprigs of fresh rosemary,
    finely chopped
105 ml/7 tbsp olive oil
about 250 ml/8 fl oz/1 cup lamb or
    vegetable stock
675 g/1½ lb potatoes, cut into
    2.5 cm/1 in cubes
a few fresh sage leaves, chopped
salt and freshly ground black pepper
lightly cooked baby carrots, to serve

serves 4

1 ▲ Preheat the oven to 230°C/450°F/ Gas 8. Using the point of a sharp knife, make deep incisions in the lamb, especially near the bone, and insert the slivers of garlic.

2 ▲ Put the lamb in a roasting tin and rub it all over with 45 ml/3 tbsp of the oil. Sprinkle over about half of the chopped rosemary, patting it on firmly, and season with plenty of salt and pepper. Roast for 30 minutes, turning once.

3 ▲ Lower the oven temperature to 190°C/375°F/Gas 5. Turn the lamb over again and add 120 ml/4 fl oz/ ½ cup of the stock.

4 Roast for a further 1¼ –1½ hours until the lamb is tender, turning the joint two or three times more and adding the rest of the stock in two or three batches. Baste the lamb each time it is turned.

5 ▲ Meanwhile, put the potatoes in a separate roasting tin and toss with the remaining oil and rosemary and the sage. Roast, on the same shelf as the lamb if possible, for 45 minutes, turning the potatoes several times until they are golden and tender.

6 ▲ Transfer the lamb to a carving board, tent with foil and leave in a warm place for 10 minutes so that the flesh firms for easier carving. Serve whole or carved into thin slices, surrounded by the potatoes and accompanied by baby carrots.

Cook's Tip

If you like, the cooking juices can be strained and used to make a thin gravy with stock and red wine.

Pork in Sweet and Sour Sauce   *Scaloppine di maiale in agrodolce*

The combination of sweet and sour flavours is popular in Venetian cooking, especially with meat and liver. This recipe is given extra bite with the addition of crushed mixed peppercorns. Served with shelled broad beans tossed with grilled bacon – it is delectable.

Ingredients
1 whole pork fillet, about 350 g/12 oz
25 ml/1½ tbsp plain flour
30–45 ml/2–3 tbsp olive oil
250 ml/8 fl oz/1 cup dry white wine
30 ml/2 tbsp white wine vinegar
10 ml/2 tsp granulated sugar
15 ml/1 tbsp mixed peppercorns,
   coarsely ground
salt and freshly ground black pepper
broad beans tossed with grilled bacon,
   to serve

serves 2

3 ▲ Heat 15 ml/1 tbsp of the oil in a wide heavy-based saucepan or frying pan and add as many slices of pork as the pan will hold. Fry over a medium to high heat for 2–3 minutes on each side until crispy and tender. Remove with a fish slice and set aside. Repeat with the remaining pork, adding more oil as necessary.

4 ▲ Mix the wine, wine vinegar and sugar in a jug. Pour into the pan and stir vigorously over a high heat until reduced, scraping the pan to incorporate the sediment. Stir in the peppercorns and return the pork to the pan. Spoon the sauce over the pork until it is evenly coated and heated through.

1 ▲ Cut the pork diagonally into thin slices. Place between two sheets of clear film and pound lightly with a rolling pin to flatten them evenly.

2 ▲ Spread out the flour in a shallow bowl. Season well and coat the meat.

Cook's Tip
Grind the peppercorns in a pepper grinder, or crush them with a mortar and pestle.

Chicken with Tomatoes and Prawns

Pollo alla marengo

This Piedmontese dish was created especially for Napoleon after the battle of Marengo.

Versions of it appear in both Italian and French recipe books.

Ingredients

120 ml/4 fl oz/½ cup olive oil
8 chicken thighs on the bone, skinned
1 onion, finely chopped
1 celery stick, finely chopped
1 garlic clove, crushed
350 g/12 oz ripe Italian plum tomatoes, peeled and roughly chopped
250 ml/8 fl oz/1 cup dry white wine
2.5 ml/½ tsp finely chopped fresh rosemary
15 ml/1 tbsp butter
8 small triangles of thinly sliced white bread, without crusts
175 g/6 oz large raw prawns, shelled
salt and freshly ground black pepper
finely chopped flat leaf parsley, to garnish

serves 4

1 ▲ Heat about 30 ml/2 tbsp of the oil in a frying pan, add the chicken thighs and sauté over a medium heat for about 5 minutes until they have changed colour on all sides. Transfer to a flameproof casserole.

2 ▲ Add the onion and celery to the frying pan and cook gently, stirring frequently, for about 3 minutes until softened. Add the garlic, tomatoes, wine, rosemary and salt and pepper to taste. Bring to the boil, stirring.

3 Pour the tomato sauce over the chicken. Cover and cook gently for 40 minutes or until the chicken is tender when pierced.

4 ▲ About 10 minutes before serving, add the remaining oil and the butter to the frying pan and heat until hot but not smoking. Add the triangles of bread and shallow fry until crisp and golden on each side. Drain on kitchen paper.

5 ▲ Add the prawns to the tomato sauce and heat until the prawns are cooked. Taste the sauce for seasoning. Dip one of the tips of each fried bread triangle in parsley. Serve the dish hot, garnished with the bread triangles.

Variation

To make the dish look more like its original, authentic version, garnish it with a few large crayfish or prawns in their shells.

Chicken with Chianti

Pollo al chianti

Together the robust, full-flavoured red wine and red pesto give this sauce a rich colour and almost spicy flavour, while the grapes add a delicious sweetness. Serve the stew with grilled polenta or warm crusty bread, and accompany with a piquant salad, such as rocket or watercress, tossed with a tasty dressing.

Ingredients

45 ml/3 tbsp olive oil
4 part-boned chicken breasts, skinned
1 medium red onion
30 ml/2 tbsp red pesto
300 ml/$\frac{1}{2}$ pint/1$\frac{1}{4}$ cups Chianti
300 ml/$\frac{1}{2}$ pint/1$\frac{1}{4}$ cups water
115 g/4 oz red grapes, halved
    lengthways and seeded if necessary
salt and freshly ground black pepper
fresh basil leaves, to garnish
rocket salad, to serve

serves 4

1 ▲ Heat 30 ml/2 tbsp of the oil in a large frying pan, add the chicken breasts and sauté over a medium heat for about 5 minutes until they have changed colour on all sides. Remove with a slotted spoon and drain on kitchen paper.

Cook's Tip

Use part-boned chicken breasts, if you can get them, in preference to boneless chicken for this dish as they have a better flavour. Chicken thighs or drumsticks could also be cooked in this way.

2 Cut the onions in half, through the root. Trim off the root, then slice the onion halves lengthways to create thin wedges.

3 ▲ Heat the remaining oil in the pan, add the onion wedges and red pesto and cook gently, stirring constantly, for about 3 minutes until the onion is softened, but not browned.

4 ▲ Add the Chianti and water to the pan and bring to the boil, stirring, then return the chicken to the pan and add salt and pepper to taste.

5 Reduce the heat, then cover the pan and simmer gently for about 20 minutes or until the chicken is tender, stirring occasionally.

6 ▲ Add the grapes to the pan and cook over a low to medium heat until heated through, then taste the sauce for seasoning. Serve the chicken hot, garnished with basil and accompanied by the rocket salad.

Variations

Use green pesto instead of red, and substitute a dry white wine such as pinot grigio for the Chianti, then finish with seedless green grapes. A few spoonfuls of mascarpone cheese can be added at the end if you like, to enrich the sauce.

Hunter's Chicken

Pollo alla cacciatora

This traditional dish sometimes has strips of green pepper in the sauce for extra colour and flavour instead of the fresh mushrooms.

Ingredients

15 g/¹/₂ oz/1 cup dried porcini
    mushrooms
30 ml/2 tbsp olive oil
15 g/¹/₂ oz/1 tbsp butter
4 chicken pieces, on the bone, skinned
1 large onion, thinly sliced
400 g/14 oz can chopped tomatoes
150 ml/¹/₄ pint/ ²/₃ cup red wine
1 garlic clove, crushed
leaves of 1 sprig of fresh rosemary,
    finely chopped
115 g/4 oz/1³/₄ cups fresh field
    mushrooms, thinly sliced
salt and freshly ground black pepper
fresh rosemary sprigs, to garnish
serves 4

1 ▲ Put the porcini in a bowl, add 250 ml/8 fl oz/1 cup warm water and soak for 20–30 minutes. Remove from the liquid and squeeze the porcini over the bowl. Strain the liquid and reserve. Finely chop the porcini.

3 ▲ Add the onion and chopped mushrooms to the pan. Cook gently, stirring frequently, for about 3 minutes until the onion has softened but not browned. Stir in the chopped tomatoes, wine and reserved mushroom soaking liquid, then add the crushed garlic and chopped rosemary, with salt and pepper to taste. Bring to the boil, stirring all the time.

4 ▲ Return the chicken to the pan and coat with the sauce. Cover and simmer gently for 30 minutes.

5 Add the fresh mushrooms and stir well to mix into the sauce. Continue simmering gently for 10 minutes or until the chicken is tender. Taste for seasoning. Serve hot, with creamed potato or polenta, if you like. Garnish with rosemary.

2 ▲ Heat the oil and butter in a large flameproof casserole until foaming. Add the chicken. Sauté over a medium heat for 5 minutes, or until golden. Remove and drain on kitchen paper.

Turkey with Marsala Cream Sauce

Tacchino al marsala

Marsala makes a very rich and tasty sauce. The addition of lemon juice gives it a sharp

edge, which helps to offset the richness.

Ingredients

6 turkey breast steaks
45 ml/3 tbsp plain flour
30 ml/2 tbsp olive oil
25 g/1 oz/2 tbsp butter
175 ml/6 fl oz/¾ cup dry Marsala
60 ml/4 tbsp lemon juice
175 ml/6 fl oz/¾ cup double cream
salt and freshly ground black pepper
lemon wedges , and chopped fresh
    parsley, to garnish
mangetouts and French beans, to serve

serves 6

1 ▲ Put each turkey steak between two sheets of clear film and pound with a rolling pin to flatten and stretch. Cut each steak in half or into quarters, cutting away and discarding any sinew.

2 ▲ Spread out the flour in a shallow bowl. Season well and coat the meat.

Variation

Veal or pork escalopes or chicken breast fillets can be used instead of the turkey, and 50 g/2 oz/¼ cup mascarpone cheese instead of the double cream.

3 ▲ Heat the oil and butter in a wide heavy-based saucepan or frying pan until sizzling. Add as many pieces of turkey as the pan will hold and sauté over a medium heat for about 3 minutes on each side until crispy and tender. Transfer to a warmed serving dish with tongs and keep hot. Repeat with the remaining turkey.

4 ▲ Lower the heat. Mix the Marsala and lemon juice in a jug, add to the pan and raise the heat. Bring to the boil, stirring in the sediment, then add the cream. Simmer, stirring constantly, until the sauce is reduced and glossy. Taste for seasoning. Spoon over the turkey, garnish with the lemon wedges and parsley and serve at once with the mangetouts and French beans.

Chicken with Parma Ham and Cheese *Pollo alla valdostana*

The name Valdostana is derived from Val d'Aosta, home of the Fontina cheese used here.

Ingredients

2 thin slices of prosciutto
2 thin slices of Fontina cheese
4 part-boned chicken breasts
4 sprigs of basil
30 ml/2 tbsp olive oil
15 g/¹/₂ oz/1 tbsp butter
120 ml/4 fl oz/¹/₂ cup dry white wine
salt and freshly ground black pepper
tender young salad leaves, to serve
serves 4

Cook's Tip

There is nothing quite like the buttery texture and nutty flavour of Fontina cheese, and it also has superb melting qualities, but you could use a Swiss or French mountain cheese, such as Gruyère or Emmental. Ask for the cheese to be sliced thinly on the machine slicer, as you will find it difficult to slice it thinly yourself.

1 ▲ Preheat the oven to 200°C/400°F/Gas 6. Lightly oil a baking dish. Cut the prosciutto and Fontina slices in half crossways. Skin the chicken breasts, open out the slit in the centre of each one, and fill each cavity with half a ham slice and a basil sprig.

2 ▲ Heat the oil and butter in a wide heavy-based frying pan until foaming. Cook the chicken breasts over a medium heat for 1–2 minutes on each side until they change colour. Transfer to the baking dish. Add the wine to the pan juices, stir until sizzling, then pour over the chicken and season to taste.

3 Top each chicken breast with a slice of Fontina. Bake for 20 minutes or until the chicken is tender. Serve hot, with tender young salad leaves.

Devilled Chicken *Pollo alla diavola*

You can tell this spicy, barbecued chicken dish comes from southern Italy because it has dried red chillies in the marinade. Versions without the chillies are just as good.

Ingredients

120 ml/4 fl oz/¹/₂ cup olive oil
finely grated rind and juice of
    1 large lemon
2 garlic cloves, finely chopped
10 ml/2 tsp finely chopped or crumbled
    dried red chillies
12 skinless, boneless chicken thighs,
    each cut into 3 or 4 pieces
salt and freshly ground black pepper
flat leaf parsley leaves, to garnish
lemon wedges, to serve
serves 4

Cook's Tip

Thread the chicken pieces spiral-fashion on the skewers so they do not fall off during cooking.

1 ▲ Make a marinade by mixing the oil, lemon rind and juice, garlic and chillies in a large, shallow glass or china dish. Add salt and pepper to taste. Whisk well, then add the chicken pieces, turning to coat with the marinade. Cover and marinate in the fridge for at least 4 hours, or preferably overnight.

2 ▲ When ready to cook, prepare the barbecue or preheat the grill and thread the chicken pieces on to eight oiled metal skewers. Cook on the barbecue or under a hot grill for 6–8 minutes, turning frequently, until tender. Garnish with parsley leaves and serve hot, with lemon wedges for squeezing.

Vegetables & Salads

....

There is no shortage of fresh and delicious vegetables in Italy, and the dishes are imaginative and varied. Most Italian cooks buy only when the vegetables are in season and at their best, so you will rarely find winter and summer vegetables together in one dish. The list of irresistible salad combinations, however, is endless, often with roasted ingredients stirred into crisp green leaves.

Roasted Plum Tomatoes and Garlic

Pomodori al forno

These are so simple to prepare yet taste absolutely wonderful. Use a large, shallow earthenware dish that will allow the tomatoes to sear and char in a hot oven.

Ingredients

8 plum tomatoes, halved
12 garlic cloves
60 ml/4 tbsp extra virgin olive oil
3 bay leaves
salt and freshly ground black pepper
45 ml/3 tbsp fresh oregano leaves,
    to garnish

serves 4

Cook's Tip

Use ripe plum tomatoes for this recipe as they keep their shape and do not fall apart when roasted at such a high temperature. Leave the stalks on, if possible.

1 ▲ Preheat the oven to 230°C/450°F/Gas 8. Select an ovenproof dish that will hold all the tomatoes snugly in a single layer. Place the tomatoes in the dish and push the whole, unpeeled garlic cloves between them.

2 ▲ Brush the tomatoes with the oil, add the bay leaves and sprinkle black pepper over the top. Bake for about 45 minutes until the tomatoes have softened and are sizzling in the pan. They should be charred around the edges. Season with salt and a little more black pepper, if needed. Garnish with oregano and serve.

Green Beans with Tomatoes

Fagiolini al pomodoro

This is a real summer favourite using the best ripe plum tomatoes and French beans.

Ingredients

30 ml/2 tbsp olive oil
1 large onion, finely sliced
2 garlic cloves, finely chopped
6 large ripe plum tomatoes, peeled,
    seeded and coarsely chopped
150 ml/¼ pint/⅔ cup dry white wine
450 g/1 lb French green beans, sliced in
    half lengthways
16 stoned black olives
10 ml/2 tsp lemon juice
salt and freshly ground black pepper
serves 4

Cook's Tip

French beans need little preparation
and now that they are grown without
the string you simply top and tail
them. When choosing make sure that
the beans snap easily – this is a good
sign of freshness.

1 ▲ Heat the oil in a large frying pan.
Add the onion and garlic and cook
for about 5 minutes until the onion
is softened but not brown.

2 ▲ Add the chopped tomatoes,
white wine, beans, olives and lemon
juice and cook over a gentle heat for
a further 20 minutes, stirring from
time to time, until the sauce is
thickened and the beans are tender.
Season with salt and pepper to taste
and serve at once.

Fennel Gratin

Finocchi gratinati

This is one of the best ways to eat fresh fennel. The fennel takes on a delicious, almost creamy, flavour, which contrasts beautifully with the sharp, strong Gruyère.

Ingredients

2 fennel bulbs, about 675 g/1½ lb
    total weight
300 ml/½ pint/1¼ cups milk
15 g/½ oz/1 tbsp butter, plus extra
    for greasing
15 ml/1 tbsp plain flour
75 g/3 oz Gruyère cheese, grated
25 g/1 oz/scant ½ cup dry
    white breadcrumbs
salt and freshly ground black pepper

serves 4

Cook's Tip

Instead of the Gruyère, Parmesan, Pecorino or any other strong cheese would work perfectly.

1 ▲ Preheat the oven to 240°C/475°F/ Gas 9. Discard the stalks and root ends from the fennel. Slice into quarters and place in a large saucepan. Pour over the milk and simmer for 10–15 minutes until tender. Butter a small baking dish.

2 Remove the fennel pieces with a slotted spoon, reserving the milk and arrange the fennel pieces in the dish.

3 ▲ Melt the butter in a small saucepan and add the flour, stir well, then gradually whisk in the reserved milk. Stir the sauce until thickened.

4 Pour the sauce over the fennel pieces, sprinkle with the white breadcrumbs and grated Gruyère. Season with salt and black pepper and bake for about 20 minutes until browned.

Sweet and Sour Onions

Cipolline in agrodolce

Onions are naturally sweet, and when they are cooked at a high temperature the sweetness intensifies. Serve with roasts and meat dishes or as part of an antipasti.

Ingredients

50 g/2 oz/¼ cup butter
75 ml/5 tbsp sugar
120 ml/4 fl oz/½ cup white wine vinegar
30 ml/2 tbsp balsamic vinegar
675 g/1½ lb small pickling onions, peeled
salt and freshly ground black pepper

serves 4

Cook's Tips

This recipe also looks and tastes delicious when made with either yellow or red onions, which are cut into either thin slices or into chunks. Cooking times will vary, depending on the size of the onion pieces.

1 ▲ Heat the butter in a large saucepan over a gentle heat. Add the sugar and heat until dissolved, stirring constantly.

2 ▲ Add the vinegars to the pan with the onions and mix together well. Season with salt and pepper and cover and cook over a moderate heat for 20–25 minutes until the onions are a golden colour and soft when pierced with a knife. Serve hot.

Roasted Potatoes with Red Onions

Patate al forno

These mouth-watering potatoes are a fine accompaniment to just about anything. The key is to use small firm potatoes; the smaller they are cut, the quicker they will cook.

Ingredients

675 g/1½ lb small firm potatoes
25 g/1 oz/2 tbsp butter
30 ml/2 tbsp olive oil
2 red onions, cut into chunks
8 garlic cloves, unpeeled
30 ml/2 tbsp chopped fresh rosemary
salt and freshly ground black pepper

serves 4

Cook's Tip

To ensure that the potatoes are crisp, make sure they are completely dry before cooking. Resist the urge to turn the potatoes too often. Allow them to brown on one side before turning. Do not salt the potatoes until the end of cooking – salting beforehand encourages them to give up their liquid, making them limp.

1 ▲ Preheat the oven to 230ºC/450ºF/ Gas 8. Peel and quarter the potatoes, rinse them well and pat thoroughly dry on kitchen paper. Place the butter and oil in a roasting tin and place in the oven to heat.

2 ▲ When the butter has melted and is foaming, add the potatoes, red onions, garlic and rosemary. Toss well then spread out in one layer.

3 Place the tin in the oven and roast for about 25 minutes until the potatoes are golden and tender when tested with a fork. Shake the tin from time to time to redistribute the potatoes. When cooked, season with salt and pepper.

Radicchio and Chicory Gratin

Radicchio e indivia gratinati

Vegetables like radicchio and chicory take on a different flavour when cooked in this way.

The creamy béchamel combines wonderfully with the bitter leaves.

Ingredients

2 heads radicchio, quartered lengthways
2 heads chicory, quartered lengthways
25 g/1 oz/½ cup drained sun-dried
    tomatoes in oil, chopped roughly
25 g/1 oz/2 tbsp butter
15 g/½ oz/1 tbsp plain flour
250 ml/8 fl oz/1 cup milk
pinch grated nutmeg
50 g/2 oz/½ cup grated
    Emmenthal cheese
salt and freshly ground black pepper
chopped fresh parsley, to garnish

serves 4

1 ▲ Preheat the oven to 180ºC/350ºF/ Gas 4. Grease a 1.2 litre/2 pint/5 cup baking dish. Trim the radicchio and chicory and pull away, discarding any damaged or wilted leaves. Quarter them lengthways and arrange in the baking dish. Scatter over the sun-dried tomatoes and brush the leaves liberally with the oil from the jar. Sprinkle with salt and pepper and cover with foil. Bake for 15 minutes, then remove the foil and bake for a further 10 minutes until the vegetables are softened.

Cook's Tip

In Italy radicchio and chicory are often grilled on an outside barbecue. To do this, simply prepare the vegetables as above and brush with olive oil. Place cut-side down on the grill for 7–10 minutes until browned. Turn and grill until the other side is browned, about 5 minutes longer.

2 ▲ Make the sauce. Place the butter in a small saucepan and melt over a moderate heat. When the butter is foaming, add the flour and cook for 1 minute, stirring. Remove from the heat and gradually add the milk, whisking all the time. Return to the heat and bring to the boil, simmer for 2–3 minutes to thicken. Season to taste and add the nutmeg.

3 Pour the sauce over the vegetables and sprinkle with the grated cheese. Bake for about 20 minutes until golden. Serve immediately, garnished with parsley.

Potato and Pumpkin Pudding

Tortino di patate e zucca

Serve this savoury pudding with any rich meat dish or simply with a mixed salad.

Ingredients

45 ml/3 tbsp olive oil
1 garlic clove, sliced
675 g/1½ lb pumpkin flesh, cut into
   2 cm/¾ in chunks
350 g/12 oz potatoes
25 g/1 oz/2 tbsp butter
90 g/3½ oz/scant ½ cup ricotta cheese
50 g/2 oz/⅔ cup grated
   Parmesan cheese
pinch grated nutmeg
4 size 3 eggs, separated
salt and freshly ground black pepper
chopped fresh parsley, to garnish
serves 4

1 Preheat the oven to 200°C/400°F/
Gas 6. Grease a 1.75 litre/3 pint/
7½ cup, shallow, oval baking dish.

Cook's Tip

You may process the vegetables in a
food processor for a few seconds,
but be careful not to overprocess, as
they will become very gluey.

2 ▲ Heat the oil in a large shallow
pan, add the garlic and pumpkin and
cook, stirring often to prevent
sticking, for 15–20 minutes or until
the pumpkin is tender. Meanwhile,
cook the potatoes in boiling salted
water for 20 minutes until tender.
Drain, leave until cool enough to
handle, then peel off the skins. Place
the potatoes and pumpkin in a large
bowl and mash well with the butter.

3 Mash the ricotta with a fork until
smooth and add to the potato and
pumpkin mixture, mixing well.

4 ▲ Stir the Parmesan, nutmeg and
plenty of seasoning into the ricotta
mixture – it should be smooth and
creamy.

5 Add the egg yolks one at a time
until mixed thoroughly.

6 Whisk the egg whites with an
electric whisk until they form stiff
peaks, then fold gently into the
mixture. Spoon into the prepared
baking dish and bake for
30 minutes until golden and firm.
Serve hot, garnished with parsley.

Fried Spring Greens

Cavolo fritto

This dish can be served as a vegetable accompaniment, or it can be enjoyed simply on its

own, with some warm crusty bread.

Ingredients

30 ml/2 tbsp olive oil
25 g/1 oz/2 tbsp butter
75 g/3 oz rindless smoked streaky
   bacon, chopped
1 large onion, thinly sliced
250 ml/8 fl oz/1 cup dry white wine
2 garlic cloves, finely chopped
900 g/2 lb spring greens, shredded
salt and freshly ground black pepper
serves 4

Cook's Tips

This dish would work just as well
using shredded red cabbage and red
wine. Leave to simmer for
10 minutes longer as red cabbage
leaves are slightly tougher than the
spring greens.

1 In a large frying pan, heat the oil
and butter and add the bacon. Fry for
2 minutes, then add the onions and
fry for a further 3 minutes until the
onion is beginning to soften.

2 Add the wine and simmer
vigorously for 2 minutes to reduce.

3 Reduce the heat and add the spring
greens and salt and pepper. Cook
over a gentle heat for about
15 minutes until the greens are
tender. (Cover the pan so that the
greens retain their colour.) Serve hot.

Fennel, Orange and Rocket Salad

Insalata di finocchio

This light and refreshing salad is ideal to serve with spicy or rich foods.

Ingredients
2 oranges
1 fennel bulb
115 g/4 oz rocket leaves
50 g/2 oz/⅓ cup black olives

For the dressing
30 ml/2 tbsp extra virgin olive oil
15 ml/1 tbsp balsamic vinegar
1 small garlic clove, crushed
salt and freshly ground black pepper
serves 4

1 With a vegetable peeler, cut strips of rind from the oranges, leaving the pith behind and cut into thin julienne strips. Cook in boiling water for a few minutes. Drain. Peel the oranges, removing all the white pith. Slice them into thin rounds and discard any seeds.

2 Cut the fennel bulb in half lengthways and slice across the bulb as thinly as possible, preferably in a food processor fitted with a slicing disc or using a mandoline.

3 ▲ Combine the oranges and fennel in a serving bowl and toss with the rocket leaves.

4 ▲ Mix together the oil, vinegar, garlic and seasoning and pour over the salad, toss together well and leave to stand for a few minutes. Sprinkle with the black olives and julienne strips of orange.

Aubergine, Lemon and Caper Salad

Caponata

This cooked vegetable relish is a classic Sicilian dish, which is delicious served as an accompaniment to cold meats, with pasta or simply on its own with some good crusty bread. Make sure the aubergine is well cooked until it is meltingly soft.

Ingredients
1 large aubergine, about 675 g/1½ lb
60 ml/4 tbsp olive oil
grated rind and juice of 1 lemon
30 ml/2 tbsp capers, rinsed
12 stoned green olives
30 ml/2 tbsp chopped fresh
    flat leaf parsley
salt and freshly ground black pepper
serves 4

Cook's Tips
This will taste even better when made the day before. Serve at room temperature. It will store, covered in the fridge, for up to 4 days. To enrich this dish to serve it on its own as a main course, add toasted pine nuts and shavings of Parmesan cheese. Serve with crusty bread.

1 ▲ Cut the aubergine into 2.5 cm/ 1 in cubes. Heat the olive oil in a large frying pan and cook the aubergine cubes over a medium heat for about 10 minutes, tossing regularly, until golden and softened. You may need to do this in two batches. Drain on kitchen paper and sprinkle with a little salt.

2 ▲ Place the aubergine cubes in a large serving bowl, toss with the lemon rind and juice, capers, olives and chopped parsley and season well with salt and pepper. Serve at room temperature.

Spinach and Roast Garlic Salad   *Insalata di spinaci con aglio arrosto*

Don't worry about the amount of garlic in this salad. During roasting, the garlic becomes sweet and subtle and loses its pungent taste.

Ingredients
12 garlic cloves, unpeeled
60 ml/4 tbsp extra virgin olive oil
450 g/1 lb baby spinach leaves
50 g/2 oz/½ cup pine nuts, lightly toasted
juice of ½ lemon
salt and freshly ground black pepper
serves 4

Cook's Tip
If spinach is to be served raw in a salad, the leaves need to be young and tender. Wash them well, drain and pat dry with kitchen paper.

1 ▲ Preheat the oven to 190°C/375°F/ Gas 5. Place the garlic in a small roasting dish, toss in 30 ml/2 tbsp of the olive oil and bake for about 15 minutes until the garlic cloves are slightly charred around the edges.

2 ▲ While still warm, tip the garlic into a salad bowl. Add the spinach, pine nuts, lemon juice, remaining olive oil and a little salt. Toss well and add black pepper to taste. Serve immediately, inviting guests to squeeze the softened garlic purée out of the skin to eat.

Sweet and Sour Artichoke Salad

Carciofi in salsa agrodolce

Agrodolce is a sweet and sour sauce which works perfectly in this salad.

Ingredients

6 small globe artichokes
juice of 1 lemon
30 ml/2 tbsp olive oil
2 medium onions, roughly chopped
175 g/6 oz/1 cup fresh or frozen broad
    beans (shelled weight)
175 g/6 oz/1¹/₂ cups fresh or frozen peas
    (shelled weight)
salt and freshly ground black pepper
fresh mint leaves, to garnish

For the salsa agrodolce

120 ml/4 fl oz/¹/₂ cup white wine vinegar
15 ml/1 tbsp caster sugar
handful fresh mint leaves, roughly torn
serves 4

1 ▲ Peel the outer leaves from the artichokes and cut into quarters. Place the artichokes in a bowl of water with the lemon juice.

2 ▲ Heat the oil in a large saucepan and add the onions. Cook until the onions are golden. Add the beans and stir, then drain the artichokes and add to the pan. Pour in about 300 ml/¹/₂ pint/1¹/₄ cups of water and cook, covered, for 10–15 minutes.

3 ▲ Add the peas, season with salt and pepper and cook for a further 5 minutes, stirring from time to time, until the vegetables are tender. Strain through a sieve and placc all the vegetables in a bowl, leave to cool, then cover and chill.

4 ▲ To make the salsa agrodolce, mix all the ingredients in a small pan. Heat gently for 2–3 minutes until the sugar has dissolved. Simmer gently for about 5 minutes, stirring occasionally. Leave to cool. To serve, drizzle the salsa over the vegetables and garnish with mint leaves.

Roasted Pepper and Tomato Salad
Peperoni arrostiti con pomodori

This is one of those lovely recipes which brings together perfectly the colours, flavours and textures of southern Italian food. Eat this dish at room temperature with a green salad.

Ingredients
3 red peppers
6 large plum tomatoes
2.5 ml/½ tsp dried red chilli flakes
1 red onion, finely sliced
3 garlic cloves, finely chopped
grated rind and juice of 1 lemon
45 ml/3 tbsp chopped fresh flat
   .leaf parsley
30 ml/2 tbsp extra virgin olive oil
salt and freshly ground black pepper
black and green olives and extra
   chopped flat leaf parsley,
   to garnish
serves 4

Cook's Tip
Peppers roasted this way will keep for several weeks. After peeling off the skins, place the pepper pieces in a jar with a tight-fitting lid. Pour enough olive oil over them to cover completely. Store in the fridge.

1 ▲ Preheat the oven to 220°C/425°F/Gas 7. Place the peppers on a baking sheet and roast, turning occasionally, for 10 minutes or until the skins are almost blackened. Add the tomatoes to the baking sheet and bake for 5 minutes more.

2 Place the peppers in a plastic bag, close the top loosely, trapping in the steam, and then set them aside, with the tomatoes, until they are cool enough to handle.

3 ▲ Carefully pull off the skin from the peppers. Remove the seeds, then chop the peppers and tomatoes roughly and place in a mixing bowl.

4 Add the chilli flakes, onion, garlic, lemon rind and juice. Sprinkle over the parsley. Mix well, then transfer to a serving dish. Sprinkle with a little salt, drizzle over the olive oil and scatter olives and extra parsley over the top. Serve at room temperature.

Marinated Courgettes
Zucchini a scapece

This is a simple vegetable dish which is prepared all over Italy using the best of the season's courgettes. It can be eaten hot or cold.

Ingredients
4 courgettes
60 ml/4 tbsp extra virgin olive oil
30 ml/2 tbsp chopped fresh mint, plus
   whole leaves, to garnish
30 ml/2 tbsp white wine vinegar
salt and freshly ground black pepper
wholemeal Italian bread and green olives,
   to serve
serves 4

Cook's Tip
Carrots, French beans, runner beans or onions can also be prepared in this way.

1 ▲ Cut the courgettes into thin slices. Heat 30 ml/2 tbsp of the oil in a wide heavy-based saucepan. Fry the courgettes in batches, for 4–6 minutes, until tender and brown around the edges. Transfer the courgettes to a bowl. Season well.

2 ▲ Heat the remaining oil in the pan, then add the mint and vinegar and let it bubble for a few seconds. Pour over the courgettes. Marinate for 1 hour, then serve garnished with mint and accompanied by bread and olives.

Stuffed Aubergines

Melanzane alla liguria

This typical Ligurian dish is spiked with paprika and allspice, a legacy from the days when spices from the East came into northern Italy via the port of Genoa.

Ingredients

2 aubergines, about 225 g/8 oz each,
    stalks removed
275 g/10 oz potatoes, peeled and diced
30 ml/2 tbsp olive oil
1 small onion, finely chopped
1 garlic clove, finely chopped
good pinch of ground allspice and paprika
1 egg, beaten
40 g/1½ oz/½ cup grated
    Parmesan cheese
15ml/1 tbsp fresh white breadcrumbs
salt and freshly ground black pepper
fresh mint sprigs, to garnish
salad leaves, to serve
serves 4

1 Bring a large saucepan of lightly salted water to the boil. Add the whole aubergines and cook for 5 minutes, turning frequently. Remove with a slotted spoon and set aside. Add the potatoes to the pan and cook for 20 minutes until soft.

2 ▲ Meanwhile, cut the aubergines in half lengthways and gently scoop out the flesh with a small sharp knife and a spoon, leaving 5 mm/¼ in of the shell intact. Select a baking dish that will hold the aubergine shells snugly in a single layer. Brush it lightly with oil. Put the shells in the baking dish and chop the aubergine flesh roughly.

Cook's Tip

The aubergines can be filled in advance, then covered with foil and kept in the fridge. Add the crumb topping just before baking.

3 ▲ Heat the oil in a frying pan, add the onion and cook gently, stirring frequently, until softened. Add the chopped aubergine flesh and the garlic. Cook, stirring frequently, for 6–8 minutes. Tip into a bowl. Preheat the oven to 190°C/375°F/Gas 5.

4 Drain and mash the potatoes. Add to the aubergine mixture with the spices and beaten egg. Set aside 15 ml/1 tbsp of the Parmesan and add the rest to the aubergine mixture, stir in salt and pepper to taste.

5 ▲ Spoon the mixture into the aubergine shells. Mix the breadcrumbs with the reserved Parmesan cheese and sprinkle the mixture over the aubergines. Bake for 40–45 minutes until the topping is crisp. Garnish with mint and serve with salad leaves.

Pepper Gratin

Peperoni gratinati

Serve this simple but delicious dish as a starter with a small mixed leaf or rocket salad and some good crusty bread to mop up the juices from the peppers.

Ingredients

2 red peppers
30 ml/2 tbsp extra virgin olive oil
60 ml/4 tbsp fresh white breadcrumbs
1 garlic clove, finely chopped
5 ml/1 tsp drained bottled capers
8 stoned black olives, roughly chopped
15 ml/1 tbsp chopped fresh oregano
15 ml/1 tbsp chopped fresh flat
    leaf parsley
salt and freshly ground black pepper
fresh herbs, to garnish

serves 4

1 ▲ Preheat the oven to 200°C/400°F/ Gas 6. Place the peppers under a hot grill. Turn occasionally until they are blackened and blistered all over. Remove from the heat and place in a plastic bag. Seal and leave to cool.

2 ▲ When cool, peel the peppers. (Don't skin them under the tap as the water would wash away some of the delicious smoky flavour.) Halve and remove the seeds, then cut the flesh into large strips.

3 ▲ Use a little of the olive oil to grease a small baking dish. Arrange the pepper strips in the dish.

4 ▲ Scatter the remaining ingredients on top, drizzle with the remaining olive oil and add salt and pepper to taste. Bake for about 20 minutes until the breadcrumbs have browned. Garnish with fresh herbs and serve immediately.

Desserts

....

An everyday Italian meal usually concludes with fresh fruit. Desserts are reserved for special occasions, and are often bought in from the local pasticceria or gelateria. This is not to say that sweet things are unpopular, but they are usually eaten with a cup of espresso coffee at other times of the day.

Tiramisu

Tiramisu

The name of this popular dessert translates as "pick me up", which is said to derive from the fact that it is so good that it literally makes you swoon when you eat it. There are many, many versions, and the recipe can be adapted to suit your own taste – you can vary the amount of mascarpone, eggs, sponge fingers, coffee and liqueur.

Ingredients

3 eggs, separated
450 g/1 lb/2 cups mascarpone cheese, at
 room temperature
1 sachet of vanilla sugar
175 ml/6 fl oz/¾ cup cold, very strong,
 black coffee
120 ml/4 fl oz/½ cup Kahlúa or other
 coffee-flavoured liqueur
18 savoiardi (Italian sponge fingers)
sifted cocoa powder and grated
 bittersweet chocolate, to finish
serves 6–8

3 ▲ Mix the coffee and liqueur together in a shallow dish. Dip a sponge finger in the mixture, turn it quickly so that it becomes saturated but does not disintegrate, and place it on top of the mascarpone in the bowl. Add five more dipped sponge fingers, placing them side by side.

4 ▲ Spoon in about one-third of the remaining mixture and spread it out. Make more layers in the same way, ending with mascarpone. Level the surface, then sift cocoa powder all over. Cover and chill overnight. Before serving, sprinkle with cocoa and grated chocolate.

1 ▲ Put the egg whites in a grease-free bowl and whisk with an electric mixer until stiff and in peaks.

2 ▲ Mix the mascarpone, vanilla sugar and egg yolks in a separate large bowl and whisk with the electric mixer until evenly combined. Fold in the egg whites, then put a few spoonfuls of the mixture in the bottom of a large serving bowl and spread it out evenly.

Stuffed Peaches with Amaretto

Pesche ripiene

Together amaretti biscuits and amaretto liqueur have an intense almond flavour, and they make a natural partner for peaches.

Ingredients

4 ripe but firm peaches
50 g/2 oz amaretti biscuits
25 g/1 oz/2 tbsp butter, softened
25 g/1 oz/2 tbsp caster sugar
1 egg yolk
60 ml/4 tbsp amaretto liqueur
250 ml/8 fl oz/1 cup dry white wine
8 tiny sprigs of basil, to decorate
ice cream or pouring cream, to serve

serves 4

3 ▲ Cream the butter and sugar together in a separate bowl until smooth. Stir in the reserved chopped peach flesh, the egg yolk and half the amaretto liqueur with the amaretti crumbs. Lightly butter a baking dish that is just large enough to hold the peach halves in a single layer.

4 ▲ Spoon the stuffing into the peaches, then stand them in the dish. Mix the remaining liqueur with the wine, pour over the peaches and bake for 25 minutes or until the peaches feel tender when tested with a skewer. Decorate with basil and serve at once, with ice cream or cream.

1 ▲ Preheat the oven to 180°C/350°F/ Gas 4. Following the natural indentation line on each peach, cut in half down to the central stone, then twist the halves in opposite directions to separate them. Remove the peach stones, then cut away a little of the central flesh to make a larger hole for the stuffing. Chop this flesh finely and set aside.

2 ▲ Put the amaretti biscuits in a bowl and crush them finely with the end of a rolling pin.

Zabaglione

Zabaglione

This sumptuous warm dessert is very quick and easy to make, but it does need to be served straight away. For a dinner party, assemble all the ingredients and equipment ahead of time so that all you have to do is quickly mix everything together once the main course is over.

Ingredients
4 egg yolks
65 g/2 ½ oz/⅓ cup caster sugar
120 ml/4 fl oz/½ cup dry Marsala
savoiardi (Italian sponge fingers), to serve
serves 6

Cook's Tip
When whisking the egg yolks, make sure that the bottom of the bowl does not touch the water or the egg yolks will scramble.

1 ▲ Half fill a pan with water and bring it to simmering point. Put the egg yolks and sugar in a large heatproof bowl and beat with a hand-held electric mixer until pale and creamy.

2 ▲ Put the bowl over the pan and gradually pour in the Marsala, whisking the mixture until it is very thick and has increased in volume.

3 Remove the bowl from the water and pour the zabaglione into six heatproof, long-stemmed glasses. Serve at once, with sponge fingers.

Lovers' Knots

Cenci

The literal translation of cenci is "rags and tatters", but they are often referred to by the more endearing term of lovers' knots. They are eaten at carnival time in February.

Ingredients
150 g/5 oz/1 ¼ cups plain flour
2.5 ml/½ tsp baking powder
pinch of salt
30 ml/2 tbsp caster sugar, plus extra for dusting
1 egg, beaten
about 25 ml/1 ½ tbsp rum
vegetable oil, for deep frying
makes 24

Cook's Tip
If you do not have a deep-fat fryer with a built-in thermostat, or a deep-fat thermometer, test the temperature of the oil before deep frying by dropping in a scrap of the dough trimmings – it should turn crisp and golden in about 30 seconds.

1 ▲ Sift the flour, baking powder and salt into a bowl, then stir in the sugar. Add the egg. Stir with a fork until it is evenly mixed with the flour, then add the rum gradually and continue mixing until the dough draws together. Knead the dough on a lightly floured surface until it is smooth. Divide the dough into quarters.

2 ▲ Roll each piece out to a 15 x 7.5 cm/ 6 x 3 in rectangle and trim to make them straight. Cut each rectangle lengthways into six strips, 1 cm/ ½ in wide, and tie into a simple knot.

3 Heat the oil in a deep-fat fryer to a temperature of 190°C/375°F. Deep fry the knots in batches for 1–2 minutes until crisp and golden. Transfer to kitchen paper with a slotted spoon. Serve warm, dusted with sugar.

Fresh Orange Granita

Granita all'arancia

A granita is like a water ice, but coarser and quite grainy in texture, hence its name. It makes a refreshing dessert after a rich main course, or a cooling treat on a hot summer's day.

Ingredients
4 large oranges
1 large lemon
150 g/5 oz/ ³⁄₄ cup granulated sugar
475 ml/16 fl oz/2 cups water
blanched pared strips of orange and
    lemon rind, to decorate
dessert biscuits, to serve
serves 6

1 ▲ Thinly pare the rind from the oranges and lemon, taking care to avoid the bitter white pith, and set aside for the decoration. Cut the fruit in half and squeeze the juice into a jug. Set aside.

2 Heat the sugar and water in a heavy-based saucepan, stirring over a gentle heat until the sugar dissolves. Bring to the boil, then boil without stirring for about 10 minutes, until a syrup forms.

3 ▲ Remove the syrup from the heat, add the pieces of orange and lemon rind and shake the pan. Cover and allow to cool.

4 ▲ Strain the sugar syrup into a shallow freezer container and add the fruit juice. Stir well to mix, then freeze, uncovered, for about 4 hours until slushy.

Cook's Tip
To make the decoration, slice extra orange and lemon rind into thin strips. Blanch for 2 minutes, refresh under cold water and dry before use.

5 ▲ Remove the half-frozen mixture from the freezer and mix with a fork, then return to the freezer and freeze again for 4 hours more or until frozen hard. To serve, turn into a bowl and allow to soften for about 10 minutes, then break up with a fork again and pile into long-stemmed glasses. Decorate with the strips of orange and lemon rind and serve with dessert biscuits.

Apple Cake

Torta di mele

This moist cake is best served warm. It comes from Genoa, home of the whisked sponge.

When whipping the cream, add grated lemon rind – it tastes delicious.

Ingredients

675 g/1½ lb Golden Delicious apples
finely grated rind and juice of
    1 large lemon
4 eggs
150 g/5 oz/¾ cup caster sugar
150 g/5 oz/1¼ cups plain flour
5 ml/1 tsp baking powder
pinch of salt
115 g/4 oz/½ cup butter, melted and
    cooled, plus extra for greasing
1 sachet of vanilla sugar, for sprinkling
very finely pared strips of citrus rind,
    to decorate
whipped cream, to serve

serves 6

1 ▲ Preheat the oven to 180°C/350°F/
Gas 4. Brush a 23 cm/9 in springform
tin with melted butter and line the
base with non-stick baking paper.
Quarter, core and peel the apples,
then slice thinly. Put the slices in a
bowl and pour over the lemon juice.

2 ▲ Put the eggs, sugar and lemon
rind in a bowl and whisk with a
hand-held electric mixture until the
mixture is thick and mousse-like. The
whisks should leave a trail.

3 ▲ Sift half the flour, all the baking
powder and the salt over the egg
mousse, then fold in gently with a
large metal spoon. Slowly drizzle in
the melted butter from the side of the
bowl and fold it in gently with the
spoon. Sift over the remaining flour,
fold it in gently, then add the apples
and fold these in equally gently.

4 ▲ Spoon into the prepared tin and
level the surface. Bake for 40 minutes
or until a skewer comes out clean.
Leave to settle in the tin for about
10 minutes, then invert on a wire
rack. Turn the cake the right way up
and sprinkle the vanilla sugar over
the top. Decorate with the citrus rind.
Serve warm, with whipped cream.

Sicilian Ricotta Cake

Cassata siciliana

The word cassata is often used to describe a layered ice cream cake. In Sicily, however, it is a traditional cake made of layers of sponge, ricotta cheese and candied peel, imbibed with alcohol, and it looks and tastes truly delicious.

Ingredients

675 g/1¹/₂ lb/3 cups ricotta cheese
finely grated rind of 1 orange
2 sachets of vanilla sugar
75 ml/5 tbsp orange-flavoured liqueur
115 g/4 oz candied peel
8 trifle sponge cakes
60 ml/4 tbsp freshly squeezed orange
    juice
extra candied peel, to decorate

serves 8–10

1 ▲ Push the ricotta cheese through a sieve into a bowl, add the orange rind, vanilla sugar and 15 ml/1 tbsp of the liqueur and beat well to mix. Transfer about one-third of the mixture to another bowl, cover and chill until serving time.

2 ▲ Finely chop the candied peel and beat into the remaining ricotta cheese mixture until evenly mixed. Set aside while you prepare the tin.

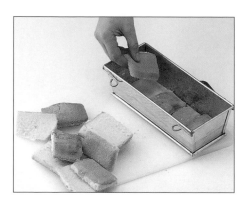

3 ▲ Line the base of a 1.2 litre/2 pint/ 5 cup loaf tin with non-stick baking paper. Cut the trifle sponges in half through their thickness. Arrange four pieces of sponge side by side in the bottom of the loaf tin and sprinkle with 15 ml/1 tbsp each of liqueur and orange juice.

4 ▲ Put one-third of the ricotta and fruit mixture in the tin and spread it out evenly. Cover with four more pieces of sponge and sprinkle with another 15 ml/1 tbsp each liqueur and orange juice as before.

5 Repeat the alternate layers of ricotta mixture and sponge until all the ingredients are used, soaking the sponge pieces with liqueur and orange juice each time, and ending with soaked sponge. Cover with a piece of non-stick baking paper.

6 ▲ Cut a piece of card to fit inside the tin, place on top of the non-stick baking paper and weight down evenly. Chill for 24 hours.

7 To serve, remove the weights, card and paper and run a palette knife between the sides of the cassata and the tin. Invert a serving plate on top of the cassata, then invert the two so that the cassata is upside down on the plate. Peel off the lining paper.

8 Spread the chilled ricotta mixture over the cassata to cover it completely, then decorate the top with candied peel, cut into fancy shapes. Serve chilled.

Cook's Tip
Don't worry if the cassata has pressed into an uneven shape when turned out. This will be disguised when the cake is covered in the chilled ricotta mixture.

Coffee and Chocolate Bombe

Zuccotto

In Italy the commercial ice cream is so good that no one would dream of making their own ice cream for this dessert. Assembling the zuccotto is impressive enough in itself.

Ingredients
15–18 savoiardi (Italian sponge fingers)
about 175 ml/6 fl oz/¾ cup
    sweet Marsala
75 g/3 oz amaretti biscuits
about 475 ml/16 fl oz/2 cups coffee ice
    cream, softened
about 475 ml/16 fl oz/2 cups vanilla ice
    cream, softened
50 g/2 oz bittersweet or plain
    chocolate, grated
chocolate curls and sifted cocoa powder
    or icing sugar, to decorate

serves 6–8

1 ▲ Line a 1 litre/1¾ pint/4 cup pudding basin with a large piece of damp muslin, letting it hang over the top edge. Trim the sponge fingers to fit the basin, if necessary. Pour the Marsala into a shallow dish. Dip a sponge finger in the Marsala, turning it quickly so that it becomes saturated but does not disintegrate. Stand it against the side of the basin, sugared-side out. Repeat with the remaining sponge fingers to line the basin fully.

2 Fill in the base and any gaps around the side with any trimmings and savoiardi cut to fit. Chill for about 30 minutes.

Cook's Tip
In Italy there are special dome-shaped moulds for making this dessert, the name for which comes from the Italian word zucca, meaning pumpkin. The shape will not be quite the same when it is made in a pudding basin.

3 ▲ Put the amaretti biscuits in a large bowl and crush them with a rolling pin. Add the coffee ice cream and any remaining Marsala and beat until mixed. Spoon into the sponge-finger-lined basin.

4 Press the ice cream against the sponge to form an even layer with a hollow. Freeze for 2 hours.

5 Put the vanilla ice cream and grated chocolate in a bowl and beat together until evenly mixed. Spoon into the hollow in the centre of the mould. Smooth the top, then cover with the overhanging muslin. Place in the freezer overnight.

6 To serve, run a palette knife between the muslin and the basin, then unfold the top of the muslin. Invert a chilled serving plate on top of the zuccotto, then invert the two so that the zuccotto is upside down on the plate. Carefully peel off the muslin. Decorate the zuccotto with the chocolate curls, then sift cocoa powder or icing sugar over. Serve at once.

Ricotta Pudding

Budino di ricotta

This creamy, rich dessert is very easy to make and, as it can be made up to 24 hours ahead, it is ideal for a dinner party. The combination of ricotta cheese and candied fruits is very popular in Sicily, where this recipe originated.

Ingredients

225 g/8 oz/1 cup ricotta cheese
50 g/2 oz/⅓ cup candied fruits
60 ml/4 tbsp sweet Marsala
250 ml/8 fl oz/1 cup double cream
50 g/2 oz/¼ cup caster sugar, plus extra
    to serve
finely grated rind of 1 orange
350 g/12 oz/2 cups fresh raspberries
strips of thinly pared orange rind,
    to decorate

serves 4–6

Cook's Tip

Buy candied fruits in large pieces from a good delicatessen – tubs of chopped candied peel are too tough to eat raw, and should only be used in baking.

1 ▲ Press the ricotta through a sieve into a bowl. Finely chop the candied fruits and stir into the sieved ricotta with half of the Marsala. Put the cream, sugar and orange rind in another bowl and whip until the cream is standing in soft peaks.

2 ▲ Fold the whipped cream into the ricotta mixture. Spoon into individual glass serving bowls and top with the raspberries. Chill until serving time. Sprinkle with the remaining Marsala and dust the top of each bowl liberally with caster sugar just before serving. Decorate with the orange rind.

Chocolate Salami

Salame al cioccolato

This after-dinner sweetmeat resembles a salami in shape, hence its curious name. It is very rich and will serve a lot of people. Slice it very thinly and serve with espresso coffee and amaretto liqueur.

Ingredients

24 Petit Beurre biscuits, broken
350 g/12 oz bittersweet or plain
 chocolate, broken into squares
225 g/8 oz/1 cup unsalted
 butter, softened
60 ml/4 tbsp amaretto liqueur
2 egg yolks
50 g/2 oz/1/2 cup flaked almonds,
 lightly toasted and thinly
 shredded lengthways
25 g/1 oz/1/4 cup ground almonds
serves 8–12

1 ▲ Place the biscuits in a food processor fitted with a metal blade and process until coarsely crushed.

2 Place the chocolate in a large heatproof bowl. Place the bowl over a saucepan of barely simmering water, add a small chunk of the butter and all the liqueur and heat until the chocolate melts, stirring occasionally.

Cook's Tip

Take care when melting chocolate that it does not overheat or it will form a hard lump. The base of the bowl containing the chocolate must not touch the water, and the chocolate must be melted very slowly and gently. If you think the water is getting too hot, remove the pan from the heat.

3 ▲ Remove the bowl from the heat, allow the chocolate to cool for a minute or two, then stir in the egg yolks followed by the remaining butter, a little at a time. Tip in most of the crushed biscuits, leaving behind a good handful, and stir well to mix. Stir in the shredded almonds. Leave the mixture in a cold place for about 1 hour until it begins to stiffen.

4 ▲ Process the remaining crushed biscuits in the food processor until they are very finely ground. Tip into a bowl and mix with the ground almonds. Cover and set aside until serving time.

5 ▲ Turn the chocolate and biscuit mixture on to a sheet of lightly oiled greaseproof paper, then shape into a 35 cm/14 in sausage with a palette knife, tapering the ends slightly so that the roll looks like a salami. Wrap in the paper and freeze for at least 4 hours until solid.

6 To serve, unwrap the "salami". Spread the ground biscuits and almonds out on a clean sheet of greaseproof paper and roll the salami in them until evenly coated. Transfer to a board and leave to stand for about 1 hour before serving in slices.

Baking

∙∙∙∙∙∙∙∙∙∙∙∙∙∙∙∙∙∙∙∙∙∙∙∙∙∙∙∙∙∙∙

The Italian tradition of baking dates back to Roman times, and Italian bakers and pastry chefs today take an enormous pride in their art. Baking at home is generally simple – rustic breads, pies and tarts, the occasional cheesecake or batch of biscuits. Elaborate confections are usually left to the professionals.

Sultana and Walnut Bread

Pane di uva con noci

This bread is delicious with soup for a first course, or with salami, cheese and salad for lunch. It also tastes good with jam, and toasts extremely well when it is a day or two old.

Ingredients

300 g/11 oz/2¾ cups strong plain flour
2.5 ml/½ tsp salt
15 ml/1 tbsp butter
7.5 ml/1½ tsp easy-blend dried yeast
115 g/4 oz/scant 1 cup sultanas
75 g/3 oz/½ cup walnuts, roughly chopped
melted butter, for brushing

makes 1 loaf

1 ▲ Sift the flour and salt into a bowl, cut in the butter with a knife, then stir in the yeast.

2 ▲ Gradually add 175 ml/6 fl oz/ ¾ cup tepid water to the flour mixture, stirring with a spoon at first, then gathering the dough together with your hands.

3 Turn the dough out on to a floured surface and knead for about 10 minutes until smooth and elastic.

Cook's Tip

Easy-blend dried yeast is sold in sachets at most supermarkets. It is a real boon for the busy cook because it cuts out the need to let the dough rise before shaping.

4 ▲ Knead the sultanas and walnuts into the dough until they are evenly distributed. Shape into a rough oval, place on a lightly oiled baking sheet and cover with oiled clear film. Leave to rise in a warm place for 1–2 hours until doubled in bulk. Preheat the oven to 220°C/425°F/Gas 7.

5 Uncover the loaf and bake for 10 minutes, then reduce the oven temperature to 190°C/375°F/Gas 5 and bake for a further 20–25 minutes.

6 ▲ Transfer to a wire rack, brush with melted butter and cover with a tea towel. Cool before slicing.

Chocolate Bread

Pane al cioccolato

In Italy it is the custom to serve this dessert bread as a snack with mascarpone or Gorgonzola cheese and a glass of red wine. Although this combination may sound unusual, it is really delicious. Chocolate bread also tastes good spread with butter at tea time, and is excellent toasted next day for breakfast and served with butter and jam.

Ingredients

450 g/1 lb/4 cups strong plain flour
2.5 ml/¹/₂ tsp salt
30 ml/2 tbsp butter
30 ml/2 tbsp caster sugar
10 ml/2 tsp easy-blend dried yeast
30 ml/2 tbsp cocoa powder
75 g/3 oz/¹/₂ cup plain chocolate chips
melted butter, for brushing
makes 2 loaves

1 ▲ Sift the flour and salt into a bowl, cut in the butter with a knife, then stir in the sugar, yeast and cocoa powder.

2 Gradually add 300 ml/¹/₂ pint/ 1¹/₄ cups of tepid water to the flour mixture, stirring with a spoon at first, then gathering the dough together with your hands.

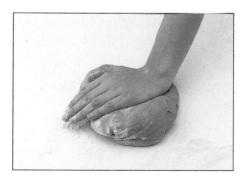

3 ▲ Turn the dough out on to a floured surface and knead for about 10 minutes until smooth and elastic.

4 ▲ Cut the dough in half and knead half the chocolate chips into each piece of dough until they are evenly distributed. Shape into rounds, place on lightly oiled baking sheets and cover with oiled clear film. Leave to rise in a warm place for 1–2 hours until the dough has doubled in bulk.

5 Preheat the oven to 220°C/425°F/ Gas 7. Uncover the loaves and bake for 10 minutes, then reduce the oven temperature to 190°C/375°F/Gas 5 and bake for a further 15–20 minutes.

6 ▲ Place the loaves on a wire rack and brush liberally with butter. Cover with a tea towel and leave to cool.

Ricotta Cheesecake

Crostata di ricotta

Low-fat ricotta cheese is excellent for cheesecake fillings because it has a good, firm texture. Here it is enriched with eggs and cream and enlivened with tangy orange and lemon rind to make a Sicilian-style dessert.

Ingredients
450 g/1 lb/2 cups low-fat ricotta cheese
120 ml/4 fl oz/$\frac{1}{2}$ cup double cream
2 eggs
1 egg yolk
75 g/3 oz/$\frac{1}{3}$ cup caster sugar
finely grated rind of 1 orange
finely grated rind of 1 lemon

For the pastry
175 g/6 oz/1$\frac{1}{2}$ cups plain flour
45 ml/3 tbsp caster sugar
pinch of salt
115 g/4 oz/8 tbsp chilled butter, diced
1 egg yolk
serves 8

1 ▲ Make the pastry. Sift the flour, sugar and salt on to a cold work surface. Make a well in the centre and put in the diced butter and egg yolk. Gradually work the flour into the diced butter and egg yolk, using your fingertips.

Variations
Add 50–115 g/2–4 oz/$\frac{1}{3}$–$\frac{2}{3}$ cup finely chopped candied peel to the filling in step 3, or 50 g/2 oz/$\frac{1}{3}$ cup plain chocolate chips. For a really rich dessert, you can add both candied peel and some grated plain chocolate.

2 ▲ Gather the dough together, reserve about a quarter for the lattice, then press the rest into a 23 cm/9 in fluted tart tin with a removable base. Chill the pastry case for 30 minutes.

3 ▲ Meanwhile, preheat the oven to 190°C/375°F/Gas 5 and make the filling. Put all the ricotta, cream, eggs, egg yolk, sugar and orange and lemon rinds in a large bowl and beat together until evenly mixed.

4 ▲ Prick the bottom of the pastry case, then line with foil and fill with baking beans. Bake blind for 15 minutes, then transfer to a wire rack, remove the foil and beans and allow the tart shell to cool in the tin.

5 ▲ Spoon the cheese and cream filling into the pastry case and level the surface. Roll out the reserved dough and cut into strips. Arrange the strips on the top of the filling in a lattice pattern, sticking them in place with water.

6 Bake for 30–35 minutes until golden and set. Transfer to a wire rack and leave to cool, then carefully remove the side of the tin, leaving the cheesecake on the tin base.

Pine Nut Tart

Pinolata

Strange though it may seem, this traditional tart is an Italian version of the homely

Bakewell tart from Derbyshire in England.

Ingredients
115 g/4 oz/8 tbsp butter, softened
115 g/4 oz/generous ½ cup caster sugar
1 egg
2 egg yolks
150 g/5 oz/1¼ cups ground almonds
115 g/4 oz/1 cup pine nuts
60 ml/4 tbsp seedless raspberry jam
icing sugar, for dusting
whipped cream, to serve (optional)

For the pastry
175 g/6 oz/1½ cups plain flour
65 g/2½ oz/⅓ cup caster sugar
1.5 ml/¼ tsp baking powder
pinch of salt
115 g/4 oz/8 tbsp chilled butter, diced
1 egg yolk
serves 8

1 ▲ Make the pastry. Sift the flour, sugar, baking powder and salt on to a cold work surface. Make a well in the centre and put in the diced butter and egg yolk. Gradually work the flour into the butter and egg yolk, using your fingertips.

2 ▲ Gather the dough together, then press it into a 23 cm/9 in fluted tart tin with a removable base. Chill for 30 minutes.

3 ▲ Meanwhile, make the filling. Cream the butter and sugar together with an electric mixer until light and fluffy, then beat in the egg and egg yolks a little at a time, alternating them with the ground almonds. Beat in the pine nuts.

Cook's Tip
This pastry is too sticky to roll out, so simply mould it into the bottom and sides of the tin with your fingertips.

4 ▲ Preheat the oven to 160°C/325°F/Gas 3. Spread the jam over the pastry base, then spoon in the filling. Bake for 30–35 minutes or until a skewer inserted in the centre of the tart comes out clean.

5 Transfer to a wire rack and leave to cool, then carefully remove the side of the tin, leaving the tart on the tin base. Dust with icing sugar and serve with whipped cream, if you like.

Baked Sweet Ravioli

Ravioli dolci al forno

These delicious sweet ravioli are made with a rich pastry flavoured with lemon and filled with the traditional ingredients used in Sicilian cassata.

Ingredients

225 g/8 oz/2 cups plain flour
65 g/2¹/₂ oz/¹/₃ cup caster sugar
90 g/3¹/₂ oz/¹/₂ cup butter
1 egg
5 ml/1 tsp finely grated lemon rind
icing sugar and grated chocolate,
    for sprinkling

For the filling

175 g/6 oz/³/₄ cup ricotta cheese
50 g/2 oz/¹/₄ cup caster sugar
4 ml/³/₄ tsp vanilla essence
1 medium egg yolk
15 ml/1 tbsp mixed candied fruits or
    mixed peel
25 g/1 oz dark chocolate, finely chopped
    or grated
1 small egg, beaten

serves 4

1 Put the flour and sugar into a food processor and, working on full speed, add the butter in pieces until fully worked into the mixture. With the food processor still running, add the egg and lemon rind. The mixture should form a dough which just holds together. Scrape the dough on to a sheet of clear film, cover with another sheet, flatten and chill until needed.

2 ▲ To make the filling, push the ricotta through a sieve into a bowl. Stir in the sugar, vanilla essence, egg yolk, peel and chocolate until combined.

3 ▲ Remove the pastry from the fridge and allow to come to room temperature. Divide the pastry in half and roll each half between sheets of clear film to make strips, measuring 15 x 56 cm/6 x 22 in. Preheat the oven to 180°C/350°F/Gas 4.

4 Arrange heaped tablespoons of the filling in two rows along one of the pastry strips, ensuring there is at least 2.5 cm/1 in clear space around each spoonful. Brush the pastry between the dollops of filling with beaten egg. Place the second strip of pastry on top and press down between each mound of filling to seal.

5 Using a 6 cm/2¹/₂ in plain pastry cutter, cut around each mound of filling to make circular ravioli. Lift each one and, with your fingertips, seal the edges. Place the ravioli on a greased baking sheet and bake for 15 minutes until golden brown. Serve warm sprinkled with icing sugar and grated chocolate.

Spicy Fruit Cake from Siena

Panforte di Siena

This is a delicious flat cake with a wonderful spicy flavour. Panforte is very rich, so should be cut into small wedges – offer a glass of sparkling wine to go with it.

Ingredients

butter for greasing
175 g/6 oz/1 cup hazelnuts,
   roughly chopped
75 g/3 oz/$\frac{1}{2}$ cup whole almonds,
   roughly chopped
225 g/8 oz/1$\frac{1}{3}$ cups mixed candied
   fruits, diced
1.5 ml/$\frac{1}{4}$ tsp ground coriander
4 ml/$\frac{3}{4}$ tsp ground cinnamon
1.5 ml/$\frac{1}{4}$ tsp ground cloves
1.5 ml/$\frac{1}{4}$ tsp grated nutmeg
50 g/2 oz/$\frac{1}{2}$ cup plain flour
115 g/4 oz/$\frac{1}{2}$ cup honey
115 g/4 oz/generous 1 cup
   granulated sugar
icing sugar, for dusting
serves 12–14

1 Preheat the oven to 180°C/350°F/Gas 4. Grease a 20 cm/8 in round cake tin with the butter. Line the base of the tin with non-stick baking paper.

2 ▲ Spread the nuts on a baking tray and place in the oven for about 10 minutes until lightly toasted. Remove and set aside. Lower the oven temperature to 150°C/300°F/Gas 2.

3 In a large mixing bowl combine the candied fruits, all the spices and the flour and stir together with a wooden spoon. Add the nuts and stir in thoroughly.

Cook's Tip

This will store in an airtight container for up to 2 weeks.

4 ▲ In a small heavy saucepan, stir together the honey and sugar and bring to the boil. Cook the mixture until it reaches 138°C/280°F on a sugar thermometer or when a small bit forms a hard ball when pressed between fingertips in iced water. Take care when doing this and use a teaspoon to remove a little mixture out of the pan for testing.

5 ▲ At this stage immediately pour the sugar syrup into the dry ingredients and stir in well until evenly coated. Pour into the prepared tin. Dip a spoon into water and use the back of the spoon to press the mixture into the tin. Bake in the preheated oven for 1 hour.

6 When ready, it will still feel quite soft but will harden as it cools. Cool completely in the tin and then turn out on to a serving plate. Dust with icing sugar before serving.

Hazelnut Bites

Nocciolini

Serve these sweet little nut cookies as petits fours with after-dinner coffee.

Ingredients

115 g/4 oz/8 tbsp butter, softened
75 g/3 oz/¾ cup icing sugar, sifted
115 g/4 oz/1 cup plain flour
75 g/3 oz/¾ cup ground hazelnuts
1 egg yolk
blanched whole hazelnuts, to decorate
icing sugar, to finish

makes about 26

1 ▲ Preheat the oven to 180°C/350°F/Gas 4. Line 3–4 baking sheets with non-stick baking paper. Cream the butter and sugar together with an electric mixer until light and fluffy.

2 ▲ Beat in the flour, ground hazelnuts and egg yolk until evenly mixed.

Cook's Tip

Don't worry that the biscuits are still soft at the end of the baking time – they will harden as they cool.

3 ▲ Take a teaspoonful of the mixture at a time and shape it into a round with your fingers. Place the rounds well apart on the baking paper and press a whole hazelnut into the centre of each one.

4 ▲ Bake the biscuits, one tray at a time, for about 10 minutes or until golden brown, then transfer to a wire rack and sift over icing sugar to cover. Leave to cool.

Ladies' Kisses

Baci di dama

These old-fashioned Piedmontese cookies make pretty petits fours.

Ingredients
150 g/5 oz/10 tbsp butter, softened
115 g/4 oz/½ cup caster sugar
1 egg yolk
2.5 ml/½ tsp almond essence
115 g/4 oz/1 cup ground almonds
175 g/6 oz/1½ cups plain flour
50 g/2 oz plain chocolate
makes 20

1 Cream the butter and sugar together with an electric mixer until light and fluffy, then beat in the egg yolk, almond essence, ground almonds and flour until evenly mixed. Chill until firm, about 2 hours.

2 Preheat the oven to 160°C/325°F/ Gas 3. Line 3–4 baking sheets with non-stick baking paper.

3 ▲ Break off small pieces of dough and roll into balls with your hands, making 40 altogether. Place the balls on the baking sheets, spacing them out as they will spread in the oven.

Cook's Tip
These biscuits look extra dainty served in frilly petit four cases.

4 Bake the biscuits for 20 minutes or until golden. Remove the baking sheets from the oven, lift off the paper with the biscuits on, then place on wire racks. Leave the biscuits to cool on the paper. Repeat with the remaining mixture.

5 ▲ When the biscuits are cold, lift them off the paper. Melt the chocolate in a bowl over a pan of hot water. Sandwich the biscuits in pairs, with the melted chocolate. Leave to cool and set before serving.

Tea Biscuits

Pastine da the

These biscuits are very quick and easy to make. If you don't want to pipe the mixture,

simply spoon it on to the baking paper and press it down with a fork.

Ingredients
150 g/5 oz/10 tbsp butter, softened
75 g/3 oz/¾ cup icing sugar, sifted
1 egg, beaten
a few drops of almond essence
225 g/8 oz/2 cups plain flour
2–3 large pieces of candied peel
makes 20

Variation
Use 10 glacé cherries instead of the candied peel. Cut them in half and press one half, cut-side down, into the centre of each biscuit.

1 Preheat the oven to 230°C/450°F/ Gas 8. Line two baking sheets with non-stick baking paper.

2 Cream the butter and sugar with an electric mixer until light and fluffy, then beat in the egg, almond essence and flour until evenly mixed.

3 ▲ Spoon the mixture into a piping bag fitted with a star nozzle and pipe 10 rosette shapes on each of the baking sheets.

4 ▲ Cut the candied peel into small diamond shapes and press one diamond into the centre of each biscuit, to decorate. Bake for 5 minutes or until golden. Transfer the biscuits on the baking paper to a wire rack and leave to cool. Lift the biscuits off the paper when cool.

Index

Index

Index

Index

Index

Acknowledgements

All the photographs are by William Adams-Lingwood and Janine Hosegood (cut-outs) except the pictures on pages 6–9, which are by John Heseltine.

The Air and Other Gases

Although we are not generally aware of it, air has mass. This can be checked directly by weighing a closed bottle of air, then pumping it out and weighing again. For a 1-liter bottle, the difference amounts to more than a gram.* The fact that air has mass becomes quite evident when it is in rapid motion, as you will find out later in this chapter.

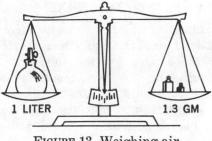

FIGURE 13. Weighing air

AIR PRESSURE

Since the air weighs something, it exerts pressure on anything immersed in it, including your own body. The reason you do not feel this pressure is that it is counterbalanced by an equal pressure from the inside—there is air in the body cavities and in the tissues and fluids. At the earth's surface, air pressure amounts to about 14.7 lb/in² (1,034 gm/cm²). This is over a ton per square foot.

EXPERIMENT 10: The existence of air pressure can be shown by removing the air from one side of an exposed surface. Get a tin can that has a tight-fitting cover or an opening provided with a screw cap. Put a little water in the can, stand it in a pan of water and boil it vigorously, with the cover removed, in order to drive out the air by means of the escaping steam. Weight the can down if it tends to upset. While still boiling, close the cap tightly, quickly transfer the can to a sink and run cold water over it to condense the steam inside. Outside air pressure will crush the vessel in a spectacular way.

The condensing (turning to liquid) of some of the steam in the last experiment left a partial **vacuum** inside the can. A vacuum is simply a place

not occupied by matter, or an empty space. For a long time, people believed that a vacuum had the mysterious power of "sucking" things into it. But how does the vacuum you create when you sip a soda succeed in getting a grip on the liquid in order to pull it up into your mouth?

THE BAROMETER

In the seventeenth century, the Duke of Tuscany decided to have a deep well dug. To his surprise, no pump was able to raise the water more than about 34 feet above the level in the well. The great scientist Galileo became interested in the question and suggested to his friend and pupil, Torricelli, that he make experiments to test "the power of a vacuum." Torricelli reasoned that if a 34-foot height of water was needed to satisfy a vacuum a much shorter column of mercury would be sufficient. Mercury is 13.6 times as dense as water, so a height of only 34/13.6, or 2½ feet, should be enough. He tried an experiment: A glass tube about a yard long, sealed at one end, was completely filled with mercury. The other end was held closed with the thumb. Then the tube was turned over and the open end set in a large dish of mercury. When the thumb was removed, the mercury dropped away from the sealed end until its upper surface came to rest about 30 inches above the liquid in the dish (Fig. 14). The mer-

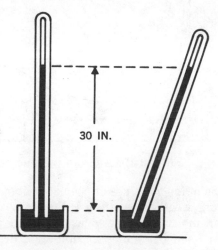

FIGURE 14. Mercury tube barometer

---

* Can you tell why, from the Table 3?

cury, in descending from the top of the tube, left a vacuum behind it, and it seemed that this vacuum was able to hold up a 30-inch column of mercury. Torricelli concluded that the liquid is supported not by any mysterious sucking action of the vacuum, but by the outside air *pressing* on the mercury in the open dish.

To complete the argument, other people carried such instruments up the side of a mountain, where the air pressure is less. Surely enough, it was observed that the mercury in the tube now stood lower, but regained its former height when brought back to the valley. Here, then, is an instrument that can be used to measure changes in air pressure. It is called a **barometer.** A more compact and convenient form of this instrument is the **aneroid** barometer (Fig. 15). It consists of a sealed metal can from which most of the air has been pumped. Changes in outside air pressure make the flexible cover bend in and out very slightly, and the motion is magnified by a lever system, moving a pointer over a scale from which the air pressure can be read off directly.

One important use of the barometer is to determine altitude. Once we know how the pressure of the air depends on altitude, we can use the barometer readings to give our height. An aneroid barometer with the scale marked directly in height units forms the **altimeter** of an airplane.

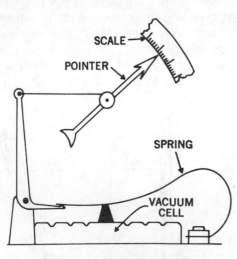

FIGURE 15. Aneroid barometer

The other main use of the barometer is in forecasting weather conditions. Contrary to general belief, moist air is *less* dense than dry air, water vapor itself being only around ⅝ as dense as dry air. Since it is less dense, moist air exerts less pressure, and so in moist weather the barometer

falls. This gives us a way of predicting what kind of weather we will have in the immediate future. A steady, high barometer indicates fair weather; a rising barometer means fair or clearing weather conditions; and a rapidly falling barometer means a storm is approaching. By combining information obtained at stations all over the country, the Weather Bureau is able to prepare and distribute maps from which forecasts can be made at any locality.

THE ATMOSPHERE

The **atmosphere** is the name we give to the whole body of air surrounding the earth. If it were not for the earth's gravity, this layer of gas would escape out into the vacuum of interplanetary space. As mentioned above, it is the weight of the air that causes it to exert pressure. But there is one important difference between the pressure due to the weight of a liquid, as discussed in the previous chapter, and the pressure of the air: Liquids are virtually incompressible, and this leads to the simple proportion between pressure and depth. But gases, such as air, are fairly easy to compress. The weight of the upper layers compresses the lower ones, with the result that the density and pressure both fall off in a more complicated way as we go upward from the surface of the earth. In going up one mile from sea level, the height of mercury in the barometer falls about 5½ inches, but in going up an additional mile from a 10 mile height, it falls only a little over ½ inch. The *rate* of falling off is a constantly decreasing one (see Fig. 16).

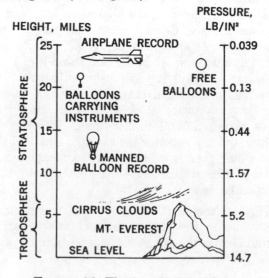

FIGURE 16. The lower atmosphere

The part of the atmosphere above about 6.5 miles is called the **stratosphere.** It is a relatively cold and calm region in which no clouds form. It has been explored to some extent by free-sailing balloons carrying instruments and, more recently, by high-altitude rockets and radar. The atmosphere continues to thin out with increasing height, and apparently has no sharp boundary. Air can still be detected at heights of several hundred miles.

GAS VOLUME: BOYLE'S LAW

When air is pumped into an automobile tire, a large volume of outside air is forced into the relatively small space inside the tube. All gases, including air, are compressible; and in order to force a gas into a small space, extra pressure must be applied to it. The greater the applied pressure, the smaller the space occupied by the gas. In the seventeenth century, Robert Boyle, an Irish scientist, discovered by experiment the exact relationship that holds: **If the temperature of the gas is kept constant,** then **the volume will be inversely proportional to the pressure.** This means that if the pressure is doubled, the volume becomes half as much; if the pressure is tripled, the volume becomes one-third of what it was, etc. In the form of an equation,

$$\frac{V_1}{V_2} = \frac{p_2}{p_1}$$

where p_1 and V_1 are, respectively, the pressure and the volume in one case and p_2 and V_2 are the values in another. In the formula, notice that on the left, the numerator has the "1" and the denominator has the "2", while on the right, it is just the other way around. This is characteristic of *inverse* proportion.

EXAMPLE 8: The air pressure in a tire is to be 30 lb/in² as read on an ordinary tire gauge, and the inside volume of the tube, assumed constant, is 0.95 ft³. What volume of outside air is needed to fill the tube to this pressure on a day when the barometric pressure is 15 lb/in²?

SOLUTION: A tire gauge reads the pressure *above* atmospheric, so the total pressure on the air in the tube is 30 + 15, or 45 lb/in². Then, if V_1 is the volume that this amount of air occupies outside, we can make the proportion

$$\frac{V_1}{0.95} = \frac{45}{15};$$

cross multiplying:

$$V_1 = \frac{0.95 \times 45}{15} = 2.85 \text{ ft}^3.$$

Buoyancy in Gases

Archimedes' law of buoyancy also holds for gases. In making very accurate weighings, the difference in the weight of air displaced by the object and by the metal weights must be taken into account. But air has such low density compared with solids, this effect can usually be neglected. A large, hollow body, such as a balloon, can displace more than its own weight of air, and so can float in air. Since the air is less dense higher up, a balloon will rise only to the level where the weight of the displaced air becomes equal to its own weight. Balloons are usually filled with hydrogen or helium. These gases are the lightest known, and provide a large lifting force.

Uses of Air Pressure

There are many uses for compressed air: It is utilized in inflating tires, in operating air brakes and tools such as the riveting hammer, and in keeping water out of underwater workings (see Experiment 1).

Low pressures have their uses, too. The vacuum cleaner is a familiar example. In making electric lamps, radio and television tubes and X-ray tubes it is extremely important to be able to remove as much air as possible. Modern pumps can reduce the air pressure in a tube to less than one-billionth of normal atmospheric pressure. Special methods can attain a billionth of this.

AIR RESISTANCE

So far, the discussion has been about air at rest. When air moves, even with moderate speed, important new forces come into play. These forces are responsible for the operation of sailboats, atomizers, parachutes, airplanes, etc. The most evident effect is the resistance that the air offers to the movement of objects through it. Hold your hand out the window of a moving car and you feel the resistance force directly. The car itself experiences such a force. At usual driving speeds, more than half the power delivered by the engine may be used up in working against air resistance.

The actual resistance force increases with the *cross-section area* of the moving body and especially with its *speed* of motion. In addition, the *shape* of the object is of great importance. What we call **streamlining** a body means giving it a suitable shape so that it will offer a minimum of opposition to the flow of air past it. This means eliminating all sharp corners and projections, approaching the general "tear-drop" shape shown in Fig. 17a. Contrary to what you might expect, the front of the body is broader than the rear. But if the body is to be a high-speed jet plane or rocket traveling faster than sound, a sharp-nosed shape gives best performance (Fig. 17b).

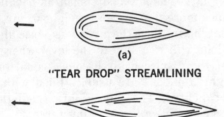

(a)

"TEAR DROP" STREAMLINING

(b)

FASTER-THAN-SOUND STREAMLINING

FIGURE 17.

Fig. 18 shows the comparative resistance, of (a) a streamlined rod, (b) a round rod and (c) a flat plate of the same cross-section and all moving at a given speed. The air flow around each is also pictured. Behind the round and flat objects, the stream lines break up into whirls, whose effect is to retard the movement of the body. The tapered tail of (a) fills in this region, allowing the flow to join smoothly at the rear.

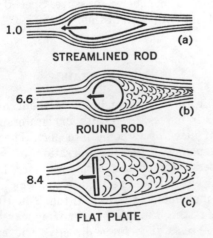

1.0

STREAMLINED ROD

(a)

6.6

ROUND ROD

(b)

8.4

FLAT PLATE

(c)

FIGURE 18. Relative resistance

Bodies falling through the air are retarded by air resistance. If not for this effect, all objects, regardless of difference in weight, would fall at the same rate.

EXPERIMENT 11: Drop a coin and a sheet of paper from shoulder height at the same instant. The coin quickly reaches the floor, while the paper flutters down slowly. To show that this result is not due to their difference in weight but only to the difference in air resistance, repeat the trial after first wadding the paper up into a small ball. This time both will be seen to hit at the same instant.

THE AIRPLANE; BERNOULLI'S LAW

Of the many applications of the physics of the air, the one that has had the greatest impact on civilization is, of course, the airplane. At the very beginning we may well ask, "What keeps an airplane up?" The answer is not at all obvious. We know that a plane must be moved rapidly through the air in order to sustain itself, and that it must have a large, slightly inclined surface—a wing—to furnish the supporting force. Seen from the moving airplane, the surrounding air streams backward, over and around it. The tilted wing surface deflects some air downward, and as a result the plane is literally "knocked" upward. But this is responsible for only a small effect. Actually, it is the flow of air around the curved *upper* surface of the wing that accounts for most of the lift. To see how this works, try an experiment:

EXPERIMENT 12: Hold one edge of a piece of letter paper against your chin, just below your lower lip, with the paper hanging over and down (Fig. 19). If you now blow above the paper, it will rise to a horizontal position as if pulled upward into the air stream.

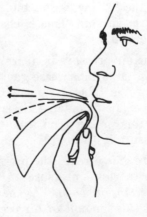

FIGURE 19.

This action is an instance of a general law discovered by the eighteenth century Swiss scientist Daniel Bernoulli: A moving stream of gas or liquid exerts less sidewise pressure than if it were at rest. The result is that things seem to be drawn into such a stream; they are really *pushed* in by the greater pressure from outside.

Bernoulli's principle gives us a way of understanding the action of air on a wing. In a properly designed wing, the airstream separates at the front of the wing and rejoins smoothly at the rear (Fig. 20). Since the air that flows over the upper surface has to travel a greater distance its average speed must be greater than that below, and so the decrease in pressure is greater on the top side, resulting in a lifting force on the entire wing. The forces on the upper side of a wing may account for over four-fifths of the whole lift.

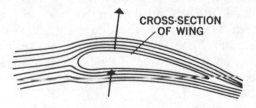

FIGURE 20. Airplane wing

The control surfaces of the airplane, as well as the propeller that moves it through the air, operate on this same principle. In the **helicopter** the airflow over the wing surfaces is produced by whirling the rotating wings, rather than by rapid motion of the whole plane through the air. As a result, a helicopter can hover over one spot on the ground, or even move in the backward direction.

Other Applications

A number of familiar observations and devices can be described in terms of Bernoulli's law. In an **atomizer** (spray gun), a stream of air is blown across the end of a small tube that dips into the liquid (Fig. 21). The decreased pressure at the side of the air stream allows normal air pressure, acting on the surface of the liquid in the bottle, to push the liquid up the tube. Here the moving air breaks it up into small drops and drives it forward. The **carburetor** of an auto works in the same way.

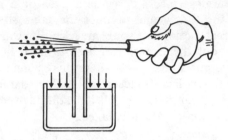

FIGURE 21. Atomizer (spray gun)

Two cars, passing each other at high speed, are in danger of sideswiping because of the decrease in air pressure in the space between them. A strong gale is capable of lifting the roof off a house. An amusing experiment shows the same effect:

EXPERIMENT 13: Lay a dime about half an inch from the edge of a table and place a saucer a few inches beyond. With your mouth at the level of the table top, blow a sudden strong breath across the top of the dime (as if whistling) and it will jump into the dish.

The curving of a baseball or of a "sliced" golf ball is explained by Bernoulli's principle. Some air is dragged around by the spin of the ball (Fig. 22). At "A" this air is moving *with* the stream of air caused by the ball's moving along, while at "B" the two *oppose* each other. The greater relative air speed at "A" makes the ball veer to that side.

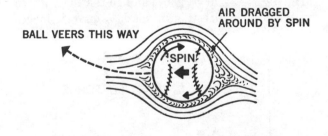

FIGURE 22. Curving of a baseball

Forces

We have described a force as a push or a pull—something that would produce the same effect as the direct action of your muscles. It was also pointed out that forces can be measured in ordinary weight units, such as grams, pounds, etc. We shall now have a closer look at forces and find out how, under certain conditions, they are capable of holding an object in balance.

REPRESENTATION OF FORCES; VECTORS

In most of the practical situations we deal with, not one but a number of forces act on the body in question. There is a simple and convenient way of representing the forces and of finding their net effect. In the first place, in order to describe a force completely, we must specify not only its *amount* (say, in pounds) but its *direction* in space; obviously it makes a difference whether a force acts to the left or to the right, or whether it acts upward or downward.

A force acting at a given point is pictured by a line drawn outward from that point in the given direction, and the *length* of the line is made to represent the *strength* of the force.

Besides forces, there are other physical quantities, to be discussed later, that have both magnitude and direction. Such a quantity is called a **vector.** Any vector may be represented by a directed line segment.

In Fig. 23 *A* stands for a force of 5 lb acting toward the northeast. The scale chosen for this drawing is "¼ in = 1 lb," and so the line, drawn in the proper direction, is made 5 quarter-inches

long. An arrow is placed at the end of the line to give its sense of direction. In the same way, *B* is an eastward force of 9 lb acting at the same point. Any convenient scale may be used in these drawings, as long as we stick to the same scale throughout the problem.

RESULTANT OF A SET OF FORCES

It is found by experience that when a number of forces act on a body they can always be replaced by a single force having a definite amount and direction. This single force, which replaces the effect of all the others, is called their **resultant.** There is a simple way of finding it by means of a drawing: Draw all the forces, end to end, until they have all been put down (the order in which you pick them off from the original drawing does not matter). Then, if you draw a line out from the starting point to the end of the last force, this line will correctly represent the resultant as to direction and amount.

EXAMPLE 9: Three forces act at a point. One is 4 lb straight down, another is 11 lb to the right and the third is 9 lb upward and to the left at an angle of 45 degrees. Find their resultant.

SOLUTION: Fig. 24 shows these forces, drawn to

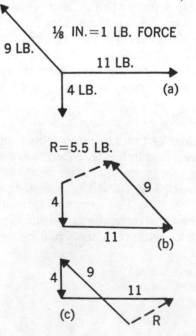

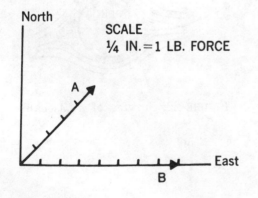

FIGURE 23. Representing force vectors

FIGURE 24. Combining vectors

scale. Now, keeping the same length and direction for each force, lay them off end to end, as in (b). Then the resultant is gotten by drawing a line from the starting point out to the end of the last force. This line, when measured, turns out to be 11/16 in. long. Therefore the resultant amounts to 11/16 divided by 1/8, or 5.5 lb, and has the direction shown. In (c) the forces have been laid off in a different order, but the resultant has the same size and direction as before.

Notice that the size (length) of the resultant is, in general, *not* equal to the sum of the magnitudes of the separate vectors. The actual value will depend on their relative positions.

If all the acting forces are in a single line (such as east-west), the magnitude of the resultant is simply the sum of all those acting to one side less the sum of all those acting toward the other. As an example, suppose a man can pull with a force of 100 lb, while a boy can pull only 70 lb. If they both pull toward the east, the combined effect is 170 lb force; if the man pulls westward and the boy eastward, the resultant is a 30 lb force toward the west (the direction of the larger force).

Another case where the resultant can easily be calculated rather than measured from a scale drawing is that of two forces at right angles to each other (Fig. 25). The resultant is the hypotenuse of a right triangle and its amount may be computed by the right triangle rule.

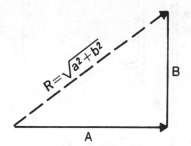

FIGURE 25. Forces at right angles

EQUILIBRIUM OF FORCES

One of the most important mechanical situations that engineers and designers must deal with is that in which all the forces acting on a body just hold it at rest. This balancing-out of the applied forces will occur if the **resultant** of all of them is **zero.** When this happens, the body is said to be

in **equilibrium.** Conversely, if a body is observed to remain at rest, we know that the resultant of all the acting forces must be zero. This fact can be used to find the values of some of the forces. An example will show how:

EXAMPLE 10: A wire-walker at the circus weighs 160 lb. When at the position shown in Fig. 26, what is the stretching force in each part of the wire?

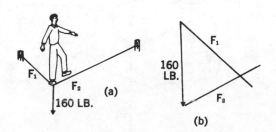

FIGURE 26. Tensions in a wire

SOLUTION: First we note that the point B is the place where the forces in question meet. One of them is the man's weight. We sketch it in the downward direction from B as shown and label it "160 lb." Acting from B along the left-hand portion of the wire is some force—call it F_1—whose value is still unknown. As yet, we can only sketch it in, but do not know how long to make it. Likewise, F_2 is the force in the other part of the wire. In general F_1 and F_2 will be different.

Since the three forces hold the point B in equilibrium, they must form a *closed triangle* by themselves (zero resultant). Off to one side, Fig. 26b, draw the weight force to scale. From the tip of this force, draw a line in parallel to BC. We do not know how long to make this force; however, if we did, we would then proceed to draw the third force from its end, heading parallel to the wire AB, and should have to land at the starting point of the weight force. It is clear what we now have to do: Simply begin at this point and draw a line back in the proper direction until it crosses the line of F_2. This crossing point fixed the lengths (or amounts) of the two forces. The force lines can now be measured, using the same scale that was employed in drawing the 160-lb weight, and so the magnitudes of F_1 and F_2 can be found. In this example they turn out to be about 165 lb and 135 lb, respectively. Try a construction like this yourself, using a weight and direction of your own choosing.

CENTER OF GRAVITY

In most of the cases we meet in practice, the forces acting on a body are not all applied at a single point, but at several different places. The weight of a body is a good example. The earth's gravity pulls downward on every particle of a material body with a force equal to the weight of that particle, as pictured in Fig. 27. However, we can replace all these separate forces by a single

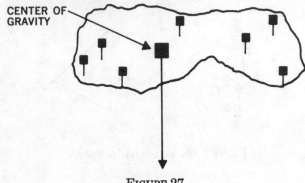

CENTER OF
GRAVITY

FIGURE 27.

one, equal to the entire weight of the object. This force must be considered to act at a given place called the **center of gravity** of the body. There is such a point for every object. If the body is made of uniform material and has a simple shape, such as a sphere, cube, straight rod, etc., the location of the center of gravity is obvious (Fig. 28a). The position of the center of gravity of an irregular object may be found by trial, by seeing where it will balance without any tendency to rotate in any direction (Fig. 28b).

(a)   (b)

FIGURE 28. Locating the center of gravity

If a body is supported at any point other than its center of gravity, it will try to move until its center of gravity is as low as possible. This explains, for instance, why it is impossible to balance a pencil on its point.

EXPERIMENT 14: Fasten a weight to the inner edge of a flat cylindrical box (Fig. 29). Placed on a sloping board, it will mysteriously roll *up* the slope when released. Notice that the center of gravity is very near the position of the concealed

weight, and that while the box goes up the hill, the center of gravity goes *down*, as it must.

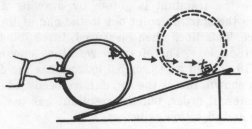

FIGURE 29. The mystery cylinder

TORQUE AND ROTATION

In general, if the forces applied to a body do not all act at a single point, there is the possibility that the body will rotate. How can we measure the ability of a force to produce rotation? Think of the example of pushing a revolving door (Fig. 30). If you want to turn the door most effectively, you push with your hand near the edge of the door rather than near the hinge. It is found that the **turning effect** of any force is given by multiplying the **amount of the force** by the **distance from the pivot** point to the line of the force. This turning effect of a force is called the **torque,** and

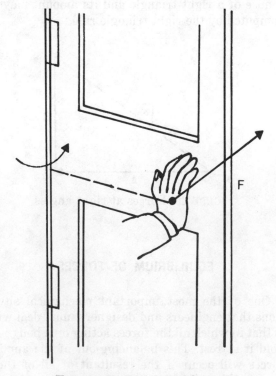

F

FIGURE 30. Revolving door

the distance mentioned is the **torque arm.** In symbols,

$$T = Fh$$

where T is the torque, F the force and h the torque arm. Notice what the units are for T: If F is in pounds and h is in feet, the units for T will be **foot pounds.** Here again we have an example of a derived quantity (p. 20).

If the body in question is not to rotate, then the net torque must be zero, that is, **the sum of all torques that tend to turn the body in one direction must be equal to the sum of all those tending to turn it in the opposite direction.** The word "direction" here refers to the sense of rotation—**clockwise** (in the direction turned by the hands of a clock), or **counterclockwise.**

In figuring the torques, we may take any point as a prospective center of turning—it need not be the place where the actual pivot or axle is located.

EXAMPLE 11: How big a downward force must be applied to the end of the crowbar shown in Fig. 31 in order just to lift the 200-lb weight? Neglect the weight of the bar itself.

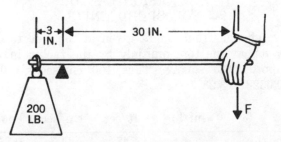

FIGURE 31. Lifting by means of a crowbar

SOLUTION: Taking the torques about the pivot point, the one due to the weight will be 200×3, or 600 in.lb. If we call the applied force F, in pounds, it will have a torque around this point of amount $30F$ in.lb. These two torques are in opposite directions: The latter one is clockwise, the other is counterclockwise. Setting the two equal, $200 \times 3 = 30F$, or $F = 20$ lb force.

EXAMPLE 12: A 5-ton truck stands 30 ft from one pier of a uniform bridge 100 ft long weighing 20 tons (Fig. 32). Find the downward force on each pier.

SOLUTION: First we must put down all the forces acting *on* the bridge: A 5-ton downward force at C; a 20-ton downward force at G, the center of gravity of the bridge structure; and at the piers, upward forces F_A and F_B whose values are

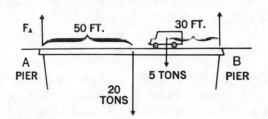

FIGURE 32. Downward force on the piers of a bridge

to be found. Take torques around A. The two weight forces tend to turn the bridge clockwise about A, and their torques amount to $20 \times 50 + 5 \times 70$, or 1,350 ft-tons. The only counter-clockwise torque is that of F_B, amounting to $100F_B$. Notice that F_A does not contribute any torque, since it has no torque arm around A. Setting the torques in the two directions equal, $100 \ F_B = 1,350$, $F_B = 13.5$ tons force. We could now repeat the process, taking torques around, say, the point B; but there is a simpler way to find the remaining force F_A: From the fact that the resultant of all the acting forces must be zero (p. 143) we have, simply because all the forces in this problem are either upward or downward, $F_A + 13.5 = 20 + 5$, so that $F_A = 11.5$ tons. So we see that by using the two equilibrium conditions that state (1) the resultant of all the forces must be zero and (2) the torques around any point must balance, we can work out any equilibrium problem.

GRAVITATION: NEWTON'S LAW

One of the greatest scientific achievements of all time was Newton's discovery of gravitation, around the middle of the seventeenth century. Earlier, the astronomer Kepler had found certain regularities about the motion of the plants around the sun. Newton, trying to explain these rules, decided that the planets must move in the observed way because they are pulled by a force exerted by the sun. He concluded that this force of gravitation exists not only between the sun and the planets but between *any* two objects in the universe, and he worked out the factors on which the amount of force depends. This is stated by his **Law of Gravitation: Any two bodies in the universe attract each other with a force that is directly proportional to their masses and inversely**

proportional to **the square of their distance apart.**
This may be stated as a formula:

$$F = \frac{Gm_1m_2}{d^2}$$

where F is the force of attraction, m_1 and m_2 are
the two masses, and d is their distance apart. G
is a constant, whose value is fixed once we have
chosen our units for F, m and d. If F and m are
measured in pounds and d in feet, the value of G
is 0.000 000 000 033. Because G is so small, the
attraction between ordinary objects is very weak,
but when the bodies concerned are very massive,

the force may be extremely large. Thus, the attractive force between the earth and the moon
amounts to about 15 million trillion tons.

The gravitational force of the earth for objects
on it—what we have been calling **gravity**—is responsible for their weight. The attraction of the
moon for the waters of the ocean is main cause
of the **tides.**

Notice that while Newton's law allows us to
calculate the amount of the attraction in any case,
it does not tell us what gravitation is, nor why
such a force exists. These are philosophical rather
than scientific questions!

Motion

In the world about us, everything moves. This
may seem to contradict the discussion where we
talked about bodies at rest. But a body at rest on
the ground is really moving with the rotation of
the whole earth, and the earth in turn moves in
its path around the sun, and so on. Rest and motion are relative terms. We will now find out how
to measure the motions of bodies, and how the
forces acting on them determine the way in which
they move.

SPEED AND VELOCITY

In any kind of motion—for example, in making
a trip—two things are of interest: What is the
rate of motion and in what *direction* does it take
place? Rate of motion is what we call **speed.** It is
measured by the distance covered divided by the
elapsed time. In symbols,

$$v = \frac{d}{t},$$

where d stands for the distance, t is the time required and v is the speed. Speed is a derived unit,
and we are at liberty to use any distance unit and
any time unit for this purpose. Table 4 gives convenient factors for changing from one common
speed unit to another.

TABLE 4

CONVERSION FACTORS FOR SPEED UNITS

To change from a unit given at the side to one
given at the top, multiply by the factor in the
appropriate square. Thus 100 cm/sec = 100 ×
0.0328 = 3.28 ft/sec.

	mi/hr	ft/sec	cm/sec	knots*
mi/hr	—	1.47	44.7	0.868
ft/sec	0.682	—	30.5	0.592
cm/sec	0.0224	0.0328	—	0.0194
knots*	1.15	1.69	51.5	—

Even where the rate of motion is not constant
over the whole journey, the above formula has a
meaning: it gives the **average speed** for the entire
trip. For instance, if a car travels to a city 90
miles away in a total time of 3 hours, the average
speed will be 90 mi/3 hr = 30 mi/hr. But no trip
of this kind is made at constant speed; there may
have been times when the car was going much
faster or much slower than this, as indicated by
the speedometer.

When the directional aspect is combined with

---

*1 knot = 1 nautical mile per hour.

the speed we have the **velocity** of motion. Velocity, like force, is a vector (p. 142), and so an arrowed line can be used to stand for a velocity. A body can have several velocities at the same time. A ball rolled across the floor of a moving railroad car (Fig. 33) has the common forward velocity of everything in the train, plus the crosswise velocity with which the ball is rolled. The **resultant velocity**

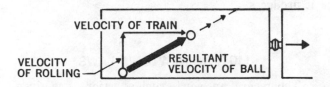

FIGURE 33. Combination of velocities

—how the ball would appear to move as seen by someone on an overhead bridge—is given by the same construction we used before. The actual path is the straight line indicated.

ACCELERATION

In most of the motions we commonly observe, the speed is not at all constant, whether it is the flight of a bird, the swinging of a pendulum or the fall of a stone. Any motion in which the speed or direction are variable is called **accelerated motion.** The **acceleration** is defined as the **rate of change** of the **velocity,** that is, the change in velocity divided by the time it takes to make that change. For instance, if a car going 25 ft/sec picks up speed until, 5 sec later, it is going 60 ft/sec, its rate of pick-up will be 60—25, or 35 ft/sec in 5 sec. Dividing, this amounts to 7 ft/sec/sec ("feet per second per second"). This means only that the car increased its speed at an average rate of 7 ft/sec *each second.* Instead of writing "ft/sec/sec," we recognize that the time unit comes in *twice* as a factor in this derived unit, and we write "ft/sec²" and read it "feet per second squared."

Motion with Constant Acceleration

One kind of motion that is readily described and computed is that where the amount of the acceleration is *constant.* This holds, for a limited time at least, when a train is gathering speed, or when it is being brought to rest by the brakes. In the latter case, the speed is *decreasing,* and this is

sometimes called decelerated motion. However, no special name is really needed; this can be taken care of merely by putting a *minus* sign in front of the value for the acceleration.

EXAMPLE 13: A car going 30 ft/sec is brought to rest by its brakes at the uniform rate of 5 ft/sec². How long must the brakes be applied?

SOLUTION: Saying that the braking acceleration amounts to −5 ft/sec² means that the car will lose speed at the rate of 5 ft/sec each second. To take away all the initial speed of 30 ft/sec will then require 30/5 or 6 sec.

How *far* will a constantly-accelerating object move in a given time? To answer such a question, you must remember that the speed of motion is changing all the while. But we can find out what is happening by making use of the *average* speed; and here, since the speed changes at a uniform rate, the average speed will be half way between the speed at the beginning and the speed at the end of the interval. The next example will show how we can compute the distance in a specific case:

EXAMPLE 14: A car going 26 ft/sec begins to accelerate at the rate of 2 ft/sec². How fast will it be going after 8 sec, and how far will it go in this time?

SOLUTION: In 8 sec, the total gain in speed will be 8 × 2 = 16 ft/sec, so the final speed will be 24 + 16, or 42 ft/sec. To find the distance traveled, we note that the speed at the beginning of the acceleration period was 26 and at the end was 42 ft/sec, so that the average speed over this interval is ½ (26 + 42) = 34 ft/sec. Going, in effect, 34 ft/sec for 8 sec, the car would cover a distance of 34 × 8, or 272 ft.

Falling Motion; Projectiles

The ancient Greek philosopher Aristotle described the motion of a freely falling body by saying that the heavier the body, the faster it would fall. This does, at first thought, seem true, but you have already performed an experiment (Experiment 11) that throws some doubt on this conclusion. In the latter part of the sixteenth century, the great Italian scientist Galileo tried some experiments that convinced him that it is merely the disturbing effect of air resistance that ordinarily makes a light object fall more slowly than a heavy one. In a vacuum, all bodies fall at the same rate.

Galileo went on to find just how a falling body

moves. He found that, when the effects of the surrounding air can be neglected, a falling body has a constant acceleration—the kind of motion we have been discussing above. This acceleration is called the **acceleration due to gravity,** and is denoted by the symbol g. Its value changes slightly from place to place on earth, and especially with height, but the standard value is close to

$$32 \text{ ft/sec}^2, \text{ or } 980 \text{ cm/sec}^2.$$

Knowing the value of g, it is not difficult to calculate the motion of a falling body. The results will be quite accurate for compact solid objects falling moderate distances. The case of a body falling great distances in air is, in general, too complicated for computation.

EXAMPLE 15: A small stone is dropped from the roof of a tall building and is seen to hit the ground 7.0 sec later. Neglecting air resistance, find the height from which the stone fell and how fast it was going when it hit the ground.

SOLUTION: In the stated time, the stone, starting from rest, picks up a speed of $7 \times 32 = 224$ ft/sec, which is its speed just before hitting the ground. Its *average* speed for the whole trip is half the sum of the speed at the start and at the finish, or $\frac{1}{2}(0 + 224) = 112$ ft/sec. Going at this speed for 7 sec, a body would cover a distance of $112 \times 7 = 784$ ft, which is the distance of fall.

A **projectile**—a thrown stone or a bullet—is really a falling body. If shot upward at an angle, it immediately begins to *fall* short of the direction of fire, just like any falling object. It continues to fall in this way while moving forward, and so follows the observed curved path. Since bullets travel at high speed, the results may be somewhat altered by air resistance.

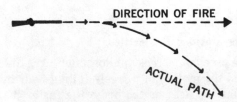

DIRECTION OF FIRE

ACTUAL PATH

FIGURE 34. Path of a projectile

EXPERIMENT 15: Place two coins at the very edge of a table, one on top of the other. A sharp blow with a knife blade held flat against the table will send the lower coin off like a projectile, while the upper one will fall almost straight down. In spite of this difference in path, both will be heard to strike the floor at the same time, since both really *fall* the same distance.

FORCE AND MOTION

In the preceding pages you learned how to describe certain types of motion, such as motion with constant speed or motion with constant acceleration, and how to figure out times, distances, etc. Now we take up the more involved question of what *causes* and *maintains* the motion of an object—that is, the relation of force to the motion it produces.

MOTION: NEWTON'S LAWS

The general answer to such questions was given by the brilliant work of Newton in the form of his **Three Laws of Motion.** These principles form the basis of the whole subject of Mechanics.

The First Law: Inertia

The First Law is called the **Law of Inertia.** Inertia was described as one of the fundamental properties of matter. Although the general idea was anticipated by Galileo, Newton succeeded in putting it into precise form:

Every body remains in a state of rest or of uniform motion in a straight line unless acted upon by forces from the outside.

This law states that motion is as natural a condition as rest. A car going along a straight, level road at constant speed is in equilibrium: The weight of the car is balanced by the supporting force of the pavement, and the forward pull of the engine counterbalances the retarding forces of friction and air resistance. The resultant force is zero, and the car is in equilibrium just as truly as if it were at rest.

Centripetal Force; Satellites

If the car comes to a curve, the pavement must furnish, through friction with the tires, an additional force to swerve the car from its natural straight path and enable it to round the curve. If the road is slippery, this force will be lacking and the car will continue straight ahead, tending to skid off the road.

The force required to hold a moving object in a circular path is called **centripetal*** force.

Many situations arise in practice where centripetal force must be taken into account. The curves

---

* The word means "toward the center."

FIGURE 35. Not enough centripetal force; the car continues along its "natural" straight path

on a road or on a bicycle racetrack are "banked," or raised at the outer edge to furnish such a force. Mud flying from the wheel of a car leaves the wheel in a straight line—it "flies off on a tangent." Laundries make use of centrifugal ("away from the center") dryers in which the wet clothes are whirled in a wire basket. Chemists and biologists use a **centrifuge** to separate suspended solid matter from a liquid. When the mixture is whirled rapidly, the difference in centripetal force on the solid material and on the less dense liquid causes the solids to collect at the outer rim. Using special arrangements, the centripetal force on a particle can be made to exceed 100 million times its weight.

A satellite following an orbit around a planet or a planet going around the sun is held in orbit by the centripetal force furnished by gravitational attraction.

The Second Law: Acceleration

Newton's First Law is limited in its usefulness, since it tells what happens only in the case where there is *no* resultant force. In the majority of actual situations, outside forces do act; the Second Law tells what can be expected under such circumstances.

In order to see what is involved, consider the particular case of a hand truck which can be pushed along on a level floor. If the truck is standing still to begin with and nobody pushes on it, it will remain at rest (First Law). What happens, now, if it is pushed in such a way that the force

acting on it is kept constant? An actual trial shows that the truck will move forward with *constant acceleration*. In general, we find that a constant force acting on a given body that is free to move will give it a constant acceleration in the direction of the force.

If we were to double the amount of force, we would find that the acceleration would become just twice as great as before. On the other hand, if the mass of the car were doubled and the same force used as before, the acceleration would be just half of its earlier value. From experiments such as these, we conclude that the acceleration is proportional to the force divided by the mass (Fig. 36).

We are now able to state the **Second Law: A body acted upon by a constant force will move with constant acceleration in the direction of the force; the amount of the acceleration will be directly proportional to the acting force and inversely proportional to the mass of the body.**

Newton's Second Law can be put into a useful form by remembering what happens to any given object when it falls under gravity: Here the acting force is equal to the weight of the body, and the acceleration is, in every case, that of gravity, g. Making a direct proportion between force and acceleration, we can write

$$\frac{F}{W} = \frac{a}{g}$$

where W is the weight of the body, F is any applied force and a is the acceleration that this force will give to the body. F and W are to be measured in the same units, and a and g are to be measured in the same units.

EXAMPLE 16: A car weighing 3,200 lb accelerates at the rate of 5 ft/sec². Neglecting friction, what is the effective forward force exerted by the engine?

SOLUTION: The proportion gives $F = W \ (a/g)$. Substituting the numbers, $F = 3200 \times 5/32 = 500$ lb force.

The Third Law; Action and Reaction

Newton's Third Law deals with the observed fact that it is not possible to exert a force on a

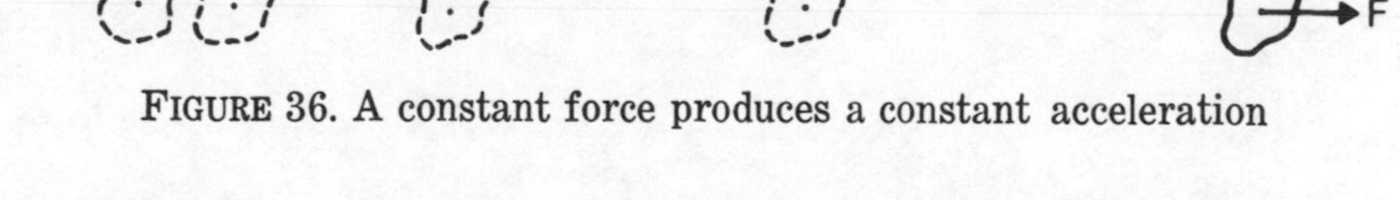

TIME   0   1 SEC.   2 SEC.   3 SEC.   4 SEC.

FIGURE 36. A constant force produces a constant acceleration

body without exerting a force in the opposite direction on some other body or bodies. There are many common illustrations of this: If you jump from a rowboat to a pier, the boat is thereby shoved backward. A gun "kicks" when the bullet goes forward. A ship's propeller can drive it forward only because it continually throws water backward.

Newton defined what is called the **momentum** of a body. It is the **mass multiplied by the velocity.** In symbols

$$M = mv,$$

where M is the momentum, m is the mass and v the velocity of the body. M is a derived quantity and any appropriate units may be used for m and v. The **Third Law** makes a simple statement about momentum. It says that **when any object is given a certain momentum in a given direction, some other body or bodies will get an equal momentum in the opposite direction.**

EXAMPLE 17: A gun has a mass of 2,500 gm and the bullets each have a mass of 100 gm. If a bullet leaves the gun with a speed of 800 meters/sec, with what speed will the gun start back?

SOLUTION: The momentum of the bullet will be 100×800 gm m/sec (gram meters per second). Calling the recoil speed of the gun V, its momentum just after firing will be $2500V$. Setting the two momenta equal, $2500\,V = 100 \times 800$, so that $V = 32$ m/sec. V comes out in m/sec because the speed of the bullet was given in these units.

If the gun and bullet were subject to no other forces after firing, the two would go in opposite directions, each continuing to move with its own constant speed forever (First Law). This would nearly be the case, for example, if the gun were fired far out in space where friction and gravitational forces are negligible. If the gun were fixed in the ground rather than free to recoil, the reaction would be transmitted to the whole earth instead of to the gun alone. Because of the earth's enormous mass, its resulting motion would be far too small to be detectable.

A jet engine or rocket gets its propelling force from the reaction of the gases discharged toward the rear at high speed. Even though the mass of gas shot out each second is not very large, its high speed makes the product mv very large. The jet plane or rocket gets an equal momentum in the forward direction. A rocket will work perfectly well in the vacuum existing in interplanetary space, provided it carries its own fuel and the oxygen needed to burn it.

EXPERIMENT 16: The reaction principle can be demonstrated by making a rubber-band slingshot on a board resting on rollers (Fig. 37). Tie the band back by means of a string and place a fairly massive stone in firing position. Release the stretched band by burning the thread and observe the recoil of the board as the stone goes forward.

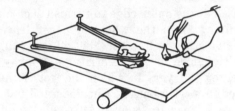

FIGURE 37. Recoil

ROTATIONAL INERTIA

Newton's laws apply to rotation as well as to the forward motion of an object as a whole. A body that is set spinning has a tendency to keep spinning—**rotational inertia.** The purpose of a heavy flywheel on an engine is to smooth out the separate power thrusts by means of its great rotational inertia.

A massive rotating wheel also has a tendency to keep its axis in a constant direction in space. This is the principle of the **gyroscope,** a rapidly rotating wheel mounted in a pivoted frame, so that the axis may hold its direction in spite of any motion of the mounting. The ability to keep its direction constant makes the gyroscope useful in the construction of several aircraft instruments, such as the turn indicator, artificial horizon, gyrocompass and automatic pilot.

CHAPTER NINE

CHEMISTRY

Matter

Strike a match. Any kind of match will do. Watch it carefully. What do you see? What did you hear? What did you smell? What do you feel? Blow it out. Did it go out completely? Try it again, this time holding the match in a horizontal position. Notice the shape of the flame. Do you see the liquid creeping just ahead of the flame? Light a wooden toothpick with the match, and then blow them both out. Blow harder on the toothpick. Blow it again. What happens? Do you have any evidence that match manufacturers are safety conscious? What differences in the properties of the match before and after burning can you find? Can the charred remnants of the match still be called a match?

A tremendous amount of chemistry has been illustrated by the phenomena which you have just observed. You will notice that in making observations we use not only our eyes, but also our other senses. The more senses we can employ in observation, the more thorough will be our findings. We will use these observations in becoming acquainted with some of the fundamental terms and ideas of chemistry. The observations will help us visualize chemical ideas and give meaning to the explanation of other phenomena of Nature.

PROPERTIES OF MATTER

We distinguish one form of matter from another by its **properties**. When you were asked to handle the match and the toothpick, you knew just what was meant because you were familiar in a general way with the properties of those objects. You are aware, of course, that a wooden match has more properties in common with a toothpick than a paper match. The wood gives the two objects a common substance. A **substance** is a definite variety of matter, all specimens of which have the same properties. Aluminum, iron, rust, salt, and sugar are all examples of substances. Notice that they are all homogeneous, or uniform in their makeup. Granite or concrete cannot be called substances because they are not homogeneous. They are made up of several different substances.

Substances have two major classes of properties: physical and chemical. **Physical** properties describe a substance as it is. **Chemical** properties describe the ability of a substance to change into a new and completely different substance.

Physical Properties

Substances have two kinds of physical properties: specific and accidental. **Specific physical properties** include those features which definitely distinguish one substance from another. Some of the important specific physical properties are:

1. Density—the weight of a unit volume of a substance. This is usually expressed as g./cc. in the metric system, or lbs./cu. ft. in the English system. Since 1 cc. of water weighs lg., its density is 1 g./cc. A cubic foot of water weighs 62.4 lbs. The density of water in the English system is 62.4 lbs,/cu. ft. Multiplying a metric density by 62.4 gives the English density of the substance. Table I lists densities of some common substances.

2. Specific Gravity—The ratio of the weight of a given volume of a substance to the weight of the same volume of water at the same temperature. Since 1 cc. of water weighs 1 g., specific gravity is numerically equal to the metric density of a substance. Both density and specific gravity have to do with the "lightness" or "heaviness" of a substance. Aluminum is "lighter" than lead. Water is "lighter" than mercury. Density is used more with solids, while specific gravity is used

TABLE I
DENSITY OF SUBSTANCES

Substance	g./cc.	lb./cu. ft.
Aluminum	2.7	168.5
Brass	8.6	536.6
Copper	8.9	555.4
Cork	0.22	13.7
Diamond	3.5	218.4
Gold	19.3	1204.3
Ice	0.917	57.2
Iron	7.9	493.2
Lead	11.3	705.1
Magnesium	1.74	108.6
Mercury	13.6	849.0
Rust	4.5	280.8
Salt	2.18	136.0
Sugar	1.59	99.0
Steel	7.83	488.8
Sulfur	2.0	124.9
Water, fresh	1.0	62.4
Water, sea	1.025	64.0
Zinc	7.1	443.0

more with liquids or solutions (acid in the battery of your car, or alcohol or glycol in the radiator of your car).

3. Hardness—Ability of the substance to resist scratching. A substance will scratch any other substance which is softer. The **MOH Hardness Scale** is used as a basis for comparing the hardness of substances. This scale is made up of various minerals of different hardness (Table II), but since so few of these minerals are commonly known, Table II also gives the approximate hardness of some familiar substances. Low hardness numbers indicate soft substances, and the higher the number, the harder the substance.

4. Odor. Many substances have characteristic odors. Some have pleasant odors, like methyl salicylate (oil of wintergreen) ; some have pungent odors, like ammonia or sulfur dioxide (a gas which forms when the head of a match burns) ; some have disagreeable odors, like hydrogen sulfide (a gas which forms in rotten eggs).

5. Color. You are familiar with the color of such

substances as gold or copper. White substances are usually described as colorless.

Normally it takes a combination of several specific physical properties to identify a given substance. A single property identifies a substance **only if the property is unique in Nature.** Thus, hardness serves to identify the diamond because diamond is the hardest known substance. The color of gold, however, is not unique as many prospectors unfortunately found out. Their "strike" of "fool's gold" looked like gold, but turned out to be pyrite, a far less valuable substance also known as iron sulfide.

Accidental physical properties are such features as *weight, dimensions,* and *volume.* They have nothing to do with the nature of the substance, but they enable us to find out how much of a given substance we have. **Objects,** particularly manufactured objects, may possess similar accidental properties, but these are in no way fundamentally related to the substances which make up the objects. Thus, matches and toothpicks are objects. Each is made according to a pattern of accidental properties. But toothpicks may be made of wood

TABLE II
HARDNESS

MOH Scale		Other Substances	
Talc	1	Graphite	0.7
Gypsum	2	Asphalt	1.3
Calcite	3	Fingernail	1.5
Fluorite	4	Rock Salt	2.0
Apatite	5	Aluminum	2.6
Feldspar	6	Copper	2.8
Quartz	7	Brass	3.5
Topaz	8	Knife Blade	5.4
Corundum	9	File	6.2
Diamond	10	Glass	6.5

or of plastic, two completely different substances with totally different specific physical properties.

Chemical Properties

The chemical properties of a substance describe its ability to form new substances under given conditions. A change from one substance to another is called a **chemical change,** or a **chemical reaction.** Hence, the chemical properties of a substance may be considered to be a listing of all the chemical reactions of a substance and the conditions under which the reactions occur.

In the striking of a match, several chemical

properties of the substances in a match are illustrated. Examine Figure 1 carefully. Notice the

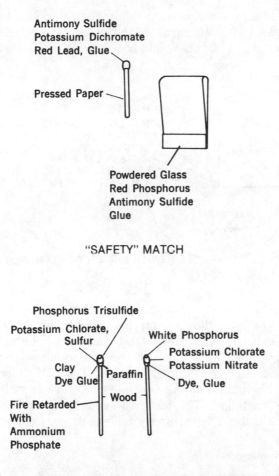

Antimony Sulfide
Potassium Dichromate
Red Lead, Glue

Pressed Paper

Powdered Glass
Red Phosphorus
Antimony Sulfide
Glue

"SAFETY" MATCH

Phosphorus Trisulfide
Potassium Chlorate,
Sulfur
White Phosphorus
Clay
Dye Glue   Paraffin   Potassium Chlorate
Potassium Nitrate
Dye, Glue
Fire Retarded   Wood
With
Ammonium
Phosphate

MODERN BANNED "STRIKE ANYWHERE"

FIGURE 1.

various substances present in each type of match. When you strike a "safety" match, the heat of friction of the head of the match rubbing on the glass is sufficient to cause the phosphorus on the scratching area to burn. This then generates enough heat to cause the substances in the head of the match to ignite. The burning of these, in turn, produces the heat necessary for the match-stick to catch fire. Notice that all of these substances burn (chemical property) but each does so at successively higher temperatures (conditions). None of the substances burns at room temperature! Since the phosphorus is contained only on the scratching area of the box or cover of the matches, they can be "struck" only on this area. (Occasionally safety matches can be struck on

glass or linoleum where rubbing produces sufficient heat to cause the head to start burning.)

The phosphorus trisulfide in the tip of the "strike anywhere" match is very sensitive to heat. Rubbing this tip on almost any moderately hard surface will produce sufficient frictional heat to cause this substance to burn. The other substances in the tip, and finally the match-stick are then ignited as the temperature rises. White phosphorus was formerly used in the tip of this type of match. This substance likewise bursts into flame at temperatures slightly above room temperature. However, the men who worked with white phosphorus and inhaled its fumes contracted a disease known as "phossy jaw" which caused their jaw bones to rot. When laws were passed prohibiting the use of white phosphorus, the company owning the patents on phosphorus trisulfide voluntarily opened them to free public use.

The charred remnants of the match-stick and toothpick consist principally of carbon, one of the new substances formed when wood or paper burn. The "after-glow" you observed in the toothpick is a chemical property of carbon. You have seen the same phenomenon in a charcoal fire. The match-stick exhibited no after-glow because it had been treated with a solution of a *fire-retardant* substance which soaked into the wood. Borax was formerly used for this purpose, but ammonium phosphate is generally considered to be more effective for this purpose and is now widely used, not only in match-sticks, but also in drapes, tapestries, and other types of decorations.

KINDS OF MATTER

As you look at the different objects about you, you are perhaps impressed by the almost endless variety of matter. Classification of the kinds of matter into fundamental groups was an impossible task until chemists began to probe into the **composition** of matter. Knowledge of composition quickly led to the discovery that all matter is made up of either pure substances or mixtures of pure substances. Substances, in turn, are of two types, either elements or compounds. Figure 2 diagrammatically shows the kinds of matter on the basis of composition.

Elements

Elements are the basic constituents of all matter. An element is the simplest form of matter. It

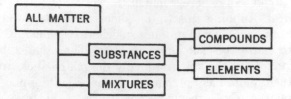

FIGURE 2.

cannot be formed from simpler substances, nor can it be decomposed into simpler varieties of matter. Some elements exist free in Nature; others are found only in combination. Free or combined, they are the building blocks which make up every different variety of matter in the universe. Table III is a list of the more commonly known elements together with their chemical **symbols.**

How many of these have you seen? How many of them have you heard of? A complete list of the 103 elements known at this time is found in Table VI.

TABLE III

Element	Symbol	Element	Symbol
Aluminum	Al	Neon	Ne
Argon	A	Nickel	Ni
Arsenic	As	Nitrogen	N
Bromine	Br	Oxygen	O
Calcium	Ca	Phosphorus	P
Carbon	C	Platinum	Pt
Chlorine	Cl	Plutonium	Pu
Copper	Cu	Potassium	K
Fluorine	F	Radium	Ra
Gold	Au	Silicon	Si
Helium	He	Silver	Ag
Hydrogen	H	Sodium	Na
Iodine	I	Sulfur	S
Iron	Fe	Tin	Sn
Lead	Pb	Uranium	U
Magnesium	Mg	Zinc	Zn
Mercury	Hg		

In general, the symbols are made up of the principal letter or letters in the name of the element. The symbols of elements known in antiquity are taken from their Latin names: Copper (Cuprum) Cu; Gold (Aurum) Au; Iron (Ferrum) Fe; Lead (Plumbum) Pb; Mercury (Hydrargyrum) Hg; Potassium (Kalium) K; Silver (Argentum) Ag;

Sodium (Natrium) Na; Tin (Stannum) Sn. Symbols are quite important in chemistry, for they represent more than merely the name of an element.

If all matter were to be broken down into the elements which form it, the percentage of each element in Nature would be as shown in Figure 3.

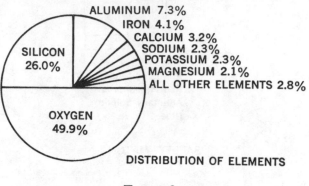

DISTRIBUTION OF ELEMENTS

FIGURE 3.

The elements in your body can easily be remembered from the advertising sign shown in Figure 4. The symbols of the most common body elements are contained in it. Use Table III to look up the names of the twelve elements represented in the figure. The last two symbols in the sign, NaCl, stand for ordinary table salt.

Compounds

A compound is a pure substance made up of elements which are chemically combined. They are perfectly homogeneous and have a definite composition regardless of origin, location, size, or shape. A compound can be decomposed into its elements only by some type of chemical change. The elements cannot be separated in a compound by any physical means.

Compounds are much more abundant than elements. Many thousands of compounds are known. Water, sand, rust, ammonia, sugar, salt, alcohol, and benzene are all examples of familiar compounds. It is important to bear in mind that when elements combine to form compounds, the elements lose all of their properties, and a new set of properties unique to the compound are created. For example, if you were to eat any sodium or inhale any chlorine, you would quickly die, for both of these elements are poisonous. But when these two elements combine, they form a compound

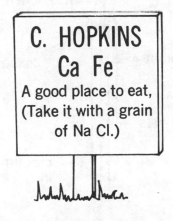

FIGURE 4.

called sodium chloride, which is ordinary table salt, a substance we must eat as part of our regular diet to maintain good health.

Mixtures

Most natural forms of matter are mixtures of pure substances. A mixture is a combination of substances held together by physical rather than chemical means. Soil and most rock, plants and animals, coal and oil, air and cooking gas, rivers and oceans, these are all mixtures. Mixtures differ from compounds in the following ways:

The ingredients of a mixture retain their own properties. If you examine a fragment of concrete you will observe that the grains of sand or gravel held together by the cement retain their identity and can be picked free. Their substance has not been changed in the formation of the concrete.

Unlike compounds which have a definite, fixed composition, **mixtures have widely varying composition.** Thus, solutions are mixtures. An infinite number of different salt water solutions can be made simply by varying the amount of salt dissolved in the water.

Mixtures can be separated into their ingredients by physical means, that is, by taking advantage of the differences in the physical properties of the ingredients. No matter how completely you mix or grind salt and pepper together, the salt can be separated from the pepper by dissolving it in water. The insoluble pepper will remain unaffected. The separation is completed by straining or **filtering** the liquid through a piece of cloth which will retain the pepper, and then evaporating the liquid (**illustrate**) to dryness of recrystallize the salt.

Perhaps you would like to try this separation for yourself. Read the following procedure fully and gather your materials before you start. Then proceed with the experiment.

EXPERIMENT 1: Mix a quarter teaspoon of salt and about half that much pepper (ground black) in a small drinking glass. Stir until a good mixture is obtained. Add about a half glass of water and stir until the salt is dissolved. Place a handkerchief or small piece of cloth loosely over the top of a small sauce pan. Filter the liquid into the pan. Notice that all the pepper remains on the cloth and that the salt solution in the pan is perfectly clear. Taste the clear filtrate to see if the salt is really there. Over a very low heat boil away the water in the pan. Be sure to remove the pan just as the last bit of liquid disappears. The white sediment is the recrystallized salt. Taste it to make sure.

The separation of mixtures into ingredients is an important operation. Almost every industry that uses natural products as raw materials employs one or more of the basic methods of separating mixtures. All of the methods take advantage of differences in physical properties of the ingredients. Some of the important methods of separating mixtures are:

Sorting. This involves a selection of the desired ingredient from the waste product in a fragmented mixture. It may be done by hand or by machine. The mining of coal is an example of this process. Here the coal is blasted loose from the inside of the earth and is then separated by sorting from the rock which accompanies the coal.

Magnetic Separation. Some iron ore is magnetic. This ore is scooped up in giant shovels from the earth, crushed, and poured on to a magnetized belt as shown in Figure 5. The non-magnetic waste ma-

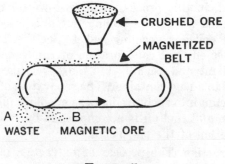

FIGURE 5.

terial drops off the belt at A, but the magnetic ore clings to the belt until it reaches B, and is thus separated.

Distillation. This process takes advantage of the difference in temperature of boiling (**boiling point**) between the ingredients of a solution. The ingredient with the lowest boiling point boils away first, leaving the higher boiling residue behind. The low boiling ingredient is said to be more **volatile** than the residue. The ingredient which boils off as a gas is then **condensed** back to a liquid by cooling and is collected in a new container.

EXPERIMENT 2: Dissolve a teapoon of sugar in a cup of water and place the solution in a tea kettle. Taste the solution to be sure it is sweet. Heat the solution to boiling. Hold a large plate vertically with the far edge just in front of the spout of the kettle so that the steam strikes it. (See Fig. 6.) Let the condensed moisture (**condensate**) run down the plate into a cup. Taste the condensate. Is it sweet? Where is the sugar? Which is more volatile, water or sugar? Remove the kettle from the burner before the solution boils completely to dryness.

PERMIT STEAM TO STRIKE PLATE

FIGURE 6.

Simple distillation effectively separates water and sugar because the boiling points of these two substances are relatively far apart. When the boiling points of ingredients to be separated are close together, a process known as **fractional distillation** is used. In this process, a large tower or column is erected above the boiling pot and fitted with cooling coils, or a cooling jacket (See Fig. 7). This provides efficient condensation of the less volatile ingredient and permits the more volatile one to escape to a new container. The separation of crude petroleum into such products as gasoline, lubricating oil, and fuel oil is accomplished by fractional distillation of the petroleum.

Extraction. The process of extraction involves the dissolving out of an ingredient from a mixture

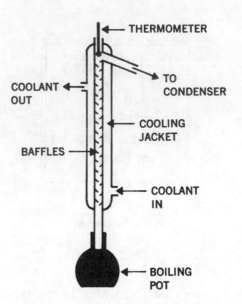

THERMOMETER

COOLANT OUT

TO CONDENSER

COOLING JACKET

BAFFLES

COOLANT IN

BOILING POT

FIGURE 7. Fractional Distillation Column

with a suitable **solvent.** Water was the solvent used to extract salt from the salt and pepper mixture in Experiment 1. Water is also used to extract the flavor of coffee from ground coffee beans in your coffee maker. Alcohol is used to extract vanillin, vanilla flavor, from vanilla beans. Other solvents like benzene, carbon tetrachloride, ether, and acetone are used to extract stains from your clothing.

Gravitation. This process takes advantage of differences in density or specific gravity of the ingredients in a mixture. In the panning of gold, the gold grains settled to the bottom of the pan because of their high density, and the lighter rocks were washed over the edge of the pan with water. In wheat harvesting, the light chaff is blown away from the denser wheat grains. The cleansing action of soap is also based upon this process. Soap bubbles surround the dense dirt particles on your skin or clothing and float the particles away.

PHYSICAL CHANGE

A physical change involves the alteration of the properties of a substance without affecting the substance itself. Hammering a piece of metal will modify its shape and increase its hardness, but the substance of the metal will remain unchanged. Freezing water to ice or boiling it to steam causes a thorough change in physical properties, but the substance remains water.

CHEMICAL CHANGE

Chemical change involves such a thorough change in a substance that an entirely new substance is formed in the process. The new substance created has its own set of properties, so physical change accompanies chemical change. Do you remember how completely the match was transformed as it burned? That was a chemical change. All burning involves chemical change. So does the rusting of iron, the toasting of bread, the drying of ink, the taking of a photograph, and the digestion of food. Chemical change is a common occurrence.

There are four principal types of chemical change: combination, decomposition, replacement, and double displacement. All chemical changes involve one or a combination of these basic varieties. Let us examine each type more carefully.

1. Combination. Combination is the direct joining of two or more simple substances, either elements or simple compounds, to form a more complex compound. For example, copper will join with oxygen in the air when heated to form a compound, copper oxide.

EXPERIMENT 3: Remove about 2 inches of insulation from a 6-inch length of copper wire. Clean the exposed metal with sandpaper to a bright copper color. Heat the copper to redness in the upper part of a gas flame for about one minute. Permit the wire to cool. Notice the black coating on the copper. This is copper oxide. Scrape it off with a knife. This exposes copper metal once more as indicated by the color. Repeat this experiment until you are satisfied that the copper is really **oxidizing** in the flame.

The reaction involved in Experiment 3 can be stated in words thus:

Copper   +   Oxygen   =   *Copper oxide
*An element   An element   A compound of the
                                          two elements*

2. Decomposition. Decomposition is the breaking down of a compound into simpler compounds or into its elements. For example, hydrogen peroxide decomposes in strong light or on contact with skin or other living tissue. Hydrogen peroxide is a compound of hydrogen and oxygen. It decomposes into water, a simpler compound of hydrogen and oxygen, and into oxygen, an element.

EXPERIMENT 4: Pour a small amount of hydrogen peroxide solution into the palm of your hand. Watch the solution closely. The bubbles which form are bubbles of oxygen gas. The rest of the peroxide forms water.

The reaction in Experiment 4 may be stated thus:

Hydrogen peroxide   =   Oxygen   +   Water
A compound   An element   A compound

3. Replacement. Replacement involves the substitution of one element for another in a compound. For example, if a piece of iron were to be dropped into a solution of sulfuric acid (the solution present in the battery of your car), hydrogen gas would be observed bubbling out of the solution. Sulfuric acid is a compound of hydrogen, sulfur, and oxygen. The iron replaces the hydrogen, liberating it as an element, and forms a new compound, iron sulfate (iron, sulfur, and oxygen), in solution. This reaction may be stated thus:

Iron   +   Sulfuric Acid   =
An element   A compound

Hydrogen   +   Iron sulfate
An element   A compound

4. Double Displacement. In double displacement reactions, two compounds react to form two new compounds by exchanging parts. To observe a reaction of this type we need a special solution. Let us make it first.

EXPERIMENT 5: Phenolphthalein is the active ingredient of many common laxatives. It can be extracted from them as follows. Crack and peel off the sugar coating from two Feen-a-mint* tablets, taking care to disturb as little as possible the yellow powder just under the coating. Place the two tablets in a small cup and add one tablespoon of rubbing alcohol. Stir until the yellow phenolphthalein is dissolved from the gum, forming a pale yellow solution.

Keep this phenolphthalein solution in a stoppered

---

* The equal sign (=) indicates that the substances on the left are transformed into the substance on the right during chemical change. As we will see later, the total weight of substances combining on the left must precisely equal the total weight of products formed on the right. The equal sign emphasizes this quantitative nature of the science of chemistry. Furthermore, many chemical changes are reversible, which means that the substances on the right can be induced to re-form the substances on the left.

---

* Trade Name.

bottle. An old well-rinsed nose-drop bottle would be excellent. We will use this solution several times. Phenolphthalein has the property of turning red in solutions of alkalis, but is colorless in acid solutions. An **alkali** is a compound which is the opposite of an **acid.** An alkali **neutralizes** an acid to water and salt solution. Such a reaction is a double displacement type. Let us observe one.

EXPERIMENT 6: Dissolve a few crystals of lye (sodium hydroxide) in one quarter cup of water. Add 2 or 3 drops of phenolphthalein solution prepared in Experiment 5. The red color shows that sodium hydroxide is an alkali. Add vinegar (acetic acid) drop by drop with stirring to the sodium hydroxide solution. When the phenolphthalein becomes colorless, the reaction is completed.

All of the substances involved in the reaction in Experiment 6 are compounds. The reaction may be stated thus:

Sodium Hydroxide	+	Acetic Acid	=	Sodium Acetate	+	Water
An alkali		*An acid*		*A salt*		

In every chemical change, energy is either given off or absorbed. **Energy** is the ability to do work. Heat, light, sound, and electricity are some of the many forms of energy. Fuel oil burns to produce heat. Magnesium burns in a flash bulb to produce light. Dynamite explodes to produce sound and

shock. On the other hand, water decomposes into its elements, hydrogen and oxygen, by absorbing electrical energy. A photograph is made by the absorption of light by the chemicals in the film.

It is important not to confuse the energy change in a reaction with the conditions under which a reaction occurs. Wood burns to produce heat, but not at room temperature. The wood must first be heated to a point considerably above room temperature before it will begin to burn. The high initial temperature is a condition under which the reaction of burning takes place. The production of heat by burning wood is a result of the reaction itself.

Many reactions take place only in the presence of a **catalyst.** A catalyst is a substance which alters the speed or rate of a chemical without becoming permanently changed itself. A catalyst which speeds up a reaction is called a **negative catalyst.** Water is a catalyst for many reactions. Perfectly dry iron will not rust in dry air. Dry crystals of acetic acid will not react as in Experiment 6 with dry crystals of sodium hydroxide.

EXPERIMENT 7: With a match, try to burn a cube of sugar. Notice that the sugar melts but does not burn. Dip the other end of the sugar cube into some cigarette or cigar ashes. *Bear in mind that these ashes have already been burned!* Apply a flame to the ash-covered end of the cube. It now burns because of the presence of a catalyst.

Structure of Matter

We have seen that chemical change involves a complete transformation of one substance into another. Early chemists reasoned that such a thorough change must in some way be related to the way matter is constructed. They sought to find out the nature of the building blocks which made up the different varieties of matter. They hoped that once they could create some sort of "model" of the fundamental particles of matter, they could then explain not only the various ways that matter was constructed, but also the behavior of substances during the process of chemical change.

As early as 450 B.C. the Greek philosophers reasoned that all matter was built up of tiny particles called **atoms.** Development of this idea was slow, but in 1802 DALTON suggested that all matter could

be broken down into elements, the smallest particles of which he referred to as atoms. By 1895, the theory that atoms existed was extended to account for particles of matter even smaller than atoms. By 1913, evidence of the presence of several subatomic particles had been gathered. The work of probing into the structure of matter continues at the present moment. We have not yet learned the full story, and many features of the behavior of matter are still unexplained. There is much room in the field of science for young people with talent.

From a chemical point of view an atomic model has been developed which is quite satisfactory. We will use it to explain all common phenomena. We will also look at some of its weaker points in order to show that science is not cut and dried, but rather is constantly changing as men of science progress toward a better understanding of Nature.

ATOMS

If we were to take a strip of aluminum or a piece of copper (elements) and subdivide them into smaller and smaller pieces, we would eventually come to a tiny particle which, if further subdivided, would no longer show the properties of the element. We call them the smallest particle of an element which has all the properties of the element an **atom.** Atoms are really quite small, too small to be seen with the most powerful microscope yet developed. It would take about 100 million atoms to make a line one inch long. You can thus see that a one inch cube would contain a fantastic number of atoms. The important thing is that atoms are both small and numerous.

ATOMIC STRUCTURE

In 1913 NEILS BOHR, a Danish scientist, suggested an atomic model which serves chemists well to the present day. He pictured the atom as consisting of three basic kinds of particles: **electrons, protons,** and **neutrons.** The electron is a particle possessing a negative (−) electrical charge. The proton is a particle consisting of a positive (+) electrical charge equal in magnitude (but opposite in type) to the charge on the electron. The neutron is a particle with no electrical

TABLE IV		
Particle	*Charge*	*Weight*
Electron	−1	0
Proton	+1	1
Neutron	0	1

charge. The proton and neutron have essentially the same weight. A weight of one unit has been assigned to each. The electron is much smaller, weighing about 1/1848 times as much as either of the other two. From a chemical point of view, we can consider the weight of the electron to be zero. Table IV summarizes the properties of these three particles which make up an atom.

In the Bohr model of the atom, protons and neutrons are considered to be packed together in the center of the atom to form what is known as the **nucleus.** Electrons travel about this nucleus in

orbits which are at relatively large distances from the nucleus. The average nucleus occupies about one-ten thousandth of the total volume of an atom. The situation is quite similar to the planets revolving about the sun in our solar system.

At this point, three important characteristics of atoms can be stated:

1. Despite the presence of electrically charged particles in atoms, all elements are observed to be electrically neutral. Therefore, the number of positive protons in the nucleus of an atom must be equal to the number of electrons surrounding the nucleus.

2. Since elements differ from one another, their atoms must differ structurally. Each element has an **atomic number.** The atomic number is more than just a catalog number. It is a special characteristic of each element. In the Bohr model, the atomic number is equal to the number of electrons revolving about the nucleus of the atom. Thus, each atom of hydrogen (atomic number 1) has a single electron spinning about the hydrogen nucleus. Each atom of uranium (atomic number 92) has 92 electrons spinning about the uranium nucleus. Since atoms are electrically neutral, the atomic number also equals the number of protons present in the nucleus of an atom.

3. Equal numbers of atoms of different elements weighed under the same conditions have a different weight. Therefore, the atoms of different elements have different atomic weights. The **atomic weight** of an **atom** is equal to the sum of the number of protons and the number of neutrons in the nucleus of the atom. Thus, all of the weight of an atom comes from its nucleus. Atomic weights are relative, which is to say they do not give the number of grams or pounds that an atom weighs, but they merely tell how much heavier or lighter an atom of one element is than another. For example, the atomic weight of oxygen is 16 and the atomic weight of helium is 4. This means that each atom of oxygen weighs 16/4, or 4 times as much as each atom of helium.

These three atomic characteristics are summarized in Table V.

It may be well to pause here to see how our atomic model is shaping up. Can you visualize a nugget or kernel like a popcorn ball with tiny specks of dust spinning round and round it? Perhaps the popcorn ball also has peanuts in it, giving it two different kinds of particles. We can think of the popcorn as protons and the peanuts as neu-

TABLE V

Characteristic	Structural Explanation
Neutral atoms	Number of electrons = Number of protons
Atomic Number	Number of electrons = Number of protons = atomic number
Atomic Weight	Number of protons + Number of neutrons = atomic weight

trons, all tightly held together in the nucleus. The specks of dust spinning around would be the electrons, equal in number to the pieces of popcorn. The specks of dust would contribute practically nothing to the total weight of our imaginary atom. A model of hydrogen would consist of a single piece of popcorn with a single speck of dust spinning around it. A uranium model would contain quite a lot of popcorn (92 pieces)

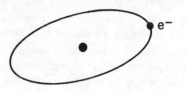

HYDROGEN
At. No. 1
At. Wt. 1

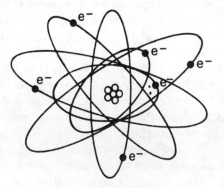

CARBON
At. No. 6
At. Wt. 12

FIGURE 8.

and many peanuts (146). It would also be quite dusty (92 specks). The sum of the particles in the uranium nucleus is 238, which is the atomic weight of uranium. Figure 8 gives us another picture of our model.

Distribution of Electrons

Our model of an atom is still incomplete. The electrons which revolve about the nucleus do so according to a definite pattern. Groups of electrons maintain definite average distances from the nucleus, thereby forming what may be called **shells** of electrons surrounding the nucleus. Each shell is capable of containing a definite number of electrons, the number increasing as the distance from the nucleus increases. The shells are designated by letters—k, l, m, n, o, p—starting with the shell nearest the nucleus. The k-shell can contain up to 2 electrons, the l-shell up to 8, the m-shell up to 18, and the n-shell up to 32. The maximum number of electrons in any shell can be calculated from the relationship:

$$\text{Number} = 2\,s^2 \qquad (1)$$

where:

Number = maximum number of electrons possible in the shell.
s = the number of the shell (k = 1, l = 2, m = 3, etc.).

The distribution of electrons by shells for the atoms of each element is given in Table VI. As you read through this list starting with element number 1, hydrogen, be sure to notice the following points:

1. In the first 18 elements the new electron is always added in the outermost shell until the shell is filled. Then a new shell is started.

2. In the higher numbered elements there can be 2 or even 3 unfilled shells of electrons.

3. Eight electrons temporarily fill each of the shells beyond the m-shell, and a new shell must be started before more electrons can be fitted into the temporarily filled shell.

TABLE VI
DISTRIBUTION OF ELECTRONS

At. No.	Element	k	l	m	n	o
1	Hydrogen	1				
2	Helium	2				
3	Lithium	2	1			
4	Beryllium	2	2			
5	Boron	2	3			
6	Carbon	2	4			
7	Nitrogen	2	5			
8	Oxygen	2	6			
9	Fluorine	2	7			
10	Neon	2	8			
11	Sodium	2	8	1		
12	Magnesium	2	8	2		
13	Aluminum	2	8	3		
14	Silicon	2	8	4		
15	Phosphorus	2	8	5		
16	Sulfur	2	8	6		
17	Chlorine	2	8	7		
18	Argon	2	8	8		
19	Potassium	2	8	8	1	
20	Calcium	2	8	8	2	
21	Scandium	2	8	9	2	
22	Titanium	2	8	10	2	
23	Vanadium	2	8	11	2	
24	Chromium	2	8	13	1	
25	Manganese	2	8	13	2	
26	Iron	2	8	14	2	
27	Cobalt	2	8	15	2	
28	Nickel	2	8	16	2	
29	Copper	2	8	18	1	
30	Zinc	2	8	18	2	
31	Gallium	2	8	18	3	
32	Germanium	2	8	18	4	
33	Arsenic	2	8	18	5	
34	Selenium	2	8	18	6	
35	Bromine	2	8	18	7	
36	Krypton	2	8	18	8	
37	Rubidium	2	8	18	8	1
38	Strontium	2	8	18	8	2
39	Yttrium	2	8	18	9	2
40	Zirconium	2	8	18	10	2
41	Niobium	2	8	18	12	1
42	Molybdenum	2	8	18	13	1
43	Technetium	2	8	18	14	1
44	Ruthenium	2	8	18	15	1
45	Rhodium	2	8	18	16	1
46	Palladium	2	8	18	18	0
47	Silver	2	8	18	18	1
48	Cadmium	2	8	18	18	2
49	Indium	2	8	18	18	3
50	Tin	2	8	18	18	4
51	Antimony	2	8	18	18	5

At. No.	Element	k	l	m	n	o	p	q
52	Tellurium	2	8	18	18	6		
53	Iodine	2	8	18	18	7		
54	Xenon	2	8	18	18	8		
55	Cesium	2	8	18	18	8	1	
56	Barium	2	8	18	18	8	2	
57	Lanthanum	2	8	18	18	9	2	
58	Cerium	2	8	18	20	8	2	
59	Pra'mium	2	8	18	21	8	2	
60	Neodymium	2	8	18	22	8	2	
61	Promethium	2	8	18	23	8	2	
62	Samarium	2	8	18	24	8	2	
63	Europium	2	8	18	25	8	2	
64	Gadolinium	2	8	18	25	9	2	
65	Terbium	2	8	18	27	8	2	
66	Dysprosium	2	8	18	28	8	2	
67	Holmium	2	8	18	29	8	2	
68	Erbium	2	8	18	30	8	2	
69	Thulium	2	8	18	31	8	2	
70	Ytterbium	2	8	18	32	8	2	
71	Lutetium	2	8	18	32	9	2	
72	Hafnium	2	8	18	32	10	2	
73	Tantalum	2	8	18	32	11	2	
74	Tungsten	2	8	18	32	12	2	
75	Rhenium	2	8	18	32	13	2	
76	Osmium	2	8	18	32	14	2	
77	Iridium	2	8	18	32	17	0	
78	Platinum	2	8	18	32	17	1	
79	Gold	2	8	18	32	18	1	
80	Mercury	2	8	18	32	18	2	
81	Thallium	2	8	18	32	18	3	
82	Lead	2	8	18	32	18	4	
83	Bismuth	2	8	18	32	18	5	
84	Polonium	2	8	18	32	18	6	
85	Astatine	2	8	18	32	18	7	
86	Radon	2	8	18	32	18	8	
87	Francium	2	8	18	32	18	8	1
88	Radium	2	8	18	32	18	8	2
89	Actinium	2	8	18	32	18	9	2
90	Thorium	2	8	18	32	18	10	2
91	Pr'tinium	2	8	18	32	20	9	2
92	Uranium	2	8	18	32	21	9	2
93	Neptunium	2	8	18	32	22	9	2
94	Plutonium	2	8	18	32	23	9	2
95	Americium	2	8	18	32	24	9	2
96	Curium	2	8	18	32	25	9	2
97	Berkelium	2	8	18	32	26	9	2
98	Californium	2	8	18	32	27	9	2
99	Einsteinium	2	8	18	32	28	9	2
100	Fermium	2	8	18	32	29	9	2
101	Mendelvium	2	8	18	32	30	9	2
102	Nobelium	2	8	18	32	31	9	2
103	Lawrencium							

4. There are never more than 8 electrons in the outermost shell.

On the basis of the distribution of electrons we can detect four different structural types of atoms in Table VI. These are:

1. Inert elements—Those with all shells filled. (These are underlined in Table VI.)

2. Simple elements—Those with only one unfilled shell.

3. Transition elements—Those with two unfilled shells.

4. Rare earth elements—Those with three unfilled shells.

At first glance, this whole problem of the distribution of electrons in our atomic model might appear to be quite imposing. Actually it is not as hard as it may seem. Remember that we want a model which is useful in explaining chemical change. Two vitally important points are basic in relating chemical change with atomic structure. These are:

Only electrons are involved in chemical change. The nuclei of atoms are in no way altered during chemical change.

In particular, **the electrons in the outermost shell are affected during chemical change.** Occasionally electrons from the second outermost shell may be affected in some of the higher numbered elements, but the influence of chemical change never penetrates the atom deeper than the second outermost shell.

ISOTOPES

Evidence is available to show that not all of the atoms of a given element are identical. They may vary in atomic weight. Atoms of an element with different atomic weights are called **isotopes** of the element.

Examine Figure 9. This shows three different kinds of hydrogen atoms. The first has an atomic weight of 1, the second has an atomic weight of 2, and the third has an atomic weight of 3. Notice that the only structural difference is the number of neutrons in the nucleus of each isotope. All three isotopes have but one electron because all are atoms of hydrogen and have atomic number 1. Similarly, all three isotopes have a single proton in the nucleus because each must remain electrically neutral. Isotopes, then, are atoms of the same element possessing different numbers of neutrons in their nuclei.

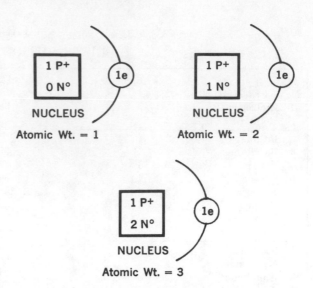

FIGURE 9. The 3 Isotopes of Hydrogen

ATOMIC WEIGHTS

Almost all of the elements have isotopes. The relative abundance of each isotope of a given element in Nature varies considerably. For example, the element chlorine has two principal isotopes, one of atomic weight 35 and one of atomic weight 37. If you were to pick up a container of chlorine, about 75% of the chlorine atoms in the container would have atomic weight 35, and the other 25% would have atomic weight 37. The average weight of all the atoms in the container would then be about 35.5. The listed atomic weight of chlorine can be found in the table on page 164. You will find it to be 35.457. This number is the average atomic weight of all the atoms present in a sample of natural chlorine. The listed **atomic weight** of any **element** is the average of the atomic weights of the isotopes of the element, taking into account the relative abundance of each isotope in a natural sample.

On a practical basis, the average atomic weight of an element is measured by comparing the weight of a given number of atoms of the element to the weight of the same number of atoms of oxygen. The weight of oxygen is taken as 16. How chemists know when they are dealing with a given number of atoms will be described later.

SYMBOLS

In Table III the symbols of some of the more common elements were given. These symbols are very important in chemistry for they represent three things:

1. The name of an element.
2. One atom of an element.
3. A quantity of the element equal in weight to its atomic weight.

For example, when we write the symbol O, we mean not only the name, oxygen, but we also represent a single oxygen atom with this symbol. What is perhaps most important of all, since oxygen has an atomic weight of 16, the symbol O stands for 16 units of weight of this element. This may be 16 grams, or 16 pounds, or 16 tons. We can select any system of weight units we need when we use symbols to indicate quantities of elements. This idea will be developed further in the next chapter.

THE BOHR MODEL

Our atomic model, as created by BOHR, is now sufficiently developed to explain chemical phenomena. It contains a nucleus composed of positive protons and neutral neutrons which supply the weight of the atom. Surrounding the nucleus are shells of electrons carrying sufficient negative charge to offset the positive charge on the nucleus. Figure 10 is a diagram of the atomic structure of an isotope of phosphorus of atomic weight 31. It shows the number of protons and neutrons in the nucleus, and the number and distruibution of electrons in the shells. The atomic weight is the sum of the number of protons and neutrons in the nucleus. The atomic number is the sum of the electrons in the shells.

If you are familiar with the properties of electricity, you know that opposite charges attract one another and like charges repel one another. As you look at Figure 10, two questions might be raised.

Why aren't the negative electrons attracted into the positive nucleus, causing our model to collapse? The answer to this is in the idea that the electrons are spinning about the nucleus. If you tie a piece of string to a ball and whirl it around, the string will get tight. The whirling motion of the ball causes it to want to fly away from your hand, but the string holds it back. In our atom, the electrical attraction of the positive nucleus and the negative electron just balances the tendency of the whirling electron to escape from the nucleus.

A second question suggested by Figure 10 is:

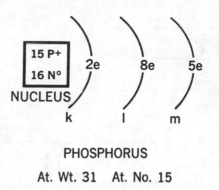

PHOSPHORUS

At. Wt. 31   At. No. 15

FIGURE 10.

Why doesn't the nucleus fly apart as a result of the repulsion of the protons on each other? In answer to this we can merely state that there is some sort of packing energy holding nuclei together. This energy is not always 100% efficient, because we know that some nuclei do break apart in a process known as **radioactivity.** This will be described later. The exact nature of the packing energy is not yet understood. At this moment scientists all over the world are at work trying to solve this secret of Nature.

THE PERIODIC TABLE

On the basis of electronic distribution, all of the elements have been arranged in a table called the **Periodic Table.** Figure 11 gives this arrangement, showing the atomic number, symbol, and atomic weight of each element. Where atomic weights have not yet been accurately measured, the approximate value is given in brackets.

The vertical columns are called **groups.** All of the elements in a group have the same electronic structure in their outermost shell. For example, all of the elements in Group I have 1 electron in the outermost shell (Check this with Table VI). Elements in Group II have 2 outermost electrons, elements in Group III have 3 outermost electrons, and so on. The inert elements at the far right of the table have 8 outermost electrons. The transition elements may be thought of as arranged in **sub-groups,** and all of these have 2 outermost electrons with the exception of the Copper-Silver-Gold subgroup which has only 1 outermost electron.

The horizontal rows of elements are called **periods.** All the elements in a given period have the same number of shells of electrons. For example, the elements in Period 1 have but one shell

PERIODIC TABLE OF ELEMENTS

PERIODS	GROUP I	GROUP II					TRANSITION ELEMENTS						GROUP III	GROUP IV	GROUP V	GROUP VI	GROUP VII	INERT Elem.
1	1 H 1.008																	2 He 4.003
2	3 Li 6.940	4 Be 9.02											5 B 10.82	6 C 12.010	7 N 14.008	8 O 16.000	9 F 19.00	10 Ne 20.183
3	11 Na 22.997	12 Mg 24.32											13 Al 26.97	14 Si 28.06	15 P 30.98	16 S 32.06	17 Cl 35.457	18 A 39.944
4	19 K 39.096	20 Ca 40.08	21 Sc 45.10	22 Ti 47.90	23 V 50.95	24 Cr 52.01	25 Mn 54.93	26 Fe 55.85	27 Co 58.94	28 Ni 58.69	29 Cu 63.57	30 Zn 65.38	31 Ga 69.72	32 Ge 72.60	33 As 74.91	34 Se 78.96	35 Br 79.916	36 Kr 83.7
5	37 Rb 85.48	38 Sr 87.63	39 Y 88.92	40 Zr 91.22	41 Nb 92.91	42 Mo 95.95	43 Tc [99]	44 Ru 101.7	45 Rh 102.91	46 Pd 106.7	47 Ag 107.88	48 Cd 112.41	49 In 114.76	50 Sn 118.70	51 Sb 121.76	52 Te 127.61	53 I 126.92	54 Xe 131.3
6	55 Cs 132.91	56 Ba 137.36	57 La 138.9 / 58 71	72 Hf 178.6	73 Ta 180.88	74 W 183.92	75 Re 186.31	76 Os 190.2	77 Ir 193.1	78 Pt 195.23	79 Au 197.2	80 Hg 200.61	81 Tl 204.39	82 Pb 207.21	83 Bi 209.00	84 Po [210]	85 At [210]	86 Rn [222]
7	87 Fr [223]	88 Ra 226.05	89 Ac [227] / 90 103															

LANTHANIDE SERIES	57 La 138.92	58 Ce 140.13	59 Pr 140.92	60 Nd 144.27	61 Pm [145]	62 Sm 150.43	63 Eu 152.0	64 Gd 156.9	65 Tb 159.2	66 Dy 162.46	67 Ho 163.5	68 Er 167.2	69 Tm 169.4	70 Yb 173.04	71 Lu 174.99

RARE EARTH ELEM. 1

ACTINIDE SERIES	89 Ac [227]	90 Th 232.12	91 Pa 231	92 U 238.07	93 Np 237	94 Pu [242]	95 Am [243]	96 Cm [243]	97 Bk [245]	98 Cf [246]	99 Es [254]	100 Fm [255]	101 Md [258]	102 No [253]	103

FIGURE 11.

of electrons. Those in Period 2 have 2 shells, and so on. It is important to note that the last element of each period is an inert element. The lanthanide series of rare earth elements is part of Period 6, and the actinide series of rare earth elements is part of Period 7.

All four structural types of elements are shown in the table. The inert elements form a group at the extreme right. The simple elements are found in Groups I through VII. The transition elements are at the center. The rare earth elements are extracted from the table and listed at the bottom.

It has been pointed out that the chemical behavior of elements is based upon the electronic structure of their atoms, particularly the structure of the outer shell. Since each *group* of elements has the same structure in the outer shell, we can expect the members of a group to show similar chemical behavior. For this reason we can expect to find much use for the Periodic Table as we explore the chemical behavior of elements.

Compounds

Elements in the free or uncombined state make up only a small fraction of matter. Most of matter occurs as compounds or mixtures of compounds. Let us now put our Bohr model of the atom to the test to see whether it is useful in explaining how elements can combine to form all the various compounds.

THE INERT ELEMENTS

Take another look at Table VI. Pay special attention to the elements which are just above the

separating lines. Notice that except for helium, all of these elements have eight electrons in the **outermost shell**. Then notice that the next element in each case has one electron in a new shell. Why doesn't this new electron go into one of the existing shells? The answer is that it simply doesn't fit, which is another way of saying that the shells of electrons in the elements just above the separating lines are, for the moment at least, filled up or saturated with electrons.

Now look up each of the elements just above the separating lines in the Periodic Table (Fig.

Property	Helium He	Neon Ne	Argon A	Krypton Kr	Xenon Xe	Radon Rn
Atomic Number	2	10	18	36	54	86
Atomic Weight	4.003	20.183	39.944	83.7	131.3	222
Density, g/cc.	0.00018	0.0009	0.00179	0.00374	0.0058	0.0099
Solubility, ml/100 ml. of water	1.49	1.5	5.6	6.0	28.4	0.000002
Parts in Million parts of dry air	4	12.3	9400	0.5	0.06	——
Boiling Point, °F.	−452.2	−410.8	−302.4	−243.4	−161.0	−79.5
Melting Point, °F.	−458.1	−416.6	−308.7	−250.8	−170.0	−96.1

TABLE VII
PROPERTIES OF INERT ELEMENTS

11). You will find all of them in the column at the far right under the heading: Inert Elements. Each of them occurs at the end of a period. Eventually, in subsequent periods in our atmosphere, the outermost shells may consist of more than eight electrons.

These inert elements all have one chemical property which is: they have no chemistry! They combine with nothing. They form no compounds either among themselves or with other elements. They are indeed chemically inert. All of these elements are gases at room temperature, and all except radon are present in inert elements; their electronic configuration obviously represents a temporarily saturated state.

You might ask why we should bring up this group of elements which form no compounds in a chapter devoted to the formation of compounds. Well, these elements possess a structure so stable that they resist compound formation. All the other elements are less stable since they do form compounds. It is suggested that when active elements combine to form compounds, they undergo a rearrangement of their electronic structures in order to gain an electronic configuration similar to that of a nearby inert element. Such a rearrangement causes the active elements to become structurally more stable.

VALENCE

The tendency of elements to form compounds through a shift of electronic structure is known as **valence.** Actually the term valence may be used to indicate two different things. One is **valence mechanism,** that is, the manner in which elements attain a stable electronic distribution. The other is **valence number,** that is, the number of electrons of an element involved in forming a compound. Let us examine first the valence mechanism, the process by which compounds are formed.

Electrovalence

Consider for a moment the structure of an atom of sodium. It has one electron in its outermost shell and eight electrons in its next outermost shell. If the lone electron were to be removed from the sodium atom, the remaining electronic structure would be identical to the structure of neon, an inert element which immediately precedes sodium in the Periodic Table. The removal of the electron would change the nature of the particle by causing it to have one excess positive charge. It would no longer be a sodium atom for, although its nucleus is still that of sodium, it would possess an insufficient number of electrons to be a sodium atom. Nor would it be neon, for its nucleus has too many protons. An electrically charged particle of the type described is called an **ion.** The one being considered is a sodium ion. Ions possess properties which are totally different from the atoms from which they come.

The idea of forming an ion from an atom is reasonable enough, but where can the electron go? The elements near sodium in the Periodic Table, like potassium or calcium or magnesium, would not accept an additional electron, for it would not bring them nearer a stable electronic configuration. But over near the other end of the Periodic Table are elements like chlorine. Chlorine has seven electrons in its outermost shell. The addition of one or more electrons would give it the same stable configuration as argon, another inert element. The addition of the electron to the chlorine atom would form a particle with one excess negative charge. It would be neither a chlorine atom nor an argon atom. It would be a **chloride ion.** Once the electron has been transferred from the sodium atom to the chlorine atom, we then have oppositely charged ions which are capable of attracting one another electrically. They do so to form the familiar compound, sodium chloride, which is ordinary table salt. Figure 12 shows the formation of this compound. The process of forming a compound through the **transfer of electrons** is called **electrovalence.**

A careful consideration of the Periodic Table will lead to the discovery of the elements which show electrovalence. Elements in Groups I, II, and III give up 1, 2, or 3 electrons respectively to form positive ions. These elements are said to exhibit **positive valence.** Elements in Groups V, VI, and VII accept 3, 2, or 1 electron respectively to form negative ions. These elements are said to exhibit **negative valence.** Table VIII gives the symbols for typical ions formed by elements in each of these groups.

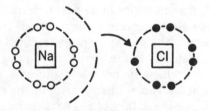

FIGURE 12. Electrovalence

Theoretically, the elements in Group IV can form ions either by gaining or by losing electrons.

It is not difficult to see that it takes energy to remove an electron from a sodium atom, or to force an electron into a chlorine atom. Similarly it seems reasonable that it takes more energy to strip the 2 electrons from a magnesium atom than to remove the 1 electron from a sodium atom. The ease with which an element loses or gains electrons is a measure of its **activity.** On the basis of energy considerations we may state the following. Elements in Groups I and VII are more active than those in Groups III and V. Only elements near the

bottom of Group IV form ions. Thus, it can be seen that activity decreases as we consider elements toward the center of the Periodic Table.

Within a given Group, there is also a range of chemical activity. Considering Group I, the negative electron to be removed from the hydrogen atom is much closer to the positive nucleus than the electron to be removed from the cesium atom. Thus it can be seen that it takes less energy to form a cesium ion than to form a hydrogen ion. Therefore, cesium is much more active than hydrogen. On the other hand, in Group VII, similar reasoning tells us that it will require more energy to force an electron into a bromine atom where the positive nucleus is buried within a cloud of negative electrons, than to force an electron into a fluorine atom where the positive nucleus is relatively close to the outermost shell and can help attract the extra electron in. On the basis of energy considerations we may state that the most active electrovalent elements are to be found in the **lower left** and **upper right** areas of the Periodic Table.

The transition and rare earth elements also form ions. However, because both their outermost and second outermost shells are unfilled, they give up not only their outermost electrons to form ions, but they may also give up some electrons from their second outermost shell as well. Thus it is common to find these elements forming two or more different positive ions.

The compounds formed by electrovalence, then, really consist of oppositely charged ions packed and held together by electrical attraction. Such compounds are called **ionic agglomerates.**

Covalence

On the basis of electrovalence, we would expect an element like carbon, which is in Group IV, to be fairly inert and form few compounds. Yet this element forms more compounds than all the other elements put together. Obviously, then, there must be some other valence mechanism.

Carbon has four electrons in its outermost shell. Hydrogen has one electron in its only shell. Suppose that four hydrogen atoms were to approach

	TABLE VIII					
	SYMBOLS OF TYPICAL IONS					
Group	*I*	*II*	*III*	*V*	*VI*	*VII*
Ionic Symbols	Na^+	Ca^{++}	Al^{+++}	N^{---}	O^{--}	F^-
	K^+	Mg^{++}			S^{--}	Cl^-

a carbon atom very closely, so closely that the shell of each hydrogen atom penetrated into the outermost shell of the carbon atom. The electrons in these interpenetrated shells would then be influenced by the nuclei of both types of atoms. Both atoms would, in a sense, be sharing electrons. What would be the net effect? Figure 13 shows us. The electron of each hydrogen atom is indicated by an x, and the carbon electrons are indicated by dots (the inner carbon atoms are not shown). We can see that two electrons are now associated with each hydrogen atom giving them the stable helium configuration, and eight electrons are associated with the carbon atom giving it the stable neon configuration. Both types of atoms have attained stable structures through this sharing

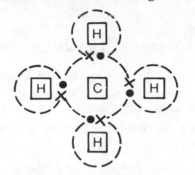

FIGURE 13. Covalence

process. The compound described is methane, the principal ingredient of natural gas used in cooking. The process of forming a compound through the sharing of pairs of electrons is called **covalence.**

A pair of electrons shared between two atoms is often called a **bond.** In methane, carbon is united to four hydrogen atoms by single bonds. Many compounds exist in which two or even three pairs of electrons are shared by two atoms. Figure 14 shows the bonding in carbon dioxide, a gas which bubbles out of carbonated water, and of acetylene, a gas commonly used in welding. Two pairs of electrons are shared between each oxygen atom and the central carbon atom in carbon dioxide, forming eight electrons around each of the three atoms present. Three pairs of electrons are shared between the two carbon atoms in acetylene, and a single pair is shared between the carbon and hydrogen atoms. Carbon dioxide is said to have two **double bonds,** and acetylene is said to have a **triple bond** between its two carbon atoms.

The net effect of covalence is to form tiny particles of compounds containing a definite number of atoms. These discreet, individual particles which possess all the properties of the compound

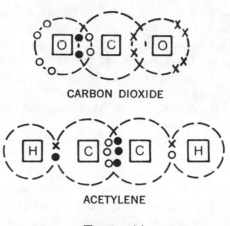

CARBON DIOXIDE

ACETYLENE

FIGURE 14.

are called **molecules.** Molecules are present only in covalent compounds. Electrovalent compounds do not have molecules, but rather, are made up of ions packed together. Table IX summarizes the differences between electrovalence and covalence.

VALENCE NUMBER

The **valence number** of an element is the number of electrons of the element involved in the formation of a compound. Since free elements are

TABLE IX

VALENCE MECHANISMS

Mechanism:	*Electrovalence*	*Covalence*
Process:	Complete transfer of electrons	Sharing of pairs of electrons
Via:	Formation of ions	Interpenetration of atoms
Product:	Ionic agglomerates	Molecules

not combined with other elements, **elements in the free state have a valence number of zero.** Most elements exhibit a variety of valence numbers depending upon the particular compound they happen to be part of. To help you determine the valence number of an element in a compound, the following general rules are given:

1. Elements of Group I of the Periodic Table normally have a valence of +1.
2. Elements of Group II normally have a valence number of +2.
3. Elements of Group VII normally have a

valence number of -1 in **binary compounds** (compounds which contain only 2 elements).

4. In electrovalent compounds in general:
   a. The valence number of an ion is numerically equal to the charge on the ion.
   b. Positive ions have positive valence numbers.
   c. Negative ions have negative valence numbers.
5. In covalent compounds in general:
   a. The valence number of an atom in a covalent compound is numerically equal to the number of its electrons shared with atoms different from itself. For example, referring again to Figure 14, the carbon atom in carbon dioxide shares all four of its outermost electrons with oxygen atoms, so its valence number is 4. But in acetylene, three carbon electrons are shared with another carbon atom while one electron is shared with a hydrogen atom. The carbon-to-carbon bonds don't count, so the valence number of carbon in acetylene is 1.
   b. Oxygen always has a valence number of -2 in its compounds (except peroxides, where its valence number is -1).
   c. Elements like carbon, silicon, nitrogen, phosphorus, sulfur, and chlorine, when they are centrally located in covalent molecules, normally have positive valence numbers.
6. The net sum of all the valence numbers exhibited in a given compound must be zero.

These rules generally apply in most chemical compounds. Where exceptions occur, they will be pointed out.

FORMULAS

The **formula** of a compound is a ratio of the number of atoms of each element present in the compound. In electrovalent compounds, the formula gives the simplest ratio of constituents in whole numbers. In covalent compounds, the formula gives the exact number of atoms of each element present in a molecule of the compound.

The symbols of the elements present are used in writing formulas. If more than one atom of an element is required in the formula, a subscript numeral is written behind the symbol of the element to indicate the number of its atoms in the formula. For example, the formula for water is H_2O. This means that in every molecule of water there are two atoms of hydrogen and one atom of oxygen. Note that when only one atom of an element is present in the formula, the subscript 1 is understood and not written. The formula for sodium chloride, $NaCl$, tells us that this compound contains equal numbers of sodium and chlorine atoms. We know from previous discussions that in this compound the atoms are actually present as ions. A formula gives no indication as to whether a compound is electrovalent or covalent. This characteristic must be ascertained from the properties of the compound.

FORMULAS AND VALENCE

If we know the valence of each element in a compound, we can easily write its formula. Let us look at a few examples.

EXAMPLE 1: A compound consists solely of magnesium and chlorine. What is its formula?

SOLUTION: Mg, a Group II element, has a valence number of $+2$. Cl, a Group VII element, has a valence number of -1.

Therefore, to form a compound in which the sum of the valence numbers is zero, it will take two chlorine atoms to nullify each magnesium atom. The formula of this compound must therefore be:
$$MgCl_2.$$

The name of this compound is magnesium chloride. The suffix, **-ide,** is used with the root of the name of the negative element in binary compounds. The terms *oxide, sulfide, nitride, phosphide, carbide, fluoride, bromide,* and *iodide* appear in the names of compounds in which these negative elements are combined with one other positive element to form a binary compound.

Look carefully at the formula of magnesium chloride, $MgCl_2$. Behind Mg, the subscript 1 is understood. Behind Cl is the subscript 2. Do you see that the valence number of each element has been criss-crossed and written as a subscript behind the symbol of the other element? Let us try this idea with another example.

EXAMPLE 2: What is the formula of aluminum oxide?

SOLUTION: Al, a Group III element, has a valence

number of $+3$. O, a Group VI element, has a valence number of -2.

Criss-crossing the valence numbers and using them as subscripts, we have the formula:

$$Al_2O_3.$$

Note that the sign of the valence numbers is ignored when we write formulas.

Does this formula for aluminum oxide satisfy the rule of zero net valence for compounds? Let's check it.

For Al: $2 \times (+3) = +6$.
For O: $3 \times (-2) = -6$.
Net valence (sum) $= 0$.

EXAMPLE 3: What is the formula of calcium sulfide?

SOLUTION; Ca, a Group II element, has a valence number of $+2$. S, a group VI element, has a valence number of -2. Criss-crossing the valence numbers and writing them as subscripts, we have the formula:

$$Ca_2S_2.$$

However, this is not the simplest formula for this compound. This formula tells us that the ratio of calcium to sulfur atoms is $2:2$. This, of course, is the same as a ratio of $1:1$. Therefore, to write this formula in its simplest form, we reduce the subscripts to 1, and the formula becomes:

$$CaS.$$

Now let's look at the relationship between formulas and valence the other way. Suppose we are given the formula of a compound and we have to find the valence numbers of the elements present. Let's look at some examples.

EXAMPLE 4: What are the valence numbers of the elements in sulfur dioxide, SO_2?

SOLUTION: Our rules tell us that oxygen has a valence number of -2. Since there are 2 oxygen atoms in our formula, the total negative valence is then -4. Therefore, to satisfy the rule of zero valence in the compound, the valence number of S in SO_2, must be $+4$.

EXAMPLE 5: What are the valence numbers of the elements in sulfuric acid, H_2SO_4?

SOLUTION: O always has a valence number of -2. H, a Group I element, has a valence number of $+1$. The 4 O atoms give us a negative valence of $4 \times (-2) = -8$. The 2 H atoms give us a positive valence of $2 \times (+1) = +2$. Therefore, in order to make the net valence of the compound zero, S in H_2SO_4 has a valence number of $+6$.

RADICALS

In many chemical compounds there are clusters of elements which behave as if they were a single element. Such a group of elements is known as a **radical.** Consider the following series of compounds.

Series A
Sodium chloride $NaCl$
Sodium hydroxide $NaOH$
Sodium nitrate $NaNO_3$

Series B
Sodium sulfide Na_2S
Sodium sulfate Na_2SO_4
Sodium carbonate Na_2CO_3

In series A, the hydroxide (OH) and the nitrate (NO_3) groups have behaved toward sodium in exactly the same way as a single chlorine atom. Similarly, in series B, the sulfate (SO_4) and carbonate (CO_3) groups have behaved toward sodium in exactly the same way as a single sulfur atom. All of these groups are radicals.

The atoms within a radical are held together by covalent bonds, but in each case, they contain either an excess or a deficiency of electrons, causing the radical to possess an electrical charge. Thus, radicals are really complex ions. They then combine as a unit with other ions to form electrovalent compounds.

Radicals possess a net valence number equal in magnitude and sign to the net charge on the radical, just like any other ion. Table X gives the names, formulas, and valence numbers of the common radicals.

TABLE X
RADICALS

Valence Number $+1$
Ammonium NH_4^+

Valence Number -1
Acetate $C_2H_3O_2^-$
Bicarbonate HCO_3^-
Chlorate ClO_3^-
Hydroxide OH^-
Cyanide CN^-
Nitrate NO_3^-
Nitrite NO_2^-
Permanganate MnO_4^-

Valence Number -2
Carbonate CO_3^{--}
Chromate CrO_4^{--}
Dichromate $Cr_2O_7^{--}$
Sulfate SO_4^{--}
Sulfite SO_3^{--}

Valence Number -3
Phosphate PO_4^{---}

Since ammonium is a positive radical, it will form

compounds with all the negative radicals. Notice how the formulas of these compounds are written.

Ammonium acetate	$NH_4C_2H_3O_2$
Ammonium carbonate	$(NH_4)_2CO_3$
Ammonium phosphate	$(NH_4)_3PO_4$

Note that it takes two ammonium ions to satisfy the valence of the carbonate ion, and three ammonium ions to satisfy the valence of the phosphate ion. (Remember ammonium phosphate from the match stick?)

Look carefully at the names and formulas of the radicals. The suffixes -ite and -ate occur repeatedly. The suffixes are used only with radicals containing oxygen atoms. Notice that "-ite" radicals contain less oxygen than "-ate" radicals. For example:

Sulfite,	SO_3	Sulfate,	SO_4
Nitrite,	NO_2	Nitrate,	NO_3

Note also that there is no definite number of oxygen atoms in either type. The formulas of each radical must be learned individually through repeated use.

FORMULA OR MOLECULAR WEIGHTS

Just as symbols represent more than just the name of an element, so formulas stand for more than merely the name of a compound. A formula stands for three things:

1. The name of a compound.
2. One molecule of the compound (if it is covalently bonded).
3. A quantity of the compound equal in weight to its **formula weight.**

This concept of the formula weight of a compound is one of the most important ideas in chemistry. Its definition is very simple. **The formula weight of a compound is the sum of all the atomic weights of the elements present in the formula of the compound.** The formula weight of sodium chloride, NaCl, is found as follows:

Atomic weight of Na   22.997

Atomic weight of Cl	35.457
Formula weight of NaCl	$\overline{58.454.}$

Similarly, the formula weight of water, H_2O, would be found thus.

Atomic weight of H $(\times 2)$	2.016
Atomic weight of O	16.000
Formula weight of H_2O	$\overline{18.016.}$

Since the formula of a covalent compound represents the constituents of a molecule of the compound, the formula weight is usually referred to as the **molecular weight** of the compound. As a matter of fact, since a formula gives no indication as to the type of bonding present in a compound, the term **molecular weight** is commonly used even with electrovalent compounds, even though no molecule is present in these compounds. Thus, in usage, the terms formula weight and molecular weight are completely interchangeable.

A quantity of a compound equal in weight to its formula weight is called a **mole.** For example, 18.016 units of weight of water is one mole of water. 18.016 grams of water would be one **gram-mole;** 18.016 pounds of water would be one **pound-mole;** etc. Any quantity of a given compound can be expressed in terms of the number of moles of the compound present. The number of moles of a compound is found by using the following expression:

$$\frac{\textbf{Actual weight}}{\textbf{Formula weight}} = \textbf{Number of moles.} \quad \textbf{(1)}$$

We will begin to see in the next chapter how fundamentally important the concept of the mole is in the science of chemistry.

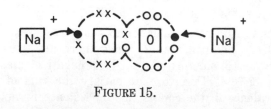

FIGURE 15.

Laws of Chemistry

We have seen how our model of an atom has given us a reasonable explanation of how atoms are combined in compounds. Now we want to look at some of the basic laws of chemistry. These laws were discovered only after years of painstaking observation of the behavior of Nature. It should

be kept in mind that *they were all known before our atomic model was created.* Each contributed to the development of our model. However, our primary concern now with these laws is with the assistance they can give us in understanding chemical change.

CONSERVATION OF MATTER

The Law of Conservation of Matter states that matter is neither created nor destroyed during chemical change. This means that the sum of the weights of the substances entering a chemical change must be precisely equal to the sum of the weights of the substance formed as a result of chemical change. This law has been verified by repeated study of chemical changes using delicate balances to measure the weights of **reactants** and **products.**

As we have seen, chemical change involves a **redistribution** of electrons, either by transfer or by sharing, but no new electrons are formed in chemical change, nor are any destroyed. The nuclei of atoms, which possess all the weight, remain unchanged and are carried along into new combinations solely as a result of the redistribution of electrons. Thus, our atomic model is consistent with the Law of Conservation of Matter.

DEFINITE PROPORTIONS

The Law of Definite Proportions states that a given compound always contains the same elements combined in the same proportions by weight. The decomposition of a compound into its elements for the purpose of finding out how much of each element is present is known as **analysis** of the compound. Repeated analysis of a compound always shows that it contains the same elements in the same weight proportions.

For example, water always contains 8 parts by weight of oxygen to 1 part by weight of hydrogen. Let us see if these results are consistent with our concepts of atomic structure and compound formation. Oxygen, with atomic weight 16.0, has 6 electrons in its outermost shell. Hydrogen, with atomic weight 1.0, has 1 electron in its shell. Oxygen needs 2 electrons to fill its outermost shell. Our concept of compound formation tells us that 2 hydrogen atoms are required to provide sufficient electrons to fill the outer shell of oxygen. Furthermore, this gives us a weight proportion of 16 parts by weight of oxygen (1 atom) to 2 parts by weight of hydrogen (2 atoms), which is consistent with the 8 to 1 proportion always found in the analysis of water.

The Law of Definite Proportions has further significance. The process of causing elements to combine to form compounds is known as **synthesis** of compounds. The Law of Definite Proportions dictates that a compound formed by synthesis must contain the same weight proportions of its elements as any other samples of this compound. Thus, water produced in a laboratory by combining oxygen and hydrogen must contain 8 parts by weight of oxygen to 1 part by weight of hydrogen, the same as any other water sample. Now suppose that one took 8 parts by weight of oxygen and 2 parts by weight of hydrogen and attempted to combine them. What would happen? Well, it can be seen that there is too much hydrogen. The 8 parts of oxygen would combine with 1 part of hydrogen, and the rest of the hydrogen would remain unchanged. In this case the oxygen is said to be the **limiting reactant,** for the amount of water formed is based upon the amount of oxygen present. Likewise, in this case, there is said to be an excess of hydrogen present, for there is more present than oxygen can combine with.

In similar fashion, if one were to begin with 10 parts by weight of oxygen and 1 part by weight of hydrogen, 8 parts of oxygen would combine with the 1 part of hydrogen to form water, and the rest of the oxygen would be left unchanged. Here, the hydrogen is the limiting reactant and an excess of oxygen is present. This concept of limiting and excess reactants is very important, for in all chemical changes that involve two or more reactants, one of the reactants will always be the limiting reactant, and the others will be in excess.

AVOGADRO'S HYPOTHESIS

Avogadro's Hypothesis states that equal volumes of gases measured at the same temperature and pressure contain equal numbers of molecules. All gases exist as molecules. By finding the ratio of weights of equal volumes of various gases, we can find the ratio of their molecular weights. For example, let us consider again the compound water, and its elements hydrogen and oxygen. We can easily convert water to a gas (steam) and weigh a given volume of it. Likewise, the same volume of hydrogen and oxygen, both gases, can be brought to the same temperature as the steam and weighed. The weight ratios found by this procedure always turn out to be as follows:

Hydrogen	1 part by weight
Oxygen	16 parts by weight
Water	9 parts by weight

The sample of oxygen weighs 16 times as much as the sample of hydrogen, and the sample of steam weighs 9 times as much as the hydrogen. Since, by Avogadro's Hypothesis, each of these samples contains the same number of molecules, the individual molecules of each of these substances must possess these same weight proportions. Now we know the weight of one of these molecules. The formula of water is H_2O, and its molecular weight, obtained by adding the atomic weights in the formula, is 18. Recalculating our weight ratio found above to a basis of 18 for water we get:

Hydrogen	2 parts by weight
Oxygen	32 parts by weight
Water	18 parts by weight

Since this ratio is a ratio of molecular weights, and since the actual molecular weight of water is 18, the actual molecular weight of hydrogen must be 2, and the actual molecular weight of oxygen must be 32.

Therefore, the molecular of hydrogen gas must contain 2 atoms of hydrogen, because the atomic weight of hydrogen is 1. Similarly the molecule of oxygen must contain 2 atoms of oxygen, because the atomic weight of oxygen is 16, one half of the molecular weight. The formula of hydrogen gas is therefore written H_2 to indicate the 2 atoms in the molecule. The formula for oxygen gas is O_2. Both of these molecules are covalently bonded.

Avogadro's Hypothesis is thus very useful in finding the molecular weight and formula of a gaseous substance, provided that its weight can be compared with the weight of a substance whose formula is known. Experimental and mathematical studies of Avogadro's Hypothesis have indicated its accuracy beyond reasonable doubt.

EQUATIONS

An equation is simply a statement of a chemical change using chemical symbols. When sulfur, or any other substance, burns, in air, it is combining with oxygen in air to produce an oxide. Let us look at this reaction in the form of a chemical equation.

$$S \quad + \quad O_2 \quad = \quad SO_2$$
Sulfur   *Oxygen*   *Sulfur dioxide*

Examine the equation closely. Is it consistent with the Law of Conservation of Matter? In other words, are there equal numbers of each type of atom on each side of the equation? Yes, we see that this is so. This equation, therefore, is said to be **balanced.** An equation is meaningless unless it is balanced.

This equation tells us more than merely that sulfur combines with oxygen to produce sulfur dioxide. It has quantitative significance just as symbols themselves do. It tells us that one atomic weight's worth of sulfur reacts with one molecular weight's worth of oxygen to produce one molecular weight's worth of sulfur dioxide. If units of grams are used, this would be:

$$S \quad + \quad O_2 \quad = \quad SO_2$$
32.1 g.   32 g.   64.1 g.

In other words, this equation tells us that one mole of sulfur combines with one mole of oxygen to produce one mole of sulfur dioxide.

Let us look at another reaction. You will recall that when copper is heated in air, black copper oxide is formed. This reaction is indicated as follows:

$$Cu \quad + \quad O_2 \quad = \quad CuO$$
Copper   *Oxygen*   *Copper oxide*

What about our Law of Conservation of Matter now? Do you see that we have apparently destroyed some oxygen? This equation is not balanced. It is called a **skeleton equation,** for it indicates only the names of the substances involved.

This equation would be balanced if we could put a subscript 2 behind the O of CuO to make it CuO_2. But this would violate the Law of Definite Proportions, because black copper oxide always has the formula CuO. In balancing equations, **the subscript in the formulas of compounds may not be changed.**

A skeleton equation is balanced by placing numbers, called **coefficients,** in front of the formulas of the substances in the reaction. Look again at our skeleton equation. An even number of oxygen atoms appears on the left side of the equation. By placing the coefficient 2 in front of CuO, we would have two oxygen atoms on each side of the equation, for the coefficient multiplies all the symbols in the formula immediately behind it. This would change our equation to read:

$$Cu + O_2 = 2CuO.$$

Now we have too much copper on the right. This

can be remedied by placing another coefficient 2 in front of the Cu, giving us the following.

$$2Cu + O_2 = 2CuO.$$

Now the equation is balanced. We have 2 copper atoms and 2 oxygen atoms on each side of the equation. The balanced equation now reads, 2 moles of copper combine with 1 mole of oxygen to produce 2 moles of copper oxide. The following expression shows how the weights of each of the substances in the balanced equation may be indicated:

$$2Cu \quad + O_2 = \quad 2CuO$$
$$2 \times 63.6 \quad 32 \quad 2(63.6 + 16)$$
$$127.2 \quad +32 = \quad 159.2$$

So, 127.2 units of weight of copper combine with 32 units of weight of oxygen to form 159.2 units of weight of copper oxide. These units of weight may be grams, pounds, tons, etc., just so long as all three weights are expressed in the same units. This weight relationship also tells us that copper and oxygen combine in a weight ratio of 127.2 parts by weight of copper to 32 parts by weight of oxygen. Similarly, 159.2 parts by weight of copper oxide are formed for every 32 parts by weight of oxygen or every 127.2 parts by weight of copper.

Let us look at one more example. Butane gas (C_4H_{10}) is commonly used as a bottled gas in rural areas. It burns with oxygen to form carbon dioxide and water. The skeleton equation is:

$$C_4H_{10} + O_2 = CO_2 + H_2O.$$

Let us balance this skeleton equation using the "even numbers" technique described in the previous example.

1. Starting with oxygen, we see an even number of oxygen atoms on the left, and an odd number on the right. The CO_2 has an even number of oxygen atoms, so we have to work with the H_2O. Let's try a coefficient of 2. This would give us:

$$C_4H_{10} + O_2 = CO_2 + 2 H_2O.$$

This gives us an even number of oxygen atoms, but we need 10 hydrogen atoms and this gives us only 4 (2×2). Therefore we need a larger coefficient.

2. A coefficient of 5 would give us the right amount of hydrogen, but 5 is an odd number, so we must go to the next even multiple of 5 which is 10. This will do, but it gives us 20 hydrogen atoms on the right. By placing another coefficient of 2

in front of the C_4H_{10} we would also have 20 hydrogen atoms on the left. This gives us:

$$2 C_4H_{10} + O_2 = CO_2 + 10 H_2O$$

Now our hydrogen is balanced and we have an even number of oxygen atoms on each side.

3. Now we look at the carbon. We have 8 carbon atoms on the left, so we need a coefficient of 8 in front of the CO_2 to balance the carbon. This gives us:

$$2 C_4H_{10} + O_2 = 8 CO_2 + 10 H_2O.$$

We still have an even number of oxygen atoms on each side.

4. Now we are finally ready to balance the oxygen. There is a total of 26 oxygen atoms on the right side of the equation. A coefficient of 13 in front of the O_2 will give us 26 oxygen atoms on the left side. Now our equation is balanced and looks like this:

$$2 C_4H_{10} + 13 O_2 = 8 CO_2 + 10 H_2O.$$

This equation reads: 2 moles of butane combine with 13 moles of oxygen to produce 8 moles of carbon dioxide and 10 moles of water. The weight proportions involved are:

$$\text{Reactants:} \begin{cases} \text{Butane:} & 2(48 + 10) = 116 \\ \text{Oxygen:} & 13(32) \quad\quad = \underline{416} \;\; 532 \end{cases}$$

$$\text{Products:} \begin{cases} \text{Carbon} \\ \text{Dioxide:} & 8(12 + 32) = 352 \\ \text{Water:} & 10(2 + 16) = \underline{180} \;\; 532 \end{cases}$$

The characteristics of a balanced equation may be summarized as follows:

1. It obeys the Law of Conservation of Matter.
2. It obeys the Law of Definite Proportions.
3. Its coefficients give the molar proportions of reactants and products involved in the reaction.

Symbols, formulas, and equations all have definite quantitative meanings. We are now ready to look at some numerical applications based upon these ideas.

PERCENTAGE COMPOSITION

If we know the formula of a compound, we can easily find the percentage by weight of each element present. A statement of the percentage of each element present in a compound is called its **percentage composition.** In chemistry, this composition is always on a weight basis unless specifically stated otherwise. Sometimes the composition of mixtures of gases is given on a volumetric basis.

The computation of percentage composition from the formula of a compound is based upon the meaning of symbols and formulas. Each symbol stands for one atomic weight's worth of the element it represents, and each formula stands for one molecular weight's worth of the compound it represents. Let us see how percentage composition calculations are carried out.

EXAMPLE 6: What is the percentage composition of water, H_2O?

SOLUTION:

	No. of Atoms	Atomic Weight	Total Weight
Hydrogen:	2	1.0	2.0
Oxygen:	1	16.0	16.0
Molecular weight of H_2O:			18.0

$$\text{Percentage of hydrogen} = \frac{2.0}{18.0} \times 100 = 11.1\%$$

$$\text{Percentage of oxygen} = \frac{16.0}{18.0} \times 100 = 88.9\%.$$

Note that the percentage of each element is found from the expression:

$$\frac{\textbf{Total wt. of element present}}{\textbf{Molecular wt. of compound}} = \% \textbf{ of element.}$$

EXAMPLE 7: What is the percentage composition of sulfuric acid, H_2SO_4?

SOLUTION:

	No. of Atoms	Atomic Weight	Total Weight
Hydrogen:	2	1.0	2.0
Sulfur:	1	32.1	32.1
Oxygen:	4	16.0	64.0
Molecular weight of H_2SO_4:			98.1

$$\text{Percentage of hydrogen} = \frac{2.0}{98.1} \times 100 = 2.0\%$$

$$\text{Percentage of sulfur} = \frac{32.1}{98.1} \times 100 = 32.7\%$$

$$\text{Percentage of oxygen} = \frac{64.0}{98.1} \times 100 = 65.3\%$$

EXAMPLE 8: Find the percentage of oxygen in calcium nitrate, $Ca(NO_3)_2$.

SOLUTION:

	No. of Atoms	Atomic Weight	Total Weight
Calcium:	1	40.1	40.1
Nitrogen:	2	14.0	28.0
Oxygen:	6	16.0	96.0
Molecular weight of $Ca(NO_3)_2$:			164.1

$$\text{Percentage of oxygen} = \frac{96.0}{164.1} \times 100 = 58.5\%.$$

Note particularly how the number of atoms of each element was obtained.

EXAMPLE 9: An iron ore field contains ferric oxide, Fe_2O_3, also known as **hematite,** mixed with rock which bears no iron. Naturally, both hematite and rock are scooped up in the giant shovels used in mining the ore. Samples taken at various spots in the ore field show that the field contains 80% hematite and 20% rock. Find the weight of pure iron in one ton of this ore, and the percentage of iron in the ore field.

SOLUTION: (1) Wt. of Fe_2O_3 per ton of ore:
$2,000 \times 0.80 = 1600$ lbs. of Fe_2O_3 per ton of ore.

(2) Percentage of Fe in Fe_2O_3:

	No. of Atoms	Atomic Weight	Total Weight
Iron:	2	55.9	111.8
Oxygen:	3	16.0	48.0
Molecular weight of Fe_2O_3:			159.8

$$\text{Percentage of Fe} = \frac{111.8}{159.8} \times 100 = 70\%$$

(3) Wt. of Fe per ton of ore:
$1600 \times 0.70 = 1120$ lbs. of Fe per ton of ore.

(4) Percentage of Fe in the field:
$$\frac{1120}{2000} \times 100 = 56.0\% \text{ Fe in the ore field.}$$

Example 9 shows how percentage composition problems may be a part of many different varieties of practical problems. Such fields as analytical chemistry, metallurgy, mining, mineralogy, and geology all make use of calculations of this type.

COMPUTATION OF FORMULAS

If we know the percentage composition of a compound, we can compute the **simplest formula** of the compound. As we have seen, a formula is a ratio of the number of atoms of each element present in the compound. The simplest formula gives this atomic ratio in terms of the smallest whole numbers of each type of atom present. For example, the true formula of hydrogen peroxide is H_2O_2. Its simplest formula would be HO. In general, the simplest formula is the true formula for all electrovalent compounds. In covalent compounds, where the formula represents the composition of the molecule of the compound, the true formula is either the same as the simplest formula, or it is some whole number multiple of it. We will learn how to calculate true formulas later, but for now, let us concentrate on finding the simplest formula of a compound.

EXAMPLE 10: A compound is analyzed and found to contain 75% carbon and 25% hydrogen. Find its simplest formula.

SOLUTION: Since each different type of atom contributes to the total weight of the compound **in parcels of weight** equal to its own atomic weight, we can divide the weight percent of a given element by its atomic weight to get the relative number of atoms of the element contributing to the total weight percent. For the compound under consideration this would be:

$$\text{Carbon:} \quad \frac{75}{12} = 6.25$$

$$\text{Hydrogen:} \quad \frac{25}{1} = 25.0$$

Thus we have 6.25 carbon atoms for every 25 hydrogen atoms in this compound. To reduce these numbers to the simplest whole numbers, we divide each by the smaller. The entire calculation would then be as follows:

$$\text{Carbon:} \quad \frac{75}{12} = 6.25; \quad \frac{6.25}{6.25} = 1.$$

$$\text{Hydrogen:} \quad \frac{25}{1} = 25; \quad \frac{25}{6.25} = 4.$$

Therefore, the simplest formula of this compound is CH_4.

EXAMPLE 11: A compound contains 21.6% sodium, 33.3% chlorine, and 45.1% oxygen. Find its simplest formula.

SOLUTION:

$$\text{Sodium:} \quad \frac{21.6}{23.0} = 0.95; \quad \frac{0.95}{0.94} = 1.$$

$$\text{Chlorine:} \quad \frac{33.3}{35.5} = 0.94; \quad \frac{0.94}{0.94} = 1.$$

$$\text{Oxygen:} \quad \frac{45.1}{16.0} = 2.82; \quad \frac{2.82}{0.94} = 3.$$

Therefore, the formula of this compound is $NaClO_3$.

EXAMPLE 12: Some crystalline solids have molecules of water forming part of their crystal structure. Such solids are known as hydrates. Ordinary household washing soda, made up of sodium carbonate and water, is a typical hydrate. The percentage of water present can be found by measuring the loss in weight of a hydrate sample dried in a hot oven. A 20.00 g. sample of washing soda is dried in an oven. After drying it is found to weigh 7.57 g. Compute:
(a) The percentage of water in washing soda.
(b) The formula of washing soda.

SOLUTION:

(a) Percentage $H_2O = \dfrac{\text{loss in wt.}}{\text{original wt.}} \times 100 =$

$$\frac{20.00-7.57}{20.00} = 62.15\%.$$

(b) The percentage of Na_2CO_3 is $100\% - 62.15\% = 37.85\%$

$$Na_2CO_3: \quad \frac{37.85}{106} = 0.357; \quad \frac{0.357}{0.357} = 1.$$

$$H_2O: \quad \frac{62.15}{18.0} \times 3.45; \quad \frac{3.45}{0.357} = 10.$$

(to the nearest whole number)

Therefore, the formula of washing soda must indicate 1 part of Na_2CO_3 and 10 parts of H_2O. Its formula is written as follows: $Na_2CO_3 \cdot 10H_2O$. This is the standard method of writing the formula of a hydrate. It indicates that the crystal contains 10 moles of water for every mole of sodium carbonate. Note particularly that since a molar ratio of constituents was sought, the molecular weights of each constituent were used in finding the molar ratio.

WEIGHT RELATIONSHIPS IN EQUATIONS

We have seen that chemical equations tell us the number of moles of each substance involved in a given reaction. For example, the equation for the rusting of iron,

$$4\text{ Fe} + 3\text{ O}_2 = 2\text{ Fe}_2\text{O}_3,$$

tells us that iron combines with oxygen in a ratio of 4 moles of iron to 3 moles of oxygen, and that 2 moles of iron oxide are produced for every 4 moles of iron entering the reaction.

These molar ratios, in turn, indicate the ratio of weights of each substance involved. The equation tells us that iron and oxygen combine in a ratio of (4×55.9) parts by weight of iron to (3×32) parts by weight of oxygen, and that (2×159.8) parts by weight of iron oxide are thereby produced in this reaction. When we multiply the coefficient of a substance in a balanced equation by the formula weight of the substance, we obtain a quantity known as the **equation weight** of the substance. **The actual weight of substances involved in a chemical reaction are in the same ratio as their equation weights.**

Therefore, if we know the balanced equation for a reaction, and the actual weight of any one substance involved in the reaction, we can find the actual weight of any other substance participating in the reaction from the following proportion:

$$\frac{\textbf{Actual wt. of one substance}}{\textbf{Its equation weight}} = \frac{\textbf{Unknown actual weight}}{\textbf{Its equation weight}}$$

Let us look at an example involving the finding of actual weights.

EXAMPLE 13: 27.95 g. of iron are oxidized completely.

(a) What weight of oxygen combined with the iron?

(b) What weight of iron oxide was produced?

SOLUTION: First we write the balanced equation for the reaction and place the equation weight of each substance involved below its formula as follows:

$$\begin{array}{ccc} 4\text{ Fe} & +\quad 3\text{ O}_2 & =\quad 2\text{ Fe}_2\text{O}_3 \\ 4 \times 55.9 & 3 \times 32 & 2 \times 159.8 \end{array}$$

Part a: Substituting in the expression above to find the actual weight of oxygen we have: (Let x represent the unknown wt.)

$$\frac{27.95}{223.6} = \frac{x}{96}$$

$$x = \frac{27.95 \times 96}{223.6}$$

$$x = 12.0 \text{ g. of oxygen.}$$

Part b: Substituting in the expression above to find the actual weight of iron oxide we have:

$$\frac{27.95}{223.6} = \frac{x}{319.6}$$

$$x = \frac{27.95 \times 319.6}{223.6}$$

$$x = 39.95 \text{ g. of iron oxide.}$$

The steps, then, in solving this type of problem are:

1. Write the **balanced** equation for the reaction.

2. Find the equation weights of the substances concerned.

3. Equate the ratios of actual weights to equation weights for each of the substances, and solve for the unknown actual weight.

EXAMPLE 14: Sodium hydroxide, NaOH, may be prepared by treating sodium carbonate, Na_2CO_3, with calcium hydroxide, $Ca(OH)_2$, according to the following equation (skeleton):

$$Na_2CO_3 + Ca(OH)_2 = NaOH + CaCO_3.$$

What weight of NaOH can be produced from 74.2 g. of Na_2CO_3?

SOLUTION: Balanced equation:

$$\begin{array}{cc} Na_2CO_3 + Ca(OH)_2 = & 2\text{ NaOH} + CaCO_3 \\ 1 \times 106 & 2 \times 40 \end{array}$$

Therefore:

$$\frac{74.2}{106} = \frac{x}{80}$$

$$x = \frac{74.2 \times 80}{106}$$

$$x = 56 \text{ g. of NaOH.}$$

Notice that it is assumed that there is sufficient calcium hydroxide present to react with all of the sodium carbonate. If any excess calcium hydroxide is used, it will remain unchanged, for the sodium carbonate is the limiting reactant in this case.

CHAPTER TEN

ASTRONOMY

A Brief History

The history of astronomy may be conveniently divided into three periods: the geocentric, the galactic, and the universal. The first had its beginnings in ancient history, and came to a close in the sixteenth century. The second extends from the seventeenth through the nineteenth centuries. And the third began and continues in the present century.

THE GEOCENTRIC PERIOD

Early astronomers believed the earth to be in the center of the universe; and assumed that the sun, moon, and stars revolved about that stationary earth. Their interest, hardly scientific in our sense of the term, was mainly in practical matters, in the real and supposed relation of celestial events to those on the earth; in searching the skies for clues to good and evil omens.

Even so, remarkable discoveries were made then. The calendar was developed with great accuracy. The apparent path of the sun among the stars—the ecliptic—was carefully defined. The complete cycle of solar and lunar eclipses was determined. And as early as the second century B.C., the motion of the earth's axis was well understood.

The great figure of Nicolaus Copernicus (1473–1543) is closely associated with the end of the primitive geocentric period in the sixteenth century.

THE GALACTIC PERIOD

Modern astronomy can be said to have begun in this period. Copernicus demonstrated that the earth, far from being the center of the universe, was merely one of the planets revolving about the central sun. Hardly unique, the earth was found to be a quite ordinary planet, going through ordinary motions in an ordinary way.

Indeed the central sun itself was realized to be merely one star among the multitudes in the heavens, one among billions of similar stars in every direction about us—some larger, some smaller, some heavier, some lighter than our sun.

In this period the approach became increasingly scientific, motivated largely by the desire to know, to understand the basic laws governing the motion of heavenly bodies, to explain what the eye saw.

Progress from the sixteenth through the nineteenth centuries resulted from the effective combination of extended observation, improved instruments, and the work of scientific genius.

Observation. Great quantities of data of fundamental importance were painstakingly gathered by careful observers, chief among whom is the great name of Tycho Brahe (1546–1601).

Instruments. The introduction of the telescope in 1610 by Galileo Galilei (1564–1642) was, of course, a milestone in the development of the science of astronomy; as was the later invention and introduction of the spectroscope. The two instruments complement one another: the telescope permits us to see the stars more clearly; the spectroscope analyzes stellar light, furnishing us with much information about the stars.

Genius. Like every science, astronomy requires for its advancement the labors of great minds that are able to apply to the observed data insight, imagination, intuition, as well as great learning.

Such minds were Johannes Kepler (1571–1630) and Sir Isaac Newton (1642–1727): Kepler by the discovery of the laws of planetary motion and Newton by the discovery of the Universal Law of Gravitation.

THE UNIVERSAL PERIOD

Now it became apparent that the galaxy of stars to which our sun belongs is merely one of many galaxies—some larger, some smaller than ours. To these much of the astronomical research of the last half century has been devoted, in an effort to achieve a "complete" picture of the universe. To aid this research ever greater optical telescopes, as well as gigantic radio telescopes, have been constructed.

The great theoretical genius associated most closely with this period in the public mind (although he was primarily a physicist and mathematician) is the late Dr. Albert Einstein (1879–1955). Cosmology and astrophysics depend more and more on his theory of relativity.

This is the astronomic period in which we live. And it is far from concluded.

The Universe

INTRODUCTION AND DEFINITIONS

For as long as man has been conscious of himself and the universe he inhabits, he has regarded the sky with awe and wonder—a source of constant and compelling fascination. Awe and wonder generate study and science; man seeking ceaselessly to conquer ignorance and solve mysteries, thus developing finally into the science of astronomy.

Astronomy is the science of the positions, motions, constitutions, histories, and destinies of celestial bodies. In the course of its development as a science, it has already discovered many of the basic laws governing those bodies. But it is the nature of scientic investigation that its work is never done—and here, as elsewhere, immense labors remain to be performed.

THE STUDY OF ASTRONOMY

We study astronomy because the intelligent, inquiring mind must ask questions and seek answers; must know "Why?" and discover "How?" And from the beginning, whenever man has looked up, there was the sky—always confronting him with seemingly imponderable problems, always challenging him to solve its mysteries.

On one level, man has stated his reaction in magic and mythology, and this has been expressed in the world's art, literature, and religions. On another level, he has attempted to explain the celestial phenomena perceived by his senses in scientific terms—and these explanations are the subject matter of the science of astronomy.

THE COMPONENTS

The earth we live on is a planet—one of a number of planets that revolve about the sun. The unassisted eye is capable of detecting the sun, several planets, one satellite (our moon), several thousands of stars, shooting stars (meteors), and once in a great while a comet.

These celestial bodies are the components that constitute the universe, in much the same way that homes, churches, hospitals, and parks are components of a community.

To the best of our knowledge, the **universe consists of stars** (billions and billions of these), nebulae, planets, planetoids, satellites, comets, etc.

STARS

Stars are large globes of intensely heated gas, shining by their own light. At their surface, they reach temperatures of thousands of degrees; in their interior, temperatures are much higher.

At these temperatures, matter cannot exist either in solid or in liquid form. The gases constituting the stars are much thicker than those on the earth usually are. The extremely high values of their density are due to enormous pressures which prevail in their interior.

Stars move above in space, although their motion is not immediately perceptible. No change in their relative position can be detected in a year. Even in a thousand years, the stars will seem not to have moved substantially. Their pattern now is almost exactly that of a thousand years ago. This seeming fixedness is due to the vast distance separating us from them. At these distances it will take many thousands of years for the stellar pattern to undergo a noticeable change: This **apparent** constancy of position accounts for the popular name "fixed stars."

NEBULAE

A **nebula is a vast cloud composed of dust and gas.** The gases which compose it are extremely thin and of low temperature. Nebulae do not shine by their own light, but are made visible by the light of neighboring stars. When they are so visible, they appear to the unaided eye not unlike a fuzzy star. Their actual size and structure, however, can be determined only with the aid of a telescope. Other nebulae are dark and obscure the stars beyond them.

PLANETS

The planets that revolve around our sun are large, solid, nearly spherical masses. The best

known to us is, of course, our own earth. All of them are relatively cool and are made visible by reflected sunlight; several can be seen at one time or another by the unaided eye. Three planets, however, can be seen only with the aid of a telescope. At first glance, planets look very much like the multitude of stars that glitter in the sky; but an observer can identify a planet by one or more of the following characteristics:

A. Planets shine with a **steady** light, while stars do not. The light reaching our eyes from stars seems to change rapidly in both color and brightness. These changes in color and brightness cause the **twinkling** of the stars.

B. Planets **wander** in the heavens: A planet which at one time was close to one star may later be observed close to another star. Stars, on the other hand, seem to keep the same positions relative to one another. See Fig. 1. The very word "planet" is derived from a Greek word meaning "wanderer."

C. Planets, when observed through telescopes, appear as **small disks** of light. The greater the magnification, the larger will be the diameter of the disk. Stars, even with the largest telescope, appear only as points of light. Even in the 200-inch telescope, they appear as mere points, having no measurable diameter.

D. Planets may be found **only in a narrow strip** in the sky. Their motions are limited to the boundaries of this strip. Stars, of course, may be found in any part of the sky.

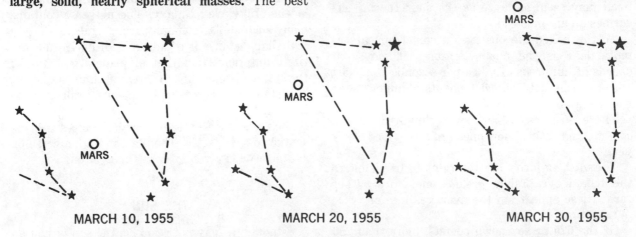

MARCH 10, 1955   MARCH 20, 1955   MARCH 30, 1955

FIGURE 1. Views of the same part of the sky on three different dates, March 10, March 20, and March 30, 1955. Note that the stars maintain the same relative position. The planet (Mars) has wandered considerably in that time.

PLANETOIDS

Planets are small, irregularly shaped solid bodies revolving, like the major planets, about the sun, and differing from planets primarily in size. They are also known either as asteroids or as minor planets. The largest planetoid, Ceres, has a diameter of 480 miles; but many of them have a diameter of only two miles. The first planetoid was discovered on January 1, 1801; many more have since been discovered. It is estimated that more than 100,000 planetoids can be photographed with one of the large telescopes.

They, too, shine by reflected sunlight; however, because of their small surface, the amount of reflected light is very small. They cannot be seen without the aid of a telescope.

SATELLITES

Six of the nine major planets have one or more moons revolving round them. These are called satellites. The earth has only one moon (satellite), while the planet Jupiter, for example, has fourteen. To date, thirty-four satellites have been discovered, the last as recently as 1975.

COMETS

Comets are celestial bodies of unique form and large size which appear from time to time. A typical comet consists of a luminous sphere, or head, connected to a long, tenuous cylinder, or tail. The head may seem as large as the sun; the tail describes an arc in the sky.

To the naked-eye observer a comet appears as motionless as the moon. Actually it moves at speeds of hundreds of miles per second. The exact speed can be determined from its changing position relative to the fixed stars.

There are less than seven hundred known comets, and several new ones are discovered every year.

The vast majority are too faint to be visible to the naked eye. Fairly great comets are rather rare; these appear, on the average, once or twice in a lifetime.

Of the 625 or so known comets, more than 259 are known to move in "closed orbits"—that is, in more or less elongated, cigar-shaped paths. The fact that the orbit is "closed," has no beginning or end, is of great importance. Comets moving in

them go round the same path continuously; many of them have been observed several times during their returns to the vicinity of the earth.

The orbits of the other 368 comets are either parabolic or hyperbolic. They very likely made only one appearance in the vicinity of the earth, coming, probably, from outer space, making a U-turn, and then left, never to be seen again.

METEOROIDS

Meteoroids are usually tiny (about the size of the head of a pin), solid objects traversing through space. Occasionally a group of meteoroids is attracted to the earth and becomes entangled in its atmosphere. The heat resulting from this encounter consumes the object; the dust resulting from this cremation falls to the earth. Hundreds of tons of meteoric dust descend each year. On rare occasions large meteoroids manage to reach the earth before they are consumed. **The light phenomenon which results from the entry of the meteoroid into the earth's atmosphere is called meteor, or "shooting star,"** the glow of which may persist several seconds.

The universe is composed of stars, nebulae, planets, comets, and other celestial bodies. Here, the components are assembled to form the design of the universe.

The planets, planetoids, satellites, comets, and meteorites revolve about a single star: the star we call the sun. Together they form the Solar System. The sun, and billions of other stars, form the community of stars known either as Our Galaxy, or the Milky Way Galaxy. The universe contains many such stellar communities, or galaxies.

Stellar distance is of an order of magnitude entirely different from that of planetary distance: the former is enormously greater than the latter.

Distances between galaxies are still greater than distances between stars. In attempting to comprehend such extraordinary distances it is essential to use a scale. The plan of the universe on such a scale is given later in this section.

THE SUN

Although it may not seem so, the sun is just an ordinary star, similar to numerous other stars that we see in the sky.

The sun appears large to us because it is, relatively speaking, near to us. All other stars appear as small points of light in the sky because they are far away. See Figs. 2a and 2b. Our interest in this star (the sun) derives from the fact that the earth receives from it both heat and light—energy of

FIGURE 2a. The sun is just an ordinary star. All the other stars look tiny, as they are so remote that we see them only as mere points of light.

FIGURE 2b. Other objects, too, appear smaller with increasing distance. Note the apparent size of the distant tree.

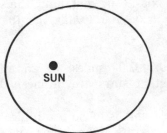

FIGURE 2c. The oval curve suggests the circumference of the whole universe. The dot represents the location of the sun.

fundamental importance in maintaining life. The oval curve in Figure 2c represents the universe and the dot the position of the sun within the universe. (Note that Fig. 2c, as well as Figs. 3, 4, and 5, are symbolic representations and not figures drawn to scale.)

PLANETS

There are nine planets revolving about the sun: Mercury, Venus, Earth, Mars, Jupiter, Saturn,

Uranus, Neptune, and Pluto. Mercury is closest to the sun, and at a somewhat greater distance is Venus; then, the earth; and the farthest known planet from the sun is Pluto.

The earth is 93 million miles from the sun. **This distance is often referred to as an Astronomical Unit.** Mercury is only four tenths the earth's distance from the sun. Pluto, the most distant planet, is forty times the earth's distance. The distance of Pluto can be stated as forty times 93 million miles, or simply as forty astronomical units.

A reducing scale may help to visualize these distances. The scale that is commonly used represents the sun-earth distance as one foot long:

93 million miles equal 1 foot; or,
1 astronomical unit equals 1 foot.

On this scale, Mercury is fourth tenths of a foot; Venus is seven tenths; and the earth is one foot away from the sun. The farthest planet is forty feet from the sun. A circular box of forty-foot radius could accommodate all the planets. The box could be quite shallow, as all the planets move approximately in the same plane.

THE SOLAR SYSTEM

The sun and the planets are the major components of the solar system. Other members of this system are:

1. the host of smaller planets known as planetoids or asteroids
2. the several moons, known as satellites, that revolve about six of these planets;
3. comets that appear from time to time;
4. the vast number of meteoroids.

The circle around the dot in Figure 3 represents the entire solar system.

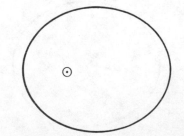

FIGURE 3. The oval curve suggests the circumference of the whole universe. The dot and the small circle represent the sun and the solar system, respectively.

THE STARS

Distances to stars are immensely greater than distances to planets. Even the star nearest our own sun is at a distance of 270,000 astronomical units. Using the scale (one foot equals one astronomical unit, or 93 million miles), the star closest to our sun would be at a distance of fifty miles.

The two units should be carefully noted. Distances between planets are stated in **feet,** while those between stars are stated in **miles.** A mental picture might help to visualize this distinction. The sun, and all the planets, could be accommodated in a circular house of forty foot radius. The closest star, by our scale, would be in a house fifty miles away. Other stars, by our scale, are at scale distances of thousands and hundreds of thousands of miles from the sun.

OUR GALAXY

These stars form a large community called Our Galaxy or the Milky Way Galaxy. It is estimated that the number of stars in our galaxy is close to a hundred billion—otherwise stated as 100×10^9, or a hundred thousand million.

The outer surface of the galaxy is often compared either to a grindstone or to a lens.

A top view of the galaxy would reveal its circular shape as well as the spiral design formed by the stars. A side view would suggest its similarity to a lens, namely, that it is thick in the center, and thins out toward the edges.

Again using the one foot scale, the diameter of the circle would be close to a million miles, while the maximum thickness is only about one sixth of the diameter.

Our galaxy is represented in Figure 4.

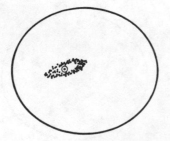

FIGURE 4. The oval curve represents the circumference of the universe. Our galaxy is indicated inside the oval. The dot and the circle represent the sun and the solar system, respectively.

OTHER GALAXIES

Ours is not the only galaxy in the universe: many have been discovered in recent years, strikingly similar to our own. The scale distances between them are from ten to twenty million miles. A highly simplified picture of the universe is shown in Figure 5.

OUTLINE OF THE UNIVERSE IN TERMS OF ACTUAL DISTANCES

The distance to the sun is 93 million miles; the distance to our nearest star, Alpha-Centauri, is

FIGURE 5. The "complete" universe consists of many galaxies. One, containing the sun, is known as our galaxy, the galaxy, or the Milky Way galaxy.

25,000,000,000,000 miles, or 25 million million miles. Distant stars are inconceivably more remote.

The mile unit is of no use in dealing with the distances of stars and galaxies—instead, astronomers use the unit "light-year": one light-year is the distance that a beam of light travels in one year. The distance covered by a beam of light in one second is 186,000 miles; hence:

One light-year =

$$186{,}000 \times 60 \left(\frac{\text{seconds}}{\text{minute}} \right) \times 60 \left(\frac{\text{minutes}}{\text{hour}} \right)$$

$$\times\, 24 \left(\frac{\text{hours}}{\text{day}} \right) \times 365\tfrac{1}{4} = 5{,}880{,}000{,}000{,}000 \text{ miles}$$

or 6 million million miles, approximately.

The star nearest the solar system is 4.3 light-years away. The diameter of our galaxy is about 100,000 light-years; its maximum thickness is 15,000 light-years. An average distance between galaxies would be approximately a million light-years.

The sun is only a minute fraction of a light-year from the earth. The distance to the sun may be stated as 8 light minutes.

Distances to heavenly bodies, when stated in terms of light, have an added meaning—for the sun, it implies that it takes a beam of sunlight 8 minutes to reach the earth.

So for the stars. A ray of light from Alpha-Centauri reaches the earth 4⅓ years after leaving the star.

The most distant object seen by the unaided eye is the Andromeda galaxy—2 million light-years away. The light entering the observer's eye has been en route for that time.

A BRIEF HISTORY OF THE UNIVERSE

The most tenable theory to date for the history of the universe is the one known as the "big bang theory." According to that theory, all the matter and all energy that is present in the universe was once concentrated in a small, enormously hot, preposterously dense ball.

Then 10, or more, thousand million years ago the ball exploded (big bang!), sending into space torrents of gas (primarily protons, neutrons, electrons, and some alpha particles), immersed in a vast ocean of radiation.

As time went on, concentration of matter formed in that turbulent gas—each concentration contracting in response to its own gravitational field, while moving outward in the ever-expanding universe.

These concentrations of gas (also known as nebulae) became galaxies when they fragmented into massive blobs to form protostars (masses of gas that in due course of time are destined to become stars).

Many of these protostars, while shrinking and flattening under influence of their own gravitational and centrifugal forces, became unstable, causing smaller masses of gas to break away and form protoplanets; and the protoplanets similarly produced protosatellites.

The protostars eventually became stars; the protoplanets and protosatellites, after proper cooling, condensing, and contracting, became planets and satellites.

To the best of our knowledge, the transition of our sun from a protostar to a star took place some 5 billion years ago. The planets and the satellites of the solar system were formed shortly thereafter.

UNAIDED OBSERVATION

On a clear night far away from city lights, the naked eye can see

A. Some 2,000 to 3,000 stars in each hemisphere of the sky. Some of these are only a few light-years away, others at distances of many hundreds of light-years.

NOTE: To the human eye, all of these stars appear equally distant and it is helpful to imagine that all these stars are attached to the inside of an imaginary large sphere called the celestial sphere. See Fig. 6.

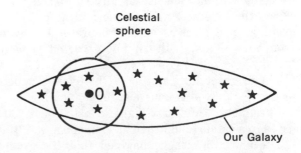

FIGURE 6. The celestial sphere is an imaginary spherical projection screen, upon which the observer, situated at the center, "sees" the stars and other celestial bodies.

B. Several planets traveling among the stars, each planet at its own characteristic velocity.

C. Meteors, five or ten every hour, each streaking across the sky and leaving a flash of light in its wake.

D. Comets, really bright ones—once or twice in a lifetime.

E. Nebulae—e.g., the great emission nebula in Orion or the dark Horsehead Nebula (also in Orion).

F. The Milky Way. An irregular belt describing a complete circuit of light on the surface of the celestial sphere. The belt varies from 5° to 50° in width. The light is due to the combined radiation emitted by the billions of stars along the long dimension of our flattened galaxy (lines AB in Figure 7). This band contrasts with the relative darkness (due to the paucity of stars) along the narrow dimension (lines AC) of the galaxy.

G. Other galaxies—e.g., the galaxy in Andromeda, that can be seen in northern latitudes and the two galaxies known as Magellanic Clouds in southern latitudes.

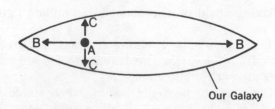

Our Galaxy

FIGURE 7. An observer at point A sees the merging light from billions of stars along lines AB. This forms the Milky Way. There are much fewer stars along lines AC, hence comparative darkness.

Identifying and Locating Stars Without a Telescope

Astronomy is one of the several sciences engaged in the study of nature. Much remains to be learned, and many important discoveries can still be made without the use of any equipment. The sky is the laboratory. The time is any fine, clear evening. The place is outdoors, preferably away from city lights, with an unobstructed view of the sky.

The brighter stars appear on the celestial sphere in groups known as constellations.

The names of forty-eight constellations are listed in a catalog published as long ago as A.D. 150.

The ancients either imagined that the groups formed pictures of gods, heroes, animals, etc., or they wanted to honor their gods, heroes, animals, etc., and named the constellations accordingly.

Modern astronomy recognizes eighty-eight constellations, each with its own clearly defined boundaries and each bearing the name originally given to it. The eighty-eight areas completely cover the celestial sphere.

NOTE: Celestial objects outside our own galaxy are also identified with the constellation in which they are seen. Hence the names "galaxy in Andromeda" or "galaxy in Ursa Major."

In this chapter, we shall pay particular attention to some thirty well-known constellations, such as Orion, the Big and Small Dippers, Cassiopeia, and so on, and we shall begin with the group that is probably easiest to identify—the Big Dipper. As its name implies, the stars form the outline of a dipper. It is important to become familiar with

that group of stars as it is with reference to it that the locations of other constellations are most often determined. The Big Dipper can be seen every clear evening in most of the northern hemisphere. This section deals primarily with the stars of that constellation.

THE STARS OF THE BIG DIPPER

Seven bright stars form the pattern of the Dipper. The four forming the "bowl" are known as Dubhe, Merak, Phecda, and Megrez, all Arabic names: Dubhe means "bear," Merak "loin," Phecda and Megrez, "thigh" and "the root of the bear's tail," respectively.

The stars forming the "handle" of the Dipper are known as Alkaid, Mizar, and Alioth, also Arabic names, meaning "the chief," and "the apron"; the precise meaning of the name "Alioth" is still disputed.

Close to Mizar is the small star Alcor. The Arabs called these two stars "the Horse and the Rider." The star Alcor was used by them in a test for good eyesight. See Fig. 8.

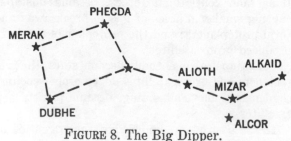

FIGURE 8. The Big Dipper.

SCALE OF ANGULAR DISTANCES

Locations of stars are stated in terms of angles or arcs. The angular distance, measured in degrees, is the angle or arc, subtended by these stars at the vantage point of the observer.

FIGURE 9. The angular distance of the full moon is about half a degree.

It is of importance to be able to gauge small angles in the sky. The diameter of the full moon is about half a degree, otherwise stated more formally as: The angle, or arc, subtended at our eye by the diameter of the full moon is .5°. See Fig. 9.

Another angular distance often used is the one between Dubhe and Merak—close to five degrees.

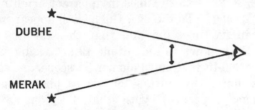

FIGURE 10. The angle subtended by Dubhe and Merak at the eye of a terrestial observer is close to 5°.

Ten moons could be placed side by side in the distance between these two stars. See Fig. 10.

PROBLEM 1:
Estimate the angular distance between Dubhe and Megrez.
Answer: 10°, approximately.

LEGENDS

One of the early names given to this constellation was the "Great Bear" and the Arabic names meaning "thigh," "loin," etc., describe parts of the bear. See Fig. 11.

FIGURE 11. The Great Bear. Note the position of the Big Dipper.

The reason for this is not known, as an observer can scarcely imagine the outline of a bear or any other animal in that constellation.

An ancient legend held that the Bear represented Callisto, a daughter of the King of Arcadia, beloved of Jupiter, who, in order to protect her, changed her into a Bear and transferred her to the skies.

Another legend held that the Great Spirit purposely put the Great Bear in the sky to act as a "calendar" for earthly bears. During the half year when the Great Bear is low in the sky, all earthly bears stay in their dens and keep warm. When the Bear is high in the sky, bears leave their dens, for summer has begun.

OTHER NAMES

The names Great Bear and Big Dipper are still in common use. The scientific name for the constellation is the Latin translation of Great Bear—Ursa Major. In England, the constellation is known as the Plough, or the Wain (for wagon).

NOTE: To be accurate, the term Big Dipper should be used to refer to the seven bright stars and the term Great Bear or Ursa Major to refer to all the stars in the constellation. Often, however, these terms are used interchangeably.

APPARENT BRIGHTNESS OF STARS

The seven stars of the Big Dipper differ materially in apparent brightness. The brightest star is Alioth; the faintest, Megrez.

Technically this is stated in terms of apparent magnitude. Alioth has the smallest apparent magnitude (1.7); Megrez, the largest (3.4).

HIPPARCHUS' CLASSIFICATION OF STARS ACCORDING TO BRIGHTNESS

The ancient Greek astronomers classified the visible stars according to their apparent brightness, into six classes. This basic classification, in the main, is still valid. To Hipparchus, who lived on the island of Rhodes in the second century B.C., goes the credit for this classification. The twenty brightest stars known to him were arbitrarily designated as stars of the **first magnitude;** and the next fifty in order of apparent brightness were designated as stars of the **second magnitude;** and so on. The designation of **sixth magnitude** was given to several hundred stars barely visible to the normal human eye. See Fig. 12. Thus a completely

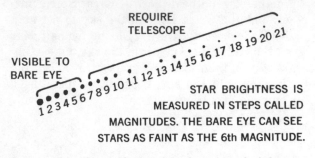

FIGURE 12. The relationship between brightness and magnitude.

arbitrary classification of stars, according to their brightness, was obtained. These magnitudes are, however, only *apparent* magnitudes. Some stars are actually bright, but appear faint because of their great distance.

DECIMAL DIVISION OF APPARENT MAGNITUDES

In the nineteenth century, the decimal division was introduced. In this classification, a star of magnitude 5.5 has an apparent brightness halfway between that of a star of magnitude 5.0 and that of a star of magnitude 6.0. Similarly, to state that the North Star (Polaris) has a magnitude of 2.1 signifies that its apparent brightness is only slightly less than the brightness of a star of magnitude 2.0. Increasingly, the decimal method of denoting magnitudes has been applied more extensively and made more precise.

RELATION BETWEEN APPARENT MAGNITUDE AND APPARENT BRIGHTNESS

There is a simple relationship between the apparent magnitude and apparent brightness.

This is based on a psychophysical law that states that if a stimulus, e.g., brightness, increases in a

geometric progression, such as 1,2,4,8,16, etc., the sensation resulting from it increases in an arithmetic progression 1,2,3,4,5, etc.

From that law it was determined empirically that magnitude 2 stars are 2.5 (more precisely, 2.512) times brighter than magnitude 3 stars. Similarly, magnitude 3 stars are 2.512 times brighter than magnitude 4 stars, and so on.

PROBLEM 1:

The star Dubhe in the constellation Ursa Major has an apparent magnitude of 2.0 An unknown star, X, had an apparent magnitude of 4.0. How much brighter is Dubhe than star X?

Solution: A decrease in one order of magnitude corresponds to an increase of 2.5 times in apparent brightness. A decrease of two orders of magnitude is the same as an increase of $2.5 \times 2.5 = 6.25$ times in apparent brightness.

Answer: To the eye, Dubhe will appear more than six times brighter than the star X.

Stars down to magnitude 19 are visible with the 200-inch Mount Palomer telescope, and stars as dim as magnitude 24 can be photographed (long exposure) with that telescope. Even fainter stars can be photographed with the aid of image tubes.

ZERO AND NEGATIVE VALUES OF APPARENT MAGNITUDE

The twenty stars originally designated as first magnitude stars were subsequently regrouped. This was necessary because some of the stars were much brighter than others. The brighter stars of this group were designated as having magnitudes of .9, .8, .7, etc., through .0 to negative numbers. The star with the greatest apparent brightness at night is Sirius. Its apparent magnitude is −1.6. On the same scale, the apparent magnitude of our sun is immensely greater: −26.7.

DETERMINING APPARENT MAGNITUDES

The method of determining the magnitude of stars by observation is rather simple. With practice, fairly accurate results (an accuracy of .1 of a magnitude) can be obtained. The method was used extensively by the German astronomer Friedrich Argelander (1799–1875) and his associates in the preparation of the great star catalog, the "B.D. Catalog." (B.D. is the abbreviation of the German title of the catalog, *Bonner Durchmusterung*—"Bonn Catalog.") By this method, the observer compares the apparent brightness of a star with two or more neighboring stars of known magnitudes. Thus, a star that appears somewhat fainter than a neighboring star of 2.4 magnitude and somewhat brighter than another neighboring star of 2.6 magnitude, will be designated as having a magnitude of 2.5. In using this method it is advisable to make sure that:

A. The star to be measured and the known magnitude stars should be at about the same distance above the horizon.
B. The known magnitude stars should be as close as possible to the star to be measured.
C. One of the known magnitude stars should be somewhat brighter and the other somewhat fainter than the star to be measured.

The following table contains a list of stars of known apparent magnitude. These can be used for the determination of magnitude of many other stars.

Star	Constellation	Apparent Magnitude
Alpheratz	Andromeda	2.2
Schedar	Cassiopeia	2.5
Diphda	Cetus	2.2
Achernar	Eridanus	.6
Hamal	Aries	2.2
Acamar	Eridanus	3.1
Aldebaran	Taurus	1.1
Rigel	Orion	.3
Capella	Auriga	.2
Bellatrix	Orion	1.7
Canopus	Carina	− .9
Sirius	Canis Major	−1.6
Procyon	Canis Minor	.5
Pollux	Gemini	1.2
Regulus	Leo	1.3
Dubhe	Ursa Major	2.0
Acrux	Crux	1.1
Arcturus	Boötes	.2
Zubenelgenubi	Libra	2.9
Shaula	Scorpius	1.7
Nunki	Sagittarius	2.1
Markab	Pegasus	2.6

NOTE: On maps these figures are rounded off to the nearest integer.

PROBLEM 2:
Determine which of the two is the brighter star, Alkaid or Merak.
Answer: Alkaid is the brighter one. The apparent magnitude of Alkaid is 1.9; that of Merak, 2.4.

PROBLEM 3:
Find three stars in the Big Dipper that appear to be of equal brightness.
Answer: Mizar, Merak, and Phecda have almost the same apparent brightness. Precisely, they are designated as being 2.4, 2.4, and 2.5 magnitude stars, respectively. Phecda is by a very slight degree fainter than the other two.

PROBLEM 4:
Determine the apparent magnitude of the North Star (Polaris).
Answer: Polaris is but slightly brighter than Merak, and slightly fainter than Dubhe. It is usually designated as a 2.1 magnitude star.

Note again, this refers to **apparent** magnitudes. Actually, Polaris is much brighter than our sun —in fact, nearly 1,500 times brighter. The great distance accounts for its being only a magnitude 2.1 star. Stated in terms of time, it takes light, traveling at the speed of 186,000 miles per second, 8⅓ minutes to reach earth from the sun; and 400 years to reach earth from Polaris.

APPARENT DAILY MOTIONS OF STARS

It is common knowledge that the sun seems to rise in the east, describe an arc in the sky, and set in the west.

The stars, too, seem to move in arcs in the sky —also from the eastern to the western part of the horizon. A complete revolution takes 23 hours, 56 minutes and 4.09 seconds. This can very easily be approximately verified any clear evening with the aid of a good watch.

PROBLEM 5:
Object: To verify a complete revolution of a star. (This period is known as a "sidereal" day, or a "starday.")

Equipment: A good watch.
Procedure:
a. Note the time at which some bright star appears just above the eastern horizon.

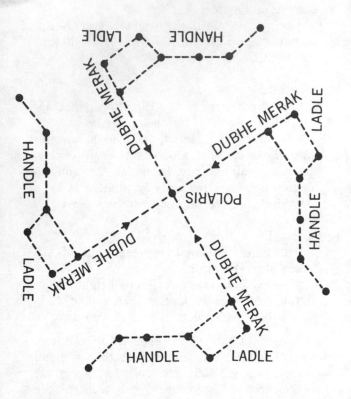

FIGURE 13. In the course of approximately 24 hours, the Big Dipper completes one revolution in the sky. Only part of that circle can actually be observed, as sunlight makes it impossible to observe the stars during the daytime. This figure shows the Big Dipper at 6-hour intervals.

b. The next day repeat the procedure under (a).
Results: The experiment demonstrates that every star completes one apparent revolution in 23 hours, 56 minutes and 4 seconds.

The term "apparent" is often repeated here for good reason. The motion is really *only* apparent; it may even be considered an optical illusion. Actually it is the earth, spinning on its axis in the opposite direction, that causes the stars to seem to move as they do.

This daily rotation can also very effectively be observed by watching a constellation, such as Ursa Major.

If, when first observed, the constellation appears level with the bowl on the right:

Six hours later it will appear with the handle pointed downward;

Twelve hours after the original observation, the Big Dipper will appear with the open part of the bowl pointing downward;

Eighteen hours after the original observation, the Big Dipper will appear to have the handle pointing upward.

In any 23 hours, 56 minutes and 4 seconds, the Big Dipper can be seen in any one of those positions.

During part of that time, the sun will interfere with the observations. The faint starlight cannot be discerned in the bright sky of day.

THE APPARENT ANNUAL MOTION OF THE STARS

The fact that stars complete a revolution in less than twenty-four hours is of great importance. It signifies, of course, that the stars make more than one revolution in a 24-hour period.

The difference between 24 and the period of revolution is:

$$\begin{array}{r} 24 \text{ hours} \\ -23 \text{ hours, 56 minutes, 4 seconds} \\ \hline 3 \text{ minutes, 56 seconds.} \end{array}$$

Thus, the stars begin the next revolution in the remaining 3 minutes and 56 seconds. This can be verified by observation.

A star that appears on the horizon, say, at eight o'clock on a Sunday evening will be slightly **above** the horizon the following evening at eight o'clock. Tuesday evening at eight o'clock, the star will be still further above the horizon and a month later at eight o'clock in the evening, the star will be substantially above the horizon.

After three months, at eight o'clock in the evening, the star will be a quarter of a circle away from the eastern horizon. At the end of a year, the star will have completed an apparent circle.

This movement of a star is also an *apparent* movement. It is due to the **real** movement of the earth about the sun. The earth completes a revolution around the sun in 12 months.

This apparent annual movement of stars obtains for constellations as well.

Thus Ursa Major at eight o'clock in the evening in October is close to the horizon with the bowl opening upward.

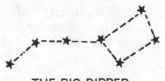

THE BIG DIPPER
8 O'CLOCK IN THE EVENING (OCTOBER)

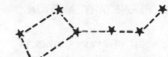

8 O'CLOCK IN THE EVENING
SIX MONTHS LATER (APRIL)

8 O'CLOCK IN THE EVENING
THREE MONTHS LATER

THE BIG DIPPER
8 O'CLOCK IN THE EVENING
NINE MONTHS LATER (JULY)

FIGURE 14.

Three months later at the same time in the evening, the handle will point downward.

In April at the same time of the evening, the Big Dipper will be high above the horizon and will appear with the bowl to the left.

In July at the same time of the evening, the Big Dipper will appear with the bowl at the bottom.

Thus in a period of 365¼ days, the Big Dipper completes 366¼ apparent revolutions: 365¼ of them are due to the rotation of the earth on its axis, and one is due to the revolution of the earth about the sun.

The Mechanics of the Solar System

INTRODUCTION

The solar system consists of the sun; the planets and their satellites; the planetoids, comets, meteorites, and dust. Both the adjective "solar" and the noun "system" are appropriate.

"Solar" indicates that the sun governs: it contains nearly 99.9 per cent of all the matter in the system. (The mass of all the planets, satellites, etc. comprises the other .1 or 1 per cent.) As a result of this division of mass, the "massive" sun is nearly stationary while all the "lighter" bodies revolve around it.

The word "system" implies that all the bodies observe great regularity in their motions. The laws governing these motions have been known for several centuries. Of great importance among the several laws are the three that are known by the name of their discoverer (Johannes Kepler) and the Universal Law of Gravitation (first stated by Isaac Newton).

KEPLER'S FIRST LAW OF PLANETARY MOTION

This law states that the orbit of every planet is an ellipse which has the sun as one of its foci.

DEMONSTRATION:

Object: To draw an ellipse.

Equipment: Pencil, piece of string, two thumbtacks, paper.

Procedure:

1. Place string to form an angle, ABC.
2. Fix the ends A and C with the thumbtacks, and place the pencil at B.
3. Keeping the string taut, move the pencil around to form the oval curve. See Fig. 15.

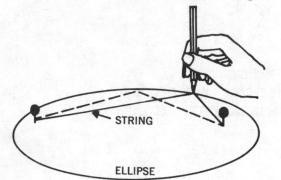

FIGURE 15. Drawing of an ellipse. Fix the end of the string at points A and C. Stretch the string to form the angle at B. Keeping the string taut at all times move the pencil about to form the oval curve. A is one focus of this ellipse. C is the other.

Result: The curve described by the pencil is an ellipse. The two points that were kept fixed by the thumbtacks are called the foci of the ellipse (sing. focus).

PROBLEM 6:

Given an ellipse. Its major axis is 5 inches long, its minor axis is 3 inches long.

Find: 1. The distance between the foci; 2. the eccentricity of the ellipse.

Solution: 1. The major axis, the minor axis, and the distance between the foci are related by a simple formula. If the length of the major axis is denoted by a; if the length of the minor axis is denoted by b; and the distance between foci is denoted by c; the formula is:

$$b^2 + c^2 = a^2 \text{ or } c = \sqrt{a^2 - b^2}.$$

In this case, $c = \sqrt{5^2 - 3^2} = 4$ inches. The distance between the foci is 4 inches. See Fig. 16.

2. **"Eccentricity"** of an ellipse is defined as the ratio of distance between foci to length of major axis. It is denoted by e.

$$e = \frac{c}{a}$$

This ratio, in the case of an ellipse, is always larger than 0 and less than 1. It indicates how "eccentric," compared with a circle, the ellipse is. When the ratio is small, say .1, the ellipse is very little eccentric. It is almost circular. When the eccentricity is large, say .8, the ellipse is highly elongated. In this problem the eccentricity is given by:

$$e = \frac{4}{5} = .8$$

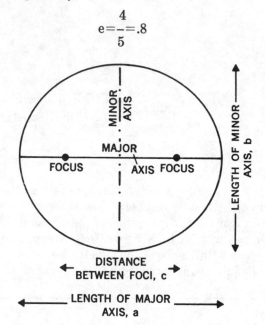

FIGURE 16. In an ellipse the length of the major axis, a, the length of the minor axis, b, and the distance between the foci, c, are related by the formula—

$$b^2 + c^2 = a^2$$

Planets move in nearly circular orbits. The eccentricities of Venus and of the earth are .01 and .02, respectively.

Comets move in elongated orbits. The orbit of Halley's Comet is an ellipse, with an eccentricity of .97.

KEPLER'S SECOND LAW OF PLANETARY MOTION

This law deals with the speed of the planets in their respective orbits. The speed is not constant, the planets moving faster the closer they are to the sun. The maximum speed of any planet is attained when it is closest to the sun, the minimum when it is farthest. The point on the orbit closest to the sun is known as perihelion, the farthest, aphelion.

Though the speeds of the planets in their orbits are not constant, another feature closely connected with speed *is* constant—namely, the speed with which the line connecting the sun and any particular planet passes over areas.

This is expressed in the formal version of Kepler's second law: **The radius vector of each planet passes over equal areas in equal intervals of time.**

The radius vector is an imaginary line that connects the sun with a planet—short at the perihelion and long at the aphelion.

The second law indicates that at aphelion, the planet moves slower than at perihelion in order to pass over equal areas of the ellipse. See Fig. 17.

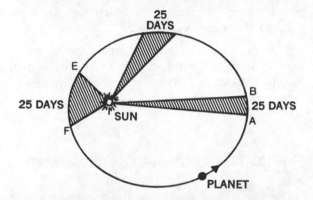

FIGURE 17. Kepler's second law of planetary motion. The radius vector would cover equal areas (three such areas are shown here shaded) in equal times (25 days).

At aphelion the planet moved relatively slowly to get from A to B. At perihelion the planet had to move at a relatively high speed to cover the distance from E to F.

The term radius vector used in the formal version of the law is an imaginary line joining the sun with the planet. The line connecting the sun to A, or the sun to B, or the sun to D, etc., is a radius vector.

The earth's average velocity along its orbit about the sun is 18.5 miles per second. Since the orbit is almost a circle, its speed does not vary materially along the path. At aphelion, the earth moves only by ½ a mile per second slower than at perihelion.

In the case of highly eccentric orbits, such as those pursued by comets, the orbital speed varies greatly. Halley's Comet, when at perihelion, has a speed of 100 miles per second; and at aphelion, of less than 1 mile per second.

KEPLER'S THIRD LAW OF PLANETARY MOTION

The third law deals with the relationship between the period of a planet and its mean distance from the sun.

The "period" is the time that it takes a planet to complete one revolution about the sun. For the earth, this is 365.26 days; for the planet Mercury, only 88 days; for Pluto, the farthest planet, 248 *years*.

Kepler's third law states that **the squares of the periods of any two planets are proportional to the cubes of their mean distances to the sun.**

This can be stated as an algebraic equation: Let the two planets be designated as A and B.

$$\frac{(\text{period of A})^2}{(\text{period of B})^2} =$$

$$\frac{(\text{mean distance of the sun to A})^3}{(\text{mean distance of the sun to B})^3}$$

If the known data for the earth are used for one of these planets, say B, the equation becomes:

$$\frac{(\text{period of A})^2}{(365.26)^2} =$$

$$\frac{(\text{mean distance of the sun to A})^3}{(93,000,000)^3}$$

This equation has two variables: the period of a planet and its mean distance. If one of these is obtained by observation, the other can be computed algebraically.

PROBLEM 7:

The period of the planet Mars is 687 days. Compute the mean distance of Mars from the sun.

Solution: Inserting the given data in the equation:

$$\frac{(\text{mean distance of Mars from sun})^3}{(93,000,000)^3} = \frac{(365)^2}{(687)^2}$$

Answer: The distance of Mars from the sun is 142,000,000 miles.

NOTE: Kepler's third law is not quite complete. The complete form was evolved by Newton. In the complete form, "the squares of the periods" have to be multiplied by the combined mass of the sun and the planet. The corrected equation reads:

$$\frac{(\text{period of A})^2(\text{mass of sun \& planet A})}{(\text{period of B})^2(\text{mass of sun \& planet B})}$$
$$= \frac{(\text{mean dist. of A})^3}{(\text{mean dist. of B})^3}$$

EVALUATION OF KEPLER'S THREE LAWS

The discovery of these laws was a milestone, not only in the history of astronomy, but also in the history of science in general. It is an eternal monument, not only to the brilliance of Kepler, but also to his devotion to science, to which he committed infinite patience and labor.

There was one shortcoming to these laws, however—a very important shortcoming. Kepler's laws did not explain the behavior of the planets, why they move in elliptical orbits, or why their speeds change as they do.

The answers were soon forthcoming in Sir Isaac Newton's epoch-making book, *Mathematical Principles of Physics*. There, Newton showed that the planets behave as they do because of a most fundamental universal law—the law of gravitation; and that Kepler's three laws are merely consequences of that universal law.

NEWTON'S UNIVERSAL LAW OF GRAVITATION

The law, dealing with forces between material objects, states that every particle of matter attracts every other particle of matter with a force, depending on three factors:

A. Mass of one object.
B. Mass of the other object.
C. The distance between the objects.

These factors are often denoted as M, m, and r, respectively.

The formal statement of the law is: **Every particle of matter in the universe attracts every other particle with a force that is proportional to the product of their masses, and inversely proportional to the square of the distance between them.**

The law can also be expressed as an algebraic equation:

$$FG = (\text{force of gravity}) \times \frac{Mm}{r^2}$$

G is known as the universal gravitational constant. Its value is 6.7×10^{-8} if M and m are expressed in grams, r in centimeters, and F in dynes. The formula for the Universal Law of Gravitation will then be:

$$F = 6.7 \times 10^{-8} \frac{Mm}{r^2}$$

PROBLEM 8:

A mass of 2,000 grams, about 4.4 pounds, is at a distance of 2.54 centimeters (about 1 inch) from another mass of 5,000 grams. Find the force of attraction between these two bodies.

$$F = 6.7 \times 10^{-8} \frac{2000 \times 5000}{(2.54)^2} = .1 \text{ dyne}$$

Answer: The force with which each mass attracts the other is .1 dyne.

A dyne is an extremely small force, much smaller than a pound of force. Approximately 500,000 dynes are equal in value to one pound of force.

APPLICATION OF THE LAW OF GRAVITATION

The law was of enormous aid in solving a host of problems. Chief among these are:

A. Freely falling bodies. Any body not properly supported, will fall toward the center of the earth.
B. Ocean tides and tides in the atmosphere.
C. Motion of comets.
D. Precession of equinoxes.
E. Motion of planets. If the gravitational force between the earth and the sun ceased to operate, the earth would go off on a tangent. It is the direct result of this law that planets revolve about the sun as they do. This result is shown in Figure 18.

The nine planets move in elliptical orbits at various distances from the sun, counterclockwise.

Although gravitation applies, of course, to the stars and galaxies as well, its effect is easier to see in the case of planets because of the presence of *one* large mass (the sun) acting on several close, smaller masses (the planets). The perturbation on these motions by distant stars is extremely small.

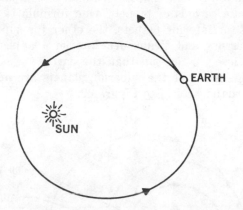

FIGURE 18. Effect of gravitational attraction. It is due to the gravitational attraction of the sun that the earth continues to move in its orbit.

In the absence of this attraction the earth would leave its elliptical orbit and go off on a tangent, such as at point A, farther and farther away from the sun.

APPARENT MOTION OF PLANETS AS SEEN FROM THE EARTH

The true motion of the planets cannot be observed from the earth, because the earth itself is constantly in motion. Observations indicate only the motion of the planets relative to that of the earth. At times a planet's relative velocity, with respect to the earth, is greater than its true velocity, as when the earth and the planet move in opposite directions; at other times the planet's relative velocity is less than its true velocity, as when a planet and the earth move in the same direction.

Of particular interest in the apparent motion of planets is the retrograde phase in which planets seem to move in a direction opposite to their normal one. See Figure 19.

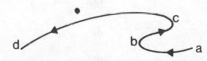

FIGURE 19. Retrograde motion. As seen against the background of the celestial sphere the planet was moving at A in the normal direction (this is called "direct motion"), and continued to do so

until point B. From B to C the motion is in a direction opposite to normal (retrograde motion). At point C, the planet makes a U-turn and continues in direct motion.

The backward or retrograde motion of several of the planets puzzled astronomers for many centuries, until finally it was explained by Copernicus. An example is of great aid in visualizing the apparent retrograde motion.

Let the inner circle in Figure 20 represent the orbit of the earth around the sun. Let the large circle represent the orbit of Mars. The earth, being closer to the sun, moves faster than Mars. Let the top of the figure represent part of the celestial sphere. The sphere serves as a background upon which the movements of Mars are observed.

When the earth is in position 1, Mars will be seen in place 1 on the celestial sphere. Several weeks later, both the earth and Mars will have moved in their orbits. Mars is now at point 2. As the earth moves through positions 3 and 4, the line described by Mars on the celestial sphere will be of a body in retrograde motion.

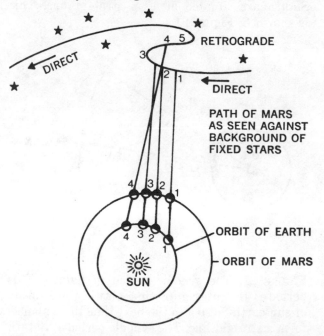

FIGURE 20. Explanation of retrograde motion. The earth, being closer to the sun than Mars, moves faster than Mars (the earth completes its circle in 365 days, Mars 687). At point 1, Mars is "ahead" of the earth; its motion is direct. At point 4 the earth is "ahead" of Mars, and the latter seems to retrograde.

SIDEREAL AND SYNODIC PERIOD OF A PLANET

In connection with planets, there are two definitions of period: (A) sidereal period; and (B) synodic period. These differ in length due to the motion of the earth.

A Sidereal Period is the time it takes the planet to complete one revolution in its orbit. Another way of saying the same thing is: It is the time required by a planet to complete a circle on the celestial sphere, as seen from the sun.

B. The Synodic Period, which involves the motion of the earth, is the interval between one time that the sun, the earth, and planet are aligned and the next time. Since both the earth and the planet are in motion, the synodic period differs materially from the sidereal.

Thus, the sidereal period of Mars is 687 days; its synodic period is 780 days.

In the case of Saturn, the sidereal and synodic periods are 29.5 years and 378 days, respectively. The former signifies that it takes Saturn nearly 30 years to complete its orbit about the sun; the latter that every 378 days, the sun, the earth, and Saturn are situated along a straight line. This is shown in Figure 21.

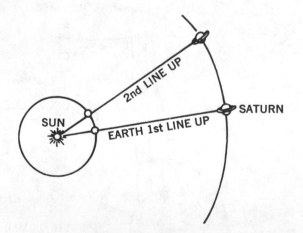

FIGURE 21. The synodic period of Saturn. This period is the interval of time between one lineup of sun-earth-Saturn to the next time these planets form a straight line. The synodic period of Saturn is 378 days. It consists of 365 days for a complete revolution of the earth plus 13 days needed for the earth to catch up with Saturn, which in the meanwhile has moved on to a new position.

The 378 days are composed of (a) 1 revolution of the earth about the sun (365 days); and (b)

13 days to catch up with Saturn which, in the meanwhile, has moved to a new position in its orbit.

There are two simple formulas to compute the synodic periods of planets. One formula is to be used for inferior planets, the other for superior.

Mercury and Venus are Inferior Plants. They are closer to the sun than the earth.

The orbits of the superior planets are outside the earth's orbit. See Figure 22.

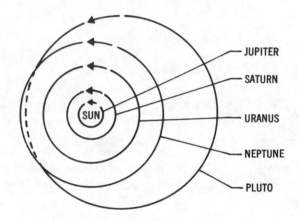

FIGURE 22. Orbits of five superior planets. The orbits are ellipses of small eccentricity, hence closely resemble circles. All the planets move in a counterclockwise direction, as shown by the arrows. The length of the arrow indicates the distance the planet travels in one year. The four other planets (not shown) move along orbits inside the orbit of Jupiter.

The formula for an inferior planet is:

$$\text{Synodic period of planet} = \frac{360}{P-E}$$

P is the number of degrees of arc that a planet moves in its orbit in one day; E is the number of degrees that the earth moves in its orbit in one day. For Mercury,

$$P = \frac{360}{88}$$

$$E = \frac{360}{365\frac{1}{4}}$$

Substituting these numbers in the formula, we then get:

$$\text{Synodic period of Mercury} = \frac{360}{\dfrac{360}{88} - \dfrac{360}{365\frac{1}{4}}}$$

$$= 116 \text{ days}$$

For a superior planet, the formula is:

$$\text{Synodic period of superior planet} = \frac{360}{E-P}$$

where E and P have the same meaning as in the previous formula.

The proof of this second formula is fairly simple. The denominator E−P stands for the number of degrees that the earth gains on a planet in *one* day. But in a synodic period, the earth gains a complete revolution (360°) on the planet; hence, that period is equal to the number of times (E−P) is contained in 360.

PROBLEM 9:

Compute the synodic period of Mars.

Given: The sidereal period of the earth is

$365\frac{1}{4}$ days, or $E = \dfrac{360}{365\frac{1}{4}}$;

and the sidereal period of Mars is 687 days, or

$$P = \frac{360}{687}$$

Answer: 780 days.

Basic Planetary Data

INTRODUCTION

For each planet there is now available a large number of data. These include dimensions as well as other physical and orbital data.

The methods used to obtain several of these values are indicated in this part.

DISTANCE TO SUN

One fairly accurate way to determine the mean distance of a planet to the sun makes use of Kepler's third law.

If distances are measured in astronomical units and sidereal periods in years, the third law can be written as

$$(\text{period of a planet})^2 = (\text{mean distance of planet to sun})^3$$

PROBLEM 10:

The sidereal period of the planet Mars is 687 days. Find the mean distance of Mars from the sun.

Solution: Changing days into years and inserting in above formula,

$$\left(\frac{687}{365.25}\right)^2 = (\text{mean distance of Mars to Sun})^3$$

The answer for mean distance is 1.52 astronomical units, or (multiplying 1.52 by 93,000,000) 142,000,000 miles.

ECCENTRICITY

The eccentricity of a planet's orbit can be found

A. By determining the distance of the planet from the sun at different times of the year.

B. By plotting a graph of date versus distance from the sun. The graph will be an ellipse.

C. By computing the eccentricity e, using the formula $e = \dfrac{c}{a}$ where c is the distance from either focus (the sun is at one of the foci) to the center of the ellipse and a is the length of half of the major axis.

NOTE: Computing actual (as opposed to mean) distances from the sun for a planet other than the earth is a more arduous task.

INCLINATION OF ORBIT TO ECLIPTIC

This is obtained from observations on the celestial sphere. The inclination is equal to the maximum angle the planet reaches above or below the ecliptic.

PERIOD OF ONE REVOLUTION, SIDEREAL

The sidereal period can be obtained by using the formulas given on page 194 and the observed synodic period.

PERIOD OF ONE REVOLUTION, SYNODIC

The synodic period is obtained by noting the interval of time between two successive conjunctions of the planet with the sun, i.e., two successive times that the planet is on the line that joins the sun and the earth.

ORBITAL VELOCITY

This is obtained by dividing the length of the circumference by the time it takes to cover that distance, i.e., by the sidereal period.

DISTANCE OF A PLANET FROM EARTH

One method that can be used to determine the distance of a planet from the earth is triangulation. In this method a line of position, say, 1,000 km long, is established on earth. The angles from both ends of the line to the planet are measured. Standard formulae from elementary trigonometry are used to find the distance to the planet.

Another method is to measure the time elapsed for a radar signal to make a round trip to the planet. The distance to the planet is obtained by multiplying half the time for the round trip by the velocity of light.

PROBLEM 11:

A radar signal was sent to the planet Venus early in 1958. The round trip took about 5 minutes (300 seconds). Find the distance to the planet at that time.

Solution: Since the velocity of light, or the velocity of radar, is 186,000 miles per second, then

$186,000 \times 150 =$ approximately 28,000,000 miles.

ANGULAR DIAMETER

The anglar diameter of a planet is determined by
 A. Sighting through a telescope one limb of the planet.
 B. Rotating the telescope to the other limb.
The angle through which the telescope has been rotated is equal to the angular diameter of the planet.

LINEAR DIAMETER

The linear diameter of a planet is obtained by multiplying the angular diameter (in radians) by the distance to the planet. The formula is:

Linear diameter = angular diameter × distance to planet

The angular diameter in this formula has to be in radian units. (A radian is an angle that subtends an arc of a circle equal to the radius of that circle; 1 radian is slightly more than 57°.) The rate of conversion from degrees to radians is 1 radian = $\dfrac{360°}{2\pi}$. The diameter will be in the same unit as that used for distance to the planet.

VOLUME

Assuming that the planet is a sphere, the geometrical formula for volume of a sphere can be used:

$$\text{Volume} = \frac{4}{3}\pi \times \text{the radius}^3$$

where π has a value of 3.14.

MASS

The mass of a planet that has a satellite orbiting around it is obtained from Kepler's third law as amended by Newton (see note following Problem 7).

One form of this amended law is

$$P^2 = \frac{4\pi^2 a^3}{G(M_1 + M_2)}$$

where

P is the sidereal period of the satellite

a is the distance from center of satellite to center of planet

G is the universal gravitational constant (in the meter-kilogram-second system $G = 6.7 \times 10^{-11}$ newtons$\times$meters$^2\times$kilograms^{-2}).

M_1 and M_2 are the masses of the planet and the satellite, respectively. The mass of the satellite (M_2) is usually so much smaller than the mass of the planet (M_1) that it may be omitted from the formula.

PROBLEM 12:

Find the mass of Mars, given that its satellite Phobos is at a distance of 5,820 miles$=9,400$ km$=9.4\times10^6$ meters and it orbits the mother planet in 7 hours 39 minutes$=27,500$ seconds.

Solution: Using meters for the unit of distance and seconds for the unit of time, then

$$M_1 = \frac{4\pi^2 \times (9.4\times10^6)^3}{6.7\times10^{-11}\times27,500^2} = 7\times10^{23} \text{ kg,}$$ approximately, for the mass of Mars, or about 11 per cent the mass of the earth.

The mass of planets that do not have natural satellites (e.g., Venus) is obtained by the use of either (A) an artificial satellite that orbits the planet or (B) determining the perturbation exerted by the planet on a close passing planetoid or spacecraft.

DENSITY

Mean density of a planet is obtained by dividing the mass by the volume. The value of a density is often stated in terms relative to the density of the earth.

SURFACE GRAVITY

The acceleration due to gravity at the surface of a planet is derived from Newton's Universal law of gravitation with M being the mass of the planet and $m=1$. In the gravity formula is $F = 6.7\times10^{-8}\frac{M}{r^2}$. In the meter-kilogram-second system, the formula is $F = 6.7\times10^{-11}\frac{M}{r^2}$. r is the radius of the planet proper units.

VELOCITY OF ESCAPE

The speed that an object must acquire in order to escape from the gravitational field of a planet is obtained from

$$V = \sqrt{2}\,\frac{Gm}{r}$$

In the centimeter-gram-second system, $G = 6.7\times10^{-8}$ the mass has to be stated in grams, and the distance of the object from the center of the planet in centimeters. The escape velocity will be in units of centimeters per second.

PERIOD OF ROTATION ABOUT AXIS

The period of rotation of planets that have identifiable features (e.g., Mars) is determined by timing a complete rotation of such a feature.

The Doppler shift in radar waves between the approaching limb and the receding limb of a planet is used to determine the period for planets that do not have identifiable features.

INCLINATION OF PLANET'S EQUATOR TO ORBIT

This is usually derived from the study of an arc described by a surface marking on the planet.

ALBEDO

Albedo pertains to the ability of an object to reflect light. Some objects—e.g., tops of clouds—reflect most of the light falling upon them; others absorb most of the light, reflecting little. Stones, rocks, and soil are poor reflectors of light.

Albedo is defined as the ratio of the quantity of light reflected to the light received by the object.

In reference to the planets, albedo is equal to the ratio:

$$\frac{\text{light reflected by the planet}}{\text{sunlight falling on the planet}}$$

The denominator can be computed from the known value of the sun's luminosity and the planet's distance from the sun. The numerator is derived from the intrinsic brightness of the planet.

CHAPTER ELEVEN

GEOLOGY

Introduction

Derived from the Greek *geo,* "earth," plus *logos,* "discourse," geology is the science which deals with the origin, structure, and history of the earth and its inhabitants as recorded in the rocks.

To the geologist, the earth is not simply the globe upon which we live—it is an ever present challenge to learn more about such things as earthquakes, volcanoes, glaciers, and the meaning of fossils. How old is the earth? Where did it come from? Of what is it made? To answer these questions, the earth scientist must study the evidence of events that occurred millions of years ago. He must then relate his findings to the results of similar events that are happening today. He attempts, for example, to determine the location and extent of ancient oceans and mountain ranges, and to trace the evolution of life as recorded in rocks of different ages. He studies the composition of the rocks and minerals forming the earth's crust in an attempt to locate and exploit the valuable economic products that are to be found there.

In pursuing his study of the earth the geologist relies heavily upon other basic sciences. For example, **astronomy** (the study of the nature and movements of planets, stars, and other heavenly bodies) tells us where the earth fits into the universe and has also developed several theories as to the origin of our planet. **Chemistry** (the study of the composition of substances and the changes which they undergo) is used to analyze and study the rocks and minerals of the earth's crust. The science of **physics** (the study of matter and motion) helps explain the various physical forces affecting our earth, and the reaction of earth materials to these forces.

To understand the nature of prehistoric plants and animals we must turn to **biology,** the study of all living forms. **Zoology** provides us with information about the animals, and **botany** gives us some insight into the nature of ancient plants. By using these sciences, as well as others, the geologist is better able to cope with the many complex problems that are inherent in the study of the earth and its history.

The scope of geology is so broad that it has been divided into two major divisions: **physical geology** and **historical geology.** For convenience in study, each of these divisions has been subdivided into a number of more specialized branches of subsciences.

PHYSICAL GEOLOGY

Physical geology deals with the earth's composition, its structure, the movements within and upon the earth's crust, and the geologic processes by which the earth's surface is, or has been changed.

The broad division of geology includes such basic geologic subsciences as **mineralogy,** the study of minerals, and **petrology,** the study of rocks. These two branches of geology provide us with much-needed information about the composition of the earth. In addition, there is **structural geology** to explain the arrangement of the rocks within the earth, and **geomorphology** to explain the origin of its surface features.

These branches of physical geology enable the

geologist to make detailed studies of all phases of earth science. The knowledge gained from such research brings about a better understanding of the physical nature of the earth.

CASUAL OBSERVATION

How can we learn more about this fascinating earth and the stories to be read from its rocks? Actually it is very simple, for geology is all around us. The geologist's laboratory is the great outdoors, and each walk through the fields or drive down the highway brings us in contact with the processes and materials of geology.

For example, pick up a piece of common limestone. There are probably fossils in it. And these fossils may well represent the remains of animals that lived in some prehistoric sea which once covered the area.

Or maybe you are walking along a river bank. Notice the silt on the bank after the last high water stage. This reminds us of the ability of running water to deposit **sediments**—sediments that may later be transformed into rocks. Notice, too, how swift currents have scoured the river banks. The soil has been removed by **erosion,** the geologic process which is so important in the shaping of the earth's surface features.

Perhaps you see a field of black fertile soil supporting a fine crop of cotton or corn. It may surprise you to learn that this dark rich soil may have been derived from an underlying chalky white limestone—still another reminder of the importance of earth materials in our everyday life.

EARTH AS A PLANET

The earth is one of nine planets comprising the solar system. It is the largest of the four planets of the inner group (Mercury, Venus, Earth, and Mars) and is third closest to the sun (Fig. 1).

Shape of the Earth. The earth has the form of an **oblate spheroid.** That is, it is almost ball-shaped, or spherical, except for a slight flattening at the poles. This flattening, and an accompanying bulge at the equator, are produced by the centrifugal force of rotation.

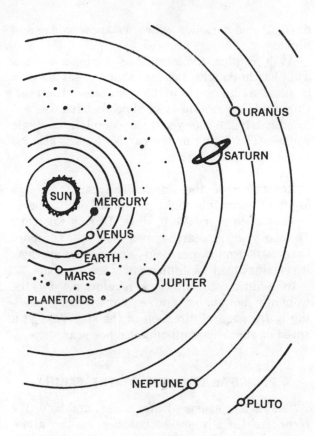

FIGURE 1. Planets of the solar system and their relation to the sun.

Size of the Earth. Although the earth is of great size, Jupiter, Saturn, Uranus, and Neptune all have greater equatorial diameters. Earth has a polar diameter of about 7900 miles (the equatorial diameter is approximately 27 miles greater because of the bulge described above). The circumference of the earth is about 24,874 miles, and the surface area comprises roughly 197 million square miles, of which only about 51 million square miles (29 per cent) are surface lands. The remaining 71 per cent of the earth's surface is covered by water.

Earth Motions. We have already learned that each of the planets revolves around the sun within its own orbit and period of revolution. In addition to its trip around the sun, the earth also rotates.

Rotation of the Earth. The earth turns on its axis (the shortest diameter connecting the poles), and this turning motion is called *rotation*. The earth rotates from west to east and makes one complete rotation each day. It is this rotating motion that gives us the alternating periods of daylight and darkness which we know as day and night.

As it rotates, the earth has a single wobble. This has to do with the fact that the earth's axis is tilted at an angle of 23½ degrees. However, this wobbling motion is so slow that it takes approximately 26,000 years to complete a single wobble. The tilting of the earth's axis is also responsible for the seasons.

Revolution of the Earth. The earth revolves around the sun in a slightly elliptical **orbit** approximately once every 365¼ days. During this time (a solar year), th earth travels at a speed of more than 60,000 miles per hour, and on the average, it remains about 93 million miles from the sun.

In addition to rotation, revolution, and the wobbling motion, our entire solar system is heading in the general direction of the star Vega at a speed of about 400 million miles per year.

PRINCIPAL DIVISIONS OF THE EARTH

The earth consists of air, water, and land. We recognize these more technically as the **atmosphere,** a gaseous envelope surrounding the earth; the **hydrosphere,** the waters filling the depressions and covering almost three-fourths of the land; and the **lithosphere,** the solid part of the earth which underlies the atmosphere and hydrosphere.

The Atmosphere. The atmosphere, or gaseous portion of the earth, extends upward for hundreds of miles above sea level. It is a mixture of nitrogen, oxygen, carbon dioxide, water vapor, and other gases (see Table 1).

GAS	PER CENT BY VOLUME
Nitrogen	78.084
Oxygen	20.946
Argon	.934
Carbon dioxide	.033
Neon	.001818
Helium	.000524
Methane	.0002
Krypton	.000114
Hydrogen	.00005
Nitrous oxide	.00005
Xenon	.0000087

TABLE 1. Analysis of gases present in pure dry air. Notice that nitrogen and oxygen comprise 99 per cent of the total volume of atmospheric gases.

Of great importance to man, the elements of the atmosphere make life possible on our planet. Moreover, the atmosphere acts as an insulating agent to protect us from the heat of the sun and to shield us from the bombardment of meteorites, and it makes possible the evaporation and precipitation of moisture. The atmosphere is an important geologic agent (see Chapter 6) and is responsible for the processes of weathering which are continually at work on the earth's surface.

The Hydrosphere. The hydrosphere includes all the waters of the oceans, lakes, and rivers, as well as **ground water**—which exists within the lithosphere. As noted earlier, most of this water is contained in the oceans, which cover roughly 71 per cent of the earth's surface to an average depth of about two and a half miles.

The waters of the earth are essential to man's existence and they are also of considerable geologic importance. Running streams and oceans are actively engaged in eroding, transporting, and depositing sediments; and water, working in conjunction with atmospheric agents, has been the major force in forming the earth's surface features throughout geologic time. The geologic work of the hydrosphere will be discussed in some detail in later chapters of this book.

The Lithosphere. Of prime importance to the geologist is the lithosphere. This, the solid portion of the earth, is composed of rocks and minerals which, in turn, comprise the continental masses and ocean basins. The rocks of the lithosphere are of three basic types, **igneous, sedimentary,** and **metamorphic.** Igneous rocks were originally in a molten state but have since cooled and solidified to form rocks such as granite and basalt. Sedimentary rocks are formed from sediments (fragments of pre-existing rocks) deposited by wind, water, or ice. Limestone, sandstone, and clay are typical of this group. The metamorphic rocks have been formed from rocks that were originally sedimentary or igneous in origin. This transformation takes place as the rock is subjected to great physical and chemical change. Marble, which in its original form was limestone, is an example of a metamorphic rock.

Most of what we know about the lithosphere has been learned through the study of the surface materials of the earth. However, by means of deep bore holes and seismological studies, geologists have gathered much valuable information about the interior of the earth. Additional geologic data are derived from rocks which were originally buried many miles beneath the ground but have been brought to or near the surface by violent earth movements and later exposed by erosion.

MAJOR PHYSICAL FEATURES OF THE EARTH

The major relief features of the earth are the **continental masses** and the **ocean basins.** These are the portions of the earth which apparently remained stable throughout all of known geologic time.

The Continental Masses. The continents are rocky platforms which cover approximately 29 per cent of the earth's surface. Composed largely of granite, they have an average elevation of about three miles above the floors of the surrounding ocean basins and rise an average of one-half mile above sea level (Fig. 2). The seaward edges of the continental masses are submerged and these are called the **continental shelves.**

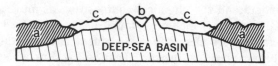

FIGURE 2. Relation between continents and ocean basins.
a—Continents.
b—Volcanic islands.
c—Sea level.

Although the continental surfaces appear to be very irregular to man, the difference in elevation between the highest mountain (Mount Everest— more than 29,000 feet above sea level) and the deepest part of the ocean (more than 35,000 feet deep, south of the Mariana Islands in the Pacific) is inconsequential when considered in relation to the size of the earth.

The Ocean Basins. The ocean basins contain the greatest part of the hydrosphere and cover more than 70 per cent of the earth's surface. The floors of the oceans were originally believed to be quite flat and featureless, but recent oceanographic studies indicate that this is not so. The surface of the ocean floor possesses as many irregularities

as the land and includes deep trenches, canyons, and submarine mountain ranges.

Of the five oceans, Arctic, Antarctic, Atlantic, Indian, and Pacific, the latter is deepest (about 35,000 feet) and largest, covering almost half of the earth. The bottoms of the deepest parts of the oceans are composed of basalt, a rather dense, dark, igneous rock. In many places the basaltic bottom is covered by layers of marine sediments.

The origin of the continents and ocean basins and their relationship to each other are discussed in later chapters.

GEOLOGIC FORCES

Geologic investigation of almost any part of the earth's surface will reveal some indication of great changes which the earth has undergone. These changes are of many kinds and most have taken place over millions of years. They are, in general, brought about by the processes of **gradation, tectonism,** and **volcanism.**

Gradation. The surface rocks of the earth are constantly being affected by gradational forces. For example, the atmosphere attacks the rocks, weathering them both physically and chemically. In addition, the rivers and oceans of the hydrosphere are continually wearing away rock fragments and transporting them to other areas where they are deposited. Gradation, then, includes two separate types of processes: **degradation,** which is a wearing down or destructive process, and **aggradation,** a holding up or constructive process.

Degradation, commonly referred to as erosion, results from the wearing down of the rocks by water, air, and ice. Here are included the work of atmospheric weathering, glacial abrasion, stream erosion, wind abrasion, etc.

Aggradation, known also as deposition, results in the accumulation of sediments and the ultimate building up of rock strata. The principal agents depositing these sediments are wind, ice, and water. The work of each of these geologic agents is discussed elsewhere in this book.

Tectonism. This term encompasses all the movements of the solid parts of the earth with respect to each other. Tectonic movements, which are indicative of crustal instability, produce **faulting** (fracture and displacement), **folding, subsidence,** and **uplift** of rock formations. Known also as **diastrophism,** tectonism is responsible for the formation of many of our great mountain ranges and for most of the structural deformation that has occurred in the earth's crust. However, these tectonic features (such as folds and faults) are not usually seen until they have been exposed by the process of degradation, or erosion.

In addition, widespread tectonic movements are responsible for certain types of metamorphism.

The intrusion of **magma,** more closely associated with volcanism, may also bring about rock deformation by folding.

Volcanism. This term, known also as vulcanism, refers to the movement of molten rock materials within the earth or upon the surface of the earth. Volcanic processes produce the lavas, ashes, and cinders which are ejected from volcanoes. Volcanism is also responsible for the rocks, once molten, which solidified at great depth within the earth.

Minerals

We now know that the geologist is primarily interested in the earth's rocky crust, but before he can study rocks it is necessary to know something about minerals, for these are the building blocks of the earth's crust. Although geologists differ when defining the term mineral, the following definition is generally accepted: **Minerals are chemical elements or compounds which occur naturally within the crust of the earth.** They are **inorganic** (not derived from living things), have a definite chemical composition or range of composition, an orderly internal arrangement of atoms (crystalline structure), and certain other distinct physical properties. It should be noted, however, that the chemical and physical properties of some minerals may vary within definite limits.

Rocks are aggregates or mixtures of minerals, the composition of which may vary greatly. Limestone, for example, is composed primarily of one mineral—calcite. Granite, on the other hand, typically contains three minerals—feldspar, mica, and quartz.

Certain minerals, such as calcite, quartz, and feldspar, are so commonly found in rocks that they are called the **rock-forming** minerals. Other minerals, like gold, diamond, uranium minerals, and silver are found in relatively few rocks.

Minerals vary greatly in their chemical composition and physical properties. Let us now become acquainted with the more important physical and chemical characteristics that enable us to distinguish one mineral from the other.

CHEMICAL COMPOSITION OF MINERALS

Although a detailed discussion of chemistry is not within the scope of this book,[1] an introduction to chemical terminology is necessary if we are to understand the chemical composition of minerals.

All matter, including minerals, is composed of one or more **elements.** An element is a substance that cannot be broken down into simpler substances by ordinary chemical means. Theoretically, if you were to take a quantity of any element and cut it into smaller and smaller pieces, eventually you would obtain the smallest pieces that still retained the characteristics of the element. These minute particles are **atoms.** Although atoms are so small that they cannot be seen with the most powerful microscope (it would take 100 million of them to make a line one inch long) we know a great deal about them. We know, for instance, that the nucleus of an atom is composed of **protons,** positively charged particles, and **neutrons,** or uncharged particles. Outside the nucleus and revolving rapidly around it are negatively charged particles called **electrons.** It is now known, of course, that certain elements have been broken down by atomic fission or "atom-smashing," but these are not considered to be "ordinary chemical means." Although there are only ninety-two elements occurring in nature, several more have been created artificially.

Some minerals, such as gold or silver, are composed of only one element. More often, however, minerals consist of two or more elements united to form a **compound.** For example, calcite is a chemical compound known as calcium carbonate. The chemical composition of a compound may be expressed by means of a chemical formula ($CaCO_3$ in the case of calcite) in which each element is represented by a symbol. The symbol is derived from an abbreviation of the Latin or English name of the element it represents. For many elements, the first letter of the element's name is used as its symbol—thus H for an atom of hydrogen, and C for an atom of carbon. If the names of two elements start with the same letter, two letters may be used for one of them to distinguish between their symbols. For example, an atom of helium may be represented as He, an atom of calcium as Ca. Some symbols have been derived from an abbreviation of the Latin name of the elements: Cu (from *cuprum*) represents an atom of copper, and Fe (from *ferrum*) an atom of iron. The small numerals used in a chemical formula represent the proportion in which each element is present. Hence, the formula for water, H_2O, indicates that there are two atoms of hydrogen for each atom of oxygen present in water.

As mentioned above, ninety-two elements have been found to be present in minerals; however, eight of these elements are so abundant that they constitute more than 98 per cent, by weight, of the earth's crust. These elements, their symbols, and the per cent by weight present in the earth's solid crust are as follows:

Oxygen (O)	46.60
Silicon (Si)	27.72
Aluminum (Al)	8.13
Iron (Fe)	5.00
Calcium (Ca)	3.63
Sodium (Na)	2.83
Potassium (K)	2.59
Magnesium (Mg)	2.09
Total	98.59

As indicated in the above table, two elements, oxygen and silicon, make up approximately three-fourths of the weight of the rocks. Both these elements are **nonmetals,** but the remaining six are **metals.** Metals are characterized by their capacity for conducting heat and electricity, their ability to be hammered into thin sheets (malleability) or to be drawn into wire (ductility), and their luster (the way light is reflected from the mineral's sur-

face). Such minerals as gold, silver, copper, and iron are included in the metals. The nonmetallic, or industrial minerals do not have the properties mentioned above. Some typical nonmetallic minerals are sulfur, diamond, and calcite.

CRYSTALS

When crystalline minerals solidify and grow without interference, they will normally adopt smooth angular shapes known as crystals. The planes that form the outside of the crystals are known as **faces.** These are related directly to the internal atomic structure of the mineral, and the size of the faces is dependent upon the frequency of the atoms in the different planes. The shape of the crystals and the angles between related sets of crystal faces are important in mineral identification.

PHYSICAL PROPERTIES OF MINERALS

Each mineral possesses certain physical properties or characteristics by which it may be recognized or identified. Although some may be identified by visual examination, others must be subjected to certain simple tests.

Physical properties especially useful in mineral identification are (1) hardness, (2) color, (3) streak, (4) luster, (5) specific gravity, (6) cleavage, (7) fracture, (8) shape or form, (9) tenacity or elasticity, and (10) certain other miscellaneous properties. The geologist must know how to test a mineral specimen for the above properties if he is to identify it correctly. Many of these tests do not require expensive laboratory equipment and may be done in the field. Some of them may be made by using such commonplace articles as a knife or a hardened steel file, a copper penny, a small magnet, an inexpensive pocket lens with a magnification of six to ten times, a piece of glass, a piece of unglazed porcelain tile, and a fingernail.

Hardness. One of the easiest ways to distinguish one mineral from another is by testing for hardness. The hardness of a mineral is determined by what materials it will scratch, and what materials will scratch it. The hardness or scratch test may be done with simple testing materials carried in the field. For greater accuracy, one may use the scale of hardness called **Mohs' scale.** This scale, named for the German mineralogist Friedrich Mohs, was devised more than one hundred years ago. In studying his mineral collection, Mohs noticed that certain minerals were much harder than others. He believed that this variation could be of some value in mineral identification, so he selected ten common minerals to be used as standards in testing other minerals for hardness. In establishing this scale, Mohs assigned each of the reference minerals a number. He designated talc, the softest in the series, as having a hardness of 1. The hardest mineral, diamond, was assigned a hardness of 10.

Mohs' scale, composed of the ten reference minerals arranged in order of increasing hardness, is as follows:

No. 1—Talc (softest)
No. 2—Gypsum
No. 3—Calcite
No. 4—Fluorite
No. 5—Apatite
No. 6—Feldspar
No. 7—Quartz
No. 8—Topaz
No. 9—Corundum
No. 10—Diamond (hardest)

Most of the minerals in Mohs' scale are common ones, which can be obtained in inexpensive collections. Diamond chips are more expensive, but not beyond reason. Note that Mohs' scale is so arranged that each mineral will be scratched by those having higher numbers, and will scratch those having lower numbers.

It is also possible to test for hardness by using the following common objects:

ITEM	HARDNESS
Fingernail	About 2½
Copper penny	About 3
Glass	5–5½
Knife blade	5½–6
Steel file	6½–7

Each of the above items will scratch a mineral of the indicated hardness. For example: the fingernail will scratch talc (hardness of 1) and gypsum (hardness of 2), but would not scratch calcite which has a hardness of 3.

In testing for hardness, first use the more common materials. Start with the fingernail; if that will not scratch the specimen, use the knife blade. If the knife blade produces a scratch, this indicates that the specimen has a hardness of between 2½ and 6 (see scale above). Referring to Mohs' scale, it is found that there are three minerals of known hardness within this range. These are: apatite (5); fluorite (4); and calcite (3). If the calcite will not scratch the specimen but the fluorite will, its hardness is further limited as between 3 and 4. Next, try to scratch the fluorite with the specimen. If this can be done, even with difficulty, the hardness is established as 4; if not, then it is between 3 and 4.

Color. Probably one of the first things that is noticed about a mineral is its color. However, the same mineral may vary greatly in color from one specimen to another, and with certain exceptions, color is of limited use in mineral identification. Certain minerals, for example, azurite, which is always blue, malachite, which is green, and pyrite, which is yellow, have relatively constant colors. Others, such as quartz or tourmaline, occur in a wide variety of colors; hence, color may be of little use in identifying these two minerals. Color variations of this sort are primarily due to minor chemical impurities within the mineral.

When using color in mineral identification, it is necessary to take into consideration such factors as (1) whether the specimen is being examined in natural or artificial light, (2) whether the surface being examined is fresh or weathered, and (3) whether the mineral is wet or dry. Each of these may cause color variations in a mineral. In addition, certain of the metallic minerals will tarnish and the true color will not be revealed except on a fresh surface.

Streak. When a mineral is rubbed across a piece of unglazed tile, it may leave a line similar to a pencil or crayon mark. This line is composed of the powdered minerals. The color of this powdered material is known as the streak of the mineral, and the unglazed tile used in such a test is called a **streak plate** (Fig. 3).

The streak in some minerals will not be the same as the color of the specimen. For example, a piece of black hematite will leave a reddish brown streak, and an extremely hard mineral such as topaz or corundum will leave no streak. This is because the streak plate has a hardness of about 7,

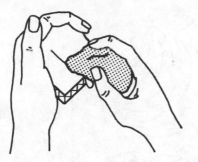

FIGURE 3. Testing for streak by means of streak plate.

and both topaz (8) and corundum (9) are harder than the streak plate, hence the mineral will not be powdered.

Luster. The appearance of the surface of a mineral as seen in reflected light is called luster. Some minerals shine like metals, for example, silver or gold. These are said to have metallic luster. Other lusters are called nonmetallic. The more important nonmetallic lusters and some common examples are shown below:

Admantine—brilliant glossy luster: typical of diamond
Vitreous—glassy, looks like glass: quartz or topaz
Resinous—the luster of resin: sphalerite
Greasy—like an oily surface: nepheline
Pearly—like mother-of-pearl: talc
Silky—the luster of silk or rayon: asbestos or satin-spar gypsum
Dull—as the name implies: chalk or clay

Submetallic luster is intermediate between metallic and nonmetallic luster. The mineral wolframite displays typical submetallic luster.

Terms such as **shining** (bright by reflected light), **glistening** (a sparkling brightness), **splendent** (glossy brilliance), and **dull** (lacking brilliance or luster) are commonly used to indicate the degree of luster present. Here too, one must take into consideration such factors as tarnish, type of lighting, and general condition of the mineral specimen being examined.

Specific Gravity. The relative weights of minerals are also useful in identification, for some minerals, such as galena (an ore of lead), are much heavier than others. The relative weight of a mineral is called its specific gravity. Specific gravity is determined by comparing the weight of the mineral specimen with the weight of an equal

volume of fresh water. Thus, a specimen of galena (specific gravity about 7.5) would be about 7½ times as heavy as the same volume of water.

In order to determine the specific gravity of a given specimen, the specimen is weighed in air on a spring scale (sometimes called a Jolly-Kraus balance); then lowered into a container of fresh water and weighed in the water. The specific gravity (Sp. Gr.) equals the weight in air divided by the loss of weight in water. When the specific gravity has been determined, it may then be compared with the known weight of other minerals in order to identify the specimen.

Cleavage and Fracture. Mineral crystals will break if they are strained beyond their plastic and elastic limits. If the crystal breaks irregularly it is said to exhibit **fracture,** but if it should break along surfaces related to the crystal structure it is said to show **cleavage.** Each break or **cleavage plane** is closely related to the atomic structure of the mineral and designates planes of weakness within the crystal. Because the number of cleavage planes

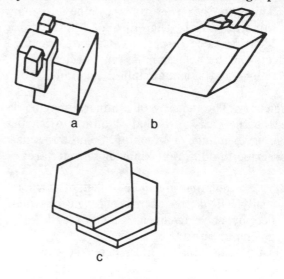

FIGURE 4. Three types of cleavage.
a—Cubic.   *b*—Rhombic.   *c*—Perfect basal.

present and the angles between them are constant for any given mineral, cleavage is a very useful aid in mineral identification.

Minerals may have one, two, three, four, or six directions of cleavage. The mineral galena, for example, cleaves in three planes (directions) at right angles to one another. Thus, if galena is struck a quick, sharp blow with a hammer, the specimen will break up into a number of small cubes. Calcite, on the other hand, has three cleavage planes that are not at right angles to one another. Therefore it will always produce a number of rhombohedral cleavage fragments. Hence, galena is said to have **cubic** cleavage, calcite **rhombohedral** cleavage.

Many minerals break or fracture in a distinctive way, and for this reason their broken surfaces (Fig. 5) may be of value in identifying minerals.

There are several types of fractures; some of the more common types (with example) are:

Conchoidal—the broken surface of the specimen shows a fracture resembling the smooth curved surface of a shell. This type of fracture is typical of chipped glass: quartz and obsidian.

Splintery or Fibrous—fibers or splinters are revealed along the fracture surface: pectolite.

Hackly—fracture surface marked by rough jagged edges: copper, silver, and certain other metals.

Uneven—rough irregular fracture of surface. This type of fracture is common in many minerals and is, therefore, of limited use in identification: jasper, a variety of quartz.

Even—as the name implies: magnesite.

Earthy—as the name implies: kaolinite.

Tenacity. The tenacity of a mineral may be defined as the resistance that it offers to tearing, crushing, bending, or breaking. Some terms used to describe the different kinds of tenacity are:

Brittle—the mineral can be broken or powdered easily. The degree of brittleness may be qualified by such terms as tough, fragile, etc.: galena or sulfur.

Elastic—the mineral, after being bent, will return to its original form or position: mica.

Flexible—the mineral will bend but will not return to its original shape upon release of pressure: talc.

Other Physical Properties. In addition to those properties discussed above, the mineral characteristics below may also aid greatly in identification. Examples of minerals exhibiting these properties are given.

Play of Colors. Some minerals show variations in color when viewed from different angles: labradorite.

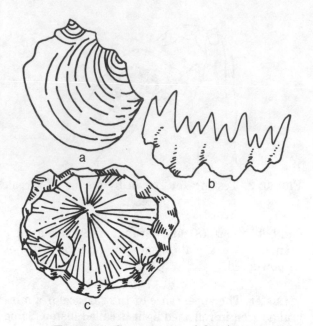

FIGURE 5. Some types of fracture.
a—Conchoidal. *b*—Hackly. *c*—Splintery.

Sectile—the mineral can be cut with a knife to produce shavings: selenite gypsum and talc.

Malleable—the mineral can be hammered into thin sheets: gold and copper.

Ductile—the mineral can be drawn out into wire: gold, silver, and copper.

Asterism. This may be observed if the mineral exhibits a starlike effect when viewed either by reflected or transmitted light: certain specimens of phlogopite or the star-sapphire.

Diaphaneity or Transparency. This property refers to the ability of a mineral to transmit light. The varying degrees of diaphaneity are:

Opaque—no light passes through the mineral: galena, pyrite, and magnetite.

Translucent—light passes through the mineral but an object cannot be seen through it: chalcedony and certain other varieties of quartz.

Transparent—light passes through the mineral and the outline of objects can be clearly seen through it: halite, calcite, clear crystalline quartz.

Magnetism. A mineral is said to be magnetic if, in its natural state, it will be attracted to an iron magnet: magnetite, or lodestone, and pyrrhotite.

Luminescence. When a mineral glows or emits light that is not the direct result of incandescence, it is said to be luminescent. This phenomena is usually produced by exposure to ultraviolet rays. Exposure to X rays, cathode rays, or radiation from radioactive substances can also cause luminescence. If the mineral is luminous only during the period of exposure to the ultraviolet rays or other stimulus, the material is said to be **fluorescent** (scheelite and willemite are fluorescent). A mineral exhibiting **phosphorescence** will continue to glow after the cause of excitation has been removed.

MINERALOIDS

Although most substances accepted as minerals are crystalline, some lack the ability to crystalize and occur instead as a hardened gel. Substances of this type are commonly referred to as mineraloids. They are also said to be amorphous—that is, without form, for example, opals.

ROCK FORMING MINERALS

Of some two thousand different minerals that are known to be present in the earth's crust, relatively few are major constituents of the more common rocks. Those minerals that do make up a large part of the more common types of rocks are called the rock-forming minerals. Most of the rock-forming minerals are silicates, that is, they consist of a metal combined with silicon and oxygen. Rock-forming minerals are such as feldspars, mica, and quartz.

RADIOACTIVE MINERALS

In this so called "atomic age," radioactive minerals have come to play an ever increasing part in modern technology. A radioactive mineral is distinguished because it emits radioactive isotopes which are detected usually with a geiger counter. Although there are a number of radioactive minerals, the two most widely known are uraninite and carnotite.

METALLIC OR ORE MINERALS

Metals are among the most valuable products known to man, and for this reason the metallic or ore minerals are of great interest to the geologist. These minerals are found in ore deposits —rock masses from which metals may be obtained commercially. Usually occurring with the valuable ore minerals are certain worthless minerals called gangue minerals. These, of course, must be separated from the more valuable ore minerals. Included here are aluminum, gold, copper, lead, and silver.

NONMETALLIC OR INDUSTRIAL MINERALS

Minerals that do not contain metals or that are not used as metals make up this group. It is in this vast category that such varied materials as coal, petroleum, sulfur, fertilizer, building stones, and gem stones are placed.

Metamorphism and Crustal Deformation

Metamorphic rocks are rocks (originally either igneous or sedimentary) that have been buried deep within the earth and subjected to high temperatures and pressures. These new physical conditions usually produce great changes in the solid rock and these changes are included under the term metamorphism (Greek *meta,* "change," and *morphe,* "form" or "shape").

During the process of metamorphism the original rock undergoes physical and chemical alterations which may greatly modify its texture, mineral composition, and chemical composition.

Thus, limestone may be metamorphosed into marble, and sandstone into quartzite. Let us now consider the types of forces that might bring about metamorphic changes.

TYPES OF METAMORPHISM

Although more technical classifications recognize several different kinds of metamorphism, only contact metamorphism, and dynamic, or kinetic, metamorphism will be considered here.

Contact Metamorphism. When country rock (the rock intruded by or surrounding an igneous intrusion) is invaded by an igneous body it generally undergoes profound change. Hence, limestone intruded by a hot magma may be altered for a distance of a few inches to as much as several miles from the igneous sedimentary contact. Some of the more simple metamorphic rocks have been formed in this so-called **baked zone** of the altered country rock (Fig. 6).

Physical change may be produced by contact metamorphism when the original minerals in the country rock are permeated by magmatic fluids which often bring about recrystallization. This process, which typically produces either new or larger mineral crystals, may greatly alter the texture of the rock. In addition, the magmatic fluids commonly introduce new elements and compounds

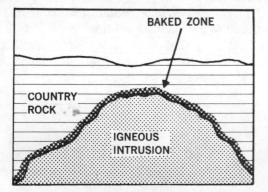

FIGURE 6. Baked zone in country rock surrounding an igneous intrusion.

which will modify the chemical composition of the original rock and result in the formation of new minerals.

Dynamic, or Kinetic, Metamorphism. Dynamic metamorphism occurs when rock layers undergo strong structural deformation during the formation of mountain ranges. The great pressures exerted as the rock layers are folded, fractured, and crumpled generally produce widespread and complex metamorphic change. Such pressures may result in tearing or crushing of the minerals, obliteration of any indication of fossils or stratification, realignment of mineral grains, and increased hardness. Because this type of metamorphism takes place on a relatively large scale it is also called **regional metamorphism.**

EFFECTS AND PRODUCTS OF METAMORPHISM

The effects of metamorphism are controlled to a large extent by the chemical and physical characteristics of the original rock and by the agent and degree of metamorphism involved. The more basic changes are in the texture and chemical composition of the rock.

TEXTURE

The rearrangement of mineral crystals during metamorphism results in two basic types of rock texture: foliated and nonfoliated.

Foliated Metamorphic Rocks. Foliated rocks are metamorphic rocks in which the minerals have been flattened, drawn out, and arranged in parallel layers or bands (Fig. 7). There are three basic types of foliation: slaty, schistose, and gneissic. Each of these, and some common rocks which exhibit them, is discussed below.

Slate. A metamorphosed shale, slate is characterized by a very fine texture in which mineral crystals cannot be detected with the naked eye. It does not show banding (see Fig. 7) and splits readily into thin even slabs. Slate occurs in a variety of colors, but is usually gray, black, green, and red. Its characteristic slaty cleavage (not to be confused with mineral cleavage) makes it especially useful for roofing, blackboards, and sidewalks.

Schist. Schist is a medium- to coarse-grained foliated metamorphic rock formed under greater pressures than those which form slate. It consists principally of micaceous minerals in a nearly parallel arrangement called **schistosity.** Schists usually split readily along these schistose laminations or folia, which are usually bent and crumpled. Commonly derived from slate, schists may also be formed from fine-grained igneous rocks. They are named according to the predominant mineral, such as mica schists, chlorite schists, etc.

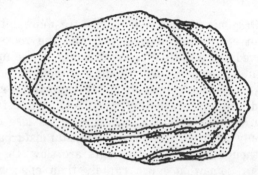

FIGURE 7. Schist, a foliated metamorphic rock.

Phyllite. Derived from the Greek word *phyllon* (a leaf), phyllites are more fine-grained than schists but coarser than slate. On freshly broken surfaces they have a characteristic silky luster or sheen due to the presence of fine grains of mica. Most have been formed from shales which have been subjected to pressures greater than those required to produce slate, but not of sufficient intensity to produce schists.

Gneiss. Gneiss (pronounced "nice") is a very highly metamorphosed coarse-grained banded rock. This rock is characterized by alternating bands of darker minerals such as chlorite, biotite mica, or graphite (Fig. 8). The bands are typically folded and contorted, and although some gneisses resemble schists, they do not split nearly as easily. Banding may be an indication of stratification in

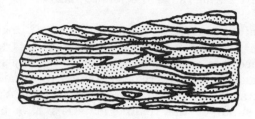

FIGURE 8. Gneiss, a banded metamorphic rock.

the original bedded sedimentary rock, or caused by the alteration of coarse-grained igneous rocks containing light- and dark-colored minerals.

In general, gneisses have undergone a greater degree of metamorphism than have schistose rocks and are commonly formed as a result of intense regional metamorphism.

Nonfoliated Metamorphic Rocks. These are metamorphic rocks which are typically massive or granular in texture and do not exhibit foliation. Although some nonfoliated rocks resemble certain igneous rocks, they can be differentiated from them on the basis of mineral composition.

Quartzite. Quartzite is formed from metamorphosed quartz sandstone. One of the most resistant of all rocks, quartzite is composed of a crystalline mass of tightly cemented sand grains. When formed from pure quartz sand, quartzite is white; however, the presence of impurities may stain the rock red, yellow, or brown.

Marble. A relatively coarse-grained, crystalline, calcareous rock, marble is a metamorphosed limestone or dolomite. It is formed by recrystallization, and any evidence of fossils or stratification is usually destroyed during the process of alteration.

ORIGINAL ROCK	METAMORPHIC ROCK
Sedimentary	
Sandstone	Quartzite
Shale	Slate, phyllite, schist
Limestone	Marble
Bituminous coal	Anthracite coal, graphite
Igneous	
Granitic textured igneous rocks	Gneiss
Compact textured igneous rocks	Schist

TABLE 2. Some common igneous and sedimentary rocks and their metamorphic equivalents.

White when pure, the presence of impurities may impart a wide range of colors to marble.

Anthracite. When bituminous, or soft, coal is strongly compacted, folded, and heated, it is transformed into anthracite, or hard, coal. Because it has undergone an extreme degree of carbonization, anthracite coal has a high fixed carbon content and almost all of the volatile materials have been driven off.

CRUSTAL MOVEMENTS

The crust of the earth has undergone great structural change during past periods of earth history. Even today the earth's crust is continually being altered by three major forces—gradation, volcanism, and tectonism. Gradation and volcanism have been discussed in earlier chapters of this book; let us now see how tectonic forces have affected our earth.

TECTONISM

As usually considered, tectonism includes those processes which have resulted in deformation of the earth's crust. Tectonic movements normally occur slowly and imperceptibly over long periods of time. But some—for example, an earthquake—may take place suddenly and violently. In some instances the rocks will move vertically, resulting in uplift or subsidence of the land. They may also move horizontally, or laterally (sidewise), as a result of compression or tension. The two major types of tectonic movements, **epeirogeny** (vertical movements) and **orogeny** (essentially lateral movements) are discussed below.

Epeirogenic Movements. Relatively slow movements accompanied by broad uplift or submergence of the continents are termed epeirogenic movements. Such movements affect relatively large areas, and typically result in tilting or warping of the land. An uplift of this type may raise wavecut benches and sea cliffs well above sea level; features of this sort are common along certain parts of the Pacific Coast. In a like manner, parts of the Scandinavian coast are rising as much as three feet per century. Subsidence of the continents may also take place. Thus, continental areas sink slowly beneath the ocean and become submerged by shallow seas. Similar movements have caused the British Isles to become isolated from continental Europe and bays to be formed in drowned valleys along the New England coast. (Submergence may, of course, also be caused by a rise in sea level.)

Rock strata involved in epeirogenic movements are not usually greatly folded or faulted (fractured). As noted above, however, such strata may undergo large-scale tilting or warping.

Orogenic Movements. These are more intense than epeirogenic movements, and the rocks involved are subjected to great stress. These movements, known also as orogenies or mountain-making movements, normally affect long narrow areas and are accompanied by much folding and faulting. Igneous activity and earthquakes also commonly occur with this type of crustal disturbance. Although orogenic movements are slow, they do occur somewhat more rapidly than epeirogenic movements.

ROCK STRUCTURES PRODUCED BY TECTONISM

Tectonic movements, whether epeirogenic or orogenic, will result in rock deformation. Under surface conditions, ordinary rocks are relatively brittle and will fracture or break when placed under great stress. Deeply buried rocks, however, are subject to such high temperatures and pressures that they become somewhat plastic. When subjected to prolonged stress these rocks are likely to warp or fold.

Warping. As noted above, warping is usually caused by raising or lowering broad areas of the earth's crust. The rock strata in such areas appear to be essentially horizontal; close study, however, indicates that the strata are gently **dipping** (inclined). Warping movements are typically epeirogenic and are accompanied by little or no local folding and faulting.

Folding. Not only may rocks be tilted and warped, they may also be folded (Fig. 9). Folds, which vary greatly in complexity and size, are formed when rock strata are crumpled and buckled up into a series of wavelike structures. This type of structural development is usually produced by great horizontal compressive forces and may result in a variety of different structures.

Anticlines (Fig. 9a) are upfolds of rock formed when strata are folded upward. **Synclines** (Fig. 9b) may be created when rock layers are folded downward. Broad uparched folds covering large areas are called **geanticlines;** large down-warped troughs are known as **geosynclines.** Great thicknesses of sediments have accumulated in certain geosynclines of the geologic past, and some of these have been elevated to form folded mountain ranges. For example, the Appalachian Geosyncline received sediments throughout much of early Paleozoic time. Then about 225 million years ago

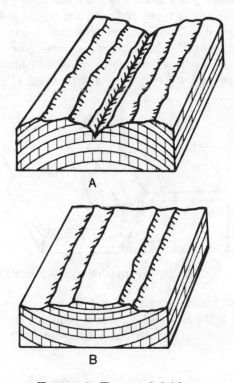

FIGURE 9. Types of folds.
a—Anticline.   *b*—Syncline.

these sediments (which had since become sedimentary rocks) were uplifted to form the Appalachian Highlands, of which the Appalachian Mountains are a part.

In studying folds we must be able to determine the **attitude** of the rock strata. Attitude—a term used to denote the position of a rock with respect to compass direction and a horizontal plane—is defined by **strike** and **dip** (Fig. 10). The strike of a formation is the compass direction of the line formed by the intersection of a bedding plane with a horizontal plane. Dip is the angle of inclination between the bedding plane and a horizontal plane. The direction of dip is always at

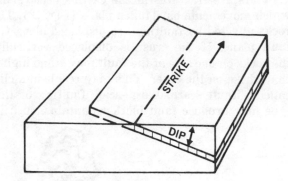

FIGURE 10. Strike and dip. The beds strike north-south and dip to the east.

right angles to the strike; thus, a rock stratum which dips due north would strike east-west.

Other types of folds include **monoclines,** simple steplike folds which dip in only one direction (Fig. 11); **domes,** a fold in which strata dip away from a common center; and **basins,** a fold in which the strata dip toward a common center.

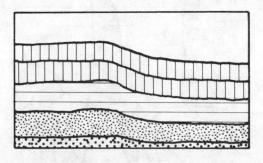

FIGURE 11. A monocline.

Fracturing. Rocks subjected to great stress near the surface are apt to fracture, thus producing joints and faults. A fracture along which there has been little or no movement is called a **joint** (Fig. 12). Joints occur in sets and are usually parallel to one another. Fractures of this sort have formed in igneous rocks as a result of contraction due to cooling and are common in certain dikes and sills. Joints are also created by tension and compression when rocks undergo stress due to warping, folding, and faulting.

Joint systems are developed when two or more sets of joints intersect. These intersecting joint patterns may be helpful in certain quarrying operations and in developing porosity in otherwise impervious rocks. Jointing will also hasten weathering and erosion, for they render the rocks more susceptible to attack from rain, frost, and streams.

Faults are fractures in the earth's crust along which movements have taken place (Fig. 13). The rocks affected by faulting are displaced along the **fault plane.** If the crust is displaced vertically, the rocks on one side of the fault may stand higher than those on the other. This may result in a cliff called a **fault scarp.** Large-scale faulting of this type may produce **fault block mountains,** such as

the Sierra Nevada in California and the Lewis Range in Montana.

Some knowledge of fault terminology is prerequisite to an understanding of the different types of faults. (The parts of faults are illustrated in Fig. 13.) The rock surface bounding the lower side of an inclined fault plane is known as the **footwall** and that above as the **hanging wall.** The **strike** of a fault is the horizontal direction of the fault plane; **dip** is determined by measuring the inclination of the fault plane at right angles to the strike. **Displacement** refers to the amount of movement that has taken place along the fault plane.

The various types of faults are classified largely by the direction and relative movement of the rocks along the fault plane. A **normal or gravity fault** is one in which the hanging wall has moved downward with respect to the footwall (Fig. 14).

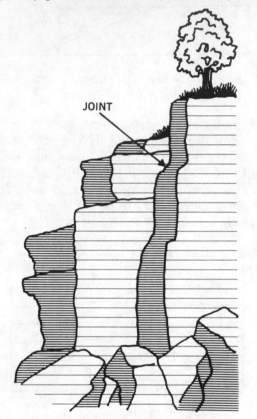

FIGURE 12. Vertical joints in limestone cliff.

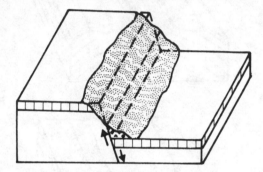

FIGURE 14. Normal or gravity fault.

If the hanging wall has moved upward with respect to the footwall, a **reverse fault** or **thrust fault** is produced (Fig. 15). A **strike-slip fault** will be

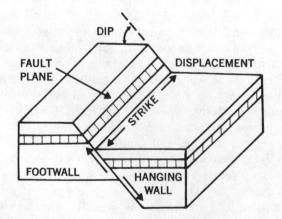

FIGURE 13. A normal fault, showing principal parts and terms used in describing faults.

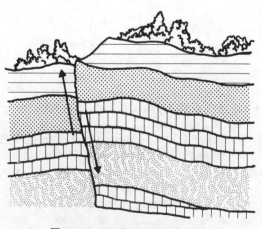

FIGURE 15. Reverse fault.

produced if the movement is predominantly horizontal parallel to the fault plane (Fig. 16).

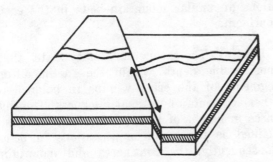

FIGURE 16. Strike-slip fault. (Note the road offset in center of block.)

In some areas a long narrow block has dropped down between normal faults, thereby producing a **graben** (Fig. 17). Large-scale grabens are called **rift valleys.** Two examples of grabens are the upper Rhine Valley and the depression containing the Dead Sea. Sometimes blocks will be raised between normal faults; these elevated blocks are called **horsts** (Fig. 18).

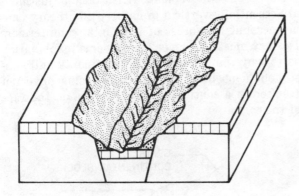

FIGURE 17. A graben.

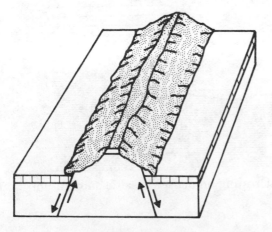

FIGURE 18. A horst.

EVIDENCE OF CRUSTAL MOVEMENTS

The rocks of the earth's crust present much evidence to show that many tectonic movements have taken place in the geologic past. We have already learned, for example, that the fossilized remains of sea plants and animals may be found thousands of feet above sea level. Common also are elevated beaches, coastal plains, and wave-cut cliffs and sea caves. Such features strongly suggest a drop in sea level or an uplift of the continent (possibly both). Similarly, drowned river valleys indicate a rising sea and/or a subsiding land mass.

The occurrence of earthquakes is evidence that similar movements are taking place today. A good example of this can be seen in the Yakutat Bay area of Alaska. Here, in 1899, faulting caused some parts of the coast to be raised as much as 47 feet. Likewise, during the San Francisco earthquake of 1906 the horizontal movement along the fault plane caused certain fences and roads to be offset as much as 20 feet.

CAUSES OF CRUSTAL MOVEMENTS

Although scientists do not agree upon the exact cause of tectonic movements, they have proposed several theories to explain them. A few of these theories are briefly outlined below.

Contraction Theory. According to this theory, the rocks of the outer crust have become crumpled and wrinkled as the interior of the earth cooled and contracted. Shrinkage may also come about as great pressures squeeze the earth into a smaller volume, or when molten rock is extruded upon the surface.

Convection Theory. It has been suggested that convection currents beneath the earth's crust may cause the rocks to expand and push upward. It is thought that the heat to produce such currents may be derived from radioactive elements such as uranium. According to this theory, circulating convection currents would exert frictional drag beneath the crust, thereby causing crustal displacement (Fig. 19).

Continental Drift Theory. This theory suggests that there was originally only one huge continent. At some time in the geologic past this continent

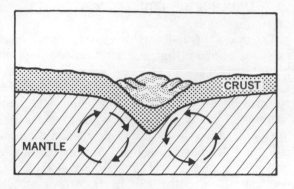

FIGURE 19. Convection currents in the mantle (circling arrows) and their relation to the overlying crust.

broke into several segments and drifted apart. This "drifting" or "floating" was possible because the continents, composed largely of granite, are lighter than the more plastic basaltic material beneath the crust. As the front of the drifting land mass moved forward, frictional drag with subcrustal material caused the continental margins to crumple up, thus forming the folded coastal mountain ranges of Europe and North and South America. Look at a globe and you will see how this idea originated. You will notice that the shorelines along both sides of the Atlantic Ocean match surprisingly well. Moreover, some of the older mountain belts in America appear to be continu-

ations of similar mountain belts in the eastern continents.

Isostasy. The theory of isostasy states that at considerable depth within the earth, different segments of the crust will be in balance with other segments of unequal thickness. The differences in height of these crustal segments is explained as the result of variations in density. Consequently, the continents and mountainous areas are higher because they are composed of lighter rocks; the ocean basins are lower because they are composed of denser (heavier) rocks (Fig. 20). As the continents are eroded and sediments deposited in the ocean, the ocean basin is depressed because of the added weight of the accumulating sediments. This causes displacement of the plastic subcrustal rocks which push the continents up. The upward displacement of the continent is aided by erosion which removes rock materials, thus making the continents lighter and more susceptible to uplift.

Because the movements of isostatic adjustment are essentially vertical in nature, this theory cannot account for forces of horizontal compression. Isostasy does, however, offer some explanation as to why the erosion of the continents and subsequent deposition in the ocean basins have not resulted in a continuous level surface on the face of the earth.

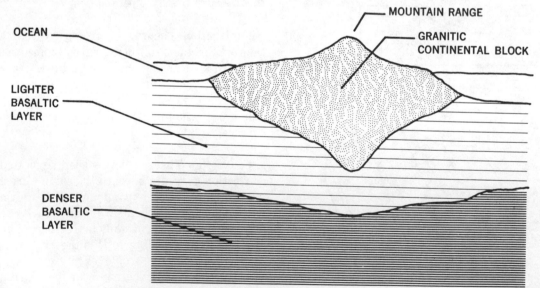

FIGURE 20. Relatively light granitic rocks of continent resting on denser basaltic substratum.

CHAPTER TWELVE

BIOLOGY

Scope and Method

Biology is the study of all living forms, plants and animals, including man, as individuals and as interdependent entities.

To the biologist—who is in the first place and above all a **natural scientist**—the human being is an object of scientific investigation; a very highly specialized protoplasmic structure, reflecting in his life processes the activity of all living animal structures. Biology demonstrates the total and absolute dependence of man—the human animal —on all other forms of life.

Biology covers so vast a field that, to make for greater accuracy and greater ease of study, it has been divided into logical subdivisions or branches. Each subdivision is so vast in itself that a lifetime of study may be devoted to each.

Depending upon his interests, the biologic scientist specializes in a single phase—if in animals, **Zoology;** if in plant life, **Botany;** if in the development of the individual from the "fertilized egg" stage through early stages of life, **Embryology;** if in the structure of the human body, **Anatomy;** if in the functions of the body, **Physiology.**

Another vital biological science is **Genetics,** which explains the phenomena of heredity. For microscope work, there is **Cytology,** the science of cell structure and function, or **Histology,** the science of living tissues. **Protozoology** is a branch of Biology which deals with one-celled animal life; **Bacteriology** is a science of one-celled plant life.

Another important and fascinating branch of Biology is **Ecology,** the study of the relationship of living things to their environment.

Frequently a person who studies Biology from intellectual curiosity becomes intensely interested in a particular division and makes it his hobby or even his lifework, his profession. Biology is the basis of such professions as Medicine, Nursing, Agriculture, Plant and Animal Breeding and even Pharmacy.

How shall we acquaint ourselves with the living world around us? Constant awareness coupled with the curiosity and desire to "dig deeper" will make our immediate surroundings a field and a laboratory for studying life.

A small patch of back yard, a vacant lot, even a window box will provide field for "exploration"; as will the public park, a local wooded area, or the seashore, crowded with plant and animal life for us to observe.

The city streets, for all their concrete pavements and huge structures, have some trees and foliage to watch as they bud in the spring, blossom in the summer, change color in the fall and become bare in the winter.

Even in the heart of the city, one hears the birds which nest nearby or pass through on their migrations. Or one sees an earthworm crawling on the pavement after a heavy rain has driven it out of the soil beneath the pavement. Where there are human beings there must be other forms of plant and animal life!

One of the most famous **Entomologists** (a biologist who specializes in the study of insects), JEAN HENRI FABRE, did most of his field work in his own back yard or in some close-by field. He spent hours watching insects in their daily activities and making notes of his observation.

While some biologists explore the lands, the waters and the skies, others prefer to work in a laboratory, the "workshop" of the scientist. If well equipped, this will have running water in a sink, connections for gas, non-corrosive table tops (usually stone) with air pressure, vacuum, and electricity outlets. In addition there will be glass beakers, jars, flasks, test tubes, bottles, porcelain crucibles, and shelves for various basic chemicals. There will probably be an oven or an incubator, a pressure cooker, and even a refrigerator in some handy place. A well-stocked library of reference books in every branch of Biology is essential.

The individual who has no access to such a laboratory can build one of his own, using materials bought in department stores or even found on the kitchen shelf or in the medicine cabinet. Actual kitchen appliances such as a stove, the pressure cooker, and the refrigerator can be very useful. One can always use cardboard boxes or wooden cheese boxes to house small animals (hamsters, white mice, guinea pigs, insects) for study. One can always plant a window box garden or even a "pocket garden" in a drinking glass to study the growth of a seedling or a sweet potato vine or an avocado pit. It is simple to leave a moist piece of bread or fruit in a warm spot in the house so that mold can grow and flourish.

With this simple equipment you can *think* scientifically and experiment. There are certain steps which a scientist follows, without bias or preconception and in logical order, when thinking scientifically. **This is known as the Scientific Method.**

1. First recognize and state clearly the problem to be solved or the question to be answered.

2. Concentrate on one part of the problem at a time.

3. Collect accurate and complete information from reliable sources.

4. Test this information with new ideas of your own.

5. Answer the question or draw conclusions.

The scientist forms an **hypothesis—a proposition which, although it remains to be tested under controlled, experimental conditions, seems to him the probable explanation of the phenomenon in question.** If subsequent experiments support the hypothesis, it will become the basis of a scientific **theory,** which may in turn be accepted as **natural law,** if it is observed to occur—without failure or variation—in nature.

In every experiment there are usually different factors involved which determine the results. Some

examples of these factors are: material used, temperature, air or water pressure, amount of moisture, sunlight and season of the year.

The scientist cannot draw any conclusions unless he has a **control** to his experiment. **This control is an omission or a change of one of the factors.** If there is any difference in the results, the difference must then be due to that one factor which has been omitted or changed. When you perform any experiment at home, you must employ the logical order of the scientific method, and make use of the control.

Let us return to the well-equipped laboratory. Here, in addition to all the equipment that has been mentioned, there must be a **microscope.** It can open to you a marvelous world of living plants and animals that normally cannot be seen at all or only barely seen with the unaided eye.

The microscope, in its simplest form, dates back to the seventeenth century when a Dutch lensmaker, ANTON VON LEEUWENHOEK, ground and polished a tiny bead of glass until it magnified whatever he looked at. To his great astonishment and awe he found that a drop of stagnant water was teeming with life never before visible to the human eye. For greater convenience, he fashioned a crude microscope of metal in which he inserted and secured this bead of glass.

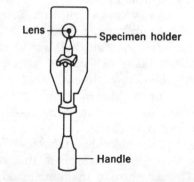

FIGURE 1. Leeuwenhoek microscope

Since that pioneering discovery of a revolutionary new use of optical lenses, there have been vast improvements and advances in magnifying lenses and microscopes. An Englishman, ROBERT HOOKE, made the first **compound microscope.** This type is used today—it can magnify objects clearly as much as 1,800 times. Such a microscope contains many lenses which, combined, *increase* magnification tremendously.

Early in this century, it was discovered that **ultraviolet** light could be used instead of light visible to the human eye, to obtain even higher magnification, as much as 4,000 times the life size of the object. This light cannot be seen by the human eye but can be photographed by the **ultraviolet microscope.**

In very recent years, engineers have developed an **electron microscope** which does not at all look like the compound microscope we are familiar with and which can produce a magnification of 20,000 times.

There is no doubt that microscopes of even greater magnification and accuracy can be de-

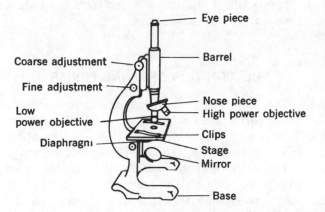

FIGURE 2. Compound microscope

veloped by the large optical companies—and will be in due course.

Because of increasing interest in the use of the microscope by individuals "at home," there are companies in this country and elsewhere which make inexpensive but adequate instruments. They do not, of course, have the magnifying power of a scientist's compound microscope but they are adequate for a home laboratory.

In this "atomic age," we are all becoming very science-conscious. Our curiosity and interests are constantly stimulated. Many newspapers have a science column, frequently biological in nature. Current science news, science facts and advice are presented so that they can be understood and appreciated by the average reader.

There are science digests, science magazines, radio and television broadcasts for the express purpose of informing the average individual. They attempt to whet his desire to seek further information.

The federal government will send literature, on written request, which will provide the most current material on many phases of biology. Write to the Department of Interior and to the Department of Agriculture for a list of their pamphlets on the branch of biology in which you are interested. These booklets may be sent to you free of charge or at a nominal cost.

Among the greatest storehouses of biologic wealth are our museums, our botanical and zoological gardens. In New York City, the Museum of Natural History houses the "story of life" from times historic to modern, with predictions of the future. There are life-size models, lifelike and accurate in every minute detail, set in carefully studied, simulated natural habitats. There are miniatures and fossilized remains. In this museum one can learn just by observing the exhibits, reading the "cards" and listening to the lecturing guides, the entire field of biology with its related subjects. There are such museums in most large cities and universities throughout the country. So, too, with "zoos," zoological gardens.

Spend a day in the springtime at a Botanical Garden. Take your camera with you—make mental pictures as well—of early spring green, of delicate new leaves fresh out of their buds, of pastel-colored blossoms—especially on the fruit trees, on vines and growing from the moist ground. Walk through the hot houses and see the vast variety of plant life which exists in climates other than yours. Smell the heavily fragrant, moist air. See the mist that halos the foliage and the damp rich soil from which it grows. Learn about plant life from growing plants.

"The Cloisters," an adjunct to the Metropolitan Museum of Art in Fort Tryon Park, New York City, has a series of tapestries, the "Unicorn Tapestries," that are world-known not only for the magnificence of their craftsmanship, design and color but for their woven pictures of every plant known in the Middle Ages. In this "imported" monastery are the Gardens of the Monks in which may be found odd flowering plants, every known herb, oddly cultured trees and many other forms of botanic life.

In cities other than New York, in many other states in the country, there are museums and collections of both living and preserved forms of plants and animals—for example, Marineland, Silver Springs, and the Everglades in lower Florida. The National Parks of the West and the Grand Canyon offer exciting and stimulating fields for biologic exploration. There are numerous places in which to study flora and fauna in their natural environments—and few experiences are more rewarding.

The Nature of Life

Biology was defined as the study of all living things, both plant and animal, including man. If we specify *living* things then we must differentiate between that which is *living* and that which is *non-living*. We may refer to substances in nature that are composed of inorganic chemicals, such as rock, air, water and parts of sand and soil as non-living. We may refer to objects fashioned by man as also being non-living. Through the years of attempting to survive and build stable communities, scientists have studied living plants and animals to determine how they have adapted or adjusted themselves. From these studies and observations, men in many fields of the arts and manufacturing have been able to fashion non-living things that in many ways imitate living things which are well-adapted to their surroundings.

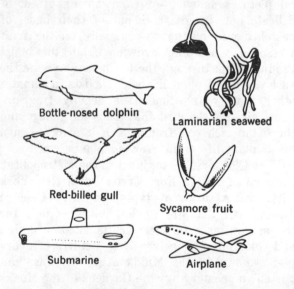

Figure 3.

Are you able to recognize man's successful imitation of living things in his building of submarines and planes? Consider the streamline shape of the dolphin, the location of the fins, the dorsally placed nostril, all **natural adaptations** for its life and activities in the water. The seaweed, though not actually propelled through the water, is continually subjected to the tidal currents. Its elongated shape and slimy covering allow the minimum of friction over its surface.

Can you see how man copied the features of

a bird when he designed airplanes, and the sycamore fruit when he designed the helicopter? The streamline shape of the bird, its wing shape and spread, its retractable legs, the feather covering for warmth and weatherproofing, the directions its feathers grow are all natural adaptations for its life and activity in the air, on land and on water. The helicopter-bladelike wings of the sycamore fruit are admirably adapted to catch wind currents which will carry it far from the parent plant to colonize new areas.

RECOGNITION OF LIVING FORMS

Yes, non-living, man-made objects resemble the living forms after which they are patterned but there are major differences which set them apart from *living forms*. These differences are:

The *self*-power of *motion* that comes from within the living plant and animal. (Boats and planes move only with the will of man and the energy of fuel he provides for them.)

The *self*-power to *grow*, to add to itself in size. (The house must be added to by the will of man and the materials he provides.)

The *self*-power to *reproduce* plants and animals each of its own kind. This is nature's lease on life. (Only the will of man and the materials he provides can produce more boats, houses, etc.)

The *self*-ability to *respond to stimuli* in the environment, or what is known as sensitivity. The plant seeks sunlight and grows in that direction. (The house must be built that way.) The roots of a tree grow downward in response to the pull of gravity and in the soil in the direction of a water supply. (The foundation of a house is placed in the ground to benefit from the pull of gravity.) Animals seek food and water when their bodies require it—so that they can carry out their daily activities of living. (A machine must be "fed" fuel by man to carry out its activity.)

In plants and simple animals, the responses to various stimuli in the environment are called tropisms.

Animals high in the animal group have specialized *systems* which enable them to respond to stimuli in their environment.

Living things are grouped according to "natural" and logical divisions. The largest and most inclusive of these divisions have been **the Plant Kingdom and the Animal Kingdom.** Yet in view of contemporary evolutionary thought, a new classification has been suggested. This classification takes into account the similarities of primitive plants and animals, but classifies higher plants and animals separately.

In studying each of these major divisions, biologists have been able to recognize a pattern of further divisions based on the simplicity or complexity of the plant or animal form. For convenience, a *classification* has been made beginning with the simplest form and carrying through to

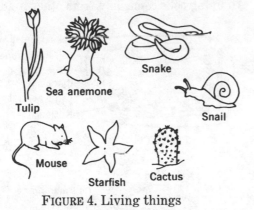

FIGURE 4. Living things

the most complex species of plants and animal life known, up to and including man.

Although all living forms have a very basic sameness, there are certain characteristics that distinguish plants from animals. Most of us think we can tell by merely looking at the living thing whether it be plant or animal. Can you easily identify which pictures are plants and which are animals? See Fig. 4.

There are forms of life, however, which exist in water, many microscopic forms, which can be grouped only after careful and detailed study, as either plants or animals. Perhaps you have seen coral growing in the warm southern waters, or highly colored sea anemones, sea urchins, or hydra, or even sponges. Have you remarked about the beauty of these underwater "flowers"? Actually they are forms of *animal* life much lower in the animal kingdom than fish or birds.

LIFE FORMS: DIFFERENCES

Perhaps you have examined a drop of water under the microscope and have seen single-celled

animated forms of life and wondered—are these plants or animals?

The outstanding characteristics which distinguish plants from animals are:

Plants generally are *stationary,* fixed to a spot. Movement of the plant is usually in response to a stimulus in the immediate environment. Plants do not have the power of *locomotion.* Animals on the other hand, can usually move about—have the power of *locomotion* to seek food and shelter.

Plant growth is *indeterminate.* That is, it is without a definite time or size limit. A plant does not die from old age, but rather from disease or some other external factor. Animal growth, however, is usually determinate.

The most outstanding difference is the ability of the *green* plant to *manufacture* food within itself using the substances in the environment in this process. **This activity or process is known as photosynthesis. All animals, including man, get their food either directly or indirectly from plants.**

In external appearance, plants are usually green, some having varied and colorful flowers and others having no apparent blossoms. Among animals there is a vast variety of sizes, shapes and colors.

The basic difference between plants and animals lies in the unit of structure and function of each, namely, the cell. Plant cells have a **cell wall** which is actually non-living in chemical nature. Animal cells do not have this.

LIFE FORMS: SIMILARITIES

In all other respects, plants and animals are alike. All other activities that keep them alive are common to both. Every plant and animal is equipped to exist in its particular environment or *natural habitat.* Some are better equipped than others, are "hardier," and therefore more likely to survive. All plants and animals are *sensitive* to the need for food, water, certain temperatures and sunlight. In addition, animals are *sensitive* to the need for shelter and protection from their natural enemies.

In plants, chemical changes within the cells occur in response to the stimuli in the environment. Very simple forms of animals respond the same way. Some animals are equipped with nervous systems to respond to these stimuli. In the simpler animals the nervous systems are relatively simple, as are the responses. In the more complex type of animal, including man, this system is highly developed and provides the power of **discrimination.**

All plants and animals require food with which to *grow* and to provide the *energy* to carry on their life activities. Plants manufacture their own food. Animals *secure* their food from external sources and change the food within themselves into materials for growth and energy.

All plants and animals, no matter how simple or complex, are made up of a basic substance called **protoplasm.** This *living material* is identical in chemical nature in all forms of life, therefore its activities are identical.

BRIEF HISTORY OF CELLS

With the advent of the microscope, biologists were able to study the physical characteristics of protoplasm. Just about the time LEEUWENHOEK made his early microscope, the English scientist, ROBERT HOOKE, studied the structure of *cork* (from the bark of an oak tree) with a strong magnifying lens. He found it to be made up of tiny "empty boxes" with thick walls. He named these boxes *cells.*

After the microscope was made available to all scientists, further investigations were made of the structure of tiny water forms, of pieces of human skin, of blood, of parts of leaves, roots and stems of plants and even of parts of insects. They were all found to contain a substance that FELIX DUJARDIN, a French scientist, described as "living stuff," jellylike, grayish matter with "granules" scattered in it.

At the same time (1835–40) in other countries, scientists began to study the basic structure of all living things. In Czechoslovakia, a scientist named EVANGELISTA PURKINJE saw the "living stuff" and gave it the name **protoplasm,** (proto—first; plasm —form). He based his conclusions on the study of embryos of certain animals.

Some fifteen years later, two German biologists, SCHLEIDEN and SCHWANN, working independently, published books on the cellular nature of all plants and animals.

ROBERT BROWN, a botanist and surgeon's mate in the British Army, made an intensive study of orchids. He recognized the cellular structure of each flower part. With the use of stains, he was able to find a slightly thicker "particle" which

appeared in every cell. This "particle" seemed to control certain activities of the cells, especially that of *reproduction.* He named this the **nucleus** of the cell.

Scientists in many countries, with the aid of microscopes, working independently and in groups, established what is known as the **Cell Theory:**

Cells are the units of structure of all living things. (All plants and animals are made up of cells.)

Cells are, therefore, the units of function of all living things. (It is within the cells that our life activities occur.)

All living cells come only from other living cells.

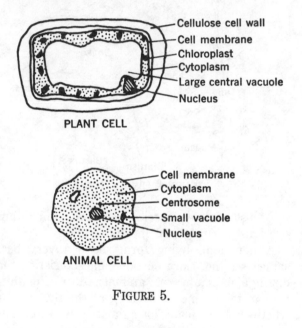

PLANT CELL

ANIMAL CELL

FIGURE 5.

CELL STRUCTURE

There are certain basic structures which appear in every cell. There are certain structures which differentiate a plant and animal cell, which make the basic differences between the plant and the animal. For convenience of study, let us look at typical plant and animal cells.

Structures present in all cells:

1. Cell membrane or **plasma membrane**—a double membrane surrounding the cell protoplasm or cytoplasm. Its function is to regulate the passage of liquids and gases into and out of the cell. It also provides a surface on which reactions may take place.

2. Cytoplasm—the protoplasm of living cells is in a colloid state; that is, it is made up of medium-sized particles hung in suspension. Its particles are too small to settle out and too large to go into solution. Because the particles are small, they provide a great surface area for cellular reactions to take place. They also permit the reaction to take place rapidly. Also, because protoplasm is not in a molecular state it cannot react chemically itself. Yet within the cytoplasm all cellular metabolic activities take place.

3. Nuclear membrane—a double membrane which controls the movement of materials into and out of the nucleus.

4. Nucleus—a definite structure within every cell. Its function is to control the activities of the cell. The nucleus contains the genetic material responsible for heredity, the *chromosomes*. It also contains the *nucleolus*, a smaller body which aids in the synthesis of protein.

5. Endoplasmic reticulum—a cell "skeletal" system. It provides a transport system between cell parts and a surface on which reactions may take place.

6. Ribosomes—small bodies which may occur on the surface of the endoplasmic reticulum or free in the cytoplasm. The ribosomes are the sites of protein synthesis.

7. Mitochondria—are often called the "power-house" of the cell. Here food is oxidized and energy is produced for use in various cellular activities.

8. Vacuoles—are storage bodies for water, minerals, etc. In unicellular organisms, vacuoles function in digestion and elimination.

Structures present only in animal cells:

1. Golgi bodies—function in the production of secretions of the cell.

2. Lysosomes—contain digestive enzymes which are released into the cytoplasm when the lysosomes burst open.

3. Centrosome or **centriole**—is located near the nucleus and functions in cell division.

Structures present only in plant cells:

1. Chloroplasts—bodies containing green chlorophyll pigments. Chloroplasts may be various shapes. The chloroplast is the site of photosynthesis or food production in a plant cell.

2. Cell wall—is composed of two layers. These layers provide support and protection for the cell. Both layers are somewhat waterproof, but they do not prevent the passage of water and sub-stances dissolved in water from passing through. The wall is composed of a substance called cellulose.

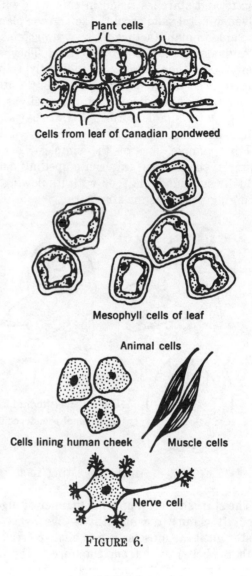

Plant cells

Cells from leaf of Canadian pondweed

Mesophyll cells of leaf

Animal cells

Cells lining human cheek   Muscle cells

Nerve cell

FIGURE 6.

INGESTION

In order to provide the necessary energy for growth and to carry on life's activities, we must take in food or eat. **This process is known as ingestion.**

In the discussion of the adaptations of plant cells it was noted that the cells are provided with structures called chloroplasts which help in the manufacture of food within the green plant. It is only in the green parts of the plant, the leaves and stems, that this food-making takes place.

Green plants in presence of light are able to take in the gas, **carbon dioxide,** from the air and combine it chemically with water to produce their carbohydrates. **This food-manufacturing process is known as photosynthesis.** By combining the sugars and starches made in this way with dissolved mineral salts from the soil, green plants are also able to manufacture their own proteins.

Animals are unable to do this. They secure their food either directly or indirectly from outside sources. Animals are adapted by nature to ingest food either directly into the cell, as in the case of very simple forms, or into parts of the body which prepare the food for all the cells to use.

For example, one of the simplest, one-celled animals, the **ameba,** (alternate spelling *amoeba*) actually surrounds its food with its flowing, everchanging protoplasmic structure.

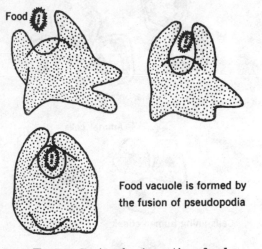

Food vacuole is formed by the fusion of pseudopodia

FIGURE 7. Ameba ingesting food

The starfish has an unusual manner of ingesting food. It clamps down with its five arms on an oyster until the muscles of the **bivalve (sea animal with 2 shells)** tire from the force. The oyster, unable to keep itself tense, relaxes. As soon as the starfish feels this, it allows the oyster shells to open, projects its own stomach into the soft tissues of the oyster and proceeds to devour it chemically.

The butterfly takes in food by uncoiling a **long tubelike structure (proboscis),** inserting it into the nectar container of a flower and sipping gently as through a straw.

The frog is an example of another type of feed-getting. He sits quietly on a leaf or log and waits for a flying insect to approach. When the unwary insect is within reach, the frog's long, cleft tongue darts out, catches the prey and directs it into his mouth. See Fig. 9.

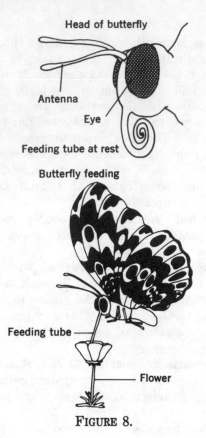

FIGURE 8.

Animals higher in the scale of life are well adapted to move around to choose, secure and to bring food to the "mouth" or part of the body which first takes in food.

DIGESTION

In both plants and animals food must be broken down into its simplest forms and made *soluble.* Only in soluble form are cells able to use food to provide energy for all life processes and to build new protoplasm and repair old. **The process of simplifying food and making it soluble is called digestion. Water is an essential substance in this process.**

The change from insoluble starch, protein and fats to soluble forms is brought about by the action of chemicals called **enzymes** which exist in both plants and animals. These enzymes bring about changes in the composition of foods without being in any way changed themselves or used up in the process. The chemist calls them **activating agents or catalysts.**

In plant cells, during the process of digestion, the starch that is manufactured in the green

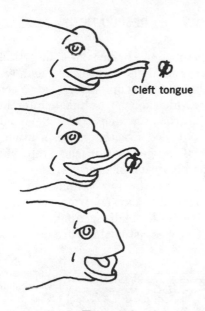

FIGURE 9.

leaves is changed into simple sugars which can be dissolved in water and carried to all other parts of the plant.

In animal cells, much the same is true. Foods containing insoluble starch, proteins, minerals and fats must be digested before they can be made available to all cells. Simple animal forms digest foods within each individual cell. Enzymes provide the necessary stimulus for this process.

More complex animals are especially fitted or adapted for digestion. In the earthworm the digestive system (series of body parts adapted solely for digestion) is extremely simple, merely a single tube extending the length of the body.

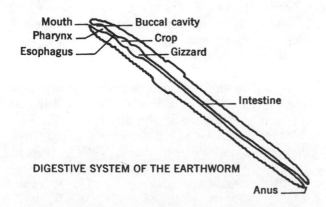

DIGESTIVE SYSTEM OF THE EARTHWORM

FIGURE 10. Digestive system of the earthworm

Higher in the animal kingdom this tube becomes divided into specialized parts each with a specific function in the process of digestion. In man and other highly developed **vertebrates (animals with backbones)** the digestive system is most specialized. Enzymes produced by glands serve as catalysts in animals as well as in plants.

ABSORPTION

Digested food must reach every cell in the living plant and animal. The cell walls of plants are porous so as to allow soluble food to pass through. The cell membranes are **selective** or **semipermeable**: that is, constructed so that only soluble substances can pass directly through into the cell protoplasm. **This process whereby digested or soluble food passes through the cell membrane is called absorption.**

In plant cells it is a simple process since all cell membranes are suitably adapted.

One-celled and other extremely simple animals contain food vacuoles in which digestion takes place. Digested food is diffused directly into the rest of the cell protoplasm.

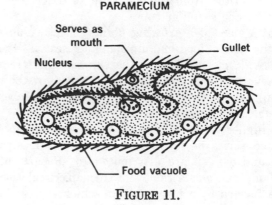

FIGURE 11.

In higher animal forms, including man, absorption takes place in specialized parts of the body. For example: in man, the small intestine is adapted to absorb digested food into the blood stream which carries it to all parts of the body.

CIRCULATION

Circulation is the life process in which soluble food and oxygen are distributed to all parts of plant and animal bodies, heat is distributed and waste removed.

The ever-moving protoplasm distributes digested food to all parts of the single-celled plant and animal.

In more highly developed plants there are tubes in the leaves and stems through which food and oxygen are circulated. **Liquid food in plants is known as sap.** Water containing dissolved minerals

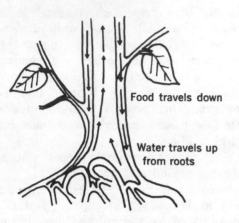

Food travels down

Water travels up from roots

FIGURE 12.

is transported from the roots up to other plant parts through similar tubes.

Cut a stem of a growing plant, especially during the active food-making summer season—the stem will "bleed." This is the sap escaping from the severed tubes. Tapping maple trees for their syrup (sap) requires cutting into the tubes through which the maple sap circulates.

In higher types of animals, there is also a specialized series of tubes through which digested food and oxygen are distributed to all parts of the body and waste removed. **In man, circulation is performed by a blood stream which courses in blood vessels (arteries, capillaries and veins) to every cell.**

ASSIMILATION

When digested food reaches the cells in all plants and animals, part of it is chemically combined with oxygen, actually burned (in the process of **oxidation**) to produce heat energy. The rest of it is changed into more protoplasm for growth and repair of cells. This process of changing digested food into protoplasm is called **assimilation.**

RESPIRATION

Another substance which all living things require is **oxygen.** This gaseous element exists in air and also dissolves in water. The mechanical process by which oxygen is taken into the body and later, carbon dioxide (CO_2) released from the body, is called *breathing.* **Respiration** is the utilization of oxygen within each cell which results in the liberation of energy.

Land-living plants and animals naturally secure the necessary oxygen from the air. Plants are provided with small openings on the under surface of leaves, stomata, through which air

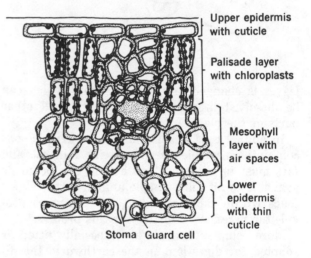

Upper epidermis with cuticle

Palisade layer with chloroplasts

Mesophyll layer with air spaces

Lower epidermis with thin cuticle

Stoma Guard cell

FIGURE 13. Cross section of a leaf

enters. Within the leaf, oxygen is selected from the air, dissolved in plant sap and circulated to all cells. Oxygen enters the cell membranes and is used by the cytoplasm to combine with digested food (oxidation) to produce the energy with which to carry on all life processes.

Characteristic of green plants is their ability to return to the atmosphere oxygen which is a by-product of photosynthesis. This replenishes the supply of oxygen in the air.

Plants that live in water select oxygen from the water via cell membranes. This is true of one-celled water-living animals as well.

Other animals are variously adapted for respiration. Fish are equipped with delicate, well-protected structures, **gills,** on each side of the head for this process. Water enters the mouth of the fish, passes back over the gills and comes out from under the scaly gill coverings. As water passes over the gills, oxygen is absorbed from the air dissolved in the water. It is carried by the blood stream to all parts of the body.

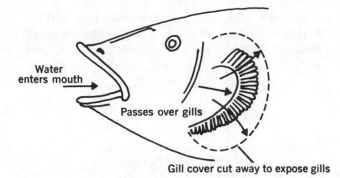

Water enters mouth

Passes over gills

Gill cover cut away to expose gills

FIGURE 14.

The earthworm, a land-living animal, breathes through its skin—which must be kept moist. Thus the earthworm always seeks damp earth into which to burrow. If the soil around it should become dry and the skin of the animal should dry up, the animal will die from its inability to carry on respiration.

After a heavy rain you will probably see many earthworms on top of the soil in the country or park and on the cement sidewalk in the city. These creatures are not adapted by nature to live under water—they will drown if unable to reach the air.

Land-living animals breathe in air containing oxygen. **Invertebrates (animals without backbones)** have varied adaptations for breathing.

Insects take in air through **spiracles** which are holes on each side of the abdomen. Air is distributed through the tubes **(trachea)** which branch throughout the body. See Fig. 15.

Most land-living vertebrates (including man)

Breathing in insects

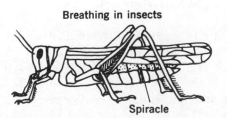

Spiracle

FIGURE 15. Grasshopper

take in air through nose and mouth from which it passes into *lungs*. The blood of these animals selects oxygen from air in the lungs and carries it to all cells where oxidation of food takes place.

The blood carries a waste gas (carbon dioxide) and excess water back to the lungs from which they are passed out of the body through the nose and mouth of the animal.

EXCRETION

After plants and animals have oxidized digested food and carried on their life activities, waste products result. Some are common to both plants and animals because of the nature of all protoplasm. These wastes are given off in the process of **excretion.**

Inability of the organism to rid itself of waste materials produces a toxic or poisonous condition within the cells. Such a condition leads to inadequate and abnormal performance of all life processes and may eventually be fatal.

The waste gas, carbon dioxide, and excess water vapor are excreted from plant cells through the stomata in the leaves of green plants. It is believed that other organic wastes accumulated in the leaves during the summer are eliminated when leaves fall in autumn.

Animals are adapted for the process of excretion. In one-celled animals (as well as plants), carbon dioxide and liquid wastes collect in vacuoles and are excreted directly through the cell membranes.

Many-celled animals, of greater specialization, produce solid wastes in addition to carbon dioxide and liquid organic wastes.

Lung-breathers eliminate carbon dioxide and some excess water through mouth and nose after these wastes have been brought by the blood to the lungs. The kidneys and the skin are specialized organs in man which collect and expel liquid wastes. The large intestine excretes solid wastes from the body.

REPRODUCTION

There are two major types of reproduction—asexual and sexual. Asexual reproduction is the more primitive type and results in "daughter" individuals identical to the "mother." Sexual reproduction is more advanced. In its evolution, male and female structures for reproduction have arisen. Sexual reproduction results in daughter individuals which are similar, but not identical, to the parents.

Simple forms of plants and animals reproduce themselves in the most primitive manner, without any special adaptation for the process. Single-celled plants and animals grow to capacity and then split into equal parts, each part becoming an individual. This method of reproduction is called **binary fission.**

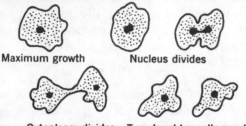

Maximum growth   Nucleus divides

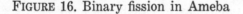

Cytoplasm divides   Two daughter cells result

FIGURE 16. Binary fission in Ameba

Multicellular (many-celled) plants are adapted in several ways for the vital function of reproduction. Mosses and ferns produce numerous spores which, when growing conditions are favorable, develop into new moss and fern plants.

Flowering plants are adapted to produce seeds. In this highly specialized form of reproduction the flower is the important part of the plant. Within separate parts of the same flower or within two separate flowers, male and female elements are developed. The combination of male and female cells results in the formation of seeds. A seed contains the **embryo** (the infant plant) which, when conditions are favorable, will develop into the new plant.

In order for most animals to reproduce their kind, male and female cells are necessary. The female reproductive cell is referred to as the **ovum** or **egg cell.** The male reproductive cell is referred to as the **sperm cell.** The union of a sperm cell with an ovum results in a **fertilized egg** which develops into the new infant animal. Since the new animal is a combination of both parent cells it inherits the characteristics of both parents.

Insects, fish, frogs, reptiles and birds produce eggs from which their young develop. Where there is little or no parental care—in the case of most fish, frogs and reptiles—large quantities of eggs are produced to insure the survival of a species.

Where there is some parental care (as in the case of birds) in providing food, shelter and protection against natural enemies, fewer eggs are produced.

Animals classified as **mammals (vertebrates that possess hair or fur and suckle their young)** produce their young alive from eggs fertilized within the body of the female or mother. Man is a member of this group of animals.

MOTION AND LOCOMOTION

Another function of all living things is the power of **motion** and, in some cases, **locomotion.** Since all protoplasm is in constant streaming motion, under normal conditions, then it follows that all living things move in some fashion.

One-celled animals move from place to place independently (locomotion) in their water surroundings.

Plants which are "rooted" in the ground do not have powers of locomotion but they do exhibit types of motion. Leaves, stems and flowers turn in the direction of the sun; tendrils of climbing plants wind about convenient supports; roots turn in the direction of water; some "sensitive" plants respond when touched.

Animals appear to be more "alive," as we commonly know the term, because, with few exceptions they have powers of locomotion. Sponges and corals grow attached at one stage of their lives—and in this way, they resemble plants.

SENSITIVITY AND BEHAVIOR

Sensitivity or **irritability** is another life function common to all protoplasm. **This refers to the response of protoplasm to stimuli or changing conditions in the environment.**

All plants and animals react or respond in some way to light, heat, need for food, physical contact and other external and internal stimuli.

Man bases his claim to superiority over the entire animal kingdom upon his ability to recognize and cope with stimuli in his environment.

The Role of Environment

Living things which exist all over the earth are numerous and extremely varied. Where conditions are favorable, plants and animals are most abundant and successful. Scientists have explored the deepest oceans and the most rarefied heights above the earth's surface and have found evidence of some life. There are relatively few places where no forms of life can exist.

ENVIRONMENT

The nature and success of living things depend upon environmental conditions. **By environment, we mean the immediate surroundings of an individual plant or animal.** The environment furnishes the basic needs for all living things to carry on their life functions.

These essentials are food, air, water and sunlight. Food is necessary to provide the energy to grow and perform life's processes. Air is necessary because it contains oxygen with which food must be oxidized to be changed to heat energy. Water is essential and waste may be removed so that substances can be made soluble for entrance into all cells through the cell membranes.

Since plants need sunlight to aid in the manufacture of food (photosynthesis) and animal food consists directly and indirectly of plants, sunlight is necessary for animals. The heat as well as the light is essential for life to exist.

In addition, the environment includes such factors as other living organisms, gravity, wind, electricity and air or water pressure.

Throughout the years of man's residence on earth, he has learned to improve his environment. To some extent, he has learned to conquer the forces that change his environment and threaten his ability to survive.

HABITAT

The same kinds of plants and animals do not live everywhere on earth. For example, polar bears normally live in frigid, polar regions. Lobsters are found among the rocks in salt water, whereas brook trout live in fresh mountain streams and lakes. The eagle builds its nest and rears its young on a craggy mountain ledge, whereas the sparrow and robin nest in an apple tree on a local farm or a maple tree in the city.

Plants, too, can be found growing in specific areas. Palm trees grow naturally in moist hot regions, whereas pines and other evergreens are more successful in drier and more northern areas. Orchids are flowers characteristic of tropical climate, whereas dandelions grow rampant on lawns in the temperate zones.

The specific environment in which a particular plant or animal or group of plants and animals is found is called its **natural habitat.** All living things are adapted to live in their natural habitats. If they are inadequately adapted, they either die or move to another area for which they are better fitted. If change in habitat occurs gradually, some plants and animals can gradually adapt themselves to the changes and live successfully.

Natural habitats vary greatly, thus the flora and fauna characteristics vary. **Flora refers to the sum of plant life** in a zone or habitat within a given length of time. **Fauna refers to the sum of animal life** of a given region and time period.

Natural habitats are distinguished from one another as follows:

Aquatic—referring to water-dwelling plants and animals. Not all types of aquatic forms live in the same kind of water. The type of indigenous (native to) life depends upon whether the water is fresh or salt, still or flowing, shallow or deep, hot, cold or moderate temperature, smooth or rocky bottom —or a combination of these factors.

Examples of fresh-water life, that is those animals whose natural habitat is ponds, lakes, streams and rivers are: algae, water cress, pondweeds and water lilies; some fish, snakes, snails, crayfish and leeches are among the animals.

Salt-water plants and animals may be divided into three groups:

Those which live on the beach or in shallow shore regions only—such as, sand eels, oysters, crabs and starfish, barnacles and seaweed.

Those which live near the surface of the ocean —such as, most sea fish, jellyfish, sea turtles, sharks, seals, porpoises; diatom plants.

Those which live in the ocean's depths where it is dark and very cold and where food is limited —such as colorless plants (diatoms and some bacteria), a few fish, some barnacles.

Terrestrial—this refers to land-living plants and animals. Although these flora and fauna live either on the surface of the ground or burrow underground, they all need some water to carry on their life processes. Terrestrial plants with few exceptions live on the surface of the ground, most of them anchored to the ground by roots or some sort of processes (stemlike growths). Trees and ferns are examples. Most terrestrial animals live on the surface of the ground. There are a few species that live part of their lives beneath the ground—for example moles, prairie dogs, gophers, earthworms and some insects.

Arboreal—this refers to animals whose existence is confined mostly to trees. Examples are some monkeys, sloths, opossums, lizards and some insects.

Aerial—refers to animals who spend a good part of their lives in the air. Examples are birds, some bats and most insects.

CLIMATE CONDITIONS

Climate conditions determine in great part the distribution of plants and animals over the world.

In Arctic regions where there is flat, frozen iceland, the flora are limited to low-growing plants such as some mosses and lichens, tough grasses, a few hardy species of dwarf poppies and even forget-me-nots. The fauna are usually confined to penguins, polar bears, seals, walruses and whales.

Plants and animals are greatly varied in **temperate** regions where there is variety in temperatures, and there are four annual seasons.

In **tropical** climates, where there is abundant rain and concentrated sunlight, plant life is luxuriant, always green and varied. Among the plant life are such trees as ebony, mahogany, rubber, date palms, bamboo, banana and thick-stemmed hardy vines; such flowers as orchids, gardenias and other heavily scented, superbly colored ones. Animals such as monkeys, apes, lemurs, sloths, elephants, parrots, birds of paradise, huge beautifully colored butterflies and innumerable insects are indigenous to this region.

In **mountainous** climates, because of characteristic high altitudes where the oxygen content of the air is less concentrated and there are strong, cold winds, both flora and fauna are relatively limited. Up to a certain line of demarcation, called the timber line, we find hardy oaks and evergreen trees, some poppies, gentians, onion-type grasses, mosses and lichens. This vegetation is low growing and extremely tenacious. Among the animals native to this region are huge spiders, eagles, bears, mountain goats and sheep.

Desert climates provide few factors favorable for most types of plants and animals. Because of the scarcity of water, the sand, and the steady intense light and heat of the sun only hardy plants like cactus, yuccas, sagebrush and tough grasses can exist. These are able to store water for long periods, have extensive roots and are tough enough to withstand the sun's burning intensity and the sharp drops in temperature at night. Such animals as rattlesnakes, horned toads, some lizards, a few more hardy rabbits, in addition to some unattractive birds, buzzards and vultures (scavengers) and a few species of insects, can exist on the desert where food is scarce and water is scarcer.

NATURAL BARRIERS

There are natural *barriers* (insurmountable obstacles) which prevent the indefinite distribution of successful growing plants and animals. These are large mountain ranges, widespread oceans, and large rivers, far-reaching deserts, soils lacking or overabundant in a certain chemical and the indestructible presence of natural enemies.

Earthquakes, the disappearance of small islands as a result of tumultuous internal earth upheavals, volcanic eruptions and large-scale glacial movements are also factors which produce natural barriers.

COMMUNITY LIVING

Within a given area or community, groups of plants and animals live together in natural coexistence. These living things are adapted or adapt themselves to all the factors in the immediate environment. In a community there always appears to be one or several dominant forms of plant and animal life which are more successful than the other plants and animals which share the community.

An example of community living can be found in a local park. There are trees which grow successfully in that particular climate and type of soil. There are birds which inhabit the trees, build nests and rear their young, feeding on the trees and other plants, and insects that grow in the area. There are insects adapted to live in the air, in the trees, on flowering plants and even in the ground.

Some insects serve as food for other animals, some help to propagate new generations of the local flora. Other animals live on the seeds, roots, stems and other parts of plants in the community. These animals contribute their share in community living by destroying harmful animal pests.

If the environmental factors remain relatively stable, then a balance of living may be achieved and all forms of flora and fauna in the area will live successfully.

PROTECTIVE ADAPTATIONS

All living things are adapted to secure the necessities of life from their immediate environment.

There appears to be a constant struggle among plants and animals to secure food and living space. Those plants and animals which are best adapted for these activities will be most successful. Those which are weakly adapted will be forced either to "fight" constantly for survival, withdraw to another community, or eventually perish.

Since every form of life has a natural enemy which will seek to destroy it, either to use it as food or in self-protection, all forms of life are adapted to protect themselves. These adaptations are called **protective adaptations.**

Among plants, the rose is a fine example of protective adaptation. Thorns on the stems discourage animals bent on destruction. Another example is the thistle with its needlelike flower cup, stems and leaves. The cactus has horny spines which are most painful to the touch.

The necessity for protective adaptation is great among animals because of their ability to move about (locomotion).

Most animals have some natural color protection from their enemies: that is, they resemble in

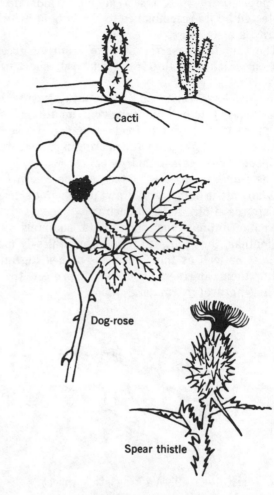

FIGURE 17.

color their natural surroundings. Most animals have other special adaptations for protection.

Insects, which are so numerous and varied, show interesting and successful adaptations. For example, the green-brown *praying mantis* with its formidable front "claws" and its wary stance, appears most menacing to a potential attacker.

FIGURE 18. Praying mantis

The *walking stick* insect, a gentle animal, is protected by its resemblance to the twig on which it crawls.

The tiny *leaf insect* looks like a spring green leaf on which it alights in its relatively short life on earth.

Beetles have claws and fierce-looking (to another insect) **mandibles (chewing mouth parts)** for protection as well as food-getting.

Bees and *wasps* have painful stinging apparatus for protection against their enemies.

The famous *chameleon* takes on the coloration of whatever it happens to crawl on when it senses the approach of a natural enemy.

Among animals such as rabbits, squirrels and chipmunks, the ability to remain breathlessly motionless as well as their keenness of hearing and sight, their alertness and speed protect them against natural marauders.

FIGURE 19. Walking stick insect

FIGURE 20. Male stag beetle

FIGURE 21. Common wasp

The *turtle* is fitted with a thick, horny "shell" which encases its soft body and into which it can withdraw completely for shelter and protection.

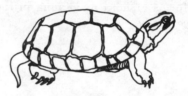

FIGURE 22. Turtle

PLANT AND ANIMAL INTERDEPENDENCE

It is obvious that in any environment one plant or one animal cannot survive by itself. All animals depend upon plants and other animals and plants depend upon other living things. Man depends upon other animals and plants for his success on earth. This mutual interdependence is what provides the balance in nature.

Most plants and animals live in groups. Some trees, for example, are adapted to a specific climate and type of soil. Hardy oak and hickory trees grow together in a temperate region where there are dry ridges. Basswood, red maple, elm, willow and birch will be found growing together in more moist areas. Evergreens (firs and pines) are usually found in more northerly climates but can grow elsewhere.

Ferns and mosses flourish together in moist shady places.

Seaweeds and algae grow together in harmony in the salty oceans.

Most animals live gregariously in "communities" or herds. Man is such an animal.

Some insects—bees and ants especially—live in communities and actually share in the many activities of food-getting, shelter-building, care of the young and protection against natural enemies.

In a warm sea-water community certain fish, coral, sponges, lobsters, crabs and jellyfish live together.

Local ponds provide community living for water bugs, frogs, snails, eels and fish.

Such animals as buffalo, elephants, cows and other cattle live in herds for mutual benefits. Wolves and coyotes travel in packs for maximum mutual strength and protection.

Relatively few animals prefer to live alone. Examples of those that do are lions, tigers, some deer and small animals like rabbits. The advantages of solitary living are few. Escape from natural enemies is perhaps easier for a swift, lonely animal; less disturbance and interference in rearing the young; less competition for mating and securing food are sometimes possible advantages.

Generally speaking there is "safety in numbers"; therefore group living is usually the most successful type of living.

SYMBIOSIS

The living together of organisms for mutual benefits is called symbiosis, the plants and animals involved are known as symbionts. An example of symbiosis among animals is the relationship between common ants and plant lice or *aphids*. The aphids suck the sap from rose or other plants. With this plant fluid they produce a sweet substance within their bodies. Ants "milk" the aphids and feed their queen and also the young. (The plant lice are known as "ant cows.") In return for this service, the ant cows are protected by their mutual benefactors against natural enemies and are also given shelter in anthills during the winter.

Another example of mutual "give and take" is found in the *termite*. This wood-eating insect provides food and shelter for a protozoan animal that lives in its intestines. The protozoa rewards its host by producing chemicals which digest the wood fibers for the termite.

Another interesting form of symbiosis between animals exists in the partnership relationship of the hermit crab and the sea anemone (a member of the jellyfish family). The hermit crab lives in a discarded snail shell which covers the soft part of the crab. The anemone lives on top of the snail-shell house and has stinging apparatus which protects it and the crab from natural enemies and captures food. It also gives protective coloration for the crab which, in turn, provides the anemone with transportation and food bits that escape its own mouth.

A classic example of plant symbiotic relationship is the *lichen* which is found growing on rocks

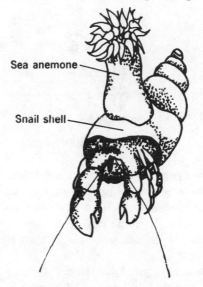

Sea anemone

Snail shell

FIGURE 23. Hermit crab

and tree trunks. This is not a single plant but a mutually beneficial combination of a nongreen fungus and a group of one-celled green plants of the algae group. The fungus cannot make its own food. It provides shelter, anchorage, protection, water and carbon dioxide for its algae companions. These simple green plants use the water and carbon dioxide to manufacture food and supply oxygen for the fungus.

PARASITISM

Some plants and animals feed on other living organisms without giving anything in return. **This relationship is known as parasitism; the offender is called a parasite, and the "meal ticket," the host.** In most cases the parasite is structurally degenerate and entirely dependent upon the host. The host may either gradually lose its vitality, be-

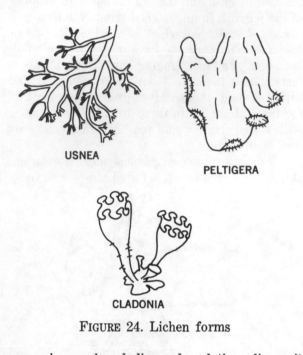

USNEA

PELTIGERA

CLADONIA

FIGURE 24. Lichen forms

The most numerous and destructive of all plant parasites are among the **bacteria (a type of single-celled plant)**. Some species cause blights on apples, pears, cabbage, cucumbers and other plants. Other species cause diseases in man and are referred to as **pathogenic** bacteria. Among the dreaded pathogenic bacteria are those which produce diphtheria, typhoid fever, Asiatic cholera, bubonic plague and other illnesses, most of which man has been able to control and prevent.

There are some animal parasites which single man out as their unfortunate hosts. Among them are protozoa which cause malaria and sleeping sickness. Hookworm and pork worm—parasitic in man—produce devastating results in their often unsuspecting hosts. Scientists have learned to prevent and control the harmful activities of these animal parasites.

come abnormal and diseased and then die or it may develop a natural protection against the parasite. It may adapt itself to live with and in spite of its burden. In some cases, the host produces a substance which either renders harmless or kills the parasite.

The *mistletoe* plant, which conjures up romantic notions, is actually a parasite incapable of manufacturing its own food, reliant on another plant for its food. Its host, usually an apple, poplar or maple tree, eventually perishes from malnutrition.

Other plant parasites which depend on and slowly devitalize their hosts, causing great economic loss to man, are wheat rust, Dutch elm disease, corn smut and chestnut blight. In each case the tree or plant mentioned in the name is the losing host to the destructive parasite plant.

There are some parasitic plants which do damage directly to man's person. These offenders are members of the **fungus group of plants, that is, a group having no chlorophyll**. The unpleasant "ringworm" and "athlete's foot" ailments are examples.

SAPROPHYTES AND SCAVENGERS

Some plants and animals depend for their existence on other, *dead* organisms. Many plants lacking chlorophyll are known as **saprophytes**, examples of which are yeasts, molds and mushrooms.

Animals that live on dead or decaying flesh of other animals are called **scavengers**. Among them are the vultures, buzzards and sea gulls. In the blood stream of man, there are **white blood cells** that resemble ameba which act as tiny scavengers by engulfing and eating unwanted particles including some disease-producing bacteria.

Man, in his position as the superior animal of our universe, has learned to change his environment, sometimes to his misfortune but generally to his advantage, and to improve the welfare of other living things. Because of his powers of observation and reasoning, he has been able, to a great extent, to control many factors of his environment.

Organization and Classification

All living things are made of **protoplasm.** The smallest unit of structure and function of protoplasm is the **cell.** All plants and animals are made up of either a single cell or many cells.

Evolutionists believe that all plants and animals originally arose from a unicellular ancestor. As can be seen by the study of lower plants and animals, particularly those of a single cell, there are many characteristics common to both those called "animals" and those called "plants." It has taken many years of evolution for organisms to acquire their distinct plant or animal-like character. In order to take into account the similarity of the lower plants and animals, recent methods of classification place them together in a group called the Protista. Traditionally, they have been classified separately.

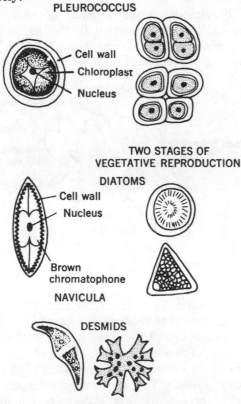

FIGURE 25. Single-celled plants

SINGLE-CELLED LIFE: PLANTS

The simplest form of plant life exists as a single cell which is able to carry on all the necessary life processes. Most one-celled plants belong to the **algae** group which live in water. There are some which live in symbiotic relationship with other plants (lichens) and with animals in a moist environment but out of the water.

A common example of a single-celled plant is the **pleurococcus** which is usually found growing on the north side of moist tree trunks and rocks in the woods. These tiny green plants are legendary

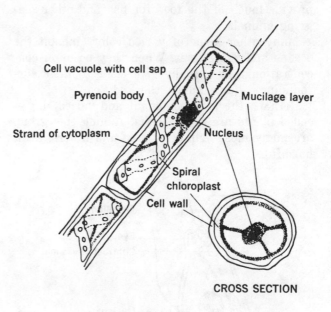

FIGURE 26. Spirogyra (common pond scum)

"Indian's Friend" and "Woodsman's Compasses" because they indicate the direction North.

They contain chlorophyll with which to combine carbon dioxide from the air and water to manufacture food. Under the microscope they appear singly or in colonies, each cell living independently within its colony. See Fig. 25.

A drop of pond water will reveal a variety of single-celled plants. What is commonly known as pond scum is a group of green threadlike colonies called **spirogyra.** They reproduce prolifically and form the greenish scum that appears on the surface of sluggish streams, small ponds and pools. See Fig. 26.

Among the independent single-celled forms which can be viewed under a microscope are the **diatoms** and **desmids.** These plants are curiously symmetrical, each kind having a specific design on its shell-like outer covering which encloses and protects the soft protoplasmic cells.

Diatoms seem to have existed in abundance centuries ago. Large deposits of their empty shells have been discovered in salt as well as fresh water and on land that shows evidence of once having been under water. These deposits, called **diatomaceous earth,** are used commercially as the basis of polishing materials and also for filtering purposes in sugar refineries.

Another common group of single-celled plant life, is found in ocean water, as part of the substance **plankton.** These are tiny green plants that provide much of the food for fish and other sea-living animals.

Many other algae of varied colors inhabit the oceans and shore lines. When they occur in concentration they actually give color to their surroundings—for example, the Red Sea.

Perhaps the most abundant and varied single-celled plants are the **bacteria.** Among this group are many most helpful to man and others, most harmful.

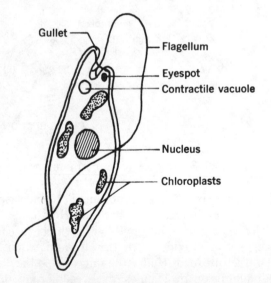

FIGURE 27. Euglena (plant or animal?)

One single-celled form of life, the **euglena,** has created dissension among biologists. Botanists consider it a simple plant because it contains chlorophyll bodies with which it manufactures its own food.

Zoologists, on the other hand, claim that it rightfully belongs to the animal kingdom for several reasons. It contains a contractile vacuole for collecting and eliminating liquid wastes. At one end of the cell there is a form of mouth and gullet into which it takes some food particles from the water. At the mouth region, there is a **whiplike projection (flagellum)** which lashes back and forth, aiding in locomotion and food-getting.

Perhaps this controversial bit of life is proof that one-celled plants and animals have a common ancestor.

SINGLE-CELLED LIFE: ANIMALS

This leads us to the fascinating group of true one-celled animals called **protozoa** (proto—first; zoa—animals). A drop of pond water reveals a variety of tiny animals, some darting about and others moving lazily.

Among the most numerous are paramecia and amebas. Each of these animals is well-equipped within its protoplasm to carry on all the life functions.

The simplest of all animals is the ameba. It has no definite or constant form. The protoplasm within the cell membrane flows into projections known as **pseudopods** or false feet. The presence

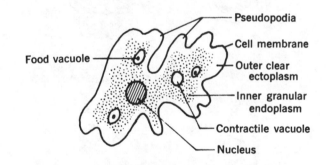

FIGURE 28. Ameba

of food particles in the water seems to stimulate the formation of these false feet which carry the rest of the cell in the direction of the food; thus the animal moves from place to place.

Food is digested within vacuoles and is absorbed directly into the surrounding cell protoplasm. Oxygen dissolved in the water is absorbed directly through any part of the cell membrane. Solid wastes are "left behind" as the ameba flows sluggishly on. A contractile vacuole regulates the water content of the animal and also collects liquid wastes which are expelled through a temporarily thin spot in the cell membrane.

The centrally located nucleus of the ameba controls all cell activities. It splits in half to produce two ameba in the process of reproduction. This simple type of reproduction is known as **binary fission.**

The paramecium, a more advanced type of one-

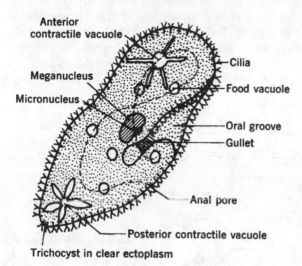

FIGURE 29. Paramecium

celled protozoa, is slipper-shaped and constant in form.

Its cell body is covered with tiny projections of protoplasm called **cilia** which wave back and forth providing means of rapid locomotion in water. Other cilia around the mouth region wave food particles into the "gullet" which is also lined with cilia to push the food into food vacuoles.

Constant flowing motion of the protoplasm within the paramecium cell body distributes each food vacuole to all parts of the cell. Digestion of food takes place in the vacuole. Digested food is absorbed directly into the surrounding protoplasm.

Oxygen dissolved in the water is absorbed directly through the cell membrane into the cell protoplasm.

Solid food wastes are expelled through a weakened area in the cell membrane called an **anal spot.** Liquid wastes are forced through the cell membrane by the contracting action of the contractile vacuoles located one at each end of the tiny animal.

Minute threads of poisonous protoplasm called **trichocysts** are imbedded just inside the cell membrane. These provide means of protection and are expelled with force when the paramecium comes in contact with a hostile form of life.

A well-developed nucleus and a "helper-nucleus" control all life activities and provide the means

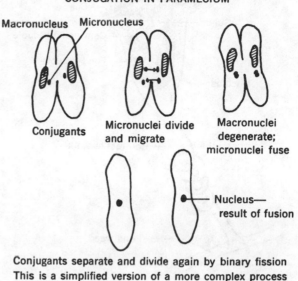

CONJUGATION IN PARAMECIUM

Conjugants separate and divide again by binary fission
This is a simplified version of a more complex process

FIGURE 30.

for reproduction. The paramecium divides by binary fission, similarly to the ameba, and also by a simple type of sexual reproduction called **conjugation.** In this type of reproduction two paramecia fuse temporarily, exchange nuclear material, separate and then each proceeds to divide by binary fission. This process seems to strengthen the species.

There are other types of protozoa which exist individually and still others which live in colonies.

The **vorticella** attaches itself by a long stalk at one end to a stationary object.

Colonial protozoa live in groups, each animal in the colony, functioning independently. Some colonies have a thick, gelatinous substance encasing them while others have glasslike coverings. The famous white cliffs of Dover (Southern England) are composed of countless chalklike shells which have accumulated through the years after the soft protoplasm of each protozoan animal has ceased to exist.

Most one-celled animals live independently but there are some which are parasites. Examples of these are the protozoa that cause malaria and African sleeping sickness in man. Each of these has an alternate host. The malarial plasmodium (protozoan that causes malaria) spends part of its life in the anopheles mosquito. The protozoan which causes sleeping sickness spends much of its life cycle in its alternate host, the tsetse fly, native to the African continent.

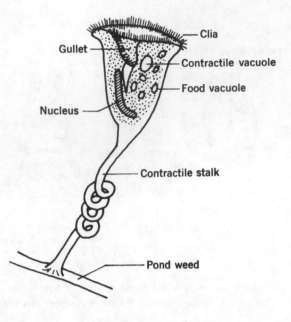

FIGURE 31. Vorticella

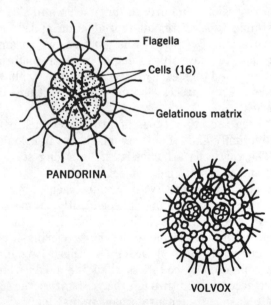

PANDORINA

VOLVOX

FIGURE 32. Colonial protozoa

CELLULAR ORGANIZATION

Living things that we can readily see and touch are usually made up of many cells, and many groups of cells. Each of these cells or groups of cells is adapted to perform a particular function.

All of the groups of cells normally work in harmony for the common welfare of the plant or animal.

One can easily see the gross structure of a geranium plant. To examine the cellular composition of any part of the plant requires a microscope.

Under the microscope the thin lower section of a geranium leaf (surface view) appears to be made up of many cells similar in size and shape, fitted together like a series of bricks in a brick wall. At intervals there are openings "guarded"

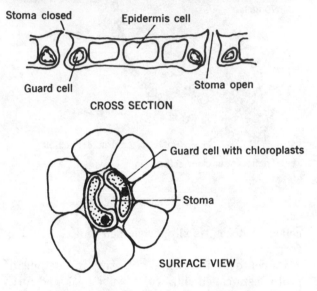

FIGURE 33. Under surface of leaf

by two kidney-shaped cells. The same view of the lower epidermis of the leaf appears to be a pattern of well-fitted flagstones among which are guarded openings. See Fig. 33.

The continuous layer of cells is adapted to protect the under surface of the leaf. The openings or **stomata** with their **guard cells** control inward or outward passage of gases. Oxygen is taken into the leaf and carbon dioxide is released during the process of respiration. During the process of photosynthesis carbon dioxide is taken in through these stomata and oxygen is released. Other cells (containing chloroplasts) in the leaf are adapted to combine carbon dioxide and water to produce food for the plant.

In a later discussion of the flowering plants, plant cells and their specialized functions in groups or tissues will be considered in detail. Note a few more examples in Figure 34.

Among many-celled animals, there are also groups of cells similar in structure with a similar common function.

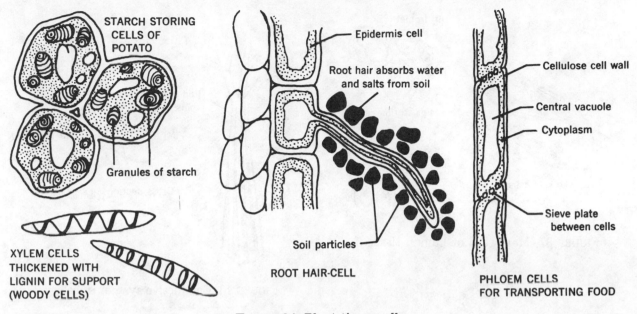

STARCH STORING
CELLS OF
POTATO

Granules of starch

XYLEM CELLS
THICKENED WITH
LIGNIN FOR SUPPORT
(WOODY CELLS)

Epidermis cell

Root hair absorbs water
and salts from soil

Soil particles

ROOT HAIR-CELL

Cellulose cell wall

Central vacuole

Cytoplasm

Sieve plate
between cells

PHLOEM CELLS
FOR TRANSPORTING FOOD

FIGURE 34. Plant tissue cells

For example, examine Figure 35 showing cells from the cheek lining of man. If a microscope is available to you, prepare a slide of cheek lining cells. (Scrape the inner surface of your cheek with the dull edge of a butter knife and mount this in a drop of water on a glass slide.)

These cells are adapted for their job of protecting the softer, inner cells of the mouth.

In Figures 36 and 37 there are surface views of several types of cells found in the human body. Note how they vary in size and shape, also in function.

Groups of cells similar in size, shape and function make up tissues: thus nerve cells working together form nerve tissue; muscle cells grouped together form muscle tissue; and cartilage cells form cartilage tissue.

There are other types of cells in the human body (as well as in all other animals and in plants) that, because of structural and functional similarities, form tissues.

Groups of different kinds of tissues working together to perform a particular function for the plant or animal are called organs.

Examples of plant organs are leaf, stem, roots, flowers, fruits and seeds.

Examples of a few organs found in the human body are larynx, trachea or windpipe and lungs.

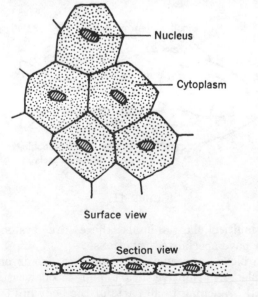

Nucleus

Cytoplasm

Surface view

Section view

FIGURE 35. Human cheek cells

Cells of human tissues

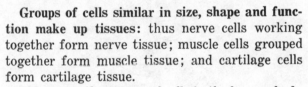

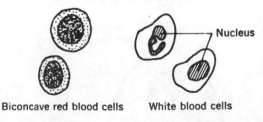

Nucleus

Biconcave red blood cells   White blood cells

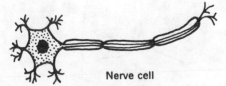

Nerve cell

FIGURE 36.

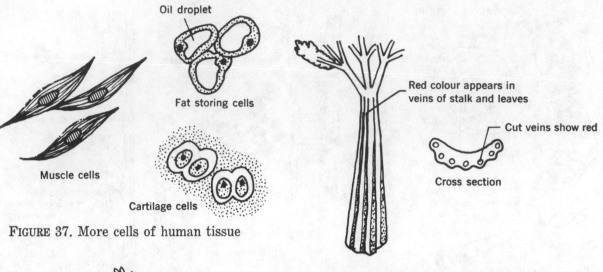

FIGURE 37. More cells of human tissue

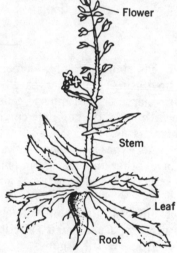

FIGURE 38. Plant organs

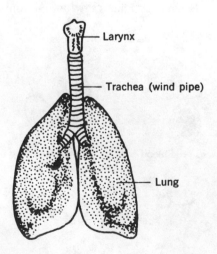

FIGURE 39. Organs of human respiration

FIGURE 40. Conductive system in celery

A group of organs working together to perform a specific life function is called a system.

A simple experiment which can be performed at home will illustrate the conductive system in plants. Place a stalk of celery (leaves included) in a solution of red ink and water for several hours. Observe the red color which apears in *tubes* or *veins* in the stalk (stem) and leaves. Cut across a piece of the stalk and observe the row of red dots in Figure 40.

This experiment indicates the conductive system through which water containing dissolved minerals from the soil rises up through the stem to all other parts of the plant.

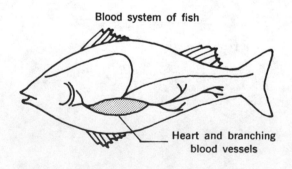

FIGURE 41.

In multicellular animals there are systems which have specialized functions.

The blood or **circulatory system** in fish is one example. A primitive heart and blood vessels (tubes) branching to all parts of the body are the organs which make up this system. Its function is to distribute blood to all cells in the fish. The blood carries digested food and oxygen to the cells and carries waste products away from the cells (to be eliminated).

In a more complex animal there are many different systems, each with a specialized job. We shall mention them briefly at this point:

Digestive system—to digest food.

Absorption system—to absorb digested food and necessary oxygen.

Circulatory system—to circulate or **deliver** digested food and oxygen to all cells **in the body** and to carry away gas and liquid waste products and distribute heat.

Respiratory system—to take in oxygen and release carbon dioxide and excess water vapor from the body.

Excretory system—to rid the body of wastes.

Reproductive system—to produce another generation of human beings.

Nervous system—to control activities of the body.

Let us analyze the digestive system to show the organs of which it is composed: the mouth, gullet or esophagus, stomach and intestines. There are glands that produce chemicals (catalysts) which aid the digestive organs in their function.

The sum total of a group of systems working together results in a complete organism, otherwise called a plant or animal.

Over a million varieties of living things have been discovered on our earth. In order that they be studied and recognized they must be grouped in some orderly fashion, or in other words, classified.

For example, books in a library are not just placed on shelves in any haphazard fashion. They are divided first into large general groups, that is, fiction and non-fiction. Each of these groups is divided further into subdivisions. For example, non-fiction are grouped according to their main topics: biography, history, science, art, etc. **Each** of these divisions is further subdivided; for example, science books are classified according to their specialties: astronomy, biology, chemistry, physiol-

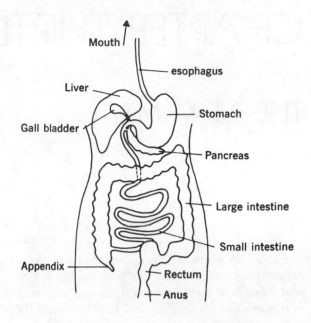

FIGURE 42. Human digestive system

ogy, etc. Subdivisions finally narrow down to individual books.

Our modern **system of classification or taxonomy** of all living things was devised by LINNAEUS (Carl von Linné) in the latter part of the eighteenth century. He used Latin names because Latin was the universal language of scholars. He gave names to plants and animals that are short and often descriptive in nature.

The largest groups of living things are the Plant and Animal kingdoms. Each of the kingdoms is divided and subdivided depending first on general and then more detailed structural and functional similarities. The smallest subdivision is the individual plant or animal. For example: The classification of Man.

Kingdom—Animal
Phylum—Chordate (with a skeletal axis)
Subphylum—Vertebrate (having backbone)
Class—Mammal (mammary glands, young born alive, have hair)
Order—Primate ("first"; opposable thumb)
Family—Hominidae (mankind)
Genus—Homo (human being)
Species—Sapiens (wise, discerning)
Man—Homo sapiens

CHAPTER THIRTEEN

THE NEW MATH

For many years the major emphasis in elementary school mathematics has been on the mechanical aspects of computation. This has created the erroneous and misleading idea that this is all there is to mathematics.

You can become very skillful in computation (learning to add, subtract, multiply, and divide) without really understanding why these mathematical processes work. With the advent of high-speed computers and desk calculators, the ability to compute is fast becoming an unsalable skill.

The tremendous advances taking place in mathematics and science demand that today's children must be taught the *why* as well as the *how* of mathematics. Today's society and, even more so, future societies will face problems that cannot even be predicted today. These problems will not be solved by rote-learned facts alone, but by the ability to think mathematically and to use mathematical methods of attacking the problems. In fact, these new problems will undoubtedly involve and require more new and as yet unknown mathematics.

This chapter is designed to help you go beyond the routine computational skills—to understand the basic structure of and organization of elementary mathematical systems. In most cases, simple illustrations from the physical world are used to help you easily understand the mathematical ideas and concepts.

Your study will be interesting and rewarding if you accept the attitude "Why does it work?" rather than "How does it work?"

Sets, Numbers, Numeration

SETS

In mathematics we are often concerned not with a single object, but with a collection of objects. For example, we hear about and speak of a collection of paintings, a row of chairs, or a set of dishes. Each of these collections is an example of a *set*.

A **set** is simply a collection of things considered as a single entity.

Definition 1:

The things contained in a given set are called **members** or **elements** of the set.

The members of a collection of paintings are the individual paintings in that set. The members of a row of chairs are the individual chairs in that row. The members of a set of dishes are the individual cups, saucers, plates, etc., in that set.

One method of naming sets is shown below.

$$A = \{\text{Bob, Bill, Tom}\}$$

This is read, "A is the set whose members are Bob, Bill, and Tom." Capital letters are usually used to denote sets. The braces, { }, merely denote a set. The names of the members of the set are listed, separated by commas, and then enclosed within braces.

An alternate use of the brace notation is illustrated below.

W = {Monday, Tuesday, Wednesday, Thursday, Friday, Saturday, Sunday}
W = {the days of the week}

The first of these examples lists or tabulates the members of the set W. In the second example a descriptive phrase is enclosed within braces. The latter example is read, "W is the set of days of the week."

Using the set W above, we can say:

Monday *is a member of* W.
Saturday *is a member of* W.

We can abbreviate the phrase "is a member of" by using the Greek letter epsilon, ε, to stand for this phrase. Then we can say:

Monday ε W
Saturday ε W

The slash line or slant bar, /, is often used to negate the meaning of a mathematical symbol. The mathematical symbol ε is read, "is not a member of." For set W we can then say:

John $\notin$ W (John is not a member of W.)
April $\notin$ W (April is not a member of W.)

The symbols denoting the individual members of a set are generally lower-case letters of our alphabet, such as *a, b, c, d,* and so on.

Exercises 1:
Name the members of each of the following sets.
1. The set of the Great Lakes
2. The set of the last 3 months of the year
3. The set of states in the U.S. bordering the Gulf of Mexico.
4. The set of men over 15 feet tall
5. The set of months in a year
6. The set of states in the U.S. whose names begin with the letter A

Write a description of each of the following sets.
7. $A = \{a,b,c,d\}$
8. $B = \{a,e,i,o,u\}$
9. $C = \{x,y,z\}$

Use the sets given in questions 7–9 above and insert the symbol ε or $\notin$ in each blank to make the following sentences true.

10. $a\_\_A$ 13. $y\_\_A$
11. $a\_\_B$ 14. $y\_\_B$
12. $a\_\_C$ 15. $y\_\_C$

THE EMPTY SET

Perhaps the preceding Exercise 4 (the set of men over 15 feet tall) caused you to wonder whether a set had been described. Although it seems natural to think of a set as having at least 2 numbers, it is mathematically convenient to consider a single object as a set (*a unit set*). It is also convenient to consider a collection containing no members as a set, called the *empty* set, or the null set, or the void set.

Definition 2:
   The empty set is the set that contains no members.

The empty set is usually denoted by Ø (a letter from the Scandinavian alphabet). Ø is read, "the empty set." We can also indicate the absence of members by denoting the empty set by { }.

Other examples of the empty set are: the set of cookies in an empty cookie jar; the set of all living men over 200 years old; or the set of months in our year which contain more than 50 years.

SUBSETS

It is often necessary to think of sets that are "part of" another set or are "sets within a set." The set of chairs (*C*) in a room is a set within the set of all pieces of furniture (*F*) in that room. Obviously, every chair in the room is a member of set *C* and also a member of set *F*. This leads to the idea of a subset.

Definition 3:
"Set *A* is a **subset** of set *B*" means that every member of set *A* is also a member of set *B*.

An equivalent definition of a subset might be:

Definition 4:
"Set *A* is a **subset** of set *B*" if set *A* contains no member that is not also in set *B*.

We can abbreviate the phrase "is a subset of" by using the conventional symbol $\subset$. $A \subset B$ means "set A is a subset of set B," or simply "A is a subset of B."

By using the symbolism already established, we can concisely state Definition 1–3 as follows:

$A \subset B$ if for every $x \, \varepsilon \, A$ then $x \, \varepsilon \, B$.
Consider the following sets.
$R = \{a,b,c,d,e\}$
$S = \{a,c,e\}$

Every member of set S is also a member of set R. Hence, $S \subset R$. R is not a subset of S ($R \not\subset S$) because R contains members (b and d) which are not members of S.

All of the possible subsets of set S are given below.

$$\{a\} \subset S \qquad \{a,c\} \subset S$$
$$\{c\} \subset S \qquad \{a,e\} \subset S$$
$$\{e\} \subset S \qquad \{c,e\} \subset S$$
$$\{ \ \} \subset S \qquad \{a,c,e\} \subset S$$

The last two subsets of S, as listed above, can lead us to some general conclusions about the subset relation.

Is the empty set a subset of every set? By Definition 1–4, the empty set contains no member which is not also a member of any given set. Hence, we say that *the empty set is a subset of every set.*

Since $S = \{a,c,e\}$ and $\{a,c,e\} \subset S$, we are tempted to ask: "Is every set a subset of itself?" Regardless of the set we choose, every member of the set is obviously a member of the set. Hence, we say that *every set is a subset of itself.*

Exercises 2:

Consider the following sets. Then write the symbol $\subset$ or $\not\subset$ in each blank so that the following become true sentences.

$A = \{a,b,c,d,e\}$ $B = \{b,d,e,g\}$ $C = \{b,d\}$

1. $B\_\_A$ 4. $C\_\_B$
2. $B\_\_C$ 5. $C\_\_A$
3. $B\_\_B$ 6. $\emptyset\_\_C$

List all of the possible subsets of each of the following sets.

7. $D = \{x,y\}$
8. $E = \{a,b,c,d\}$

Compare the number of subsets and the number of members of set D, E, and the previously used set $S = \{a,c,e\}$.

9. Can you discover a formula for finding the number of subsets of any set?

SET EQUALITY

Consider the following sets.

$A = \{r,s,t,u\}$
$B = \{t,r,u,s\}$

Since each set contains identically the same members, we say that set A *is equal to* set B or simply $A = B$.

Definition 5:

If A and B are names for sets, $A = B$ means that set A has identically the same members as set B, or that A and B are two names for the same set.

Note that the order in which the members are named does not matter. For example, $\{a,b,c\} = \{c,a,b\} = \{b,a,c\}$.

Whenever the equal sign ($=$) is used, as in $A = B$ or $1 + 2 = 3$, it means that the symbols on either side of it name precisely the same thing.

Consider the following sets.

$K = \{p,q,r,s\}$
$M = \{r,v,x,z\}$

Since K and M do not contain identically the same members, we say K *is not equal to* M, or simply $K \neq M$.

Exercises 3:

Use the sets named below and write $=$ or $\neq$ in each blank so that true sentences result.

$A = \{1,2,3,4\}$
$B = \{a,e,i,o,u\}$
$C = \{$the first four counting numbers$\}$
$D = \{$the vowels in our alphabet$\}$
$E = \{3,2,1,4\}$
$F = \{o,i,a,w\}$

1. $A\_\_B$ 6. $B\_\_C$
2. $A\_\_C$ 7. $B\_\_D$
3. $A\_\_D$ 8. $B\_\_E$
4. $A\_\_E$ 9. $B\_\_F$
5. $A\_\_F$ 10. $E\_\_F$

EQUIVALENT SETS

Suppose you had a set of cups and a set of saucers. Someone asks, "Are there more cups or more saucers?" Would you have to count the objects in each set to answer the question?

All you need do is place one cup on each saucer until all of the members of one of the sets have been used. If there are some cups left over, then there are more cups than saucers. If there are some saucers left over, then there are more saucers. In case each cup is paired with one and only one saucer and each saucer is paired with one and only one cup, we say the sets are matched one-to-one or that there is a one-to-one correspondence between the sets.

Definition 6:

There is a **one-to-one correspondence** between sets A and B if every member of A is paired with one member of B and every member of B is paired with one member of A.

The following illustration shows the six ways of establishing a one-to-one correspondence between the two sets.

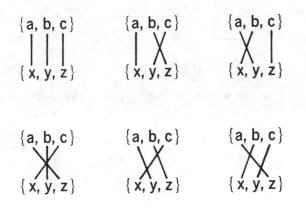

The existence of a one-to-one correspondence between two sets has nothing to do with the way in which the pairing is done.

Definition 7:

Two sets are **equivalent** if there is a one-to-one correspondence between the two sets.

Note that the idea of equivalent sets is not the same as that of equal sets. That is, two sets are equal if they have identically the same members. Two equivalent sets may have different members just so there exists a one-to-one correspondence between them. For example:

$\{a,b,c,d\}$ is equivalent to $\{r,s,t,u\}$.
$\{a,b,c,d\}$ is not equal to $\{r,s,t,u\}$.
$\{a,b,c,d\}$ is equal to $\{c,a,d,b\}$.
$\{a,b,c,d\}$ is equivalent to $\{c,a,d,b\}$.

Exercises 4:

Draw matching lines to show a one-to-one correspondence between the sets in each pair.

1. $\{a,b,c,d\}$

   $\{w,x,y,z\}$

2. $\{1,2,3,4,5,6\}$

   $\{2,4,6,8,10,12\}$

NUMBERS

Let us consider the collection of all sets that are equivalent to $\{a,b,c\}$. For convenience, let us denote a set by drawing a ring around the collection of objects.

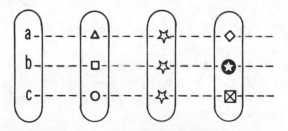

The only thing alike about all of these sets is that their members can be matched one-to-one. That is, they are equivalent sets. The thing that is alike about these sets is called the *number three*.

Of course, other sets belong to this collection also—the set of wheels on a tricycle, the set of people in a trio, and the set of sides of a triangle.

The number three has many names—III, $2 + 1$, 3, and many more. Each of these names is called a **numeral**. A *numeral* is a name for a number. The simplest numeral for the number three is 3.

With every collection of equivalent sets is associated a number, and with each number is associated a simplest numeral.

Set	Number	Simplest Numeral
{ }	zero	0
$\{a\}$	one	1
$\{c,d\}$	two	2
$\{x,y,z\}$	three	3
•	•	•
•	•	•
•	•	•

The dots indicate that we can extend each of the above columns. The set of numbers so derived is called the set of cardinal numbers or the set of *whole numbers*.

Since we usually begin counting "one, two, three,..." we call {1,2,3,4,5, ...} the set of counting numbers or the set of *natural numbers*.

Set of whole numbers: {0,1,2,3,4, ...}
Set of natural numbers: {1,2,3,4, ...}

Exercises 5:

Write the simplest numeral for the number associated with each of the following sets.

1. {q,r,s,t,w,x,y,z}
2. {the days of the week}
3. {1,2,3,4,5,6,7,8,9}
4. {the months of the year}
5. {all three-dollar bills}
6. {John, James, Jean, Joe}
7. {Presidents of the U.S.}
8. {states in the U.S.}

BASE-TEN NUMERATION

Because of the random arrangement of the members of the set shown below, you may have a hard time determining quickly the number of members in the set.

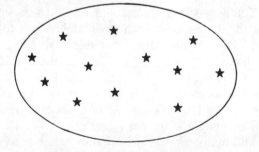

It is easier to determine the number of members if they are arranged as follows.

Since man has ten fingers, he probably matched members of a set one-to-one with his fingers and thereby grouped the objects as follows.

This led to his writing the symbol 12 to mean 1 set of ten and 2 more.

Finally it dawned on man that he could make any kind of grouping in his mind. Then he might group the members and name the number of members in any of the following ways.

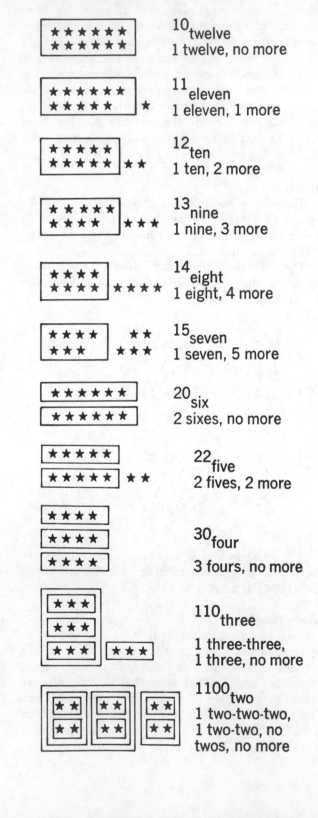

Through the years man has found use for several of these methods of naming the number of the set. But his early ten-finger matching was deep-seated in his memory, and he most frequently grouped by tens. It is this grouping that leads to the *decimal* or *base-ten numeration* system.

Definition 8:

A *numeration system* is a planned scheme or way of naming numbers.

Let us agree that when a numeral is written without a number word to the lower right, such as 23, we shall mean base ten or grouping by tens. Then the numeral 23 means:

2 tens and 3 more

or

2 tens and 3 ones

Since 2 tens can be thought of as 2×10, and 3 ones can be thought of as 3×1, let us name 23 as follows:

$$23 = (2 \times 10) + (3 \times 1)$$

This is called the *expanded numeral* or *the expanded notation* for 23.

How can we name 427 in expanded notation? The numeral 427 means 4 ten-tens, 2 tens, and 7 ones. Since a ten-ten means 10×10 or 100, we can show the expanded notation for 427 as follows.

$$427 = (4 \times 100) + (2 \times 10) + (7 \times 1)$$

In a similar way we can write the expanded numeral for 3256 as follows.

3 ten-ten-tens, 2 ten-tens, 5 tens, and 6 ones
$(3 \times 10 \times 10 \times 10) + (2 \times 10 \times 10) +$
$(5 \times 10) + (6 \times 1)$

or

$(3 \times 1000) + (2 \times 100) + (5 \times 10) + (6 \times 1)$

Exercises 6:

Write the simplest numeral for each of the following.

1. $(8 \times 10) + (5 \times 1)$
2. $(5 \times 100) + (3 \times 10) + (9 \times 1)$
3. $(7 \times 100) + (3 \times 10) + (0 \times 1)$
4. $(7 \times 100) + (7 \times 10) + (7 \times 1)$
5. $(3 \times 1000 + (4 \times 100) + (3 \times 10) + (2 \times 1)$
6. $(6 \times 1000) + (0 \times 100) + (5 \times 10) + (1 \times 1)$

Write the expanded numeral for each of the following.

7. 46
8. 124
9. 629
10. 82
11. 3426
12. 2041

EXPONENTS

It is inconvenient to write such things as $10 \times 10 \times 10$ and $5 \times 5 \times 5 \times 5$ whenever we express a number in expanded notation. Let us invent a short way of saying such things.

In $10 \times 10 \times 10$ we see that 10 is used 3 times in the multiplication. So let us write 10^3 to mean $10 \times 10 \times 10$.

Then $5 \times 5 \times 5 \times 5 = 5^4$ since 5 is used 4 times in the multiplication.

In 10^3, the number 10 is called the *base*, the number 3 is called the *exponent*, and the number named by 10^3 is called the *power*.

Base	*Exponent*
The number used in the multiplication	How many times the base is used

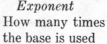

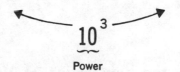

Power

Exercises 7:

Name each of the following as a power.

1. $10 \times 10 \times 10 \times 10 \times 10$
2. 10×10
3. $10 \times 10 \times 10 \times 10$
4. $7 \times 7 \times 7 \times 7$
5. $4 \times 4 \times 4 \times 4 \times 4 \times 4$

Write the meaning of each of the following.

6. 10^3
7. 10^5
8. 10^7
9. 6^4

PLACE VALUE

We have already seen that the place a symbol occupies in the simplest numeral for a number indicates a specific value. For example:

$$328 = (3 \times 10 \times 10) + (2 \times 10) + (8 \times 1)$$

or

$$= (3 \times 10^2) + (2 \times 10^1) + (8 \times 1)$$

Then we can show the meaning of greater numbers by following this pattern of grouping by tens.

$3256 = (3 \times 10^3) + (2 \times 10^2) + (5 \times 10^1) +$
$\quad (6 \times 1)$

$41865 = (4 \times 10^4) + (1 \times 10^3) + (8 \times 10^2) +$
$\quad (6 \times 10^1) + (5 \times 1)$

From this we develop place value in base-ten numeration as indicated in the following illustration.

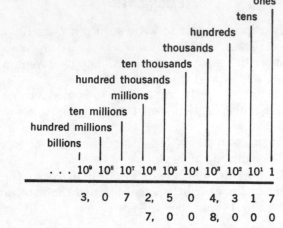

	3,	0	7	2,	5	0	4,	3	1	7
			7,	0	0	8,	0	0	0

The commas are inserted merely to make it easy to read a numeral. They give no meaning whatsoever to the numeral.

The first numeral above is read: *three billion, seventy-two million, five hundred four thousand, three hundred seventeen.*

The second numeral above is read: *seven million, eight thousand.*

Exercises 8:

Write the simplest numeral for each of the following.

1. one billion, one hundred million, two thousand, eight hundred twenty-six

2. five million, one

3. seven hundred twelve thousand, three hundred nine

4. fifty-two million, eighteen

Addition and Subtraction of Whole Numbers

UNION OF SETS

We are accustomed to joining sets in our daily activities. For example, when you put some coins in your purse, you are joining two sets of coins— the set of coins already in your purse and the set of coins about to be put in your purse. This, and many more examples, form the basis for the idea of the *union* of two sets.

Definition 9:

The **union** of set A and set B, denoted by $A \cup B$, is the set of all objects that are members of set A, of set B, or of both set A and set B.

Consider the following sets.

$R = \{a,b,c,d\}$
$S = \{r,s,t\}$
$T = \{c,d,e,f\}$

According to the definition of union, we can form the following sets.

$R \cup S = \{a,b,c,d,r,s,t\}$
$R \cup T = \{a,b,c,d,e,f\}$
$S \cup T = \{r,s,t,c,d,e,f\}$

For $R \cup T$ there is no need of repeating the names of members c and d. For example, suppose you are referring to a set of 3 girls—named Jane, Mary, and Pam. Then {Jane, Mary, Pam, Mary} is correct but not preferred since Mary is named twice and there are only 3 girls in the set.

Another way of illustrating sets and set operations is to use Venn diagrams. A Venn diagram is merely a closed figure used to denote the set of all points within the figure.

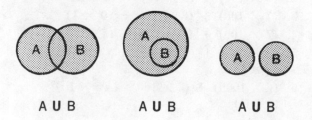

    A ∪ B   A ∪ B   A ∪ B

The shaded region in each of these illustrations indicates $A \cup B$. Note that the union of two sets includes all of the members in both of the sets.

Exercises 9:

Use the following sets to form the union of each pair of sets given below.

$K = \{3,5,7,9\}$ $M = \{2,4,6,8\}$
$J = \{1,2,3\}$ $N = \{0,5,9\}$

1. $J \cup K$ 5. $J \cup N$
2. $K \cup M$ 6. $M \cup N$
3. $K \cup N$ 7. $N \cup M$
4. $J \cup M$ 8. $K \cup K$

INTERSECTION OF SETS

Suppose a teacher asked a class, "How many of you went to the game last night?" Then several children raised their hands. Those who raised their hands are members of the set of children in the class *and* they are also members of the set of all children who went to the game last night.

By using a Venn diagram we can illustrate this situation. Let $A = \{$all children in the class$\}$ and let $B = \{$all children who went to the game last night$\}$.

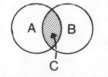

Then $C = \{$all children in A and also in $B\}$, and C is called the intersection of A and B.

Definition 10:

The **intersection** of set A and set B, denoted by $A \cap B$, is the set of all objects that are members of both set A *and set* B.

For example, the shaded region in each of the following illustrations represents $A \cap B$.

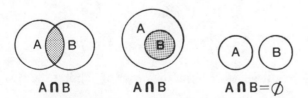

ANB   ANB   ANB=∅

Consider the following sets.

$X = \{g,h,i,j\}$
$Y = \{e,f,g,h\}$
$Z = \{a,b,c,d,e\}$

Then: $X \cap Y = \{g,h\}$
        $X \cap Z = 0$
        $Y \cap Z = \{e\}$
        $X \cap X = \{g,h,i,j\}$

Exercises 10:

Use the following sets to form the intersection of each pair of sets given below.

$C = \{2,3,4,5,6\}$
$D = \{1,2,3,7,8\}$
$E = \{3,4,5,6\}$
$F = \{7,8,9,10\}$

1. $C \cap D$ 5. $D \cap E$
2. $D \cap C$ 6. $D \cap F$
3. $C \cap E$ 7. $E \cap F$
4. $C \cap F$ 8. $E \cap E$

DISJOINT SETS

It is obvious that some sets have no members in common—such as $\{a,b,c\}$ and $\{r,s,t\}$.

Definition 11:

Set A and set B are called disjoint sets if they have no members in common. Or, set A and set B are *disjoint sets* if $A \cap B = \emptyset$.

In the following diagram, set A and set B do not intersect. Therefore, A and B are disjoint sets.

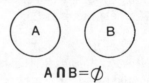

A∩B=∅

Consider the following sets.

$R = \{f,g,h,j\}$
$S = \{a,b,c\}$
$T = \{a,h,j\}$

Sets R and S have no members in common. Hence, R and S are disjoint sets.

Sets R and T are not disjoint sets since they both have h and j as members. Sets S and T are not disjoint sets since they both have a as a member.

Exercises 11:

Tell whether each statement below is *true* or *false*.

1. $\{q,r,s,t\}$ and $\{x,y,z\}$ are disjoint sets.
2. If $Q \cap R = \emptyset$, then Q and R are disjoint sets.
3. If $Q \subset R$, then Q and R are disjoint sets.

4. If $Q \subset R$ and $R \subset Q$, then $R = Q$.
5. If $R \cup Q = R$, then $Q \subset R$.
6. If $R \cap Q = R$, then $R \subset Q$.
7. If $R \cap Q = R \cup Q$, then $R = Q$.
8. If $C \cap D = \{5\}$, then $5 \,\varepsilon\, C$ and $5 \,\varepsilon\, D$.
9. If $C \cup D = \{3,4,5,6,7\}$, and $5 \,\varepsilon\, C$ and $5 \,\varepsilon\, D$.
10. If $x \,\varepsilon\, H$, then $x \,\varepsilon\, H \cup G$.

ADDITION

We already know that with each set there is associated a number. Let us use the symbol $n(A)$ to mean "the number of set A." It is important to note that $n(A)$ is a name for a number.

For $A = \{a,b,c\}$, we have $n(A) = 3$.
For $B = \{g,h\}$, we have $n(B) = 2$.

Let us begin with two disjoint sets, C and D, and find $C \cup D$. That is, we will join set D to set C.

$$C = \{\square, \triangle, \star\} \qquad D = \{\bigcirc, \bigstar\}$$

$$C \cup D = \{\square, \triangle, \star, \bigcirc, \bigstar\}$$

$$n(C) = 3 \qquad n(D) = 2$$
$$n(C \cup D) = 5$$

From this illustration we can say what is meant by addition of whole numbers.

Definition 12:
For *disjoint sets A and B*, the **sum** of $n(A)$ and $n(B)$, denoted by $n(A) + n(B)$, is $n(A \cup B)$ or the number of the union set.

For the above illustration, we have $n(C) = 3$, $n(D) = 2$, and $n(C \cup D) = 5$.
$$n(C) + n(D) = n(C \cup D)$$
$$3 + 2 = 5$$

In an addition statement, the numbers being added are called **addends** and the resulting number is called the **sum.**

Caution! We *add numbers*, not sets. We write $3 + 2$, but we do not write $A + B$ for sets. We find the *union of sets*, not numbers. We write $A \cup B$, but we do not write $5 \cup 4$.

To find the sum of 6 and 4, we could think of disjoint sets A and B such that $n(A) = 6$ and $n(B) = 4$. Suitable sets might be:

$A = \{a,b,c,d,e,f\}$
$B = \{r,s,t,u\}$
$A \cup B = \{a,b,c,d,e,f,r,s,t,u\}$

$$n(A) + n(B) = n(A \cup B)$$
$$6 + 4 = 10$$

The numbers six and four are addends. The number ten is the sum. The numerals $6 + 4$ and 10 are two names for the sum. The numeral 10 is the simplest name for the number ten.

Exercises 12:
Find each sum.

1.
6	7	8	9	7
+5	+3	+4	+5	+6

2.
4	5	8	2	9
+3	+7	+6	+8	+9

3.
7	5	8	4	7
+9	+5	+8	+5	+8

4.
6	4	9	7	5
+9	+9	+3	+4	+8

5.
3	1	6	7	6
+8	+9	+4	+7	+6

ADDITION IS COMMUTATIVE

If you are to join two sets, you may wonder which set to join to which. Does the order of joining the sets change the union set? Let us examine such a situation.

$$A = \{\square, \bigcirc, \triangle\} \quad \text{join} \atop \text{B to A} \quad B = \{a, b, c, d\}$$

$$A \cup B = \{\square, \bigcirc, \triangle, a, b, c, d\}$$

$$n(A) + n(B) = n(A \cup B)$$
$$3 + 4 = 7$$

Now let us reverse the order of joining the two sets.

$$A = \{\square, \bigcirc, \triangle\} \quad \text{join} \atop \text{A to B} \quad B = \{a, b, c, d\}$$

$$B \cup A = \{\square, \bigcirc, \triangle, a, b, c, d\}$$

$$n(B) + n(A) = n(B \cup A)$$
$$4 + 3 = 7$$

We notice that the union set is unchanged when the order of joining is reversed. We also note the following.

$$3 + 4 = 7 \text{ and } 4 + 3 = 7$$
$$\text{or}$$
$$3 + 4 = 4 + 3$$

The order of the addends can be changed but the sum remains the same. That is,

For all whole numbers a and b.

$$a + b = b + a.$$

We call this idea the *commutative property of addition*. Or we say that *addition is commutative*.

The phrase "for all whole numbers a and b" means that a and b can be replaced by numerals for any numbers in the set of whole numbers. They may be replaced by the same numeral or by different numerals. When a, b, or any other symbol is used in this manner, it is called a **placeholder** or a **variable** over a specified set of numbers.

Even though we may not know the sum of 557 and 3892, we know the following is true because addition is commutative.

$$557 + 3892 = 3892 + 557$$

Exercises 13:

Think of doing one activity of each pair given below and then doing the other. Do the following pairs illustrate a commutative property?

1. Put on your sock; put on your shoe
2. Take two steps forward; take two steps backward
3. Swim; eat
4. Write the letter "O"; then write the letter "N"
5. Go outside; close the door
6. Eat; brush your teeth

Complete each of the following sentences by using the commutative property of addition.

7. $3 + 7 = 7 + \underline{\quad}$
8. $\underline{\quad} + 15 = 15 + 8$
9. $36 + \underline{\quad} = 17 + 36$
10. $156 + 13 = \underline{\quad} + 156$
11. $129 + 47 = \underline{\quad} + \underline{\quad}$
12. $\underline{\quad} + \underline{\quad} = 218 + 326$
13. $327 + \underline{\quad} = 56 + \underline{\quad}$
14. $651 + 87 = \underline{\quad} + \underline{\quad}$

IDENTITY NUMBER OF ADDITION

Study the following unions of sets.

$$\{ \ \} \cup \{a,b,c\} = \{a,b,c\}$$
$$\{a,b,c\} \cup \{ \ \} = \{a,b,c\}$$

Notice that joining the empty set to a given set, or joining a given set to the empty set, does not change the given set.

The addition statements that correspond to the set operations above are:

$$0 + 3 = 3$$
$$3 + 0 = 3$$

Are the following sentences true?

$$7 + 0 = 7 \qquad 115 + 0 = 115 \qquad 721 = 0 + 721$$

Adding zero to any whole number b, or adding any whole number b to zero, leaves the number b unchanged.

Since zero is the only number with this special property, the number zero is called the **identity number of addition.**

For any whole number b,

$$0 + b = b = b + 0.$$

ADDITION IS ASSOCIATIVE

There are occasions when we join three sets. For example, we might combine a set of forks, a set of spoons, and a set of knives to form a set of silverware.

We might join the spoons to the forks, and then join the knives. Or we might join the knives to the spoons, and then join this set to the forks. Does the method of joining the sets change the resulting set?

Consider joining these sets.

$$A = \{a,b,c\} \qquad B = \{g,h,j,k\} \qquad C = \{t,v\}$$
$$A \cup B = \{a,b,c,g,h,j,k\} \qquad B \cup C = \{g,h,j,k,t,v\}$$
$$(A \cup B) \cup C = \{a,b,c,g,h,j,k,t,v\}$$
$$A \cup (B \cup C) = \{a,b,c,g,h,j,k,t,v\}$$

The ( ) in the last two statements indicate which two sets are joined first.

$(A \cup B) \cup C$ means to find $A \cup B$ first.
$A \cup (B \cup C)$ means to find $B \cup C$ first.

Joining sets makes us think of addition. We can add only two numbers at a time. How can we find the sum of three numbers, such as 3, 4, and 2?

Let us use the pattern established for joining three sets.

$$3 + 4 + 2 = (3 + 4) + 2$$
$$= \quad 7 \quad + 2$$
$$= 9$$
$$3 + 4 + 2 = 3 + (4 + 2)$$
$$= 3 + \quad 6$$
$$= 9$$

The ( ) in $(3 + 4) + 2$ means that 4 was added to 3 first. The ( ) in $3 + (4 + 2)$ mean that 2 was added to 4 first.

When finding the sum of three numbers we can group the first two addends or the last two addends and always get the same sum.

This idea is called the **associative property of addition.** Or we say that *addition is associative.*

For all whole numbers a, b, and c,

$$(a + b) + c = a + (b + c).$$

We can add these first,

$$7 + 3 + 6$$

or we can add these first.

We can add these first, or add these first.

Notice that when we use the associative property of addition the order of the addends is *not* changed as it is when we use the commutative property of addition.

Exercises 14:

Three things are to be combined in each exercise below. Do not change their order, only the grouping. Do the combinations show an associative property?

1. Water, lemon juice, sugar
2. Sand, cement, water
3. Blue paint, red paint, green paint

Complete each of the following sentences by using the associative property of addition.

4. $5 + (7 + 6) = (5 + \_\_) + \_\_$
5. $17 + (15 + 32) = (\_\_ + \_\_) + 32$
6. $(9 + 8) + 7 = \_\_ + (\_\_ + \_\_)$
7. $\_\_ + (\_\_ + \_\_) = (13 + 12) + 6$
8. $(\_\_ + \_\_) + \_\_ = 72 + (31 + 46)$

Find each sum below by using whichever grouping of addends makes the addition easier.

9. $7 + 3 + 6$ 11. $5 + 5 + 3$
10. $12 + 8 + 7$ 12. $9 + 13 + 7$

USING THE PROPERTIES OF ADDITION

We can show that $5 + (9 + 7) = 7 + (9 + 5)$ without using any addition facts.

$$5 + (9 + 7) = (5 + 9) + 7 \quad \text{Assoc. prop.}$$
$$= (9 + 5) + 7 \quad \text{Comm. prop.}$$
$$= 7 + (9 + 5) \quad \text{Comm. prop.}$$

Exercises 15:

Each of the following sentences is true because of the commutative property of addition, the associative property of addition, or both. Write the letter C, A, or both C and A to tell which property or properties are used.

1. $(9 + 8) + 3 = 9 + (8 + 3)$
2. $(9 + 8) + 3 = 3 + (9 + 8)$
3. $6 + (7 + 12) = 6 + (12 + 7)$
4. $6 + (7 + 12) = (6 + 12) + 7$
5. $(13 + 5) + 14 = 14 + (5 + 13)$
6. $(32 + 9) + 8 = 9 + (32 + 8)$
7. $13 + (9 + 7) = (13 + 9) + 7$
8. $13 + (9 + 7) = (9 + 7) + 13$
9. $13 + (9 + 7) = (13 + 7) + 9$
10. $a + (b + c) = (a + b) + c$

ORDER OF WHOLE NUMBERS

If two sets are not equivalent, then one set contains more members than the other set. For example:

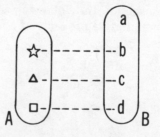

Set B has some members left unmatched after all of the members of set A have been matched. Set B has more members than set A, or set A

has fewer members than set B. We use the symbol $<$ (read: *is less than*) and the symbol $>$ (read: *is greater than*) when comparing the numbers of two sets that are not equivalent.

$$n(A) < n(B) \text{ or } n(B) > n(A)$$
$$3 < 4 \text{ or } 4 > 3$$

THE SUM OF MORE THAN TWO ADDENDS

We can save time and effort by looking for sums of ten, sums of one hundred, and so on, when finding the sum of more than two addends. Think of finding the simplest numeral for the following sum.

$$3 + 6 + 5 + 4 + 7$$

We know that addition is associative, so we can use any grouping we please. We also know that addition is commutative, so we can change the order of addends as we please. By using these two properties of addition, we can think of the addition as follows:

$$3 + 6 + 5 + 4 + 7 = (3 + 6) + (5 + 4) + 7$$
$$= (5 + 4) + (3 + 6) + 7$$
$$= (5 + 4) + (6 + 3) + 7$$
$$= 5 + (4 + 6) + (3 + 7)$$
$$= 5 + 10 + 10$$
$$= 25$$

This type of thinking is used when we think about $3 + 6 + 5 + 4 + 7$ as follows:

$$3+6+5+4+7=$$
$$10+10+5=25$$

Exercises 16:

Find each sum. Look for sums of ten or one hundred.

1.
5	8	13	25	97
6	2	4	32	9
+5	+7	+7	+75	+3

2.
7	4	24	19	37
6	5	8	7	60
4	5	2	1	13
+3	+6	+6	+2	+40

THE ADDITION ALGORISM

Everyday problems make us aware of the need to have an easy method for operating with greater numbers. For example, we may want to find the sum of 725 and 273. Both of these numbers have many names. We strive to name the numbers so that it is easy to find their sum.

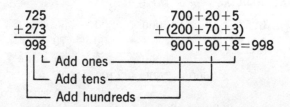

Another situation might require us to find the sum of 3528 and 4361.

$$
\begin{array}{ll}
3528 & 3000 + 500 + 20 + 8 \\
+4361 & + (4000 + 300 + 60 + 1) \\
\hline
7889 & 7000 + 800 + 80 + 9 = 7889
\end{array}
$$

This procedure, or algorism, of writing numerals and renaming numbers can be extended to finding the sum of greater numbers.

Exercises 17:
Find each sum.

1.
342	3751	35285
+536	+4248	+24713

2.
235	5041	60027
+542	+3806	+28951

3.
624	1826	1423
+65	+153	+36504

4.
43	320	10726
+325	+6468	+8070

RENAMING SUMS IN ADDITION

It may well be the case that the sum of the ones is greater than nine, or the sum of tens is greater than ninety, and so on. All we need do is rename such sums as shown in the following examples.

Rename the sum of the ones:

$$
\begin{array}{r}
427 \\
+256 \\
\hline
\end{array}
\quad
\begin{array}{l}
400 + 20 + 7 \\
+ (200 + 50 + 6) \\
\hline
600 + 70 + 13 = \\
600 + 70 + (10 + 3) = \\
\qquad\qquad\qquad \text{Assoc. prop.} \\
600 + (70 + 10) + 3 = \\
600 + 80 + 3 = 683
\end{array}
$$

Rename the sum of the tens:

$$
\begin{array}{r}
3258 \\
+471 \\
\hline
\end{array}
\quad
\begin{array}{l}
3000 + 200 + 50 + 8 \\
 + (400 + 70 + 1) \\
\hline
3000 + 600 + 120 + 9 = \\
3000 + 600 + (100 + 20) + 9 = \\
\qquad\qquad\qquad\qquad \text{Assoc. prop.} \\
3000 + (600 + 100) + 20 + 9 = \\
3000 + 700 + 20 + 9 = 3729
\end{array}
$$

Rename sums of tens and ones:

$$
\begin{array}{r}
3456 \\
+2378 \\
\hline
\end{array}
\quad
\begin{array}{l}
3000 + 400 + 50 + 6 \\
+ (2000 + 300 + 70 + 8) \\
\hline
5000 + 700 + 120 + 14 = \\
5000 + 700 + (100 + 20) + (10 + 4) = \\
\qquad\qquad\qquad\qquad\qquad \text{Assoc. prop.} \\
5000 + (700 + 100) + (20 + 10) + 4 = \\
5000 + 800 + 30 + 4 = 5834
\end{array}
$$

This procedure can be abbreviated by thinking about the addition as follows.

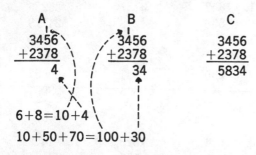

In A, $6 + 8 = 14$ and $14 = 10 + 4$. Write the 4 in ones place of the sum numeral and name the ten by writing a small reminder numeral 1 above the 5 in tens place of the first addend.

In B, $10 + 50 + 70 = 130$ and $130 = 100 + 30$. Write 3 in tens place of the sum numeral to name thirty; then write a reminder numeral 1 above the 4 in hundreds place in the first addend to name the hundred.

In C, the sum of hundreds is less than 1000 and the sum of the thousands is less than 10,000, so renaming is not needed.

The above procedure can be extended for addition of more than two numbers and for numbers whose numerals have a greater number of digits.

Exercises 18:
Find each sum.

1.
$$
\begin{array}{r} 3426 \\ +2595 \\ \hline \end{array}
\qquad
\begin{array}{r} 61897 \\ +17973 \\ \hline \end{array}
\qquad
\begin{array}{r} 567428 \\ +340754 \\ \hline \end{array}
$$

2.
$$
\begin{array}{r} 3058 \\ +4963 \\ \hline \end{array}
\qquad
\begin{array}{r} 47569 \\ +10753 \\ \hline \end{array}
\qquad
\begin{array}{r} 640596 \\ +365437 \\ \hline \end{array}
$$

3.
$$
\begin{array}{r} 3246 \\ 503 \\ +1174 \\ \hline \end{array}
\qquad
\begin{array}{r} 97654 \\ 7965 \\ +89348 \\ \hline \end{array}
\qquad
\begin{array}{r} 297254 \\ 34135 \\ +343048 \\ \hline \end{array}
$$

4.
$$
\begin{array}{r} 756 \\ 82 \\ +1429 \\ \hline \end{array}
\qquad
\begin{array}{r} 507 \\ 4296 \\ +39204 \\ \hline \end{array}
\qquad
\begin{array}{r} 30729 \\ 1075 \\ +298264 \\ \hline \end{array}
$$

INVERSE OPERATIONS

Many things we do can be "undone." If you take 2 steps backward, you can return to your original position by taking 2 steps forward. If you add 6 to a number, you can obtain the original number by subtracting 6 from the sum.

Any process or operation that "undoes" another process or operation is called an *inverse operation*.

Of course, there are some activities that cannot be undone. Talking cannot be undone by being silent.

Exercises 19:
For each activity given below, tell how to undo it.

1. Close your eyes

2. Stand up

3. Go to school

4. Close your book

5. Take 5 steps forward

6. Untie your shoe

7. Add seven

8. Subtract thirteen

SUBTRACTION

Three ways of thinking about the meaning of subtraction are explained below. The first two ways are helpful for interpreting a physical situation in terms of mathematics. However, their disadvantages will be pointed out. The last way defines subtraction for any mathematical situation.

1. Removing a subset:

John had 7 pennies and spent 4 of them. How many pennies did he have left?

We might illustrate the problem with Venn diagrams. Let $H = \{$pennies he had$\}$ and let $S = \{$pennies he spent$\}$. Each circular region in the following drawing represents a distinct penny.

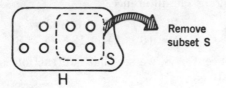

Definition 13:

The difference between $n(H)$ and $n(S)$, denoted by $n(H) - n(S)$, is the number of members in H but not in S.

When subset S is removed from set H, only 3 pennies remain.

$$n(H) - n(S) = 3$$
$$7 - 4 = 3$$

This idea is suitable only for whole numbers and the particular type of problem illustrated.

2. Comparing sets:

Bob has 5 stamps and Jane has 9 stamps. How many more stamps does Jane have than Bob?

Let each $\square$ in the following diagram represent a distinct stamp. Let $B = \{$Bob's stamps$\}$ and let $J = \{$Jane's stamps$\}$.

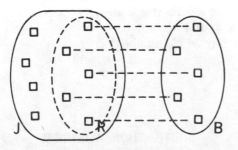

Select a subset R of J by establishing a one-to-one correspondence between set B and subset R. Since $n(R) = n(B)$, we can treat sets J and R as in the previous method.

$$n(J) = 9 \qquad n(B) = n(R) = 5$$
$$n(J) - n(B) = 4$$
$$9 - 5 = 4$$

We now have a method of treating two types of subtraction problems, but as yet subtraction is not defined for all numbers. That is, neither of the above methods is practical for fractional numbers, only for whole numbers.

3. Inverse of Addition:

By using either of the previous methods, we see that addition and subtraction are related—addition and subtraction undo each other. Addition and subtraction are inverse operations.

$$7 - 4 = 3 \text{ and } 3 + 4 = 7$$
$$9 - 5 = 4 \text{ and } 4 + 5 = 9$$

Definition 14:

For any numbers a, b, and c, if $c + b = a$, then c is the **difference** between a and b, denoted by $a - b$.

Note that $a - b$ names a number such that $(a - b) + b = a$. That is, we begin with the number a, subtract b, then add b, and the result is the number a with which we started. This shows the *do-undo* relationship between addition and subtraction.

Also note that $(a + b)$ names a number such that $(a + b) - b = a$. In this case subtraction undoes addition.

Exercises 20:

Write the simplest numeral for each of the following.

1. $(15 - 7) + 7$ 5. $57 + (756 - 57)$
2. $621 + (754 - 621)$ 6. $(39 - 17) + 17$
3. $(69 + 83) - 83$ 7. $(312 + 179) - 179$
4. $(26 - 15) + 15$ 8. $(r + s) - s$

Find the simplest numeral for each difference. Think of the corresponding addition if necessary.

9. $15 - 7$ 13. $18 - 9$
10. $11 - 8$ 14. $13 - 6$
11. $14 - 6$ 15. $12 - 5$
12. $9 - 3$ 16. $17 - 8$

FINDING UNNAMED ADDENDS

Think about solving the following problem. Randy bought 12 pieces of candy. He ate some of them and has 5 pieces left. How many pieces of candy did he eat?

We might think: If we add the number of pieces of candy he has left (5) to the number of pieces of candy he ate (□), the sum should be the number of pieces of candy he bought (12).

$$5 + □ = 12$$

Now how can we determine the simplest numeral to replace □ so that $5 + □ = 12$ becomes a true sentence?

Using the inverse idea between addition and subtraction, we have

$$5 + □ = 12 \text{ so } 12 - □ = 5.$$

We see that this approach is not too helpful. We might start over again by using the commutative property of addition.

$$5 + □ = 12 \text{ so } □ + 5 = 12$$

Now use the inverse idea.

$$□ + 5 = 12 \text{ so } 12 - 5 = □$$
$$7 = □$$

Randy ate 7 pieces of candy.

Note that we could have used any other symbol to represent the number of pieces of candy he ate. That is, we could have used △, ◯, a, b, c, or any other symbol to hold a place for the numeral. Then, instead of $5 + □ = 12$, we could have written $5 + △ = 12$, $5 + ◯ = 12$, $5 + a = 12$, $5 + b = 12$, $5 + c = 12$, and so on.

Exercises 21:

Find the unnamed addend in each of the following.

1. $9 + □ = 15$ 4. $8 + □ = 16$
2. $7 + x = 11$ 5. $5 + k = 14$
3. $6 + n = 14$ 6. $3 + y = 12$

Write a number sentence for each problem. Solve the number sentence and write an answer for the problem.

7. A boy had 9 scout awards. He earned some more awards, and now he has 12 awards. How many more awards did he earn?

8. Jane made 15 cupcakes. Her brothers ate some of them and there are 7 left. How many of the cupcakes did her brothers eat?

9. Diane invited 12 children to her birthday party. If only 8 of the children came, how many were invited but did not attend?

10. Randy picked 7 apples from one tree and some from another tree. He picked 13 apples in all. How many did he pick from the second tree?

PROPERTIES OF SUBTRACTION

Is subtraction commutative? That is, can we change the order of the numbers without changing the difference?

$$7 - 3 = 4 \text{ but } 3 - 7$$

does not name a whole number, let alone being equal to 4. Hence, subtraction is *not* commutative.

Is subtraction associative? That is, can we change the grouping of the numbers without changing the difference?

$$(12 - 6) - 2 = 6 - 2 = 4$$
$$12 - (6 - 2) = 12 - 4 = 8$$

Since $4 \neq 8$, we see that subtraction is *not* associative.

ZERO IN SUBTRACTION

If the empty set (set of no members) is removed from $A = \{a,b,c,d\}$, the result is set A.

$$n(A) - n(\emptyset) = n(A)$$
$$4 - 0 = 4$$

Since this is true for all sets, it is also true for all whole numbers.

If set A is removed from itself, the result is the empty set.

$$n(A) - n(A) = n(\emptyset)$$
$$4 - 4 = 0$$

Since this is true for all sets, it is also true for all whole numbers.

We can summarize these two special properties of zero as follows:

For any whole number a,
$$a - 0 = a, \text{ and}$$
$$a - a = 0.$$

SUBTRACTION ALGORISM

As with addition, we should like to devise a scheme of writing the numerals for greater numbers so that subtraction can be done quickly and easily. For example, we may want to find the difference between 758 and 326.

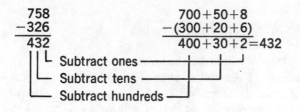

$$758 \qquad 700+50+8$$
$$-326 \qquad -(300+20+6)$$
$$\overline{432} \qquad \overline{400+30+2}=432$$

Subtract ones
Subtract tens
Subtract hundreds

Follow the same procedure for still greater numbers.

$$6975 \qquad 6000 + 900 + 70 + 5$$
$$-3864 \qquad -(3000 + 800 + 60 + 4)$$
$$\overline{3111} \qquad \overline{3000 + 100 + 10 + 1} = 3111$$

Exercises 22:
Find each difference.

1.	756	9384	67859
	−531	−4150	−21536
2.	526	7925	82756
	−413	−4912	−62412
3.	837	5987	49758
	−216	−2852	−15047

RENAMING NUMBERS IN SUBTRACTION

Think about subtracting 592 from 857.

$$857 \qquad 800 + 50 + 7$$
$$-592 \qquad -(500 + 90 + 2)$$
$$\overline{} \qquad \overline{? + 5}$$

We notice that 90 is greater than 50, and 50–90 does not name a whole number. But we can name any number in many different ways. Let us rename 857 so that we can subtract the tens.

$$857 \qquad 700 + 150 + 7$$
$$-592 \qquad -(500 + 90 + 2)$$
$$\overline{} \qquad \overline{200 + 60 + 5} = 265$$

Another example might be the following, where we must rename 3548 so that we can subtract the ones.

$$3548 \qquad 3000 + 500 + 30 + 18$$
$$-2419 \qquad -(2000 + 400 + 10 + 9)$$
$$\overline{} \qquad \overline{1000 + 100 + 20 + 9} = 1129$$

In still other cases we find it impossible to subtract ones or tens or hundreds, and so on, or any combination of these. We merely rename the number subtracted from until subtraction becomes possible in every place-value position.

$$3426 \qquad 3000 + 400 + 10 + 16$$
$$-1358 \qquad -(1000 + 300 + 50 + 8)$$
$$\overline{} \qquad \overline{? + 8}$$

Rename 3426 in another way so that subtraction of the tens is possible.

$$3426 \qquad 3000 + 300 + 110 + 16$$
$$-1358 \qquad -(1000 + 300 + 50 + 8)$$
$$\overline{} \qquad \overline{2000 + 0 + 60 + 8} = 2068$$

This procedure may be abbreviated as shown in the following examples.

$$315 \qquad 200 + 110 + 5 \qquad \overset{2\ 11}{\cancel{3}\cancel{1}5}$$
$$-172 \qquad -(100 + 70 + 2) \qquad -172$$
$$\overline{} \qquad \overline{100 - 40 - 3} \qquad \overline{143}$$

$$752 \qquad 700 + 40 + 12 \qquad \overset{4\ 12}{7\cancel{5}\cancel{2}}$$
$$-328 \qquad -(300 + 20 + 8) \qquad -328$$
$$\overline{} \qquad \overline{400 + 20 + 8} \qquad \overline{424}$$

Exercises 23:
Find each difference.

1.	315	3427	56349
	−163	−2109	−21467
2.	408	5382	47009
	−226	−3475	−20858
3.	725	6243	70000
	−537	−3856	−43197

CHECKING SUBTRACTION

Since addition and subtraction are inverse operations, we can use addition to check subtraction.

Subtraction	*Check*
715	432
−432	+283
283	715

Exercises 24:
Check the subtraction in Exercises 23.

Multiplication and Division of Whole Numbers

USING SETS IN MULTIPLICATION

We have described addition of whole numbers in terms of joining disjoint sets. It is also possible to describe multiplication in this way.

A sandwich menu lists three kinds of meat—beef, ham, pork. You can have either white bread or rye bread. What are all the possible kinds of sandwiches if you choose one kind of meat and one kind of bread? The answer might be shown as follows.

(beef, white)   (ham, white)   (pork, white)
(beef, rye)   (ham, rye)   (pork, rye)

We notice that there are 3 choices of meat, 2 choices of bread, and 6 possible kinds of sandwiches. Somehow we have performed an operation on 2 and 3 to obtain 6.

Another example might involve finding the number of street intersections formed by the following situation.

{1st Ave., 2nd Ave., 3rd Ave., 4th Ave.}
{A St., B St., C St.}

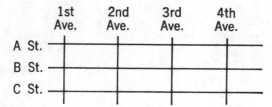

Notice that there are 4 avenues, 3 streets, and 12 intersections. Somehow we have performed an operation on 3 and 4 to obtain 12.

In a game you are to pick one letter from set A below and then pick one number from set B.

$A = \{a,b,c,d,e\}$
$B = \{1,2,3\}$

To show all the possible pairs we could construct the following array.

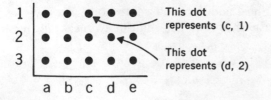

This dot represents (c, 1)
This dot represents (d, 2)

We are to choose first from set A, so let us agree to list the members of this set horizontally when making the array. We are to choose second from set B, so let us agree to list the members of this set vertically.

In other words, the number of columns in the array is the number of the first set and the number of rows is the number of the second set. In this case, the number of columns is $n(A)$ or 5 and the number of rows is $n(B)$ or 3.

Note that the 15 dots indicate that there are 15 possible combinations for picking one letter and one number.

Exercises 25:

Tell how many dots there are in the array for picking one member from the first set below and one member from the second set.

1. {Ed, Bill, Al} and {Jo, Mary, Susan}
2. {?, *} and {a,b,c,d}
3. {cake, cookies} and {coffee, tea, milk}
4. {a,b,c,d,e,f} and {7,8,9,10}

DEFINITION OF MULTIPLICATION

Thinking of arrays for two sets enables us to define the operation of multiplication. Suppose we are given sets A and B such that $n(A) = a$ and $n(B) = b$. We could make an array for these sets so that it has a columns and b rows.

Definition 15:

The **product** of any two whole numbers a and b, denoted by $a \times b$, is the number of dots in the array having a columns and b rows. The numbers a and b are called **factors.**

The symbol $a \times b$ is read "a times b" or "the product of a and b." Hence, 4×5 is read "4 times 5" or "the product of 4 and 5." For a pictorial representation of 4×5 we can set up an array having 4 columns with 5 dots in each column, and then count the number of dots in the array.

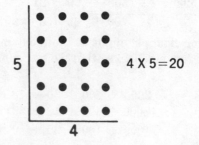

$4 \times 5 = 20$

Exercises 26:

Draw an array if necessary and find the simplest numeral for each product below.

1. 3×5	5. 2×8	9. 9×3
2. 4×6	6. 4×4	10. 4×7
3. 2×5	7. 8×3	11. 6×3
4. 7×2	8. 5×6	12. 3×3

MULTIPLICATION AS REPEATED ADDITION

Any array can be thought of as the union of equivalent sets.

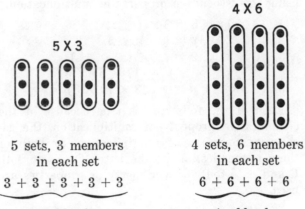

5 X 3

5 sets, 3 members
in each set

$3 + 3 + 3 + 3 + 3$

5 addends

4 X 6

4 sets, 6 members
in each set

$6 + 6 + 6 + 6$

4 addends

These drawings illustrate another way to think about multiplication of whole numbers.

$$5 \times 3 = 3 + 3 + 3 + 3 + 3 = 15$$
$$4 \times 6 = 6 + 6 + 6 + 6 = 24$$

This is sometimes referred to as the repeated addition description of multiplication.

Exercises 27:

Write the meaning of each product as repeated addition and give the simplest numeral for the product.

1. 6×2	4. 4×5	7. 6×7
2. 6×1	5. 5×4	8. 4×9
3. 1×6	6. 3×7	9. 5×7

Write each of the following as a product of two factors. Then give the simplest numeral for each product.

10. $8 + 8 + 8 + 8$
11. $5 + 5 + 5 + 5 + 5 + 5$
12. $1 + 1 + 1 + 1 + 1$
13. $9 + 9 + 9 + 9 + 9$
14. $9 + 9$
15. $2 + 2 + 2 + 2 + 2 + 2 + 2 + 2 + 2$

MULTIPLICATION IS COMMUTATIVE

An array having 4 columns and 3 rows can be changed into an array having 3 columns and 4 rows as shown below.

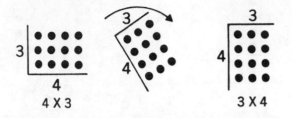

4 X 3   3 X 4

Since $4 \times 3 = 12$ and $3 \times 4 = 12$, we notice that the order of the factors can be changed but the product remains the same.

That is, for all whole numbers a and b,

$$a \times b = b \times a.$$

We call this idea the **commutative property of multiplication**. Or we say that *multiplication is commutative*.

This property of multiplication can also be shown by repeated addition.

$$5 \times 4 = 4 + 4 + 4 + 4 + 4 = 20$$
$$4 \times 5 = 5 + 5 + 5 + 5 = 20$$

Therefore, $5 \times 4 = 4 \times 5$.

Exercises 28:

Complete each of the following sentences by using the commutative property of multiplication. Do not find any of the products.

1. $5 \times 9 = 9 \times \underline{\quad}$
2. $\underline{\quad} \times 8 = 8 \times 7$
3. $31 \times 7 = \underline{\quad} \times 31$
4. $12 \times \underline{\quad} = 6 \times 12$
5. $9 \times 17 = \underline{\quad} \times \underline{\quad}$
6. $23 \times \underline{\quad} = 5 \times \underline{\quad}$
7. $\underline{\quad} \times \underline{\quad} = 18 \times 9$
8. $\underline{\quad} \times 13 = \underline{\quad} \times 27$
9. $357 \times 6 = \underline{\quad} \times \underline{\quad}$
10. $\underline{\quad} \times \underline{\quad} = 127 \times 43$

IDENTITY NUMBER OF MULTIPLICATION

Recall that zero is the identity number of addition because for any whole number a, $a + 0 = a = 0 + a$.

We would expect the identity number of multiplication to be some number such that for any whole number a, $a \times \underline{\quad} = a = \underline{\quad} \times a$.

Each array below has but *one* column, and hence the number of dots in the array is the same as the number of dots in the single column.

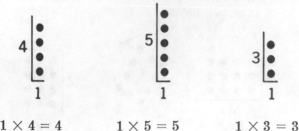

$$1 \times 4 = 4 \qquad 1 \times 5 = 5 \qquad 1 \times 3 = 3$$

Or we can interpret 1×4 as using 4 as an addend only once.

$$1 \times 4 = 4$$

Since multiplication is commutative, we know that $1 \times 4 = 4 \times 1$, and we conclude that $1 \times 4 = 4 = 4 \times 1$.

Multiplying any given whole number by one, or multiplying one by any given whole number, leaves the given number unchanged. Since one is the only number with this special property, we call the number one the **identity number of multiplication.**

For any whole number a, $a \times 1 = a = 1 \times a$.

MULTIPLICATION IS ASSOCIATIVE

Recall that the pattern of the associative property of addition is

$$(a + b) + c = a + (b + c).$$

for all whole numbers a, b, and c.

Is there such a property for multiplication? Let us look at a few examples.

$$(2 \times 3) \times 4 = 6 \times 4 = 24$$
$$2 \times (3 \times 4) = 2 \times 12 = 24$$

Therefore, $(2 \times 3) \times 4 = 2 \times (3 \times 4)$.

$$(3 \times 5) \times 2 = 15 \times 2 = 30$$
$$3 \times (5 \times 2) = 3 \times 10 = 30$$

Therefore, $(3 \times 5) \times 2 = 3 \times (5 \times 2)$.

When finding the product of three numbers, we can group the first two factors or the last two factors and always get the same product.

This idea is called the **associative property of multiplication.** Or we say that *multiplication is associative.*

For all whole numbers a, b, and c,

$$(a \times b) \times c = a \times (b \times c).$$

We can multiply these first

or multiply these first.

Notice that when we use the associative property of multiplication, the order of the factors is *not* changed as it is when we use the commutative property of multiplication.

Exercises 29:

Complete each of the following sentences by using the associative property of multiplication.

1. $(3 \times 7) \times 5 = 3 \times (\_\_ \times \_\_)$
2. $4 \times (2 \times 3) = (\_\_ \times \_\_) \times 3$
3. $(6 \times 3) \times 2 = \_\_ \times (\_\_ \times \_\_)$
4. $\_\_ \times (\_\_ \times \_\_) = (17 \times 8) \times 5$
5. $(\_\_ \times \_\_) \times \_\_ = 13 \times (9 \times 3)$

Each of the following is true because of the commutative property of multiplication, the associative property of multiplication, or both of these properties. Write the letter C, A, or both C and A to tell which property or properties are used.

6. $(9 \times 8) \times 3 = 9 \times (8 \times 3)$
7. $(9 \times 8) \times 3 = 3 \times (9 \times 8)$
8. $6 \times (7 \times 12) = 6 \times (12 \times 7)$
9. $6 \times (7 \times 12) = (6 \times 12) \times 7$
10. $(13 \times 5) \times 14 = 14 \times (5 \times 13)$
11. $(32 \times 9) \times 8 = 9 \times (32 \times 8)$
12. $r \times (s \times t) = (r \times s) \times t$

ZERO IN MULTIPLICATION

What number is named by 3×0? By thinking of repeated addition,

$$3 \times 0 = 0 + 0 + 0 = 0.$$

Since multiplication is commutative, we know that $3 \times 0 = 0 \times 3$ and that 0×3 must be equal to 0.

It appears that when zero is one of the factors, then the product is zero. That is, for any whole number a,

$$a \times 0 = 0, \text{ and}$$
$$0 \times a = 0.$$

What can we say about the factors if the product is zero? That is, what do we know about the factors a and b if $a \times b = 0$? The only way we can get a product of zero is to use zero as one of the factors. That is:

If $a \times b = 0$, then $a = 0$, $b = 0$, or both factors are zero.

THE DISTRIBUTIVE PROPERTY

Four boys and three girls are planning a party. Each child is to bring 2 gifts. How many gifts did they bring in all?

Two ways of thinking about solving this problem are given below.

1. There are $4 + 3$ or 7 children. Each child will bring 2 gifts. Then, all together they will bring

$(4 + 3) \times 2$ or 7×2 or 14 gifts.

2. Each of the 4 boys will bring 2 gifts. Then the boys will bring 4×2 gifts. Each of the 3 girls will bring 2 gifts. Then the girls will bring 3×2 gifts. All together the children will bring

$(4 \times 2) + (3 \times 2)$ or $8 + 6$ or 14 gifts.

From these ways of thinking about the problem we see that

$(4 + 3) \times 2 = (4 \times 2) + (3 \times 2)$.

Since multiplication is commutative, we know that we can change the order of the factors. Hence,

$(4 + 3) \times 2 = 2 \times (4 + 3)$,
$4 \times 2 = 2 \times 4$, and
$3 \times 2 = 2 \times 3$.

Then the sentence

$(4 + 3) \times 2 = (4 \times 2) + (3 \times 2)$

can be written

$2 \times (4 + 3) = (2 \times 4) + (2 \times 3)$.

Let us investigate such a pattern with different numbers.

$2 \times (5 + 3) = 2 \times 8 = 16$
$(2 \times 5) + (2 \times 3) = 10 + 6 = 16$

Hence $2 \times (5 + 3) = (2 \times 5) + (2 \times 3)$.

$(4 + 6) \times 3 = 10 \times 3 = 30$
$(4 \times 3) + (6 \times 3) = 12 + 18 = 30$

Hence, $(4 + 6) \times 3 = (4 \times 3) + (6 \times 3)$.

This pattern is also visible in an array.

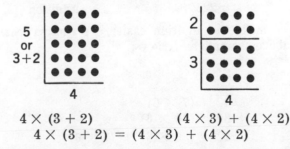

$4 \times (3 + 2)$ $(4 \times 3) + (4 \times 2)$
$4 \times (3 + 2) = (4 \times 3) + (4 \times 2)$

By drawing a horizontal line in the array we can separate it into two arrays, one having 2 rows and 4 columns and the other having 3 rows and 4 columns. We have not discarded any of the dots, so the number of dots remains the same.

This property is called the **distributive property of multiplication over addition.**

For all whole numbers a, b, and c,

$$a \times (b + c) = (a \times b) + (a \times c)$$
$$\text{and}$$
$$(b + c) \times a = (b \times a) + (c \times a).$$

It is important that we realize that the distributive property involves both addition and multiplication. Furthermore, it is important that we are able to "undistribute" as follows.

$$(5 \times 3) + (5 \times 6) = 5 \times (3 + 6)$$
$$(4 \times 6) + (7 \times 6) = (4 + 7) \times 6$$

Exercises 30:

Use the distributive property to complete each of the following sentences.

1. $7 \times (2 + 5) = (7 \times \underline{\ }) + (7 \times \underline{\ })$
2. $4 \times (3 + 6) = (\underline{\ } \times \underline{\ }) + (\underline{\ } \times \underline{\ })$
3. $(4 + 5) \times 3 = (\underline{\ } \times 3) + (\underline{\ } \times 3)$
4. $(8 + 9) \times 6 = (\underline{\ } \times \underline{\ }) + (\underline{\ } \times \underline{\ })$
5. $(5 \times 2) + (7 \times 2) = (\underline{\ } + \underline{\ }) \times 2$
6. $(6 \times 3) + (8 \times 3) = (\underline{\ } + \underline{\ }) \times \underline{\ }$

BASIC MULTIPLICATION FACTS

We can use addition or an array to determine and memorize the basic multiplication facts as shown in the following multiplication table. The first factor is named in the left column and the second factor is named in the top row.

X	0	1	2	3	4	5	6	7	8	9
0	0									
1	0	1								
2	0	2	4							
3	0	3	6	9						
4	0	4	8	12	16					
5	0	5	10	15	20	25				
6	0	6	12	18	24	30	36			
7	0	7	14	21	28	35	42	49		
8	0	8	16	24	32	40	48	56	64	
9	0	9	18	27	36	45	54	63	72	81

Since multiplication is commutative, we need not compute products for the shaded portion of the table. If we need to compute 3×7, we merely commute, $3 \times 7 = 7 \times 3$, and use the table to find that $7 \times 3 = 21$.

Even some of the basic facts can be found in other ways. For example:

$7 \times 8 = 7 \times (3 + 5)$ Rename 8 as $3 + 5$
$\quad = (7 \times 3) + (7 \times 5)$ Dist. prop.
$\quad = 21 + 35$ Multiplication
$\quad = 56$ Addition

$9 \times 5 = (5 + 4) \times 5$ Rename 9 as $5 + 4$
$\quad = (5 \times 5) + (4 \times 5)$ Dist. prop.
$\quad = 25 + 20$ Multiplication
$\quad = 45$ Addition

FACTORS OF 10, 100, OR 1000

When finding the product of two factors we might draw the array and count the dots. Or we might restate the multiplication as repeated addition and find the sum. Either of these methods become time-consuming and tedious when the factors are greater numbers, such as 615×352. Hence, we should like to discover some "streamlined" way of finding a product.

Let us begin by investigating products where one of the factors is 1, 10, 100, or 1000.

$$5 \times 1 = 1 + 1 + 1 + 1 + 1 = 5$$
$$5 \times 10 = 10 + 10 + 10 + 10 + 10 = 50$$
$$5 \times 100 = 100 + 100 + 100 + 100 + 100 = 500$$
$$5 \times 1000 = 1000 + 1000 + 1000 + 1000 + 1000 = 5000$$

$$7 \times 1 = 1 + 1 + 1 + 1 + 1 + 1 + 1 = 7$$
$$7 \times 10 = 10 + 10 + 10 + 10 + 10 + 10 + 10 = 70$$
$$7 \times 100 = 100 + 100 + 100 + 100 + 100 + 100 + 100 = 700$$
$$7 \times 1000 = 1000 + 1000 + 1000 + 1000 + 1000 + 1000 + 1000 = 7000$$

From these examples it is evident that to multiply by 10, annex one zero; to multiply by 100, annex two zeros; to multiply by 1000, annex three zeros.

Exercises 31:
Write the simplest numeral for each product.

1. 6×10 3. 3×10
2. 9×100 4. 8×100

5. 2×100 8. 4×1000
6. 4×10 9. 100×4
7. 4×100 10. 1000×4

Now let us investigate the case where one or both factors are multiples of a power of ten, such as 30, 400, 70, or 900.

$8 \times 20 = 8 \times (2 \times 10)$ Rename 20
$\quad = (8 \times 2) \times 10$ Assoc. prop.
$\quad = 16 \times 10$ Multiplication
$\quad = 160$ Mult. by 10

$50 \times 70 = (5 \times 10) \times (7 \times 10)$ Rename factors
$\quad = [(5 \times 10) \times 7] \times 10$ Assoc. prop.
$\quad = [7 \times (5 \times 10)] \times 10$ Comm. prop.
$\quad = [(7 \times 5) \times 10] \times 10$ Assoc. prop.
$\quad = (7 \times 5) \times (10 \times 10)$ Assoc. prop.
$\quad = 35 \times 100$ Multiplication
$\quad = 3500$ Mult. by 100

Exercises 32:
Write the simplest numeral for each product.

1. 7×30 3. 50×90 5. 40×600
2. 8×400 4. 70×20 6. 700×200

TECHNIQUES OF MULTIPLICATION

To find products of greater numbers, we simply use the properties in such a way that calculation is easy. Notice how the renaming of numbers and the properties of the operations are used in the following examples.

$8 \times 24 = 8 \times (20 + 4)$ Rename 24
$\quad = (8 \times 20) + (8 \times 4)$ Dist. prop.
$\quad = 160 + 32$ Multiplication
$\quad = 192$ Addition

$37 \times 6 = (30 + 7) \times 6$ Rename 37
$\quad = (30 \times 6) + (7 \times 6)$ Dist. prop.
$\quad = 180 + 42$ Multiplication
$\quad = 222$ Addition

To make the addition easier, we can write the above example as follows.

$$\begin{array}{r} 37 \\ \times 6 \\ \hline 42 = (7 \times 6) \\ 180 = (30 \times 6) \\ \hline 222 = (30 \times 6) + (7 \times 6) \end{array}$$

The distributive property of multiplication over addition is used as the factors become greater.

$372 \times 4 = (300 + 70 + 2) \times 4$ Rename 372

                    Dist. prop.

$= (300 \times 4) + (70 \times 4) + (2 \times 4)$

                    Multiplication

$= 1200 + 280 + 8$

                    Addition

$= 1488$

This same product can be computed as follows.

$$
\begin{array}{r}
372 \\
\times 4 \\
\hline
8 = (2 \times 4) \\
280 = (70 \times 4) \\
1200 = (300 \times 4) \\
\hline
1488
\end{array}
$$

Exercises 33:

Find the simplest numeral for each product.

1. 56×3 4. 354×6

2. 78×5 5. 37×8

3. 124×6 6. 426×9

7. $\begin{array}{r} 47 \\ \times 4 \\ \hline \end{array}$ 9. $\begin{array}{r} 173 \\ \times 6 \\ \hline \end{array}$ 11. $\begin{array}{r} 457 \\ \times 3 \\ \hline \end{array}$

8. $\begin{array}{r} 29 \\ \times 5 \\ \hline \end{array}$ 10. $\begin{array}{r} 321 \\ \times 8 \\ \hline \end{array}$ 12. $\begin{array}{r} 634 \\ \times 9 \\ \hline \end{array}$

Now let us see what happens when both factors are named by two-digit numerals.

$24 \times 63 = 24 \times (60 + 3)$ Rename 63

                     Dist. prop.

$= (24 \times 60) + (24 \times 3)$

                     Rename 60

$= [24 \times (6 \times 10)] + (24 \times 3)$

                     Assoc. prop.

$= [(24 \times 6) \times 10] + (24 \times 3)$

                     Multiplication

$= (144 \times 10) + (24 \times 3)$

                     Mult. by 10

$= 1440 + 72$

                     Addition

$= 1512$

Another way to think about 24×63 is shown below.

                    Rename factors

$24 \times 63 = (20 + 4) \times (60 + 3)$

                    Dist. prop.

$= [(20 + 4) \times 60] + [(20 + 4) \times 3]$

                    Dist. prop.

$= [(20 \times 60) + (4 \times 60)] + (20 \times 3) + (4 \times 3)$

                    Assoc. prop.

$= (20 \times 60) + (4 \times 60) + (20 \times 3) + (4 \times 3)$

                    Multiplication

$= 1200 + 240 + 60 + 12$

                    Addition

$= 1512$

This, too, can be shown in vertical arrangement.

$$
\begin{array}{r}
24 \\
\times 63 \\
\hline
12 = (4 \times 3) \\
60 = (20 \times 3) \\
240 = (4 \times 60) \\
1200 = (20 \times 60) \\
\hline
1512
\end{array}
$$

Exercises 34:

Find the simplest numeral for each product.

1. $\begin{array}{r} 38 \\ \times 13 \\ \hline \end{array}$ 4. $\begin{array}{r} 24 \\ \times 54 \\ \hline \end{array}$ 7. $\begin{array}{r} 83 \\ \times 49 \\ \hline \end{array}$

2. $\begin{array}{r} 27 \\ \times 24 \\ \hline \end{array}$ 5. $\begin{array}{r} 78 \\ \times 52 \\ \hline \end{array}$ 8. $\begin{array}{r} 57 \\ \times 68 \\ \hline \end{array}$

3. $\begin{array}{r} 47 \\ \times 35 \\ \hline \end{array}$ 6. $\begin{array}{r} 17 \\ \times 58 \\ \hline \end{array}$ 9. $\begin{array}{r} 25 \\ \times 93 \\ \hline \end{array}$

THE MULTIPLICATION ALGORISM

The previous exercises enable us to find the product of still greater factors. You should have noticed by now that the distributive property of multiplication over addition is a powerful tool in making multiplication easy.

$$
\begin{array}{r}
523 \\
\times 7 \\
\hline
21 = (3 \times 7) \\
140 = (20 \times 7) \\
3500 = (500 \times 7) \\
\hline
3661
\end{array}
$$

$$
\begin{array}{r}
346 \\
\times 24 \\
\hline
24 = (6 \times 4) \\
160 = (40 \times 4) \\
1200 = (300 \times 4) \\
120 = (6 \times 20) \\
800 = (40 \times 20) \\
6000 = (300 \times 20) \\
\hline
8304
\end{array}
\qquad
\begin{array}{r}
346 \\
\times 24 \\
\hline
1384 \\
6920 \\
\hline
8304
\end{array}
$$

By doing 346×4 mentally, we can write 1384 in the arrangement at the right. Then write 6920 by doing 346×20 mentally.

$$
\begin{array}{r}
243 \\
\times 312 \\
\hline
486 = (243 \times 2) \\
2430 = (243 \times 10) \\
72900 = (243 \times 30) \\
\hline
75816
\end{array}
$$

We can erase the indicated products at the right, and omit writing the final 0's of 2430 and 72,900, and write the short form as follows:

$$
\begin{array}{r}
243 \\
\times 312 \\
\hline
486 \\
243 \\
729 \\
\hline
75816
\end{array}
$$

Exercises 35:
Find each product.

1. $624 \atop \times 3$	4. $432 \atop \times 312$	7. $3426 \atop \times 4$
2. $532 \atop \times 24$	5. $675 \atop \times 123$	8. $4521 \atop \times 32$
3. $324 \atop \times 31$	6. $843 \atop \times 324$	9. $3421 \atop \times 322$

ESTIMATING A PRODUCT

Often we are interested in estimates rather than the exact answers. Knowing how to multiply by multiples of powers of ten helps us find an estimate of a product very quickly and easily. Suppose you are to find the value of n in $n = 28 \times 53$.

$20 < 28$ and $50 < 53$,
so $20 \times 50 < n$ or $1000 < n$.
$30 > 28$ and $60 > 53$,
so $30 \times 60 > n$ or $1800 > n$.

Hence, we know that $1000 < n < 1800$, which is read: 1000 is less than n and n is less than 1800. Another way of saying this is "n is between 1000 and 1800."

Another example might be to find the value of x and $x = 72 \times 587$.

$70 < 72$ and $500 < 587$,
so 70×500 or $35000 < x$.
$80 > 72$ and $600 > 587$,
so 80×600 or $48000 > x$.

Hence, $35000 < x < 48000$, or the value of x is between 35000 and 48000.

Exercises 36:
Find a rough estimate for n in each sentence. Then find the exact answer.

1. $n = 27 \times 65$	5. $n = 47 \times 367$
2. $n = 82 \times 75$	6. $n = 77 \times 492$
3. $n = 39 \times 58$	7. $n = 826 \times 52$
4. $n = 43 \times 94$	8. $n = 572 \times 67$

DIVISION

Division is related to multiplication in much the same way that subtraction is related to addition. When two numbers are added, the addition can be undone by subtraction. Similarly, when two numbers are multiplied, the multiplication can be undone by division. Hence, multiplication and division are inverse operations.

Addition	Subtraction
$5 + 7 = 12$	$12 - 7 = 5$
$29 + 5 = 34$	$34 - 5 = 29$

Multiplication	Division
$7 \times 6 = 42$	$42 \div 6 = 7$
$24 \times 3 = 72$	$72 \div 3 = 24$

Knowing that multiplication and division are inverse operations, we can interpret $8 \div 2$ as that factor which, when multiplied by 2, yields a product of 8. That is,

$$(8 \div 2) \times 2 = 8.$$

If we should think of an array as we did for multiplication, $8 \div 2$ would be the number of columns in an array of 8 dots having 2 dots in each column.

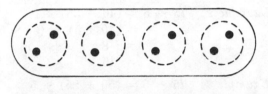

8 ÷ 2 or 4

Or we can think of 8 ÷ 2 as the number of disjoint subsets formed when a set of 8 objects is separated into disjoint subsets having 2 objects each.

8 ÷ 2 = 4
Set of 8 objects separated into 4 disjoint subsets having 2 objects each.

Exercises 37:

Think of an array or separating a set into disjoint equivalent subsets to tell the number named by each of the following.

1. 12 ÷ 3	5. 20 ÷ 4	9. 24 ÷ 8
2. 6 ÷ 2	6. 18 ÷ 2	10. 24 ÷ 12
3. 15 ÷ 5	7. 14 ÷ 7	11. 24 ÷ 3
4. 16 ÷ 4	8. 24 ÷ 6	12. 24 ÷ 4

ZERO IN DIVISION

First let us investigate a division such as $7 \div 0 = n$. Since multiplication and division are inverse operations, the above division can be restated as a multiplication.

$7 \div 0 = n$ so $n \times 0 = 7$

But we already know that when one of the factors is zero, the product is zero. Hence, there is *no* number n such that $n \times 0 = 7$. That is, $7 \div 0$ does not name a number.

Now let us investigate the special case $0 \div 0 = n$. Restate this as a multiplication.

$0 \div 0 = n$ so $n \times 0 = 0$

In this case, any number we choose for n yields a product of 0. That is, $5 \times 0 = 0$, $721 \times 0 = 0$, $9075 \times 0 = 0$, and so on. If we accept $0 \div 0$ as a name for a number, then we are forced to accept

that it names *every* number. This is certainly not very helpful.

The fact that in the first case *no* number is named and in the second case *every* number is named is a source of difficulty in division. Let us rule out both of these cases by agreeing to the following.

Division by zero is meaningless. This means that we shall not define division by zero.

Now let us investigate a case such as $0 \div 8 = n$. Restate this as a multiplication.

$0 \div 8 = n$ so $n \times 8 = 0$

We already know that if the product is zero, at least one of the factors must be zero. Since $8 \neq 0$, then n must be equal to zero. Hence, $0 \times 8 = 0$ and $0 \div 8 = 0$.

This is true regardless of what number we choose for a, except $a = 0$, in the following.

$0 \div a = 0$ if $a \neq 0$.

We can state our finding as follows. When zero is divided by any nonzero number the result is zero.

DEFINITION OF DIVISION

Now let us state a definition of division.

Definition 16:

If $a \times b = c$ and $b \neq 0$, then $c \div b = a$.

We read $c \div b$ as "c divided by b."

The number named by $c \div b$ is called the **quotient,** the number named by b is called the **divisor,** and the number named by c is called the **dividend.**

We can show the relationship between these numbers and the numbers in a multiplication as follows.

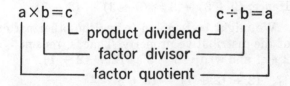

Hence, we see that in a division we are given the product and one of the factors, and we are to find the other factor.

From this definition, and knowing the basic multiplication facts, we can determine the basic definition facts.

Exercises 38:
Find each quotient.

1. $42 \div 7$	5. $36 \div 4$	9. $25 \div 5$
2. $35 \div 5$	6. $21 \div 3$	10. $49 \div 7$
3. $48 \div 8$	7. $45 \div 9$	11. $27 \div 3$
4. $81 \div 9$	8. $32 \div 8$	12. $28 \div 7$

PROPERTIES OF DIVISION

Is division commutative? That is, do $12 \div 4$ and $4 \div 12$ name the same number? $12 \div 4 = 3$, but $4 \div 12$ does not name a whole number, let alone three. Hence, $12 \div 4 \neq 4 \div 12$. Division is *not* commutative.

Is division associative? That is, do $(12 \div 6) \div 2$ and $12 \div (6 \div 2)$ name the same number?

$(12 \div 6) \div 2 = 2 \div 2 = 1$
$12 \div (6 \div 2) = 12 \div 3 = 4$

Hence, $(12 \div 6) \div 2 \neq 12 \div (6 \div 2)$. Division is *not* associative.

Since division is not commutative, we know that $8 \div 1 \neq 1 \div 8$. But let us see what happens when the divisor is 1.

$8 \div 1 = n$ so $n \times 1 = 8$

Since 1 is the identity number of multiplication, we see that $n = 8$ and $8 \div 1 = 8$. That is, when the divisor is 1, the dividend and the quotient are the same.

For all whole numbers a,

$a \div 1 = a$.

If we are to find the value of n in $12 \div 3 = n$, we might rename 12 as $(9 + 3)$. Could it be that division distributes over addition? Let us try it.

$(9 + 3) \div 3 = 12 \div 3 = 4$
$(9 \div 3) + (3 \div 3) = 3 + 1 = 4$

Hence, $(9 + 3) \div 3 = (9 \div 3) + (3 \div 3)$.

We might be tempted to try the other pattern of the distributive property. That is, rename 3 as $2 + 1$ and write $12 \div 3$ as $12 \div (2 + 1)$.

$12 \div (2 + 1) = 12 \div 3 = 4$
$(12 \div 2) + (12 \div 1) = 6 + 12 = 18$

Hence, $12 \div (2 + 1) \neq (12 \div 2) + (12 \div 1)$.

However, it is important to remember that for all whole numbers a, b, and c, where $c \neq 0$,

$(a + b) \div c = (a \div c) + (b \div c)$.

We say that *division distributes over addition, but only when the divisor is distributed.*

Study the following examples which show the use of this property.

Example 1:
$$
\begin{aligned}
32 \div 4 &= (20 + 12) \div 4 \\
&= (20 \div 4) + (12 \div 4) \\
&= \quad 5 \quad\quad + \quad 3 \\
&= \quad 8
\end{aligned}
$$

Example 2:
$$
\begin{aligned}
75 \div 5 &= (40 + 35) \div 5 \\
&= (40 \div 5) + (35 \div 5) \\
&= \quad 8 \quad\quad + \quad 7 \\
&= \quad 15
\end{aligned}
$$

Example 3:
$$
\begin{aligned}
75 \div 5 &= (50 + 25) \div 5 \\
&= (50 \div 5) + (25 \div 5) \\
&= \quad 10 \quad\quad + \quad 5 \\
&= \quad 15
\end{aligned}
$$

Exercises 39:
Rename the dividend in each of the following and use the distributive property of division over addition to find each quotient.

1. $16 \div 2$	4. $44 \div 4$	7. $52 \div 4$
2. $65 \div 5$	5. $84 \div 7$	8. $72 \div 6$
3. $39 \div 3$	6. $24 \div 4$	9. $95 \div 5$

REMAINDERS IN DIVISION

If we think of separating a set into disjoint equivalent subsets, we find that some divisions do not yield a whole number as a quotient.

12 objects, 3 disjoint sets,
4 objects in each subset
$12 \div 4 = 3$

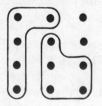

12 objects, 2 disjoint subsets
of 5 objects each, *and* 2 objects
left over

$$12 = (2 \times 5) + 2$$
$$\qquad\quad \uparrow \qquad\qquad \uparrow$$
$$\quad\text{quotient} \qquad \text{remainder}$$

As long as we are operating only with whole numbers, we shall give the remainder as such. Later in this book we will extend the number system so that we can carry out division without having to use remainders.

A final comment regarding the remainder is the following.

$$20 = (4 \times 5) + 0,$$
so $20 \div 5 = 4$ with remainder 0.

Let us agree that every division of whole numbers has a remainder. That is, for whole numbers a and b, $b \neq 0$, the division $a \div b$ can be stated as

$$a = (q \times b) + r$$

where q is the quotient and r is the remainder. Furthermore, $r = 0$ or $r > 0$ and $r < b$. This means that the remainder is either zero or some whole number between 0 and b.

Exercises 40:

Find each quotient and remainder.

1. $17 \div 5$ 4. $31 \div 5$ 7. $55 \div 4$
2. $21 \div 6$ 5. $40 \div 9$ 8. $73 \div 8$
3. $15 \div 7$ 6. $33 \div 6$ 9. $67 \div 6$

ONE-DIGIT DIVISORS

The definition of division does not tell us how to carry out a division. We should like to discover some method of writing the numerals so that division becomes easy, especially where greater numbers are involved.

Suppose we want to find the simplest numeral for $43 \div 5$. In terms of multiplication we can estimate the result by thinking of $n \times 5 = 43$. Knowing the multiples of 5 helps us in making this estimate.

$$8 \times 5 = 40 \text{ and } 40 < 43$$
$$9 \times 5 = 45 \text{ and } 45 > 43$$

Obviously, $43 \div 5$ does not name a whole number. Perhaps we can state the result in the form $a = (q \times b) + r$. So let us rename 43 as a sum of two addends, the first of which is 40 since we already know it can be named as 8×5.

$$43 = 40 + 3$$
$$\quad = (8 \times 5) + 3$$
$$\qquad\quad \uparrow \qquad\qquad \uparrow$$
$$\quad\text{quotient} \qquad \text{remainder}$$

Another way of writing this is:

$$\begin{array}{r} 8 \\ 5)\overline{43} \\ 40 \\ \hline 3 \end{array} = (8 \times 5) \qquad \text{or} \qquad \begin{array}{r} 8 \\ 5)\overline{43} \\ 40 \\ \hline 3 \end{array}$$

Now let us find the simplest numeral for $256 \div 8$.

Think of $n \times 8 = 256$ to estimate the result.

$$10 \times 8 = 80 \text{ and } 80 < 256$$
$$20 \times 8 = 160 \text{ and } 160 < 256$$
$$30 \times 8 = 240 \text{ and } 240 < 256$$
$$40 \times 8 = 320 \text{ and } 320 > 256$$

Hence, the result is between 30 and 40. So let us rename 256 as the sum of two addends, the first addend being 240.

$$256 = 240 + 16$$

We notice that the second addend cannot be the remainder since $16 > 8$. Further, we notice that 16 is a multiple of 8. Then we can use the distributive property of division over addition.

$$256 \div 8 = (240 + 16) \div 8$$
$$= (240 \div 8) + (16 \div 8)$$
$$= 30 \quad + \quad 2$$
$$= 32$$

Another way to write this is:

$$\begin{array}{r} 30 + 2 = 32 \\ \hline 8)\overline{256} \quad 8)\overline{240} + 16 \end{array}$$

Or a more concise method is to think of place value.

$$\begin{array}{r} 3 \\ 8)\overline{256} \\ 240 \\ \hline 16 \end{array} = (30 \times 8) \qquad \begin{array}{r} 32 \\ 8)\overline{256} \\ 240 \\ \hline 16 \\ 16 = (2 \times 8) \\ \hline 0 \end{array}$$

Exercises 41:

Find each quotient.

1. $105 \div 7$ 4. $315 \div 5$ 7. $3320 \div 8$
2. $156 \div 6$ 5. $288 \div 4$ 8. $2526 \div 6$
3. $272 \div 8$ 6. $201 \div 3$ 9. $2464 \div 7$

TWO-DIGIT DIVISORS

Let us extend division to the case where the divisor is expressed by a two-digit numeral. For example, let us carry out the division $624 \div 32$.

We are not as familiar with the multiples of 32 as we are with the multiples of the numbers 1 through 10, so let us think of renaming 624 as the sum of more than two addends. Let us do this by thinking of multiples of powers of 10 as shown below.

$$10 \times 32 = 320 \text{ and } 320 < 624$$
$$20 \times 32 = 640 \text{ and } 640 > 624$$

Now we can rename 624 as follows.

$$624 = 320 + 304$$
$$= (10 \times 32) + 304$$

Certainly 304 cannot be the remainder since $304 > 32$. Now rename 304 as a sum of two addends where the first addend is a multiple of 32. Since 304 is nearly 320 we can expect the value of n in $n \times 32 = 304$ to be nearly 10.

$$8 \times 32 = 256 \text{ and } 256 < 304$$
$$9 \times 32 = 288 \text{ and } 288 < 304$$
$$10 \times 32 = 320 \text{ and } 320 > 304$$

Now we can rename 624 so that the division can be completed easily.

$$624 = 320 + 288 + 16$$
$$= (10 \times 32) + (9 \times 32) + 16$$
$$= (19 \times 32) + 16$$

quotient   remainder

Again, to make the subtraction (necessary in the renaming) easy, let us proceed as follows.

Think		Write
$\left.\begin{array}{c}9\\10\end{array}\right\}10 + 9 = 19$		19
32)624		32)624
320	$= (10 \times 32)$	320
304		304
288	$= (9 \times 32)$	288
16		16

Exercises 42:
Carry out each division.

1. $415 \div 25$	4. $328 \div 45$	7. $2091 \div 17$
2. $534 \div 31$	5. $408 \div 24$	8. $2115 \div 17$
3. $715 \div 64$	6. $638 \div 53$	9. $3400 \div 17$

THE DIVISION ALGORISM

The vertical method makes the division easier to complete since it makes subtraction easy. However, we are faced with subtracting the greatest multiple of the divisor. Suppose we illustrate this with $329 \div 14$.

$$\begin{array}{r} 1 \\ 14\overline{)329} \\ 140 \quad = (10 \times 14) \\ \hline 189 \end{array}$$

We see that $189 > (10 \times 14)$, so 10×14 is not the greatest multiple of 14 that we could have subtracted in this process. So let us start over again.

$$\begin{array}{r} 2 \\ 14\overline{)329} \\ 280 \quad = (20 \times 14) \\ \hline 49 \end{array}$$

Now estimate the value of n in $n \times 14 = 49$ to obtain the next digit in the answer.

$$3 \times 14 = 42 \text{ and } 42 < 49$$
$$4 \times 14 = 56 \text{ and } 56 > 49$$

Hence, the next digit in the answer must be 3.

Think		Write
23		23
14)329		14)329
280	$= (20 \times 14)$	280
49		49
42	$= (3 \times 14)$	42
7		7

Study the following examples and notice how this process is used.

167		81	
21)3526		58)4708	
2100	$= (100 \times 21)$	4640	$= (80 \times 58)$
1426		68	
1260	$= (60 \times 21)$	58	$= (1 \times 58)$
166		10	
147	$= (7 \times 21)$		
19			

Exercises 43:
Carry out each division.

1. $217 \div 34$	5. $5806 \div 47$	9. $8059 \div 25$
2. $836 \div 22$	6. $7052 \div 35$	10. $6072 \div 253$
3. $759 \div 18$	7. $3431 \div 25$	11. $2448 \div 24$
4. $342 \div 32$	8. $5284 \div 25$	12. $6794 \div 79$

Solving Equations and Problems

RELATION SYMBOLS

By using mathematical symbols, we are constantly building a language. In many respects it is more concise than the English language. Because of its brevity we must have a thorough understanding of the meaning of the symbols used in writing a number sentence. Study the meaning of each symbol given below.

$$= \quad \textit{is equal to}$$
$$\neq \quad \textit{is not equal to}$$
$$< \quad \textit{is less than}$$
$$> \quad \textit{is greater than}$$

These symbols serve as verbs in number sentences. Since they show how two numbers are related, they are called *relation symbols*.

The sentence $5 + 3 = 8$ is true since $5 + 3$ and 8 are two names for the same number. But the sentence $7 - 3 = 8$ is false since $7 - 3$ and 8 do not name the same number.

What relation symbol can we write between $7 - 3$ and 8 so that a true sentence is formed? Since $7 - 3$ is not equal to 8, we see that $7 - 3 \neq 8$ is a true sentence.

The sentence $5 - 2 < 4 + 3$ is true since $5 - 2$ or 3 is less than $4 + 3$ or 7. But the sentence $8 + 5 < 9 - 6$ is false since $8 + 5$ or 13 is greater than $9 - 6$ or 3. Hence, $8 + 5 > 9 - 6$ is a true sentence.

The sentence $17 - 5 < 12$ is false since $17 - 5$ or 12 is equal to 12. Hence, we can change the relation symbol $<$ to the relation symbol $=$ and form the true sentence $17 - 5 = 12$.

Exercises 44:

Write T before each true sentence below, and write F before each false sentence.

1. $7 + 6 = 15$
2. $14 < 17 + 3$
3. $8 + 2 = 10$
4. $15 - 5 > 6$
5. $23 > 29 + 1$
6. $7 + 6 < 11 - 3$
7. $6 + 9 = 23 - 8$
8. $9 + (-1) = 3 - (-5)$
9. $32 - 2 = 2 \times 15$
10. $3 \times 4 < 5 \times 2$

GROUPING SYMBOLS

Punctuation marks are used in any language to make clear what we want to say. Study how punctuation marks change the meaning of the following unpunctuated sentence.

Bob said Betty is cute.
Bob said, "Betty is cute."
"Bob," said Betty, "is cute."

Punctuation marks are just as important in number sentences as they are in English sentences.

Study the following expression. What number does it name?

$$7 \times 2 + 5$$

Without being told by a symbol or some other means, we do not know whether to do the multiplication or the addition first.

If we multiply first:

$$7 \times 2 + 5 = 14 + 5 = 19$$

If we add first:

$$7 \times 2 + 5 = 7 \times 7 = 49$$

To avoid the confusion of such an expression naming two different numbers, let us use parentheses ( ) to indicate which operation is to be done first.

$$(7 \times 2) + 5 = 14 + 5 = 19$$
$$7 \times (2 + 5) = 7 \times 7 = 49$$

When part of a number sentence is enclosed within parentheses, think of that part as naming but one number. Think of (7×2) as naming 14 and think of $(2 + 5)$ as naming 7.

It is commonly agreed that when more than one operation, or all of the operations, are indicated in the same expression, we multiply and divide first, then add and subtract.

$$5 + 3 \times 4 \text{ means } 5 + (3 \times 4)$$
$$7 - 6 \div 2 \text{ means } 7 - (6 \div 2)$$
$$7 + 3 \times 8 - 5 \text{ means } 7 \times (3 \times 8) - 5$$

In case only addition and subtraction are indicated in an expression (or only multiplication and division), we will perform the operations in the order indicated from left to right.

$$8 + 6 - 9 \text{ means } (8 + 6) - 9$$
$$6 \times 4 \div 3 \text{ means } (6 \times 4) \div 3$$

It is not always necessary to write the multiplication sign. Multiplication is indicated in each of the following.

$$6 \ (5 + 4) \text{ means } 6 \times (5 + 4)$$
$$9 \ (15) \text{ means } 9 \times 15$$
$$12n \text{ means } 12 \times n$$
$$(n + 2) \ (7 - 5) \text{ means } (n + 2) \times (7 - 5)$$

Study how the parentheses are handled in the following sentences.

$$(16 \div 2) \ (7 + 6) = 8 \times 13 = 104$$
$$(13 - 4) + (12 \div 3) = 9 + 4 = 13$$

Sometimes the sentence becomes so complicated that we need more than one set of parentheses. Instead of two sets of parentheses, let us use brackets [ ] for the second set. In such cases, we handle the innermost groupings first.

$$[4 \times (3 + 2)] - 8 = [4 \times 5] - 8$$
$$= 20 - 8$$
$$= 12$$
$$60 + [(8 \div 2) \times (4 + 3)] = 60 + [4 \times 7]$$
$$= 60 + 28$$
$$= 88$$

Exercises 45:

What number is named by each of the following?

1. $(12 - 8) \times 7$ 6. $[6 + (7 - 2)] + 8$
2. $9 \times (32 \div 8)$ 7. $40 \div [(18 \div 3) + 2]$
3. $(11 - 6) + 12$ 8. $[4 + (7 - 2)] \ (9 - 3)$
4. $(4 \times 2) \ (20 \div 5)$ 9. $[14 \div (6 + 1)] \div 2$
5. $28 \div (10 - 7)$ 10. $8 - [7(5 - 3) - 6]$

Write parentheses, brackets, or both parentheses and brackets in each of the following expressions so that it will name the number indicated after it.

11. $30 - 12 \div 3 \times 2$ Number: 3
12. $30 - 12 \div 3 \times 2$ Number: 52
13. $30 - 12 \div 3 \times 2$ Number: 12
14. $30 - 12 \div 3 \times 2$ Number: 28
15. $30 - 12 \div 3 \times 2$ Number: 22

NUMBER SENTENCES

The symbols used in writing a number sentence are members of one of the following sets.

Number symbols or numerals:
    $0, \frac{2}{3}, 4.7, 5, 72, 119, \ldots$

Operation symbols:
    $+, -, \times, \div, \ldots$

Relation symbols:
    $=, \neq, <, >, \ldots$

Grouping symbols:
    $(\ ), [\ ], \ldots$

Placeholder symbols or variables:
    $\square, n, x, y, t, \ldots$

To write a number sentence we write a relation symbol between two different combinations of the other symbols.

A very important property of a number sentence which does not contain a placeholder symbol is that it is either true or false, but not both. For example, the following number sentences are classified as true or false.

True	*False*
$4 + 7 = 19 - 8$	$6 + 9 = 17 - 8$
$5 \times 3 < 14 + 6$	$27 - 5 < 2 \times 9$
$48 \div 16 \neq 5$	$5 + 4 > 5 \times 4$

Exercises 46:

Write T before each true sentence below and write F before each false sentence.

1. $5 \ (3 + 4) = 21 + 14$
2. $(8 \div 4) + 7 < 4 \times 6$
3. $3 \times 4 > 20 - 8$
4. $6 + 8 \neq 15 \div 3$
5. $3(4 + 2) = (3 \times 4) + 2$
6. $(3 + 4) \ (5 - 5) < 5$

OPEN SENTENCES

In previous lessons we determined whether certain sentences were true or false. Now let us examine the following sentences to learn more about when a number sentence is true, when it is false, and when we are unable to determine which it is.

1. Harry Truman was elected President of the United States.
2. Julius Zulk was elected President of the United States.
3. He was elected President of the United States.

You know that sentence 1 is true, and a little checking of history will show that sentence 2 is false. But what about sentence 3?

Until the word *he* is replaced by the name of a person, we are unable to tell whether sentence 3 is true or false.

Now consider the following number sentences.

$$7 + 6 = 13$$
$$9 - 5 = 27$$
$$8 + n = 15$$

Certainly, $7 + 6 = 13$ is true and $9 - 5 = 27$ is false, but we cannot tell whether $8 + n = 15$ is true or false until n is replaced by a numeral.

Definition 17:

Mathematical sentences that contain letters (or some other symbols) to be replaced by numerals, and are neither true nor false, are called *open sentences*.

Examples of open sentences are given below.

$$n - 15 = 7 \qquad 3x + 2 < 12$$
$$(-14)\, t = 64 \qquad 26(y - 3) > 47$$

Exercises 47:

Before each sentence below write T if it is true, F if it is false, and O if it is open.

1. $(5 + 3) \div k = 2$
2. $4 - (-6) = 10$
3. $4y + (18 \div 6) < 4$
4. $3 + (-8) = 17 - (2 \times 10)$
5. $72 > (24 \div x) + 56$
6. $(16 \div 4) + 13 < (3 \times 4) + 5$

REPLACEMENT SET

Consider the replacements for the pronoun *she* in the following sentence.

She was a great musician.

Certainly it would be sensible to replace *she* with the name of a person. It would not be sensible to replace *she* with the name of a state, a building, a ship, and so on. If we want the resulting sentence to be meaningful, we must know the set from which we can select the replacements for the pronoun *she*.

This idea also underlies an open sentence. We must know which set of numbers we are allowed to use when replacing a placeholder symbol or variable with a numeral.

Definition 18:

The set of numbers whose names are to be used as replacements for a variable is called the *replacement set*.

Solution Set

Use $\{1,2,3,4,5,6\}$ as the replacement set for x in the following open sentence.

$$3 + x < 7$$

We can replace x by each of the numerals 1, 2, 3,

4, 5, and 6 to determine which of them make the resulting sentence true.

True	*False*
$3 + 1 < 7$	$3 + 4 < 7$
$3 + 2 < 7$	$3 + 5 < 7$
$3 + 3 < 7$	$3 + 6 < 7$

We see that only the numerals 1, 2, and 3 can replace x to make the resulting sentence true. Hence, $\{1,2,3\}$ is called the *solution set* for $3 + x < 7$.

Definition 19:

The set of replacements for the variable in an open sentence that make the resulting sentence true is called the *solution set*. Each member of the solution set is called a *solution* or a *root* of the open sentence.

In the previous example, $\{1,2,3\}$ is the solution set, and the roots of the open sentence are 1, 2, and 3.

Study the following examples of finding a solution set.

Example 1: Find the solution set of $n + 8 = 17$ if the replacement set is the set of whole numbers. We know that $9 + 8 = 17$, so 9 is a solution and belongs in the solution set. If n represents any whole number other than 9, the sentence is false. Hence, the only root is 9 and the solution set is $\{9\}$.

Example 2: Find the solution set of $7 - y = 10$ if the replacement set is the set of whole numbers. Since 0 is the least of the whole numbers and $7 - 0 = 7$, we know that y must represent a number less than zero. There is no such whole number, so the solution set is $\emptyset$. This does not mean that there is no solution set. It merely means that there is no solution in the set of whole numbers.

Example 3: Find the solution set of $7 - y = 10$ if the replacement set is the set of integers. Since $7 - (-3) = 10$, we know that -3 is a root. We could try other integer replacements for y to convince ourselves that this is the only root. Hence, the solution set is $\{-3\}$.

Exercises 48:

Using $\{-5,-4,-3,-2,-1,0,1,2,3,4,5,\}$ as the replacement set, find the solution set of each of these open sentences.

1. $n + 7 = 9$
2. $3x + 2 = -7$
3. $3 + k < 1$
4. $7 - r < 0$
5. $(n \div 2) + 3 = 5$
6. $4t - 7 < 10$

7. $21 - n = 21$
8. $13 \times k = -13$
9. $3(2 + n) = 0$
10. $4(15 \div n) = -12$

EQUATIONS

Those number sentences that state that two expressions are names for the same number are called *equations*. The following are examples of an equation.

$$7 + 6 = 13 \quad n = 9$$
$$5 + 2 = 76 \quad 4(5 + r) = 28$$

We see that an equation might be true, such as $7 + 6 = 13$, or it might be false, such as $5 + 2 = 76$, or it might be an open sentence.

If an equation is not an open sentence, all we need do is determine whether it is true or false. Hence, we are primarily concerned with those equations that are open sentences. When no confusion is possible, let us refer to such open sentences as equations.

Definition 20:

To *solve an equation* means to find its solution set.

Throughout this chapter consider the replacement set to be the set of integers for all equations, unless directed otherwise.

In an equation such as $n = 5$ or $k = -56$, the solution set is obvious. We can guess to find the solution set of an equation such as $n + 3 = 5$ or $5t = 15$.

Study how the following equations might be solved mentally.

Solve $3n + 5 = 11$.

By previous agreement, the replacement set for n is the set of integers. Ask yourself: What number plus 5 gives a sum of 11? Since $6 + 5 = 11$, then $3n = 6$. Then ask yourself: 3 times what number gives a product of 6? Since $3 \times 2 = 6$, then $n = 2$. The solution set is $\{2\}$. Check your answer by replacing n by 2 in the original equation ($3n + 5 = 11$) and compute to see if this replacement makes the resulting sentence true.

Exercises 49:

Solve these equations.

1. $n + 5 = 12$
2. $5k = 35$
3. $36 \div y = 4$
4. $16 + x = 10$
5. $7 + 3t = 19$
6. $4r + 20 = 0$
7. $x(12 - 8) = 28$
8. $8k \div 2 = -16$

ADDITION PROPERTY OF EQUATIONS

As we attempt to solve more complicated equations, we become aware that a more systematic or logical procedure is needed. That is, we should like to develop a sequence of reasoning for restating an equation until it becomes simple enough for us to solve mentally. However, each step in the reasoning process should be based on the properties of numbers, the properties of the operations, or on the properties of equations that we shall assume.

Suppose we are to solve $r + 5 = 17$. We already know that $r = 12$ since $12 + 5 = 17$, but let us examine more closely how to arrive at such a root. Can we somehow restate the equation so that only r remains on one side of the equal sign?

Let us begin by thinking of $r + 5$. We can undo the adding of 5 by adding its additive inverse, which is -5.

$$(r + 5) + (-5) = r + [5 + (-5)] \quad \text{Assoc. prop. } +$$
$$= r + 0 \quad \text{Additive inverses}$$
$$= r \quad \text{Identify number } +$$

Since $r + 5 = 17$ means that $r + 5$ and 17 are two names for the same number, we must also add -5 to 17 in order that the two new expressions still name the same number. Hence, we could solve the equation as illustrated below.

$$r + 5 = 17$$
$$(r + 5) + (-5) = 17 + (-5) \quad \text{Assoc. prop. } +$$
$$r + [5 + (-5)] = 12$$
$$\quad \text{Additive inverses}$$
$$r + 0 = 12$$
$$\quad \text{Identity number } +$$
$$r = 12$$

The first step in the above solution uses what we call the **addition property of equations.**

For all integers a, b, and c.
if $a = b$, then $a + c = b + c$.

In other words, we can add the same number to both sides of an equation. Of course, we know that adding a negative integer is equivalent to subtracting its opposite. Hence, we do not need such a property for subtraction.

Study the following examples.

Example 1: Solve $17 = n - 8$.

Add. prop. of equations

$17 + 8 = (n - 8) + 8$

Addition

$25 = [n + (-8)] + 8$

Assoc. prop. +

$25 = n + [(-8) +]$

Additive inverses

$25 = n + 0$

Identity number +

$25 = n$

Example 2: Solve $12 + x = 31$.

Since addition is commutative, we can add -12 on the right or on the left of $12 + x$ and 31.

$12 + x = 31$

Add. prop. of equations

$(-12) + (12 + x) = (-12) + 31$

Assoc. prop. +

$[(-12) + 12] + x = 19$

Additive inverses

$0 + x = 19$

Identity number +

$x = 19$

Exercises 50:
Find the solution set for each equation.

1. $k + 7 = 21$
2. $29 + x = 36$
3. $y - 12 = 43$
4. $8 + r = -9$
5. $-5 + n = 72$
6. $t + 6 = -18$
7. $17 = r + 6$
8. $n - (-3) = 11$
9. $-7 = r + 15$
10. $76 + n = 76$

MULTIPLICATION PROPERTY OF EQUATIONS

We can denote division by several symbols. In an equation such as $n \div 3 = 17$ it is convenient to state $n \div 3$ as $\dfrac{n}{3}$.

Again, to restate the equation so that it can be solved mentally, we should like to restate the equation so that only n remains on one side of the equal sign.

We can think of undoing the dividing by 3 by multiplying by 3, since multiplication and division are inverse operations.

$$n \div 3 = 17$$
$$(n \div 3) \times 3 = 17 \times 3$$
$$n = 51$$

Another way of writing this is:

$$\frac{n}{3} = 17$$
$$\frac{n}{3} \times 3 = 17 \times 3$$
$$\frac{n \times 3}{3} = 51$$
$$n \times \frac{3}{3} = 51$$
$$n \times 1 = 51$$
$$n = 51$$

In the first step of this solution we used the **multiplication property of equations.**

For all integers a, b, and c, if $a = b$, then $a \times c = b \times c$.

Study how this property is used in solving the following equation.

$$-14 = \frac{a}{4}$$
$$(-14)(4) = \frac{a}{4} \times 4$$
$$-56 = \frac{a \times 4}{4}$$
$$-56 = a \times \frac{4}{4}$$
$$-56 = a \times 1$$
$$-56 = a$$

Fractions occurred in both of the preceding examples. You are probably familiar with the operations on these fractional numbers. These operations will be fully explained in the chapter dealing with rational numbers.

Exercises 51:
Solve the following equations.

1. $\dfrac{c}{5} = 8$
2. $\dfrac{x}{-3} = 9$
3. $21 = \dfrac{n}{10}$
4. $0 = \dfrac{t}{3}$
5. $\dfrac{n}{-4} = -7$
6. $\dfrac{x}{12} = -6$
7. $25 = \dfrac{c}{3-4}$
8. $\dfrac{a}{-9} = 1$
9. $\dfrac{a}{2+5} = 8$
10. $\dfrac{t}{4(-5)} = -8$
11. $3(-6) = \dfrac{n}{5}$
12. $\dfrac{r}{-1} = 1$

DIVISION PROPERTY OF EQUATIONS

Consider solving the equation $4n = 32$. In this case n is multiplied by 4. Since multiplication and division are inverse operations, we can undo multiplying by 4 by dividing by 4. So we might divide both $4n$ and 32 by 4, as shown in the following example.

$$4n = 32$$
$$\frac{4n}{4} = \frac{32}{4}$$
$$\frac{4}{4} \times n = 8$$
$$1 \times n = 8$$
$$n = 8$$

In this case we have used the **division property of equations.**

For all integers a, b, and c, where $c \neq 0$, if $a = b$, then $\dfrac{a}{c} = \dfrac{b}{c}$.

We might ask why we have a division property and no subtraction property. Once we have invented the set rational (fractional) numbers, we can show that the division property is no longer needed. Until that time we will use this property of equations.

Study how this property is used in the following examples.

Example 1: Solve $5n = 35$.

$$5n = 35$$
$$\frac{5n}{5} = \frac{35}{5} \quad \text{Div. prop. of equations}$$
$$\frac{5}{5} \times n = 7$$
$$1 \times n = 7$$
$$n = 7$$

Example 2: Solve $-8c = 56$.

$$-8c = 56$$
$$\frac{-8c}{-8} = \frac{56}{-8} \quad \text{Div. prop. of equations}$$
$$\frac{-8}{-8} \times c = -7$$
$$1 \times c = -7$$
$$c = -7$$

Exercises 52:
Solve these equations.

1. $4n = 36$
2. $42 = -6r$
3. $-7k = 63$
4. $-5x = -75$
5. $-k = 47$
6. $72 = 8x$
7. $-52 = -a$
8. $t(5 + 2) = 91$
9. $n(5 - 9) = -24$
10. $x(21 \times 3) = 0$

SOLVING EQUATIONS

As we attempt to solve more and more complicated equations, we may need to use more than one of the properties of equations or use the same property more than once.

In solving an equation such as $5t + 6 = 21$ it is generally advisable to use the property that is most convenient for changing the expression $5t + 6$ to $5t$ first. Then use the property for changing $5t$ to t. Study the following example.

$$5t + 6 = 21$$

Addition property of equations

$$(5t + 6) + (-6) = 21 + (-6)$$

Assoc. prop. +

$$5t + [6 + (-6)] = 21 + (-6)$$

Addition

$$5t + 0 = 15$$

Identity number +

$$5t = 15$$

Division property of equations

$$\frac{5t}{5} = \frac{15}{5}$$

Division

$$t = 3$$

Then we can check our work by replacing t by 3 in the original equation.

$$5t + 6 = 21$$
$$5(3) + 6 = 21$$
$$15 + 6 = 21$$
$$21 = 21$$

Since we have shown that $5(3) + 6$ and 21 name the same number, we know that 3 is a root of the equation.

Since we know that adding a number and its additive inverse is equivalent to adding zero, we can combine some of the steps when writing the previous solution. Also, we may make some of the calculations mentally in the process. However, the example shows the thinking steps necessary in solving the equation.

As you study the following examples, think of the reason or reasons for each step.

Example 1: Solve $\dfrac{n}{4} - 13 = 3.$

$$\dfrac{n}{4} - 13 = 3$$

$$\left[\dfrac{n}{4} + (-13)\right] + 13 = 3 + 13$$

$$\dfrac{n}{4} = 16$$

$$\dfrac{n}{4} \times 4 = 16 \times 4$$

$$n = 64$$

Example 2: Solve $\dfrac{x-5}{4} = 6.$

$$\dfrac{x-5}{4} = 6$$

$$\dfrac{x-5}{4} \times 4 = 6 \times 4$$

$$x - 5 = 24$$

$$(x - 5) + 5 = 24 + 5$$

$$x = 29$$

Example 3: Solve $\dfrac{3t+7}{2} = 26.$

$$\dfrac{3t+7}{2} = 26$$

$$\dfrac{3t+7}{2} \times 2 = 26 \times 2$$

$$3t + 7 = 52$$

$$(3t + 7) + (-7) = 52 + (-7)$$

$$3t = 45$$

$$\dfrac{3t}{3} = \dfrac{45}{3}$$

$$t = 15$$

Example 4: Solve $5(2t - 14) = 60.$

Solution 1:
$$5(2t - 14) = 60$$

$$\dfrac{5(2t - 14)}{5} = \dfrac{60}{5}$$

$$2t - 14 = 12$$

$$(2t - 14) + 14 = 12 + 14$$

$$2t = 26$$

$$\dfrac{2t}{2} = \dfrac{26}{2}$$

$$t = 13$$

Solution 2:
$$5(2t - 14) = 60$$

$$10t - 70 = 60$$

$$(10t - 70) + 70 = 60 + 70$$

$$10t = 130$$

$$\dfrac{10t}{10} = \dfrac{130}{10}$$

$$t = 13$$

Exercises 53:

Solve these equations. Check your answers by replacing the variable in the original equation with the root you have found.

1. $3n + 4 = 19$

2. $14 = \dfrac{a}{2} - 6$

3. $-26 = 1 - 3x$

4. $15 + 3t = 0$

5. $3t + 5 = 29$

6. $\dfrac{r}{4} + 8 = 7$

7. $4(k + 4) = 0$

8. $\dfrac{3n}{4} = 9$

9. $\dfrac{2c}{5} + 6 = 10$

10. $\dfrac{n+7}{5} = 16$

11. $\dfrac{5n}{3} - 13 = 2$

12. $12 = 11t - 10$

13. $4 = \dfrac{3n-4}{8}$

14. $7t - 18 = 73$

15. $3(4n - 1) = 21$

16. $\dfrac{n+14}{3} = 20$

MORE ABOUT SOLVING EQUATIONS

If a variable occurs more than once in the same equation, it must be replaced by the same numeral in both instances. For example, if either of the letters k in $5k + 2 = 7 + k$ is replaced by the numeral 3, then the other must also be replaced by 3.

Before solving equations where the same variable occurs more than once, let us investigate some expressions of this type.

What is a simpler name for $2y + 5y$? Our first guess would probably be $7y$. We could test our guess for a few replacements of y to see if $2y + 5y = 7y$. For example:

If we replace y by 3, then
$$2y + 5y = 2(3) + 5(3) = 6 + 15 = 21$$
$$7y = 7(3) = 21$$

If we place y by -5, then
$$2y + 5y = 2(-5) + 5(-5) = -10 + (-25)$$
$$= -35$$
$$7y = 7(-5) = -35$$

At least for these two replacements of y the sentence $2y + 5y = 7y$ is true. Since it is impossible to test this equation for all values of y, let us use the properties of numbers and their operations to verify that $2y + 5y = 7y$.

$$2y + 5y = (2 \times y) + (5 \times y)$$
$$= (2 + 5) \times y \qquad \text{Dist. prop.}$$
$$= 7 \times y \qquad \text{Addition}$$
$$= 7y$$

We can also use the distributive property to show that $9x - 5x = 4x$.
$$9x - 5x = 9x + (-5x)$$
$$= [9 + (-5)]x$$
$$= 4x$$

Since a placeholder or variable names a number, we can treat it just as we do a numeral when solving an equation, as shown in the following.

Example 1: Solve $9t - 40 + t$.
$$9t = 40 + t$$
$$9t + (-t) = (40 + t) + (-t)$$
$$8t = 40$$
$$\frac{8t}{8} = \frac{40}{8}$$
$$t = 5$$

Example 2: Solve $5(2n - 3) = 21 + n$.
$$5(2n - 3) = 21 + n$$
$$10n - 15 = 21 + n$$
$$(10n - 15) + (-n) = (21 + n) + (-n)$$
$$(-n) + [10n + (-15)] = 21 + 0$$
$$[(-n) + 10n] + (-15) = 21$$
$$9n + (-15) = 21$$
$$[9n + (-15)] + 15 = 21 + 15$$
$$9n = 36$$
$$\frac{9n}{9} = \frac{36}{9}$$
$$n = 4$$

Exercises 54:
Solve these questions.

1. $7k + 8 = 11k$
2. $8n = 14 + n$
3. $4t - 5 = t + 1$
4. $7r + 3r = 130$
5. $17x - 11x = 42$
6. $c + 3(5 + c) = 23$
7. $a + 14 = 5(a - 2)$
8. $2t + 18 = t + 6$
9. $3(2t - 18) = 11 + t$
10. $15 - t = 2(6 + t)$

TRANSLATING ENGLISH PHRASES

One of the most important skills in problem-solving is the ability to translate a problem stated in the English language into the language of mathematics. That is, we want to write an open sentence that says essentially the same thing as a "story problem."

We know from our study of the English language that sentences may contain phrases. Before translating sentences, let us investigate what we shall call *open phrases*, such as $k + 5$.

Suppose we want to express John's age 6 years ago and we do not know what John's age is now. We might think as follows.

Number of years in John's age now_____ n
Number of years in John's age 6
years ago _____ $n - 6$
Suppose Bob's age is 5 years more than 3 times his sister's age. How can we express Bob's age?
Number of years in his sister's age_____ s
3 times the number of years in his sister's age _____ $3s$
5 years more than 3 times the number of years in his sister's age____ $3s + 5$.

In making the translation from English to mathematics, we first choose some letter to use as the variable. Then decide which operation or operations say essentially the same thing as the English words.

Exercises 55:
Translate the following English phrases into open phrases. Use the letter n for the variable in each open phrase.

1. Seven more than some number
2. Three less than 2 times some number
3. The sum of a number and twice the number
4. Mary's age 8 years from now
5. The number of cents in n nickels and $(7 - n)$ dimes
6. A man's age is 9 years greater than 2 times his son's age
7. The sum of 3 times some number and 4 times the number
8. Five more than twice the number of dollars Jim has
9. The number of feet in the distance around a square
10. Bob's score on a test if he answered 3 problems incorrectly

TRANSLATING ENGLISH SENTENCES

We usually describe a problem situation in the English language. Some of the English sentences can be translated into mathematical sentences and others cannot be so translated. For example, the sentence "The rose is red" does not lend itself to a mathematical translation.

Consider the following sentence.

John is 14 years old.

This sentence is just as meaningful if stated as follows. Then we can easily translate it into the language of mathematics.

The number of years
in John's age   is   14.

$$n \qquad\qquad = \qquad 14$$

Now consider the following sentence.

Six years ago John was 8 years old.

This sentence is just as meaningful if stated as follows.

The number of years in John's
age 6 years ago   was   8.

$$n \qquad\qquad\qquad = \quad 8$$

Notice that both of these sentences were rewritten in order to emphasize that the variable, in this case n, represents a *number*.

Exercises 56:

Translate each of these English sentences into open sentences. Use the letter t for the variable in each open sentence.

1. If Mark spends 3 dollars he will have 4 dollars left.
2. The product of some number and 12 is 32.
3. The difference between 3 times some number and 8 is 7.
4. Alice received 51 votes, which is 7 more votes than George received.
5. When a certain number is divided by 5 the quotient is -9.

SOLVING PROBLEMS

There is no one set of rules for solving problems, nor is there one way to apply mathematics to the physical world. However, some suggestions can be made for solving problems.

a. Study the problem carefully and think about the situation in terms of which operation or operations to use and what open sentence you might write for the problem.

b. Translate the problem into an open sentence.

c. Solve the open sentence.

d. Use the root or roots of the open sentence to answer the problem.

Study how each of the following problems are translated into an open sentence and how the root of the open sentence is used to answer the problem.

Example 1:

The George Washington Bridge has two end spans of the same length and a center span that is 3600 feet long. The overall length of the bridge is 4800 feet. How long is each end span?

Let $f =$ the number of feet in the length of each end span

$$2f + 3600 = 4800$$
$$(2f + 3600) + (-3600) = 4800 + (-3600)$$
$$2f = 1200$$
$$\frac{2f}{2} = \frac{1200}{2}$$
$$f = 600$$

Each end span is 600 feet long.

Example 2:

Jim and Ed were the only candidates for president. Jim received 52 more votes than Ed. If 264 votes were cast, how many votes did each boy receive?

Let $e =$ the number of votes for Ed
$e + 52 =$ the number of votes for Jim

$$e + (e + 52) = 264$$
$$(e + e) + 52 = 264$$
$$2e + 52 = 264$$
$$(2e + 52) + (-52) = 264 + (-52)$$
$$2e = 212$$
$$\frac{2e}{2} = \frac{212}{2}$$
$$e = 106$$

Ed received 106 votes.
Jim received $e + 52$ or 158 votes.

Example 3:

Jean's age is 7 years more than twice her sister's age. If Jean is 19 years old, how old is her sister?

Let s = the number of years in her sister's age

$$2s + 7 = 19$$
$$(2s + 7) + (-7) = 19 + (-7)$$
$$2s = 12$$
$$s = 6$$

Her sister is 6 years old.

Exercises 57:

Solve these problems.

1. The sum of two times a certain number and 6 is 22. What is the number?

2. One number is 3 more than a second number. Their sum is 67. What are the two numbers?

3. Ted weighs 9 pounds less than Roger. Their combined weight is 239 pounds. How much does each boy weigh?

4. A rope 26 feet long is cut into 2 pieces so that one piece is 8 feet longer than the other. How long is the shorter piece of rope?

5. A rectangle is 12 inches long. Its perimeter is 44 inches. How wide is the rectangle?

6. The sum of a number and 4 times the number is 75. What is the number?

7. Rita said, "If I had 40 cents more than twice what I have, I would have $3.30." How much money does Rita have?

8. Robert pays 5 cents each for papers and sells them for 8 cents each. Last week he earned $2.70 by selling papers. How many papers did he sell last week?

9. The difference between a number and 5 times the number is 32. What is the number? (Hint: There are two possible answers—one positive and one negative.)

Answers to Exercises

Ex. 1:
1. {Iluron, Superior, Erie, Michigan, Ontario}
2. {October, November, December}
3. {Texas, Louisiana, Mississippi, Alabama, Florida}
4. Ø or the empty set
5. {January, February, March, April, May, June, July, August, September, October, November, December}
6. {Alaska, Alabama, Arizona, Arkansas}
7. The set of the first 4 letters of the English alphabet
8. The set of vowels in the English alphabet
9. The set of the last 3 letters of the English alphabet

10. ε   12. ∉   14. ∉
11. ε   13. ∉   15. ∉

Ex. 2:
1. ⊄   3. ⊂   5. ⊂
2. ⊄   4. ⊂   6. ⊂

7. {x,y}, {x}, {y}, Ø
8. {a,b,c,d}, {a,b,c}, {a,b,d}, {a,c,d},

{b,c,d}, {a,b}, {a,c}, {a,d}, {b,c}, {b,d}, {c,d}, {a}, {b}, {c}, {d}, Ø

9. If a set contains n members, then it contains 2^n subsets.

Ex. 3:
1. ≠   3. ≠   5. ≠   7. =   9. ≠
2. =   4. =   6. ≠   8. ≠   10. ≠

Ex. 4:
Answers may vary.
1. {a, b, c, d}

{w, x, y, z}
2. {1, 2, 3, 4, 5, 6}

{2, 4, 6, 8, 10, 12}

Ex. 5:
1. 8   3. 9   5. 0   7. 36
2. 7   4. 12   6. 4   8. 50

Ex. 6:
1. 85   2. 539   3. 730

4. 777   5. 3432   6. 6051

7. $(4 \times 10) + (6 \times 1)$
8. $(1 \times 100) + (2 \times 10 + (4 \times 1)$
9. $(6 \times 100) + (2 \times 10) + (9 \times 1)$
10. $(8 \times 10) + (2 \times 1)$
11. $(3 \times 1000) + (4 \times 100) + (2 \times 10) + (6 \times 1)$
12. $(2 \times 1000) + (0 \times 100) + (4 \times 10) + (1 \times 1)$

Ex. 7:
1. 10^5 3. 10^4 5. 4^6
2. 10^2 4. 7^4

6. $10 \times 10 \times 10$
7. $10 \times 10 \times 10 \times 10 \times 10$
8. $10 \times 10 \times 10 \times 10 \times 10 \times 10 \times 10$
9. $6 \times 6 \times 6 \times 6$

Ex. 8:
1. 1,100,002,826   3.   712,309
2.   5,000,001   4. 52,000,018

Ex. 9:
1. $J \cup K = \{1,2,3,5,7,9\}$
2. $K \cup M = \{2,3,4,5,6,7,8,9\}$
3. $K \cup N = \{0,3,5,7,9\}$
4. $J \cup M = \{1,2,3,4,6,8\}$
5. $J \cup N = \{0,1,2,3,5,9\}$
6. $M \cup N = \{0,2,4,5,6,8,9\}$
7. $N \cup M = \{0,2,4,5,6,8,9\}$
8. $K \cup K = K$

Ex. 10:
1. $C \cap D = \{2,3\}$ 5. $D \cap E = \{3\}$
2. $D \cap C = \{2,3\}$ 6. $D \cap F = \{7,8\}$
3. $C \cap E = E$ 7. $E \cap F = \emptyset$
4. $C \cap F = \emptyset$ 8. $E \cap E = E$

Ex. 11:
1. T   4. T   7. T   10. T
2. T   5. T   8. T
3. F   6. T   9. F

Ex. 12:
1. 11, 10, 12, 14, 13
2. 7, 12, 14, 10, 18
3. 16, 10, 16, 9, 15
4. 15, 13, 12, 11, 13
5. 11, 10, 10, 14, 12

Ex. 13:
1. No   2. Yes   3. No

4. No   5. No   6. No

7. $3 + 7 = 7 + 3$
8. $8 + 15 = 15 + 8$
9. $36 + 17 = 17 + 36$
10. $156 + 13 = 13 + 156$
11. $129 + 47 = 47 + 129$
12. $326 + 218 = 218 + 326$
13. $327 + 56 = 56 + 327$
14. $651 + 87 = 87 + 651$

Ex. 14:
1. Yes   2. Yes   3. Yes

4. $5 + (7 + 6) = (5 + 7) + 6$
5. $17 + (15 + 32) = (17 + 15) + 32$
6. $(9 + 8) + 7 = 9 + (8 + 7)$
7. $13 + (12 + 6) = (13 + 12) + 6$
8. $(72 + 31) + 46 = 72 + (31 + 46)$
9. 16   10. 27   11. 13   12. 29

Ex. 15:
1. A   4. C, A   7. A   10. A
2. C   5. C   8. C
3. C   6. C, A   9. C, A

Ex. 16:
1. 16, 17, 24, 132, 109
2. 20, 20, 40, 29, 150

Ex. 17:
1. 878, 7999, 59998
2. 777, 8847, 88978
3. 689, 1979, 37927
4. 368, 6788, 18796

Ex. 18
1. 6021,   79870,   908182
2. 8021,   58322,   1006033
3. 4923,   194967,   674437
4. 2267,   44007,   330068

Ex. 19:
1. Open your eyes
2. Sit down (or lie down)
3. Return from school
4. Open your book
5. Take 5 steps backward
6. Tie your shoe
7. Subtract seven
8. Add thirteen

Ex. 20:
1. 15   2. 754   3. 69   4. 26

5. 756   6. 39   7. 312   8. r

9. 8   12. 6   15. 7
10. 3   13. 9   16. 9
11. 8   14. 7

Ex. 21:
1. 6   3. 8   5. 9
2. 4   4. 8   6. 9

7. $9 + n = 12$, 3 awards
8. $15 - n = 7$, 8 cupcakes
9. $12 - 8 = n$, 4 children
10. $7 + n = 13$, 6 apples

Ex. 22:
1. 225, 5234, 46323
2. 113, 3013, 20344
3. 621, 3135, 34711

Ex. 23:
1. 152, 1318, 34882
2. 182, 1907, 26151
3. 188, 2387, 26803

Ex. 24:

1.	163	2109	21467
	+152	+1318	+34882
	315	3427	56349
2.	226	3475	20858
	+182	+1907	+26151
	408	5382	47009
3.	537	3856	43197
	+188	+2387	+26803
	725	6243	70000

Ex. 25:
1. 9   2. 8   3. 6   4. 24

Ex. 26:
1. 15   4. 14   7. 24   10. 28
2. 24   5. 16   8. 30   11. 18
3. 10   6. 16   9. 27   12. 9

Ex. 27:
1. $2 + 2 + 2 + 2 + 2 + 2$; 12
2. $1 + 1 + 1 + 1 + 1 + 1$; 6
3. 6; 6
4. $5 + 5 + 5 + 5$; 20
5. $4 + 4 + 4 + 4 + 4$; 20

6. $7 + 7 + 7$; 21
7. $7 + 7 + 7 + 7 + 7 + 7$; 42

8. $9 + 9 + 9 + 9$; 36
9. $7 + 7 + 7 + 7 + 7$; 35

10. $4 \times 8 = 32$ 13. $5 \times 9 = 45$
11. $6 \times 5 = 30$ 14. $2 \times 9 = 18$
12. $5 \times 1 = 5$ 15. $9 \times 2 = 18$

Ex. 28:
1. $5 \times 9 = 9 \times 5$ 6. $23 \times 5 = 5 \times 23$
2. $7 \times 8 = 8 \times 7$ 7. $9 \times 18 = 18 \times 9$
3. $31 \times 7 = 7 \times 31$ 8. $27 \times 13 = 13 \times 27$
4. $12 \times 6 = 6 \times 12$ 9. $357 \times 6 = 6 \times 357$
5. $9 \times 17 = 17 \times 9$ 10. $43 \times 127 = 127 \times 43$

Ex. 29:
1. $(3 \times 7) \times 5 = 3 \times (7 \times 5)$
2. $4 \times (2 \times 3) = (4 \times 2) \times 3$
3. $(6 \times 3) \times 2 = 6 \times (3 \times 2)$
4. $17 \times (8 \times 5) = (17 \times 8) \times 5$
5. $(13 \times 9) \times 3 = 13 \times (9 \times 3)$

6. A   8. C   10. C   12. A
7. C   9. C, A   11. C, A

Ex. 30:
1. $7 \times (2 + 5) = (7 \times 2) + (7 \times 5)$
2. $4 \times (3 + 6) = (4 \times 3) + (4 \times 6)$
3. $(4 + 5) \times 3 = (4 \times 3) + (5 \times 3)$
4. $(8 + 9) \times 6 = (8 \times 6) + (9 \times 6)$
5. $(5 \times 2) + (7 \times 2) = (5 + 7) \times 2$
6. $(6 \times 3) + (8 \times 3) = (6 + 8) \times 3$

Ex. 31:
1. 60   4. 800   7. 400   10. 4000
2. 900   5. 200   8. 4000
3. 30   6. 40   9. 400

Ex. 32:
1. 210   3. 4500   5. 24000
2. 3200   4. 1400   6. 140000

Ex. 33:
1. 168   4. 2124   7. 188   10. 2568
2. 390   5. 296   8. 145   11. 1371
3. 744   6. 3834   9. 1038   12. 5706

Ex. 34:
1. 494   4. 1296   7. 4067
2. 648   5. 4056   8. 3876
3. 1645   6. 986   9. 2325

Ex. 35:
1. 1872   3. 10044   5. 83025
2. 12768   4. 134784   6. 273132

7. 13704   8. 144672   9. 1101562

Ex. 36:
1. $1200 < n < 2100$, 1755
2. $5600 < n < 7200$, 6150
3. $1500 < n < 2400$, 2262
4. $3600 < n < 5000$, 4042
5. $12000 < n < 20000$, 17249
6. $28000 < n < 40000$, 37884
7. $40000 < n < 54000$, 42952
8. $30000 < n < 42000$, 38324

Ex. 37:
1. 4	4. 4	7. 2	10. 2
2. 3	5. 5	8. 4	11. 8
3. 3	6. 9	9. 3	12. 6

Ex. 38:
1. 6	5. 9	9. 5
2. 7	6. 7	10. 7
3. 6	7. 5	11. 9
4. 9	8. 4	12. 4

Ex. 39:
1. 8	4. 11	7. 13
2. 13	5. 12	8. 12
3. 13	6. 6	9. 19

Ex. 40:
1. 3 $r2$	4. 6 $r1$	7. 13 $r3$
2. 3 $r3$	5. 4 $r4$	8. 9 $r1$
3. 2 $r1$	6. 5 $r3$	9. 11 $r1$

Ex. 41:
1. 15	4. 63	7. 415
2. 26	5. 72	8. 421
3. 34	6. 67	9. 352

Ex. 42:
1. 16 $r15$	4. 7 $r13$	7. 123 $r0$
2. 17 $r7$	5. 17 $r0$	8. 124 $r7$
3. 11 $r11$	6. 12 $r2$	9. 200 $r0$

Ex. 43:
1. 6 $r13$	5. 123 $r25$	9. 322 $r9$
2. 38 $r0$	6. 201 $r17$	10. 24 $r0$
3. 42 $r3$	7. 137 $r6$	11. 102 $r0$
4. 10 $r22$	8. 211 $r9$	12. 86 $r0$

Ex. 44:
1. F	4. T	7. T	10. F
2. T	5. F	8. T	
3. T	6. F	9. T	

Ex. 45:
1. 28	4. 32	7. 5	10. 0
2. 36	5. 4	8. 54	
3. 17	6. 19	9. 1	

11. $(30 - 12) \div (3 \times 2)$
12. $[30 - (12 \div 3)] \times 2$
13. $[(30 - 12) \div 3] \times 2$
14. $30 - [12 \div (3 \times 2)]$
15. $30 - [(12 \div 3) \times 2]$

Ex. 46:
1. T	3. F	5. F
2. T	4. T	6. F

Ex. 47:
1. O	3. O	5. O
2. T	4. F	6. F

Ex. 48:
1. $\{2\}$
2. $\{-3\}$
3. $\{-3, -4, -5\}$
4. $\varnothing$
5. $\{4\}$
6. $\{-5, -4, -3, -2, -1, 0, 1, 2, 3, 4\}$
7. $\{0\}$
8. $\{-1\}$
9. $\{-2\}$
10. $\{-5\}$

Ex. 49:
1. 7	3. 9	5. 4	7. 7
2. 7	4. -6	6. -5	8. -4

Ex. 50:
1. 14	3. 55	5. 77	7. 11	9. -22
2. 7	4. -17	6. -24	8. 8	10. 0

Ex. 51:
1. 40	4. 0	7. -25	10. 160
2. -27	5. 28	8. -9	11. -90
3. 210	6. -72	9. 56	12. -1

Ex. 52:
1. 9	4. 15	7. 52	10. 0
2. -7	5. -47	8. 13	
3. -9	6. 9	9. 6	

Ex. 53:
1. 5	5. 8	9. 10	13. 12
2. 40	6. -4	10. 73	14. 13
3. 9	7. -3	11. 9	15. 2
4. -5	8. 12	12. 2	16. 46

Ex. 54:

1. 2	4. 13	7. 6	10. 1
2. 2	5. 7	8. −12	
3. 2	6. 2	9. 13	

Ex. 55:

1. $n + 7$
2. $2n - 3$
3. $n + 2n$
4. $n + 8$
5. $5n + 10(7 - n)$
6. $2n + 9$
7. $3n + 4n$
8. $2n + 5$
9. $4n$
10. $n - 3$

Ex. 56:

1. $t - 3 = 4$
2. $12t = 32$
3. $3t - 8 = 7$
4. $t + 7 = 51$
5. $t \div 5 = -9$

Ex. 57:

Typical solutions.

1. $2n + 6 = 22$; 8
2. $n + (n + 3) = 67$; 32 and 35
3. $r + (r - 9) = 239$; Roger 124 pounds and Ted 115 pounds
4. $p + (p + 8) = 26$; 9 feet
5. $2(w + 12) = 44$; 10 inches
6. $n + 4n = 75$; 15
7. $2a + 40 = 330$; $1.45
8. $p(8 - 5) = 270$; 90 papers
9. $5n - n = 32$ or $n - 5n = 32$; 8 or −8

CHAPTER FOURTEEN

ALGEBRA

Ratio and Proportion

RATIO

A *ratio* is the relation between two like numbers or two like values. The ratio may be written as a fraction, $\frac{3}{4}$; as a division, $3 \div 4$; or with the colon or *ratio sign* (:), 3 : 4. When the last of these forms is used, it is read, 3 *to* 4; or 3 *is to* 4. Ratios may be expressed by the word *per* as in miles per hour, or revolutions per second. In arithmetic these are written miles/hour, revolutions/minute, volts/ampere. Whatever the manner of writing the ratio, its value in arithmetical computations is always the same.

Since a ratio may be regarded as a fraction, you will recognize the following principle as being true:

Rule 1: *Multiplying or dividing both terms of a ratio by the same number does not change the value of the ratio.*

Thus, 2 : 4 = 4 : 8 (multiplying both terms by 2)

or 2 : 4 = 1 : 2 (dividing both terms by 2)

To reduce a ratio to its lowest terms, *treat the ratio as a fraction and reduce the fraction to its lowest terms.*

EXAMPLE 1: Express $\frac{2}{3}$ to $\frac{4}{9}$ in its lowest terms.

SOLUTION: $\frac{2}{3}$ to $\frac{4}{9} = \frac{2}{3} \div \frac{4}{9} = \frac{2}{3} \times \frac{9}{4} = \frac{3}{2}.$

Hence $\frac{2}{3}$ to $\frac{4}{9}$ is the same as 3 to 2.

To separate a quantity according to a given ratio, *add the terms of the ratio to find the total number of parts. Find what fractional part each term is of the whole. Divide the total quantity into parts corresponding to the fractional parts.*

EXAMPLE 2: Three hundred tents have to be divided between two army divisions in the ratio of 1 : 2. How many does each division get?

1 + 2 = 3 (adding the terms)

$\left.\begin{array}{l} \frac{1}{3} \times 300 = 100 \\ \frac{2}{3} \times 300 = 200 \end{array}\right\}$ ANS. (Taking corresponding fractional parts of total quantity)

Check: 100 : 200 or $\frac{100}{200} = \frac{1}{2}$ or 1 : 2.

EXAMPLE 3: 1,600 lbs. of coffee have to be distributed to 3 wholesale dealers in the ratio of 8 : 11 : 13. How many lbs. should each dealer receive?

SOLUTION:
8 + 11 + 13 = 32

$\frac{8}{32}, \frac{11}{32}, \frac{13}{32}$ are the fractional parts

$\left.\begin{array}{l} \frac{8}{32} \times 1,600 = 400 \\ \frac{11}{32} \times 1,600 = 550 \\ \frac{13}{32} \times 1,600 = 650 \end{array}\right\}$ ANS.

Practice Exercise No. 1

PROBLEMS

1   Reduced to its lowest terms, 24 : 32 equals what?

(A) $\frac{1}{3}$ _____   (C) $\frac{6}{8}$ _____

(B) $\frac{1}{2}$ _____   (D) $\frac{3}{4}$ _____

2   What is the value of the ratio $7 \times 9 : 8 \times 7$?

(A) $\frac{8}{9}$ _____   (C) $8 : 9$ _____

(B) $1\frac{1}{8}$ _____   (D) $1\frac{23}{49}$ _____

3   If 5 lbs. of vegetables lose 10 oz. in drying, what part of the original weight was water?

(A) $\frac{1}{6}$ _____   (C) 12% _____

(B) $\frac{1}{8}$ _____   (D) $\frac{1}{2}$ _____

4   A mixture requires 2 parts of water to 3 parts of alcohol. What percentage of the mixture is water?

(A) 40% _____   (C) 60% _____

(B) 50% _____   (D) $66\frac{2}{3}\%$ _____

5   Bronze consists of 6 parts tin to 19 parts copper. How many pounds of tin are there in a 500-lb. bronze statue?

(A) 100 _____   (C) 140 _____

(B) 120 _____   (D) 200 _____

6   \$2,000 is to be distributed among 3 members of a family in the ratio of $5 : 14 : 21$. How much greater is the largest share than the smallest share?

(A) \$900 _____   (C) \$500 _____

(B) \$800 _____   (D) \$750 _____

PROPORTION

A **proportion** is a statement of equality between two ratios. It may be written with the double colon or **proportion sign** ($::$), or with the sign of equality ($=$).

Thus, $2 : 6 :: 3 : 9$ is a proportion that is read, 2 *is to* 6 *as* 3 *is to* 9; or $\frac{2}{6}$ *equals* $\frac{3}{9}$.

In any proportion the first and last terms are called the extremes and the second and third terms are called the **means.** In $2 : 6 :: 3 : 9$ the *extremes* are 2 and 9; and the *means* are 6 and 3.

Multiply the two extremes and the two means of the proportion $2 : 6 :: 3 : 9$ and compare the products.

Extremes: $2 \times 9 = 18$,
Means: $6 \times 3 = 18$.

This result illustrates **Rule 2:** *The product of the* means *is equal to the product of the* extremes.

If you write the proportion in the form of $\frac{2}{6} = \frac{3}{9}$, note that the means and extremes are diagonally opposite each other. This affords another way to pick out your equation.

No proportion is a true proportion unless the two ratios are equal. This is another way of saying that Rule 2 must be satisfied.

By means of this rule you can find the missing term of any proportion if the other 3 terms are given.

EXAMPLE 1: $2 : 6 = 8 : ?$ Find the value of the missing term. The letter x is traditionally used to denote a missing term or an unknown quantity. Rewriting the proportion we get
$2 : 6 :: 8 : x$.

(a) 2 times $x = 6$ times 8
$2x = 48$
(b) $\frac{2x}{2} = \frac{48}{2}$
$x = 24$, ANS.

a. Product of the extremes equals product of the means.
b. Both sides of any equation may be divided by the same number without changing the equation.

The above process is the equation method of solving problems containing an unknown. This process will be treated at greater length in Chapter Eight, which deals with elementary algebra.

If you wish to use a strict arithmetic method of finding the missing term in a proportion, you may employ the following two rules.

Rule 3: *The product of the means divided by either extreme gives the other extreme as the quotient.*

$2 : 6 :: 8 : 24$;
$6 \times 8 = 48$, $48 \div 2 = 24$, $48 \div 24 = 2$.
Thus if given $? : 6 = 8 : 24$,
multiply the two means, $6 \times 8 = 48$,
and divide this product by the known extreme; $48 \div 24 = 2$. The quotient here is the unknown term.

Rule 4: *The product of the extremes divided by either mean gives the other mean as a quotient.*

$2 : 6 = 8 : 24$;
$2 \times 24 = 48$, $48 \div 6 = 8$, $48 \div 8 = 6$.
Thus if given $2 : ? :: 8 : 24$,
multiply the two extremes, $2 \times 24 = 48$, and divide this product by the known means; $48 \div 8 = 6$. The quotient again is the unknown term.

Practice Exercise No. 2

Find the missing term.

1 $2 : 3 :: 4 : ?$ 6 $5 : ? :: 25 : 20$
2 $20 : 10 :: ? : 6$ 7 $? : 5 :: 12 : 20$
3 $2 : ? :: 8 : 24$ 8 $? : 25 :: 10 : 2$
4 $18 : ? :: 36 : 4$ 9 $9 : ? :: 24 : 8$
5 $12 : 4 :: ? : 7$ 10 $24 : 4 :: ? : 3$

PROBLEMS IN PROPORTION

In solving problems by the ratio and proportion method it is first necessary to recognize whether a proportion exists and if so what kind it is.

A direct proportion is indicated when two quantities are so related that an increase in one causes a corresponding increase in the other or when a decrease in one causes a corresponding decrease in the other.

The following is a list of typical quantitative expressions in which the variables are directly related when other quantities remain unchanged.

   a. The faster the speed, the greater the distance covered.
   b. The more men working, the greater the amount of work done.
   c. The faster the speed, the greater the number of revolutions.
   d. The higher the temperature of gas, the greater the volume.
   e. The taller the object, the longer the shadow.
   f. The larger the quantity, the greater the cost.
   g. The smaller the quantity, the lower the cost.
   h. The greater the length, the greater the area.
   j. The greater the base, the larger the discount, commission, interest and profit.

EXAMPLE 2: If 20 men assemble 8 machines in a day, how many men are needed to assemble 12 machines in a day?

SOLUTION:

8 machines need 20 men
12 machines need ? men
$8 : 12 :: 20 : x$
$8x = 240$
$x = 30$,   ANS.

EXPLANATION: Place corresponding values on the same line. Put *like numbers* together. The more machines, the more men needed. ∴ The values are a direct proportion. Solve for x.

EXAMPLE 3: If 12 drills cost $8.00, how much will 9 drills cost?

SOLUTION:

12 drills cost $8.00
 9 drills cost   ?
$12 : 9 :: 8 = x$
$12x = 72, x = \$6.$

EXPLANATION: The fewer the drills the lower the cost. ∴ The values are in direct proportion. Solve for x.

Examples 2 and 3 are easily recognized as direct proportions since more men can assemble more machines, and fewer drills cost less money.

CUES IN SOLVING PROPORTION PROBLEMS

In every proportion both ratios must be written in the same order of value, for instance in Example 2:

$$\frac{\text{Smaller no. mach's}}{\text{Larger no. of mach's}} = \frac{\text{Smaller no. of men}}{\text{Larger no. of men}}$$

In Example 3:

$$\frac{\text{Larger no. of drills}}{\text{Smaller no. of drills}} = \frac{\text{Larger cost}}{\text{Smaller cost}}$$

An inverse proportion is indicated when two quantities are so related that an increase in one causes a corresponding decrease in the other, or vice versa.

The following are quantitative expressions in which the variables are inversely related.

   a. The greater the speed, the less the time.
   b. The slower the speed, the longer the time.
   c. The greater the volume, the less the density.
   d. The more men working, the shorter the time.
   e. The fewer men working, the longer the time.

EXAMPLE 4: When two pulleys are belted together the revolutions per minute (rpm) vary inversely as the size of the pulleys. A 20-in. pulley running at 180 rpm drives an 8-in. pulley. Find the revolutions per minute of the 8-in. pulley.

SOLUTION:

20 in. makes 180 rpm
 8 in. makes ? rpm
$\dfrac{8}{20} = \dfrac{180}{x}$
$8x = 3,600$
$x = 450$ rpm,   ANS.

EXPLANATION: First make a table of corresponding values. Put *like numbers* together. The smaller the pulley, the greater the number of revolutions; ∴ the quantities are in inverse ratio. Inverting the first ratio, write the proportion. Solve for x.

CUE: If you write your proportion in this form, $\dfrac{8}{20} = \dfrac{180}{x}$, you may note that in the inverse proportion the corresponding numbers are arranged diagonally, *i.e.*, 20 in. and 180 rpm, and 8 in. and x rpm are diagonally opposite each other.

In the direct proportion as in Example 3, $\dfrac{12}{9} = \dfrac{8}{x}$, the corresponding numbers are arranged directly on a line with each other, *i.e.*, 12 drills and $8, 9 drills and $$x$.

Practice Exercise No. 3
PROBLEMS

1   If a pole 18 ft. high casts a shadow 20 ft. long, how long a shadow would a pole 27 ft. high cast?

(A) 10 _____   (C) 30 _____
(B) 25 _____   (D) 36 _____

2   If a soldier walks 9 miles in 2 hrs. how long will it take him to walk 30 miles?

(A) 6 _____   (C) $8\frac{1}{2}$ _____
(B) $6\frac{2}{3}$ _____   (D) 9 _____

3   If an automobile runs 90 miles on 5 gal. of gas, how far will it run on a full 20-gal. tank?

(A) 300 _____   (C) 450 _____
(B) 360 _____   (D) 280 _____

4   An army camp has provisions for 240 men for 28 days; but only 112 men are sent to the camp. How long will the provisions last?

(A) 60 _____   (C) $13\frac{2}{3}$ _____
(B) 56 _____   (D) 76 _____

5   A train takes 26 hrs. at a speed of 35 miles per hr. to go from Chicago to New York. How fast must the train travel to make the trip in 20 hours?

(A) $39\frac{1}{2}$ _____   (C) $26\frac{12}{13}$ _____
(B) 40 _____   (D) $45\frac{1}{2}$ _____

6   The flywheel on an engine makes 220 revolutions in 2 seconds. How many revolutions does it make in 8 seconds?

(A) 1,7600 _____   (C) 880 _____
(B) 55 _____   (D) 800 _____

Signed Numbers and Algebraic Expressions

Up to the present, all the numbers used here have been positive numbers. That is, none was less than zero (0). In solving some problems in arithmetic it is necessary to assign a *negative* value to some numbers. This is used principally for numbers with which we wish to represent opposite quantities or qualities, and can best be illustrated by use of a diagram. For example consider a thermometer, as in Fig. 1.

If temperatures *above* zero are taken as *positive*, then temperatures *below* zero are considered *negative*.

In measuring distances east and west, as in Fig. 2, if distance *east* of a certain point is taken as *positive*, then distance *west* of that point is considered *negative*.

FIGURE 1

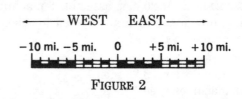

FIGURE 2

Another good example may be taken from commercial bookkeeping, where money in the bank and other *assets* may be considered as *positive* amounts, while money *owed* represents *negative* amounts.

Thus, in general, positive and negative numbers are used to distinguish between opposite qualities. Values above zero are considered positive and take the + sign, while values below zero are considered negative and are written with the − sign. These then become signed numbers, as they are called.

The + and − also continue to be used as signs of addition and subtraction. When no sign is indicated the + sign is understood.

Learning to use signed numbers is an introduction to some of the special rules for algebraic operations and also a preparation for the equation method of solving some difficult arithmetic problems in easier ways.

ADDING SIGNED NUMBERS

To add numbers of like signs, *add the numbers as in arithmetic and give to the result the common sign.*

EXAMPLE 1: -14 added to $-8 = -22$.

EXAMPLE 2: Add $+4$, $+12$, and $+16$. ANS. $+32$.

To add numbers of unlike signs, *combine all positive and negative quantities, subtract the smaller from the larger and give the result the sign of the larger combination.*

EXAMPLE 1: Add $-4 -8 +2 +6 +10$.

SOLUTION: $(-4) + (-8) = -12$;
$\qquad 2 + 6 + 10 = 18$
$\qquad 18 - 12 = 6$, ANS.

EXAMPLE 2: Add $3 + 19 + 4 - 45$

SOLUTION: $26 - 45 = -19$, ANS.

What has been done above is called finding the **algebraic sum.** Similarly we can combine numbers that are represented by similar symbols.

EXAMPLE 3: Add $5b - 11b + 14b$.

SOLUTION: $19b - 11b = 8b$, ANS.

We cannot arithmetically add terms containing unlike symbols. For instance, if we let b stand for books and p for plates we know from arithmetic that we couldn't combine books and plates as a single quantity of either. Therefore, **to add quantities containing unlike symbols,** *collect like terms and express them separately in the answer.*

EXAMPLE 4: Add $5b + 2p + 7p + 3b$.

SOLUTION: Collecting like terms,

$\qquad 5b + 3b = 8b$
$\qquad 2p + 7p = 9p$

Expressing unlike terms separately we get $8b + 9p$, which is an algebraic expression containing two terms, as the answer.

Practice Exercise No. 4

ADDITION OF SIGNED NUMBERS

1 $+5 + 18 =$
2 $-5 - 17 - 14 =$
3 $+7 - 12 - 6 + 4 =$
4 $-14d - 6d =$
5 $7b - 3b =$
6 $+22 - 14 - 17 - 12 + 18 =$
7 $5x - 7x + 14x =$
8 $3a + 4b + 2a - 2b =$
9 $6a + 3b + 9a - 5b =$
10 $6a + 3b + 9a - 5 =$

SUBTRACTING SIGNED NUMBERS

Subtraction means finding the difference between two numbers, or the difference between two values on a scale.

If you were asked what is the difference between $-4°$ centigrade and $+5°$, your answer would be $9°$. You would do this mentally. Now how did you arrive at the answer? First you counted from $-4°$ to zero, then add 5 to that. The rule for subtraction of signed numbers is therefore:

To subtract signed numbers, *change the sign of the subtrahend and apply the rules for addition.*

EXAMPLE 1: Subtract $+20$ from $+32$.

SOLUTION:

$+20$ is the subtrahend or number to be subtracted. Changing its sign and adding, we get $32 - 20 = 12$, ANS.

EXAMPLE 2: From -18 subtract -12.

SOLUTION:

-12 is the subtrahend. Changing its sign and adding, we get $-18 + 12 = -6$, ANS.

Practice Exercise No. 5

SUBTRACTION OF SIGNED NUMBERS

1	$+47$ $+19$	4	$+54$ -12	7	$(-5) - (-8)$
2	-26 -17	5	80 -50	8	$(-7) - (-4)$
3	-42 -18	6	$-22ab$ $+18ab$	9	$(-9) - (+16)$

MULTIPLICATION AND DIVISION OF SIGNED NUMBERS

Law of signs for multiplication of signed numbers—Rule: *The product of any two numbers that have like signs is positive (+), and the product of any two numbers that have unlike signs is negative (−).*

EXAMPLE 1: Multiply −8 by −6.

SOLUTION: The signs are the same.
∴ −8 × −6 = +48,   ANS.

EXAMPLE 2: Multiply +3 by −4.

SOLUTION: The signs are unlike.
∴ 3 × −4 = −12,   ANS.

EXAMPLE 3: Multiply −2 by +5 by −3 by +4.

SOLUTION: (−2) × (+5) = −10,
(−10) × (−3) = +30,
+ (+30) × (+4) = +120,   ANS.

Division of signed numbers is carried out by the same process as division in arithmetic, but *the sign of the quotient is positive if the divisor and dividend have the same sign, and negative if the divisor and dividend have opposite signs.*

EXAMPLE 4: Divide −16 by −2.

SOLUTION: $\dfrac{-16}{-2} = +8$,   ANS.

Same signs, ∴ answer is plus (+).

EXAMPLE 5: Divide −35 by +5.

SOLUTION: $\dfrac{-35}{5} = -7$,   ANS.

Opposite signs, ∴ answer is minus (−).

Practice Exercise No. 6

Do the following examples:

1   2 + −16 =
2   −18 × −12 =
3   −4 × −6 × 3 =
4   4 × 3 × −2 × 6 =
5   72 ÷ −24 =
6   −68 ÷ −17 =
7   −14 ÷ −5 =
8   −24 × 4 ÷ 8 =

ALGEBRAIC EXPRESSIONS

Working with signed numbers is an introduction to using algebraic expressions. An **algebraic expression** is one in which letter symbols are used to represent numbers.

A letter symbol or other type of symbol that represents a number is called a **literal number.**

If you know the numerical values of the symbols and understand the arithmetic signs of an algebraic expression, then you can find the numerical value of any algebraic expression. *Thus:*

$a + b$ means that b is added to a.
If $a = 2$ and $b = 3$, then $a + b = 5$.

$b - a$ means that a is subtracted from b.
If $b = 6$ and $a = 4$, $b - a = 2$.

$a \times b$ means that b is multiplied by a.
If $a = 7$ and $b = 3$, $a \times b = 21$.

Multiplication can be indicated in four ways in algebra. a multiplied by b can be written $a \times b$, $a \cdot b$, $(a) (b)$, or ab. That is, multiplication can be expressed by a cross ×, by a dot ·, by adjacent parentheses, and by directly joining a letter and its multiplier with no sign between them. *Thus 2a means 2 times a, and ab means a times b.*

a^2 means $a \cdot a$. You read it: a *squared.*
If $a = 3$, then $a^2 = 3 \cdot 3$ or 9.

a^3 means $a \cdot a \cdot a$. You read it: a *cubed.*
If $a = 3$, then $a^3 = 3 \cdot 3 \cdot 3$ or 27.

$a^2 + b^3$ means that b^3 is to be added to a^2.
If $a = 3$ and $b = 2$, then $a^2 + b^3 = 9 + 8$, or 17.

The small 2 and 3 placed to the right and slightly above the a and the b in writing a^2 and b^3 are called **exponents.**

The number a is called the **base.** a^2 and a^3 are called **powers** of the *base a.*

$3a^2 - 2b^2$ means that $2b^2$ is subtracted from $3a^2$.

The $3a^2$ and $2b^2$ are known as **terms** in the algebraic expression.

The numbers placed before the letters are called **coefficients.** *Thus,* in $3a^2 - 2b^2$, 3 is called the *coefficient* of a^2, 2 is the *coefficient* of b^2. The coefficient so placed indicates multiplication, *i.e.,* $3a^2$ means $3 \times a^2$.

Practice Exercise No. 7

In each of the following write the algebraic expression and find its numerical value if $x = 2$, $y = 3$ and $z = 4$.

1   x added to y =
2   x, y and z added together =
3   Twice x added to twice y =
4   z subtracted from the sum of x and y =
5   The square of x added to the square of y =
6   3 less than y =
7   Twice the product of x and z =

Algebraic Formulas and Equations

In the preceding sections rules in words were used to describe methods to be followed in solving various types of problems. For example, to find the amount of a discount the rule is to multiply the base or price by the rate of discount. By the use of symbols this rule can be expressed in a brief form known as a **formula.**

Thus a short way to express the rule in question is:

a. Discount = Base × Rate

A still shorter way is:

b. $D = B \times R$,

in which D, B and R means discount, base and rate respectively.

The shortest and algebraic way to express this is:

c. $D = BR$.

DEFINITIONS

A **formula** is a shorthand method of expressing a rule by the use of symbols or letter designations (literal numbers).

At the same time it must be remembered that a formula is an equation. And what is an equation?

An **equation** is a statement that two expressions are equal.

For example, $D = BR$ states that D, the discount, is equal to B, the base, multiplied by R, the rate of discount. Before we can start working with formulas and equations there are a few things that have to be learned about them.

An equation has two equal sides or members. In the equation $D = BR$, D is the left side and BR is the right side.

Terms are made up of numbers or symbols combined by multiplication or division.

For example, $6DR$ is a term in which the factors 6, D and R are combined by *multiplication;* $\dfrac{M}{4}$ is a term in which the quantities M and 4 are combined by *division* or in which the factors M and ¼ are combined by multiplication.

An expression is a collection of terms combined by addition, subtraction, or both, and frequently grouped by parentheses, as in: $(3a + 2b)$, $(2c - 4c + 3b)$, $2x - 3y$.

USING PARENTHESES

Parentheses ( ) or **brackets** [ ] mean that quantities are to be grouped together, and that quantities enclosed by them are to be considered as one quantity. The line of a fraction has the same significance in this respect as a pair of parentheses.

Thus, $18 + (9 - 6)$ is read 18 *plus the quantity* $9 - 6$.

Rule: To solve examples containing parentheses, *do the work within the parentheses first; then remove the parentheses and proceed in the usual way. Within parentheses and in examples without parentheses do multiplications from left to right before doing additions and subtractions.*

It is extremely important to observe this method of procedure, since it is otherwise impossible to solve algebraic problems.

EXAMPLE 1: $94 - (12 + 18 + 20) = ?$
$94 - 50 = 44$, ANS.

EXAMPLE 2: $12(3 + 2) = ?$
$12 \times 5 = 60$, ANS.

EXAMPLE 3: $\dfrac{18}{2(4 - 1)} = ?$
$\dfrac{18}{2 \times 3} = \dfrac{18}{6} = 3$, ANS.

EXAMPLE 4: $3 \times 6 - 4$
$18 - 4 = 14$, ANS.

Note: If in this example the 4 had been subtracted from the 6 before multiplying, the answer would have been 6, but this would be wrong according to the laws of algebra. This example illustrates the absolute necessity of *doing multiplication first* in any cases similar to this.

Practice Exercise No. 8

Clear parentheses and solve.

1   $18 + (19 - 14) =$
2   $22(3 + 2) =$

3   $42 - 9 - (18 + 2) =$

4   $(6 - 4)(8 + 2) =$

5   $(18 \div 3)(9 - 7) =$

6   $(7 \times 8) - (6 \times 4) + (18 - 6) =$

7   $(6 \times 8) \div (8 \times 2) =$

8   $19 + (18 - 14 + 32) =$

9   $(7 \times 6)(6 \times 5) =$

10 $69 \div [35 - (15 - 3)] =$

TRANSLATING WORD STATEMENTS INTO FORMULAS AND ALGEBRAIC EXPRESSIONS

To express word statements as formulas or as brief algebraic expressions, letters and symbols are substituted for words.

EXAMPLE 1: Express briefly, *What number increased by 6 gives 18 as a result?*

Substituting the letter N for the unknown *what number*, we get

$$N + 6 = 18,$$
$$N = ? \quad \text{ANS.}$$

EXAMPLE 2: Express briefly, *The product of two numbers is 85. One is 5, find the other.*

$$5N = 85, N = ? \quad \text{ANS.}$$

EXAMPLE 3: Express briefly, *Fifteen exceeds a certain number by 6. What is the number?*

$$15 - 6 = N, N = ? \quad \text{ANS.}$$

EXAMPLE 4: Express briefly, *Two thirds of a number is 20. Find the number.*

$$\tfrac{2}{3}N = 20, N = ? \quad \text{ANS.}$$

In algebra, however, the regular method of writing fractions is to place all factors, as far as may be possible, above or below a single horizontal line. The form $\tfrac{2}{3}N$, while mathematically correct, is less regular than $\dfrac{2N}{3}$. Hence to express our problem in approved form we arrive at:

$$\frac{2N}{3} = 20, N = ? \quad \text{ANS.}$$

The foregoing illustrates in simple form the general method of making algebraic statements. In engineering, scientific, industrial and commercial practice, it is common to express certain kinds of facts in algebraic *formulas*. The usual way is to state the formula with symbolic letters and to follow it immediately with an explanation (starting with the words *in which*) to make intelligible to the reader any symbols that may require definition. Examples of this method of formula statement follow.

EXAMPLE 1: The cost equals the selling price minus the margin of profit.

FORMULA: $C = S - M$, in which C stands for cost, S for selling price and M for margin of profit.

EXAMPLE 2: The area of a rectangle equals the base times the height.

FORMULA: $A = bh$, in which A stands for area, b for base and h for height.

EXAMPLE 3: To determine the resistance in ohms of an electrical circuit, divided the number of volts by the number of amperes.

FORMULA: $O = \dfrac{V}{A}$, in which O stands for ohms, V for volts and A for amperes.

Practice Exercise No. 9

Write the following statements as equations. *Note:* Most of the statements represent formulas commonly used by draftsmen, designers, carpenters, engineers and clerks.

1   The perimeter (p) of a rectangle equals twice its length (l) added to twice its width (w).

2   The distance (d) traveled by an object that moves at a given rate of speed (r) for a given time (t) equals the rate multiplied by the time.

3   To get the horsepower (H) of an electric motor multiply the number of volts (v) by the number of amperes (a) and divide by 746.

4   Interest (I) on money is figured by multiplying the principal (P) by the rate (R) by the time (T).

5   The amperage (A) of an electrical circuit is equal to the wattage (W) divided by the voltage (V).

6   Profit (P) equals the margin (M) minus the overhead (O).

7   The distance (d) that an object will fall in any given time (t) is equal to the square of the time multiplied by 16.

8   The area (A) of a square figure is equal to the square of one of its sides (S).

9 Centigrade temperature (C) is equal to Fahrenheit temperature (F) minus 32°, multiplied by $\frac{5}{9}$.

10 The speed (R) of a revolving wheel is proportional to the number of revolutions (N) it makes in a given time (T).

RULE FOR SOLVING EQUATIONS

When you solve an equation you are finding the value of the unknown or literal number in terms of what has been given about the other numbers in the equation. To do this you must learn the following rules of procedure for treating equations. Primarily, *what you do to one side of an equation you must also do to the other*. This might be called the golden rule of algebra. Its observance is imperative in order to preserve equality.

Rule 1. *The same number may be added to both sides of an equation without changing its equality.*

EXAMPLE 1: If $x - 4 = 6$, what does x equal?

SOLUTION:
$x - 4 + 4 = 6 + 4$. Adding 4 to both sides,
$x = 10$,   ANS.

To check the solution of algebraic examples, *substitute the value of the unknown quantity as determined in the answer for the corresponding symbol in the original equation. If both sides produce the same number, the answer is correct.*

EXAMPLE 1: Check the correctness of 10 as the solution of $x - 4 = 6$.

METHOD:
$x - 4 = 6$, original equation,
$10 - 4 = 6$, substituting answer for symbol,
$6 = 6$, proof of correctness.

Rule 2. *The same number may be subtracted from both sides of an equation.*

EXAMPLE 2: If $n + 6 = 18$, what does n equal?

SOLUTION:
$n + 6 - 6 = 18 - 6$. Subtracting 6 from both sides, $n = 12$,   ANS.

Check by substituting 12 for n in the original equation. *Thus,* $n + 6 = 18$ becomes $12 + 6 = 18$ or $18 = 18$, which is correct.

Rule 3. *Both sides of an equation may be multiplied by the same number.*

EXAMPLE 3: If $\frac{1}{3}$ of a number is 10, find the number.

SOLUTION:
$\frac{1}{3} n$ or $\frac{n}{3} = 10$,

$\frac{n}{3} \times 3 = 10 \times 3$, multiplying both sides by 3,

$\frac{n}{\cancel{3}} \times \cancel{3} = 10 \times 3$, cancelling,

$n = 30$,   ANS.
Check the answer.

Rule 4. *Both sides of an equation may be divided by the same number.*

EXAMPLE 4: Two times a number is 30. What is the number?

SOLUTION:
$2n = 30$,

$\frac{2n}{2} = \frac{30}{2}$, dividing both sides by 2.

$n = 15$,   ANS.
Check the answer.

TRANSPOSITION

Transposition is the process of moving a quantity from one side of an equation to the other side by changing its sign of operation. This is exactly what has been done in carrying out the rules in the four examples above.

Division is the operation opposite to multiplication.

Addition is the operation opposite to subtraction.

Transposition is performed in order to obtain an equation in which the unknown quantity is on one side and the known quantity on the other.

Rule: *A term may be transposed from one side of an equation to the other if its sign is changed from + to −, or from − to +.*

Rule: *A factor (multiplier) may be removed from one side of an equation by making it a divisor in the other. A divisor may be removed from one side of an equation by making it a factor (multiplier) in the other.*

Observe again the solution to Example 1.

$x - 4 = 6$,   EXPLANATION: To get x by it-
$\quad x = 6 + 4$,   self on one side of the equa-
$\quad x = 10$.   tion, the −4 was transposed

from the left to the right side and made $+4$.

Observe again the solution to Example 2.

$n + 6 = 18$,   EXPLANATION: To get n by it-
$n = 18 - 6$,   self on one side of the equa-
$n = 12$.   tion, the $+6$ was transposed from the left to the right side and made -6.

Observe again the solution to Example 3.

$\dfrac{n}{3} = 10$,   EXPLANATION: To get n by itself on one side of the equation, the divisor 3 on the left was changed
$n = 10 \times 3$,   to the multiplier $3(\frac{3}{1})$ on the
$n = 30$.   right.

Observe again the solution to Example 4.

$2n = 30$,   EXPLANATION: To get n by itself on
$n = \dfrac{30}{2}$,   one side of the equation, the multi-plier 2 on the left was changed to
$n = 15$.   the divisor 2 on the right.

Note that transposition is essentially nothing more than a shortened method for performing like operations of addition, subtraction, multiplication or division on both sides of the equation.

Changing $x - 4 = 6$ to $x = 6 + 4$ is the same as adding 4 to both sides:

$$\begin{array}{rcl} x - 4 & = & 6 \\ +4 & = & +4 \\ \hline x & = & 10 \end{array}$$

Changing $n + 6 = 18$ to $n = 18 - 6$ is the same as subtracting 6 from both sides:

$$\begin{array}{rcl} n + 6 & = & 18 \\ -6 & = & -6 \\ \hline n & = & 12 \end{array}$$

Changing $\dfrac{n}{3} = 10$ to $n = 10 \times 3$ is the same as multiplying both sides by 3:

$\dfrac{n}{3} \times 3 = 10 \times 3$, in which the 3s on the left cancel.

Changing $2n = 30$ to $n = \dfrac{30}{2}$ is the same as dividing both sides by 2:

$\dfrac{2n}{2} = \dfrac{30}{2}$, in which the 2s on the left cancel.

When terms involving the unknown quantity occur on both sides of the equation, *perform such transpositions as may be necessary to collect all the unknown terms on one side (usually the left) andl all the known terms on the other.*

EXAMPLE 5: If $3x - 6 = x + 8$ what does x equal?

SOLUTION:

$3x = x + 8 + 6$,   transposing -6 from left to right.

$3x - x = 14$,   transposing x from right to left.

$2x = 14$,   transposing 2 as a multiplier from left to a di-
$x = \dfrac{14}{2}$,   visor at the right.

$x = 7$,   ANS.

Check:
$3x - 6 = x + 8$,
$21 - 6 = 7 + 8$,   substituting 7 for x,
$15 = 15$.   proof of correctness.

When using an algebraic formula in actual practice, it may be necessary to change its form from that in which it has been originally expressed. Such changes are effected by tranposition.

EXAMPLE 6: If $R = \dfrac{WC}{L}$, solve for W, C, and L.

SOLUTION:

$R = \dfrac{WC}{L}$, original formula

$\dfrac{LR}{C} = W$. To separate W, C and L are transposed.

$\dfrac{LR}{W} = C$. To separate C, L and W are transposed.

$L = \dfrac{WC}{R}$. To separate L, L and R are transposed.

Practice Exercise No. 10

Solve by transposition:

1	$p + 3 = 8$	$p = ?$
2	$2n = 25$	$n = ?$
3	$\frac{1}{2}x = 14$	$x = ?$
4	$5c - 3 = 27$	$c = ?$
5	$18 = 5y - 2$	$y = ?$
6	$\frac{2}{3}n = 24$	$n = ?$

7   $\dfrac{a}{2} + \dfrac{a}{4} = 36$ $a = ?$

8   $W = \dfrac{b}{c}$ $b = ?$

9   $V = \dfrac{W}{A}$ $A = ?$

10   $H = \dfrac{P}{AW}$ $W = ?$

FUNDAMENTAL OPERATIONS

Addition is performed thus:

$$
\begin{array}{r}
3a - 4b + 2c \\
-8a + 6b - 3c \\
6a - 4b + 8c \\
\hline
a - 2b + 7c
\end{array}
$$

EXPLANATION: The terms are arranged in columns in such a way that all like terms are in the same column.

Subtraction is performed thus:

$$
\begin{array}{r}
8a - 4b + 2c \\
5a - 6b + 8c \\
\hline
3a + 2b - 6c
\end{array}
$$

EXPLANATION: To subtract algebraically, whenever you cannot directly subtract a smaller from a larger quantity of like sign, mentally change the sign of the subtrahend and perform an addition.
$8a - 5a = 3a;$ $-4b + 6b = +2b;$
$2c - 8c = -6c.$

Multiplication is performed thus:

$$
\begin{array}{r}
a^2 - 2ab + b^2 \\
a - b \\
\hline
a^3 - 2a^2b + ab^2 \\
- a^2b + 2ab^2 - b^3 \\
\hline
a^3 - 3a^2b + 3ab^2 - b^3
\end{array}
$$

EXPLANATION: Each term in the multiplicand is multiplied separately by a and then by b. Like terms are set under each other and the whole is added. $+ \times +$ gives $+$; $- \times -$ gives $+$; $+ \times -$ gives $-$.

Division is performed thus:

$$\frac{3a^2b + 3ab^2 + 3a}{3a} = ab + b^2 + 1, \text{ or } b^2 + ab + 1.$$

EXPLANATION: $3a$ is a factor of each term in the dividend. Separate divisions give us $ab + b^2 + 1$. This is changed to $b^2 + ab + 1$ because it is customary to place algebraic terms in the order of their highest powers.

Practice Exercise No. 11

USE OF FORMULAS AND EQUATIONS

1   Diameters of pulleys are inversely proportioned to their rpm. $\dfrac{D}{d} = \dfrac{r}{R}$. An 18″ diameter pulley turning at 100 rpm is driving a 6″ diameter pulley. What is the rpm of the smaller pulley?

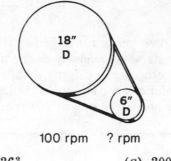

100 rpm   ? rpm

(A) $36\frac{2}{3}$ _____   (C) 300 _____
(B) 600 _____   (D) 900 _____

2   What size pulley at 144 rpm will drive a 9″ pulley at 256 rpm?

(A) 24″ _____   (C) 16″ _____
(B) $5\frac{1}{6}$″ _____   (D) 32″ _____

3   Three times a certain number plus twice the same number is 90. What is the number?

(A) 16 _____   (C) 20 _____
(B) 18 _____   (D) 24 _____

4   The larger of two numbers is seven times the smaller. What is the larger if their sum is 32?

(A) 28 _____   (C) 25 _____
(B) 36 _____   (D) 39 _____

5   Six hundred pairs of shoes are to be divided up among three army units. The second unit is to get twice as many as the first, and the third unit is to get as many as the first and second units together. How many pairs of shoes does the second unit get?

(A) 100 _____   (C) 300 _____
(B) 200 _____   (D) 400 _____

6   Two aviators are 3,000 miles part. They start toward each other, one at a rate of 200 miles per hour and the other at 300 miles per hour. How much distance does the faster one cover up to the time they meet? $R \times T = D$.

(A) 1,200 _____   (C) 1,600 _____
(B) 1,400 _____   (D) 1,800 _____

7 Two soldiers start out from camp in opposite directions. One travels twice as fast as the other. In 10 hours they are 24 miles apart. What is the rate of the faster soldier?

(A) $\frac{4}{5}$ mi. hr. _____   (C) $1\frac{4}{5}$ mi. hr. _____
(B) 1 mi. hr. _____   (D) $1\frac{3}{5}$ mi. hr. _____

8 A man has 3 times as many nickels as quarters. How many nickels has he if the value of both together is $8.00? Hint: Let n = no. of quarters and $3n$ = no. of nickels and multiply each by their value.

(A) 20 _____   (C) 60 _____
(B) 40 _____   (D) 80 _____

9 When two gears run together the revolutions per minute vary inversely as the number of teeth. A 48-tooth gear is driving a 72-tooth gear. Find the revolutions per minute of the larger gear if the smaller one is running at 160 rpm.

(A) $106\frac{2}{3}$ rpm _____   (C) $66\frac{2}{3}$ rpm _____
(B) 240 rpm _____   (D) 180 rpm _____

10 A teeter board is a form of lever. It is balanced when the weight times the distance on one side equals the weight times the distance on the other side. A weight of 120 lbs. is placed $4\frac{1}{2}$ feet from the fulcrum. What weight is needed to balance this at a distance of 5 feet from the fulcrum on the other end?

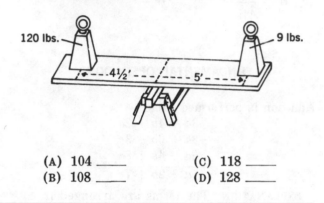

(A) 104 _____   (C) 118 _____
(B) 108 _____   (D) 128 _____

Factors and Roots

A **factor** of a number is an exact divisor of that number. Thus 2 is a factor of 6 because $6 \div 2 = 3$ exactly; 3 is the other factor of 6.

For the number 9, 3 and 3 are equal factors; and for 8, 2, 2 and 2 are equal factors. These equal factors are called roots of the number. Thus:

The number 3 is a *root* of 9.

The number 2 is a *root* of 8.

A root of a number is therefore one of the equal factors which, if multiplied together, produce the number.

The **square root** of a number is one of TWO equal factors which, if multiplied together, produce that number.

$3 \times 3 = 9$, hence 3 is the *square root* of 9.

The **cube root** of a number is one of THREE equal factors which if multiplied together produce that number.

$3 \times 3 \times 3 = 27$, hence 3 is the *cube root* of 27.

A **fourth root** of a number is one of FOUR equal factors; the fifth root is one of five, and so on.

The square root is the one most frequently used in mathematics.

The sign indicating square root is $\sqrt{}$. It is placed over the number whose root is to be found. $\sqrt{25}$ means the square root is 25. It is called the **square root sign** or **radical sign**.

To indicate a root other than square root a small figure called the **index** of the root is placed in the radical sign. Thus: $\sqrt[3]{8}$ means the cube root of 8.

The square root of 4 = 2, of 36 = 6, or 49 = 7.

To check that you have obtained the correct square root of a number, *multiply it by itself. If the product is equal to the original number the answer is correct.*

Practice Exercise No. 12

Find the roots indicated and check.

1 $\sqrt{64}$ 7 $\sqrt[3]{1000}$
2 $\sqrt{100}$ 8 $\sqrt{1}$
3 $\sqrt{81}$ 9 $\sqrt{.04} = \sqrt{.2 \times .2} = .2$

4 $\sqrt[3]{27}$ 10 $\sqrt{.09}$

5 $\sqrt[3]{125}$ 11 $\sqrt{1.44}$

6 $\sqrt{144}$ 12 $\sqrt{.0025}$

Not all numbers have exact square roots. Nor can we always determine square root by *inspection* as you have done above. (Inspection means "trial and error.") There is an arithmetic method of extracting the square roots of numbers whereby an answer may be found that will be correct to any necessary or desired number of decimal places.

METHOD FOR FINDING SQUARE ROOTS

Find the square root of 412,164.

1. Place the square root sign over the number, and then, beginning at the right, divide it into *periods* of two figures each. Connect the digits in each period with tie-marks as shown. In the answer there will be one digit for each period.

$$\sqrt{41\ 21\ 64}$$

2. Find the largest number which, when squared, is contained in the first left-hand period. In this case 6 is the number. Write 6 in the answer over the first period. Square it, making 36, and subtract 36 from the first period. Bring down the next period, making the new dividend 5 21.

$$\begin{array}{r} 6 \\ \sqrt{41\ 21\ 64} \\ \underline{36} \\ 5\ 21 \end{array}$$

3. Multiply the root 6 by 2, getting 12. Place the 12 to the left of 5 21, since 12 is the new trial divisor. Allow, however, for one more digit to follow 12. The place of this missing digit may be indicated by a question mark. To find the number belonging in this place, ignore (cover over) the last number in the dividend 5 21, and see how many times 12 goes into 52. Approximately 4. Place the 4 above its period, 21, and put it in place of the ? in the divisor.

$$\begin{array}{r} 6\ \ 4 \\ \sqrt{41\ 21\ 64} \\ \underline{36} \\ 12\overset{?}{_4}\ \big)\ 5\ 21 \end{array}$$

4. Multiply the divisor 124 by the new number in the root, 4. 124 × 4 = 496. Place this product under 521 and subtract. Bring down the next period, 64.

$$\begin{array}{r} 6\ \ 4 \\ \sqrt{41\ 21\ 64} \\ \underline{36} \\ 124\ \big)\ 5\ 21 \\ \underline{4\ 96} \\ 25\ 64 \end{array}$$

5. Multiply 64 by 2 to get 128 as the new trial divisor. 128 goes into 256 two times. Place the 2 above the next period in the root and also in the divisor. Then multiply the divisor 1282 by the new root 2, to get 25 64. Subtracting, the remainder is zero. 642 is therefore the exact square root.

$$\begin{array}{r} 6\ \ 4\ \ 2 \\ \sqrt{41\ 21\ 64} \\ \underline{36} \\ 124\ \big)\ 5\ 21 \\ \underline{4\ 96} \\ 128\overset{?}{_2}\ \big)\ 25\ 64 \\ \underline{25\ 64} \\ 0 \end{array}$$

6. CHECK: 642 × 642 = 412,164.

FINDING THE SQUARE ROOT OF DECIMALS

A slight variation in method is necessary when it is required to find the square root of a decimal figure.

Mark off periods beginning at the decimal point. Count to the right for the decimal quantities and to the left for the whole numbers. If the last period of the whole numbers contains one figure, leave it by itself, but remember that in such a case the first figure in the root cannot be more than 3 because the square of any number greater than 3 is a two-place number. If the last period of the decimal numbers contains only one figure you may add a zero to it. This is because two digits are necessary to make up a period, while the addition of a zero at the right of a decimal figure does not change its value.

The square root of a decimal will contain as many decimal places as there are periods, or half as many decimal places as the given number.

The operations in obtaining the square root of a decimal number are the same as for whole numbers.

Follow the steps in the example following.

EXAMPLE 1: Find the square root of 339.2964.

1. Beginning at decimal point, mark off periods to left and right.

2. 1 is the largest whole-number square root that is contained in 3, which constitutes the first period.

3. Place decimal point in root after the 8 because the root of the next period has a decimal value.

4. Bring down 29 next to the 15, making 1529 the new dividend. Multiply the root 18 by 2, making 36 the new divisor.

5. Covering the 9 of 1529, 36 seems to be contained about 4 times in this number. Place a 4

$$\begin{array}{r} 1\ \ 8.\ 4\ \ 2 \\ \sqrt{3\ 39.29\ 64} \\ \underline{1} \\ 2\overset{?}{_8}\ \big)\ 2\ 39 \\ \underline{2\ 24} \\ 36\overset{?}{_4}\ \big)\ 15\ 29 \\ \underline{14\ 56} \\ 368\overset{?}{_2}\ \big)\ 73\ 64 \\ \underline{73\ 64} \\ 0 \end{array}$$

in the root above 29, and multiply 364 by 4 to get 1456. Substract this from 1529.

6. Bring down the 64 and repeat the previous process. Since the number is a perfect square, the remainder is zero.

When the given number is not a perfect square, *add zeros after the decimal point, or after the last figure if the original number is already in decimal form, and carry out the answer to the required or desired number of decimal places. Usually two places are sufficient.*

Note: In working a square root example, when a divisor is larger than the corresponding dividend, write zero in the trial divisor and bring down the next period. This is illustrated in the next example.

EXAMPLE 2: Find the square root of 25.63 to three decimal places.

$$
\begin{array}{r}
5.\ 0\ \ 6\ \ 2+,\ \text{ANS.} \\
\sqrt{25.63\ 00\ 00} \\
25 \\
100\tfrac{?}{6}\overline{|\ 0\ 63\ 00} \\
60\ 36 \\
1012\tfrac{?}{2}\overline{|\ 2\ 64\ 00} \\
2\ 02\ 44 \\
61\ 56\ \text{remainder}
\end{array}
$$

To find the square of a fraction, determine separately the square roots of the numerator and of the denominator, and reduce to lowest terms or to a decimal.

EXAMPLE 3: $\sqrt{\dfrac{33}{67}}$.

$$\sqrt{\frac{33}{67}} = \frac{5.745}{8.185} = .701,\ \text{ANS.}$$

USE OF SQUARE ROOTS

Although in many test situations the student may be required to work out square roots as above, in actual practice it is inconvenient to stop work for such calculations. Most mathematics books therefore contain tables giving powers and roots of numbers. Such a table is found on page 854 of the Quick Reference Encyclopedia.

Any formula or problem containing the square of a number or factor, requires a knowledge of square roots for its solution. You will find many such problems and formulas in the material contained in Chapter Fourteen on geometry.

EXAMPLE 1: Find the length of one side of a square whose area is 225 square feet.

SOLUTION: Let x = length of one side.

Area = base $\times$ height. $\therefore$ Area = x^2,

$x^2 = 225$,

$x = 15$, extracting the square root of both sides of the equation.

EXAMPLE 2: $d = 16t^2$ (in which d is distance and t is time) is the formula for measuring the distance an object will fall in t seconds irrespective of its weight. If an object fell 10,000 feet, how long would it take to reach the ground?

SOLUTION:

$10000 = 16t^2$,

$\dfrac{10000}{16} = t^2$, dividing both sides by 16

$625 = t^2$,

$25 = t$,   extracting square root of both sides of the equation.

Practice Exercise No. 13

Work out examples 1–5. Find answers in Table V for 6–10.

1	$\sqrt{5329}$	6	$\sqrt{676}$
2	$\sqrt{1225}$	7	$\sqrt{1849}$
3	$\sqrt{2937.64}$	8	$\sqrt{3136}$
4	$\sqrt{312.649}$	9	$\sqrt{7225}$
5	$\sqrt{428}$ to 2 places	10	$\sqrt{9409}$

Powers

To square a number is to use that number as a factor twice. Thus $4 \times 4 = 16$, and 16 is said to be the **square** of 4. This is also called raising a number to its **second power.** Using a number as a factor three times (for instance, $4 \times 4 \times 4 = 64$) is called raising it to the **third power.** The given case would be written 4^3, and be read *four cubed.* 4^4 is read *four to the fourth power,* 4^5 is read *four to the fifth power,* etc.

A **power** of a number is the product obtained by multiplying the number by itself a given number of times. Raising a number to a given power is the opposite process of finding the corresponding root of a number.

To raise a given number to its indicated power, multiply the number by itself as many times as the power indicated. Thus, $3^5 = 3 \times 3 \times 3 \times 3 \times 3 = 243$. The small five used in writing 3^5 is called an *exponent,* while the number 3 is called the base.

An **exponent** indicates the power to which a number is to be raised. *Thus, x^3 means that x is to be raised to the third power.*

$$\text{If } x^3 = 125,$$
$$x = ?$$

To raise a fraction to a given power, *raise both the numerator and the denominator to the given power.*

$$(\tfrac{1}{3})^2 = \tfrac{1}{3} \times \tfrac{1}{3} = \tfrac{1}{9},$$
$$(\tfrac{3}{5})^2 = \tfrac{3}{5} \times \tfrac{3}{5} = \tfrac{9}{25}.$$

Any power or root of 1 is 1, because 1 multiplied or divided by 1 any number of times is 1.

Any number **without an exponent** is considered to be the first power or first root of itself. Neither the exponent nor the index 1 is written. *Thus, x means x^1.*

Any number raised to the **zero power,** such as 5^0, is equal to 1. The reason for this will appear when we consider the multiplication of powers of numbers.

When a number has a **negative exponent,** *i.e.,* when the exponent is preceded by the minus sign, as in 3^{-3}, it indicates the reciprocal of the indicated power of the number. Since $3^3 = 27$, $3^{-3} = \frac{1}{27}$, the reciprocal of 27. 12^{-2} means the reciprocal of 12^2, or $\frac{1}{144}$.

When a number has a **fractional exponent** with a numerator of 1, as has $x^{\frac{1}{2}}$, it signifies that the corresponding *root* is to be taken of the number. In other words, $16^{\frac{1}{2}} = \sqrt{16} = 4$.

When a fractional exponent has a numerator greater than one, as has $x^{\frac{2}{3}}$, the numerator indicates the power to which the number is to be raised, while the denominator indicates the root that is to be taken. Accordingly, $4^{\frac{3}{2}} = \sqrt{4^3} = \sqrt{64} = 8$. To reverse this example, $8^{\frac{2}{3}} = \sqrt[3]{8^2} = \sqrt[3]{64} = 4$.

POWERS OF 10

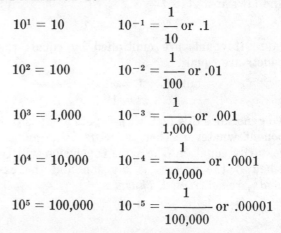

$$10^1 = 10 \qquad 10^{-1} = \frac{1}{10} \text{ or } .1$$
$$10^2 = 100 \qquad 10^{-2} = \frac{1}{100} \text{ or } .01$$
$$10^3 = 1{,}000 \qquad 10^{-3} = \frac{1}{1{,}000} \text{ or } .001$$
$$10^4 = 10{,}000 \qquad 10^{-4} = \frac{1}{10{,}000} \text{ or } .0001$$
$$10^5 = 100{,}000 \qquad 10^{-5} = \frac{1}{100{,}000} \text{ or } .00001$$

From this it is apparent that 10 raised to any positive power is equal to a multiple of 10 bearing as many zeros as are represented by the quantity of the exponent.

Also, 10 raised to any negative power is equal to a multiple of 10 containing as many decimal places as the quantity of the negative exponent.

The above forms are used for writing very large and very small numbers in an abbreviated way. *Thus,*

$$32{,}000 \text{ may be written as } 32 \times 10^3,$$
$$6{,}900{,}000 \text{ may be written as } 6.9 \times 10^6,$$
$$.000008 \text{ may be written as } 8 \times 10^{-6},$$
$$.0000000235 \text{ may be written as } 2.35 \times 10^{-8}.$$

A positive exponent moves the decimal point a corresponding number of places to the right. *Thus,* $8.2 \times 10^7 = 82{,}000{,}000.$

A negative exponent moves the decimal point a corresponding number of places to the left. *Thus,* $6.3 \times 10^{-5} = .000063.$

LAWS OF EXPONENTS

To multiply powers of the same base, *add their exponents.*

> *Thus,*　2^2 times $2^3 = 2^5$.
> PROOF:　$2^2 = 4$; $2^3 = 8$; $2^5 = 32$;
> 　　　　$4 \times 8 = 32$.

To divide powers of the same base, *subtract the exponent of the divisor from the exponent of the dividend.*

> *Thus,*　$3^5 \div 3^3 = 3^2$.
> PROOF:　$3^5 = 243$; $3^3 = 27$; $3^2 = 9$;
> 　　　　$243 \div 27 = 9$.

It will now become apparent why *any* number with an exponent of zero is equal to 1. According to the laws just stated—

$$x^3 \times x^0 = x^{3-0} = x^3$$

because if equals are multiplied by equals the products are equal;

$$\text{but } x^3 \times 1 = x^3,$$
$$\therefore x^0 = 1.$$

To generalize this fact, let *n* denote any positive exponent whatever. Then $x^n \times x^0 = x^n$ and x^0 necessarily equals 1. The same conclusion will be reached if the process is division and the exponents are subtracted. *Thus,*

$$x^n \div x^0 = x^{n-0} = x^n, \therefore x^0 = 1.$$

Practice Exercise No. 14

Perform the indicated operations.

1	$6^2 =$	9	$43 \times 10^6 =$
2	$9^3 =$	10	$6.2 \times 10^5 =$
3	$25^{\frac{1}{2}} =$	11	$(\frac{2}{3})^2 =$
4	$4^{-3} =$	12	$6^{\frac{3}{2}} =$
5	$432^2 =$	13	$2.8 \times 10^{-7} =$
6	$8^5 =$	14	$25 \times 10^{-4} =$
7	$\sqrt{81} =$	15	$12.2 \times 10^7 =$
8	$\sqrt[3]{125} =$		

METHOD FOR FINDING CUBE ROOTS

In studying the following example, read step by step the rule that follows it and note how the example illustrates the rule.

EXAMPLE: What is the cube root of 264,609,288?

$$\sqrt[3]{\overline{264}\ \overline{609}\ \overline{288}}$$
$$\quad 6 \quad 4 \quad 2$$

			$6^3 = 216$
1st Part. Div.	3×60^2	$=$	10800 ⌉ 48 609
	$3 \times 60 \times 4$	$=$	720
	4^2	$=$	16
1st Comp. Div.			11536 ⌉ 46 144
			2 465 288
2nd Part. Div.	3×640^2	$= 1228800$	
	$3 \times 640 \times 2$	$= 3840$	
	2^2	$= 4$	
2nd Comp. Div.		1232644	2 465 288

The following rule is more readily understood if we bear in mind the formula for the cube of the sum of two numbers:

$$(a + b)^3 = a^3 + 3a^2b + 3ab^2 + b^3$$

Rule: 1. *Separate the given number into periods of three figures each, beginning at the right, and place over it the radical sign with the proper index.*

The extreme left-hand period may contain one, two or three figures.

2. *Determine the greatest cube that is smaller than the first left-hand period, and write its cube root, in the position shown, as the first figure of the required root.*

This root corresponds to *a* in the formula.

3. *Subtract the cube of this root from the first period and annex the next period to the remainder.*

4. *Multiply this root mentally by ten and write three times the square of this as a partial divisor.*

5. *Make a trial division to determine what the next figure in the root will be and write it in its proper place.*

6. *Add to the partial divisor* (1) *the product of 3 times the first part of the root considered as tens multiplied by the second part of the root; and* (2) *the square of the second part of the root. The sum of these numbers is the complete divisor.*

7. *Multiply the complete divisor by the second part of the root and subtract the product from the new dividend.*

Note in the example that at this point $a = 60$ and $b = 4$. When we subtracted 216 we took 216,000 or a^3 out of the given figure. When we multiply the first complete divisor by 4, this is equivalent to multiplying $3a^2$ (10800) by *b*, producing $3a^2b$; $3ab$ (720) by *b*, producing $3ab^2$; and b^2 (16) by *b*, producing b^3. Hence when we write 46144 previous to performing the subtraction we have fulfilled up to this point all the requirements of the formula

$$(a + b)^3 = a^3 + 3a^2b + 3ab^2 + b^3.$$

8. *Bring down the next period and continue the same process until all the figures of the root have been determined.*

When the third figure of the root is found in the example a becomes 640 and b becomes 2. The student should check the manner in which multiplication of the second complete divisor by 2 fulfills the requirements of the formula. The correctness of the complete extraction may of course be checked by multiplying the determined root to its third power.

APPROXIMATE ROOTS OF FRACTIONS

We have seen that the square root of a fraction is the square root of its numerator placed over the square root of the denominator, subject to further reduction or to conversion to a decimal.

When the terms of a fraction are not perfect squares it is often desirable to approximate a square root without going to the trouble of making an exact calculation. This is done by multiplying the terms of the fraction by any number that will make the denominator a perfect square, as in the following example.

EXAMPLE: What is the approximate square root of $\frac{19}{8}$?

$\frac{19}{8} = \frac{38}{16}$, of which the approximate square root, $\frac{6}{4}$, is correct to within $\frac{1}{4}$; or

$\frac{19}{8} \times \frac{32}{32} = \frac{608}{256}$, of which the approximate square root, $\frac{25}{16}$, is correct to within $\frac{1}{16}$.

EXPLANATION: We select a factor that will make the denominator a perfect square. We then extract the square root of the denominator and the square root of the perfect square that is nearest to the numerator. If we write the fraction as $\frac{38}{16}$, the square root of the denominator is 4 and the square root of the nearest perfect square to 38 is 6. The resulting approximate square root, $\frac{6}{4}$, reducible to $\frac{3}{2}$, is correct to within $\frac{1}{4}$.

If we want a closer approximation than this, we multiply by a larger factor. Using 32 as a factor, we get $\frac{608}{256}$. The square root of the denominator is 16. The nearest perfect square to

608 is 625, the square root of which is 25. The resulting approximate square root, $\frac{25}{16}$, is correct to within $\frac{1}{16}$.

It will be noted that the larger the factor the more closely will the result approximate the correct value.

The approximate cube root of a fraction may be found by a similar process.

EXAMPLE: Find the approximate cube root of $\frac{173}{32}$.

$\frac{173}{32} = \frac{346}{64}$, of which the approximate cube root, $\frac{7}{4}$, is correct to within $\frac{1}{4}$; or

$\frac{173}{32} = \frac{2768}{512}$, of which the approximate cube root, $\frac{14}{8}$, is correct to within $\frac{1}{8}$.

EXPLANATION: The denominator has been multiplied by two different factors in order to demonstrate again that the higher factor produces the more nearly accurate answer. It will be noted that the final result in both cases has the same ultimate value since $\frac{19}{8} = \frac{7}{4}$. If, however, we had not worked out the second solution we would not know that $\frac{7}{4}$ is actually correct to within $\frac{1}{8}$.

HIGHER ROOTS

If the index of a higher root contains no other prime factors than 2 and 3, we can find the required root by repeated extraction of square or cube roots, according to the nature of the problem.

EXAMPLE 1: What is the fourth root of 923521?

SOLUTION: $\sqrt{923521} = 961$,
$$\sqrt{961} = 31, \quad \text{ANS.}$$

EXPLANATION: Since the fourth power of a number is its square multiplied by its square, we find the fourth root of a given number representing such a power by extracting the square root of the square root.

EXAMPLE 2: What is the sixth root of 191102976?

SOLUTION: $\sqrt{191102976} = 13824$,
$$\sqrt[3]{13824} = 24, \quad \text{ANS.}$$

EXPLANATION: The sixth root is found by taking the cube root of the square root. The order of making the extractions is of course immaterial.

Higher roots with indexes that are prime to 2 and 3 are found by methods based on the same general theory as that underlying the methods for extracting square and cube roots. Thus if it be required to find the fifth root of a number, we consider that $(a + b)^5 = a^5 + 5a^4b + 10a^3b^2 + 10a^2b^3 + 5ab^4 + b^5$. After subtracting a^5 from the first period we must construct a complete divisor which when multiplied by b will satisfy the whole formula. Dividing what follows a^5 in the formula by b we get as the requirement of our complete divisor, $5a^4 + 10a^2b + 10a^2b^2 + 5ab^3 + b^4$. We use the first term of this, $5a^4$, as a trial divisor, but where the complete divisor is so complex several estimates may have to be tried before finding the correct value for b. In actual practice, however, higher roots are more commonly found by the use of logarithms and the slide rule, as in Chapter Twelve.

HANDY ALGEBRAIC FORMULAS

The following formulas should be memorized.

$$(a + b)^2 = a^2 + 2ab + b^2$$
$$(a - b)^2 = a^2 - 2ab + b^2$$
$$(a + b)(a - b) = a^2 - b^2$$
$$(a + b)^3 = a^3 + 3a^2b + 3ab^2 + b^3$$

These formulas have many applications, and they are particularly applicable to doing arithmetic by short-cut methods. Compare what is said below with the methods of multiplication starting on page 23.

TRANSLATING NUMBERS INTO ALGEBRA

In the following consider that a represents a number of the tens order, like 10, 20, 30, etc., while b represents a number of the units order.

Squaring a number:

EXAMPLE 1: Multiply 63 by 63.

60×60 combined with $3 \times 3 = 3609$,
6×60, or 360, added to 3609 = 3969, ANS.

EXPLANATION: 60×60 represents the a^2 of the formula, to which we at once add 9 as the b^2. The $2ab$ is most quickly figured out as $2 \times 3 \times 60$.

EXAMPLE 2: What is the square of 65?

60×70 combined with $25 = 4225$, ANS.

EXPLANATION: Doing this example by the previous method we would get $3625 + (2 \times 5 \times 60)$. But $(2 \times 5) \times 60 = 10 \times 60$. Hence we at once multiply 60 by 10 more than we otherwise would, or 70.

EXAMPLE 3: What is the square of 89?

8100 combined with 1 = 8101,
8101 − 180 = 7921, ANS.

EXPLANATION: Since the digits are large and 89 is near 90 it is preferable here to use the square of $a - b$, taking a as 90 and b as 1. $a^2 + b^2 = 8101$; $2ab = 2 \times 1 \times 90$ or 180, which in accordance with the formula is subtracted from 8101.

Multiplying a sum by a difference:

EXAMPLE 4: How much is 53×47?

$2500 - 9 = 2491$, ANS.

EXPLANATION: $a = 50$, $b = 3$. $53 = a + b$; $47 = a - b$. $(a + b)(a - b) = a^2 - b^2 = 2500 -$. Note that this method is applicable whenever the units add up to 10 and the tens differ by 10.

Cubing a number:

EXAMPLE: What is the cube of 23?

$$\begin{array}{r} 8027 \\ (69 \times 60) \quad 4140 \\ \hline 12167, \quad \text{ANS.} \end{array}$$

EXPLANATION: $(a + b)^3 = a^3 + 3a^2b + 3ab^2 + b^3$. $a^3 + b^3$ may be quickly written down as 8027. $3a^2b + 3ab^2 = 3ab(a + b)$. $a + b$ is the given number, in this case 23. We therefore want 3×23 or 69 multiplied by ab or 3×20 or 60. In other words, to the cubes of the digits properly placed add three times the number multiplied by the product of its digits with an added 0. A little practice makes all this quite simple. For small numbers the method is very much quicker than performing separate multiplications.

In solving examples like the preceding there is of course no reason why a may not represent a number of the hundreds plus the tens order instead of one of the tens order. Consider a few examples:

EXAMPLE 1: Square 116.
$12136 + 1320 = 13456$, ANS.

EXAMPLE 2: Square 125.
130×120 combined with $25 = 15625$, ANS.

EXAMPLE 3: Multiply 127 by 113.
$14400 - 49 = 14351$, ANS. from $(a^2 - b^2)$.

Practice Exercise No. 15

Find the required roots (approximate in the case of fractions).

1	$\sqrt[3]{2460375}$	11	$\sqrt[3]{\frac{2}{3}}\ (\times\frac{72}{72})$		
2	$\sqrt[3]{11089567}$	12	$\sqrt[3]{\frac{2}{3}}\ (\times\frac{15552}{15552})$		
3	$\sqrt[3]{40353607}$	13	$\sqrt[3]{\frac{2}{3}}\ (\times\frac{124416}{124416})$		
4	$\sqrt[3]{403583419}$	14	$\sqrt[3]{5\frac{13}{32}}(\times\frac{2}{2})$		
5	$\sqrt[3]{115501303}$	15	$\sqrt[3]{\frac{125}{256}}(\times\frac{2}{2})$		
6	$\sqrt{\frac{2}{3}}\ (\times\frac{48}{48})$	16	$\sqrt[4]{6561}$		
7	$\sqrt{\frac{38}{5}}(\times\frac{5}{5})$	17	$\sqrt[6]{117649}$		
8	$\sqrt{\frac{45}{7}}(\times\frac{343}{343})$	18	$\sqrt[4]{29\frac{52}{81}}$		
9	$\sqrt{10\frac{1}{2}}(\times\frac{200}{200})$	19	$\sqrt[4]{104\frac{536}{625}}$		
10	$\sqrt{7\frac{1}{8}}(\times\frac{20000}{20000})$	20	$\sqrt[6]{11\frac{25}{64}}$		

Do the following mentally by algebraic methods.

21	21^2		$(a-b)^2$
22	23^2	32	39^2
23	33^2	33	99^2
24	37^2	34	28^2
25	39^2	35	38^2
26	35^2	36	19×21
27	65^2		$(a+b)(a-b)$
28	95^2	37	28×32
29	105^2	38	37×43
30	205^2	39	46×54
31	29^2	40	48×72

Algebraic Processes

DEFINITIONS

A **monomial** is an algebraic expression of one term. *Thus,* $8a$ and $16a^2b$ and $\sqrt{3ax}$ are monomials.

A **polynomial** is an algebraic expression of more than one term. *Thus,* $a + b$, and $a^2 + 2ab + b^2$, and $a^3 + 3a^2b + 3ab^2 + b^3$, are three different *polynomials.*

A **binomial** is a polynomial that contains *two* terms. *Thus,* $a + b$, and $a + 1$, and $\sqrt{2} + \sqrt{3}$, are *binomials.* A **trinomial** contains *three* terms.

FACTORING

Factoring is the process of separating, or resolving, a quantity into factors.

No general rule can be given for factoring. In most cases the operation is performed by inspection and trial. The methods are best explained by examples.

Principle: *If every term of a polynomial contains the same monomial factor, then that monomial is one factor of the polynomial, and the other factor is equal to the quotient of the polynomial divided by the monomial factor.*

EXAMPLE: Factor the binomial $8a^2x^2 + 4a^3x$.

SOLUTION: $8a^2x^2 + 4a^3x = 4a^2x(2x + a)$.

EXPLANATION: We see by inspection that $4a^2x$ is a factor common to both terms. Dividing by $4a^2x$ we arrive at the other factor.

Principle: *If a trinomial contains three terms two of which are squares and if the third term is equal to plus or minus twice the product of the square roots of the other two, the expression may be recognized as the square of a binomial.*

Thus, $a^2x^2 + 2acx + c^2 = (ax + c)^2$, and $9a^2b^2 - 24a^2bc + 16a^2c^2 = (3ab - 4ac)^2$.

Principle: *If an expression represents the difference between two squares, it can be factored as the product of the sum of the roots by the difference between them.*

Thus, $4x^2 - 9y^2 = (2x + 3y)(2x - 3y)$, and $25a^4b^4x^4 - 4z^2 = (5a^2b^2x^2 + 2z)(5a^2b^2x^2 - 2z)$.

Principle: *If the factors of an expression contain like terms, these should be collected so as to present the result in the simplest form.*

EXAMPLE: Factor $(5a + 3b)^2 - (3a - 2b)^2$.

SOLUTION: $(5a + 3b)^2 - (3a - 2b)^2$
$= [(5a + 3b) + (3a - 2b)][(5a + 3b) - (3a - 2b)]$
$= (5a + 3b + 3a - 2b)(5a + 3b - 3a + 2b)$
$= (8a + b)(2a + 5b)$, ANS.

Principle: *A trinomial in the form of $a^4 + a^2b^2 + b^4$ can be written in the form of the difference between two squares.*

EXAMPLE: Resolve $9x^4 + 26x^2y^2 + 25y^4$ into factors.

SOLUTION:
$$9x^4 + 26x^2y^2 + 25y^4$$
$$+ 4x^2y^2 \qquad\quad - 4x^2y^2$$
$$\overline{(9x^4 + 30x^2y^2 + 25y^4) - 4x^2y^2}$$
$$= (3x^2 + 5y^2)^2 - 4x^2y^2$$
$$= (3x^2 + 5y^2 + 2xy)(3x^2 + 5y^2 - 2xy)$$
$$= (3x^2 + 2xy + 5y^2)(3x^2 - 2xy + 5y^2)$$

EXPLANATION: We note that the given expression is nearly a perfect square. We therefore add $4x^2y^2$ to it to make it a square and also subtract from it the same quantity. We then write it in the form of a difference between two squares. We resolve this into factors and rewrite the result so as to make the terms follow in the order of the powers of x.

Principle: *If a trinomial has the form $x^2 + ax + b$ and is factorable into two binomial factors, the first term of each factor will be x; the second term of the binomials will be two numbers whose product is b and whose sum is equal to a, which is the coefficient of the middle term of the trinomial.*

EXAMPLE 1: Factor $x^2 + 10x + 24$.

SOLUTION: $x^2 + 10x + 24 = (x + 6)(x + 4)$.

EXPLANATION: We are required to find two numbers whose product is 24 and whose sum is 10. The following pairs of factors will produce 24: 1 and 24, 2 and 12, 3 and 8, 4 and 6. From among these we select the pair whose sum is 10.

EXAMPLE 2: Factor $x^2 - 16x + 28$.

SOLUTION: $x^2 - 16x + 28 = (x - 14)(x - 2)$.

EXPLANATION: We are required to find two numbers whose product is 28 and whose algebraic sum is -16. Since their product is positive they must both have the same sign, and since their sum is negative they must both be negative. The negative factors that will produce 28 are -1 and -28, -2 and -14, -4 and -7. We select the pair whose algebraic sum is -16.

EXAMPLE 3: Factor $x^2 + 5x - 24$.

SOLUTION: $x^2 + 5x - 24 = (x + 8)(x - 3)$.

EXPLANATION: We are required to find two numbers whose product is -24 and whose algebraic sum is 5. Since their product is negative the numbers must have unlike signs, and since their sum is $+5x$, the larger number must be positive. The pairs of numbers that will produce 24, without considering signs, are 1 and 24, 2 and 12, 3 and 8, 4 and 6. From these we select the pair whose difference is 5. This is 3 and 8. We give the plus sign to the 8 and the minus sign to the 3.

EXAMPLE 4: Factor $x^2 - 7x - 18$.

SOLUTION: $x^2 - 7x - 18 = (x - 9)(x + 2)$.

EXPLANATION: We are required to find two numbers whose product is -18 and whose algebraic sum is -7. Since their product is negative the signs of the two numbers are unlike, and since their sum is negative, the larger number must be negative. The pairs of numbers that will produce 18, without considering signs, are 1 and 18, 2 and 9, 3 and 6. We select the pair whose difference is 7, giving the minus sign to the 9 and the plus sign to the 2.

EXAMPLE 5: Factor $x^2 - 7xy + 12y^2$.

SOLUTION: $x^2 - 7xy + 12y^2 = (x - 4y)(x - 3y)$.

EXPLANATION: We are required to find two terms whose product is $12y^2$ and whose algebraic sum is $-7y$. Since their product is positive and their sum negative they must both be negative terms. From the pairs of negative terms that will produce $+12y^2$ we select $-4y$ and $-3y$ as fulfilling the requirements.

When a trinomial factorable into two binomials has the form $ax^2 \pm bx \pm c$, it is resolved into factors by a process of trial and error which is continued until values are found that satisfy the requirements.

EXAMPLE 1: Factor $4x^2 + 26x + 2$

$$4x + 11$$
$$\diagdown$$
$$+ 11x + 8x = 19x \; (reject),$$
$$\diagup$$
$$x + 2$$

$$x + 11$$
$$\diagdown$$
$$+ 44x + 2x = 46x \; (reject),$$
$$\diagup$$
$$4x + 2$$

$$2x + 11$$
$$\diagdown$$
$$22x + 4x = 26x \; (correct).$$
$$\diagup$$
$$2x + 2$$

$\therefore 4x^2 + 26x + 22 = (2x + 11)(2x + 2)$, ANS.

EXPLANATION: We use what is called the *cross multiplication* method to find the required binomials. We consider the pairs of terms that will produce the first and last terms of the trinomials. We write down the various forms of examples that can be worked out with these, and we reject one trial result after another until we find the arrangement that will give us the correct value for the middle term of the given trinomial.

Instead of making a separate example out of each of the possibilities, the process is shortened by simply listing the possible factors involved, in the following manner:

$$\begin{array}{ccc} 1 & 4 & 2\,|\,11 \\ 4 & 1 & 2\,|\,\ 2 \end{array}$$

Factors to the left of the vertical line represent possible coefficients of x; those to the right of the line represent possible numerical values of second terms. Each pair of x coefficients is written in two positions (1 over 4, 4 over 1, etc.). Accordingly, it is not necessary to write second-term values in more than one position in order to exhaust the possibilities. We proceed with cross multiplication of the numbers on both sides of the vertical line. $(1 \times 2) + (4 \times 11) = 46$ *(too large—reject)*; $(4 \times 2) + (1 \times 11) = 19$ *(too small—reject)*; $(2 \times 2) + (2 \times 11) = 26$ *(correct.)*

EXAMPLE 2: Factor $24x^2 - 2x - 15$

SOLUTION:

$$\begin{array}{ccccccccc} 24 & 1 & 2 & 12 & 3 & 8 & 4 & 6 & |\ 1\ \ 3 \\ 1 & 24 & 12 & 2 & 8 & 3 & 6 & 4 & |\ 15\ 5 \end{array}$$

We select $\dfrac{4}{6}$ and $\dfrac{3}{5}$ as the combination of numbers that will give us the required middle term. $\therefore 24x^2 - 2x - 15 = (4x + 3)(6x - 5)$, ANS.

EXPLANATION: We write down the possible numerical values in the manner previously described. Inasmuch as the third term of the trinomial is negative the two second terms of its binomial factors must have unlike signs. Considering that the given middle term has a very small value, we conclude that we are more likely to find the answer quickly if we start our cross multiplication at the right of the numerical arrangement rather than at the left. In carrying out this cross multiplication we give the negative sign in each case to the larger of the two products involved. *Thus:* $6(-5) + 4(+3) = -18$ *(reject)*; $4(-5) + 6(+3) = -2$ *(cor-*

rect). We have been fortunate in finding the correct values so soon. Otherwise we should have had to continue the process of trial and error with the numerical listing—though this is not as lengthy a process as may appear, since many of the wrong results are recognized at a glance without taking the trouble to calculate them. Having selected the correct combination of numbers, we write the factors as $4x + 3$ and $6x - 5$.

Practice Exercise No. 16

Resolve the following into factors

1	$7a^2bc^3 - 28abc$	9	$x^2 + 10x + 21$
2	$15a^2cd + 20ac^2d - 15acd^2$	10	$x^2 - 18x + 45$
3	$4x^2 + 12xy + 9y^2$	11	$x^2 + 5x - 36$
4	$9a^2b^2 - 24a^2bc + 16a^2c^2$	12	$x^2 - 13x + 48$
5	$9a^2x^2 - 16a^2y^2$	13	$x^2 - 14xy + 33y^2$
6	$49x^4 - 16y^2$	14	$6x^2 + 21x + 9$
7	$(2x + y + z)^2 - (x - 2y + z)^2$	15	$15x^2 - 6x - 21$
8	$a^4 + a^2 + 1$	16	$12x^2 + 27x - 39$
	(Hint: add and subtract a^2)		

SIMULTANEOUS EQUATIONS

Simultaneous equations are equations involving the same unknown quantities. *Thus,* $a + 2b = 11$ and $2a + b = 10$ are *simultaneous equations* since they both involve the same unknowns, namely, a and b.

Simultaneous equations involving two unknown quantities are solved as follows:

Rule 1. *Eliminate one of the unknowns.*
Rule 2. *Solve for the other unknown.*
Rule 3. *Find the value of the unknown previously eliminated.*

Elimination may be performed by any one of three different methods:

1. *By addition or subtraction.*
2. *By substitution.*
3. *By comparison.*

ELIMINATION BY ADDITION
OR SUBTRACTION:

Rule 1. *Multiply one or both of the equations by such a number or numbers as will give one of the unknowns the same coefficient in both equations.*

Rule 2. *Add or subtract the equal coefficients according to the nature of their signs.*

EXAMPLE: $5x + 2y = 32, 2x - y = 2$. Find x and y.

SOLUTION:

$5x + 2y = 32$
$\underline{4x - 2y = \ \ 4}$, multiplying $2x - y$ by 2,
$9x \qquad\ = 36$
$x \qquad\ = 4.$
$20 \ + 2y = 32$, substituting 4 for x in first equation,
$2y = 32 - 20$, transposing
$y = 6.$

ELIMINATION BY SUBSTITUTION:

Rule 1. *From one of the equations find the value of one of the unknowns in terms of the other.*

Rule 2. *Substitute the value thus found for the unknown in the other of the given equations.*

EXAMPLE: $2x + 4y = 50, 3x + 5y = 66$. Find x and y.

SOLUTION:

$2x + 4y = 50,$
$2x \qquad = 50 - 4y$, transposing,
$x \qquad = 25 - 2y.$
$3(25 - 2y) + 5y = 66$, substituting for x in other equation,
$75 - 6y + 5y = 66,$
$-y = 66 - 75 = -9, y = 9.$
$2x + 36 = 50, \qquad$ substituting 9 for y in first equation,
$2x = 50 - 36 = 14, x = 7.$

ELIMINATION BY COMPARISON:

Rule 1. *From each equation find the value of one of the unknowns in terms of the other.*

Rule 2. *Form an equation from these equal values.*

EXAMPLE: $3x + 2y = 27, 2x - 3y = 5$. Find x and y.

SOLUTION:

$3x + 2y = 27, 3x = 27 - 2y, x = \dfrac{27 - 2y}{3}.$

$2x - 3y = 5, 2x = 5 + 3y, x = \dfrac{5 + 3y}{2}.$

$\dfrac{27 - 2y}{3} = \dfrac{5 + 3y}{2}$, both being equal to x,

$27 - 2y = \dfrac{3(5 + 3y)}{2}$, multiplying both sides by 3,

$2(27 - 2y) = 3(5 + 3y)$, multiplying both sides by 2,

$54 - 4y = 15 + 9y$, carrying out multiplication,

$-4y - 9y = 15 - 54 = -39, y = 3.$
$3x + 6 = 27, 3x = 21, x = 7.$

Of the foregoing methods, select the one which appears most likely to make the solution simple and direct.

Practice Exercise No. 17

PROBLEMS

1　The hands of a clock are together at 12 o'clock. When do they next meet? (x = minute spaces passed over by minute hand; y = number passed over by hour hand.)

2　A man has $22,000 invested and on it he earns $1,220. Part of the money is out at 5% interest and part at 6%. How much is in each part?

3　Jack is twice as old as Joe. Twenty years ago Jack was four times as old as Joe. What are their ages?

4　There are two numbers: the first added to half the second gives 35; the second added to half the first equals 40. What are the numbers?

5　The inventory of one department of a store increased by one-third of that of a second department amounts to $1,700; the inventory of the second increased by one-fourth of that of the first amounts to $1,800. What are the inventories?

6　Find two numbers such that $\frac{1}{2}$ of the first plus $\frac{1}{3}$ of the second shall equal 45, and $\frac{1}{2}$ of the second plus $\frac{1}{5}$ of the first shall equal 40.

7　A and B invest $918 in a partnership venture and clear $153. A's share of the profit is $45 more than B's. What was the contribution of each one to the capital?

8　Two girls receive $153 for baby sitting. Ann is paid for 14 days and Mary for 15. Ann's pay for 6 days' work is $3 more than Mary gets for 4. How much does each earn per day?

9　In 80 lbs. of an alloy of copper and tin there are 7 lbs. of copper to 3 of tin. How much copper must be added so that there may be 11 lbs. of copper to 4 of tin?

10　Brown owes $1,200 and Jones $2,500, but neither has enough money to pay his debts. Brown says to Jones, "Lend me one-eighth of your bank account and I'll pay my creditors." Jones says to Brown, "Lend me one-ninth of yours and I'll pay mine." How much money has each?

FRACTIONS

To reduce a fraction to its lowest terms, *resolve the numerator and the denominator into their prime factors and cancel all the common factors, or divide the numerator and the denominator by their highest common factor.*

EXAMPLE 1: Reduce $\dfrac{12a^2b^3c^4}{9a^3bc^2}$.

SOLUTION: $\dfrac{12a^2b^3c^4}{9a^3bc^2} = \dfrac{2 \times 2 \times 3a^2bc^2(b^2c^2)}{3 \times 3a^2bc^2(a)}$

$= \dfrac{4b^2c^2}{3a}$, ANS.

EXPLANATION: The numerical parts of the fraction are separated into their prime factors, and the algebraic parts are divided by their highest common factor. The terms that cancel out are then eliminated. As a guide for determining the highest common factor of monomial terms note that such a factor is made up of the lower (or lowest) of the given powers of each letter involved.

EXAMPLE 2: Reduce $\dfrac{12x^2 + 15x - 63}{4x^2 - 31x + 42}$.

SOLUTION: $\dfrac{12x^2 + 15x - 63}{4x^2 - 31x + 42} = \dfrac{(3x + 9)(4x - 7)}{(x - 6)(4x - 7)}$

$= \dfrac{3x + 9}{x - 6}$, ANS.

EXPLANATION: Numerator and denominator are factored, and the common factor is then cancelled.

A fraction may be reduced to an integral or mixed expression if the degree (power) of its numerator equals or exceeds that of its denominator.

To reduce a fraction to an integral or mixed expression, *divide the numerator by the denominator.*

EXAMPLE 1: Reduce $\dfrac{x^2 - y^2}{x - y}$ to an integral expression.

SOLUTION: $\dfrac{x^2 - y^2}{x - y} = \dfrac{(x - y)(x + y)}{x - y} = x + y$.

EXAMPLE 2: Reduce $\dfrac{x^2 + y^2}{x + y}$ to a mixed expression.

SOLUTION: $\dfrac{x^2 + y^2}{x + y} = \dfrac{(x^2 - y^2) + 2y^2}{x + y}$

$= \dfrac{(x + y)(x - y) + 2y^2}{x + y}$

$= x - y + \dfrac{2y^2}{x + y}$, ANS.

EXPLANATION: While $x^2 + y^2$ is not evenly divisible by $x + y$, we recognize that it would be so divisible if it were $x^2 - y^2$. Hence we subtract $2y^2$ to convert it to $x^2 - y^2$ and also add to it the same amount. We divide $x^2 - y^2$ by $x + y$ and write the remainder as a fraction that has $x + y$ for its denominator.

To reduce a mixed expression to a fraction, *multiply the integral expression by the denominator of the fraction; add to this product the numerator of the fraction and write under this result the given denominator.*

EXAMPLE: Reduce $x + 1 + \dfrac{x + 1}{x - 1}$ to a fraction.

SOLUTION: $\left(x + 1 + \dfrac{x + 1}{x - 1}\right)\left(\dfrac{x - 1}{x - 1}\right)$

$= \dfrac{x^2 - 1 + x + 1}{x - 1} = \dfrac{x^2 + x}{x - 1}$, ANS.

To reduce fractions to their lowest common denominator, *find the lowest common multiple of the denominators and proceed on the same principles that govern arithmetical fractions.*

EXAMPLE: Reduce $\dfrac{1}{x^2 + 3x + 2}$, $\dfrac{2}{x^2 + 5x + 6}$ and $\dfrac{3}{x^2 + 4x + 3}$ to fractions having the lowest common denominator.

SOLUTION: $\dfrac{1}{x^2 + 3x + 2}$, $\dfrac{2}{x^2 + 5x + 6}$, $\dfrac{3}{x^2 + 4x + 3}$

$= \dfrac{1}{(x + 1)(x + 2)}$, $\dfrac{2}{(x + 2)(x + 3)}$, $\dfrac{3}{(x + 1)(x + 3)}$

The LCD is $(x + 1)(x + 2)(x + 3)$.

Dividing this by each of the denominators and multiplying each numerator by the resulting quotient we obtain

$$\frac{x+3}{(x+1)(x+2)(x+3)}, \frac{2x+2}{(x+1)(x+2)(x+3)},$$

$$\frac{3x+6}{(x+1)(x+2)(x+3)}, \text{ Ans.}$$

ADDITION AND SUBTRACTION OF FRACTIONS

EXAMPLE 1: Simplify

$$\frac{2a-4b}{4} - \frac{a-b+c}{3} + \frac{a-b-2c}{12}.$$

SOLUTION: $\dfrac{2a-4b}{4} - \dfrac{a-b+c}{3} + \dfrac{a-b-2c}{12}$

$$= \frac{6a-12b-4a+4b-4c+a-b-2c}{12}$$

$$= \frac{3a-9b-6c}{12} = \frac{a-3b-2c}{4}, \text{ Ans.}$$

EXAMPLE 2: Simplify $\dfrac{a+2x}{a-2x} - \dfrac{a-2x}{a+2x}.$

SOLUTION: $\dfrac{a+2x}{a-2x} - \dfrac{a-2x}{a+2x}$

$$= \frac{(a+2x)^2 - (a-2x)^2}{a^2-4x^2}$$

$$= \frac{a^2+4ax+4x^2-a^2+4ax-4x^2}{a^2-4x^2}$$

$$= \frac{8ax}{a^2-4x^2}, \text{ Ans.}$$

MULTIPLICATION AND DIVISION OF FRACTIONS

Principle: *The product of two or more fractions is equal to the product of the numerators multiplied together, divided by the product of the denominators multiplied together.*

EXAMPLE 1: Multiply $\dfrac{7x}{5y}$ by $\dfrac{3a}{4c}$.

SOLUTION: $\dfrac{7x}{5y} \cdot \dfrac{3a}{4c} = \dfrac{21ax}{20cy}$, Ans.

EXAMPLE 2: Multiply $\dfrac{2x}{x-y}$ by $\dfrac{x^2-y^2}{3}$.

SOLUTION: $\left(\dfrac{2x}{x-y}\right)\left(\dfrac{x^2-y^2}{3}\right) = \dfrac{2x(x+y)(x-y)}{3(x-y)}$

$$= \frac{2x(x+y)}{3}, \text{ Ans.}$$

EXAMPLE 3: Multiply $\dfrac{2(x+y)}{x-y}$ by $\dfrac{x^2-y^2}{x^2+2xy+y^2}$.

SOLUTION: $\left[\dfrac{2(x+y)}{x-y}\right]\left[\dfrac{x^2-y^2}{x^2+2xy+y^2}\right]$

$$= \frac{2(x+y)(x+y)(x-y)}{(x-y)(x+y)^2} = 2, \text{ Ans.}$$

Principle: *Division by a fraction is equivalent to multiplication by the reciprocal of the fraction, i.e., the fraction inverted.*

EXAMPLE: Divide $\dfrac{3a^2}{a^2-b^2}$ by $\dfrac{a}{a+b}$.

SOLUTION: $\dfrac{3a^2}{a^2-b^2} \div \dfrac{a}{a+b} = \dfrac{3a^2}{a^2-b^2} \cdot \dfrac{a+b}{a}$

$$= \frac{3a^2(a+b)}{a(a+b)(a-b)} = \frac{3a^2}{a(a-b)} = \frac{3a}{a-b}, \text{ Ans.}$$

Practice Exercise No. 18

1 Reduce $\dfrac{45x^3y^3z}{36abx^2y^2z}$ to its lowest terms.

2 Reduce $\dfrac{x^2+2ax+a^2}{3(x^2-a^2)}$ to its lowest terms.

3 Reduce $\dfrac{x^2+a^2+3-2ax}{x-a}$ to a mixed quantity.

4 Reduce $a + \dfrac{ax}{a-x}$ to a fraction.

5 Reduce $1 + \dfrac{c}{x-y}$ to a fraction.

6 Reduce $\dfrac{x+a}{b}, \dfrac{a}{b}$ and $\dfrac{a-x}{a}$ to fractions with the LCD.

7 Reduce $\dfrac{x}{1-x}$, $\dfrac{x^2}{(1-x)^2}$ and $\dfrac{x^3}{(1-x)^3}$ to fractions with the LCD.

8 Add $\dfrac{x+y}{2}$ and $\dfrac{x-y}{2}$.

9 Add $\dfrac{2}{(x-1)^3}$, $\dfrac{3}{(x-1)^2}$ and $\dfrac{4}{x-1}$.

10 Subtract $2a - \dfrac{a-3b}{c}$ from $4a + \dfrac{2a}{c}$.

11 Subtract $\dfrac{x}{a+x}$ from $\dfrac{a}{a-x}$.

12 Multiply $\dfrac{2}{x-y}$ by $\dfrac{x^2-y^2}{a}$.

13 Multiply $\dfrac{x^2-4}{3}$ by $\dfrac{4x}{x+2}$.

14 Divide $\dfrac{3x}{2x-2}$ by $\dfrac{2x}{x-1}$.

15 Divide $\dfrac{(x+y)^2}{x-y}$ by $\dfrac{x+y}{(x-y)^2}$.

Logarithms

Logarithms are a means of simplifying the manipulation of numbers containing many digits or decimal places. The system of common logarithms, which is the one in most common use, is based on powers of 10.

By this system **the logarithm of a given number** *is the exponent to which* 10 *must be raised to obtain that number. Thus:*

$10^1 = 10$; $\therefore$ the logarithm of 10 is 1.
$10^2 = 100$; $\therefore$ the logarithm of 100 is 2.
$10^3 = 1,000$; $\therefore$ the logarithm of 1,000 is 3.
$10^4 = 10,000$; $\therefore$ the logarithm of 10,000 is 4.

and so on up.

The logarithm of a number between 10 and 99 is therefore an exponent greater than 1 and less than 2.

The logarithm of a number between 100 and 200 is an exponent greater than 2 and less than 3.

The logarithm of any number other than a multiple of 10 is therefore a whole number plus a decimal.

FINDING THE LOGARITHM OF A NUMBER

The logarithm of 45 should be between 1 and 2. That is, it must be 1 plus something. To find out what this something is, we refer to what is known as a **table of logarithms,** and then we find the logarithm of 45 to be equal to 1.6532. This is written:

Log 45 = 1.6532.

The method of finding a logarithm from the table will be explained in detail later.

The **characteristic** is the whole number part of the logarithm. In the above case the *characteristic* is 1.

The **mantissa** is the decimal part of the logarithm, and is the part found in the table of logarithms. In the above case the *mantissa* is .6532.

Finding the Characteristic. *The characteristic is not found in the table but is determined by rule. It is positive for numbers equal to 1 or greater, and negative for numbers less than 1.*

By definition,

For numbers between these limits	the characteristic is
10,000 and 100,000 *minus*	4
1,000 and 10,000 *minus*	3
100 and 1,000 *minus*	2
10 and 100 *minus*	1
1 and 10 *minus*	0
.1 and 1 *minus*	−1
.01 and .1 *minus*	−2
.001 and .01 *minus*	−3
.0001 and .001 *minus*	−4

Note: The characteristic 4 would apply to numbers from 10,000 to 99,999.999999+ carried to any number of places; characteristic 3, from 1,000 to 9,999.999999 . . . etc. For the sake of simplicity the latter numbers in these groups are expressed as 100,000 minus, 10,000 minus, 1,000 minus, etc.

Rule 1. *For whole numbers the characteristic is one less than the number of figures to the left of the decimal point.*

EXAMPLE 1: What is the characteristic of 82,459.23?

SOLUTION: There are 5 figures to the left of the decimal. $5 - 1 = 4$. ∴ the characteristic is 4.

Rule 2. *The characteristic of decimal numbers is equal to minus the number of places to the right from the decimal point to the first significant figure* (number other than zero).

EXAMPLE 2: What is the characteristic of .001326?

SOLUTION: From the decimal point to 1, the first significant figure, there are 3 places. ∴ the characteristic is −3.

EXAMPLE 3: What is the characteristic of .443?

SOLUTION: There is but one place from the decimal point to the first significant figure. ∴ the characteristic is −1.

Note: If the characteristic of a number (.023) is −2, and the mantissa is 3617, the whole logarithm is written 2.3617. The mantissa is always considered positive, and therefore negative characteristics are denoted by the placing of the minus sign *above* the characteristic. Another notation used for negative characteristics is 8.3617 − 10. In this the negative *characteristic* is subtracted from 10, the remainder is made the new characteristic, and the −10 is placed after the mantissa to indicate a negative characteristic.

Practice Exercise No. 19

Write the characteristics of the following.

1	17	6	67.48
2	342	7	7.4
3	78,943	8	.000571
4	4,320	9	.021
5	.42	10	1

Finding the mantissa. The mantissa is found in the table of logarithms on page 843. The mantissa

is not related to the position of the decimal point in any number. For example the mantissa of 34,562 is the same as the mantissa of 3,456.2 or 345.62. But the logarithm of these numbers differs with respect to the *characteristic*, which you have learned to find by inspection of the number.

Note: The reason why the mantissa for a given set of digits does not change, no matter how they may be pointed off decimally, will appear from the following. Let us assume that *m* is any number and the logarithm of this number is $n + p$, in which *n* is the characteristic and *p* the mantissa. By definition $m = 10^{n+p}$. If we multiply or divide 10^{n+p} by 10, 100, 1,000, etc. we make corresponding changes in the decimal pointing of *m*. But by the laws of algebra multiplication or division of 10^{n+p} by 10, 100, 1,000, etc., would be performed by adding or subtracting the exponents of 10^1, 10^2, 10^3, etc. Hence to arrive at any desired decimal pointing of the number *m*, only the whole-number part of the exponent of 10^{n+p} is modified. This part is *n*, the characteristic. The mantissa, *p*, always remains unchanged. Similar considerations will also make it clear why the mantissa still remains positive even when the characteristic is negative.

Let us now use the table of logarithms on page 843 to find the mantissa of the number 345. Find 34 in the left-hand column headed by No. Then move across to the column headed 5. The mantissa is 5378. The characteristic is 2; therefore log 345 = 2.5378.

By using the same mantissa and simply changing the characteristic we arrive at the following logarithms for various decimal pointings of the digits 345:

log 34.5 = 1.5378
log 3.45 = .5378
log .345 = 1.5378, or 9.5378 − 10
log .0345 = 2.5378, or 8.5378 − 10

EXAMPLE 1: Find the log of .837.

SOLUTION: Find 83 in the column headed No., move across to column headed 7. The mantissa is .9227; the characteristic is −1.
∴ log .837 = $\overline{1}$.9227 or 9.9227 − 10,   ANS.

Interpolation is an arithmetic method used to find the value of a mantissa when the original number contains more than three significant (nonzero) figures. (The table printed in the Encyclopedia gives direct answers only for numbers up to 999.)

EXAMPLE 2: Find the log of 6484.

SOLUTION:

log 6480 = 3.8116 ⎫ The difference between
log 6490 = 3.8122 ⎭ these two logs is .0006.
Difference between 6490 and 6480 is 10.
Difference between 6484 and 6480 is 4.
Difference between mantissas is .0006.
$\frac{4}{10}$ × .0006 = .00024 increment,
.8116 + .00024 = .81184.
log 6484 = 3.81184, ANS.

EXAMPLE 3: Find the log of .05368.

SOLUTION:

log .05360 = $\overline{2}$.7292,
log. 05370 = $\overline{2}$.7300.
Difference between logs = .0008.
Difference between numbers is 8.
.0008 × .8 = .00064 increment,
.7292 + .00064 = .72984,
log .05368 = 2.72984, ANS.

Practice Exercise No. 20

Find the logarithms of the following:

1	354	6	.234
2	76	7	.00352
3	8	8	6.04
4	6346	9	.0005324
5	3.657	10	672.8

Finding the antilogarithm. The number which corresponds to a given logarithm is called its **antilogarithm.**

The antilogarithm of a logarithm is found by obtaining the number corresponding to the mantissa and determining the position of the decimal point from the characteristic.

EXAMPLE 1: Find the antilogarithm of 1.8531.

SOLUTION: Look for mantissa 8531 in the body of the table on page 843. In the No. column to the left of the row where you have located 8531, you will find the first two figures of the number (71). The third figure (3) is found at the top of the column in which 8531 is located. Since the characteristic is 1, mark off two decimal places in the number, counting from the *left,* to give 71.3.

Usually the mantissa cannot be found exactly in the tables. It is then necessary to interpolate between the two numbers corresponding to the two nearest logarithms.

EXAMPLE 2: Find the antilog of 3.5484.

SOLUTION: Given mantissa 5484 is between 5478 and 5490. Hence the first three significant figures of the antilog are 353.
Diff. bet. 5490 and 5478 = 0012 ⎫ $\frac{0006}{0012}$ ⎫ = .5
Diff. bet. 5484 and 5478 = 0006 ⎭ ⎭
The first four significant figures are therefore 3535. Since the characteristic is 3, antilog = .003535, ANS.

HOW TO USE LOGARITHMS

To multiply by the use of logarithms, *add the logarithms of the numbers to be multiplied and find the antilogarithm corresponding to this sum.*

EXAMPLE: Multiply 25.31 by 42.18.

SOLUTION: log 25.31 = 1.4033,
log 42.18 = 1.6251,
Sum = 3.0284,
Product = antilog of 3.0284 = 1067.5, ANS.

To divide by the use of logarithms, *substract the logarithm of the divisor from the logarithm of the dividend; the difference is the logarithm of the quotient.*

EXAMPLE 1: Divide 5,280.4 by 67.82.

SOLUTION: log 5,280.4 = 3.7226,
log 67.82 = 1,8313,
difference = 1.8913,
Quotient = antilog 1.8913 = 77.86, ANS.

EXAMPLE 2: Divide 5,280.4 by .06782.

SOLUTION:

log 5,280.4 = 13.7226 − 10
log .06782 = 8.8313 − 10
difference = 4.8913,
antilog = 77860, ANS.

EXPLANATION: log .06782 is negative with a characteristic of −2. In order to perform a subtraction with it we write it as 8.8313 − 10, but before subtraction is possible we must make a corresponding change in the minuend. This we do by both adding to it and subtracting from it the number 10, an operation that does not affect its value. The two −10s are eliminated when we subtract and the resulting logarithm has the correct characteristic.

EXAMPLE 3: Divide 52.804 by 6782.

$$\log 52.804 = 11.7226 - 10$$
$$\log 6782 = \underline{3.8313}$$
$$\overline{7.8913 - 10}$$
$$= 3.8913$$
$$\text{antilog} = .007786, \quad \text{Ans.}$$

EXPLANATION: In this case we have to increase and decrease the upper logarithm by 10 in order to perform the subtraction, but the -10 is not eliminated and hence has the effect of giving the remainder a negative characteristic.

To raise to a given power by the use of logarithms, *multiply the logarithm of the number by the given exponent of the number and find the antilogarithm.*

The reason for this may be explained as follows. Let m be a number and n its logarithm. Then—

$$m = 10^n,$$
$$m^2 = 10^n \times 10^n = 10^{n+n} = 10^{2n},$$
$$m^3 = 10^{3n}, \text{ etc.}$$

EXAMPLE 1: Find 46^4.

SOLUTION: $\log 46 = 1.6628$
$$\underline{\times 4}$$
$$\log 46^4 = \overline{6.6512,}$$
$$46^4 = \text{antilog } 6.6512 = 4,479,000, \quad \text{Ans.}$$

To find a given root by the use of logarithms, *divide the logarithm of the number by the index of the root and find the antilogarithm.*

This may be demonstrated thus:

$$\text{Let} \quad m = 10^n.$$
$$\text{Then} \quad \sqrt{m} = \sqrt{10^n} = 10^{\frac{n}{2}},$$
$$\sqrt[3]{m} = 10^{\frac{n}{3}}, \text{ etc.}$$

EXAMPLE 1: Find $\sqrt[3]{75}$.

SOLUTION: $\log 75 = 1.8751,$
$$\frac{1.8751}{3} = .62503,$$

Root $= $ antilog $.62503 = 4.217, \quad$ ANS.

EXAMPLE 2: Find $\sqrt{.251}$.

SOLUTION: $\log .251 = \overline{1}.3997$ or $9.3997 - 10,$
$$\frac{9.3997 - 10}{2} = 4.69985 - 5 = \overline{1}.69985,$$

Root $=$ antilog $\overline{1}.69985 = .5015, \quad$ ANS.

EXAMPLE 3: Find $\sqrt[3]{.75}$.

SOLUTION:
$$\log .75 = \quad 9.8751 - 10$$
$$+ 20 \qquad - 20$$
$$\overline{29.8751 - 30,}$$

$$\frac{29.8751 - 30}{3} = 9.9583 - 10 = \overline{1}.9583,$$
$$\text{antilog} = .9084, \quad \text{Ans.}$$

EXPLANATION: Starting in this case with a negative characteristic, we cannot make a direct division by 3 because dividing 10 by 3 would result in a fractional characteristic, which is impossible. We therefore increase and decrease the logarithm by 20 in order to make the division possible and to produce a -10 in the remainder.

Practice Exercise No. 21

Solve by logarithms.

1 3984×5.6	11 $\dfrac{5}{-7}$
2 25.316×42.18	12 $\dfrac{-17}{32}$
3 220.2×2209	13 $\dfrac{6+3}{4}$
4 $5280 \div 33.81$	14 $\dfrac{8+7}{7}$
5 $7256.2 \div 879.26$	15 $\dfrac{13-9}{3}$
6 $9783 \div .1234$	16 $\dfrac{11}{16-7}$
7 77^3	17 $\dfrac{8}{3 \times 5}$
8 $\sqrt[3]{85}$	18 $\dfrac{4 \times 6}{11}$
9 $\sqrt[5]{356.07}$	19 $\dfrac{7 \div 3}{4}$
10 2.43^5	20 $\dfrac{16}{18 \div 5}$

The principal use of logarithms is in connection with trigonometry, the branch of mathematics that has to do with the measurement of triangles.

Exercise No. 1

1 $\frac{24}{32} = \frac{3}{4}$

2 $63 : 56 = \frac{63}{56} = 1\frac{7}{56} = 1\frac{1}{8}$

3 1 lb. = 16 oz., 5 lb. = 80 oz., $\frac{10}{80} = \frac{1}{8}$.

4 2 parts + 3 parts = 5 parts. Since 2 parts are water, then $\frac{2}{5}$ of total is water, or 40%.

5 6 parts tin + 19 parts copper = 25 parts to

make bronze. The amount of tin in 500 lbs. of bronze is $\frac{6}{25} \times 500$ or 120.

6 $5 + 14 + 21 = 40$ parts $=$ the total of $2,000. $\frac{21}{40} \times 2,000 = \$1,050$ as the largest share; $\frac{5}{40} \times 2,000 = \$250$ as the smallest share; $1,050 - 250 = \$800$ difference.

Exercise No. 2

1 6	3 6	5 21	7 3	9 3
2 12	4 2	6 4	8 125	10 18

Exercise No. 3

1 $\frac{18}{27} = \frac{20}{x}$ Direct prop. $18x = 540$, $x = \frac{540}{18} = 30$

2 $\frac{9}{30} = \frac{2}{x}$ Direct prop. $9x = 60$, $x = \frac{60}{9} = 6\frac{2}{3}$

3 $\frac{5}{20} - \frac{90}{x}$ Direct prop. $5x = 1,800$, $x = \frac{1,800}{5} = 360$

4 $\frac{112}{240} = \frac{28}{x}$ Inverse prop. $112x = 6,720$, $x = \frac{6,720}{112} = 60$

5 $\frac{26}{20} = \frac{x}{35}$ Inverse prop. $20x = 910$, $x = \frac{910}{20} = 45\frac{1}{2}$

6 $\frac{220}{x} = \frac{2}{8}$ Direct prop. $2x = 1,760$, $x = \frac{1,760}{2} = 880$

Exercise No. 4

1 23	5 $4b$	8 $5a + 2b$
2 -36	6 -3	9 $15a - 2b$
3 -7	7 $12x$	10 $15a + 3b - 5$
4 $-20d$		

Exercise No. 5

1 28	4 66	7 3
2 -9	5 130	8 -3
3 -24	6 $-40ab$	9 -25

Exercise No. 6

1 -32	3 72	5 -3	7 $2\frac{4}{5}$
2 216	4 -144	6 4	8 -12

Exercise No. 7

1 $x + y = 5$ 5 $x^2 + y^2 = 13$

2 $x + y + z = 9$ 6 $y - 3 = 0$

3 $2x + 2y = 10$ 7 $2xz = 16$

4 $x + y - x = 1$

Exercise No. 8

1 23	4 20	7 3	9 1,260
2 110	5 12	8 55	10 3
3 13	6 44		

Exercise No. 9

1 $p = 2l + 2w$ 6 $P = M - O$

2 $d = rt$ 7 $d = 16t^2$

3 $H = \frac{av}{746}$ 8 $A = S^2$

4 $I = PRT$ 9 $C = \frac{5}{9}(F - 32°)$

5 $A = \frac{W}{V}$ 10 $R = \frac{N}{T}$

Exercise No. 10

1 $p = 5$ 6 $n = 36$

2 $n = 12\frac{1}{2}$ 7 $a = 48$

3 $x = 28$ 8 $b = Wc$

4 $c = 6$ 9 $A = \frac{W}{V}$

5 $y = 4$ 10 $W = \frac{P}{AH}$

Exercise No. 11

1 Since $\frac{D}{d} = \frac{r}{R}$ then $rd = DR$, and $r = \frac{DR}{d}$; substituting, $r = \frac{18 \times 100}{6} = \frac{1,800}{6} - 300.$

2 Since $DR = dr$, and D is the unknown, then $D = \frac{dr}{R}$; substituting, $D = \frac{9 \times 256}{144} = \frac{2,304}{144} = 16.$

3 Let n represent the number. Then $3n + 2n = 90$, $5n = 90$, $n = \dfrac{90}{5} = 18$

4 Let n represent the smaller number. Then $n + 7n = 32$, $8n = 32$, $n = \frac{32}{8} = 4$, and $7n = 7 \times 4$ or 28.

5 Let $x =$ the amount the first unit gets. Then the second unit receives $2x$, and the third unit receives $x + 2x$ or $3x$. The total $x + 2x + 3x = 6x = 600$, $x = 100$, and $2x = 200$.

6 Rate $\times$ Time = Distance; $R \times t = D$. They both travel the same amount of time. Let t equal the time they travel. Then $300t + 200t = 3,000$ mi., $500t = 3,000$, $t = \dfrac{3,000}{500} = 6$ hrs. $300 \times 6 = 1,800$ mi.

7 $R \times t = D$. Let $R =$ rate of slower soldier. Then $2R =$ rate of faster one. $10R + 20R = 24$ mi., $30R = 24$, $R = \frac{24}{30}$ or $\frac{4}{5}$, and $2R = \frac{8}{5}$ or $1\frac{3}{5}$ mi. per hr.

8 Let $n =$ number of quarters the man has. Then $3n =$ number of nickels, and $.25(n) + .05(3n) = 8.00$ or his total money.

$.25n + .15n = .40n = 8.00$, $n = \dfrac{8.00}{.40} = 20$

CHECK: $3n = 60$. $20 \times .25 = \$5.00$, and $60 \times .05 = \$3.00$, $\$5.00 + \$3.00 = \$8.00$.

9 Let T and t represent no. of teeth in large and small gears and let R and r represent rpm.

Then $\dfrac{T}{t} = \dfrac{r}{R}$, and $\dfrac{72}{48} = \dfrac{160}{R}$, $72R = 7,680$,

$R = \dfrac{7,680}{72} = 106\frac{2}{3}$.

10 Weight $\times$ Distance = Weight $\times$ Distance. $\therefore 120 \times \frac{9}{2} = x \times 5$. $5x = 540$, $x = 108$.

Exercise No. 12

1	8	4	3	7	10	10	.3
2	10	5	5	8	1	11	1.2
3	9	6	12	9	.2	12	.05

Exercise No. 13

1	73	4	17.68	7	43	9	85
2	35	5	20.69	8	56	10	97
3	54.2	6	26				

Exercise No. 14

1	36	6	32,768	11	$\frac{4}{9}$
2	729	7	9	12	14.6969
3	5	8	5	13	.00000028
4	$\frac{1}{64}$	9	43,000,000	14	.0025
5	186,624	10	620,000	15	122,000,000

Exercise No. 15

1	135	11	$\frac{5}{6}$	21	441	31	841
2	223	12	$\frac{31}{36}$	22	529	32	1521
3	343	13	$\frac{63}{72}$	23	1089	33	9801
4	739	14	$\frac{7}{4}$	24	1369	34	784
5	487	15	$\frac{6}{8}$	25	1521	35	1444
6	$\frac{10}{12}$	16	9	26	1225	36	399
7	$\frac{14}{5}$	17	7	27	4225	37	896
8	$\frac{124}{49}$	18	$2\frac{1}{3}$	28	9025	38	1591
9	$\frac{65}{20}$	19	$3\frac{1}{5}$	29	11025	39	2484
10	$\frac{1068}{400}$	20	$1\frac{1}{2}$	30	42025	40	3456

Exercise No. 16

1 $7abc\,(ac^2 - 4)$
2 $5acd\,(3a + 4c - 3d)$
3 $(2x + 3y)\,(2x + 3y)$
4 $(3ab - 4ac)\,(3ab - 4ac)$
5 $(3ax + 4ay)\,(3ax - 4ay)$
6 $(7x^2 + 4y)\,(7x^2 - 4y)$
7 $(3x - y + 2z)\,(x + 3y)$
8 $(a^2 + a + 1)\,(a^2 - a + 1)$
9 $(x + 7)\,(x + 3)$
10 $(x - 15)\,(x - 3)$
11 $(x + 9)\,(x - 4)$
12 $(x - 16)\,(x + 3)$
13 $(x - 11y)\,(x - 3y)$
14 $(3x + 9)\,(2x + 1)$
15 $(5x - 7)\,(3x + 3)$
16 $(4x + 13)\,(3x - 3)$

Exercise No. 17

1 Let $x =$ no. of min. spaces passed over by min. hand; $y =$ no. passed by hr. hand. $12y = x$; $y = x - 60$. Subtracting, $11y = x - (x - 60) = 60$; $y = 5\frac{5}{11}$. $5\frac{5}{11}$ min. spaces past 12 o'clock gives $1.05\frac{5}{11}$ o'clock.

2 Try elimination by substitution. $x =$ part inv. at 5%; $y =$ part inv. at 6%. $.05x + .06y = \$1,220$; $x + y = \$22,000$. Multiplying $.05x$ etc. by 20 we get $x + 1.20y = \$24,400$, from

which $x = \$24,000 - 1.20y$. Substituting this value in other equation, $\$24,000 - 1.20y + y = \$22,000$; $-.20y = -\$2,400$; $y = \$12,000$; hence $x = \$10,000$.

3 Try elimination by comparison. $a =$ Jack's age; $b =$ Joe's age. $a = 2b$; $a - 20 = 4(b - 20)$; $a = 4(b - 20) + 20$; hence $2b = 4b - 80 + 20$; $2b - 4b = -60$; $b = 30$ years for Joe; $2 \times 30 = 60$ years for Jack.

4 $a =$ first; $b =$ second. $a + \dfrac{b}{2} = 35$; $\dfrac{a}{2} + b = 40$. Multiply first equation by 2, $2a + b = 70$. Subtracting second equation from this $1\frac{1}{2}a = 30$; $a = 20$; $a + \dfrac{b}{2} = 35$; $\dfrac{b}{2} = 35 - 20$; $\dfrac{b}{2} \doteq 15$; $b = 30$.

5 $a + \dfrac{b}{3} = \$1700$; $\dfrac{a}{4} + b = \$1800$. Multiplying first equation by 3, $3a + b = \$5100$. Subtracting second equation, $2\frac{3}{4}a = \$3300$; $a = \$1200$. Substituting in first equation $\$1200 + \dfrac{b}{3} = \$1700$; $\dfrac{b}{3} = \$1700 - \$1200 = \$500$; $b = \$1500$.

6 $\dfrac{a}{2} + \dfrac{b}{3} = 45$; $\dfrac{a}{5} + \dfrac{b}{2} = 40$. Multiplying both equations, $a + \dfrac{2b}{3} = 90$; $a + \dfrac{5b}{2} = 200$. Subtracting the first from the second $\dfrac{11b}{6} = 110$; $b = 60$. Substituting in first equation, $\dfrac{a}{2} + 20 = 45$; $\dfrac{a}{2} = 25$; $a = 50$.

7 $a =$ A's profit; $b =$ B's profit. $a + b = \$153$; $a - b = \$45$. Adding, $2a = \$198$; $a = \$99$; $b = 54$. Dividing \$918 in the proportions of 99 and 54, $\$918 \div 153 = 6$; $\$99 \times 6 = \$594$ for A; $\$54 \times 6 = \$324$ for B.

8 Try substitution. $14A + 15M = \$153$; $6A - 4M = \$3$; $6A = \$3 + 4M$, whence $A = \$.50 + \dfrac{2M}{3}$. Substituting in other equation \$7 +

$\dfrac{28M}{3} + 15M = \$153$; $9\frac{1}{3}M + 15M = \$153 - \$7$. $\dfrac{73M}{3} = \$146$; $M = \$6$. Substituting in original equation, $6A - \$24 = \$3$; $6A = \$27$; $A = \$4.50$.

9 There are several ways to solve problems like this. The method by simultaneous equations might be as follows. Select letters to represent values that do not change. $a =$ wt. of copper to be added; $b =$ wt. of tin. $b = 80 - \dfrac{7b}{3} = 24$. $a = \dfrac{11b}{4} - \dfrac{7b}{3} = 66 - 56 = 10$ lbs.

10 Eliminate by comparison. $B + \dfrac{J}{8} = \$1200$; $\dfrac{B}{9} + J = \$2500$. $B = \$1200 - \dfrac{J}{8}$; $B = \$22,500 - 9J$; $\$1200 - \dfrac{J}{8} = \$22,500 - 9J$; $9J - \dfrac{J}{8} = \$22,500 - \$1200$; $\dfrac{71J}{8} = \$21,300$; $J = \$2400$; $B + \dfrac{J}{8} = \$1200$; $B + \$300 = \$1200$; $B = \$900$.

Exercise No. 18

1 $\dfrac{5xy}{4ab}$

2 $\dfrac{x + a}{3(x - a)}$

3 $x - a + \dfrac{3}{x - a}$

4 $\dfrac{a^2}{a - x}$

5 $\dfrac{x - y + c}{x - y}$

6 $\dfrac{a(x + a)}{ab}$, $\dfrac{a^2}{ab}$, $\dfrac{b(a - x)}{ab}$

7 $\dfrac{x(1 - x)^2}{(1 - x)^3}$, $\dfrac{x^2(1 - x)}{(1 - x)^3}$, $\dfrac{x^3}{(1 - x)^3}$

8 x

9 $\dfrac{4x^2 - 5x + 3}{(x - 1)^3}$

12 $\dfrac{2(x + y)}{a}$

10   $2a + \dfrac{3(a-b)}{c}$ 13 $\dfrac{4x(x-2)}{3}$

11   $\dfrac{a^2 + x^2}{a^2 - x^2}$ 14 $\frac{3}{4}$

    15   $x^2 - y^2$

Exercise No. 19

1	1	4	3	7	0	9	−2
2	2	5	−1	8	−4	10	0
3	4	6	1				

Exercise No. 20

1	2.5490	4	3.8025	7	3.5465	9	4.7262
2	1.8808	5	.56312	8	.7810	10	2.8279
3	.9031	6	1.3692				

Exercise No. 21

1	22,310	4	156.2	7	456,500	9	3.238
2	1,068	5	8.252	8	4.396	10	84.72
3	486,400	6	79,280				

11   Log 5 = .6990, log 7 = .8451, antilog 1.8539 = .71. Prefix minus sign.

12   Log 17 = 1.2304, log 32 = 1.5051, antilog $\overline{1}$.7253 = .53. Prefix minus sign.

13   First perform addition. Log 9 = .9542, log 4 = .6061, antilog .3521 = 2.25.

14   First perform addition. Log 15 = 1.1761, log 7 = .8451, antilog .3310 = 2.14.

15   First perform subtraction. Log 4 = .6021, log 3 = .4771, antilog .1250 = 1.33.

16   First perform subtraction. Log 11 = 1.0414, log 9 = .9542, antilog .0872 = 1.22.

17   First multiply. Log 8 = .9031, log 15 = 1.1761, antilog $\overline{1}$.7270 = .53.

18   First multiply. Log 24 = 1.3802, log 11 = 1.0414, antilog .3388 = 2.18.

19   $\dfrac{7 \div 3}{4} = \dfrac{7}{12}$. Log 7 = .8451, log 12 = 1.0792, antilog $\overline{1}$.7659 = .58.

20   $\dfrac{16}{18 \div 5} = \dfrac{80}{18} = \dfrac{40}{9}$. Log 40 = 1.6021, log 9 = .9542, antilog .6479 = 4.44.

CHAPTER FIFTEEN

GEOMETRY

DEFINITIONS AND TERMS

Elementary geometry is the branch of mathematics that deals with space relationships.

Application of the principles of geometry requires an ability to use arithmetic and elementary algebra as taught in the previous sections of this book. A knowledge of geometry in addition to simple algebra and arithmetic is basic to so many occupations (carpentry, stone-masonry, dress design, hat design, display design, sheet metal work, machine-shop work, tool-making, architecture, drafting, engineering, etc.) that no serious student should be without it.

A **geometric figure** is a point, line, surface, solid, or any combination of these.

A **point** is the *position* of the intersection of two lines. It is *not* considered to have length, breadth, or thickness.

A **line** is the intersection of two surfaces. It has *length* but neither breadth nor thickness. It may be *straight*, *curved*, or *broken*.

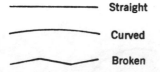

Straight

Curved

Broken

A **surface** has *two* dimensions: *length* and *breadth*. A *flat* surface may be called a **plane**.

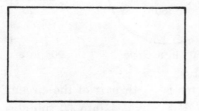

Plane Surface

A **solid** has *three* dimensions: *length, breadth,* and *thickness*.

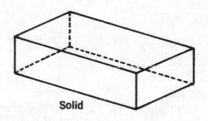

Solid

In solving geometric problems we apply certain general principles called **theorems.** These are systematically demonstrated by means of more basic principles called *axioms* and *postulates*.

Different writers use these last two terms somewhat differently. We may think of the **axioms** used in geometry, however, as *basic mathematical principles* which are so elementary that they cannot be demonstrated by means of still simpler principles. They were once widely called "self-evident truths." Note that the first seven "axioms" listed below are the principles with which you have already become familiar in performing operations upon algebraic equations (starting page 54).

The **postulates** used in geometry are of two different, but closely related, kinds. Some are merely restatements of more general mathematical axioms in specific geometric terms. Others are axiom-like statements which apply only to geometry. For instance, the last three "axioms" below may also be thought of as *geometric postulates*.

AXIOMS

1. Things equal to the same thing are equal to each other.

2. If equals are added to equals, the sums are equal.

3. If equals are subtracted from equals, the remainders are equal.

4. If equals are multiplied by equals, the products are equal.

5. If equals are divided by equals, the quotients are equal.

6. The whole is greater than any of its parts, and is equal to the sum of all its parts.

7. A quantity may be substituted for an equal one in an equation or in an inequality.

8. Only one straight line can be drawn through two points.

9. A straight line is the shortest distance between two points.

10. A straight line may be produced to any required length.

SYMBOLS

The following is a list of symbols used so frequently that they should be memorized.

= equality sign	∠ angle
< is less than	° degree
> is greater than	▱ parallelogram
∴ therefore	⊙ circle
‖ parallel	△ triangle
⊥ perpendicular	≠ unequal

LINES

A **horizontal** line is a straight line that is level with the horizon.

A **vertical** line is a straight line that is perpendicular to the horizon.

Two lines are **perpendicular** to each other when the angles at which they intersect are all equal. Such lines are said to be at right angles to each other.

An **oblique** line is neither horizontal nor vertical.

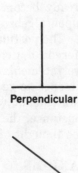

Horizontal

Vertical

Perpendicular

Oblique

Parallel lines are two or more straight lines which are equally distant from each other at all points and would never meet no matter how far they might be extended.

Parallel

ANGLES

An **angle** is the figure formed by two lines proceeding from a common point called the **vertex.** The lines that form an angle are called its **sides.** If three letters are used to designate an angle, the *vertex* is read between the others. Thus, Fig. 3 is written ∠*ABC,* and is read *angle ABC;* the sides are *AB* and *BC.*

A

B   C

FIG. 3

In measuring an angle remember that you can think of it as composed of the spokes or radii emanating from a point (the vertex) which is at the center of a circle. As shown, there are 360 degrees around a point. The unit of measure for angles is the *degree* (°).

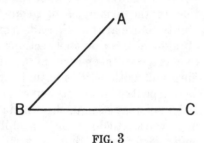

180°

180° in a straight angle

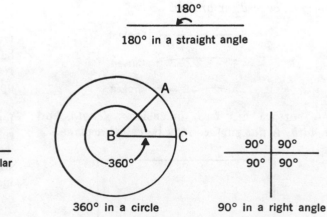

360° in a circle   90° in a right angle

One degree is $\frac{1}{360}$th part of the circumference of a circle. It is divided into 60 minutes (′). The minute is divided into 60 seconds (″). An angle of 85 degrees, fifteen minutes, three seconds would be written 85° 15′ 3″.

A **straight angle** is one of 180°. Its two sides lie in the same straight line.

A **right angle** is one of 90°. Hence it is half a straight angle.

An **acute angle** is any angle that is less than (<) a right angle. Thus it must be less than 90°.

An **obtuse angle** is greater than (>) a right angle but less than (<) a straight angle. Hence, it must be *between 90° and 180°*.

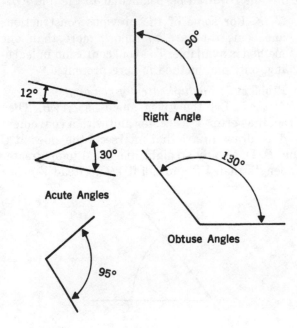

MEASURING ANGLES

Angles are measured by determining the part of a circle that the sides intersect. Therefore one measures the *opening between* the sides of an angle rather than the length of the sides. To measure or lay off angles one uses a protractor as shown in the illustration.

To measure an angle with protractor: *Place the center of the protractor at the vertex of the angle, and the straight side on a line with one side of the angle. Read the degrees where the other side of the angle crosses the scale of the protractor.*

To draw an angle with a protractor: *Draw a straight line for one side of the angle. Place the center of the protractor at the point of the line that is to be the vertex of the angle, and make the*

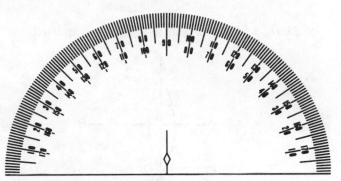

Protractor for Measuring and Laying off Angles

straight side of the protractor coincide with the line. Place a dot on your paper at the point on the scale of the protractor that corresponds to the size of the angle to be drawn. Connect this dot and the vertex to obtain the desired angle.

Practice Exercise No. 1

1 Draw a straight angle.
2 Draw a right angle.
3 Draw an acute angle of 30°.
4 Draw an obtuse angle of 120°.

Use the diagram for the following problems.

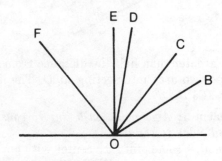

5   Measure angle *AOB*.
6   Measure angle *AOC*.
7   Measure angle *AOD*.
8   Measure ∠*AOE*.
9   Measure ∠*AOF*.
10 Measure ∠*BOF*.
11 Measure ∠*BOD*.

GEOMETRICAL CONSTRUCTIONS

Geometrical constructions, in the strict sense, involve only the use of a straight-edge (un-scaled ruler) and a pair of compasses. These are the only instruments needed to carry out the following constructions. Of course, in actual mechanical drawing the draftsman is not thus limited.

Problem 1: *To bisect a straight line.* (Bisect means to divide in half.)

Method: With *A* and *B* as centers and with a

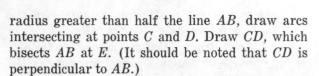

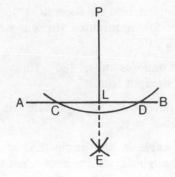

radius greater than half the line *AB*, draw arcs intersecting at points *C* and *D*. Draw *CD*, which bisects *AB* at *E*. (It should be noted that *CD* is perpendicular to *AB*.)

Problem 2: *To bisect any angle.*

Method: With the vertex as center and any radius draw an arc cutting the sides of the angle at *B* and *C*. With *B* and *C* as center and with a

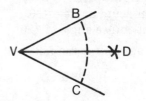

radius greater than half the distance from *B* to *C*, describe two arcs intersecting at *D*. The line *DV* bisects ∠*CVB*.

Problem 3: *At a point on a line to construct a perpendicular to the line.*

Method: From point *P* as center with any radius describe an arc which cuts the line *AB* at *M* and *N*. From *M* and *N* as centers and with a radius

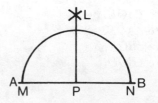

greater than *MP*, describe arcs which intersect at *L*. Draw the line *PL*, which is the required perpendicular.

Problem 4: *From a given point away from a straight line to drop a perpendicular to the line.*

Method: From the given point *P* as center and with a large enough radius describe an arc which cuts line *AB* at *C* and *D*. From *C* and *D* as centers and with a radius greater than half *CD*, describe

two arcs that intersect at *E*. Connect *PE*. The line *PL* is the required perpendicular to the line *AB*.

Note: For some of the previous constructions and some that are to follow, more than one method is available. To avoid confusion in learning, only one method is here presented.

Problem 5: *To duplicate a given angle.*

Method: Let the given angle be ∠*AVB*. Then from the vertex *V* as center and with a convenient radius, draw an arc that intersects the sides at *C* and *D*. Draw any straight line equal to or greater in length than *VB* and call it *V'B'*. (Read *V* prime

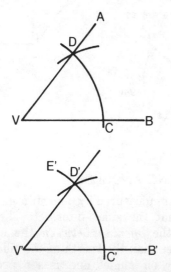

B prime.) With *V'* as center and with the same radius, describe an arc *C'E* that cuts the line at *C'*. From *C'* as center and with a radius equal to *DC*, describe an arc intersecting arc *C'E* at *D'*. Draw *D'V'*. ∠*D'V'C'* is the required angle.

Problem 6: *To duplicate a given triangle.*

Method: Draw any straight line from any point *D* as center, and with a radius equal to *AB* lay off *DE* equal to *AB*. With *E* as center and *BC* as radius, draw an arc. With *D* as center and *AC* as

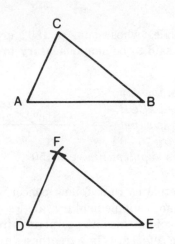

radius, draw an arc which intersects the other arc at *F*. Draw *FE* and *FD*. *DEF* is the required triangle.

Problem 7: *To construct a line parallel to a given line at a given distance.*

Method: If the given line is *AD* and the given distance is one inch, then at any two points *C* and *D* on the given line *AB* erect perpendiculars to *AB*. (See Problem 3.) With *C* and *D* as centers

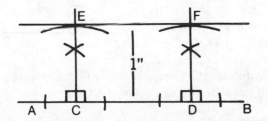

and with a radius equal to one inch, describe arcs cutting the perpendiculars at *E* and *F*. Draw the line *EF*, which is the required parallel line at a distance of one inch from *AB*.

Problem 8: *To divide a line into a given number of equal parts.*

Method: If *AB* is the given line, and if it is to be divided into six parts, then draw line *AC* making an angle (most conveniently an acute angle) with *AB*. Starting at *A* mark off on *AC* with a compass six equal divisions of any convenient length. Connect the last point *I* with *B*. Through points *D*, *E*, *F*, *G* and *H* draw lines parallel to

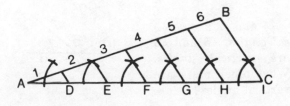

IB by making equal angles. The parallel lines divide *AB* into six equal parts.

Problem 9: *To find the center of a circle or arc of a circle.*

Method: Draw any two chords *AB* and *DE*. Draw the perpendicular bisectors of these chords.

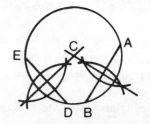

(See Problem 1.) The point *C* where they intersect is the center of the circle or arc.

Problem 10: *To inscribe a regular hexagon in a circle.*

Note: A regular hexagon is a polygon with six equal sides and six equal angles. The length of a side of a hexagon is equal to the radius of a circle circumscribing it.

Method: The radius of the circle is equal to *AG*. Starting at any point on the circle and using the length of the radius as the distance, lay off suc-

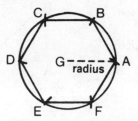

cessive points *B*, *C*, *D*, *E*, *F* on the circumference of the circle. Connect the points with straight lines to obtain the required hexagon.

LINE AND ANGLE RELATIONSHIPS

Having learned some basic geometric definitions, axioms and constructions, you are now prepared to understand some important relationships between lines and angles.

In demonstrating these relationships it is necessary to introduce additional *definitions*, *postulates*, *propositions*, *theorems* and *corollaries*.

For example, the following are important *postulates*.

Postulate 1. *A geometric figure may be moved from one place to another without changing its size or shape.*

Postulate 2. *Two angles are equal if they can be made to coincide.*

Postulate 3. *A circle can be drawn with any point as center.*

Postulate 4. *Two straight lines can intersect in only one point.*

Postulate 5. *All straight angles are equal.*

A **corollary** is a geometric truth that follows from one previously given and needs little or no proof.

For example, from Postulate 3 above we derive the *corollary:*

Corollary 1. *An arc of a circle can be drawn with any point as center.*

Adjacent angles are angles that have a common vertex and a common side between them.

For example, ∠*CPB* is adjacent to ∠*BPA* but not to ∠*DRC*.

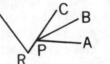

ADDING ANGLES

Postulate 6. *Adjacent angles can be added.* *Thus:*

∠*AOB* + ∠*BOC*
= ∠*AOC*.
∠*DOC* + ∠*COB*
+ ∠*BOA*
= ∠*DOA*.
∠*EOD* + ∠*DOC* + ∠*COB*
= ∠*EOB*.

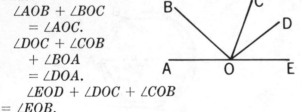

Postulate 7. *The sum of all the adjacent angles about a point on one side of a straight line is equal to one straight angle. Thus:*

If you measure ∠*AOB* + ∠*BOC* + ∠*COD* + ∠*DOE*, it should total 180°. Does it?

COMPLEMENTS AND SUPPLEMENTS

Two angles whose sum is 90°, or one right angle, are called **complementary.** Each of the angles is called the **complement** of the other. *Thus:*

∠*AOB* is the *complement* of
  ∠*BOC*,
or 35° *is complementary to*
  55°,
or 55° *is complementary to*
  35°.

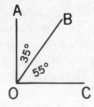

Two angles whose sum is 180° or a straight angle are said to be **supplementary** to each other. *Thus:*

∠*AOC* is the *supple-*
  ment of ∠*COB*,
or 150° *is supple-*
  mentary to 30° ,
or 30° *is supplementary to* 150°.

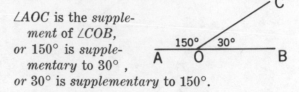

The postulates that follow concerning complementary and supplementary angles are mostly corollaries of axioms and postulates already stated. Hence, the references in parentheses are to axioms and postulates at the beginning of this chapter and this page.

Postulate 8. *All right angles are equal.* Since all straight angles are equal (POST. 5) and halves of equals are equal (AX. 5).

Postulate 9. *When one straight line meets another, two supplementary angles are formed.*

∠1 + ∠2 = ∠*AOB*
which is a straight
angle. (AX. 6)

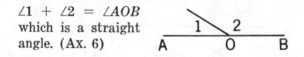

Postulate 10. *Complements of the same angle or of equal angles are equal.* (AX. 3)

Postulate 11. *Supplements of the same angle or of equal angles are equal.* (AX. 3)

Postulate 12. *If two adjacent angles have their exterior sides in a straight line, they are supplementary.*

Postulate 13. *If two adjacent angles are supplementary, their exterior sides are in the same straight line.*

Vertical angles are the pairs of opposite angles formed by the intersection of straight lines. *Thus:*

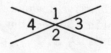

∠1 and ∠2 are *vertical angles.* ∠5 and ∠6 are *vertical angles.* What other pairs are vertical angles?

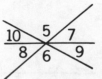

THE METHOD OF DEMONSTRATION IN GEOMETRY

A **proposition** is a statement of either a *theorem* or a *problem*.

A **theorem** is a relationship to be demonstrated.

A **problem** is a construction to be made.

In proving theorems or the correctness of constructions, the procedure is as follows.

If the proposition is a *theorem* requiring proof, you break it up into its two parts: the *hypothesis* and the *conclusion*. In the *hypothesis* certain facts are assumed. You use these given facts in conjunction with other previously accepted geometric propositions to prove the conclusion.

If the proposition is a *problem*, you make the construction and then proceed to prove that it is correct. You do this by listing the given elements and bringing forward previously established geometric facts to build up the necessary proof of correctness.*

For example, let us take the statement, *vertical angles are equal*. This theorem is given as Proposition No. 1 in many geometry textbooks, and is presented as follows.

Given: Vertical angles 1 and 2 as in the diagram next to the definition of vertical angles.

To prove: ∠1 = ∠2.

Steps	Reasons
1. ∠2 is the supplement of ∠3.	1. Two angles are supplementary if their sum is a straight ∠.
2. ∠1 is the supplement of ∠3.	2. Same as Reason 1.
3. ∠1 = ∠2.	3. Supplements of the same ∠ are equal. (Post. 4)

---

* This is the method of procedure followed in most geometry textbooks for demonstrating the truth of established geometric principles. For the purposes of this book, however, it will not be necessary to give formal demonstrations of theorems and problems. It is our purpose to give you a working knowledge of the essential geometric principles, facts and skills that can be put to practical application in office and in shop, in following military pursuits, in indulging a hobby, or in studying higher mathematics as presented in this book and in other more advanced textbooks.

ABBREVIATIONS

The following abbreviations are used:

adj.	adjacent	def.	definition
alt.	alternate	ext.	exterior
	altitude	hyp.	hypotenuse
ax.	axiom	iden.	identity
comp.	complementary	int.	interior
cong.	congruent	rt.	right
const.	construction	st.	straight
cor.	corollary	supp.	supplementary
corr.	corresponding	vert.	vertical

It should also be noted that the plurals of a number of the symbols listed on page 81 are formed by inserting an *s* in the symbol. Thus, ⧠ means angles; ⧍, triangles; |S|, parallels; Ⓢ, circles; ⧠, parallelograms, etc.

Practice Exercise No. 2

1   ∠1 coincides with ∠2. ∠1 = 30°. Find ∠2.

2   *BD* is the bisector of ∠*ABC*, which is 45°. Find ∠*ABD*.

3   ∠1 = ∠5, ∠2 = ∠1 and ∠3 = ∠5. What is the relationship between:

    (a) ∠1 and ∠3
    (b) ∠2 and ∠5
    (c) ∠4 and ∠7

4   In the same figure list the pairs of adj. ⧠.

5   In the same figure list the pairs of vertical angles.

6   In the accompanying figure the opposite ⧠ are vertical ⧠; ∠1 = 30° and ∠3 = 100°. Find the remaining four angles.

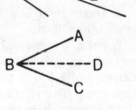

7   In the same figure find the values of ∠*AOC*, ∠*AOD*, ∠*BOE* and ∠*FOB*.

8   How many degrees are there in (a) $\frac{3}{4}$ of a rt. ∠, (b) $\frac{2}{3}$ rt. ∠, (c) $\frac{1}{2}$ rt. ∠, (d) $\frac{1}{8}$ rt. ∠, (e) $\frac{1}{4}$ rt. ∠?

9   Find the complement of (a) 68°, (b) 45°, (c) 55°, (d) 32°, (e) 5°, (f) 33° 30′.

10 What is the supplement of (a) 25°, (b) 125°, (c) 44°, (d) 88°, (e) 74° 30′, (f) 78° 30′?

PARALLEL LINES

Postulates Concerning Parallels

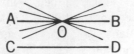

1. Through a given point only one line can be drawn parallel to a given line.

In the diagram, the only line that can be drawn ‖ to *CD* through point *O* is *AB*.

2. Two intersecting lines cannot both be parallel to a third straight line.

3. Two straight lines in the same plane, if produced, either will intersect or else are parallel.

Definitions

A **transversal** is a line that intersects two or more other lines.

When a **transversal** cuts two parallel or intersecting lines, various angles are formed. The names and relative positions of these angles are important. The relationship of angles as shown in the following diagram should be memorized.

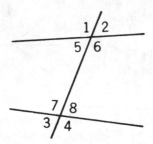

∠1, 2, 3, 4 are termed exterior angles.
∠5, 6, 7, 8 are termed interior angles.

∠1 and 4 } { are pairs of **alternate exterior**
∠2 and 3 }   { angles.

∠5 and 8 } { are pairs of **alternate interior**
∠6 and 7 }   { angles.

∠1 and 7 }
∠2 and 8 } { are pairs of **corresponding**
∠5 and 3 } { angles.
∠6 and 4 }

Theorem 1. If two straight lines are parallel to a third straight line, they are parallel to each other.

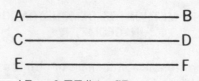

Given: *AB* and *EF* ‖ to *CD*.
To prove: AB ‖ *EF*.

If *AB* is not ‖ to *EF* the two lines would intersect and they would then be two intersecting lines parallel to a third straight line. But this is impossible according to Parallel Postulate 2. Hence *AB* must be parallel to *EF*.

Relationships Formed by Parallels and a Transversal

If two parallel lines are cut by a transversal, certain definite relationships will always be found to exist among the angles that are formed by the parallel lines and the transversal.

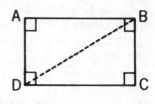

If we take the rectangle *ABCD*, we know that the opposite sides are parallel and equal and that all the angles are right angles. If we then draw the diagonal *DB* we have formed two triangles, △*DAB* and △*DCB*.

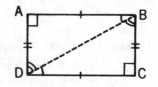

In △*DAB* and *DCB* we know *AD* = *CB*, *AB* = *DC* and ∠*A* = ∠*C*. As will be shown in the section on triangles, when two sides and the included ∠ of one △ are equal to two sides and the included ∠ of another, the two triangles are said to be congruent. This means that all their corresponding sides and angles are equal. (In the diagram the corresponding sides and angles of each triangle are marked with matched check marks.)

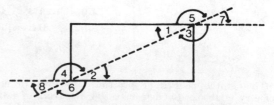

If we extend lines *AB* and *CD*, we have two ‖ lines cut by a transversal. We number the related angles for convenience, and the following relationships become evident.

∠1 = ∠2 (Corr. ∠s of cong. △.)
∠1 = ∠7 and ∠2 = ∠8 (Vert. ∠s are equal.)

∴ ∠7 = ∠8 = ∠1 = ∠2 (Things = to the same thing are = to each other.)

∠5 is supp. ∠7 (Ext. sides form a st. ∠s)

∴ ∠6 = ∠4 and ∠3 = ∠5 (Vert. ∠ are equal.)

∴ ∠3 = ∠6, ∠5 = ∠6 and ∠3 = ∠4 (Things = to the same thing are = to each other. Ax. 1.)

Presenting the above conclusions verbally, the angle relationships that occur when two parallel lines are cut by a transversal may be stated as follows.

1. The alternate interior angles are equal.

∠1 = ∠2, and ∠3 = ∠4

2. The alternate exterior angles are equal.

∠5 = ∠6, and ∠7 = ∠8

3. The corresponding angles are equal.

∠4 = ∠5, ∠3 = ∠6,   ∠2 = ∠7, ∠1 = ∠8

4. The two interior angles on the same side of a transversal are supplementary.

∠1 supp. ∠4, and ∠3 supp. ∠2

5. The two exterior angles on the same side of a transversal are supplementary.

∠5 supp. ∠8, and ∠7 supp. ∠6

These angle relationships may now be employed to prove that certain straight lines are parallel. Such proofs are represented by the *converses* of statements 1 to 5, in the form of the following theorems.

Theorems on Parallel Lines

Two lines are parallel if:

Theorem 2. *A transversal to the lines makes a pair of alternate interior angles equal.*

Theorem 3. *A transversal to the lines makes a pair of alternate exterior angles equal.*

Theorem 4. *A transversal to the lines makes a pair of corresponding angles equal.*

Theorem 5. *A transversal to the lines makes a pair of interior angles on the same side of the transversal supplementary.*

Theorem 6. *A transversal to the lines makes a pair of exterior angles of the same side of the transversal supplementary.*

A *corollary* that follows from these theorems is the following.

Corollary 1. *If two lines are perpendicular to a third line they are parallel.*

This can be easily proved by showing alt. int. ∠s equal as ∠1 = ∠2, or corr. ∠s equal, as ∠1 = ∠2, etc.

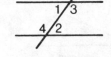

We may summarize the relationships of the angles formed by parallel lines cut by a transversal as follows:

(a) *The four acute angles formed are equal.*

(b) *The four obtuse angles formed are equal.*

(c) *Any one of the acute angles is the supplement of any one of the obtuse angles; that is, their sum equals 180°.*

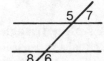

Practice Exercise No. 3

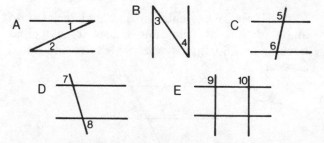

1   In the above diagram identify the kinds of angles indicated.

2   If ∠3 = 50°, what is the value of ∠1, ∠2 and ∠4?

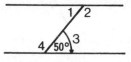

3   If ∠5 = 40°, what is the value of ∠6, ∠7 and ∠8?

4   *AB* is ⊥ to *CD*. Why would any other line that makes a 90° angle with *CD* be ‖ to *AB*?

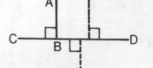

5   Tell why *AB* ‖ *CD* if given:
(a) ∠3 = ∠6
(b) ∠1 = ∠5
(c) ∠2 = ∠7

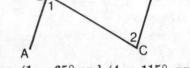

6   If given ∠1 = ∠2, prove that *AB* ‖ *CD*.

7   Given ∠1 = 65° and ∠4 = 115°, prove that the two horizontal lines are ‖.

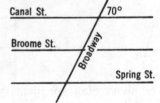

8   If Broadway cuts across Canal Street at an angle of 70°, at what angle does it cut across Broome and Spring Streets, which are ‖ to Canal Street?

9   Given ∠*ABC* = 60°, construct a line ‖ to *BC* using the principle of corresponding angles being equal.

10   Using the drawing-board, T-square and triangle pictured, how would you construct two angles the sides of which are ‖ to each other?

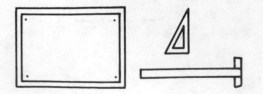

TRIANGLES

A **triangle** is a three-sided figure, the sides of which are straight lines. If you close off any angle a triangle is formed.

Triangles are classified according to their sides as *scalene, isosceles* and *equilateral.*

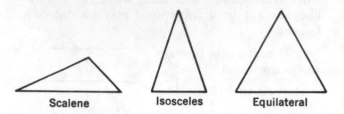

A **scalene triangle** is one in which no two sides are equal. An **isosceles triangle** is one in which two sides are equal. An **equilateral triangle** is one with three sides equal.

Triangles may also be classified with respect to their angles as *equiangular, right, acute* and *obtuse.*

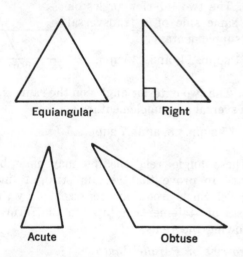

An **equiangular triangle** is one in which all the angles are equal (each measuring 60°).

A **right triangle** (or *right-angled triangle*) contains one right angle (often indicated by placing a small square in the 90° angle).

An **acute triangle** is one in which all angles are less than right angles.

An **obtuse triangle** has one angle greater than a right angle.

Note that an *equiangular triangle* is always *equilateral;* a *right* triangle may be *scalene* or *isosceles,* an *acute* triangle may be *scalene, isosceles,* or *equilateral* (equiangular is merely a special case of acute) ; an *obtuse* triangle may be *scalene* or *isosceles*.

Note also that either the scalene or the isosceles triangle may be *right*, *acute* or *obtuse*. The scalene cannot be *equiangular*, but the isosceles can, since the equilateral may be considered a special type of the isosceles.

It is a basic theorem that the sum of the angles of any triangle is equal to 180°. (See Theorem 14.)

TRIANGULAR MEASUREMENT

The **height** or **altitude** of a triangle is the perpendicular distance from the base to the vertex of the opposite angle. In Fig. 4, *AC* represents height or altitude of the triangles.

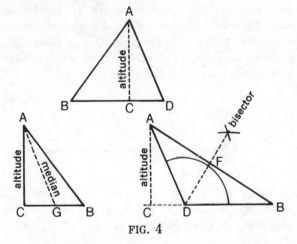

FIG. 4

A **median** is a line drawn from any vertex of a triangle to the middle of the opposite side. *AG* in Fig. 4.

The **bisector** of an angle is the line which divides it into two equal angles. *DF* bisects ∠*BDA* in Fig. 4.

The **perimeter** of any figure is *the entire distance around the figure.*

Rule: *The area of a triangle equals one half the product of the base and the height.*

Expressed as a **formula:**

$$A = \tfrac{1}{2}bh \text{ or } A = \frac{bh}{2}.$$

EXAMPLE 1: Find the area of the triangle shown.

SOLUTION: $A = \dfrac{bh}{2}$

$$= \frac{6 \times 8}{2}$$

$$= 24 \text{ sq. in.,} \quad \text{ANS.}$$

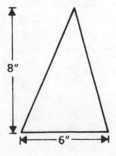

EXAMPLE 2: What is the height of a triangle if its area is 1 sq. ft. and its base 16 in.?

SOLUTION: $A = \dfrac{bh}{2} \ \therefore \ h = \dfrac{2A}{b}$

$$= \frac{2 \times 144}{16} = 18 \text{ in.,} \quad \text{ANS.}$$

FACTS ABOUT RIGHT TRIANGLES

The **hypotenuse** of a right triangle is the side opposite the right angle.

In the figure below it is shown that the square drawn on the hypotenuse of a right triangle is equal in area to the sum of the areas of the squares drawn on the other two sides.

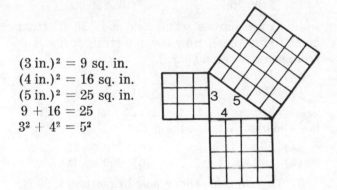

(3 in.)² = 9 sq. in.
(4 in.)² = 16 sq. in.
(5 in.)² = 25 sq. in.
9 + 16 = 25
3² + 4² = 5²

Rule: *The square of the hypotenuse of a right triangle is equal to the sum of the squares of the other two sides.*

From this there arise several self-evident formulas with reference to the right triangle.

Let c = hypotenuse, a = altitude, b = base; then:

Formula 1: $c^2 + a^2 + b^2$

Formula 2: $c = \sqrt{a^2 + b^2}$. (Taking the square root of both sides of the first equation.)

Formula 3: $a^2 = c^2 - b^2$; or, by transposition, $b^2 = c^2 - a^2$.

EXAMPLE 3: Find the hypotenuse of a right triangle whose base is 18 inches and altitude 26 inches.

$c = \sqrt{a^2 + b^2}$ (formula)

$= \sqrt{(18)^2 + (26)^2}$ (substituting)

$= \sqrt{324 + 676}$ (squaring)

$= \sqrt{1000}$ (adding)

$= 31.62$, ANS., extracting the square root.

Practice Exercise No. 4

1 A derrick standing perpendicular to the ground is 45 ft. high, and is tied to a stake in the ground by a cable 51 ft. long. How far is the foot of the derrick from the stake?

  (A) 68 ft. _____   (C) 24 ft. _____
  (B) 6 ft. _____   (D) 96 ft. _____

2 The base of a triangle is 18 in.; the altitude is $3\frac{1}{2}$ times the base. What is the area?

  (A) 1,296 sq. in. _____   (C) 567 sq. in. _____
  (B) 600 sq. in. _____   (D) 648 sq. in. _____

3 How much will it cost to fence off an isosceles shaped lot if one side is 75 ft. and the base is 50 ft.? Fencing costs $2.00 a foot.

  (A) $40.00 _____   (C) $25.00 _____
  (B) $400.00 _____   (D) $50.00 _____

4 In a square baseball field it is 90 ft. from home to first base. How far in a straight line is it from home to second base?

  (A) 127 ft. _____   (C) 120 ft. _____
  (B) 180 ft. _____   (D) 135 ft. _____

5 The base of a triangle is 20 feet; the altitude is $\frac{1}{2}$ the base. What is the area?

  (A) 80 sq. ft. _____   (C) 120 sq. ft. _____
  (B) 100 sq. ft. _____   (D) 200 sq. ft. _____

6 To hold a telephone pole in position a 26-ft. wire is stretched from the top of the pole to a stake in the ground 10 ft. from the foot of the pole. How tall is the pole?

  (A) 24 ft. _____   (C) 12 ft. _____
  (B) 40 ft. _____   (D) 36 ft. _____

7 What must be the length of a ladder to reach to the top of a house 40 ft. high, if the bottom of the ladder is placed 9 ft. from the house?

  (A) 36 ft. _____   (C) 41 ft. _____
  (B) 45 ft. _____   (D) 54 ft. _____

8 A tree is 100 ft. in a horizontal line from a river and its base is 20 ft. above the river. It is 160 ft. high. A line from its top to the opposite shore of the river measures 500 ft. How wide is the river?

  (A) 250.93 ft. _____   (C) 342.89 ft. _____
  (B) 366.47 ft. _____   (D) 329.65 ft. _____

DEMONSTRATING THE CONGRUENCE OF TRIANGLES

In demonstrating some fundamental relationships between lines and angles of triangles, a method of proving triangles to be *congruent* is employed.

Congruent figures are those which can be made to coincide or fit on one another. Thus if two triangles can be made to coincide in all their parts, they are said to be congruent.

The symbol for congruence is ≅.

In triangles that are congruent the respective equal angles and equal sides that would coincide if one figure were placed on top of the other, are termed **corresponding** angles and *corresponding* sides.

Corresponding parts are also called *homologous* parts. From what has been said it follows that corresponding parts of congruent figures are equal.

In geometry the corresponding or homologous parts of corresponding figures are frequently indicated by using *corresponding check marks* on the respective parts. For example, the corresponding parts in the congruent triangles below are marked with check marks of the same kind.

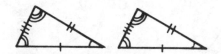

Seven Theorems on Congruence

Theorem 7. *Two triangles are congruent if two sides and the included angle of one are equal respectively to two sides and the included angle of the other.*

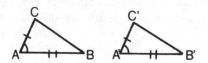

According to this theorem you are given $\angle ABC \cong \triangle A'B'C$, with $AC = A'C'$, $AB = A'B'$ and $\angle A = \angle A'$.

If you construct the figures with the given equal parts and then place $\triangle ABC$ on $\triangle A'B'C'$ so that the given equal parts correspond, it will be seen that the third line, CB, coincides with $C'B'$, making the triangles congruent at all points. Thus all the corresponding parts not given may also be assumed to be respectively equal.

For example, construct AC and $A'C'$ to equal $\frac{3}{8}''$; $\angle A$ and $\angle A' = 60°$; AB and $A'B' = \frac{3}{4}''$. Then measure the distances between CB and $C'B'$, and you will find them to be equal. If you measure $\angle C$ and C' and $\angle B$ and B', you will find these pairs to be equal as well.

Proving congruence by this theorem is known as the *side angle side* method. It is abbreviated *s.a.s.* = *s.a.s.*

By employing a similar approach you can readily verify the following theorems on the correspondence of triangles.*

Theorem 8. *Two triangles are congruent if two angles and the included side of one are equal respectively to two angles and the included side of the other.*

This is known as the *angle side angle* theorem, and is abbreviated *a.s.a.* = *a.s.a.*

Theorem 9. *Two triangles are congruent if the sides of one are respectively equal to the sides of the other.*

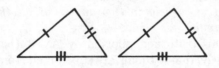

This is known as the *side side side* theorem, and is abbreviated *s.s.s.* = *s.s.s.*

Theorem 10. *Two triangles are congruent if a side and any two angles of one are equal to the corresponding side and two angles of the other.*

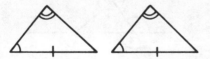

This is known as the *side angle angle* theorem, and is abbreviated *s.a.a.* = *s.a.a.*

Theorem 11. *Two right triangles are equal if the sides of the right angles are equal respectively.*

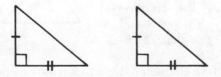

———
*Formal proofs employing geometric axioms, postulates and theorems to illustrate these cases of congruent triangles are given in regular school textbooks on geometry. The student interested in academic study should refer to such books.

Since the included right angles are equal, this theorem is really a special case of *s.a.s.* = *s.a.s.*

Theorem 12. *Two right triangles are equal if the hypotenuse and an acute angle of one are equal to the hypotenuse and an acute angle of the other.*

Since the right angles are equal, this theorem is a special case of *s.a.a.* = *s.a.a.*

Theorem 13. *Two right triangles are congruent if a side and an acute angle of one are equal to a side and corresponding acute angle of the other.*

Since the right angles are equal, this is again a special case of *s.a.a.* = *s.a.a.*

Practice Exercise No. 5

Note: Mark corresponding parts with corresponding check marks as previously explained. Use the method of demonstration shown under Theorem 14, following lines of reasoning similar to that used in connection with Theorem 7.

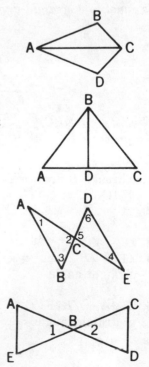

1   *Given* $AB = AD$
    $\angle 1 = \angle 2$
    Prove
    $\triangle ABC \cong \triangle ADC$

2   *Given* $BD \perp ACD$ is
    the mid-point
    of AC
    Prove
    $\triangle ABD \cong \triangle CBD$

3   *Given* $\angle 3 = \angle 5$ AE
    is the bisec-
    tor of BD
    Prove
    $\triangle ABC \cong \triangle EDC$

4   *Given* AD and CE
    bisect each
    other
    Prove $AE \parallel CD$

5   *Given* $AD = BC$
         $AC = BD$
   Prove
    $\triangle BAD \cong \triangle ABC$
     and $\angle 1 = \angle 2$

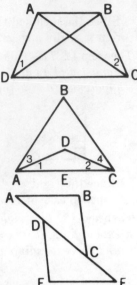

6   *Given* $AB = CB$
         $AD = CD$
   Prove $\angle 1 = \angle 2$
    Hint: Draw *BD*
   and then extend it
   to meet *AC* at *E*.

7   *Given* $AB = EF$
         $AB \parallel EF$
         $BC \parallel DE$
   Prove $BC = DE$

FACTS ABOUT TRIANGLES IN GENERAL

The general properties of the triangle not only form the foundation of trigonometry, but also find a wide application in the analysis and measurement of straight-sided plane figures of every kind.

One of the most important facts about triangles in general is that, regardless of the shape or size of any triangle, *the sum of the three angles of a triangle is equal to a straight angle, or 180°.* Presented as a theorem this proposition is easily proved.

Theorem 14. *The sum of the angles of a triangle is equal to a straight angle.*

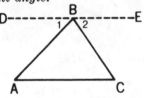

Given: $\triangle ABC.$
To prove: $\angle A + \angle B + \angle C =$ a straight angle.

Steps	*Reasons*
1. Through *B* draw *DE* $\parallel$ *AC*.	1. Parallel postulate No. 1.
2. $\angle 1 = \angle A$.	2. Alt. int. $\angle$s of $\parallel$ lines are =.
3. $\angle 2 = \angle C$.	3. Same reason as 2.
4. $\angle 1 + \angle B + \angle 2 =$ a straight angle.	4. By definition, since the exterior sides lie in a straight line.
5. $\therefore \angle A + \angle B + \angle C =$ a straight angle.	5. Substituting $\angle A$ and $\angle C$ for $\angle 1$ and $\angle 2$ in step 4 by Axiom 7.

From this knowledge of the sum of the angles of a triangle the following corollaries concerning triangles in general become self-evident.

Corollary 1. *Each angle of an equiangular triangle is 60°.*

Since the angles of an equiangular triangle are equal, each angle = 180° ÷ 3, or 60°.

Corollary 2. *No triangle may have more than one obtuse angle or right angle.*

180° minus 90° or more leaves 90° or less, to be split between the two remaining angles, and therefore each of the two remaining angles must be acute, *i.e.*, less than 90°.

Corollary 3. *The acute angles of a right triangle are complementary.*

180° minus 90° leaves two angles whose sum equals 90°.

Corollary 4. *If two angles of one triangle are equal respectively to two angles of another, the third angles are equal.*

This truth is supported by Ax. 3 (page 81), namely, that if equals are subtracted from equals the remainders are equal.

Corollary 5. *Any exterior* angle of a triangle is equal to the sum of the two remote interior angles.*

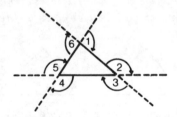

Thus in $\triangle ABC$ if you extend *AC* to *D* and draw *CE* $\parallel$ *AB*, you have the two $\parallel$ lines *AB* and *CE* cut by the transversal *AD*. $\therefore$ $\angle 1 = \angle B$ and $\angle 2 = \angle A$, so that $\angle 1 + \angle 2$, or $\angle BCD = \angle A + \angle B$.

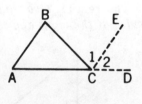

A few characteristic properties of special triangles frequently used are worth noting at this point.

---

*An exterior angle of a triangle is the angle formed by a side and the extension of its adjacent side. Every triangle has six exterior angles as shown in the diagram.

Theorem 15. *The base angles of an isosceles triangle are equal.*

By definition the sides of an isosceles triangle are equal.

∴ if you draw the bisector *BD* of ∠*B* it is readily seen that △*ABD* ≅ △*CBD* by *s.a.s.* = *s.a.s.* Hence ∠*A* = ∠*C*.

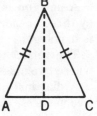

This theorem may be stated in another way, namely:

Theorem 16. *If two sides of a triangle are equal, the angles opposite those sides are equal.*

The following corollaries may readily be seen to follow from this theorem.

Corollary 1. *If two sides of a triangle are equal, the angles opposite these sides are equal and the triangle is isosceles.*

Corollary 2. *The bisector of the apex angle of an isosceles triangle is perpendicular to the base, bisects the base and is the altitude of the triangle.*

Corollary 3. *An equilateral triangle is equiangular.*

Theorem 17. *If one acute angle of a right triangle is double the other, the hypotenuse is double the shorter side.* Or

In a 30°–60° right triangle the hypotenuse equals twice the shorter side.

The following properties of bisectors, altitudes and medians of triangles are frequently applied in the practical problems of geometric design and construction that arise in shop and office.

Theorem 18. *Every point in the perpendicular bisector of a line is equidistant from the ends of that line.*

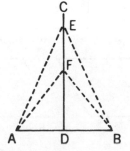

If   CD is ⊥ bisector of *AB*
Then DA = DB
        FA = FB, etc.

Theorem 19. *Every point in the bisector of an angle is equidistant from the sides of the angle.*

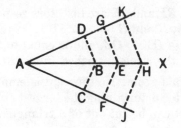

If   AX is the bisector of ∠*A*
Then BC = BD, EF = EG, HJ = HK, etc.

Theorem 20. *The perpendicular is the shortest line that can be drawn from a point to a given line.*

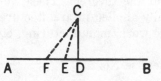

If   CD ⊥ *AB*
Then CD < CE ,CD < CF, etc.

Theorem 21. *The three bisectors of the sides of a triangle meet in one point which is equidistant from the three vertices of the triangle.*

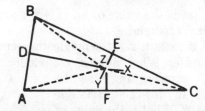

If   DX, EY and *FZ* are bisectors of the sides
          AB, BC and *CA*
Then AO = BO = CO, and is equal to the radius of the circle circumscribing △*ABC*

Note: This fact is often used as a method for finding the center of a circular object. The procedure consists in inscribing a triangle in the circle and constructing the bisectors of the sides. The point at which they meet is the center of the circle.

Theorem 22. *The three bisectors of the angles of a triangle meet in one point which is equidistant from the three sides of the triangle.*

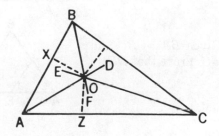

If   *AD*, *BF* and *CE* are bisectors respectively of
     ∡*A*, *B* and *C*
Then OX = OY = OZ, and is equal to the radius
     of the circle inscribed in △*ABC*.

Note: This geometric theorem is employed as a method for determining the largest circular pattern that can be cut out of a triangular piece of material.

For practical purposes you should carry out the constructions involved in the theorems of this section. Check the accuracy of your constructions by determining whether the constructed parts fit the hypothesis of the theorem. These very constructions are daily applied in architecture, carpentry, art, machine work, manufacturing, etc.

Practice Exercise No. 6

1   Two angles of a triangle are 62° and 73°. What does the third angle equal?

2   How many degrees are there in the sum of the angles of a quadrilateral?

Hint: Draw the figure and then construct a diagonal.

3   What is the value of an exterior angle of an equilateral triangle?

4   In a certain right triangle the acute angles are 2*x* and 7*x*. What is the size of each angle?

5   An exterior angle at the base of an isosceles triangle equals 116°. What is the value of the vertex angle?

6   In a certain triangle one angle is twice as large as another and three times as large as the third. How many degrees are there in each angle?

7   Draw an equilateral triangle and by it find the ratio between the diameter of the inscribed circle and the radius of the circumscribed circle.

Hint: Refer to Theorems 20 and 22.

8   Given ∠1 = ∠4, prove that △*ABC* is isosceles.

9   Given *BA* = *BC* and DE ∥ *BC*, prove that *DE* = *DA*.

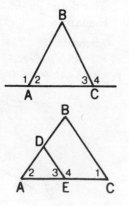

POLYGONS

A **polygon** is a plane geometric figure bounded by three or more sides. Any triangle, for instance, is a polygon.

The **vertices** of a polygon are the angle points where two sides meet.

A **diagonal** of a polygon joins two nonconsecutive vertices. How many diagonals has a triangle? None. How many diagonals can a four-sided figure have? Two.

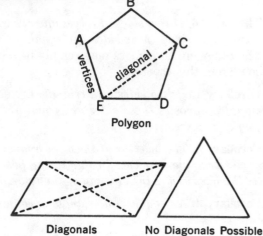

Polygon

Diagonals   No Diagonals Possible

Polygons derive their names from the number of and nature of the sides and the types of angles included.

Quadrilaterals are polygons with four sides. There are six types of quadrilaterals: the *rectangle*, the *square* (a special form of rectangle), the *rhomboid*, the *rhombus*, the *trapezoid* and the *trapezium*.

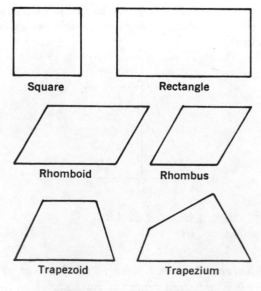

Square   Rectangle

Rhomboid   Rhombus

Trapezoid   Trapezium

TYPES OF QUADRILATERALS

A **parallelogram** is a quadrilateral in which the opposite sides are parallel and the opposite angles are equal.

A **square** is a parallelogram in which the angles are all right angles and the sides are all equal.

A **rectangle** is a parallelogram that has 4 right angles and in which opposite sides are equal.

A **rhomboid** has opposite sides parallel but no right angles.

A **rhombus** is a parallelogram having four equal sides but no right angles.

A **trapezoid** is a quadrilateral having one pair of parallel sides.

A **trapezium** is a quadrilateral in which no two sides are parallel.

(*Note:* In England these last two definitions are interchanged.)

SURFACE MEASUREMENT OF QUADRILATERALS

The **height** or **altitude** of a **parallelogram** is the distance perpendicular from the base to the opposite side.

Rule: *The area of a rectangle equals the base multiplied by the height.*

Formula: $A = bh$.

EXAMPLE 1: Find the area of a rectangle that is 3 inches high with a 4-inch base.

SOLUTION:

$A = bh$, formula.
$A = 4 \times 3 = 12$.
12 sq. inches, ANS.

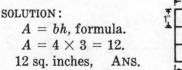

Note: The diagram has been drawn to scale on a $\frac{3}{16}$ basis. There are 4 columns and 3 rows of sq. in. units. The number of sq. in. by count is seen to be 12. The area is thus 12 sq. in.

EXAMPLE 2: Find the height of a rectangle with a 16 ft. base and an area of 80 sq. ft.

SOLUTION: $A = bh. \therefore h = \dfrac{A}{b}$

$= \frac{80}{16} = 5$ ft., ANS.

Rule: *The area of a square is equal to the square of one of its sides.*

Formula: $A = S^2$.

EXAMPLE 3: Find the side of a square whose area is 121 sq. in.

SOLUTION: $A = S^2. \therefore \sqrt{A} = S$

$= \sqrt{121} = 11$ ft., ANS.

Rule: *The perimeter of a square is equal to four times the square root of the area.*

Formula. $P = 4\sqrt{A}$ or $P = 4S$, where $P =$ perimeter, $A =$ area, and $S =$ side of a square.

EXAMPLE 4: Find the perimeter of a square whose area is 144 sq. in.

SOLUTION: $P = 4\sqrt{A}$, $P = 4 \times 12 = 48$ in., ANS.

Rule. *The diagonal of a square equals the square root of twice the area.*

diagonals

Formula: $D = \sqrt{2A}$

Note: Check back on your right triangle formula.

EXAMPLE 5: Find the diagonal of a square if the area is 49 sq. inches.

SOLUTION: $D = \sqrt{2A}$, $D = \sqrt{98} = 9,899$, ANS.

SOLUTION by rt. triangle formula: $c^2 = a^2 + b^2$, in which c represents the diagonal or hypotenuse while a and b are the sides. Then $c^2 = 7^2 + 7^2$, $c^2 = 98$

$c = \sqrt{98} = 9.899$, ANS.

Any parallelogram can be converted to a rectangle without changing its area. This is shown in the following diagram.

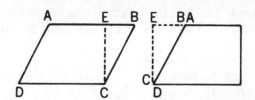

By taking the triangle EBC from the figure at the left and changing its position as shown in the figure at the right, we create a rectangle without adding to or deducting from the total area. Hence—

Rule: *The area of a parallelogram is equal to the product of the base times the height.*

EXAMPLE 6: Find the area of a rhomboid whose base is 12 inches and whose height is 8 inches.

SOLUTION: $A = bh. \therefore A = 12 \times 8 = 96$ sq. in.

Rule: *The area of a trapezoid equals half the sum of the parallel sides multiplied by the height.*

PROOF:

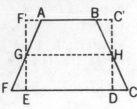

Make a rectangle of the trapezoid *ABCF* by drawing a line *GH* ∥ to the two ∥ sides and midway between them. The length of this line is the average of the two ∥ sides *AB* and *FC*. Perpendiculars from the midline *GH* to the larger base *FC* cut off triangles that are exactly equal to the triangles needed above the midline to form a rectangle of the new figure.

Formula: A of trapezoid $= \dfrac{B + b}{2} \times h$, in which h is the ⊥ height and B, b are the parallel sides.

EXAMPLE 7: Find the area of a trapezoid whose bases are equal to 20 in. and 30 in. and whose height is 15 inches.

SOLUTION: $A = \dfrac{B + b}{2} \times h$; $A = \dfrac{30 + 20}{2} \times 15$
$= 25 \times 15 = 375$ sq. in.,   ANS.

Practice Exercise No. 7

PROBLEMS

1   An apartment house is rectangular in shape. If its front is 550 ft. and it goes back 390 ft., how far is it all around the house?

  (A) 940 ft. ____   (C) 1,880 ft. ____
  (B) 1,800 ft. ____   (D) 1,100 ft. ____

2   A rectangular hangar is to house an airplane. What must its area be if you desire a 20-foot allowance on all sides and if the plane is 110 feet wide by 64 feet long?

  (A) 23,200 sq. ft. ____
  (B) 14,420 sq. ft. ____
  (C) 15,600 sq. ft. ____
  (D) 14,000 sq. ft. ____

3   How much would it cost to resurface a square plot 75 ft. long at a cost of 20¢ a sq. foot?

  (A) $6,000 ____   (C) $1,000 ____
  (B) $1,600 ____   (D) $1,125 ____

4   A square field whose area is 1,024 sq. feet is to be completely covered by flagstones 4 ft. square. How many flags will be needed to cover the field?

  (A) 32 ____   (C) 64 ____
  (B) 56 ____   (D) 84 ____

5   How much barbed wire would be needed to go diagonally across a rectangular piece of land that is 66 ft. wide by 88 ft. long?

  (A) 90 ft. ____   (C) 110 ft. ____
  (B) 100 ft. ____   (D) 120 ft. ____

6   If you had a square frame for the floor of a tent and if it contained 288 sq. ft., how long a piece of lumber would be needed to brace the frame from one corner to the other?

  (A) 12 ft. ____   (C) 21 ft. ____
  (B) 17 ft. ____   (D) 24 ft. ____

7   If molding cost 6 cents a ft., how much would it cost to put a border of molding around a square window that had an area of 81 sq. ft.?

  (A) $4.86 ____   (C) $1.08 ____
  (B) $.54 ____   (D) $2.16 ____

8   What is the area of the figure shown below?

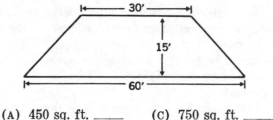

  (A) 450 sq. ft. ____   (C) 750 sq. ft. ____
  (B) 675 sq. ft. ____   (D) 2,700 sq. ft. ____

9   What is the area of the figure below?

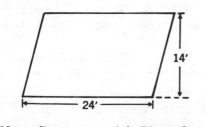

  (A) 168 sq. ft. ____   (C) 76 sq. ft. ____
  (B) 336 sq. ft. ____   (D) 206 sq. ft. ____

10   What is the area of the figure to the right?

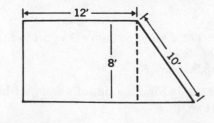

  (A) 120 sq. ft. ____   (C) 160 sq. ft. ____
  (B) 140 sq. ft. ____   (D) 180 sq. ft. ____

CIRCLES

A **circle** is a curved line on which every point is equally distant from a point within called the **center.**

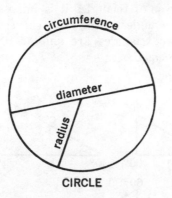

CIRCLE

A **radius** of a circle is a line drawn from the center to the outer edge.

The **diameter** of a circle is a straight line drawn from any point on the outer edge through the center to the outer edge on the opposite side. It is equal to twice any radius.

The **circumference** of a circle is the line representing its outer edge and is equal to the complete distance around the circle. It is analogous to perimeter.

Pi, written π, is the name given to the ratio expressed by dividing the circumference of any circle by its diameter. In quantity it is a constant approximately equal to $3\frac{1}{7}$ or 3.1416. If you measure the distance around any circle, and its diameter, and then divide the distance by the diameter you will always get a result of approximately $3\frac{1}{7}$.

Formula: $\pi = \dfrac{C}{d}$, where C = circumference

and d = diameter; or $\pi = \dfrac{C}{2r}$, where r = radius.

Rule: *To find the circumference of a circle multiply the diameter by π.*

Formula: $C = \pi d$; or $C = 2\pi r$.

EXAMPLE 1: The spoke of a wheel is 21 inches. Find its circumference.

SOLUTION: $C = 2\pi r$

$$= 2 \times \frac{22}{7} \times \overset{3}{\cancel{21}} = 132 \text{ in.}, \quad \text{Ans.}$$

EXAMPLE 2: The circumference of a pulley is 33 inches. What is its diameter?

SOLUTION: $C = \pi d, \therefore d = \dfrac{C}{\pi}$.

$$d = \frac{33}{\dfrac{22}{7}} = \overset{3}{\cancel{33}} \times \frac{7}{\underset{2}{\cancel{22}}} = \frac{21}{2} = 10\tfrac{1}{2} \text{ in.}, \quad \text{Ans.}$$

AREA OF A CIRCLE

Rule: *The area of a circle equals one-half the product of the circumference and the radius.*

This can be reasoned informally as follows. Any circle can be cut to form many narrow triangles as shown in Fig. 5. The altitude of each triangle would be equal to a radius r. The base would be a part of the circumference C. We know the area of

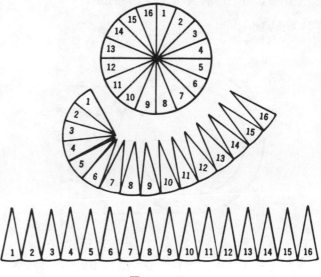

FIGURE 5

each triangle to be equal to $\frac{1}{2}$ the base times the altitude. Since r is the altitude, and the sum of the bases equal the circumference, the area $= \frac{1}{2}r \times C$. Since $C = 2\pi r$, $A = \frac{1}{2}r \times 2\pi r$. $\therefore A = r \times \pi r = \pi r^2$.

Rule: *The area of a circle in terms of the radius is π times the radius squared.*

Formula: $A = \pi r^2$.

EXAMPLE 3: Find the area of a circle that has a 6-in. radius.

SOLUTION: $A = \pi r^2 = 3.1416 \times (6)^2$
$$= 113.10 \text{ sq. in.,} \quad \text{ANS.}$$

EXAMPLE 4: The area of a circle is 396 sq. in. Find its radius.

SOLUTION:

$$A = \pi r^2, \quad \frac{A}{\pi} = r^2, \quad \sqrt{\frac{A}{\pi}} = r,$$

$$r = \sqrt{\frac{396}{\frac{22}{7}}} = \sqrt{396 \times \frac{7}{22}} = \sqrt{126} = 11.18 \text{ in.}$$

Rule: *The area of a circular ring equals the area of the outside circle minus the area of the inside circle.*

Formula: $A = \pi R^2 - \pi r^2$, where R = radius of larger circle and r = radius of smaller circle.

EXAMPLE: In a circular ring the outside diameter is 8″ and the inside diameter is 6″. What is the area of a cross-section of the ring?

SOLUTION:
$$A = \pi R^2 - \pi r^2. \qquad D = 8, \therefore R = 4.$$

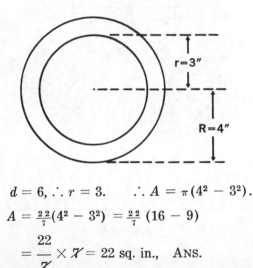

$$d = 6, \therefore r = 3. \qquad \therefore A = \pi(4^2 - 3^2).$$
$$A = \tfrac{22}{7}(4^2 - 3^2) = \tfrac{22}{7}(16 - 9)$$
$$= \frac{22}{\not{7}} \times \not{7} = 22 \text{ sq. in.,} \quad \text{ANS.}$$

SIMILAR PLANE FIGURES

In ordinary language plane figures are similar when they are alike in all respects except size. For instance, all circles are obviously similar.

Two polygons are **similar** when the angles of one are respectively equal to the angles of the other in the same consecutive order.

If the *consecutive* order of the angles is the same, it makes no difference if they follow each other clockwise in one figure and counter-clockwise in the other. Such figures will still be similar because either may be considered as having been reversed like an image in a mirror.

In the case of triangles it is impossible *not* to arrange the angles in the same consecutive order, so that two triangles are similar if only their angles are equal.

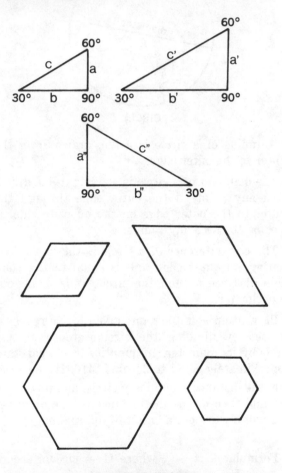

SIMILAR POLYGONS

In the preceding diagram all three triangles are similar because they all have the same angles.

The two rhombuses are similar, though the direction of the lines in one reverses that in the other.

All *regular* polygons with a given number of sides are similar.

Rule 1: *If two figures are similar, the ratio of any line in one to the corresponding line in the other applies to all the lines that correspond in the two figures.*

Rule 2: *If two figures are similar, the ratio of their areas is that of the squares of corresponding lines.*

These rules apply not only to simple geometric figures but to drawings, photographs, engravings, blueprints, etc. presenting the greatest complexity of lines. Because of the broad applicability of the rules governing similar polygons, we have generalized the whole subject.

To find the length of any line in a plane figure that is similar to another plane figure, *apply the ratio that exists between any other two corresponding lines.*

EXAMPLE: In a rhombus measuring 4 inches on a side the longer diagonal is $5\frac{1}{2}$ inches. How long would this diagonal be in a similar rhombus measuring 7 inches on a side?

SOLUTION:

$$D : d :: S : s,$$

$$\frac{D}{5\frac{1}{2}} = \frac{7}{4},$$

$$D = \frac{7 \times 5\frac{1}{2}}{4} = \frac{38\frac{1}{2}}{4} = \frac{77}{2 \times 4} = 9\frac{5}{8} \text{ in., ANS.}$$

To find the area of a plane figure that is similar to another plane figure having a known area, *determine the ratio of any two corresponding lines in the two figures and make the required area proportional to the squares of these lines.*

EXAMPLE: A trapezium in which one of the sides measures 6 inches has an area of 54 square inches. What would be the area of a similar trapezium in which a corresponding side measured 15 inches?

SOLUTION:

$$A' : A :: S^2 : s^2,$$

$$\frac{A'}{54} = \frac{15^2}{6^2},$$

$$A' = \frac{225 \times 54}{36} = \frac{225 \times 3}{2} = 337\frac{1}{2} \text{ in., ANS.}$$

SOLID GEOMETRY

Plane geometry treats of surfaces or of figures having *two* dimensions, namely *length* and *breadth.* **Solid** geometry treats of **solids** or of bodies having *three* dimensions, namely, *length, breadth,* and *thickness.*

RECTANGULAR SOLIDS

A rectangular solid is one in which all the faces are rectangles. The **cube** is a special type of rectangular solid in which all the faces are equal.

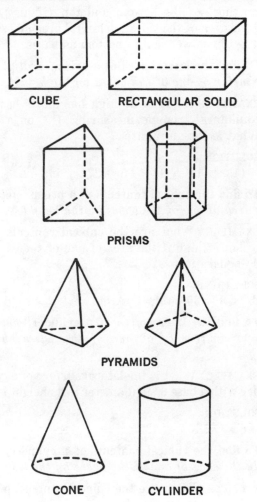

CUBE   RECTANGULAR SOLID

PRISMS

PYRAMIDS

CONE   CYLINDER

To find the area of the faces of a rectangular solid, *add the areas of the three different forms of face and multiply by 2.*

EXAMPLE: A rectangular solid measures $6'' \times 4'' \times 3''$. What is the total area of its faces?

SOLUTION: It has two faces measuring $6'' \times 4''$, two measuring $6'' \times 3''$ and two measuring $4'' \times 3''$.

$(6 \times 4) + (6 \times 3) + (4 \times 3) = 54$ sq. in.

$2 \times 54 = 108$ sq. in., ANS.

To find the area of the faces of a cube, *multiply the area of one face by six.*

To find the cubical contents of a rectangular solid, *multiply together the three dimensions.*

EXAMPLE: What are the cubical contents of a box measuring $11'' \times 6'' \times 4\frac{1}{2}''$?

$11 \times 6 \times 4\frac{1}{2} = 297$ cu. in.,   ANS.

With solids other than rectangular ones we consider the surfaces and areas of the sides as distinct from those of the bottom and top (if any). We call the area of the sides the **lateral area** and speak of the top as well as the bottom as **bases.**

To find the lateral area of a prism, *multiply the perimeter of one of the bases by the height.*

EXAMPLE: A prism 6'' high has as its base an equilateral triangle measuring $1\frac{1}{2}''$ on a side. What is its lateral area?

SOLUTION:

$(1\frac{1}{2} + 1\frac{1}{2} + 1\frac{1}{2}) \times 6 = 27$ sq. in.,   ANS.

To find the cubical contents of a prism, *multiply the area of one of the bases by the height.*

EXAMPLE: What are the cubical contents of a prism 8'' high if the area of one of the bases is $3\frac{3}{4}$ square inches?

SOLUTION:

$3\frac{3}{4} \times 8 = 30$ cu. in.,   ANS.

To find the lateral area of a cylinder, *multiply the circumference of one of the bases by the height.*

EXAMPLE: What is the lateral surface of a cylinder with a base 6'' in diameter if its height is 7''?

SOLUTION:

$6 \times \frac{22}{7} \times 7 = 132$ sq. in.,   ANS.

To find the cubical contents of a cylinder, *multiply the area of one of the bases by the height.*

EXAMPLE: What are the cubical contents of the cylinder in the preceding example?

SOLUTION:

$3^2 \times \frac{22}{7} \times 7 = 9 \times 22 = 198$ cu. in.,   ANS.

To find the lateral area of a pyramid, *multiply its slant height by the perimeter and divide by two.*

EXAMPLE: What is the lateral area of a triangular pyramid having a base measuring 2'' on a side and a slant height of 9''?

SOLUTION:

$(2 + 2 + 2) \times 9 \div 2 = 27$ sq. in.,   ANS.

To find the cubical contents of a pyramid, *multiply the area of the base by the altitude* (not slant height) *and divide by three.*

EXAMPLE: A square pyramid 10 inches high has a base measuring 4 inches on a side. What are its cubical contents?

SOLUTION:

$$\frac{4 \times 4 \times 10}{3} = \frac{160}{3} = 53\frac{1}{3} \text{ cu. in., \quad ANS.}$$

To find the lateral area of a cone, *multiply its slant height by the circumference of the base and divide by two.* (Compare this with the rule for finding the lateral area of a pyramid as given above.)

To find the cubical contents of a cone, *multiply the area of the base by the altitude and divide by three.* (Compare this with the rule for finding the cubical contents of a pyramid as given above.)

To find the area of the surface of a sphere, *multiply the square of the radius by 4π.*

EXAMPLE: What is the surface area of a sphere one foot in diameter?

SOLUTION:

$6^2 \times 4\pi = 36 \times 4 \times \frac{22}{7}$
$= \frac{3168}{7} = 452\frac{4}{7}$ sq. in.,   ANS.

To find the cubical contents of a sphere, *multiply the cube of the radius by $\dfrac{4\pi}{3}$.*

EXAMPLE: What are the cubical contents of a sphere one foot in diameter?

SOLUTION:

$$6^3 \times \frac{4\pi}{3} = \frac{216 \times 4 \times 22}{3 \times 7} = \frac{6336}{7}$$
$$= 905\frac{1}{7} \text{ cu. in., \quad ANS.}$$

Practice Exercise No. 8

PROBLEMS

1 The diameter of an automobile tire is 28''. What is its circumference?

   (A) 66''____   (C) 88''____
   (B) 77''____   (D) 99''____

2 The circumference of a wheel is 110 inches. How long is one of its spokes?

   (A) 35''____   (C) 15''____
   (B) $17\frac{1}{2}''$____   (D) $12\frac{1}{2}''$____

3 To make a circular coil for a magnet you need 49 turns of wire. How much wire will you need if the diameter of the coil is 4''?

   (A) $12\frac{4}{7}$ in.____   (C) 324 in.____
   (B) $84\frac{2}{7}$ in.____   (D) 616 in.____

4 How many square inches of tin are needed for the top of a can that is 14 inches in diameter?

(A) 616 sq. in. ____　　(C) 462 sq. in. ____

(B) 308 sq. in. ____　　(D) 154 sq. in. ____

5 You have a circular grazing field 96 ft. in diameter, which is roped around. Concentric with that you have a circular trotting track 128 ft. in diameter. How much will it cost to regravel the trotting track at a price of 10¢ per sq. ft.?

(A) \$426.00　　　　(C) \$826.40

(B) \$563.20　　　　(D) \$968.20

6 The area of canvas needed to just cover the muzzle of a cannon is $50\frac{1}{4}$ sq. in. What is the diameter of the muzzle?

(A) 12 in. ____　　(C) 6 in. ____

(B) 8 in. ____　　(D) 5 in. ____

7 If the radius of a circle is twice as great as the radius of a smaller circle, how many times as large will the area of the greater circle be than the area of the smaller circle?

(A) 2 ____　　(C) 6 ____

(B) 4 ____　　(D) 8 ____

8 You have 4 circular garden plots, each having a 14-foot radius. What must the radius be of one large circular plot that will have as much area as the four combined?

(A) 28 ft. ____　　(C) 20 ft. ____

(B) 21 ft. ____　　(D) 64 ft. ____

9 How much will it cost to re-surface a circular swimming tank that has a diameter of 56 ft. if surfacing costs 25 cents a sq. ft.?

(A) \$154.00 ____　　(C) \$462.00 ____

(B) \$308.00 ____　　(D) \$616.00 ____

10 If you wish to convert a circular field that has a diameter of 56 feet to a square field with the same area, how long will a side of the square be?

(A) 28 ft. ____　　(C) 49.6 ft. ____

(B) 36.8 ft. ____　　(D) 46.0 ft. ____

Exercise No. 1

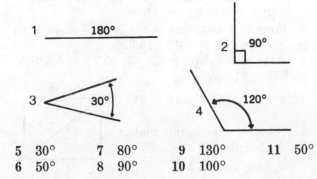

| 5 | 30° | 7 | 80° | 9 | 130° | 11 | 50° |
| 6 | 50° | 8 | 90° | 10 | 100° | | |

Exercise No. 2

1 $\angle 2 = 30°$. ∡s that coincide are =.

2 $\angle ABD = 22° 30'$. A bisector divides an ∠ in half.

3 (a) $\angle 1 = \angle 3$ ⎫
(b) $\angle 2 = \angle 5$ ⎭ Ax. 1, p. 80
(c) Relationship unknown

4 $\angle 1$ and $\angle 2$, $\angle 2$ and $\angle 3$, $\angle 3$ and $\angle 4$, $\angle 4$ and $\angle 5$, $\angle 5$ and $\angle 6$, $\angle 6$ and $\angle 7$, $\angle 7$ and $\angle 1$

5 $\angle 1$ and $\angle 5$, $\angle 2$ and $\angle 6$

6 $\angle 2 = 50°$, $\angle 4 = 30°$, $\angle 5 = 50°$, $\angle 6 = 100°$

7 $\angle AOC = 80°$, $\angle AOD = 180°$, $\angle BOE = 180°$, $\angle FOB = 130°$

8 (a) 67° 30', (b) 60°, (c) 45°, (d) 30°, (e) 22° 30'

9 (a) 22°, (b) 45°, (c) 35°, (d) 58°, (e) 85°, (f) 56° 30'

10 (a) 155°, (b) 55°, (c) 136°, (d) 92°, (e) 105° 30', (f) 101° 30'

Exercise No. 3

1 (a) alt. int., (b) alt. int., (c) corr., (d) alt. ext., (e) corr.

2 $\angle 1 = 50°$, $\angle 2 = 130°$, $\angle 4 = 130°$

3 $\angle 6 = 140°$, $\angle 7 = 140°$, $\angle 8 = 40°$

4 Two lines ⊥ to a third line are ∥

5 (a) alt. int. ∡s are =
(b) corr. ∡s are =
(c) alt. ext. ∡s are =

6 If a pair of alt. int. ∡s are = the lines are ∥.

7 $\angle 3$ is sup. to 115°. ∴ $\angle 3 = 65°$, making corr. ∡s =.

8 70°

9 Extend AB to D and construct $\angle BDE =$ to 60°. Then $DE \parallel BC$ because corr. ∡s are =.

10 If the triangle is moved along the edge of the T-square into any two different positions, then lines drawn along side a will be ∥ to each other, and lines drawn along side b will also be ∥ to each other.

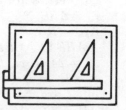

Exercise No. 4

1 $b^2 = c^2 - a^2$, $b = \sqrt{(51)^2 - (45)^2}$ $= \sqrt{2,601 - 2,025} = \sqrt{576} = 24$

2 $A = \dfrac{bh}{2}; \dfrac{18\,(63)}{2} = 567$ sq. in.

3 Perimeter = sum of 3 sides. In isosceles $\triangle$ 2 sides are equal.
$75 + 75 + 50 = 200; 200 \times \$2.00 = \$400.00$

4 $c^2 = a^2 + b^2$
$c = \sqrt{90^2 + 90^2} =$
$\sqrt{8{,}100 + 8{,}100} =$
$\sqrt{16{,}200} = 127.27$

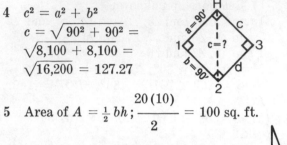

5 Area of $A = \frac{1}{2} bh; \dfrac{20\,(10)}{2} = 100$ sq. ft.

6 $a^2 = c^2 - b^2$, $a = \sqrt{(c)^2 - (b)^2} =$
$\sqrt{(26)^2 - (10)^2} =$
$\sqrt{676 - 100} = \sqrt{576} = 24$

7 Let l = length of ladder, h = height of house, and b = distance from house at base. Then $l = \sqrt{h^2 + b^2} = \sqrt{1600 + 81} = \sqrt{1681} = 41$

8 Form the triangle and make the necessary deduction afterward. Let h = height of tree + elevation = $160 + 20 = 180$; l = line from top of tree to opposite shore; d = horizontal distance from tree to opposite shore. Then $d = \sqrt{l^2 - h^2} = \sqrt{500^2 - 180^2} = \sqrt{250000 - 32400} = \sqrt{217600} = 466.47$. Subtracting 100 ft. leaves 366.47 as the width of the river.

Exercise No. 5

1 $AB = AD$, $\angle 1 = \angle 2$ and $AC = AC$ (by identity) $\therefore \triangle ABC \cong ADC$ by s.a.s. = s.a.s.

2 $AD = DC$, $BD = BD$, and $\angle ADB = \angle CDB$ (all rt. ∡ are =)
$\therefore \triangle ABD \cong \triangle CBD$ by s.a.s. = s.a.s.

3 $\angle 3 = \angle 5$, $BC = CD$ (bisected line) and $\angle 2 = \angle 6$ (vert. ∡ are =)
$\therefore \triangle ABC \cong \triangle EDC$ by a.s.a. = a.s.a.

4 $AB = BD$, $EB = BC$, $\angle 1 = \angle 2$ (vert. ∡)
$\triangle ABE \cong \triangle CBD$ by s.a.s. = s.a.s.
$\angle 3 = \angle 4$ (corr. ∡ of cong. ∡)
$\therefore AE \parallel CD$ (two lines are $\parallel$ if a pair of alt. int. $\angle$ are =)

5 $AD = BC$, $AC = BD$, $AB = AB$ by identity
$\therefore \triangle BAD \cong \triangle CBA$ by s.s.s. = s.s.s.
$\therefore \angle 1 = \angle 2$ (corr. $\angle$ of cong. $\triangle$ are =)

6 $AB = CB$, $AD = CD$,
$DB = DB$ by identity

$\therefore \triangle ABD \cong \triangle CBD$ by s.s.s. = s.s.s.
$\therefore \angle 5 = \angle 6$ (corr. ∡ of cong. ∡)
$\therefore \angle 7 = \angle 8$ (supp. of = ∡ are =)
$DE = DE$ by identity
$\therefore \triangle ADE \cong \triangle CDE$ by s.a.s. = s.a.s.
$\therefore \angle 1 = \angle 2$ (corr. ∡ of cong. ∡)

7 $AB = EF$, $\angle A = \angle F$ (alt. int. ∡) and $\angle C = \angle D$ (alt. int. ∡)
$\therefore \triangle ABC \cong \triangle DEF$ by s.a.a. = s.a.a.
$\therefore BC = DE$ (corr. sides of cong. ∡)

Exercise No. 6

1 $45°$

2 $360°$ (any quad. can be divided into 2 ∡)

3 $120°$ (∡ of equilateral $\triangle$ = $60°$, and ext. $\angle$ = sum of 2 int. ∡)

4 $20°$ and $70°$ (acute ∡ of a rt. $\triangle$ are comp. . . $9x = 90°$, $x = 10°$)

5 $52°$ (supp. $116° = 64°$; base $\angle$ of isos. $\triangle$ are = $\therefore 180 - (64° + 64°) = 52°$

6 $32\frac{8}{11}°$, $49\frac{1}{11}°$, $98\frac{2}{11}°$ (Let x = angle; then $x + \frac{1}{2}x + \frac{1}{3}x = 180°$ and $x = 98\frac{2}{11}°$.)

7 Ratio is $1 : 1$ or equal.

8 $\angle 2$ supp. $\angle 1$ and $\angle 3$ supp. $\angle 4$
$\therefore \angle 2 = \angle 3$ (Ax. 1, page 103)
$\therefore AB = BC$ and $\triangle ABC$ is isos. (if 2 ∡ of a $\triangle$ are = the sides opp. are = and the $\triangle$ is isos.)

9 In $\triangle ABC$ $\angle 1 = \angle 2$ (base ∡ of an isos. $\triangle$ are =)
$\angle 1 = \angle 3$ (corr. ∡ of $\parallel$ lines are =)
$\therefore \angle 3 = \angle 2$ (Ax. 1)
$\therefore DA = DE$ (if two ∡ of a $\triangle$ are =, the sides opp. are =)

Exercise No. 7

1 Perimeter = sum of 4 sides, and the opposite sides of a rectangle are equal. $\therefore P = 550 + 550 + 390 + 390 = 1{,}880$

2 Area of a rectangle = $l \times w$. $110 + 40 \times 64 + 40 = 150 \times 104 = 15{,}600$

3 Area of a square = S^2. $75 \times 75 = 5{,}625 \times .20 = \$1{,}125$

4 $4^2 = 16$; $1{,}024 \div 16 = 64$

5 Diag. of a rectangle makes 2 rt. angles. $c^2 = a^2 + b^2$.
$\therefore c = \sqrt{a^2 + b^2}$,

$c = \sqrt{(88)^2 + (66)^2} = \sqrt{4,356 + 7,744} = 110$

6 Side of a square is equal to the square root of the area. $S = \sqrt{A} = \sqrt{288}$. Diagonal makes a rt. triangle in which $c^2 = a^2 + b^2$ or $c = \sqrt{288 + 288} = \sqrt{576} = 24$. By formula, diag. of a sq. $= \sqrt{2A}$ or $\sqrt{2 \times 288} = \sqrt{576} = 24$

7 Perimeter = sum of 4 sides. If area = 81, side = $\sqrt{81}$ or 9; $9 \times 4 = 36$; $36 \times .06 = \$2.16$

8 Area of a trapezoid = $\dfrac{B + b}{2} \times h = \dfrac{60 + 30}{2} \times 15 = 45 \times 15 = 675$ sq. ft.

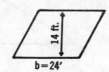

9 Area of a parallelogram equals base times height. $A = bh. \therefore = 24 \times 14 = 336$ sq. ft.

10 To find unknown segment use formula for area of rt. triangle. $c^2 = a^2 + x^2$, or $x = \sqrt{c^2 - a^2} = \sqrt{(10)^2 - (8)^2} = \sqrt{100 - 64} = \sqrt{36} = 6$.

Area of trapezoid = $\dfrac{B + b}{2} \times h; \dfrac{18 + 12}{2} \times 8 = 15 \times 8 = 120$

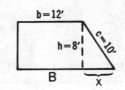

Exercise No. 8

1 $C = \pi d. C = \frac{22}{7} \times 28 = 88$ in.

2 $C = 2\pi r. r = \dfrac{C}{2\pi}, r = \dfrac{110}{\frac{44}{7}} = 110 \times \dfrac{7}{44} = \dfrac{35}{2} = 17\frac{1}{2}$ in.

3 $C = \pi d. C = \frac{22}{7} \times 4 = \frac{88}{7}, \frac{88}{7} \times 49 = 616$ in.

4 $A = \pi r^2, D = 2r$. If $D = 14$, then $r = 7; A = \frac{22}{7} \times (7)^2 = 154$ sq. in.

5 Area of ring $= \pi R^2 - \pi r^2$. $D = 128, d = 96, R = 64, r = 48$
$A = \pi(64^2 - 48^2) = \frac{22}{7}(4,096 - 2,304) = \frac{22}{7} \times 1792 = 5,632; 5,632 \times .10 = \$563.20$

6 $A = \pi r^2, r^2 = \dfrac{A}{\pi}; r = \sqrt{\dfrac{A}{\pi}} = \sqrt{\dfrac{50\frac{1}{4}}{\frac{22}{7}}} = \sqrt{50\frac{1}{4} \times \frac{7}{22}} = \sqrt{\frac{1407}{88}} = \sqrt{16.1}$. Discarding the decimal, $r = 4; D = 2 \times 4$ or 8.

7 Since $A =$ constant times R^2, areas are to each other as the squares of their radii, or $A : a :: R^2 : r^2$. If $R = 2$ and $r = 1$, then $A = \pi \times (2)^2$, and $a = \pi(1)^2$, or 4 to 1. Answer is 4.

8 $R = \sqrt{r^2 + r^2 + r^2 + r^2} = \sqrt{(14)^2 + (14)^2 + (14)^2 + (14)^2} = \sqrt{4(196)} = \sqrt{784} = 28$

9 Area $= \pi R^2 = \frac{22}{7} \times 28^2$. Cost is $\frac{22}{7} \times 28 \times 28 \times \frac{1}{4} = 22 \times 28 = \$616$.

10 Area of circle $= \pi R^2$. Side of equal square $= \sqrt{\pi R^2} = \sqrt{\frac{22}{7} \times 28 \times 28} = \sqrt{88 \times 28} = \sqrt{2464} = 49.6$ ft.

CHAPTER SIXTEEN

TRIGONOMETRY

Trigonometry is the branch of mathematics that deals with the measurement of triangles. (The word *trigonometry* comes from the Greek and means *to measure a triangle*.) Trigonometry enables us to find the unknown parts of triangles by arithmetical processes. For this reason it is constantly used in surveying, mechanics, navigation, engineering, physics and astronomy.

From geometry you learned that there are many shapes of triangles. For our purpose we can start with the simple case of a right triangle. Starting from this, you will eventually be able to work with all types of triangles because any triangle can be broken down into two right triangles.

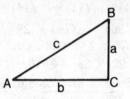

In the right triangle *BAC* you know from geometry that

(a) $\angle A + \angle B = 90$,

(b) $c^2 = a^2 + b^2$.

From equation (a) you can find one of the acute angles if the other is given, and from equation (b) you can determine the length of any side if the other two are given. But as yet you do not have a method for finding angle *A* if given the two sides *a* and *b*, even though by geometry you could construct the triangle with this information. And this is where trigonometry makes its contribution. It gives you a method for calculating the angles if you know the sides or for calculating the sides if you know the angles.

TRIGONOMETRIC FUNCTIONS OF AN ANGLE

If we take the triangle in the previous figure

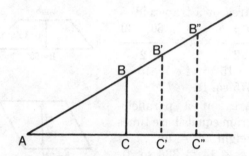

and extend lines *AB* and *AC*, and then drop perpendiculars from points *B′* and *B″* to *AC*, we form three similar triangles:

$$\triangle CAB, \triangle C' AB' \text{ and } \triangle C'' AB''$$

When two triangles are similar, the ratio of any two sides of one triangle equals the ratio of corresponding sides of the second triangle. Thus in the three triangles of the figure,

$$\frac{BC}{AC} = \frac{B'C'}{AC'} = \frac{B''C''}{AC''}, \text{ or}$$

$$\frac{BC}{AB} = \frac{B'C'}{AB'} = \frac{B''C''}{AB''}.$$

Similar equalities hold for the ratios between the other sides of the triangles.

These equalities between the ratios of the corresponding sides of similar triangles illustrate the fact that *no matter how the size of a right triangle may vary, the values of the ratios of the sides remain the same so long as the acute angles are unchanged.* In other words each of the above ratios is a **function** of angle *A*.

From algebra and geometry we learn that a variable quantity which depends upon another quantity for its value is called a **function** of the latter value.

Therefore in the above figure the value of the ratio $\dfrac{BC}{AC}$ is a function of the magnitude of angle A; and as long as the magnitude of angle A remains the same, the value of the ratio $\dfrac{BC}{AC}$ will be the same.

DESCRIPTION OF THE TANGENT FUNCTION

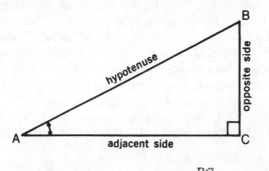

The constant ratio or function, $\dfrac{BC}{AC}$, is termed the **tangent** of angle A. It will be noted that this function represents the ratio of the side *opposite* angle A divided by the side next to angle A, called the *adjacent* side—that is, the side next to it other than the hypotenuse. Accordingly,

$$\textbf{tangent } \angle A = \frac{\text{opposite side}}{\text{adjacent side}},$$

or $\qquad\qquad \textbf{tan } A = \dfrac{\text{opp}}{\text{adj}}.$

MAKING A TABLE OF TRIGONOMETRIC FUNCTIONS

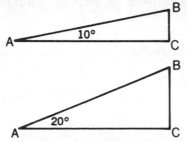

If you construct $\angle A$ equal to 10° and measure BC and AC and then compute the value of $\dfrac{BC}{AC}$, you will find it to be .176. Then if you construct $\angle A$ to equal 20°, you will find $\dfrac{BC}{AC}$ equal to .364.

For $\angle A$ at 30° you will find $\dfrac{BC}{AC}$ equal to .577. This means that thereafter you will know that the

tangent of any angle of 10° in a right triangle is equal to .176, and the tangent of any angle of 20° is equal to .364. Thus by computing the values of the ratios of $\dfrac{BC}{AC}$ for all angles from 1° to 90° you would obtain a complete table of tangent values. A sample of such a table is shown below.

SAMPLE TABLE OF TRIGONOMETRIC FUNCTIONS

Angle	Sine	Cosine	Tangent
68	.9272	.3746	2.4751
69	.9336	.3584	2.6051
70	.9397	.3420	2.7475
71	.9455	.3256	2.9042
72	.9511	.3090	3.0777

This sample table and the more complete table at the end of this chapter give the tangents of angles to four decimal places. For instance in the table above, to find the value of the tangent of an angle of 69° you first look in the column head *Angle* and find 69°. Then on the same horizontal line in the column headed *Tangent* you find the value 2.6051. This means that tan 69° = 2.6051.

The following example will show how you can solve problems in trigonometry by the use of the table of tangents.

EXAMPLE: An airplane is sighted by two observers. One observer at A indicates it to be directly overhead. The other observer at B, 3,000 feet due west of A, measures its angle of elevation (*see below*) at 70°. What is the altitude of the airplane?

SOLUTION:

$$\tan \angle B = \frac{\text{(opp side)}}{\text{(adj side)}} = \frac{CA}{BA}$$

Since $\angle B = 70°$,
$\qquad\qquad \tan \angle B = 2.7475.$
$\qquad\qquad$ (*see table above*)

Substituting, $2.7475 = \dfrac{CA}{3000}.$

Transposing, $CA = 3000 \times 2.7475$
$\qquad\qquad\qquad = 8242.5$ ft.

Altitude of airplane is 8242.5 ft.,
$\qquad\qquad\qquad\qquad$ ANS.

PRACTICAL OBSERVATION OF ANGLES

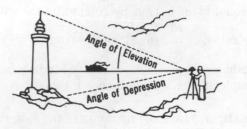

The *angle of elevation or depression* of an object is the angle made between a line from the eye to the object and a horizontal line in the same vertical plane. If the object is above the horizontal line it makes an *angle of elevation;* if below the horizontal line it makes an *angle of depression.*

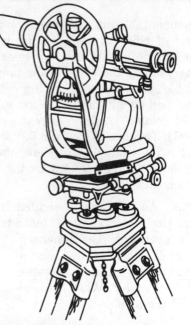

Courtesy of Keuffel & Esser Co., New York

For measuring both vertical and horizontal angles out of doors an engineer's *transit* or *theodolite* is used. As may be seen from the illustration, the instrument combines a telescope with a horizontal and a vertical plate, each of which is graduated by degrees, minutes and seconds. By moving the telescope to right or left, horizontal angles can be measured on the horizontal plate. Vertical angles are measured on the vertical disc by moving the telescope up and down.

THE SIX TRIGONOMETRIC FUNCTIONS

As has been previously pointed out, ratios other than those involved in the *tangent function* exist

between the sides of the triangle, and have, like the tangent, an equality of value for a given magnitude of angle, irrespective of the size of the triangle. It is to be expected, therefore, that problems involving the solution of right triangles can be solved by other known trigonometric ratios or functions of the selfsame angle. As a matter of fact, there exist six important ratios or functions for any acute angle of a right triangle. The description and definition of these functions follows.

The sides and angles of triangle *CAB* in the following diagram have been marked in the manner traditionally employed in trigonometry. It is the custom to have the angles represented by capital letters and the sides indicated by the small letter

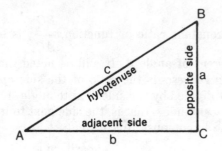

corresponding to the angle opposite the side. Thus the right angle is designated by *C* while the hypotenuse, which is opposite to it, is designated by *c*. Similarly, side *a* is opposite ∠*A*, and side *b* is opposite ∠*B*. Thus we have these six ratios:*

$\dfrac{a}{c}$ — is the **sine** of ∠*A* (written **sin** *A*).

$\dfrac{b}{c}$ — is the **cosine** of ∠*A* (written **cos** A).

$\dfrac{a}{b}$ — is the **tangent** of ∠*A* (written **tan** *A*).

$\dfrac{b}{a}$ — is the **cotangent** of ∠*A* (written **cot** *A*).

$\dfrac{c}{b}$ — is the **secant** of ∠*A* (written **sec** *A*).

$\dfrac{c}{a}$ — is the **cosecant** of ∠*A* (written **csc** *A*).

---

* Two additional functions which are little used are: versed sine ∠*A* = 1 − cos *A* (written **vers** *A*), and coversed sine ∠*A* = 1 − sin *A* (written **covers** *A*).

TABLE I

TABLE OF NATURAL TRIGONOMETRIC FUNCTIONS

For explanation of the use of this table see following page.

Angle	Sin	Cos	Tan	Cot	Sec	Csc	
0°	.0000	1.0000	.0000	∞	1.0000	∞	90°
1	.0175	.9998	.0175	57.2900	1.0002	57.2987	89
2	.0349	.9994	.0349	28.6363	1.0006	28.6537	88
3	.0523	.9986	.0524	19.0811	1.0014	19.1073	87
4	.0698	.9976	.0699	14.3007	1.0024	14.3356	86
5°	.0872	.9962	.0875	11.4301	1.0038	11.4737	85°
6	.1045	.9945	.1051	9.5144	1.0055	9.5668	84
7	.1219	.9925	.1228	8.1443	1.0075	8.2055	83
8	.1392	.9903	.1405	7.1154	1.0098	7.1853	82
9	.1564	.9877	.1584	6.3138	1.0125	6.3925	81
10°	.1736	.9848	.1763	5.6713	1.0154	5.7588	80°
11	.1908	.9816	.1944	5.1446	1.0187	5.2408	79
12	.2079	.9781	.2126	4.7046	1.0223	4.8097	78
13	.2250	.9744	.2309	4.3315	1.0263	4.4454	77
14	.2419	.9703	.2493	4.0108	1.0306	4.1336	76
15°	.2588	.9659	.2679	3.7321	1.0353	3.8637	75°
16	.2756	.9613	.2867	3.4874	1.0403	3.6280	74
17	.2924	.9563	.3057	3.2709	1.0457	3.4203	73
18	.3090	.9511	.3249	3.0777	1.0515	3.2361	72
19	.3256	.9455	.3443	2.9042	1.0576	3.0716	71
20°	.3420	.9397	.3640	2.7475	1.0642	2.9238	70°
21	.3584	.9336	.3839	2.6051	1.0711	2.7904	69
22	.3746	.9272	.4040	2.4751	1.0785	2.6695	68
23	.3907	.9205	.4245	2.3559	1.0864	2.5593	67
24	.4067	.9135	.4452	2.2460	1.0946	2.4586	66
25°	.4226	.9063	.4663	2.1445	1.1034	2.3662	65°
26	.4384	.8988	.4877	2.0503	1.1126	2.2812	64
27	.4540	.8910	.5095	1.9626	1.1223	2.2027	63
28	.4695	.8829	.5317	1.8807	1.1326	2.1301	62
29	.4848	.8746	.5543	1.8040	1.1434	2.0627	61
30°	.5000	.8660	.5774	1.7321	1.1547	2.0000	60°
31	.5150	.8572	.6009	1.6643	1.1666	1.9416	59
32	.5299	.8480	.6249	1.6003	1.1792	1.8871	58
33	.5446	.8387	.6494	1.5399	1.1924	1.8361	57
34	.5592	.8290	.6745	1.4826	1.2062	1.7883	56
35°	.5736	.8192	.7002	1.4281	1.2208	1.7434	55°
36	.5878	.8090	.7265	1.3764	1.2361	1.7013	54
37	.6018	.7986	.7536	1.3270	1.2521	1.6616	53
38	.6157	.7880	.7813	1.2799	1.2690	1.6243	52
39	.6293	.7771	.8098	1.2349	1.2868	1.5890	51
40°	.6428	.7660	.8391	1.1918	1.3054	1.5557	50°
41	.6561	.7547	.8693	1.1504	1.3250	1.5243	49
42	.6691	.7431	.9004	1.1106	1.3456	1.4945	48
43	.6820	.7314	.9325	1.0724	1.3673	1.4663	47
44	.6947	.7193	.9657	1.0355	1.3902	1.4396	46
45°	.7071	.7071	1.0000	1.0000	1.4142	1.4142	45°
	Cos	Sin	Cot	Tan	Csc	Sec	Angle

Using self-explanatory abbreviations, we thus have by definition:

$$\sin A = \frac{\text{opp}}{\text{hyp}} = \frac{a}{c}, \qquad \cos A = \frac{\text{adj}}{\text{hyp}} = \frac{b}{c},$$

$$\tan A = \frac{\text{opp}}{\text{adj}} = \frac{a}{b}, \qquad \cot A = \frac{\text{adj}}{\text{opp}} = \frac{b}{a},$$

$$\sec A = \frac{\text{hyp}}{\text{adj}} = \frac{c}{b}, \qquad \csc A = \frac{\text{hyp}}{\text{opp}} = \frac{c}{a}.$$

This table of definitions of the trigonometric functions should be committed to memory.

Practice Exercise No. 1

1 In the preceeding figure, $\tan B = \frac{b}{a}$. Write the other five functions of $\angle B$.

2 Which is greater, $\sin A$ or $\tan A$?

3 Which is greater, $\cos A$ or $\cot A$?

4 Which is greater, $\sec A$ or $\tan A$?

5 Which is greater, $\csc A$ or $\cot A$?

6 $\sin A = \frac{3}{5}$. What is the value of $\cos A$?
    Hint: Use rt. $\triangle$ formula $c^2 = a^2 + b^2$ to find side b.

7 $\tan A = \frac{3}{4}$. What is the value of $\sin A$?

8 $\sin A = \frac{8}{17}$. Find $\cos A$.

9 $\cot A = \frac{15}{8}$. Find $\sec A$.

10 Find the value of the other five functions of A if $\sin A = \frac{5}{13}$.

RELATIONS BETWEEN FUNCTIONS OF COMPLEMENTARY ANGLES

If you observe the relations between the functions of the two acute angles of the same right triangle, you will note that every function of each of the two acute angles is equal to a different function of the other acute angle. These correspondences of value are demonstrated in the following.

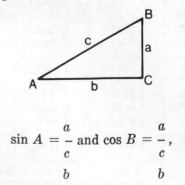

$$\sin A = \frac{a}{c} \text{ and } \cos B = \frac{a}{c},$$

$$\frac{b}{b}$$

$$\cos A = \frac{b}{c} \text{ and } \sin B = \frac{b}{c},$$

$$\tan A = \frac{a}{b} \text{ and } \cot B = \frac{a}{b}, \text{ etc.}$$

Thus we have:

$$\begin{aligned}
\sin A &= \cos B, & \cot A &= \tan B \\
\cos A &= \sin B, & \sec A &= \csc B \\
\tan A &= \cot B, & \csc A &= \sec B
\end{aligned}$$

From these equalities it will be evident that any function of an acute angle of a right triangle equals the co-function of the complement of that angle.*

For example, $\tan 40° = \cot 50°$; $\sin 70° = \cos 20°$; $\csc 41° \, 20' = \sec 48° \, 40'$.

Since angles A and B are complementary, another way of writing these equations is as follows:

$$\begin{aligned}
\sin (90° - A) &= \cos A, & \cot (90° - A) &= \tan A \\
\cos (90° - A) &= \sin A, & \sec (90° - A) &= \csc A \\
\tan (90° - A) &= \cot A, & \csc (90° - A) &= \sec A
\end{aligned}$$

Practice Exercise No. 2

Fill in the blanks in examples 1–6 with the equivalent co-functions

1 $\sin 26° =$ 4 $\cot 88° \, 50' =$

2 $\tan 43° =$ 5 $\sec 6° \, 10' =$

3 $\cos 24° \, 28' =$ 6 $\csc 77\frac{1}{2}° =$

7 How many degrees must $\angle A$ be if $90° - A = 5A$?

8 What is the value of $\angle A$ if $\tan A = \cot A$?

9 Find A if $90° - A = A$.

10 Find A if $\cos A = \sin 2A$.

HOW TO USE A TABLE OF TRIGONOMETRIC FUNCTIONS

From the foregoing it becomes apparent that you can easily compute the functions of any angle greater than 45° if you know the functions of all angles between 0° and 45°. Therefore in a table of trigonometric functions, such as appears on the preceding page, it is only necessary to have a direct table of functions for angles from 0° to 45°, since the function of any angle above 45° is equal to the co-function of its complement.

---

*The name *cosine* means *complement's sine*. It is a contraction from the Latin *complementi sinus*. The words *cotangent* and *cosecant* were derived in the same manner.

To find the functions of angles from 0° to 45° read the table from the top down, using the values of angles at the left and the headings at the top of the table. To find the functions of angles from 45° to 90° read from the bottom up, using the values of angles at the right and the function designations at the bottom of the table.

If you know the value of the function of an angle and wish to find the angle, look in the body of the table in the proper column and then read the magnitude of the angle in the corresponding row of one or the other of the angle columns.

For example, you are told that the sine of a certain angle is .5000 and wish to find the angle. Look in the *Sin* column, locate .5000 and read the angle value (30°) from the left *Angle* column. If this value had been given to you as a cosine, you would have noted that it does not appear in the column headed *Cos* at the top but does appear in the column that has *Cos* at the bottom. Hence you would then use the *Angle* column at the right and find .5000 to be the cosine of 60°.

You should become thoroughly familiar with the use of the table. To this end you can supplement the following exercise by making up your own examples.

Practice Exercise No. 3

From the table of trigonometric functions find the values required in examples 1–15:

1	sin 8°	6	cos 25°	11	cos 62°
2	sin 42°	7	csc 14°	12	tan 56°
3	tan 40°	8	sin 78°	13	sin 58°
4	cot 63°	9	cot 69°	14	cos 45°
5	sec 22°	10	sec 81°	15	sin 30°

16 Find the angle whose sine is .2588.
17 Find the angle whose tangent is .7002.
18 Find the angle whose cosine is .5000.
19 Find the angle whose secant is 2.9238.
20 Find the angle, whose cotangent is 5.6713.

FUNCTIONS OF 45°, 30°, AND 60° ANGLES

For some rather common angles the exact values of their functions can be easily found by the application of elementary principles of geometry.

Functions of a 45° Angle

In the isosceles right triangle *ACB*, if $\angle A = 45°$, then $\angle B = 45°$, and therefore side $a =$ side b. Now if we let side a equal 1 or unity, then from the right triangle formula of

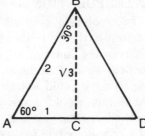

$$a^2 + b^2 = c^2$$

we get

$$c = \sqrt{1} + 1 \text{ or } \sqrt{2}$$

(taking the square root of both sides of the equation). Now since any trigonometric function of an acute angle is equal to the corresponding co-function of its complement, therefore

$$\sin 45° = \frac{1}{\sqrt{2}} \text{ or } \tfrac{1}{2}\sqrt{2} = \cos 45°,$$

$$\tan 45° = \frac{1}{1} \text{ or } 1 = \cot 45°,$$

$$\sec 45° = \frac{\sqrt{2}}{1} \text{ or } \sqrt{2} = \csc 45°.$$

Functions of 30° and 60° Angles

In the equilateral triangle *ABD* the three sides are equal and the three angles each equal 60°. If we drop a perpendicular from *B* to *AD*, it bisects $\angle B$ and the base *AD* at *C*.

If we let the length of each of the sides equal 2 units, then $AC = CD = 1$; and in the right triangle *ACB*.

$$\angle B = 30°, \angle C = 90°, \angle A = 60°$$

$$AC = 1, AB = 2$$

Then, since $(AB)^2 = (AC)^2 + (BC)^2$, it follows that $(BC)^2 = 3$ and $BC = \sqrt{3}$.

Thus in the right triangle *ACB*

$$\sin 30° = \tfrac{1}{2} \qquad\qquad = \cos 60°,$$

$$\tan 30° = \frac{1}{\sqrt{3}} \text{ or } \tfrac{1}{3}\sqrt{3} = \cot 60°,$$

$$\sec 30° = \frac{2}{\sqrt{3}} \text{ or } \tfrac{2}{3}\sqrt{3} = \csc 60°,$$

$$\cos 30° = \frac{\sqrt{3}}{2} \qquad\qquad = \sin 60°,$$

$$\cot 30° = \frac{\sqrt{3}}{1} \text{ or } \sqrt{3} = \tan 60°,$$

$$\csc 30° = \frac{2}{1} \text{ or } 2 = \sec 60°.$$

It is an advantage to know the values of the 30°, 45° and 60° angles by heart. To help yourself memorize them, fill in the outline of the table below with the proper values of the functions.

Function	30°	60°	45°
Sine			
Cosine			
Tangent			
Cotangent			
Secant			
Cosecant			

INTERPOLATION

Interpolation is used in trigonometry in connection with the table of functions. For example, if given the function of an angle that is measured in degrees and minutes, such as sin 30° 40′, its exact value could not be found directly from the table but would have to be computed by the method of interpolation. Again, if given the value of a trigonometric function such as tan A = .7400, which does not appear in the body of the table, it means that the corresponding angle is expressed in units more exact than the nearest degree and must be found by interpolation. The following examples will illustrate the method of performing interpolations with reference to the table of trigonometric functions.

EXAMPLE 1: Find sin 30° 40′.

SOLUTION: sin 30° 40′ is between sin 30° and sin 31°.

Since there are 60′ in 1°, 40′ = $\frac{2}{3}$ of 1°

From the table   sin 30° = .5000
sin 31° = .5150
Difference = .0150
sin 30° = .5000
$\frac{2}{3}$ of .0150 = .0100
sin 30° 40′ = .5100,   ANS.

Note: In this case we added the proportional part of the difference (.0100) to the value of sin 30° because the sine of an angle *increases* as the angle increases.

EXAMPLE 2: Find cos 59° 48′.

SOLUTION: cos 59° 48′ is between cos 59° and cos 60°.

48′ is $\frac{4}{5}$ of 1°.

From the table   cos 59° = .5150
cos 60° = .5000
Difference = .0150
cos 59° = .5150
$\frac{4}{5}$ of .0150 = .0120
cos 59° 48′ = .5030,   ANS.

Note: In this case we subtracted the proportional part of the difference (.0120) from the value of cos 59° because the cosine of an angle *decreases* as the angle increases.

EXAMPLE 3: Find $\angle A$ if tan A = .7400.

SOLUTION: From the table, in the tan column, we see that .7400 is between tan 36° and tan 37°.

tan 37° = .7536
tan 36° = .7265
Difference = .0271
tan A = .7400
tan 36° = .7265
Difference = .0135

The proportional difference between tan A and tan 36° is .0135. The difference between tan 36° and tan 37° is .0271.

$\frac{.0135}{.0271}$ of 1° or 60′ equals $\frac{1}{2}$° or 30′

∴ tan A = 36° + 30′ = 36° 30′,   ANS.

Further familiarity with the table of functions will indicate the following about variations of the trigonometric functions.

As an angle increases from 0° to 90°, its:

sine   *increases* from 0 to 1,
cosine   *decreases* from 1 to 0,
tangent   *increases* from 0 to ∞,
cotangent *decreases* from ∞ to 0,
secant   *increases* from 1 to ∞,
cosecant *decreases* from ∞ to 1.

Also note that:

sines and cosines are never > 1,
secants and cosecants are never < 1,
tangents and cotangents may have any value from 0 to ∞.*

---

* The symbol ∞ denotes "infinity" and is used in mathematics to represent a number that is indefinitely large, or larger than any preassignable quantity. The sign > means greater than, and < means less than.

Practice Exercise No. 4

Find by interpolation the values of the functions in examples 1–5:

1   sin 15° 30′
2   cos 25° 40′
3   tan 47° 10′
4   cot 52° 30′
5   sec 40° 30′

Find by the interpolation method the value of ∠A to the nearest minute in examples 6–10:

6   sin A = .0901
7   tan A = .3411
8   cos A = .4173
9   cot A = .8491
10   csc A = 1.4804

RECIPROCALS AMONG THE FUNCTIONS

If you inspect the ratios of the six functions of ∠A, you will readily note that they are not independent of each other. In fact, if you line them up as follows:

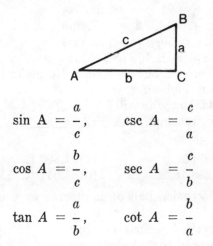

$$\sin A = \frac{a}{c}, \qquad \csc A = \frac{c}{a}$$

$$\cos A = \frac{b}{c}, \qquad \sec A = \frac{c}{b}$$

$$\tan A = \frac{a}{b}, \qquad \cot A = \frac{b}{a}$$

it becomes obvious that *the sine is the reciprocal of the cosecant, the cosine is the reciprocal of the secant, and the tangent is the reciprocal of the cotangent.* Accordingly,

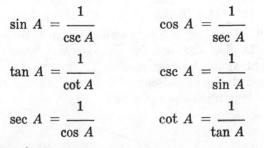

$$\sin A = \frac{1}{\csc A} \qquad \cos A = \frac{1}{\sec A}$$

$$\tan A = \frac{1}{\cot A} \qquad \csc A = \frac{1}{\sin A}$$

$$\sec A = \frac{1}{\cos A} \qquad \cot A = \frac{1}{\tan A}$$

Therefore:

$$\sin A \times \csc A = 1, \quad \cos A \times \sec A = 1$$

$$\tan A \times \cot A = 1$$

In accordance with the usual algebraic method of notation (by which ab is equivalent to $a \times b$) these relationships are usually written:

$$\sin A \csc A = 1, \quad \cos A \sec A = 1$$

$$\tan A \cot A = 1$$

To illustrate such a relation, find, for example, in the table of functions the tangent and the cotangent of 30°.

$$\tan 30° = .5774, \quad \cot 30° = 1.7321$$

$$\tan 30° \cot 30° = .5774 \times 1.7321$$
$$= 1.00011454$$

INTERRELATIONS AMONG THE FUNCTIONS

Since $\tan A = \dfrac{a}{b}$, $\sin A = \dfrac{a}{c}$, and $\cos A = \dfrac{b}{c}$, it follows that

$$\tan A = \frac{\sin A}{\cos A}, \text{ and } \sin A = \tan A \cos A.$$

The student will the more readily grasp these interrelations if instead of considering only abstract values, he translates these into actual numbers. The 3–4–5 right triangle in the diagram will serve this purpose.

From the interrelations of sine, cosine and tangent it follows that if we know two of these values, we can always find the third.

From the Pythagorean theorem of the right triangle we know that $a^2 + b^2 = c^2$. If we divide both sides of this equation by c^2, we get

$$\frac{a^2}{c^2} + \frac{b^2}{c^2} = 1.$$

Since $\dfrac{a}{c} = \sin A$ and $\dfrac{b}{c} = \cos A$, it follows that

(1) $\sin^2 A + \cos^2 A = 1$*

Therefore

(2) $\sin A = \sqrt{1 - \cos^2 A}$ and

(3) $\cos A = \sqrt{1 - \sin^2 A}$

---

* $(\sin A)^2$ is customarily written as $\sin^2 A$, and likewise for the other functions.

MAKING PRACTICAL USE OF THE FUNCTIONS

With the information on trigonometry outlined in the previous pages you will be able to solve many triangles if you know three parts one of which is a side. And in the case of the right triangle, since the right angle is a part of it, you need only to know two other parts one of which must be a side.

As will be brought out in the practice exercises that follow, these trigonometric methods of solving triangles are used daily in handling problems that arise in military operations, engineering, navigation, shopwork, physics, surveying, etc.

You should adopt a planned method of procedure in solving problems. One such method is as follows.

1. After reading the problem, draw a figure to a convenient scale, and in it show those lines and angles which are given and those which are to be found.

2. Write down all the formulas that apply to the particular problem.

3. Substitute the given data in the proper formulas, and solve for the unknowns.

4. Check your results.

Incidentally we would suggest that you work with a hard lead pencil or a fine-pointed pen. Nothing is of greater help to accuracy in mathematics than neatness of work, and neatness is next to impossible if you use writing instruments that make thick lines and sprawly figures.

Applying the Sine Function,

$$\sin A = \frac{\text{opp}}{\text{hyp}} = \frac{a}{c}$$

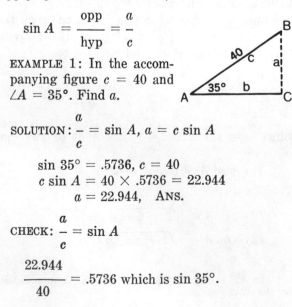

EXAMPLE 1: In the accompanying figure $c = 40$ and $\angle A = 35°$. Find a.

SOLUTION: $\dfrac{a}{c} = \sin A,\ a = c \sin A$

$$\sin 35° = .5736,\ c = 40$$
$$c \sin A = 40 \times .5736 = 22.944$$
$$a = 22.944, \quad \text{ANS.}$$

CHECK: $\dfrac{a}{c} = \sin A$

$$\frac{22.944}{40} = .5736 \text{ which is } \sin 35°.$$

EXAMPLE 2: Given $c = 48$ and $\angle B = 22°$, find a by means of the sine formula.

SOLUTION: $\dfrac{a}{c} = \sin A,\ a = c \sin A,$

$$\angle A = 90° - \angle B,\ \angle A = 90° - 22° = 68°,$$
$$\sin 68° = .9272,\ c = 48,$$
$$c \sin A = 48 \times .9272 = 44.5056,$$
$$a = 44.50+, \quad \text{ANS.}$$

CHECK: $\dfrac{a}{c} = A.$

$$\frac{44.5056}{48} = .9272 \text{ which is } \sin 68°.$$

Practice Exercise No. 5

The problems in this exercise should be solved by using the sine function. Answers need be accurate only to the first decimal place.

1. Given $c = 100$, $\angle A = 33°$, find a.
2. Given $c = 10$, $\angle A = 20°$, find a.
3. Given $a = 71$, $c = 78$, find $\angle A$.
4. Given $a = 14$, $\angle A = 28°$, find c.
5. Given $c = 50$, $a = 36$, find $\angle A$.

6. An airplane is 405 feet above a landing field when the pilot cuts out his motor. He glides to a landing at an angle of 13° with the field. How far will he glide in reaching the field?

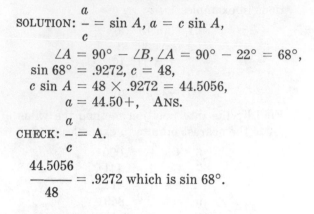

   (A) 300 ft. _____   (C) 1,800 ft. _____
   (B) 1,248 ft. _____ (D) 1,641 ft. _____

7. An ascension balloon is moored by a rope 150 ft. long. A wind blowing in an easterly direction keeps the rope taut and causes it to make an angle of 50° with the ground. What is the vertical height of the balloon from the ground?

   (A) 180 ft. _____   (C) 177.5 ft. _____
   (B) 114.9 ft. _____ (D) 189.4 ft. _____

8. A carpenter has to build a ramp to be used as a loading platform for a carrier airplane. The height of the loading door is 12 ft., and the required slope or gradient of the ramp is to be 18°. How long must the ramp be?

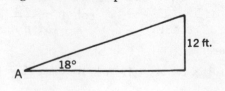

(A) 24 ft. _____ (C) 48.42 ft. _____
(B) 38.83 ft. _____ (D) 10.14 ft. _____

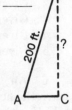

9 The fire department has a new 200-ft. ladder. The greatest angle at which it can be placed against a building with safety is at 71° with the ground. What is the maximum vertical height that the ladder can reach?

(A) 189.1 ft. _____ (C) 300 ft. _____
(B) 209.4 ft. _____ (D) 162.3 ft. _____

10 A road running from the bottom of a hill to the top is 625 ft. long. If the hill is $54\frac{1}{2}$ ft. high, what is the angle of elevation of the road?

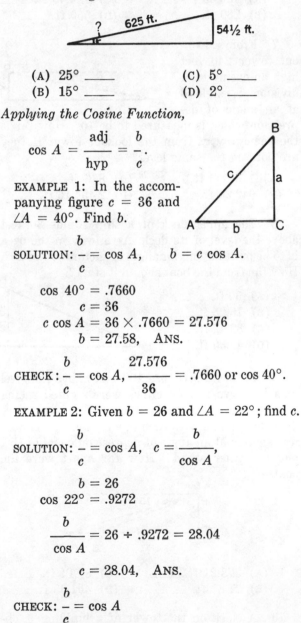

(A) 25° _____   (C) 5° _____
(B) 15° _____   (D) 2° _____

Applying the Cosine Function,

$$\cos A = \frac{adj}{hyp} = \frac{b}{c}.$$

EXAMPLE 1: In the accompanying figure $c = 36$ and $\angle A = 40°$. Find b.

SOLUTION: $\frac{b}{c} = \cos A$, $b = c \cos A$.

$\cos 40° = .7660$
$c = 36$
$c \cos A = 36 \times .7660 = 27.576$
$b = 27.58$, ANS.

CHECK: $\frac{b}{c} = \cos A$, $\frac{27.576}{36} = .7660$ or $\cos 40°$.

EXAMPLE 2: Given $b = 26$ and $\angle A = 22°$; find c.

SOLUTION: $\frac{b}{c} = \cos A$, $c = \frac{b}{\cos A}$,

$b = 26$
$\cos 22° = .9272$

$\frac{b}{\cos A} = 26 \div .9272 = 28.04$

$c = 28.04$, ANS.

CHECK: $\frac{b}{c} = \cos A$

$\frac{26}{28.04} = .9272$ which is $\cos 22°$.

Practice Exercise No. 6

Use this cosine function in solving the problems in this exercise.

1 Given $c = 400$, $b = 240$; find $\angle A$.
2 Given $c = 41$, $\angle A = 39°$; find b.
3 Given $c = 67.7$, $\angle A = 23° 30'$; find b.
4 Given $c = 187$, $b = 93\frac{1}{2}$; find $\angle A$.
5 Given $b = 40$, $\angle A = 18°$, find c.

6 A carpenter has to build a triangular roof to a house. The roof is to be 30 feet wide. If the rafters are 17 feet long, at what angle will the rafters be laid at the eaves?

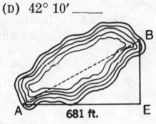

(A) 34° _____   (C) 28° 05' _____
(B) 19° 30' _____   (D) 42° 10' _____

7 Desiring to measure distance across a pond, a surveyor standing at point A sighted on a point B across the pond. From A he ran a line AC, making an angle of 27° with AB. From B he ran a line perpendicular to AC. He measured the line AC to be 681 feet. What is the distance across the pond from A to B?

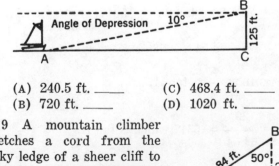

(A) 100 ft. _____   (C) 681 ft. _____
(B) 764.3 ft. _____   (D) 862.8 ft. _____

8 A scout on a hill 125 feet above a lake sights a boat on the water at an angle of depression of 10° as shown. What is the exact distance from the scout to the boat?

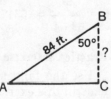

(A) 240.5 ft. _____   (C) 468.4 ft. _____
(B) 720 ft. _____   (D) 1020 ft. _____

9 A mountain climber stretches a cord from the rocky ledge of a sheer cliff to a point on a horizontal plane, making an angle of 50° with the ledge. The cord is 84 feet

long. What is the vertical height of the rocky ledge from its base?

(A) 45 ft. ____ (C) 76.8 ft. ____
(B) 82 ft. ____ (D) 54 ft. ____

10 A 100-foot ladder is placed against the side of a house with the foot of the ladder $16\frac{1}{2}$ feet away from the building. What angle does the ladder make with the ground?

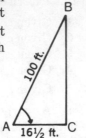

(A) 65° ____
(B) 25° 40′ ____
(C) 80° 30′ ____
(D) 72° 20′ ____

Applying the Tangent Function,

$$\tan A = \frac{opp}{adj} = \frac{a}{b}.$$

EXAMPLE 1: In the accompanying figure $a = 40$ and $b = 27$. Find $\angle A$.

SOLUTION: $\frac{a}{b} = \tan A$, $a = 40$, $b = 27$,

$$\frac{40}{27} = 1.4815,$$

$\tan A = 1.4815$, $\angle A = 55° 59′$, ANS.

CHECK: $a = b \tan A$; $27 \times 1.4815 = 40$ which is a.

EXAMPLE 2: Given angle $A = 28°$ and $a = 29$. Find b.

SOLUTION: $\frac{a}{b} = \tan A$, $b = \frac{a}{\tan A}$,

$a = 29$, $\tan 28° = .5317$, $\frac{29}{.5317} = 54.54$,

$b = 54.54$, ANS.

CHECK: $\frac{a}{b} = \tan A$,

$$\frac{29}{54.54} = .5317 \text{ which is } \tan A.$$

Practice Exercise No. 7
Use the tangent function in solving the problems in this exercise.

1 Given $a = 18$, $b = 24$; find $\angle A$.
2 Given $b = 64$, $\angle A = 45°$; find a.
3 Given $b = 62$, $\angle A = 36°$; find a.
4 Given $\angle A = 70°$, $a = 50$; find b.
5 Given $\angle A = 19° 36′$, $b = 42$; find a.

6 An engineer desires to learn the height of a cone-shaped hill. He measures its diameter to be 280 feet. From a point on the circumference of the base he determines that the angle of elevation is 43°. What is the altitude?

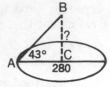

(A) 130.55 ft. ____ (C) 125.45 ft. ____
(B) 260 ft. ____ (D) 560 ft. ____

7 From a lookout tower 240 feet high an enemy tank division is sighted at an angle of depression which is measured to be 10°. How far is the enemy away from the lookout tower if they are both on the same level?

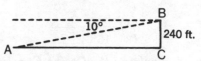

(A) 1,361.11 ft. ____ (C) 866 ft. ____
(B) 642.25 ft. ____ (D) 2,434.16 ft. ____

8 The upper deck of a ship stands 30 feet above the level of its dock. A runway to the deck is to be built having an angle of inclination of 20°. How far from the boat should it start?

(A) 60 ft. ____
(B) 76.25 ft. ____
(C) 82.42 ft. ____
(D) 42.30 ft. ____

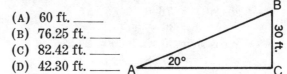

9 From a boathouse 100 feet above the level of a lake two rowing crews were sighted racing in the direction of the boathouse. The boats were directly in a line with each other. The leading boat was sighted at an angle of depression equal to 15°, and the other at 14°. How far apart were the boats?

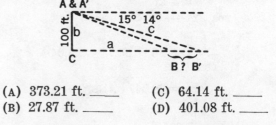

(A) 373.21 ft. ____ (C) 64.14 ft. ____
(B) 27.87 ft. ____ (D) 401.08 ft. ____

10 A clock on the tower of a building is ob-

served from two points which are on the same level and in the same straight line with the foot of the tower. At the nearer point the angle of elevation to the clock is 60°, and at the farther point it is 30°. If the two points are 300 feet apart, what is the height of the clock?

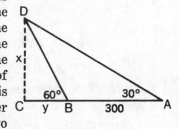

(A) 130.8 ft. ____   (C) 259.8 ft. ____
(B) 400 ft. ____   (D) 360.4 ft. ____

THE OBLIQUE TRIANGLE

As previously stated, you can use right triangle methods to solve most oblique triangles by introducing perpendiculars and resolving the oblique triangle into two right triangles.

For example:

1. Triangle *ABC* can be resolved into right triangles *ADC* and *BDC* by introducing the perpendicular *CD*.

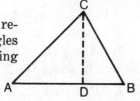

2. Triangle *DEF* can be resolved into right triangles *DGF* and *EGF* by extending *DE* and dropping the perpendicular *FG*.

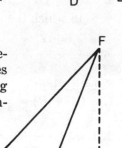

3. Triangle *HJK* can be resolved into right triangles *HLJ* and *KLJ* by introducing the perpendicular *JL*.

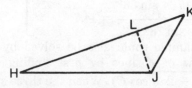

In practical problems, however, it is often impossible or too cumbersome to use a right triangle,

and in such cases formulas for oblique angles are needed.*

There are three important formulas that may be used in the solution of triangles of any shape. They are known as the *law of sines*, the *law of cosines* and the *law of tangents*.

For our purposes it will be sufficient to state the law, give the corresponding formulas and show the application of the law to the solution of problems involving oblique triangles.†

The law of sines: *The sides of a triangle are proportional to the sines of their opposite angles:*

$$\frac{a}{\sin A} = \frac{b}{\sin B} = \frac{c}{\sin C}, \text{ or}$$

$$\frac{a}{b} = \frac{\sin A}{\sin B}, \frac{b}{c} = \frac{\sin B}{\sin C}, \frac{a}{c} = \frac{\sin A}{\sin C}.$$

The law of cosines: *The square of any side of a triangle is equal to the sum of the squares of the other two sides minus twice their product times the cosine of the included angle.*

$$a^2 = b^2 + c^2 - 2bc \cos A,$$
$$b^2 = a^2 + c^2 - 2ac \cos B,$$
$$c^2 = a^2 + b^2 - 2ab \cos C, \text{ or}$$
$$a = \sqrt{b^2 + c^2 - 2bc \cos A},$$
$$b = \sqrt{a^2 + c^2 - 2ac \cos B},$$
$$c = \sqrt{a^2 + b^2 - 2ab \cos C}.$$

The law of tangents: *The difference between any two sides of a triangle is to their sum as the tangent of half the difference between their opposite angles is to tangent of half their sum.*

$$\frac{a - b}{a + b} = \frac{\tan \frac{1}{2}(A - B)}{\tan \frac{1}{2}(A + B)},$$
$$\frac{a - c}{a + c} = \frac{\tan \frac{1}{2}(A - C)}{\tan \frac{1}{2}(A + C)},$$
$$\frac{b - c}{b + c} = \frac{\tan \frac{1}{2}(B - C)}{\tan \frac{1}{2}(B + C)},$$

---

* For work with oblique triangles a more detailed table of functions graduated by tenths of degrees appears at the end of this section. Use of this table will obviate much of the extra arithmetic ordinarily employed in interpolation procedures.

† The interested reader can obtain from any standard textbook on trigonometry a detailed description of the mathematics involved in deriving these formulas.

or if $b > a$, then

$$\frac{b-a}{b+a} = \frac{\tan\frac{1}{2}(B-A)}{\tan\frac{1}{2}(B+A)}.$$

SOLVING OBLIQUE TRIANGLES

Any triangle has six parts, namely, three angles and the sides opposite the angles.

In order to solve a triangle three independent parts must be known in addition to the fact that the sum of the angles of any triangle equals 180°.

In problems involving triangles there occur the following four combinations of parts which if known will determine the size and form of the triangle.

I. *One side and two angles are known*

II. *Two sides and the included angle are known*

III. *Three sides are known*

IV. *Two sides and the angle opposite one of them is known.**

APPLYING THE LAWS OF SINE, TANGENT AND COSINE TO OBLIQUE TRIANGLES

Case I: **One side and two angles are known**

EXAMPLE: Given $\angle A = 56°$, $\angle B = 69°$ and $a = 467$; find b and c.

SOLUTION: We use the law of sines.

Formulas needed:
1. $C = 180° - (\angle A + \angle B)$

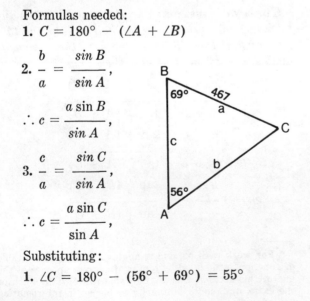

2. $\dfrac{b}{a} = \dfrac{\sin B}{\sin A}$,

$\therefore c = \dfrac{a \sin B}{\sin A}$,

3. $\dfrac{c}{a} = \dfrac{\sin C}{\sin A}$,

$\therefore c = \dfrac{a \sin C}{\sin A}$,

Substituting:
1. $\angle C = 180° - (56° + 69°) = 55°$

---

* This combination is considered an ambiguous case because it is often possible to form more than one triangle to satisfy the given conditions.

2. $b = \dfrac{467 \times .9336}{.8290} = 525.9$

3. $c = \dfrac{467 \times .8192}{.8290} = 461.5$ } ANS.

Case II: **Two sides and the included angle are known**

EXAMPLE: Given $a = 17$, $b = 12$ and $\angle C = 58°$; find $\angle A$, $\angle B$ and c.

SOLUTION: We use the law of tangents to obtain $\angle A$ and $\angle B$ and the law of sines to obtain c.

Formulas needed:
1. $A + B = 180° - C$ and
$\frac{1}{2}(A + B) = \frac{1}{2}(180° - C)$

When $\frac{1}{2}(A + B)$ has been determined $\frac{1}{2}(A - B)$ is found by the following

2. $\dfrac{a-b}{a+b} = \dfrac{\tan\frac{1}{2}(A-B)}{\tan\frac{1}{2}(A+B)}$

$\therefore \tan\frac{1}{2}(A - B) = \dfrac{a-b}{a+b} \times \tan\frac{1}{2}(A+B)$

3. $\angle A = \frac{1}{2}(A + B) + \frac{1}{2}(A - B)$
in which the Bs cancel out

4. $\angle B = \frac{1}{2}(A + B) - \frac{1}{2}(A - B)$,
in which the As cancel out

5. $\dfrac{c}{a} = \dfrac{\sin C}{\sin A}$, $\therefore c = \dfrac{a \sin C}{\sin A}$.

Substituting:
1. $\frac{1}{2}(A + B) = \frac{1}{2}(180° - 58°) = 61°$

2. $\tan\frac{1}{2}(A - B) = \dfrac{17-12}{17+12} \times \tan 61° = .3110$,

which is the tan of 17° 16′ and equal to $\frac{1}{2}(A - B)$

3. $\angle A = 61° + 17° 16′ = 78° 16′$

4. $\angle B = 60° - 17° 16′ = 43° 44′$

5. $c = \dfrac{17 \times \sin 58°}{\sin 78° 16′} = 14.7$ } ANS.

This example could also be solved by the use of the law of cosines by first finding c ($c = \sqrt{a^2 + b^2 - 2ab \cos C}$). When the three sides and $\angle C$ are known the law of sines can be employed to find $\angle A$ and $\angle B$. For purposes of a check, do this example by the second method.

Case III: **Three sides are known**

EXAMPLE: Given $a = 5$, $b = 6$ and $c = 7$; find $\angle A$, $\angle B$ and $\angle C$.

SOLUTION: We use the law of cosines and the law of sines.

Formulas needed:

1. $a^2 = b^2 + c^2 - 2bc \cos A$

$\therefore \cos A \dfrac{b^2 + c^2 - a^2}{2bc}$

2. $\dfrac{a}{b} = \dfrac{\sin A}{\sin B}$, $\qquad \therefore \sin B = \dfrac{b \sin A}{a}$

3. $\angle C = 180° - (A + B)$

Substituting:

$\cos A = \dfrac{36 + 49 - 25}{2(6 \times 7)} = .7143$

which is the cos of $44° \, 25'$

$\sin B = \dfrac{6 \times .69995}{5} = .8399,$

which is the sin of $57° \, 45'$

$\angle C = 180° - (44° \, 25' + 57° \, 45' = 77° \, 50'$

$\left.\begin{array}{l} \angle A = 44° \, 25' \\ \angle B = 57° \, 45' \\ \angle C = 77° \, 50' \end{array}\right\}$ ANS.

Case IV (the ambiguous case): **Two sides and the angle opposite one of them are known**

When given two sides of a triangle and the angle opposite one of them, there is often a possibility of two solutions unless one of the solutions is excluded by the statement of the problem.

This fact may be clarified by the next figure. It will be seen in the triangle *ABC* that if $\angle A$ and

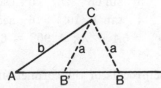

sides a and b are given, either of the triangles *ABC* or *AB'C* meet the given conditions.

By varying the relative lengths of a and b and the magnitude of $\angle A$, the following possibilities can be recognized.

If $a > b$, $\angle A > \angle B$, which makes $\angle B$ less than $90°$, and allows for only on solution.

If $a = b$, $\angle A = \angle B$; both angles are less than $90°$ and only an isosceles triangle can be formed.

If $a < b$ and $\angle A$ is acute, two triangles are possible.

If $a = b \sin A$, the figure is a right triangle and only one solution is possible.

If $a < b \sin A$, no triangle is possible.

Before doing a problem of this type you can generally determine the number of possible solutions by making an approximate small-scale drawing of the given parts.

In the cases where there are two possible solutions and the unknown parts are $\angle B$, $\angle C$ and side c, the second set of unknown parts should be designated as $\angle B'$, $\angle C'$ and side c'. They will then be found as follows:

$B' = 180° - B$, because when an angle is determined by its sine, it has two possible values that are supplementary to each other.

$C' = 180° - (A + B')$.

$c' = \dfrac{a \sin C'}{\sin A}.$

EXAMPLE: Given $a = 5$, $b = 8$ and $\angle A = 30°$; find $\angle B$, $\angle C$ and side c.

Here $a < b$ and $\angle A$ is acute. $\therefore$ two triangles are possible.

Formulas needed for $\triangle ABC$:

1. $\dfrac{b}{a} = \dfrac{\sin B}{\sin A}$, $\qquad \therefore \sin B = \dfrac{b \sin A}{a}.$

2. $\angle C = 180° - (A + B)$.

3. $\dfrac{c}{a} = \dfrac{\sin C}{\sin A}$, $\qquad \therefore c = \dfrac{a \sin C}{\sin A}.$

Substituting:

1. $\sin B = \dfrac{8 \times .5000}{5} = .8000,$

which is the sin of $53° \, 8'$

2. $\angle C = 180° - (30° + 53° \, 8') = 96° \, 52'$

3. $c = \dfrac{5 \times .9928}{.5000} = 9.928$

$\left.\begin{array}{l} \angle B = 53° \, 8' \\ \angle C = 96° \, 52' \\ c = 9.928 \end{array}\right\}$ ANS.

To find $\angle B'$, $\angle C'$ and c':

$\angle B' = 180° - B = 126° 52'$, ANS.

$\angle C' = 180° - (A + B') = 23° 8'$, ANS.

$$c' = \frac{a \sin C'}{\sin A} = \frac{5 \times 3.929}{5} = 3.929, \text{ ANS.}$$

Practice Exercise No. 8

In working out the problems in this exercise apply the principles for solving oblique triangles.

1   Given $\angle A = 45°$, $\angle B = 60°$ and $c = 9.562$; find a and b.

2   Given $a = 43$, $\angle A = 43°$ and $\angle B = 68°$; find $\angle C$, b and c.

3   Given $c = 22$, $b = 13$ and $\angle C = 68°$; find $\angle A$, $\angle B$ and c.

4   Given $a = 27$, $b = 26$, $c = 34$; find $\angle A$, $\angle B$ and $\angle C$.

5   Given $a = 8$, $b = 5$ and $\angle A = 21$; find c, $\angle A$ and $\angle B$.

6   Two airplane spotters, A and B, are 1.83 miles apart on the same level of ground. B is due north of A. At the same instant they both spot an airplane to the north, which makes an angle of elevation of 67° 31′ at A and 82° 16′ at B. What is the altitude of the airplane from the ground?

(A) 2.5 mi. ____   (C) 4 mi. ____
(B) 6.6 mi. ____   (D) 3.2 mi. ____

7   An observer on a boat anchored offshore sights on two points, A and B, on the shore. He determines the distance from himself to point A to be 985 feet, and the distance between A and B as 1,460 feet. The angle to the observer subtended by the points on shore is 64° 20′. How far is it from the observer to point B?

(A) 1,585.6 ft. ____   (C) 1,760 ft. ____
(B) 1,242.6 ft. ____   (D) 927.7 ft. ____

8   An observer at a fire tower spots a fire in a forest area extending across a stretch of land from point A to point B. The distance from the tower to A is 5 miles, and to B, $5\frac{1}{2}$ miles. The angle subtended by the stretch of land to the tower is 50°. What is the distance across which the fire extends? (*Note: For practice purposes solve by the tangent law.*)

(A) 6 mi. ____   (C) 3.42 mi. ____
(B) 4.46 mi. ____   (D) 8.5 mi. ____

9   Two scouts start from a point C at the same time and branch out at an angle of 33° to each other. If one scout travels at the rate of 1 mile per hour while the other travels at the rate of 3 miles per hour, how far apart will they be at the end of 2 hours? (*Note: Solve by cosine law.*)

(A) 3 mi. ____   (C) 4.46 mi. ____
(B) 5.42 mi. ____   (D) 8.56 mi. ____

10   A cannon is placed in position at point A to fire upon an enemy fort located on a mountain. The airline distance from the gun to the fort has been determined as 5 miles. The distance on a horizontal plane from the gun to a point C at the base of the mountain is $3\frac{1}{2}$ miles. From this point at the base to the fort itself the distance is 1.8 miles. (a) At what angle of elevation will the cannon have to be set in order to score a direct hit upon the fort? (b) What is the angle of depression from the fort to the cannon?

(a)   (A) 27° 21′ ____   (C) 13° 40′ ____
      (B) 38° 59′ ____   (D) 16° 8′ ____

(b)   (A) 38° 59′ ____   (C) 22° 16′ ____
      (B) 27° 21′ ____   (D) 13° 40′ ____

Exercise No. 1

1   $\sin B = \dfrac{b}{c}$, $\cos B = \dfrac{a}{c}$, $\cot B = \dfrac{a}{b}$, $\sec B = \dfrac{c}{a}$, $\csc B = \dfrac{c}{b}$

2   $\tan A$ 6 $\cos A = \frac{4}{5}$ 10 $\cos A = \frac{12}{13}$,

3   $\cot A$ 7 $\sin A = \frac{3}{5}$ $\tan A = \frac{5}{12}$

4   $\sec A$ 8 $\cos A = \frac{15}{17}$ $\cot A = \frac{12}{5}$,

5   $\csc A$ 9 $\sec A = \frac{17}{15}$ $\sec A = \frac{13}{12}$,

$\csc A = \frac{13}{5}$

Exercise No. 2

1   $\cos 64°$ 3 $\sin 65° 32'$ 5 $\csc 83° 50'$

2   $\cot 47°$ 4 $\tan 1° 10'$ 6 $\sec 12\frac{1}{2}°$

7   15° ($90° = 5A + A$; $\therefore 90° = 6A$, and $A = 15°$)

8   45° (reciprocals of the cofunctions are $=$, $\therefore \angle A = 45°$)

9   45° ($90° - A = A$; $90° = 2A$; $A = 45°$)

10   30° ($\cos A = \sin 90° - A$; since $\cos A = \sin 2A$, then $\sin 90° - A = \sin 2A$, $90 - A = 2A$; $3A = 90°$ and $A = 30°$)

Exercise No. 3

1	.1392	6	.9063	11	4695	16	15°
2	.6691	7	4.134	12	1.4826	17	35°
3	.8391	8	.9781	13	.8480	18	60°
4	.5095	9	.3839	14	.7071	19	70°
5	1.079	10	6.3925	15	.5000	20	10°

Exercise No. 4

1	.2672	5	1.315	8	cos 65° 20′
2	.9013	6	sin 5° 10′	9	cot 49° 40′
3	1.079	7	tan 18° 50′	10	csc 42° 30′
4	.7674				

Exercise No. 5

1   $a = 54.46$ 4 $c = 29.82$

2   $a = 3.42$ 5 $\angle A = 46° 03′$

3   $\angle A = 65° 33′$

6   $\dfrac{a}{c} = \sin A, c = \dfrac{a}{\sin A} = \dfrac{405}{.2250} = 1{,}800$ ft.

7   $a = c \sin A = 150 \times .7660 = 114.9$ ft.

8   $c = \dfrac{a}{\sin A} = \dfrac{12}{.3090} = 38.83$ ft.

9   $a = c \sin A = 200 \times .9455 = 189.1$ ft.

10   $\dfrac{a}{c} = \sin A = \dfrac{54.5}{625} = .0872$ which is the sin of 5°

Exercise No. 6

1   $\angle A = 53° 8′$ 4 $\angle A = 60°$

2   $b = 31.86$ 5 $c = 42$

3   $b = 62.08$

6   $\dfrac{b}{c} = \cos A = \dfrac{15}{17} = .8823$ which is the cos of 28°

7   $\dfrac{b}{c} = \cos A, c = \dfrac{b}{\cos A} = \dfrac{681}{.8910} = 764.9$

8   $\angle B = 90° - 10° = 80°, \cos B = \dfrac{a}{c},$

     $c = \dfrac{a}{\cos B} = \dfrac{125}{.1736} = 720.04$

9   $\cos B = \dfrac{a}{c}, a = c \cos B = 84 \times 64828 =$

$53.9952 = 54$

10   $\cos A = \dfrac{b}{c} = \dfrac{16.5}{100} = .165$ which is the cos of 80° 30′

Exercise No. 7

1	36° 52′	3	45.04
2	64	4	18.19
5	15		

6   $\dfrac{a}{b} = \tan A, b = \frac{1}{2}$ of $280 = 140$ ft., $a = b \tan A$

     $= 140 \times .9325 = 130.55$ ft.

7   $\tan B = \dfrac{b}{a}, \angle B = 90° - 10° = 80°, b = a \tan B = 240 \times 5.6713 = 1361.11$ ft.

8   $\tan A = \dfrac{a}{b}, b = \dfrac{a}{\tan A} = \dfrac{30}{.3640} = 82.42$ ft.

9   $\angle A = 90° - 15° = 75°, \angle A' = 90° - 14° = 76°$

     $CB = b \tan A = 100 \times 3.7321 = 373.21$ ft.

     $CB' = b \tan A' = 100 \times 4.0108 = 401.08$ ft.

     $CB' - CB = BB' = 401.08 - 373.21 = 27.87$ ft.

10   Let x = height of tower

     y = distance from nearer point to foot of tower

From $\triangle ACD, \dfrac{x}{300 + y} = \tan 30°$; $\tan 30°$

$= \dfrac{1}{\sqrt{3}} \therefore y = \sqrt{3}x - 300$

From $\triangle BCD, \dfrac{x}{y} = \tan 60°, \tan 60° = \sqrt{3} \therefore y = \dfrac{x}{\sqrt{3}}$

Equating the values of y, $\sqrt{3}x - 300 = \dfrac{x}{\sqrt{3}}$

$2x = 300 \times 1.732, x = 259.8$

Exercise No. 8

1   $a = 7, b = 8.57$

2   $\angle C = 69°, b = 58.91, c = 58.44$

3   $\angle A = 76° 52′, \angle B = 35° 8′, c = 20.95$

4 $\angle A = 51° \; 24'$, $\angle B = 48° \; 49'$, $\angle C = 79° \; 47'$

5 $\angle B = 12° \; 56'$, $\angle C = 146° \; 4'$, $c = 12.43$

6 $\angle ABC = 97° \; 44'$

$\angle BCA = 180° - (67° \; 31' + 97° \; 44') = 14° \; 45'$

$\dfrac{a}{c} = \dfrac{\sin A}{\sin C}$, $a = \dfrac{c \sin A}{\sin BCA}$

$= \dfrac{1.83 \times .9241}{.2546}$

$= 6.656$

$\sin 82° \; 16' = \dfrac{x}{6.656}$,

$x = .9909 \times 6.656 = 6.595 = 6.6$ mi.

7 $\dfrac{b}{c} = \dfrac{\sin B}{\sin C}$, $\sin B$

$= \dfrac{b \sin C}{c}$

$= \dfrac{985 \, (\sin 64° \; 20')}{1460}$

$= .6081$ which is sin $37° \; 27'$

$\angle A = 180° - (64° \; 20' + 37° \; 27') = 78° \; 13'$

$\dfrac{a}{b} = \dfrac{\sin A}{\sin B}$, $a = \dfrac{b \sin A}{\sin B} = \dfrac{985 \times .9789}{.6081}$

$= 1585.6$ ft.

8 $A + B = 180° - 50° = 130°$, $\frac{1}{2}A + B = 65°$

$\tan\frac{1}{2}(A - B) =$

$\dfrac{a - b}{a + b} \times \tan\frac{1}{2}(A + B)$

$= \dfrac{5.5 - 5}{5.5 + 5} \times 2.145 = .102$

which is the tan of $5° \; 50'$

$\angle A = \frac{1}{2}(A + B) + \frac{1}{2}(A - B) = 70° \; 50'$

$\dfrac{c}{a} = \dfrac{\sin C}{\sin A}$, $c = \dfrac{a \sin C}{\sin A} = \dfrac{5.5 \times .7660}{.9446} = 4.46$ mi.

9 By cos law, $c = \sqrt{a^2 + b^2 - 2ab \cos C}$

$c = \sqrt{2^2 + 6^2 - 2(2 \times 6) \cos 33°}$

$= \sqrt{19.87}$

$= 4.46$ mi.

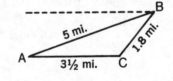

10 By cos law, $a^2 = b^2 + c^2 - 2bc \cos A$

$\therefore \cos A = \dfrac{b^2 + c^2 - a^2}{2bc}$

(a) $\cos A = \dfrac{3.5^2 + 5^2 - 1.8^2}{2(3.5 \times 5)} = .9717$

which is the cos of $13° \; 40'$

(b) alt. int. $\angle$s of $\parallel$ lines are $=$;

$\therefore$ angle of depression $= 13° \; 40'$

TABLE II
TABLE OF NATURAL TRIGONOMETRIC FUNCTIONS

Degrees	Sin	Cos	Tan	Cot	Sec	Csc	
0° 00′	.0000	1.0000	.0000	——	1.000	——	90° 00′
10	029	000	029	343.8	000	343.8	50
20	058	000	058	171.9	000	171.9	40
30	.0087	1.0000	.0087	114.6	1.000	114.6	30
40	116	9999	116	85.94	000	85.95	20
50	145	999	145	68.75	000	68.76	10
1° 00′	.0175	.9998	.0175	57.29	1.000	57.30	89° 00′
10	204	998	204	49.10	000	49.11	50
20	233	997	233	42.96	000	42.98	40
30	.0262	.9997	.0262	38.19	1.000	38.20	30
40	291	996	291	34.37	000	34.38	20
50	320	995	320	31.24	001	31.26	10
2° 00′	.0349	.9994	.0349	28.64	1.001	28.65	88° 00′
10	378	993	378	26.43	001	26.45	50
20	407	992	407	24.54	001	24.56	40
30	.0436	.9990	.0437	22.90	1.001	22.93	30
40	465	989	466	21.47	001	21.49	20
50	494	988	495	20.21	001	20.23	10
3° 00′	.0523	.9986	.0524	19.08	1.001	19.11	87° 00′
10	552	985	553	18.07	002	18.10	50
20	581	983	582	17.17	002	17.20	40
30	.0610	.9981	.0612	16.35	1.002	16.38	30
40	640	980	641	15.60	002	15.64	20
50	669	978	670	14.92	002	14.96	10
4° 00′	.0698	.9976	.0699	14.30	1.002	14.34	86° 00′
10	727	974	729	13.73	003	13.76	50
20	756	971	758	13.20	003	13.23	40
30	.0785	.9969	.0787	12.71	1.003	12.75	30
40	814	967	816	12.25	003	12.29	20
50	843	964	846	11.83	004	11.87	10
5° 00′	.0872	.9962	.0875	11.43	1.004	11.47	85° 00′
10	901	959	904	11.06	004	11.10	50
20	929	957	934	10.71	004	10.76	40
30	.0958	.9954	.0963	10.39	1.005	10.43	30
40	987	951	992	10.08	005	10.13	20
50	.1016	948	.1022	9.788	005	9.839	10
6° 00′	.1045	.9945	.1051	9.514	1.006	9.567	84° 00′
10	074	942	080	9.255	006	9.309	50
20	103	939	110	9.010	006	9.065	40
30	.1132	.9936	.1139	8.777	1.006	8.834	30
40	161	932	169	8.556	007	8.614	20
50	190	929	198	8.345	007	8.405	10
7° 00′	.1219	.9925	.1228	8.144	1.008	8.206	83° 00′
10	248	922	257	7.953	008	8.016	50
20	276	918	287	7.770	008	7.834	40
30	.1305	.9914	.1317	7.596	1.009	7.661	30
40	334	911	346	7.429	009	7.496	20
50	363	907	376	7.269	009	7.337	10
8° 00′	.1392	.9903	.1405	7.115	1.010	7.185	82° 00′
10	421	899	435	6.968	010	7.040	50
20	449	894	465	6.827	011	6.900	40
30	.1478	.9890	.1495	6.691	1.011	6.765	30
40	507	886	524	6.561	012	6.636	20
50	536	881	554	6.435	012	6.512	10
9° 00′	.1564	.9877	.1584	6.314	1.012	6.392	81° 00′
	Cos	Sin	Cot	Tan	Csc	Sec	Degrees

TABLE OF NATURAL TRIGONOMETRIC FUNCTIONS (*Continued*)

Degrees	Sin	Cos	Tan	Cot	Sec	Csc	
9° 00′	.1564	.9877	.1584	6.314	1.012	6.392	81° 00′
10	593	872	614	197	013	277	50
20	622	868	644	084	013	166	40
30	.1650	.9863	.1673	5.976	1.014	6.059	30
40	679	858	703	871	014	5.955	20
50	708	853	733	769	015	855	10
10° 00′	.1736	.9848	.1763	5.671	1.015	5.759	80° 00′
10	765	843	793	576	016	665	50
20	794	838	823	485	016	575	40
30	.1822	.9833	.1853	5.396	1.017	5.487	30
40	851	827	883	309	018	403	20
50	880	822	914	226	018	320	10
11° 00′	.1908	.9816	.1944	5.145	1.019	5.241	79° 00′
10	937	811	974	066	019	164	50
20	965	805	.2004	4.989	020	089	40
30	.1994	.9799	.2035	4.915	1.020	5.016	30
40	.2022	793	065	843	021	4.945	20
50	051	787	095	773	022	876	10
12° 00′	.2079	.9781	.2126	4.705	1.022	4.810	78° 00′
10	108	775	156	638	023	745	50
20	136	769	186	574	024	682	40
30	.2164	.9763	.2217	4.511	1.024	4.620	30
40	193	757	247	449	025	560	20
50	221	750	278	390	026	502	10
13° 00′	.2250	.9744	.2309	4.331	1.026	4.445	77° 00′
10	278	737	339	275	027	390	50
20	306	730	370	219	028	336	40
30	.2334	.9724	.2401	4.165	1.028	4.284	30
40	363	717	432	113	029	232	20
50	391	710	462	061	030	182	10
14° 00′	.2419	.9703	.2493	4.011	1,031	4.134	76° 00′
10	447	696	524	3.962	031	086	50
20	476	689	555	914	032	039	40
30	.2504	.9681	.2586	3.867	1.033	3,994	30
40	532	674	617	821	034	950	20
50	560	667	648	776	034	906	10
15° 00′	.2588	.9659	.2679	3.732	1.035	3.864	75° 00′
10	616	652	711	689	036	822	50
20	644	644	742	647	037	782	40
30	.2672	.9636	.2773	3.606	1.038	3.742	30
40	700	628	805	566	039	703	20
50	728	621	836	526	039	665	10
16° 00′	.2756	.9613	.2867	3.487	1.040	3.628	74° 00′
10	784	605	899	450	041	592	50
20	812	596	931	412	042	556	40
30	.2840	.9588	.2962	3.376	1.043	3.521	30
40	868	580	994	340	044	487	20
50	896	572	.3026	305	045	453	10
17° 00′	.2924	.9563	.3057	3.271	1.046	3.420	73° 00′
10	952	555	089	237	047	388	50
20	979	546	121	204	048	356	40
30	.3007	.9537	.3153	3.172	1.049	3.326	30
40	035	528	185	140	049	295	20
50	062	520	217	108	050	265	10
18° 00′	.3090	.9511	.3249	3.078	1.051	3.236	72° 00′
	Cos	Sin	Cot	Tan	Csc	Sec	Degrees

TABLE OF NATURAL TRIGONOMETRIC FUNCTIONS (*Continued*)

Degrees	Sin	Cos	Tan	Cot	Sec	Csc	
18° 00′	.3090	.9511	.3249	3.078	1.051	3.236	72° 00′
10	118	502	281	047	052	207	50
20	145	492	314	018	053	179	40
30	.3173	.9483	.3346	2.989	1.054	3.152	30
40	201	474	378	960	056	124	20
50	228	465	411	932	057	098	10
19° 00′	.3256	.9455	.3443	2.904	1.058	3.072	71° 00′
10	283	446	476	877	059	046	50
20	311	436	508	850	060	021	40
30	.3338	.9426	.3541	2.824	1.061	2.996	30
40	365	417	574	798	062	971	20
50	393	407	607	773	063	947	10
20° 00′	.3420	.9397	.3640	2.747	1.064	2.924	70° 00′
10	448	387	673	723	065	901	50
20	475	377	706	699	066	878	40
30	.3502	.9367	.3739	2.675	1.068	2.855	30
40	529	356	772	651	069	833	20
50	557	346	805	628	070	812	10
21° 00′	.3584	.9336	.3839	2.605	1.071	2.790	69° 00′
10	611	325	872	583	072	769	50
20	638	315	906	560	074	749	40
30	.3665	.9304	.3939	2.539	1.075	2.729	30
40	692	293	973	517	076	709	20
50	719	283	.4006	496	077	689	10
22° 00′	.3746	.9272	.4040	2.475	1.079	2.669	68° 00′
10	773	261	074	455	080	650	50
20	800	250	108	434	081	632	40
30	.3827	.9239	.4142	2.414	1.082	2.613	30
40	854	228	176	394	084	595	20
50	881	216	210	375	085	577	10
23° 00′	.3907	.9205	.4245	2.356	1.086	2.559	67° 00′
10	934	194	279	337	088	542	50
20	961	182	314	318	089	525	40
30	.3987	.9171	.4348	2.300	1.090	2.508	30
40	.4014	159	383	282	092	491	20
50	041	147	417	264	093	475	10
24° 00′	.4067	.9135	.4452	2.246	1.095	2.459	66° 00′
10	094	124	487	229	096	443	50
20	120	112	552	211	097	427	40
30	.4147	.9100	.4557	2.194	1.099	2.411	30
40	173	088	592	177	100	396	20
50	200	075	628	161	102	381	10
25° 00′	.4226	.9063	.4663	2.145	1.103	2.366	65° 00′
10	253	051	699	128	105	352	50
20	279	038	734	112	106	337	40
30	.4305	.9026	.4770	2.097	1.108	2.323	30
40	331	013	806	081	109	309	20
50	358	001	841	066	111	295	10
26° 00′	.4384	.8988	.4877	2.050	1.113	2.281	64° 00′
10	410	975	913	035	114	268	50
20	436	962	950	020	116	254	40
30	.4462	.8949	.4986	2.006	1.117	2.241	30
40	488	936	.5022	1.991	119	228	20
50	514	923	059	977	121	215	10
27° 00′	.4540	.8910	.5095	1.963	1.122	2.203	63° 00′
	Cos	Sin	Cot	Tan	Csc	Sec	Degrees

TABLE OF NATURAL TRIGONOMETRIC FUNCTIONS (*Continued*)

Degrees	Sin	Cos	Tan	Cot	Sec	Csc	
27° 00′	.4540	.8910	.5095	1.963	1.122	2.203	63° 00′
10	566	897	132	949	124	190	50
20	592	884	169	935	126	178	40
30	.4617	.8870	.5206	1.921	1.127	2.166	30
40	643	857	243	907	129	154	20
50	669	843	280	894	131	142	10
28° 00′	.4695	.8829	.5317	1.881	1.133	2.130	62° 00′
10	720	816	354	868	134	118	50
20	746	802	392	855	136	107	40
30	.4772	.8788	.5430	1.842	1.138	2.096	30
40	797	774	467	829	140	085	20
50	823	760	505	816	142	074	10
29° 00′	.4848	.8746	.5543	1.804	1.143	2.063	61° 00′
10	874	732	581	792	145	052	50
20	899	718	619	780	147	041	40
30	.4924	.8704	.5658	1.767	1.149	2.031	30
40	950	689	696	756	151	020	20
50	975	675	735	744	153	010	10
30° 00′	.5000	.8660	.5774	1.732	1.155	2.000	60° 00′
10	025	646	812	720	157	1.990	50
20	050	631	851	709	159	980	40
30	.5075	.8616	.5890	1.698	1.161	1.970	30
40	100	601	930	686	163	961	20
50	125	587	969	675	165	951	10
31° 00′	.5150	.8572	.6009	1.664	1.167	1.942	59° 00′
10	175	557	048	653	169	932	50
20	200	542	088	643	171	923	40
30	.5225	.8526	.6128	1.632	1.173	1.914	30
40	250	511	168	621	175	905	20
50	275	496	208	611	177	896	10
32° 00′	.5299	.8480	.6249	1.600	1.179	1.887	58° 00′
10	324	465	289	590	181	878	50
20	348	450	330	580	184	870	40
30	.5373	.8434	.6371	1.570	1.186	1.861	30
40	398	418	412	560	188	853	20
50	422	403	453	550	190	844	10
33° 00′	.5446	.8387	.6494	1.540	1.192	1.836	57° 00′
10	471	371	536	530	195	828	50
20	495	355	577	520	197	820	40
30	.5519	.8339	.6619	1.511	1.199	1.812	30
40	544	323	661	501	202	804	20
50	568	307	703	1.492	204	796	10
34° 00′	.5592	.8290	.6745	1.483	1.206	1.788	56° 00′
10	616	274	787	473	209	781	50
20	640	258	830	464	211	773	40
30	.5664	.8241	.6873	1.455	1.213	1.766	30
40	688	225	916	446	216	758	20
50	712	208	959	437	218	751	10
35° 00′	.5736	.8192	.7002	1.428	1.221	1.743	55° 00′
10	760	175	046	419	223	736	50
20	783	158	089	411	226	729	40
30	.5807	.8141	.7133	1.402	1.228	1.722	30
40	831	124	177	393	231	715	20
50	854	107	221	385	233	708	10
36° 00′	.5878	.8090	.7265	1.376	1.236	1.701	54° 00′
	Cos	Sin	Cot	Tan	Csc	Sec	Degrees

TABLE OF NATURAL TRIGONOMETRIC FUNCTIONS (*Continued*)

Degrees	Sin	Cos	Tan	Cot	Sec	Csc	
36° 00′	.5878	.8090	.7265	1.376	1.236	1.701	54° 00′
10	901	073	310	368	239	695	50
20	925	056	355	360	241	688	40
30	.5948	.8039	.7400	1.351	1.244	1.681	30
40	972	021	445	343	247	675	20
50	995	004	490	335	249	668	10
37° 00′	.6018	.7986	.7536	1.327	1.252	1.662	53° 00′
10	041	969	581	319	255	655	50
20	065	951	627	311	258	649	40
30	.6088	.7934	.7673	1.303	1.260	1.643	30
40	111	916	720	295	263	636	20
50	134	898	766	288	266	630	10
38° 00′	.6157	.7880	.7813	1.280	1.269	1.625	52° 00′
10	180	862	860	272	272	618	50
20	202	844	907	265	275	612	40
30	.6225	.7826	.7954	1.257	1.278	1.606	30
40	248	808	.8002	250	281	601	20
50	271	790	050	242	284	595	10
39° 00′	.6293	.7771	.8098	1.235	1.287	1.589	51° 00′
10	316	753	146	228	290	583	50
20	338	735	195	220	293	578	40
30	.6361	.7716	.8243	1.213	1.296	1.572	30
40	383	698	292	206	299	567	20
50	406	679	342	199	302	561	10
40° 00′	.6428	.7660	.8391	1.192	1.305	1.556	50° 00′
10	450	642	441	185	309	550	50
20	472	623	491	178	312	545	40
30	.6494	.7604	.8541	1.171	1.315	1.540	30
40	517	585	591	164	318	535	20
50	539	566	642	157	322	529	10
41° 00′	.6561	.7547	.8693	1.150	1.325	1.524	49° 00′
10	583	528	744	144	328	519	50
20	604	509	796	137	332	514	40
30	.6626	.7490	.8847	1.130	1.335	1.509	30
40	648	470	899	124	339	504	20
50	670	451	952	117	342	499	10
42° 00′	.6691	.7431	.9004	1.111	1.346	1.494	48° 00′
10	713	412	057	104	349	490	50
20	734	392	110	098	353	485	40
30	.6756	.7373	.9163	1.091	1.356	1.480	30
40	777	353	217	085	360	476	20
50	799	333	271	079	364	471	10
43° 00′	.6820	.7314	.9325	1.072	1.367	1.466	47° 00′
10	841	294	380	066	371	462	50
20	862	274	435	060	375	457	40
30	.6884	.7254	.9490	1.054	1.379	1.453	30
40	905	234	545	048	382	448	20
50	926	214	601	042	386	444	10
44° 00′	.6947	.7193	.9657	1.036	1.390	1.440	46° 00′
10	967	173	713	030	394	435	50
20	988	153	770	024	398	431	40
30	.7009	.7133	.9827	1.018	1.402	1.427	30
40	030	112	884	012	406	423	20
50	050	092	942	006	410	418	10
45° 00′	.7071	.7071	1.0000	1.000	1.414	1.414	45° 00′
	Cos	Sin	Cot	Tan	Csc	Sec	Degrees

CHAPTER SEVENTEEN

PHILOSOPHY AND RELIGION

Philosophy is the conscious attempt to clarify the basic concepts and values of an individual or a society. It also attempts to organize those concepts and values into a coherent system. Philosophy thus has a dual function: analysis and synthesis. Even though different ages may stress one function at the expense of the other (ours, for example, is primarily an age of analysis), both are to be found operating throughout the history of philosophy.

No area of human concern is exempt from philosophic inquiry. But not all areas are of equal philosophic interest. Philosophic problems may be roughly divided into three general domains: (1) Theories of Method, (2) Theories of Value, and (3) Theories of Being or Reality.

Methodology is concerned with the ways in which knowledge is obtained and verified. It has two main subdivisions—*Logic*, the study of correct reasoning, and *Epistemology*, the theory of knowledge.

Axiology is concerned with questions of value. It has two main subdivisions—*Ethics*, the study of the morally good and the right, and *Aesthetics*, the study of the artistically good and beautiful.

Metaphysics is concerned with the most general characteristics of whatever exists. There are four major schools of metaphysical philosophy—*Materialism, Idealism, Naturalism,* and *Existentialism.*

Methodology

Logic is the study of the basic principles of valid reasoning. It is concerned with the *form* rather than the *content* of arguments. The form of an argument determines its validity or invalidity.

VALIDITY AND TRUTH

Validity is a characteristic of formal arguments. It should not be confused with truth, a characteristic of factual statements. Thus "Warren Burger is a Justice of the Supreme Court" is true. But the

argument, "All Justices of the Supreme Court are U.S. citizens. Warren Burger is a Justice of the Supreme Court. Therefore, Warren Burger is a U.S. citizen," is neither true nor false, but *valid*. It has the valid logical form:

All J is C
B is J
Therefore, B is C

This kind of argument is called a *syllogism*. It was first analyzed in detail by Aristotle (384–322 B.C.). It consists of two premises and a conclusion,

Aristotle

containing three and only three terms. To be valid, it must conform to certain rules regarding its structure. That determines its validity or invalidity.

Although validity is a question of argument form, it does involve truth in one very important way. No *valid* argument can derive a false conclusion from true premises. If the argument is valid and the conclusion is false, at least one premise must be false. If the argument is valid and the premises are true, the conclusion must be true.

DEDUCTION AND INDUCTION

Strictly speaking, only deductive reasoning can be valid. But we use another type of reasoning called *inductive* reasoning. Deduction proceeds from the general to the particular; induction proceeds from the particular to the general. Deduction alone can provide demonstration, or *proof*. A demonstration, or *proof*, is a set of general expressions, from which other more specific expressions can be

derived. In valid deductive arguments, the truth of the premises provides *conclusive* evidence for the truth of the conclusion.

Induction proceeds from specific instances to a generalization. It provides no such "proof." The instances only provide *some* evidence for the generalized conclusion. The evidence is *probable,* but not *conclusive.* Another set of instances may disprove it. For example, the discovery of black swans contradicted the old inductive generalization, "All swans are white."

SYMBOLIC LOGIC

Symbolic, or *mathematical, logic* is the attempt to develop an artificial language by constructing a special notation with rules for its use. The purpose of this language is to provide a richer, more fruitful logical apparatus than any available in the ancient or medieval periods. Aristotelian logic—the dominant logic down to the last century—also used symbols. But its techniques were too narrow to treat many philosophical problems.

A pioneer in the new symbolism was the German mathematician, G. W. von Leibniz (1646–1716). He suggested a symbolic logic but did not develop it. In the nineteenth century, his suggestion was taken up in the work of the Englishman George Boole (1815–1864), the American C. S. Peirce (1839–1914), and the German G. Frege (1848–1925), among others. The culmination of their work occurred in the monumental *Principia Mathematica* (1910–1913) by A. N. Whitehead (1861–1947) and Bertrand Russell (1872–1970). This work was a culmination of previous efforts and a truly important work for this century. The authors attempted to develop a logical apparatus that would let them derive all of mathematics from five basic axioms. Though they did not succeed, their work provoked hundreds of other works in logic and mathematics. Since symbolic logic is the basis of computer mathematics, this abstract work has had many practical results.

Epistemology

Epistemology is the study of the sources of knowledge. Does reason or sensation provide the more reliable source for knowledge? Can we ever know any self-evident truths? Can we ever know what transcends sense experience? What verifies knowledge? Such questions are the proper concern of epistemology. Unlike psychology (which is concerned with how we come to know), epistemology is concerned with what we do know and the conditions which make such knowledge possible.

RATIONALISM

The rationalist holds that the human mind is the sole source of knowledge. Sensation is fluctuating and contradictory. It yields only opinions. The sun seems now the size of an orange, now the size of a basketball, yet we can not accept either opinion. Such opinions do not stand to reason. Although sensation might provide occasions for the exercise of reason, it can not yield genuine knowledge. Only reason can do that. Knowledge is not based on sense experience (*a posteriori*); it is independent of sense experience (*a priori*).

The human mind not only analyzes the facts of the world; it uses intuition. Learning is either a kind of remembering what was known before birth or an illumination of certain "ideas" stemming from God. These ideas are "innate," and can be brought to light by "the natural light of reason." They are "the material out of which" necessary and universal *a priori* truths are developed. Such *a priori* truths are self-evident; they require only clear and distinct formulation by intuitive reason. What is clearly *seen* to be true needs no further verification.

EMPIRICISM

The empiricist holds that sense experience is the sole source of knowledge. Reason may classify, direct, and unify our investigations; but the data of experience entirely constitutes knowledge. Empiricism is thus traditionally opposed to rationalism (see above).

Empiricism denies the existence of "self-evident" truths. All hypotheses must be validated by experience. Similarly, empiricism denies the existence of innate or intuitive knowledge, because all knowledge is derived from sense experience. Consequently, there are no factual *a priori* truths.

Historically, the rejection of "innate ideas" and the notion that the mind is "a blank tablet" at birth goes back to Aristotle (384–322 B.C.). The most famous version of the position occurs, however, in the philosophy of the Englishman John Locke (1632–1704). The Irishman George Berkeley (1685–1753) and the Scotchman David Hume (1711–1776) followed Locke's lead and tried to show that knowledge was wholly derived from sense experience. Berkeley showed that there was no good reason to believe in Isaac Newton's concept of "matter." Hume concluded that there was no ground for accepting the notions of "matter," "cause," or "self." We acquire such notions by habit. Immanuel Kant (1724–1804) attempted to bring empiricism and rationalism together. He argued that experience provides the *content* (the data of knowledge) while reason provides the *structure* (the intelligibility of knowledge).

Plato

PRAGMATISM

Pragmatism studies the *consequences* of concepts and beliefs in determining their validity and value. It is *not,* however, the naïve belief that "Whatever works is true."

Pragmatism was first formulated by C. S. Peirce (1839–1914) as a method for clarifying scientific concepts. He regarded it as a technique, not a doctrine. The technique was this: If you want to understand what a given concept *means,* consider all the experimentally repeatable effects that result from that concept. Then you have found "the entire meaning of the concept." William James (1842–1910) made pragmatism famous by reformulating it as a theory of truth and value—somewhat to Peirce's dismay.

James was more interested in humanistic questions. For James, the meaning of an idea is found in all the effects "of a practical kind" that follow from it. Moreover, James decided that an idea is not so much *given* as true as *made true* by effects which are good. Faced with what James called "a genuine option," indecision is a decision in itself. In such a case, James argued that belief in the fact helps create the fact. He took this to be especially true in certain areas of religious belief.

John Dewey (1859–1952) reformulated pragmatism as both a theory of knowledge and a theory of value. *Instrumentalism,* he preferred to call it. Dewey's basic notion is that of problematic *situation.* Experience is an interaction between an organism and its situation. To the extent that the situation does not suit the needs of the organism, it is problematic. The intelligent organism uses the scientific method to transform an unfavorable situation into a more favorable one. Situations are, however, always in process. Consequently, we must modify all our solutions in the light of experience. The process of drawing on past experience to meet new situations is called "inquiry." Belief is the result of successful inquiry.

LOGICAL POSITIVISM

Logical positivism, or *logical empiricism,* studies the logic of language. The logical positivist insists that the only legitimate function of philosophy is to clarify the meaning of terms. Its domain is thus *semantics,* the study of language in terms of meaning.

Not all sentences are meaningful. Sentences which are not capable of being either true or false are meaningless. This is called the Verification Principle. In other words, the meaning of a statement is its means of verification. If you cannot stipulate the conditions under which a claim can be tested, then it is meaningless.

The logical positivist uses this principle with great effect against traditional philosophy, especially metaphysics. Since metaphysical statements are not subject to test, they are meaningless. Traditional problems of philosophy are, on this view, not problems to be solved, but "pseudo-problems." This is the negative side of logical positivism.

Logical positivism, especially in the work of Rudolf Carnap (1891–1970), tried to construct a unified language to be used by all the sciences. The enterprise remains unrealized. Moreover, it has been accused by Bertrand Russell (1872–1970) of involving a Platonic metaphysic in disguise. In addition, critics point out that the Verification Principle itself is empirically unverifiable. They argue that it is "metaphysical." Defenders reply that it is a "definition."

LINGUISTIC ANALYSIS

Philosophy is analysis of the meanings of terms used in ordinary language, according to the logical analyst. Where the logical positivist distinguished the problems of science from the so-called

John Locke

"pseudo-problems" of philosophy, the linguistic analyst accepts philosophic problems as genuine puzzles.

Linguistic analysis is informal. It is based on the use of ordinary language. Whatever linguistic usage has survived "the constant test of use" can be trusted, since it reflects a certain good sense developed through long common usage. Like other games, the word game has its own implicit set (or sets) of rules. The philosopher must collate and apply those implicit rules of the word game.

This philosophy of language which is currently popular in both England and America derives a great deal from the philosophy of G. E. Moore (1873–1958) and the later philosophy of Ludwig Wittgenstein (1889–1951).

Axiology

Aesthetics is the study of beauty (or ugliness) and its expression in works of art. It attempts both to account for the experience of beauty and to set up standards of judgment for works of art. It must be admitted, however, that there is no general consensus as to the nature of art. Among other things, the essential nature of art has been argued to be:

Imitation (Plato and Aristotle): Art copies some individual or universal aspect of life. Our recognition of the copy serves as an emotional release (Aristotle).

Insight into Reality (Plato and Schopenhauer): Art expresses a direct insight into some reality that cannot be directly sensed.

Expression (Croce): Art is the expression of intuitions, lyric visions, or particular experiences.

Play (Schiller): Art releases surplus energy in imaginative play.

Wish Fulfillment (Freud): Art expresses repressed desires.

Infectiousness (Tolstoi): Art transmits emotion.

Pleasure Objectified (Santayana): Art is pleasure, regarded as the quality of a thing.

Experience Intensified (Dewey): Art is experience fulfilled.

Economically Conditioned (Marx): Art expresses economically determined class values.

ETHICS

Ethics is the study of the good or bad, the right or wrong. Questions as to the nature of the good are a matter of ethical values; questions as to the nature of the right are a matter of ethical obligation.

A basic division occurs between those who stress values and those who stress obligation. For example, is it ever right to break a promise? A philosopher such as Immanuel Kant (1724–1804), who emphasizes obligation, would claim that it could never be right. A philosopher such as William James (1842–1910), who emphasizes values, would claim that it might be right under certain conditions. Kant's ethic regards the right as *categorical;* what is right is right in every case. James would say an act is right if it leads to ends which are good. His is a *teleological* ethic.

The problem then becomes: Is there any ultimate good, any highest good *(Summum Bonum),* desirable for its own sake? If so, what is the highest good? Many answers have been given. To consider a few:

Subjectivism (Moral Skepticism). The subjectivist argues that to say "Hitler is bad," is to say, (1) "Hitler. Bah!" or perhaps, (2) "I disapprove of Hitler," or perhaps, (3) "My crowd disapproves of Hitler." The first version merely expresses emotion with no cognitive value. The second has *some* cognitive value; it tells you about the speaker's attitudes. The third tells you about the attitudes of the speaker's society. (This version is usually referred to as *ethical relativism.*) All three versions would give equal *moral* weight to the contrary statements, "Hitler is good," and "Hitler is bad."

Hedonism. The hedonist argues that pleasure is the ultimate good. Pain is the ultimate evil. The good life has a maximum of pleasure and a minimum of pain. That is happiness. Pleasure is not limited, however, to physical pleasure. The most famous of the ancient hedonists, Epicurus (341–271 B.C.), advocated a life of tranquillity with a moderate satisfaction of needs. For him, the highest point of pleasure was the removal of pain. The problem for a resolute hedonist is: If I do enjoy my pleasure, why should I care about your pleasures and pains?

Utilitarianism. The utilitarian agrees that pleasure is the good, but he hastens to add a social dimension. Pleasure, he argues, is a *social* good. The less pain there is in society, the "happier" will that society be. The test of right and wrong is: Always act for the greatest happiness for the greatest number, *or* to avoid suffering.

Jeremy Bentham (1748–1832) and John Stuart Mill (1806–1873) are the most famous utilitarians. They do not see eye to eye on the nature of pleasure. For Bentham, pleasures differed only in degree; all pleasures were of the same kind.

Mill, on the other hand, argued that pleasures differed in kind as well as in degree. He argued that a man dissatisfied was better than a pig satisfied, and that Socrates dissatisfied was better than a fool satisfied. The good for Mill was the pleasure of intelligent and cultivated minds. Mill makes pleasure itself *subject to* moral evaluation, whereas Bentham had taken pleasure to be the *criterion of* evaluation.

The greatest impact of the utilitarians was probably in the area of politics. Politics, they argued, should bring human happiness. Bentham's treatises on legislation and government and J. S. Mill's *On Liberty* are perhaps their most permanent contributions.

Eudaemonism. Eudaemonism argues that happiness is the good. But happiness is not equated with pleasure; pleasure is only a sign of the good at best. In this view, happiness involves the realization of what is potential. Aristotle (384–322 B.C.) first developed this view in detail. For him, happiness was the life of one who habitually chose the moderate course of action (the mean).

Metaphysics

As we noted above, *metaphysics* is a branch of philosophy that probes the general nature of existence. Political philosophy, religious philosophy, and many other studies must rely on the concepts developed by metaphysics.

MATERIALISM

Materialism contends that the universe is ultimately reducible to physical matter. Everything mental or spiritual can be ultimately explained in physical terms.

Atomism

Atomism states that the world is made up of simple, individual, impenetrable, and indivisible units or *atoms* (the term originally meant "unsplittable"), moving in a void or vacuum. Objects are made up of clusters of atoms which blindly collided and became entangled.

Remember that atomism is a metaphysical world view, not a physical theory. Atomism is *not* the atomic theory in physics—although it may well be its ancestor.

Leucippus and Democritus (fifth century B.C.) first proposed atomism as an imaginative vision. In fact, Democritus distrusted sense experience. So, too, when Pierre Gassendi (1592–1655) revived atomism in the seventeenth century, it was to *account for* the new Galilean science. It was only when John Dalton (1766–1844) devised "a theory of atoms" in chemistry that the scientific hypothesis was developed. Dalton's atomic hypothesis stands or falls in relation to experimental evidence. No amount of experimental evidence could refute Democritus.

Atomism raises the problem of free will and determinism. If the world is a completely determined system, how can man's willful efforts have any effect on it? He himself is part of the determinism and his "freedom" of action is only an illusion. If the atoms blindly run on in an impersonal universe, then human effort is futile. Epicurus (341–

Epicurus

270 B.C.) tried to avoid this futility by introducing an accidental "swerve" from time to time in the running atoms. It is questionable if this helps. If the "swervings" are *sheer accidents,* then they can not be anticipated or predicted. Man then remains a victim of both "swerving" and regular atoms. He is helpless before the accidental as well as before the regular course of nature.

The appeal of atomism is probably at its strongest in *De Rerum Natura (On the Nature of Things)* by the Roman poet, Lucretius (98–55 B.C.). Materialism has never had a more eloquent spokesman.

Dialectical Materialism

Dialectical materialism is the name generally given to the philosophy of Karl Marx (1818–1883) and Friedrich Engels (1820–1895). For Marx, the material world is not the material world of the atomist. The atomist's world is a determined system to which men are irrelevant spectators. Knowledge for him is merely a "seeing" of blindly running atoms. For Marx, knowledge is active. Its function is not to understand the world but to change it. Therefore, the material world is essentially historical and the historical process essentially material.

According to Marx, man can have a distinctively human life only by working to transform his mate-

rial environment. But as a worker he is also involved with other men, which requires a division of labor. Thus labor leads to the creation of classes due to its division of functions. Human history then is the history of class warfare.

A man's class in society is determined by his relationship to the means of production. The means of production consist of (1) the forces of production (raw materials, equipment, workers, etc.), and (2) the relations of production (property relations determining classes).

Marx borrowed his historical "dialectic" from George Hegel (1770–1831). It is a logic by which one stage of a process (a *thesis*) passes into its opposite (its *antithesis*) and then both are comprehended in a wider unified stage (the *synthesis*) of the process. Marx distinguished five stages of labor evolving in this manner: (1) primitive communal, (2) slave, (3) feudal, (4) capitalist, and (5) communist. Under the first, the means of production are socially owned. However, it generates its antithesis, the slave society, in which the slave owner owns the means of production. This, in turn, generates a synthesis of the first two: feudal society, in which the means of production are partly owned by the lord, and partly owned by his men. Feudal society becomes a new thesis generating its antithesis, capitalist society, in which the means of production are owned by the capitalist and not by his workers—though he does not own his workers. Marx believed the new synthesis is in the process of being generated. Under the communist mode, the workers will own the means of production. The mechanism of conflict between the forces of production and the relations of production will then be eliminated. History as we have known it will then come to a close.

IDEALISM

Idealism is the world view that the universe is spiritual. The material world is formed by consciousness. The characteristics of mind and of spirit permeate reality.

Subjective Idealism

According to the system of subjective idealism, only subjective minds or spirits and their experience exist. Experience consists of ideas, actively held by God and passively perceived by human minds. There is no objective material world beyond experience. The order of nature is constituted by ideas in the mind of God. "Things" are constructed of ideas in mind. Thus a cherry is a complex of ideas and sensible impressions. It is only what it is experienced to be. To be, in fact, is to be perceived (*Esse est percipi*).

Critical Idealism

According to this system, philosophy is the radical criticism of knowledge. There is no knowledge, no science, of what things really are in themselves (*noumena*). There is only knowledge of how things appear (*phenomena*) to our understanding. The content of knowledge is given by sense experience. The form is given by the human understanding in terms of necessary and universal principles of order. Whatever is necessary and universal in experience is brought to it by the understanding. Science must use certain necessary and universal principles to organize sense experience. Yet even though the scientific understanding cannot legitimately go beyond experience, human reason does have a natural disposition to do so.

The human mind thus has two functions: *understanding* (which organizes sense experience along necessary lines of coherence) and *reason* (which transcends sense experience and proposes "ideas" for the purpose of orientation). Where the understanding only tells us what *is,* reason demands what *ought* to be. It goes beyond sense experience to propose a law unto itself. God, freedom, and immortality are "ideas" of reason. This view was espoused by Immanuel Kant (1724–1804).

Objective Idealism

Objective idealism takes the natural world as being thoroughly spiritual. The most representative form of this philosophy is probably that of G. W. F. Hegel (1770–1831), whose view is sometimes called absolute idealism.

Absolute idealism holds that reality is the "unfolding" of the Absolute or World Spirit.* This "unfolding" will create *every* theoretical possibility which is implicit in the World Spirit. There is a dialectic in every phase of the "unfolding" or embodiment of the World Spirit in nature. Any given stage (e.g., a bud) is a *thesis* which generates its opposite, its *antithesis* (e.g., a blossom). The dialectical tension between these two stages generates a larger unifying *synthesis* (e.g., the fruit), wherein

*The terms *Absolute* and *World Spirit* are capitalized because they are synonymous with an impersonal divinity.

George Hegel

the earlier stages are absorbed. The *synthesis* cancels out the limitations of the earlier stages and yet keeps their essential characteristics. The *synthesis,* in turn, serves as a *thesis* for a new dialectic. The World Spirit then expresses itself as a complex dialectical order which embodies itself in nature and history.

Hegel believed that human history is the embodiment of the World Spirit. The Spirit expresses itself in various national cultures (e.g., Greek, Roman, German.) Each national culture is the expression of a particular National Spirit (*Volksgeist*), which is a form of the World Spirit. The Spirit of the Nation is to be found in the State. So the warfare between states is a necessary part of the dialectical tension within the process of history. The rise and fall of nations is part of the march of Spirit in the world. Great men such as Caesar and Napoleon may think that they move events, but they are wrong. They are in fact "historical" men only because they serve as agents of the advance of reason in history.

HUMANISTIC NATURALISM

Humanistic naturalism is the view that reality is a combination of matter and spirit. Neither can be explained as a form of the other. Material im-

George Santayana

pulses without spiritual ideas are futile; spiritual ideas disconnected from material impulses are insane. Man, the rational animal, represents the fusion of matter and mind. "He is constituted by ideas which have ceased to be visionary and actions which have ceased to be vain" (George Santayana [1863–1952], *The Life of Reason: Reason in Common Sense,* p. 6).

Aristotle used the orders of form and matter to explain things and processes in nature. Consider the bronze statue. Its matter is bronze; its form is horse and rider. Then consider something alive which is undergoing process—say, an oak tree or a man. The matter of an oak tree is its wood pulp, sap, leaves, branches, etc.; its form is its "oak tree-ness," the kind of thing it is. The matter of a man is his flesh, blood, muscles, organs, nerves, etc.; his form is his rational humanity, the kind of thing he is. Knowledge grasps forms, but essential forms exist only as matter. This is a static view of a thing or process.

When a material thing represents its kind, it may be said to be "realizing its nature." The tree, living as a distinctive oak tree, is realizing its nature.

EXISTENTIALISM

Existentialism is the world view that man is radically free in a universe that has no objective value. Man's freedom to determine values gives his life meaning.

Essential values cannot be *given;* they must be *chosen.* Every individual is thrust into an existential situation (his own) in which he must define himself. Humanity cannot be given to him. Man makes himself human. He is responsible for determining his humanity. But in determining himself, he determines the nature of mankind.

So choice is not merely a private affair. In choice, the individual is defining not only himself, but mankind as well. But why does he have to accept this burden? Why is he "condemned" to be free?

First, he cannot escape his freedom by surrendering it to some authority, for then he is choosing to remain in servitude. He always has the option of resistance—even if the price of resistance is death. Secondly, he cannot escape his freedom because he is aware that he must at some time die. Death is a real possibility *present* in every moment of life. It is this awareness that makes man *dread* his condition. The only appropriate response to dread is *authentic engagement* in the responsibilities of freedom. Man must create courses of action for which he can accept responsibility as man. Then, even if he fails, his failure is not meaningless.

The existentialist movement is generally taken to have begun with Søren Kierkegaard (1813–1855), whom many regard as the greatest theologian of the last century. Today, theologians such as Karl Jaspers (1883–1969) and Paul Tillich (1886–1965) are closely associated with this world view.

PHILOSOPHIC TERMS

Agnostic—One who claims that the evidence for or against a given position is inadequate to justify a judgment. It is usually applied to the question of the existence of God, where it refers to anyone who suspends judgment as to whether God exists or not (*see* Atheist).

Analytic Proposition—Any statement which is necessarily true because its denial is a self-contradiction (*see* Synthetic Proposition.)

A posteriori knowledge—*See* Epistemology.

A priori knowledge—*See* Epistemology.

Atheist—One who claims that the evidence is sufficient to justify the claim that there is no God. The problem often arises as to whether or not the *atheist* is denying all meanings of the term, *God,* or just one specific meaning (*see* Agnostic).

Behaviorism—The study of actions to determine the mental states of the agents.

Conceptualism—The doctrine that "universals" have a mental status but do not exist in real things (*see* Nominalism; Realism).

Conventionalism—The theory that alternative theories may be constructed to explain the same data. The choice between them is a matter of "convention."

Deduction—*See* Logic.

Determinism—The belief that every event is an instance of inviolable causal laws. Human freedom is illusory (*see* Atomism).

Dualism—The belief in the opposition of two basic concepts or principles—e.g., mind-matter, subject-object, God-nature, form-matter.

Efficient Cause—The agency *by which* something is caused. The sculptor is the efficient cause of the statue (*see* Final Cause; Formal Cause; Material Cause).

Final Cause—The purpose *for which* anything happens or is done. To commemorate the memory of a public figure might be the final cause of the statue (*see* Efficient Cause; Formal Cause; Material Cause).

Formal Cause—The way *in which* anything happens or is done, its essence. The shape (horse and rider) might be the formal cause of the statue (*see* Efficient Cause; Final Cause; Material Cause).

Genetic Fallacy—Any explanation that gives the *origins* of something under the guise of explaining its *function.* Origins do not explain function. Genetic explanation is properly used to explain malfunction—that is, how the particular disorder came about. The most successful use of genetic explanation has been in the field of medical pathology.

Humanism—(1) A Renaissance attitude of sympathy with, and interest in, the literature of classical antiquity. (2) Any non-theological, "man-centered" world view (*see* Humanistic Naturalism).

Hylomorphism—Any philosophy which takes the terms *form* and *matter* to be basic (*see* Humanistic Naturalism; Neo-Thomism).

Hypostatize—To make a thing out of something insubstantial.

Induction—*See* Logic.

Material Cause—That *out of which* anything is made. Bronze might be the material cause of the statue (*see* Efficient Cause; Final Cause; Formal Cause).

Mechanism—The view that regards the world as a vast machine, running under its own rules. Human purposes and values are a cosmic irrelevance (*see* Atomism).

Monism—The belief that everything can be explained in terms of some single principle.

Neo-Thomism—The revived philosophy of St. Thomas Aquinas (1225–1274). It is a form of Christian Aristotelianism (*see* Humanistic Naturalism).

Nominalism—The doctrine that "universals" have neither objective existence nor legitimate mental status (*see* Conceptualism; Realism).

Noumenon—*See* Critical Idealism.

Operationalism—Theory that the meaning of a scientific concept is defined by the operations of its use.

Pantheism—Belief that God permeates the universe.

Personalism—The form of pluralistic objective idealism which argues that only persons are real.

Plurality—The belief that experience cannot be explained by any one or any few principles.

Realism—(1) The doctrine that "universals" have an objective existence. (2) The doctrine that the object of knowledge exists in its own right, independent of its being known. (3) In aesthetics, the belief that works of art should copy or express recognizable natural and social conditions. (4) In politics, the belief that conditions as they are must determine our decisions.

Romanticism—The belief in exalting the ego and intensifying the emotions. In the arts, a nineteenth-century movement which emphasized those values.

Scholasticism—The general name for the rationalistic methods and problems of medieval philosophy. It has come to be an unfavorable term suggesting pedantry.

Socratic Method—A method of question-and-answer to clarify terms. Socrates (470–399 B.C.) would ironically profess his ignorance on a given subject to provoke a popular opinion which he would reduce to absurdity by his questions. Then he would begin again with a new, more refined proposal in order to find a universal definition for some moral term, such as *justice.* However, the usual result was inconclusive.

Synthetic Proposition—Any statement that is neither necessarily true nor false (*see* Analytic Proposition).

Tautology—(1) a redundancy; (2) an Analytic Proposition.

Universal—Whatever holds in common for any group of elements.

Verification Principle—*See* Logical Positivism.

Voluntarism—Any philosophy which emphasizes the primacy of the human will.

RELIGION

Of all the forces in world history, religion has been one of the most potent and influential. The word *religion* (from the Latin *religio,* meaning "respect for what is sacred") refers to a system of belief in a superhuman power to be worshiped, obeyed, and served. Most religions emphasize moral values, right conduct, and concern for one's fellow man. Perhaps the Latin root word *religare* (meaning "to bind") best describes the historical function of religion: It serves as a bond between God and man, and between man and man. "Thou shalt love the Lord thy God" (Deut. 6:5) and "Love thy neighbor as thyself" (Lev. 19:18) illustrate the imperatives of most religions.

Religion has been a great civilizing force throughout history. Albert Einstein called cosmic religious experience "the strongest and noblest driving force behind scientific research."

Religion has preserved the great cultural contributions of the ages and transmitted them from generation to generation. Man has found many varied avenues of expression to articulate his religious needs and feelings. Painfully aware of his finite nature, man has sought to establish contact with the infinite.

The three major monotheistic religions—Judaism, Christianity, and Islam—are described in this section in the chronological order of their founding.

JUDAISM

Judaism derives its name from Judah, the most prominent tribe of Israel. It is variously called the Jewish religion, the Hebrew religion, or the religion of Israel. It traces its origins to the great historical event of God's revelation at Mt. Sinai which occurred 34 centuries ago, and even beyond to the exile in Egypt and the age of the patriarchs Abraham, Isaac, and Jacob.

Judaism is the oldest of the great monotheistic religions and one which has been practiced since the time of Moses, lawgiver, prophet, and greatest personality in Jewish history. (Today the world Jewish population stands at close to twelve million.)

The outstanding feature of Judaism is to be found in the affirmation of faith, or *Shema:* "Hear, O Israel, the Lord is our God, the Lord is One" (Deut. 6:4–9). This strict belief in one God has characterized the Hebrew faith throughout its history.

Judaism teaches that God chose Israel to tell the rest of mankind about him. Israel is to adhere to a special discipline of *Mitzvoth* (commandments) taught by the written *Torah* (Old Testament) and amplified by the *Oral Torah* (Talmud) to enable it to serve him faithfully while it fulfills its mission to mankind.

The three "branches" of contemporary Judaism are Orthodoxy, which subscribes to the traditional authority of the Jewish law (*Halacha*); Reform,

Touro Synagogue—Oldest Jewish Synagogue in the United States Newport, Rhode Island (Built 1759-1763)

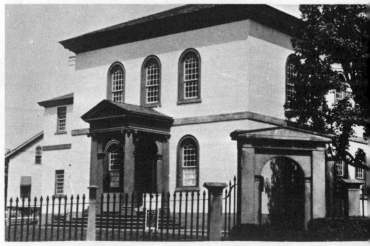

which rejects many of the restrictions of Jewish law and reduces much of the ritual; and Conservatism, which attempts to follow a course midway between the two.

Judaism has no religious hierarchy. A *Rabbi* is a teacher of religion and the chief religious functionary in the synagogue. The *Hazan,* or Cantor, chants the service as he leads the congregation.

CHRISTIANITY

In speaking of Christianity we must take into account the many religious groups which are based on the teachings of Jesus. Christianity is rooted in the faith that God manifested himself in the person of his Son, Jesus, who lived among men and died on the cross as an atonement for the sins of mankind. Only in Christianity does incarnation occupy so central a position. Christianity proclaims the character of God in the person of Jesus.

The chief literature of Christianity is in the Gospels and Epistles of the New Testament. Much of early Christianity remains buried in legend and folklore. This absence of objective historical data has given rise to fundamental differences of belief within Christendom. Christianity is divided into a traditionalist wing, comprising the Roman Catholic and the Eastern Orthodox churches, and the reformed wing, which includes the Protestant churches and various independent groups. The traditionalists claim that they derive their authority from the early practices of Christianity; the reformers claim to have eliminated the dogma and ritual that accumulated in the course of time, and to have returned to original Scripture and its pure ways.

Christianity proclaims one God, with Jesus as his mediator. It offers salvation or a place in the kingdom of heaven to all men.

Almost twenty centuries have passed since Jesus of Nazareth proclaimed his gospel in the cities and villages of Judeah and Galilee.

Today about 900 million people profess his faith on every continent of the earth.

Roman Catholic Church.
The Roman Catholic Church, with a constituency of over 450 million people, is today the largest religious body in Christendom. It acknowledges the Pope as the head of the church on earth. It establishes his claim to supremacy on the belief that the Apostle Peter was the first Bishop of Rome

Church of the Holy Sepulchre—Erected upon the site of Jesus' crucifixion, burial, and resurrection, Jerusalem

and that Jesus founded his church on the "rock" of "Petrine supremacy."

The doctrines of the Roman Catholic church are rooted in the faith received by the apostles from Jesus, as well as the decisions of various councils. These are subject to the authority of the Pope. When he is speaking *ex cathedra* (that is, in his capacity as head of the church), he defines Catholic doctrine.

Roman Catholics express their faith mainly in formulated creeds. The most widely held is the Apostles' Creed, which summarizes the basic tenets of Catholicism: "I believe in God, the Father Almighty, Creator of heaven and earth; and in Jesus Christ, His only Son, Our Lord; who was conceived by the Holy Ghost, born of the Virgin Mary, suffered under Pontius Pilate, was crucified, died, and was buried. He descended into hell; the third day He arose again from the dead; He ascended into heaven, sitteth on the right hand of God, the Father Almighty; from thence He shall come to judge the living and the dead. I believe in the Holy Ghost, the Holy Catholic Church, the communion of saints, the forgiveness of sins, the resurrection of the body and life everlasting. Amen."

One of the most important elements in the Catholic faith is the doctrine that God's grace is conveyed to man directly through the sacraments. These are ceremonial observances which are said to bestow grace. There are seven sacraments: the Eucharist (or Mass), baptism of infants, confirmation, penance (forgiveness of sins), matrimony, holy orders (the giving of church offices and duties), and extreme unction (anointing individuals just before death).

St. Peter's Basilica—Center of Catholicism, Vatican City, Rome

Other important features of Roman Catholicism are a well-organized hierarchy, a widespread parochial and secondary school system, and a wide variety of lay organizations for men, women, and youth.

Catholics are obliged to hear Mass on Sundays and holy days, receive Holy Communion at Easter time, confess to a priest at least once a year, contribute to the support of the church, and follow the marriage rules of the church.

A Catholic enters the church through the sacrament of baptism, which "cleanses from original sin and initiates the life of grace in the soul." The church is all-inclusive. It consists of Christians both living and dead, the Virgin Mary, the saints in heavens, and those consigned to purgatory.

Many leaders have attempted to reform the Roman Catholic Church. The most recent attempt was the Ecumenical Council called by the late Pope John XXIII and continued by his successor, Pope Paul VI. Pope John Paul I and Pope John Paul II have indicated that they want to continue this reforming trend, but with more moderation.

Eastern Orthodox Churches.

Eastern Orthodoxy consists of a number of national churches that are administratively independent but essentially united in doctrine and form of worship. The churches reject the authority or primacy of the Pope; they accept the decrees of the first seven ecumenical (worldwide) councils.

Differences within the early church slowly led to the great schism between East and West. In the ninth century Photius challenged the authority of

Rome; in 1054, Pope Leo IX condemned the Patriarch of Constantinople.

The Orthodox churches recognize Jesus as the head of the church. They disagree with Roman Catholics in their belief that the Holy Ghost proceeds only from the Father and not from the Son.

The Orthodox accept the doctrine of the Virgin birth. They honor Mary as the mother of God, although their theology does not accept the immaculate conception of Mary.

Membership in the church is by baptism which is immediately followed by *chrismation* (confirmation). Holy Communion is offered after confession and absolution (except in the case of children under seven, of whom confession is not required).

The Orthodox worship service is solemn. The sacraments are largely the same as those in the Roman rite. Priests are usually married, but monks and bishops not.

The rise of Communism in Russia and in neighboring countries which have concentrations of Orthodoxy makes it difficult to know the exact number of Orthodox believers. The number stands at about one hundred and sixty million.

Protestants.

Protestantism began with the Reformation in the sixteenth century—originally a reform movement within the Catholic Church. The revolt against the authority of the church was triggered by the invention of printing, the Renaissance, church-state friction, the development of commerce, and the rise of a middle class.

Protestantism began with Martin Luther posting his celebrated 95 theses on the door of the church in Wittenberg on October 31, 1517. This was followed by an attack on the authority of the church and open defiance of Rome. By insisting that each believer be allowed to read the Bible, Luther gave the individual greater responsibility for his own salvation. He replaced justification by sacraments, good works, and church power with justification by faith alone.

Much has transpired since that fateful day in 1517. Wars have been fought—on battlefields as well as in seminaries—to heal that breach in Christendom. Within Protestantism itself there have been many doctrinal differences.

John Calvin was perhaps the most influential theologian of the Reformation. In 1536, he established in Geneva a center of Protestantism whose influence extended far and wide, including England and eventually the United States. The word *Protestant* has a negative ring, yet Protestantism does much more than merely "protest." It is very positive in the doctrines it teaches.

Protestantism is actually a very broad term. In the United States it includes several major confessional bodies: Lutheran; Presbyterian and Reformed; Episcopalian (or Anglican); and "independent" or "free" churches, which include Congregationalists, Disciples of Christ, Baptists, and many others.

Common to most Protestant denominations is their belief in the Trinity (Father, Son, and Holy Ghost), justification by faith, the authority of the Bible, the priesthood of all believers in Christ, the church as a fellowship of all believers, belief in eternal life with God, and a fervent belief in freedom for all religions.

No one can draw up an accurate definition of what constitutes a Protestant or a Protestant denomination. Yet it is safe to estimate the Protestant population in the world today at about two hundred and twenty-five million. They belong to more than two hundred and fifty denominations.

ISLAM

Islam (which means "submission," *Aslama*), is the third of the three great monotheistic religions. It absorbed much from Judaism and Christianity, including the prophets of the Hebrew Scriptures. Muslims believe Jesus was an ordinary prophet, who will return at the end of the world as the *Mahdi* (divine guide) to lead the faithful.

Muslims do not prefer the name "Mohammedanism" for their religion. Though they believe Mohammed was the greatest and "seal of the prophets," he was only a *human* messenger with no divine pretensions. He was God's instrument, used to transmit his Word, which is recorded in the *Koran,* the Islamic scripture.

Mohammed was born in Mecca about A.D. 573. He led a simple, virtuous life as a camel driver. He married Khadiya, a wealthy widow, who supplied him with the economic freedom that enabled him to turn his attention to spiritual matters. In a cave outside Mecca he received the call (A.D. 610): "Recite thou in the name of the Lord who created"— and a new religion was born.

Mohammed's early efforts met with little success. In 622 he was forced to flee for his life. This *Hegira* (or "flight") from Mecca to Medina is regarded by Muslims as the turning point in history, and the year 622 is the beginning of the Muslim era.

The major Islamic articles of faith include belief in God, his angels, his divine books, his prophets, and in Mohammed as the last of the prophets. Muslims also expect a Judgment Day. The Muslim

The Door of the Schlosskirche (Castle Church)—Wittenberg, Germany. Luther posted his 95 points on this door.

Mosque of Omar—Moslem Shrine in Mount Moriah
(Built Seventh Century)

creed is *La ilaha illa Allah!* "There is no God but Allah and Mohammed is His Prophet."

Islam is based on the Word of God contained in the *Koran,* supplemented by the *Hadith* (traditions ascribed to Mohammed's experiences and sayings).

Islam has no organized priesthood. The *imam* is a layman who leads the service, while the *mufti* is an authority on religious law.

Today one of every seven persons in the world is a Muslim, and responds to the call of the *muezzin* (crier who calls the faithful to worship).

BUDDHISM

Buddhism is the world's fourth largest faith. It began in India with a handsome Indian prince, Gautama, six centuries before the advent of Christianity. The young prince was overwhelmed by the four facts of life which he saw personified in a sick man, an old man, a dead man, and a holy man. First he fled to a forest to seek enlightenment. He finally achieved *nirvana* ("enlightenment") after meditating for 49 days under a sacred Bodhi tree.

Buddha now began his ministry, wandering throughout India. He had nothing to say about God or divine judgment. He taught that *Dharma,* the law of cause and effect, governs the fortunes of man.

Buddha's teachings may be summed up in the Four Noble Truths: (1) Man suffers all his life and continues to suffer from one life to the next. (2) Craving for pleasure, possessions, and freedom from pain are the source of man's suffering. (3) One should detach himself from everything, including himself. (4) Detachment is achieved by means of the eightfold path: right views, right intentions, right speech, right conduct, right livelihood, right effort, right mindfulness, and right meditation.

An important institution in Buddhism is the *Sangha,* a large body of monks and nuns. The two great traditions in Buddhism are the *Hinayana,* or the Lesser Vehicle, and the *Mahayana,* or Greater Vehicle. *Hinayana* is more austere; it limits *nirvana* to members of the *Sangha.* The *Mahayana* offers hope of *nirvana* to all. Mahayana also stresses compassion for humanity and looks upon the *bodhisattva* ("enlightened one") as the acme of perfection.

About one hundred fifty million people profess the Buddhist faith. This system stresses that man's final goal is *nirvana* (Sanskrit: annihilation), a positive state of enhanced consciousness and infinitely developed personality.

India was the birthplace of Buddhism. Yet the Buddhist population in that country is insignificant as compared with the vast multitudes of Buddhists in China, Burma, Japan, and other countries of the Orient.

Many Americans have become familiar with Zen Buddhism, a subdivision of the *Mahayana* that was taken over by the Japanese and brought to these shores by Japanese immigrants. Zen stresses prolonged meditation to achieve *satori,* or *nirvana.*

HINDUISM

Hinduism is the religion of more than three hundred million people, most of them residing in India. They consider it more a way of life than a religion. Hinduism cannot be traced to a "founder"; it has its roots in the ancient civilization of India and in that land's ancient religions.

Hinduism has no canonized scripture. However, the *Rig Veda, Brahmanas,* and *Bhagavad-Gita* are important sacred writings to Hindus. The *Upanishads* (which form the foundation of Hindu philosophy) are a more highly sophisticated religious

Buddhist Shrine—A roadside shrine to Buddha, Ceylon

literature which teach the doctrine of a universal spirit to which all souls will be reunited after the conquest of *Maya* (the illusion of time and space).

Hinduism has gone through many stages in its long history. It was always prepared to absorb concepts from other systems of religion and philosophy. To this day Hinduism permits numerous cults and sects to engage in what other religions would consider to be heretical practices and teachings.

Modern Hinduism teaches that there is a triune deity: *Brahma,* the creator of the universe; *Vishnu,* the preserver; and *Siva,* the destroyer. In the *Bhagavad-Gita,* the most popular of Hindu sacred writings, ethical teachings, *Krishna,* is presented as the supreme God. Hindus believe the images they worship are but incarnations of a spiritual God, made concrete to enable the masses to worship a personal deity.

Hinduism does not maintain an organized priesthood. Priests are supported through the generosity of worshipers, who also build and maintain the numerous temples and shrines in India. Countless *sannyasins* (monks dedicated to a life of pious devotion) wander throughout the land, subsisting on the offerings of the faithful.

Out of Hinduism have grown other great religions such as Buddhism, Jainism, and Sikhism—as well as scores of sects which still are within the Hindu communion.

Hinduism, like all Indian and Oriental religions, is not missionary in nature. Yet one of its

sects, the Ramakrishna Movement (also known as the Vedanta Society), actively tries to interest people in the Hindu religion.

CONFUCIANISM

Three hundred million people follow the teachings of Confucius. Many of them also confess Buddhism or Taoism, in the spirit of the proverbial tolerance of Oriental religion.

The religion of Confucius is exceptionally rational and humanistic. Indeed, many regard it as a philosophy rather than as a religion. Confucius taught mainly that man's nature is good and that he possesses freedom of choice. He also emphasized that virtue is its own reward, and that one should not do to others what he does not want others to do to him. Confucius urged the cultivation of "the princely man" as the cornerstone of the "good society."

Confucius was an observer and formulator of the people's religion, rather than a creative philosopher. His lectures were recorded in the *Classics.* Other works by the sage are: *The Book of Poetry, The Book of Changes,* and in later years, his *Book of Rites. The Confucian Analects* are his posthumously collected words of wisdom.

Ironically, Confucius had little to say about the gods, yet he became an object of veneration. The honored position of the founder of Confucianism is highlighted by the Chinese name for that religion: *Ju Chaio*—"the scholar's teachings."

MINOR ORIENTAL RELIGIONS

India and the Orient abound in religions, cults, and sects. Most of them are very simple in theology and practice.

Taoism ("The Way") was founded by Lao-Tzu (or Tze) in the sixth century B.C. It has a following of about fifty million, many of whom are also Buddhists or Confucianists.

Many of Lao-Tzu's teachings have a distinct Judaeo-Christian ring, referring to love, peace, and human ennoblement. Today, however, Taoism bears little resemblance to the teachings of its founder.

Lao-Tzu advocated periods of silence and repaying evil with good. He also spoke of immortality and the supremacy of the spiritual world.

Sikhism was founded by Nanok (born 1469), an Indian Hindu influenced by Islam. *Sikh* means "disciple" or "follower," and Sikhism today has a body of over six million followers.

Sikhism teaches that there is one immortal God and Creator, from whom salvation is obtained through obedience. Idols and asceticism are forbidden. Nanok was the first *Guru* or teacher of a long line, the tenth of which led a conquering army of Sikhs into the Punjab.

Jainism, another offspring of Hinduism, is a reform movement among the Hindus founded by Mahavira. Jainism has little to say about gods, but Mahavira did preach the doctrine of *Kharma* and rebirth. Jainism emphasizes asceticism and teaches an austere self-discipline.

The three basic principles of Jainism are Right Knowledge, Right Faith, and Right Conduct. The 1,500,000 Jainists in the world today follow the teachings of pacifism, nonviolence, and noninjury to living beings. Their concern for all living creatures causes them to be vegetarians. Their sacred scriptures, the *Agamas,* equate "the good life" with monastic isolation.

Shinto (known as " the way of the Kami," or the gods) is the national religion of Japan. There are two wings of Shinto: One is the original natural religion, which emphasizes mythology. The other is the state Shinto taught in the schools as a national system of ethics; it emphasizes religious patriotism.

About fifty-nine million people profess Shinto; the usual broad tolerance typical of most Oriental religions permits Shinto worshippers to participate in other religions.

National defeat after World War II and the Emperor's renunciation of his divine status brought decline for Shinto. However, there has been a growing renewal of interest in the faith.

CHAPTER EIGHTEEN

WESTERN ART

Art is a visual record of general history and, in some cases, as in the ancient cultures of Assyria and Egypt, the only evidence we have of the life of bygone times. From the ritualistic cave paintings of the Paleolithic period to the great cathedrals of the late Renaissance, art is a reflection of the religious beliefs of each culture. The increased wealth and more closely knit political structure of the late Gothic and early Renaissance city-states are directly expressed by the great commissions given to the artists of those times. The daily life of humble people from the Renaissance period was recorded for later ages by the painters of Germany, Holland, and Flanders.

Art often records something more than a reflection of concrete facts. In Classical Greek sculpture there is an idealized beauty of the human form. In Gothic architecture the spiritualism of the time is expressed in lofty stone arches and spires. Purely intellectual ideas are given life in Cubist paintings and Dadist sculptures. Individual human energy is the only real subject matter of Abstract Expressionism. Through art we are given a glimpse into the inner aspirations and ideals of individuals, nations, and civilizations.

Further, art introduces the fascinating study of what man has considered beautiful throughout the ages. Various trends have been introduced, changed, and refined, only to die and reappear hundreds of years later in new and interesting ways. The repetition of a single motif, such as the shell or scroll, can be traced through thousands of years of artistic representation, each time reappearing as a fresh and seemingly new utilization.

Although each age is shaped by many complicated influences, it does leave a distinctive mark on what we call artistic style. The recognized artistic periods are given here in chronological order.

Since the decorative arts, the arts of the Orient, and the arts of primitive cultures are so specialized, each requiring exhaustive treatment, they have not been included. The following is a description of the major artistic styles of the Western world from the beginning of recorded history to the present day.

PREHISTORIC

Paleolithic (before 5000 B.C.) Small sculptures and cave paintings from the Paleolithic period are the oldest works of art known. They were formed with flint tools and sometimes decorated with charcoal and earth pigments. Despite their primitive nature, the simple shapes of these paintings and sculptures convey a feeling for power and movement.

The great cave paintings in southwestern France, such as those at Lascaux, France, and in northern Spain, probably were created in a magic rite to insure a successful hunt.

The sculptures are highly stylized images of humans and animals cut from bone, horn, and stone and were probably used as fertility figures. Examples of Paleolithic sculpture are found in the collections of the Museum of Natural History, Vienna, and the Louvre, Paris.

Neolithic (ca. 8000–3000 B.C.) By this time man had formed settled communities and had begun to build houses, towns, and walls, of stone and wood. Huge monuments of a religious nature like Stonehenge in England are, in mid-twentieth century, just becoming sites of archaeological excavation.

The basic materials of works of art of the Neolithic period are those found in nature, that is, shell, horn, clay, bone, and stone of various kinds. These materials were often worked in simple geometric designs and polished by crude means to decorate implements and weapons of daily use. Examples of these tools can be found in the Natural History Museum, Berlin.

ANCIENT

Sumerian (ca. 3000–1000 B.C.) The Sumerian civilization flourished in the fertile valley between the Tigris and Euphrates rivers. Sumerian art is characterized by heavy masonry temples such as the White Temple at Uruk, Iraq, built on earth and stone platforms into which steps were cut.

The sculpture of the Sumerians was small in size, carved of stone, and modeled for bronze castings. The figures were usually blocky and symmetrical with crude features and clothing, but with large, staring eyes. Animals were more realistically represented, often performing human tasks as part of the mythology of the time. Examples of Sumerian art are in the permanent collections of the Metropolitan Museum of Art, New York, the Louvre, Paris, and the Iraq Museum, Baghdad.

Assyrian (ca. 1000–600 B.C.) The Assyrian Empire extended along the Tigris-Euphrates Valley from the Sinai Peninsula to Armenia. It was known for the great palaces and cities, such as that built at Khorsbad, made of brick and slabs of stone carved in relief. These shallow stone reliefs depicted in detail the conquests of royal armies with inscriptions in cuneiform to further describe the glories of the king. Another favorite subject was the royal lion hunts in which the sinews and muscles of both animals and men were emphasized. The proportions of the figure were heavy, with simple drapery; wavy lines were used to depict hair and beards. The position of the figure, as in the art of Egypt, combined both the frontal and profile views in order to depict the most characteristic features of each. Another development peculiar to Assyria was the massive, free-standing sculptures of winged, man-headed lions. These figures usually stood as guardian figures at the entrances to the palaces. Examples of Assyrian sculpture can be seen at the British Museum, London, and the Metropolitan Museum of Art, New York.

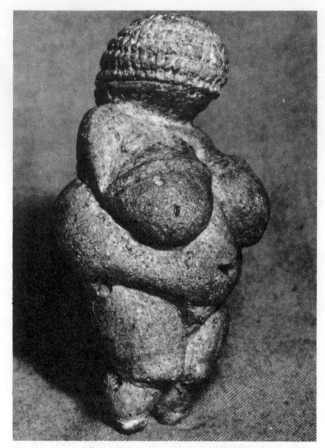

Paleolithic—_Venus of Willendorf_

Egyptian (ca. 3000–500 B.C.) Egyptian art derived its form almost entirely from the political and religious customs of the country. The Pharaoh, or king, ruled absolutely and was divine in the eyes of his people. There was a small aristocratic class, and the rest of society provided a vast source of labor to build the monumental tombs and temples which are characteristic ofhEgyptian art.

The dominant religious belief of the people that shaped their art so completely was their preoccupation with life after death. Very little of their daily life is known, but of their funeral customs we know a great deal. They believed that the spirit of the individual lived on forever after mortal life had ended and that the spirit needed all the objects necessary during life, or reasonable models of them, to carry on a happy existence. Thus the tombs of the ancient Egyptians were more important to them than the actual houses in which they lived. These tombs were lavishly furnished and were built to last forever, often with hidden entrances or massive stonework designed to conceal the actual tomb, as in the pyramids at Gizeh.

Neolithic—Stonehenge, Wiltshire, England

Many artifacts were placed in the tombs, like that of Tutankhamen, such as gold and silver jewelry inlaid with semiprecious stones; jars containing ointments and cosmetics; furniture, chariots; etc. The walls of the tombs were decorated with painted scenes of occupations the deceased particularly enjoyed, plus representations of his household staff which were to provide him with necessary food, drink, and entertainment for the afterlife.

The art of the entire period does not vary a great deal stylistically. The paintings all tell a story, often simplifying the subjects so that they become mere signs or symbols–very much like hieroglyphics, which were the Egyptian form of writing, and which often appeared as part of the actual painting or sculpture. The human figure was painted to show its most characteristic form so that often the frontal and profile views were combined. The profile of the face, arms, and legs were used together with the frontal views of eyes, torso, and shoulders, which produced a rather stiff pose, tempered by the graceful outline of each individual part. Facial features were simplified into several basic lines, but headdresses and garments often included each curl and fold.

The emphasis in Egyptian art was on order, completeness, and decoration rather than on realism and movement. Examples of Egyptian art are to be found in the permanent collections of the museums in Berlin, Cairo, Paris, New York, and Boston.

Cycladic (2600–1100 B.C.) The people who inhabited the Cyclades Islands in the Aegean Sea have left little in the way of art with the exception of a number of marble idols ranging in size from three inches to life-size. These idols were often of the nude figure and were flat, with wedge-shaped bodies and featureless faces except for the ridge of the nose. Despite their simplicity, they have an elegance of line which was sparingly used to indicate roundness of body and subtle transitions from one part of the body to another. Excellent examples of these idols can be seen at the Metropolitan Museum of Art, New York, and the National Museum, Athens.

Minoan (ca. 2000–1500 B.C.) The Minoan civilization flourished on the island of Crete, which was then a rich trading center. Most of what we know of the art of this period we surmise from the ruins of what must have been open, rambling palaces with small intimate areas set off for particular persons. These palaces were primarily located at Knossos and were decorated with wall paintings showing primarily scenes from nature—animals, birds, fish, and vegetation—painted with rhythmic, undulating line and movement that produced a floating or dreamlike quality. The pottery of this period was well formed and also painted with naturalistic, swirling ornament. The largest collection of Minoan art is to be found in the Museum at Candia, Crete.

Sumerian—*Head of Ur-Ningirsu, son of Gudea*

Mycenaean (ca. 1600–1100 B.C.) The Mycenaeans lived on the Greek mainland and built massive hilltop fortresses and walls of huge stone blocks. Very little of these fortresses remains, and we can only imagine the richness of the decoration from the gold and ivory artifacts that have been unearthed from the rather modest tombs. The objects found in these tombs were most often pieces of personal equipment—jewelry, drinking vessels, and weapons. They are characterized by the bold expression of animal and human activities and by excellent workmanship. Examples of Mycenaean art are in the permanent collection of the National Museum, Athens.

Greek (ca. 1100–100 B.C.) The Greek civilization was comprised of many small city-states located on the Greek mainland and nearby islands. Greek painting, architecture, and sculpture fall into four distinct stylistic periods: the Geometric (ca. 1100–700 B.C.), the Archaic (ca. 700–500 B.C.), the Classical (ca. 500–350 B.C.), and the Hellenistic (ca. 350–100 B.C.).

The major art forms of the Geometric period were large, highly patterned stone vases that served as grave monuments. These vases were decorated with bands of commemorative scenes in which the human figure was represented with a circle for a head, a triangle for a body, and lines for arms and legs. The intervening spaces were filled with abstract shapes, usually geometric in nature.

The Archaic period introduces a softening of lines and shapes used in painting and sculpture, but the linear concept still remains. The painting to be found on pottery is all that remains of this art form in ancient Greece. Painted murals and panels undoubtedly existed but there is very little trace of them left today. We know that painting was a great art of the time, however, because many of the vases of this period were signed not only by the potters who made them but by the painters who decorated them. Essentially the vase paintings of the Archaic period were outline drawings filled in with solid, flat colors. They usually represented one or two figures of the gods performing a deed connected with his legend.

Archaic stone and marble sculptures were usually limited to the representation of the human form, clothed or nude. Free-standing figures were often life-size, stiffly posed, and oversimplified with wiglike treatment of the hair. Parts of the body were compartmentalized and treated as separate units. Drapery of fabric was achieved by incised parallel lines and facial expressions were

Cycladic—*Seated Man With Harp*

Egyptian—*Nefret-iry Playing Draughts* (copy)
From the Tomb of Nefret-iry

Assyrian—*Winged Bull,* From the Palace of Ashur-nasir-apal II
At Kalhu, modern Nimrod

Mycenaean—Lion Gate to the Acropolis of Mycenae

quite blank except for an often-recurrent, slight smile.

Architecture of the Archaic period set the style for later Greek temples and palaces. The rectangular building based on the post-and-lintel system, surrounded by a columned portico, topped by a gently sloping gable roof with triangular pediments at the short ends, appeared around 650 B.C. and was developed and redeveloped in later periods. As in all Greek architecture, the outside of the building was the most important and the interior enclosure was small and often quite dark. Sculpture in high relief was used to decorate the pediments and friezes, and elaborate systems or "orders" for the parts of the building and its decoration were devised. The three "orders" devised by the Greeks were the Doric, the Ionic, and the Corinthian. The most outstanding example of the Doric temple is the Parthenon, built in Athens during the Classical period. The Parthenon stands today and has been widely used as a model for public buildings from the Renaissance down to the twentieth century.

The Classical period of Greek art is marked by the reign of Pericles in Athens; it is often called the Golden Age of Greek art. Sculpture of this period is marked by two great innovations, namely, the easy, naturalistic pose and the glorification of the human body. Heretofore, all representations of the human figure were placed or posed by the artist in order to convey an idea to the viewer. Classical Greek sculpture seems to take its stance from natural movement—*Nike Loosening Her Sandal,* the *Discus Thrower,* or the reclining *Three Fates* from the Parthenon pediment. Further, emphasis on the human body, not the anatomically correct proportions but rather the beauty and grace of the ideal form, dominates the sculpture of this period. Drapery is indicated by realistic folds, but is never allowed to interfere with the indication of shape or movement of the human body beneath.

Hellenistic sculpture is likewise concerned with the glory of the human body, but it takes on a more frenzied pose. Figures act out more emotional scenes and are aided by swirling drapery and arrested movement, as in the *Nike of Samothrace.* The impact of the *Laocoön* group is heightened not only by the tortured poses of the three figures involved, but by the sinuous, twisting snakes that encompass the whole composition.

Examples of Greek art can be found in most of the great museums of the world, but primarily

Greek (Classical)—*The Nike of Samothrace* (copy)
Original in the Louvre, Paris

can be found in all of these countries today. The Romans built great temples, palaces, baths, triumphal arches, and columns, as well as more practical things such as bridges, roads, sewers, and aqueducts. These buildings used the post-and-lintel system but incorporated the arch, barrel, and groined vault ceilings as well as the dome. Some buildings, such as the Colosseum and Pantheon in Rome and the Pont-du-Gard aqueduct in Nîmes, France, remain as examples of the high engineering skill of the Romans.

Stylistically the Romans borrowed heavily from the Greeks, often combining the Doric, Ionic, and Corinthian orders in the same building. Roman architecture, however, is heavier, more richly decorative, and more complex than the Greek. The Romans were the first to develop the idea of grandiose interior space as well as impressive exterior façades. They also developed a domestic architecture that was comfortable and gracious. Their houses usually were built around a central courtyard onto which most of the rooms opened, in order to enjoy the breeze and pleasant view. These homes were lavishly decorated with frescoes and stucco decoration depicting mythology and landscapes.

Roman sculpture relied a great deal on Greek

Minoan—*Vase With Three Handles*
Said to be from Knossos, Crete

those in London, Paris, Athens, Berlin, Munich, and Rome.

Etruscan (ca. 700–500 B.C.) The Etruscan people occupied the area in Italy between Rome and Florence and are known primarily for their tombs, which were buried underground and often took on the shape of actual houses. Life-size clay effigy figures often decorated the tops of the coffins. These figures were elastic and gently rounded in form and often portrayed with vivacious gestures. Wall paintings of hunting, dancing, and banqueting scenes were rhythmic and lively. The Etruscans also produced quantities of bronze works—engraved mirrors and small, elongated statuettes of excellent craftsmanship.

Etruscan wall paintings can still be seen *in situ* in Tarquinia, Italy; sculptures and bronzes are to be found in the museums in Rome, Berlin, and Vienna.

Roman (ca. 500 B.C.–A.D. 325) The Roman Empire extended throughout Italy, Greece, North Africa, the Near East, Spain, and north into France and England. Examples of Roman architecture

forms and ideas, but with greater emphasis on realism. Military, literary, and political persons were often honored by having likenesses of themselves put on public display, and for the first time facial features were allowed to reveal lines of character and personality. Historical events were also recorded as narrative reliefs on altars, arches, and triumphal columns. Specific events enacted by specific people were recorded, and realistic spatial relationships and proportions were carefully thought out.

The excavations at Pompeii and Herculaneum, which were buried by the eruption of Mount Vesuvius in A.D. 79, have revealed most of what we know of Roman painting. The paintings uncovered there were primarily wall decorations in the homes of well-to-do people. The painters of these wall decorations were interested in spatial illusion and often painted in false window frames, niches, and cupboards, as well as mythological scenes, charming landscapes, or vast architectural vistas. Perspective was still not a carefully thought-out

Etruscan
Mirror with engraved design of
the Dioscuri and two women

rule but even so the Roman painter knew enough to use the elements of perspective to create realistic effects. The colors of these frescoes are amazingly vivid today and contain a surprising variety and subtle combination of shades.

Examples of Roman painting are to be found *in situ* at Pompeii and Herculaneum, the National Museum, Naples, and the Metropolitan Museum of Art, New York. Outstanding collections of Roman sculpture are those of the Vatican and Capitoline museums in Rome.

EARLY CHRISTIAN

Early Christian (ca. A.D. 200–800) Even before the fall of the Roman Empire the Christian religion had grown to such an extent that churches were needed in which to worship. The earliest of these were based on the Roman basilica form which had a long nave lit by high windows, two side aisles, and a wooden roof, such as San Apollinare in Classe in Ravenna. This form provided a large interior in which to assemble, and demanded decorative paintings and mosaics to cover the walls in order to create a proper atmosphere in which to worship. In fact the interior decoration of the churches became increasingly the focus of Early Christian art and their exteriors grew to be quite plain and unadorned. Glass mosaic imbedded in the wall plaster, because of its more brilliant color, gradually overtook painting as the prime means of decorating the interior walls.

Greek (Archaic)—Statue of a Votary or Priest

Roman—Wall Painting, Found at Boscoreale

The illusionistic devices of Roman wall paintings gradually gave way to a more symbolic depiction of scenes from the Old and New Testaments. The exact narrative was not as important as the gestures that conveyed a general idea. Thus, much of Early Christian art became involved in signs and symbols meant to express an idea about Christ and the saints and prophets rather than any realistic representation of their acts.

NEAR EASTERN

Fayum (ca. A.D. 200–400) The Fayum is a district in lower Egypt known for the very realistic burned-in portraits on wooden panels placed over the coffins of the deceased. The immediacy and lifelike quality of these portraits have rarely been surpassed in the entire history of art. Several well-known examples of Fayum paintings can be seen in the Metropolitan Museum of Art, New York.

Byzantine (ca. A.D. 500–1450) Byzantine art originated in Constantinople with the building of domed, octagonal Christian churches. Oddly enough, the Byzantine churches of the Near East have been long since destroyed or changed (Hagia

Sophia in Constantinople), whereas those built after their types in the West still remain, such as San Vitale in Ravenna and St. Mark's in Venice. The octagonal church permits windows at many levels and so the interiors are filled with light. This adds greatly to the effect of the glittering mosaics used to cover the interior walls. The figures in these mosaics are tall and slender with large, dark eyes and long noses.

Later developments of the Byzantine style occur in Russia and Greece in elaborate church architecture and icon painting of impressive and severe simplicity. Examples of Russian icon painting can be found in the Art Institute, Chicago, and the National Gallery, Washington, D.C.

Islamic (ca. 700–1700 B.C.) The rise of Islamic art coincides with the spread of Mohammedanism throughout the Near East, North Africa, Spain, and east into India. The Moslem conquerors built large, many-aisled mosques supported by arched colonnades topped by colored tiles, lacy stucco dec-

Fayum—Portrait, Panel from a mummy

oration, and light, airy domes. The effect of the interior space is thus one of airy, limitless, honeycombed areas. The Alhambra in Spain is a good example of this type of architecture. Islamic decoration was primarily floral or geometric in nature with many Arabic inscriptions worked into the all-over patterns.

Islamic art is also known for quantities of richly worked textiles, metal and leatherwork, and illuminated manuscripts. These artifacts are heavily patterned with animal, floral, geometric, and handwriting motifs of great intricacy. The British Museum, London, the Freer Gallery of Art, Washington, D.C., and the Metropolitan Museum of Art, New York, have good collections of Islamic art.

MEDIEVAL

Romanesque (ca. A.D. 1050–1200) Western Europe had become predominantly Christian by this time and the unity of religious feeling had started the Crusades. The consequent opening of trade routes resulted in new industries and the growth of cities throughout the area. The churches built during this period are characterized by the Latin-cross plan with a long nave (main sanctuary), two side aisles, transept (side galleries), and ambulatory around the altar at the east end. They were built of heavy masonry and used the vaulted ceilings. The interiors were long, tall, dim, and ponderously architectural with heavy piers and exposed ribs of vaulting. The exteriors were more

Byzantine—Detail of a panel showing Empress Theodora (copy). Original in mosaic, San Vitale, Ravenna, Italy

richly architectural with applied semi-circular arches and columns and stone relief sculptures set into niches and portals.

The figures in Romanesque sculpture are thin-limbed, with linear drapery and eloquent gestures; they often express a nightmarish quality with grotesque and monsterish forms. Animal and human figures and Christian symbols were widely used to tell Old and New Testament stories in a powerful and mystical manner.

Examples of Romanesque architecture and sculpture can be found in the churches of San Ambrogio in Milan and the cathedrals of Autun, Moissac, and Vézelay in France.

Gothic (ca. A.D. 1150–1450) Gothic architecture originated in France and spread throughout western Europe. The intellectual spirit that dominated the society and politics of the times sought artistic expression in the great cathedrals erected during this period. Church interiors became more lofty, and walls and columned piers became lighter in weight because most of the masonry supporting the building was moved to the exterior in the form of elaborate buttressing. The shell-like walls permit more windows, which were elaborately filled with stained glass and lacy stonework. The pointed arches extend upward into elaborate fan

Early Christian—Mosaic: Separation of Sheep and Goats (copy). Original in San Apollinare Nuovo, Ravenna, Italy

and groin vault ceilings that seem to float high above the floor. Exteriors are vertical in emphasis, with towers and turrets extending well above the roof line. Rich sculptural decoration covers much of the exterior face of these buildings, especially around the pointed arch portals.

Gothic sculpture, although still attached to the building, became more and more sculpture-in-the-round. Figures are elongated and become increasingly graceful with ornate drapery. Faces take on national characteristics and while the whole figure is firmly anchored to its base, the poses become more naturalistic. Architectural Gothic sculpture was designed primarily as ornament for the carefully organized façades of Gothic cathedrals but stands well as an art form of its own. So vast were the areas to be covered that several generations of sculptors were needed to complete the decoration of a single cathedral. Differences of style can be noted from one part of the building to another; late in the period certain sculptors, such as Nicola Pisano and Lorenzo Ghiberti, were known to have executed doors, pulpits, tombs, and statues.

Islamic—Incense Burner

Renaissance—van Eyck, Ghent Altarpiece, center panel

Romanesque—Capital from the Abbey of St. Michael and St. Germain, Cuxa

Outstanding examples of the Gothic Cathedral are to be found in Chartres Cathedral and Notre Dame (Paris), Salisbury Cathedral in England, and the Milan and Florence cathedrals.

Late in the Gothic period in Italy, about A.D. 1300, painting began to overtake stained glass and manuscript illumination as the major pictorial art. Monumental altar panels and wall frescoes were used to decorate church interiors. These paintings borrowed heavily from late Roman landscape painting and from Byzantine and Early Christian icons by using architectural framing elements and rigid, frozen poses. Gradually the symbolism of the earlier periods gave way to a softening of drapery, a definition of spatial relationships, a rounding of forms, and strong grouping of figures which produced lifelike tableaux of great power and simplicity.

Outstanding painters of the late Gothic period are Cimabue, Duccio, and Giotto.

Realism—Daumier, *The Third-Class Carriage*

Gothic—Tomb of Armengol VII, Count of Urgel

Mannerism—El Greco, *The Adoration of the Shepherds*

RENAISSANCE

Renaissance (ca. 1350–1525) The Renaissance period began in Italy and spread gradually northward to France, Flanders, Germany, England, and all of western Europe. It began as an intellectual and cultural reawakening of interest in the arts of antiquity and grew to become a pursuit of general learning, humanism, and individualism.

Renaissance painters made great use of the new technique of oil painting first used about 1400 in Flanders, as well as the older techniques of fresco and egg tempera. The individual artist began to work out techniques and a style of his own, and wealthy persons as well as the Church began to commission works of art to beautify public buildings and homes. The great artistic achievements of the Renaissance period in painting included a scientific working out of the rules of perspective, a new interest in the development of light and shadow, an increased skill and interest in depicting reality, spontaneous action, and dramatic movement. Subject matter expanded to include not only religious figures, who were often depicted in contemporary dress, but also scenes from classical mythology, contemporary history, portraits, scenes of everyday living, still life, and landscape. Outstanding Italian painters of this period include Botticelli, Leonardo, Mantegna, Masaccio, Piero della Francesca, Raphael, and Titian.

Painting of the Renaissance period in Holland, Flanders, Germany, and France differs from the painting in Italy in that the northern artists placed more emphasis on piety and realism. Medieval religious symbolism was often combined with realistic, contemporary, everyday settings, perhaps in an effort to relate spiritual and secular life. Extremely realistic portraits containing great detail was another achievement of the Renaissance in the north. Outstanding artists of the Renaissance movement in the north are Bruegel, van Eyck, Dürer, Grünewald, and Holbein.

Architecture of the Renaissance period was directly influenced by the rise of the strong city-state which dominated the political life of western Europe throughout the period. Civic enthusiasm in combination with the increased wealth gave rise to commissions for houses and public buildings as well as churches.

Renaissance architecture is known for its symmetry and order as well as the universal use and reworking of Greek and Roman architectural elements—the rounded arch, fluted columns (now often flattened against walls as pilasters), pediments, entablatures, moldings, cornices, and domes. Renaissance buildings were often set off by spacious piazzas such as St. Peter's in Rome or by long approach vistas found in the great manor houses of England and the country châteaux of France. Façades are imposing, regular, always symmetrical; plans were often based on mathematical formulas to the detriment of the function of the building. The amazing variety of creative solutions in Renaissance architecture, especially between different geographic areas, is a comment on the new reliance on individual architects instead of blind acceptance of a prevailing style. Michelangelo, Brunelleschi, and Alberti were outstanding architects of the Renaissance period.

Renaissance sculpture also marked a return to classic forms and, further, a more positive interest in realism. Sculpture was used on church facades and interiors but was freed from being simply a religious decoration and became a full-fledged art form in itself. The nude figure returned as a subject for free-standing statues. Major sculptural works of the Renaissance appeared as portrait busts, equestrian and fountain sculpture, and tombs. Large marble carvings and small bronze works were created to beautify homes and public buildings.

The renewed interest in the human figure was not a mere copying of Greek and Roman statues. Emotion and power in combination with personal immediacy call forth a far different response from the viewer of Renaissance sculpture as opposed to the impersonal, idealized beauty of classic art. The pent-up energy, large size, and graceful, natural stance of Michelangelo's *David* is a good example of Renaissance sculpture. Other outstanding sculptors of the Renaissance period were Donatello, Verrocchio, and Luca della Robbia.

Mannerism (ca. 1525–1600) Mannerism is a term applied to Late Renaissance art in which the artist seemed to create works of art "in the manner of" the last half of the Renaissance period. Painting became exaggerated, more elegant and elongated in line, more frenzied in movement, with light flickering over colorful forms. Dramatic ecstasy of religious or mythological legend was often a subject portrayed by artists of this period.

Sculpture also took on more elegant lines, and forms were often smoothed, rounded, and elongated to produce richly decorative sculptures and architectural ornament. Cellini, El Greco, and Tintoretto were outstanding artists of this period.

Art Nouveau—Beardsley, *The Toilet of Salome*

Rococo—Fragonard, *The Meeting*
Copyright, The Frick Collection

Romanticism—Delacroix, *The Abduction of Rebecca*

Post-Impressionism—van Gogh, *Cypresses*

Baroque (ca. 1600–1750) Baroque art became highly decorative, ornate, and flamboyant on the one hand and extremely natural and worldly on the other. These tendencies were produced in part by the rise of the absolute monarchy and the reaffirmation of spiritual enthusiasm of the Counter Reformation. Commissions for new and splendid churches abounded. While the classical feeling was dominant, dramatic new forms and combinations became evident. Typical elements were towering domes, twisted columns, broken pediments, curved façades, and a fondness for concave and convex forms. There were grandiose combinations of architectural, sculptural, and painted decorations of a rhythmic and asymmetrical nature. San Carlo alle Quattro Fontane in Rome and the Monastery of Melk in Austria are excellent examples of Baroque architecture.

Baroque sculpture and painting showed the same fondness for the grandiose scale, asymmetrical composition, swirling movement, and drapery. There was a tendency to represent biblical and everyday scenes of great simplicity, set in contemporary surroundings. Still life and everyday life painting came into their own as subjects for seri-

ous work. The concept known as "painterly" became evident through the use of visible brushwork, spontaneous composition on the canvas, and use of light and color almost as subjects rather than tools of painting.

Outstanding artists of the Baroque period were Bernini, Caravaggio, Chardin, van Dyck, Hals, Rembrandt, Rubens, Vermeer, and Velázquez.

Classicism (ca. 1630–1685) Classicism was a tendency, primarily in France, that showed an admiration for the form and spirit of antiquity and the Italian Renaissance, furthered by French thought in philosophy and humanism. Mythological and classical legends were dominant subjects for painting, which was executed with great clarity, balance, and restraint. Architecture, such as the Palace of Versailles, also exhibited great clarity, order, and formality. The best-known painters of this period were Lorraine and Poussin.

Rococo (ca. 1725–1775) Rococo is a more playful and lighter version of the Baroque style occurring primarily in France. Architecture and painting become more intimate in scale. Subjects for painting and sculpture include fetes, lovers, cupids, and other mythical characters, rendered in

Fauve—Matisse, *The Blue Window*

a poetic and lyrical manner. Interior decoration in the Rococo style becomes the major concern of the architects of the time who catered to individual fancy and made great use of rich materials, swags, arabesques, painted medallions, and shell motifs. Outstanding artists of the Rococo period are Boucher, Fragonard, and Watteau.

EIGHTEENTH CENTURY

Neoclassicism (ca. 1775–1850) Neoclassicism was a revival of authentic Greek and Roman architectural motifs, freely applied. This revival took place primarily in France, England, and the United States. Archeological excavations provided specific material for the construction of Neoclassic buildings. An attempt was made to copy the form of the classical buildings for decorative effect without regard to function.

Neoclassic painting and sculpture also made an attempt to revive the classical spirit in depicting Greek history, contemporary events, and portraits. Clarity, order, and precision of details—as well as observant but detached unemotionalism regarding the subject matter—separate Neoclassic painting from Romantic painting of classical subjects of this same time.

Outstanding artists of the Neoclassical period were Adam, David, and Ingres.

Classicism—Poussin, *The Rape of the Sabine Women*

NINETEENTH CENTURY

Romanticism (ca. 1750–1850) Romanticism began in England with a newly developed interest in the past and spread throughout Europe and the United States. Due to increased literacy, publications, and the political revolutionary activity of the times, the people of the late eighteenth and early nineteenth centuries desired to turn against what was current and to return to nature, the past, or the sublime. Thus began a search for the picturesque in architecture with revivals of the Greek, Roman, Egyptian, and Gothic styles.

Romantic painting did not borrow so heavily from past styles but used the literature of the past and present as a source of inspiration. Subjects for Romantic painting are highly emotional, mystical, and sometimes imaginary. It was during this period that landscape painters first began to paint out-of-doors, often concentrating, however, on nature's more dramatic moods. Outstanding artists of the Romantic period are Constable, Corot, Delacroix, Gericault, and Turner.

Realism (ca. 1800–1860) The Realist movement is not an attempt to depict lifelike detail; it is an attempt to portray—with paint, brushes, and canvas—the reality of life that goes on about us. The subject can be a manual laborer, or the artist and model in his studio. Most often the subject is depicted in a matter-of-fact way with visible brush strokes and flat areas of color. Realism had its strongest influence in France and the United States. Artists of the Realist period include Courbet, Daumier, Eakins, Homer, and Millet.

Impressionism—Degas, *The Rehearsal*
Copyright, The Frick Collection

Leading painters of the Impressionist period were Degas, Manet, Monet, Pissarro, and Renoir.

Post-Impressionism (ca. 1880–1900) Post-Impressionism is a continuation of the Impressionist ideas of using broken areas of color to produce the effect of light, but the Post-Impressionists as a general rule laid more emphasis on form. Each of the artists of this period produced an individual interpretation of what painting should be and each in his own way helped to set the stage for the various developments of the twentieth century. Outstanding Post-Impressionist artists are Cezanne, Gauguin, Seurat, Toulouse-Lautrec, and van Gogh.

Art Nouveau (ca. 1895–1900) Examples of Art Nouveau appeared simultaneously in painting, sculpture, architecture, and the decorative arts of Europe and the United States during this brief period. The dominating factor of this style is tenu-

Expressionism—Kirchner, *The Street* (1913)

Cubism—Picasso, *Ma Jolie* (Woman with a Zither or Guitar)

Impressionism (ca. 1860–1880) The Impressionist painters believed that the most real part of a painting was its painted surface. In France, England, and the United States, the movement grew out of the school of Realism with its impasto (thickly applied paint) and brushwork. The Impressionists painted out-of-doors and from café and bedroom life, but the subject matter was not most important. Their main concentration was on the small patches of color that actually made up the painting and on how light and shadow affect color and the reflection of light. In effect, they put on canvas what appeared in a fleeting moment of vision, thereby preserving their impression of it.

The composition of the Impressionist paintings also helped to create the idea of a momentary pose by viewing the human subject from an oblique angle or in the midst of a routine activity. The composition of Japanese prints, widely circulated in France at this time, and the development of the new art of photography influenced the compositions of Impressionist painters.

ous, sensual, twisting line, particularly adaptive to depiction of nature forms—trees, vines, foliage, flowers—used primarily as a decorative element. Aubrey Beardsley was a representative artist of this movement.

TWENTIETH CENTURY

Fauvism (ca. 1905–1914) *Fauve,* a term meaning "wild beast," was applied with derision to a group of French painters of the first decade of the twentieth century. These painters began to use color as an independent structural element. Colors were not in relation to their natural elements; that is, pink trees, green houses, etc., were used to intensify expression and give movement to the painting as a whole. Matisse was the foremost painter of the Fauve period.

Expressionism (ca. 1905–1940) Expressionism began with the attempt by a group of German painters to distort form, color, and space in order to produce a heightened expression of emotional reality. Common subject matter was war, insanity,

Futurism—Boccioni, *Unique Forms of Continuity in Space*

and deformity. The distortion of everyday subjects as well gave Expressionist paintings a disquieting, violent, and grotesque aspect. Outstanding artists of the period are Beckmann, Kirchner, and Nolde.

Cubism (ca. 1907–1920) Cubistic painting began in France with the breaking up of forms, such as the human body, into angular shapes. These shapes were combined in such a way that the background became intermixed with the foreground, and spatial relationships disappeared entirely. Concave and convex forms were widely used, but it became difficult to distinguish which parts of the paintings were meant to recede and which were meant to advance. This has been described as the analytical phase of Cubism—the breaking down of volume, forms, and space to produce an almost purely abstract painting.

A later phase of Cubism, called the synthetic or building phase, began around 1912. Bits and pieces of real objects, such as paper, lettering, and cloth, were combined with painting in a technique called "collage." This type of painting used the overlapping of actual forms to create real space—not the modeled or linear perspective space used since the Renaissance. This new concept of nonperspective space set the stage for the truly abstract painting of the later twentieth century. Three major artists of Cubism were Braque, Gris, and Picasso.

Dada—Duchamp, *The Bride* (1912)

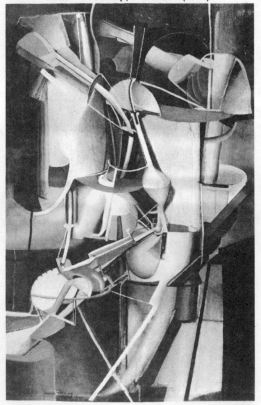

Futurism (ca. 1910–1915) The Futurist artists were a small group of Italian painters and sculptors who took the fractured forms of Cubism and used them to depict dynamic motion. Subjects were chosen from anything that moved, such as a speeding train or a running figure, and were then broken down into angular planes which were repeated over and over to indicate violent movement. The Futurist paintings and sculptures were intended as comments on the fast-moving pace of modern, mechanized society. Two artists of the period are Boccioni and Severini.

Dadism (ca. 1916–1920) Dada art became the visible reaction of a small group of artists against the horrible realities of World War I. Nonsense, the laws of chance, the irrational, and the meaninglessness of life became the inspiration for their art. Dadism ranges from highly imaginative paintings to "ready-made" objects, such as pieces of plumbing mounted as sculpture. Duchamp and Ernst were leaders in the Dada movement.

Surrealism (ca. 1916–1940) The realm of the imagination became the subject matter of Surrealist painters. Some artists painted their interpretation of the subconscious or dream world, while others drew upon fanciful legend or fantasy for inspiration. Natural and imaginary forms were often combined in unreal settings to produce creative but provocative and unsettling pictures. Outstanding Surrealist artists are Dali, Chagall, Chirico, Klee, and Miró.

Abstract Expressionism (ca. 1945–1960) Abstract Expressionism began in the United States shortly after World War II, and is often referred to as Action Painting. The artists involved in this movement exert their energy on painting in a visible way—by dribbling, smearing, and otherwise manipulating paint to produce a completely abstract canvas with an exceedingly active surface. Paint applied with controlled exhilaration by the artist is the subject matter of Abstract Expressionist art. Pollock and DeKooning were leaders of the movement.

Recent Trends (1960–present) Changes in art have been taking place at such lightning speeds during this period that it is virtually impossible to point to one major trend. The period has seen Pop art (in which objects from our commercial culture are glorified and exaggerated), Op art (in which the artist creates mind-warping optical illusions), Kinetic art (in which objects move or alter shape, often at the command of the observer), Environmental art (in which the viewer may find himself a part of the work), and even the so-called "Impossible" art. In other developments, artists have put themselves or live models into their works; they have created art meant to be temporary, often destroyed at the end of one showing; and they have designed art that bombards the observer with sound, lights, and smell. While some artists in the early 1970s have shown a distaste for such trends and returned to a form of realism, there is apparently no end to such innovative approaches.

Surrealism—Dali, *The Persistence of Memory*

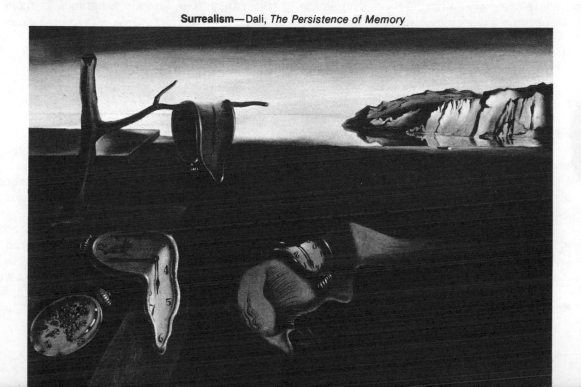

CHAPTER NINETEEN

SPORTS

ARCHERY

When you leaf through the pages of a telephone directory, you can see plenty of evidence of the bow and arrow's effect on our civilization; archery figured so prominently in history that many family names are based on archery terms. You'll see names like Archer, Arrowsmith, Bowman, Bowyer, Boyer, Fletcher, Yeoman, and others which originated as a result of archery. The bow and arrow, instead of being discarded as historical relics, are being put to practical use in the modern world—in industry, science, and, once again, in the field of warfare.

Perhaps the best thing about archery is that it can be fun for everybody—all ages, all sizes, all income groups, and in all places. In addition to the bowmen who take part in organized shooting programs, there are thousands of archers who like to plink informally at backyard targets; and there are thousands more who get a bang out of hunting with the bow and arrow for both big and small game. There's hardly a good-sized community in the country without at least one archery club, where you'll find men and women, boys and girls, shooting regularly at different kinds of targets.

Members of most archery clubs shoot throughout the year, many of them entering tournaments held in different parts of their state every weekend. Tournament shooting reaches its peak during the summer months, when state and national championships take place.

The field-archery course is usually laid out in a wooded tract, and sometimes you'll see animal targets instead of bull's-eyes.

That's how the sport of field archery was started. A group of bowhunters wanted a type of practice that would help to keep them in condition and sharpen their shooting eyes between hunting seasons. The idea spread, clubs were organized, and now there is a National Field Archery Association, with many thousands of members in hundreds of affiliated clubs. The clubs hold tournaments regularly, in which the archers shoot in various classes, arranged so that shooters of the same degree of skill will compete against one another. States hold shoots to determine their star bowmen, and the top field archers in the country prove themselves at the annual national field-archery tournament.

Target archery is the other important branch of organized archery, vastly different and much older than field archery. While shooting on a field course is something like hunting, the grounds of a target-archery club are in some ways similar to a rifle range. The shooting distance is fixed; the ground is level; the target is always the same size. The emphasis is on controlled, precision shooting, which requires a great amount of disciplined practice and skill.

AUTO RACING

The natural attachment between modern man and his car can easily be seen by the tremendous sums of money poured into racing car events by manufacturers, parts suppliers, tire makers, and other allied companies.

Actually, auto racing preceded Henry Ford and the mass-production concepts he pioneered. The first auto race of major importance was held in 1894, from Paris to Rouen, France, and was won by a steam car which achieved a speed of approximately eleven miles per hour. A year later a round-trip race from Paris to Bordeaux produced the breathless speed of 15.01 miles per hour. American enthusiasts who witnessed the event returned to the United States extolling the virtues of auto racing. Within the next five years a number of exhibitions were held in America, although there was little, if any, supervision involved in the running of the events.

In 1901, Henry Ford entered a 10-mile race at Grosse Point, Michigan, and won with an average speed of 44.8 miles per hour. The prize money and publicity that followed enabled Ford to start his own company, which soon became one of America's automotive giants. Oddly, Ford never again raced in competition after the Grosse Point event.

By 1908, auto makers in America were beginning to match the Europeans in styling and technology. Newspapers of that era carried almost daily reports of daredevils who risked their lives in high-powered racing machines. But American innovators felt that the answer to open highway racing, where the failure to make a turn sometimes meant an abrupt collision with a tree or brick wall, lay in auto speedways on closed, banked tracks.

It was around this time that American specialists pooled their ideas and resources to build the Indianapolis Motor Speedway, a 2.5-mile oval course. And in 1908, the racing car was still far ahead of cars being mass-produced for Americans.

From 1913 to 1923, Europeans dominated the track against American challengers like Barney Oldfield and World War I fighter pilot Eddie Rickenbacker. Early cars included the Marmon, Buick, Fiat, Mercer, Stutz, Simplex, National, and the Mercedes. During the Roaring Twenties, regulations for cars were altered to exclude these *Beasts of Indy* from the nation's highways.

A major revolution occurred in 1961 when Grand Prix driver Jack Brabham showed up with a flimsy-looking light Cooper-Climax racing car equipped with an engine mounted in the rear. While he did not win the Indy that year, Brabham prophesied that before long all other cars with front engines would be "a million dollars worth of obsolete machinery." By 1964, almost all road racing cars were rear-engined.

Meanwhile, road racing was sweeping America on such tracks as Watkins Glen and Riverside. With it, big money from auto manufacturers flooded the sport, and purses for the Indianapolis 500 and nine other big-car races in 1972 totaled nearly $2.5 million.

Great drivers like Mario Andretti, A. J. Foyt, Joe Leonard, Al Unser, and Jackie Stewart have earned phenomenal incomes during their careers. Stewart collected his third world drivers' championship in 1973, then announced his retirement. However, before doing so, he had racked up an all-time record of 27 major auto-race victories.

The United States Auto Club (USAC) rules all big-car races in America, while the National Association for Stock Car Auto Racing (NASCAR) regulates most stock car events. NASCAR's influence extends to Canada and into Germany, where stock car racing interest is increasing rapidly. Richard Petty is the most successful of all stock car drivers, having topped a million dollars in earnings.

Along with the USAC and NASCAR organizations, the Sports Car Club of America (SCCA) plays its part in governing amateur and professional racing as well as supervising hundreds of rallies and driver schools in the United States.

BADMINTON

Badminton was developed from a game called "poona," which was originated in India, then adapted and brought home by English Army officers. It is not an offshoot of tennis or other court games, as is generally surmised.

The Anglicized version was launched in 1873 at a party thrown by the Duke of Beaufort at his country manor, called Badminton, in Gloucestershire. The mansion's name stuck and became official. The English considered the Indian rules confusing and contradictory. It was the Bath Badminton Club that laid out standardized rules. In 1895, the Badminton Association of England was formed to take over the Bath Club, and the modified rules that were laid down continue to more or less govern the sport today. The first All-England Championships were held for men in 1899, with a pioneer all-women tournament scheduled a year later.

Badminton quickly spread to the United States and Canada. All organized competition is played indoors. California has produced some of the most brilliant players.

Badminton is played with rackets that resemble smaller versions of a tennis racket, and a shuttlecock, or "birdie," made of cork and feathers, which is struck back and forth over a net by the opponents.

BASEBALL

Although ball playing of some sort has existed down through the ages it had little to do with baseball, our national game. The exceptions are the games of rounders and cricket, which the early settlers brought with them from England. Our early-Americans played with a ball and bat on public greens with equipment and ideas from the English games. Changes came soon and by the early 1800s, rounds became innings, bowlers became pitchers, and strikes or wickets became bases. The Americans definitely liked more action, and the stakes had to be fastened down as the players soon learned to lunge for them with desperate slides. The bat was soon changed so that it was round rather than oblong. This was desirable because it could be "whipped" with much greater force.

Town teams developed and various contests were played with neighboring groups. Local ground rules determining base distances, pitcher's stance, positions, number of players, and length of games were established by the captains. The base distance was generally determined by the site of the playing area; and "plugging," hitting a runner with the ball while between bases, was a popular play.

Abner Doubleday, an Army general, is credited with laying out the first real diamond in Cooperstown, New York in 1839. A baseball museum is now located there and the Hall of Fame players are honored there each year.

By 1846, metropolitan New York teams were playing under organized rules at the Elysian Fields in Hoboken, New Jersey. New teams were mushrooming throughout the East and Midwest. In 1859, the game reached the college level when Amherst met Williams.

The Civil War interrupted the growth of baseball for a time but the Union soldiers took the game with them and the Southerners picked it up as they saw prisoners playing it. After the Civil War the game spread everywhere.

In 1869, the Cincinnati Red Stockings became the first professional baseball team; they were sensational and very well received wherever they played. They were undefeated in 1869 with 55 victories and one tie game.

In 1876, the National League was formed with notable help from the immortal A. G. Spalding.

The American League became strong enough in 1903 to challenge the National League for

Lou Gehrig, the "Iron Man", holds the major league record for consecutive games played with 2,130.

supremacy in professional baseball and the first "World Series" was played. This annual event has become a national institution.

Baseball has retained its popularity because it has speed, action, skill, daring, suspense, drama, and is easily understood by the average person. Fans are able to learn the rules of the game quickly and they retain their knowledge as there has been no major rule change in sixty years. It is a game of standards and records so comparisons can be readily made. The rules are the same for professionals, for schools, and for independent play.

Perhaps the most important standard in the game has been the ball itself. The ball weighs from five to five and a quarter ounces, and the circumference is nine to nine and a quarter inches—the standard weight and size since 1872. There are exactly one hundred and eight hand stitches carrying eighty-eight inches of waxed twine. However, the ball is decidedly livelier as scientific tests have shown.

There is more "rabbit," or liveliness, in the ball. This developed when the manufacturer wrapped the ball twine tighter to give extra home-run resilience.

BASKETBALL

In 1891, Dr. James A. Naismith of Springfield College, Springfield, Massachusetts, devised a game to occupy the students in physical education classes during the winter months. He nailed a peach basket to the side of the balcony at each end of the gymnasium into which a ball was to be tossed. A janitor sat on a ladder to retrieve the ball from the basket after a player had made a goal. From this primitive beginning came the game now played by thousands of people throughout the world. In the United States, basketball attracts more spectators than any other sport. Moreover, more athletes participate in the game of basketball than in any other sport. Basket rings attached to a garage, tree, or clothespole are not an uncommon sight.

In the early days of basketball the two forwards did most of the scoring. The guards very seldom took a shot, and the center was used mainly to get the tap on center jumps after each field goal. In 1937, when the center jump was abolished by the high school, college, and professional associations, the nature of the game changed entirely.

The use of the fast break and the development of one-hand shots, particularly the jump shot, have made basketball a game requiring a degree of skill unknown in its early days. In a single game today individual players often score as many points as an entire team did before the center jump was abolished.

The way the game is played today the two forwards, the two guards, and the center all have many of the same responsibilities. All are expected to be good scorers and to play sound defense. Instead of having two scorers we now have five, so that many more shots are taken during a game. Consequently, we have a far more interesting game.

In basketball today, every player must be a scorer. A basketball team of five scorers keeps the defense alert. The defense must watch all five men instead of concentrating on one or two high-scoring players. The many defensive tactics used today can play havoc with a team of one or two scorers. Very seldom are there five players of equal scoring ability, but every player must be a scoring threat.

A team must be drilled in the ability to get possession of the ball once they fall behind during the closing minutes of a game. The half-court press and the full-court press are the attacks used.

In the half-court press, the offensive players are picked up as soon as they reach or are near the ten-second line. The ten-second line on most courts is the mid-court line. On courts that are not standard another line further back may be used. In the full-court press the offensive players are played all over the court.

The defense's objective is to gain possession of the ball. Effective use of the press makes the offense speed up its game. In doing this, the defense hopes to make the offense commit costly errors, such as bad passes, hurried shots, palming, running with the ball, and violation of the ten-second rule.

The defense may apply the press not only when they are behind, but they may use it as a surprise

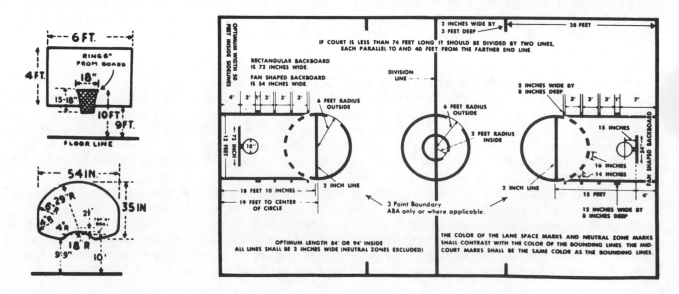

Norm Van Lier, the Chicago Bulls' playmaking guard, is shown here scoring during a game against the Milwaukee Bucks.

maneuver during any part of the game. This can sometimes prove disastrous to an inexperienced team.

Some teams use the press throughout the game. This type of defense requires a player to be in tip-top condition.

BOWLING

Bowling has an appeal that is not easily matched by any other sport. It is simple to play, it can be played by an entire family, and even a novice has a chance to bowl a perfect game.

There are more than sixty million bowlers today, throwing *strikes, spares, splits,* and *turkeys* in 47 nations of the world. The individual and organizational craze for bowling has even reached the White House, where lanes have been installed in the basement for presidential relaxation.

Bowling was known to have existed as early as 5200 B.C. in Egypt, and small bowling-type stones were used by the ancient Polynesians to play a primitive form of bowling, named *ula maika.* The Rome of the Caesars had its own version called *boccie.* Modern-day bowling, however, was developed in Germany. As far back as the fourth century, German peasants set up *kegels* (small

clubs) in the cloisters of churches and bowled round stones at them. It was part of their religious devotion, in which each kegel represented a nonbeliever. Knocking down all the kegels was a good omen.

The game eventually spread to other countries and found its way to the United States in the seventeenth century, when Dutch immigrants made it a flourishing pastime in New York City. To this day, a section of lower Manhattan is referred to as Bowling Green.

The American Bowling Congress was formed in 1895, and by the early 1970s had five million members on its rolls. But the real revolution of bowling occurred in the 1950s when automatic pin-setting machines replaced the pin boys (who worked behind the pins and reset them after each bowler had a turn), and modern, air-conditioned lanes provided day-and-night facilities for the vastly increasing number of enthusiasts. Organized bowling is now a major entertainment source, with both amateur and professional leagues set up all over the world. In the United States, the emphasis is on professional bowling, with individual and team prizes amounting to hundreds of thousands of dollars given out each year.

The idea of the game is to knock down all 10 pins, which are set on spots within a 36-inch triangle at the far end of the alley. The distance from the *foul line* to the head pin is 60 feet; and the alley, made of pine or maple boards, is 42 inches wide. On either side of the alley are *gutters* (shallow grooves). There is an approach area of approximately 15 feet behind the foul line. Bowling balls must not be more than 8.59 inches in diameter or 27 inches in circumference, and must weigh no more than 16 pounds. Each ball has two or three holes for finger placement.

A game consists of 10 *frames.* A perfect score is 300. If the player knocks down all pins with the first ball, he or she is awarded a strike.

A *spare* is credited when all pins are cleared in two shots. A *turkey* is three strikes in a row. To record a perfect 300 score, the bowler must make 12 successive strikes—one in each of the 10 frames—and an additional two strikes, in the final frame.

Duckpins is a smaller version of regular bowling, using little pins to conform with a six-inch bowling ball. Introduced in 1900, it is now supervised under the aegis of the National Duckpin Bowling Congress, which claims over one hundred thousand members in the United States.

BOXING

From ancient times, when Homer described a boxing match held as part of a celebration commemorating the fall of Troy, to the present, when more than 300 million people witnessed the second Muhammad Ali-Joe Frazier fight in 1974—boxing has had a charismatic hold on the sports public.

Historically, England is credited as the true organizer of the sport. Broughton's rules in 1743, the London Prize Ring Rules in 1838 and 1853, and the Marquis of Queensberry Rules in 1867, set the pattern for all boxing matches to follow.

In the early days, under London Prize Ring Rules, bare knuckles were used and a round ended when a fighter was knocked or wrestled to the ground. Under the later Marquis of Queensberry Rules, devised by John Sholto Douglas, no wrestling or hugging was allowed, each round lasted three minutes with a minute's rest between rounds, a man knocked to the canvas had to get up before the count of 10, and boxing gloves had to be worn. With minor variations, these rules are still used today in every country where boxing exists.

Both amateur and professional boxing are divided into various weight divisions, thus equalizing the boxer's chances. The divisions are as follows: Heavyweight (over 175 pounds), Light Heavyweight (not over 175 pounds), Middleweight (not over 160 pounds), Junior Middleweight (not over 154 pounds), Welterweight (not over 147 pounds), Junior Welterweight (not over 140 pounds), Lightweight (not over 135 pounds), Junior Lightweight (not over 130 pounds), Featherweight (not over 126 pounds), Bantamweight (not over 118 pounds), and Flyweight (not over 112 pounds).

Designated officials keep scorecards and give points to each fighter. Boxing matches are held in a ring measuring not less than 14 feet square or more than 20 feet square and surrounded by three ropes. Each corner post must be padded. The fighters wear trunks and gloves. The gloves range from 6 ounces for flyweights to welterweights, and 8 ounces for all heavier weight classes.

The number of rounds in a fight varies with the importance of the fight. Newcomers to the professional ranks are generally restricted to four or six three-minute rounds, and seasoned fighters are permitted to engage in 8-, 10-, and 12-round contests. Championship matches must be no less than 15 rounds.

There are a number of scientifically executed

A weary Muhammad Ali leans against the ropes after taking a right to the mid-section thrown by Leon Spinks in the final round of their heavyweight title bout Feb. 15, 1978. Spinks, a 12-1 underdog, won a split 15-round decision and the crown in only his eighth professional fight.

blows that are called for in order for a fighter to have a chance against his opponent. The fighter must know how to deliver a *jab,* a *left* and *right cross,* an *uppercut,* and a *hook,* and be able to attack his opponent's head and midsection during *in-fighting* exchanges.

The *break* requires both boxers to step back and push themselves away from each other. One must come out of a *clinch* on a signal from the referee, and no blow can be struck after a *clean break* until the referee orders the fight to be resumed. Hitting below the belt is illegal and can result in disqualification.

Throughout the history of boxing there have been classic and controversial fights that are still being discussed today. The Dempsey-Firpo fight in 1923 was one. Seven times in the first round Dempsey drove Firpo to the canvas. But Firpo, the Wild Bull of the Pampas, came back with a crushing right that sent Dempsey sprawling through the ropes. Pushed back into the ring by sportswriters, Dempsey weathered the round, and came back in the second to finish off his man.

The Dempsey "long count" match against Gene Tunney in 1927 was another. So was the famed

Jack Johnson-Jess Willard heavyweight fight held in Havana in 1915, when Johnson seemed to be napping on the canvas, under a bright sun, and lost his title in the 26th round.

Many of boxing's great moments were produced when two equally matched boxers pitted their skills against one another in a series of fights. Among these fights were those of Muhammad Ali and Joe Frazier (two heavyweight title fights and one non-title bout), Rocky Graziano and Tony Zale (three championship fights for the middleweight crown), and Willie Pep and Sandy Saddler (four featherweight championships). The first Rocky Marciano-Jersey Joe Walcott match (for the heavyweight title) and the second Joe Louis-Max Schmeling heavyweight championship bout were also classics, the latter probably the most brutal, one-sided contest in the history of boxing.

CANOEING

The word *canoe* is an Indian term. This is fitting, as the craft was developed by them, with the white man merely providing some refinements in design and materials. The word was Arawakan in origin, initially spelled *canoa,* and was carried back to Europe by Columbus, eventually to be Anglicized as "canoe."

Canoes are light, handy craft of various forms, and have been widely used by aboriginal peoples throughout the world. A variety of materials was used in their construction. Some were made of reeds or rushes, bound together in a long and narrow shape. Some were chopped or burned out of large logs. Others had frameworks of wood or bone, covered with skin. Still others were framed in wood and covered with bark. A few were made only of bark. These required a minimum of effort to construct. A long, wide layer of bark about three-eighths of an inch thick was stripped from a tree, soaked until soft and fairly pliable, then pressed and tied into a rough canoe-like shape. When the bark dried, it held this form; and then the bottom was smeared with a resinous gum to waterproof it.

In the skin-covered canoes the framework determined the form, for the skin followed the contour of the frame. In the bark canoe, however, the framing largely followed the contour of the bark shell. It was the birchbark canoe, primarily developed by the Indian tribes of the north central and northeastern states, as well as the Canadian maritime provinces, that served as the model for today's craft.

The birchbark canoe was not nearly as fragile as many seem to believe. History proves this; no fragile craft could have withstood the usage this one received. For example, in the seventeenth century when Père Marquette, the Jesuit missionary and explorer, made the trip from Lake Michigan to what is now northern Louisiana, he and his party used two birchbark canoes. Their journey led them up the Fox River to Lake Winnebago, over a long portage to the Wisconsin River, and then on to the Mississippi which they followed until they reached the mouth of the Arkansas. They returned by way of the Illinois River which meant a portage once more to reach the lake. The canoes were still sound at the end of their long journey.

The modern canoe, whether of aluminum, fiberglass, or wood and canvas, is light, sturdy, and stable and requires no more care and maintenance than other small boats of similar size and capacity. The overall design shows surprisingly little change, although the tendency has been to broaden the beam for greater stability, and some models are built with a thin keel, which not only protects the bottom during grounding but also aids directional movement.

Almost every manufacturer now offers models with square sterns for ease in mounting the outboard motor. These are satisfactory for lake use; however, the canoeist who plans much river running would be advised to avoid them. Square-sterned canoes are less maneuverable for downstream running in fast water, especially in circumstances where the canoe must be brought to a quick stop in order to check the water ahead for the best course. Water tends to back up against the flat surface, sometimes with considerable force. For those who may use an outboard on occasion, brackets are available that are adequate for the purpose.

CRICKET

Cricket, the game of the British Commonwealth, has been played in England for at least seven hundred years and possibly longer. The name is derived from an ancient Anglo-Saxon word, *Cryce,* meaning "a wooden stick used to hit a ball." The game in its present form, played between two teams of eleven men, has flourished for almost three centuries.

Cricket and baseball have many terms in common. Among them are batter, innings, runs, and umpire. Cricket is popular in England, Australia, New Zealand, India, and the West Indies.

The first recorded match was in 1697, and the first game between two English counties—the pattern of modern English cricket—in 1719. The most famous cricket club, at Hambledon in the South of England, was flourishing in 1777 and scored a famous victory against All-England in a match that ranks as a milestone in cricket history.

The English Championship, contested between 17 county teams, began in 1864. Test matches between England and Australia have been a regular feature of the game since 1880. South Africa started playing test matches against England in 1888; the West Indies entered this select group in 1928, New Zealand in 1929, India in 1932, and Pakistan in 1934.

Cricket is played on a field of unspecified size. The playing pitch, or wicket, is a strip 22 yards long in the center of the field, with three wooden sticks or stumps, surmounted by "bails" or cross-pieces, at each end. One team bats while the opposing team bowls and fields.

The bowler, or pitcher, delivers the ball with a stiff arm action and the batsman aims to hit the ball and score runs—one for every time he and his partner at the opposite end of the pitch make a complete run from wicket to wicket, four every time he hits the ball over the boundary on the field, six if he hits it over the boundary without bouncing.

The batsman is out if the ball hits his stumps (bowled), if he makes a stroke and the ball is caught by a fieldsman before it touches the ground (caught), if the ball hits his legs and in the umpire's opinion would have hit the stumps (leg before wicket), if he attempts a run and the fielding side throws the stumps down before he reaches base (run out), or if he steps outside the batting crease, or box, and the wicket-keeper removes the bails from the top of the stumps with the ball in his hand (stumped).

One team continues batting until its batsmen are out. Then the other team has its turn at bat. The total number of runs scored by each team decides the match—sometimes on the basis of one inning a side, more often on two innings a side.

FISHING

From time immemorial, man has fished and hunted, first for food; then, gradually, his means of livelihood turned into a great sport. Fly fishing started before the birth of Christ when men and women tied bits of feathers to crude hooks and the fish came up to them. Since then anglers have been perfecting their lures, tackle, and techniques in order to better the game of fun with fish.

Fishing tackle developed when man first coiled a rope, tied a hook to the end of it, and threw it into the water. First, single-action reels were developed and attached to poles. Then, years later someone developed the revolving-spool reel that has not changed basically since. *Spinning*, that is fishing with a reel with a stationary spool, then came along as the latest, and some consider the best, development in fishing's history.

Before choosing the type of tackle you will be using, it is best to know the three basic types and their uses.

Fly-fishing equipment is used for casting very, very light artificial flies on delicate leaders a long distance from the angler. The rod comes in lengths from six to ten feet and is made of split bamboo or tubular glass fibers. The action is a wavy type, the line guides are many, to keep the line close to the rod so that the bend is under equal pressure. The close guides allow the line to be cast freely. The line is tapered so as to balance with the action of the rod. Some lines are double tapered from thin to thick to thin and come marked so that the right line can be bought for the right rod. This is what is known as matched or balanced tackle. The wrong line with the very best rod will render it almost useless, for it will cast poorly.

Spinning tackle is a middle-of-the-road choice between fly- and bait-casting equipment. The rod is usually not as long as the fly rod but longer than the conventional bait-casting rod. The reason it is so long and limber is that it is used to throw light lures which are heavier than flies but lighter than regulation bait-casting plugs and spoons. The spinning rod, made either from split bamboo or tubular glass, is lined with very large-holed guides for the reason that the line peels off the rim of the spool, rather than straight out as in the case of the single-action fly or bait-casting reel.

The line used is braided nylon or monofilament, the latter being preferred by most anglers because it sinks better and does not have the tendency to fray and wear. It also has a certain amount of stretch that can mean the difference sometimes between a lost or creeled fish.

Bait-casting equipment is older in design than spinning gear, but it is still irreplaceable in the opinion of many anglers. The shorter, stiffer rod with its smaller guides casts medium or heavy-weight lures and baits with great accuracy. The rod is generally from four to five and a half feet long, fairly stiff, made of steel, glass, or split bamboo. The line is braided nylon line which is attached to a short piece of leader, wire, or monofilament, depending on the conditions.

The big advantage of the bait-casting rod is that it is much more practical for deep-water trolling. It is also much more responsive for a quick strike to a heavy fish, especially if you have to strike against a bobber or heavy plug. The bait-casting rig had its start as the traditional outfit for bass fishing with plugs and spoons. It is used also for the bigger species of fish such as the pike and muskie. In light salt water fishing, it is tops when a quick fast strike is necessary and where generally heavier lures are used.

Most of the salt water fishing is done from some kind of a boat. The flounder fisherman casually rows out a few feet from the dock, anchors, and drops his lines overboard. The outboarder uses his craft to quickly get to and from the favorite fishing grounds, or trolls for stripers and blues at night. The owner of an open-water sea skiff wanders well off shore in search of blues and sailfish, or wanders up and down the inland waterways. The cabin cruiser man ventures out into the deep sea. They all belong to the clan and fish their respective ways.

FOOTBALL

In any of the early forms of football, as played by the Greeks, the Romans, people of medieval days, and nineteenth-century Englishmen, the main rule was that the ball be kicked, not carried, toward the goal. Originally called "futballe" it became better known as soccer a hundred years ago.

During a class game one late fall afternoon in 1823 at a boys' school at Rugby, England, a strange thing happened. William Ellis suddenly took the ball in his arms and ran across the opposing goal line. This impulsive act stunned those present. The score was not allowed and Ellis was somewhat mortified and looked down on for deliberately violating the rules. However, the seed had been planted for the possibilities of running with the ball and this was directly responsible for the game of rugby. The American game of football descended directly from rugby.

Football probably came to America with the English colonists at Jamestown in 1607. In the early days a pig bladder was used as a ball. Early in the nineteenth century, Yale and Harvard had class scrimmages of "Football Fightum." The first intercollegiate football game grew out of a rivalry between Princeton and Rutgers universities in New Jersey. On November 6, 1869, this first game was played at Rutgers, located at New Brunswick, New Jersey. Rutgers defeated Princeton 6 goals to 4. There were 25 players on each side, and this was strictly the soccer-type game. The Football Hall of Fame has voted to erect a permanent museum for football on the site where the first game was played.

Other colleges picked up the sport, but it was still soccer as we know it. When McGill University of Montreal visited Harvard in 1874 to play a game of football, preliminary practice revealed that their conception of the game was the rugby ver-

Denver's Craig Morton, a former Dallas quarterback, is about to be lassoed by Cowboys' Randy White (54), Harvey Martin (79), and Ed Jones (72) during Super Bowl XII in New Orleans. Morton completed only four of 19 passes and was intercepted a game record four times as Dallas won the NFL crown, 27-10.

sion. The Harvard captain and the Harvard team, as proper hosts, played the visitor's rules. It is remarkable how quickly ball-carrying and tackling was learned, as the game ended in a scoreless tie.

It soon was very apparent that rugby was the preferred version of football with young Americans. The boys liked to get the ball and to run with it.

Many men helped to develop football. Walter Camp played and coached at Yale. He served on all the early rules-making bodies and he was the authoritative selector of All-American teams until his death in 1925. He influenced the change from 15 players on a side to 11. Camp cooperated in redeeming the game from brutality. Mass plays involving hedges, locked hands aiding the ballcarrier, and no neutral zone on the line of scrimmage were aspects of play that caused serious injuries and some deaths. Tough players, called "ringers," appeared during the football season and were permitted to play at some colleges. Subversive tactics so disgusted such schools as Army at West Point and Navy at Annapolis that they were among those schools which dropped the game for a time. President Theodore Roosevelt called Walter Camp and other experts to the White House in 1905 to review the game. The result was that the game was changed and opened up. On offense a

team was permitted four downs to make 10 yards replacing the five yards necessary in three downs. The big feature was that the forward pass was legalized. By opening up the game, mass play was virtually eliminated.

Amos Alonzo Stagg coached for more than sixty years, and his long tenure at the University of Chicago (1892–1933) enabled him to be instrumental in founding the Western Conference, now the Big Ten. Stagg worked for clean amateur athletics, and he set standards for eligibility of play. He hated recruiting of athletes, a sentiment which pervades college athletics today. A great rival of Stagg was "Hurry Up" Yost of Michigan, a truly great coach who developed point-a-minute teams.

Glenn S. "Pop" Warner, a Cornell man, became coach at the Carlisle Indian School in 1899. His legendary Indian teams, led by the fabulous Jim Thorpe, made football history. Warner later coached very successfully at Stanford, Pittsburgh, and Temple; and he invented both the single and double wing-back formations.

Notre Dame, Knute Rockne, and football rang across that national football scene and it stood for quality–the best. Rockne was a great teacher, a real leader, and an astute coach. As a player, he helped to revolutionize football in 1913 as he caught Gus Dorais' passes in Notre Dame's monumental (39-13) upset of Army at West Point. Coach Rockne developed the shift and the forward

O.J. Simpson of the Buffalo Bills (32) was an AP Award winner in 1973. The Juice set an NFL record that year by rushing for 2,003 yards. He was traded to San Francisco on March 24, 1978.

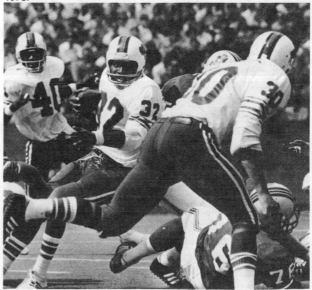

pass to its highest degree. His inspirational leadership helped to defeat many a superior foe.

With the impetus and intelligent spark given by President Theodore Roosevelt, the rules were improved by 1906. The game was changed from one of ultraroughness to one of finer and cleaner play. The philosophy of the game changed from trying to maim or disable your opponent to playing to outmaneuver him. This called for brainwork with agility as well as for brawn, which always helps in football. The NCAA code and all other rules pertaining to football clearly depict the spirit and the intent of the rules. The core of the rules state that traditionally football is the game of schools and colleges. As such, only the highest standards of sportsmanship and conduct are expected of players, coaches, and others associated with the game.

Today's players are usually numbered with the ends in the 80s, tackles in the 70s, guards in the 60s, and the centers in the 50s. The quarterbacks are numbered from 10 to 19 and the other backs from 20 through 49. Numbered jerseys were first worn in the Pittsburgh *vs.* Washington and Jefferson game in 1908. By 1915, all players wore numbers on their backs; and in 1936, the rules required all players be numbered both front and back.

Football has come a long way since the early days when a player was considered a coward if he left the game during play under his own power. Players go at top speed today and are removed for fresh reserves as substitution rules are very liberal. Specialists are used for spot plays.

Game officials have improved along with the game and now retain complete control of it.

Everyone seems to know that the field is 100 yards long with 10-yard end zones, but few know the football field is 160 feet wide.

Football involves stress, strain, hope, despair, success in winning, and disappointment in losing. Success and disappointment are measured only partly in winning and losing because a game can be won by one team only. Real success is measured by how the game was played by both teams.

GOLF

Golf is among the most commercially popular outdoor activities in the world. Presidents and kings play golf; comedians crack jokes about it; weekend duffers groan over it; millions watch it; and a small handful of professionals have made a fortune from it.

As early as the fifteenth century, King James II of Scotland was taking royal swings at a golf ball. Mary Queen of Scots learned to play golf at a young age, continuing a tradition that led to the establishment of the famous St. Andrews course—recognized as the birthplace of golf—in 1552. Two hundred years later (1754), the Society of St. Andrews Golfers—eventually named the Honourable Company of the Royal and Ancient Club—was founded. Its members adopted the "13 articles" that still apply as the basic rules governing the sport today.

Although the Scots played golf with great passion, it inevitably spread elsewhere. The first logical inheritors of the game were the Irish and the English. Ships sailing from the British Isles in the mid-nineteenth century deposited golf-playing enthusiasts on Canadian and American soil, and they promptly extolled the virtues of the game to their North American friends.

Golf was slow to catch on in the United States. In the 1880s, most Americans were caught up in action-packed sports such as baseball and football, while the imported product from Scotland languished far behind, much too snobbish and boring for the average citizen. As one New Yorker of the period explained, "Golf . . . is for those who get more pleasure from hitting a small ball into a hole than putting their shoulders into an honest day's work."

Although several areas claim the achievement, most historians credit a transplanted Scotsman, John Reid, with having laid out the first golf course in the United States in Yonkers, New York, on February 22, 1888. The United States then moved quickly to become the world's leading golf-playing nation.

The Amateur Golf Association of the United States (United States Golf Association) was formed in 1894; and one year later, the first U.S. Open and Amateur championships were held at Newport, Rhode Island, with Charles Blair Macdonald winning the title, beating Charles E. Sands 12 and 11.

But it took the appearance of a lanky, sad-eyed gardener's son to lift golf in the United States to a popularity it had never seen. The lad was Francis Ouimet, a 20-year-old ex-caddy who lived across the road from the Brookline Country Club in Massachusetts. When the club was selected as the site for the 1913 U.S. Open, Ouimet entered the competition. The best players were still English and Scottish, and when two elite British professionals,

"I never thought I'd do it," said Al Geiberger after shooting an incredible 59 in the second round of the 1977 Danny Thomas Memphis Open. It was the greatest competitive 18-hole round ever played, breaking the record of 60, held by seven men.

Harry Vardon and Ted Ray, joined other notable golfers, such as England's Wilfrid Reid and France's Louis Tellier, in the championship event, it was not a question of whether an American had a chance but which Englishman would win.

Ouimet and another 20-year-old American from Rochester, New York, an "unknown" by the name of Walter Hagen, were tied at 151 after 36 holes, four strokes off the pace. But on the final day of the tournament, Ouimet scrambled for a share of the lead with Harry Vardon and Ted Ray by sinking two birdie putts during the final six holes.

The crowd buzzed with excitement the next day as the two vaunted Englishmen and the American ex-caddy teed up for the playoffs. By the 15th hole, Ray was out of it when he lined a tee shot off a spectator's derby and ended the hole with a bogey six. Ouimet was visibly nervous earlier in the morning, but as the day wore on it became apparent that he was not to be denied. Vardon fell to a disastrous double bogey six while coming down the home stretch, and on the final hole, Ouimet calmly sank a four-foot putt for a par and the championship. The news of Ouimet's stunning upset was front-page copy in newspapers across the country, and soon the man on the street began to turn to golf links to rid himself of the day's frustrations. Golf was here to stay.

Ouimet's sensational win in 1913 produced the seeds that brought other fabulous American golfers to the fore in the decade of the 1920s. There was Ouimet's good friend and fellow competitor in the 1913 Open, Walter Hagen; and the immortal Robert Tyre "Bobby" Jones, who stood supreme over the amateurs in the Golden Age of Sports. Jones finished his career in 1930 by sweeping the U.S. Open and the British Open—to complete a Grand Slam victory over the best golfers in the world. He was only 28 when he called it quits, but he could look back to 13 national titles, accumulated during his sensational reign between 1923 and 1930. Throughout his golfing life, Jones remained an amateur.

Hagen, who was universally known as The Haig, was the king of the pros. A Professional Golf Association winner five times, victor in two U.S. Opens (1914 and 1919), holder of 11 national championships and four successive U.S. professional titles, Hagen played on five continents and knew the first names of royalty and commoners alike. He approached the *tees* of the world's fairways with a regal stride that entranced galleries for a quarter of a century—and earned over $1 million before retiring in 1940.

The 1930s had golfing heroes galore: Lawson Little, Paul Runyon, Denny Shute, Craig Wood, Johnny Revolta, and Ralph Guldahl. Then, with the approaching clouds of war, other magnificent golfers from the United States emerged. The irrepressible Ben Hogan, Byron Nelson, Lloyd Mangrum, Jimmy Demaret, and Jug McSpaden, all from Texas, and Virginia's Sam Snead dominated professional golf into the 1950s.

The sixties were the decade of Arnold Palmer, South Africa's Gary Player, Jack Nicklaus, Lee Trevino, Billy Casper, Julius Boros, Tom Weiskopf, and Frank Beard. Both Palmer and Nicklaus were the true giants of that era. Between them, and through "the magic of television," they captured the fancy of millions, and turned thousands of bystanders into Sunday golf players.

Meanwhile, the women have also played golf as enthusiastically as their male counterparts. Competing in major tournaments such as the Ladies Professional Golf Association (LPGA) and the USGA Women's Open, female golfers have developed into formidable players. In the early 1930s, Pam Barton opened the door for future women champions. Mildred "Babe" Zaharias, Louise Suggs, Mickey Wright, Donna Caponi, Carol Mann, Kathy Whitworth, Sandra Haynie, and Judy Rankin have all entered the inner circle of golf greatness through the years. Women's purses have increased, too, suggesting that in future years the gals may well be in the same money-earning position as the men.

Nadia Comaneci, a 14-year-old Romanian, captivated television audiences with her coordination, daring, and skill in gymnastics during the 1976 Olympic Games. She was chosen The AP female athlete of the year.

GYMNASTICS

Running, jumping, and wrestling were probably the first human sports. They were played by prehistoric children for the same reason that a couple of puppies snarl and roll in mock combat. They were learning through play how to survive in a hostile world.

In the beginning our first tumbler developed his art from the necessity of jumping, diving, rolling, and running to escape his enemies. Experience and accident taught him that certain ways of falling were less painful than others.

Later he learned that teamwork produced more than any one person could achieve alone. The spectacular human pyramids we see acrobatic teams doing today were most likely born at this time. Growing intelligence showed that if one caveman held his brother on his shoulders they could reach fruit on limbs too high for either to reach.

Some historians believe the Chinese were the first formal gymnasts. They supposedly created the sport more than five thousand years ago, both for military use and as an aid to health.

Old pictures carved on the walls of Egyptian ruins clearly show that pyramid-building routines and acrobatic balancing were popular in that country at least four thousand years ago.

The art of tumbling reached its peak in Crete, the Mediterranean island, about three thousand five hundred years ago. Not in the one thousand five hundred year history of tumbling to that time nor in the 35 centuries since has anything been done that can match the Cretan's amazing tumbling feats.

The Cretan tumblers climaxed their acrobatic exhibitions with a stunt called "bull jumping," surely the most dangerous and difficult acrobatic stunt ever performed. It combined the thrills of bullfighting and acrobatics.

A bull, the most ferocious obtainable, was made wild with rage before it was turned into the arena pit. The acrobat met the enraged beast head on. Just when it appeared he would be gored to death, the jumper leaped into the air. He caught the bull's horns exactly the way a gymnast today grabs the pommels of his side horse. Using the rushing bull's horns for leverage, the acrobat flipped himself over for an aerial somersault to land on the ground behind the frustrated beast.

The feat is so dangerous that no one has shown much enthusiasm for reviving it in modern times. Steer bulldogging in today's rodeo cannot anywhere near approach it.

Following the Cretans, the Greeks developed gymnastics to a fine art and gave us the word *gymnastics,* which means "to exercise naked." In their gymnasiums and in the famed Olympic games the participants wore no clothing of any kind.

The Olympic games spurred gymnastics until the decline of Greek civilization. After that the sport survived primarily as training for war. The popular side-horse vaulting grew directly from the need of knights and cavalry soldiers to get on their mounts in a hurry.

During this long period from the decline of the Greeks to recent times, the lot of the common man was to toil from dawn to dusk. He got all the exercise he needed and wanted from his labor. He left it to the soldier and the leisure class to play for fun. His day started to dawn in the late eighteenth century when the first modern book on scientific gymnastics was written by a German enthusiast.

Since then the popularity of gymnastics has grown until today it has a greater following than at any other time in history.

HANDBALL

Handball is the invention of the Irish, who played the sport in the tenth century. It was then called *fives,* and soon became a favorite national pastime. It wasn't until late in the nineteenth century that handball caught on in other countries. Credit should go to Meham Baggs of Tipperary, who applied sheer wizardry to the game. Baggs learned how to control his shots, making the ball spin, curve, and rebound in amazing fashion. Soon others began to learn his tricks, and the ultimate refinements led to handball's adoption outside of Ireland.

In the early 1880s, an Irish handball star named Phil Casey migrated to Brooklyn, New York. He found a dearth of handball players and courts but soon set to work to rectify the situation. Casey built a court of his own, instructed players, charged fees, and made a profit. This enabled him to build more courts and, in turn, led his pupils to spread four-wall to other parts of the United States.

During Casey's time, professional handball was extremely popular. To remain in good physical condition, firemen participated in the sport, and hardly a firehouse in New York existed without a friendly but high-spirited game going on during the few leisure hours afforded to engine company members.

When Casey (who had beaten Irish champion John Lawlor in 11 out of 17 matches) ran out of opponents, the sport slipped into relative nonexistence. If it hadn't been for the Amateur Athletic Union, it might have succumbed completely. The AAU sponsored the first four-wall national championship in 1919 as well as the first one-wall championship, which was held in New York in 1924. By that time, there were hundreds of one-wall courts springing up in the beach areas, playgrounds, and gymnasiums of New York. To this day four-wall handball is played with high enthusiasm almost everywhere in the United States.

Handball is played on either four-, three-, or one-wall courts. The ball is made of hard rubber, and players wear protective gloves to cushion the impact of the hit and to put spins on the ball.

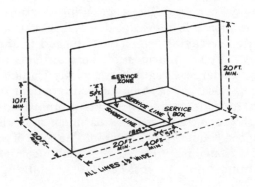

Competition handball is played in singles and by doubles teams. A team or player must win his serve first in order to have a chance to score, and points are won when an opposing player fails to return a shot from the wall. A game consists of 21 points; matches, best of three games.

HORSE RACING

Thoroughbred horse racing is known as the "Sport of Kings," and rightly so. Its history, which dates back to the days of Richard II and Henry IV of England, has long been associated with the nobility of early times, when high-quality horses from Spain and Italy were imported for purposes of running them in matches set up by reigning kings. Elizabeth I loved horse racing so much that she and her court attended the races at Croyden, which became a gathering place for English fashion.

Horse racing began in the United States a hundred years before the Declaration of Independence, when Richard Nicolls, then the colonial governor of New York, laid out a course on Salisbury Plain, Long Island, and donated a silver trophy to commemorate the races that could be run in the spring and fall.

"Racing is for the improvement of the breed," said Nicolls. "It is not for the divertissement of youth." To this day, that well-turned phrase is still quoted throughout turfing circles.

Today, more than one hundred tracks hold meets in the 30 American states where horse racing is legal. Nearly fifty million people pay their way for the privilege of betting close to four billion dollars annually on the races. Add this to the legalized off-track betting that is now an important means of revenue to local communities around the country, and suddenly the betting dollars climb to astronomical sums.

Racing is a year-round sport in the United States, although the tracks in the northern states usually limit their seasons to nine or ten months.

The decades have witnessed the comings and goings of champion jockeys and expert trainers, but it is the thoroughbreds, such as Man o' War, Whirlaway, Gallant Fox, Swaps, Majestic Prince, Secretariat, and Forego, that have become part of our American Heritage. Many elements go into making a champion thoroughbred—bloodlines, age, conditioning, handling—but they are all part

Seattle Slew, with Jean Cruguet aboard, streaks to victory in the 1977 Kentucky Derby. Slew went on to become the first Triple Crown winner since Secretariat in 1973, and was named Horse of the Year.

of one goal: speed. And it is speed that makes the thoroughbred king of horses.

With the advent of starting stalls, electric timers, and other modern advances, horse racing has become a very precise sport, leaving almost no room for faulty handling of the races.

Purses are given by the tracks to winning owners, who in turn compensate their riders with a percentage of the prize money.

Claiming races are run so that any horse can be claimed by a buyer for its entered price, but the claim must be made at least 15 minutes before the advertised time of the race.

Handicaps are races for which the weights are adjusted for purposes of equalizing the chances of all the entries.

There are a number of restrictions on the type of horse that may run in any particular race. Some limit it to sex; some admit horses of certain age groups; some are *maiden* races, for horses which have never won a race—and so on.

Once a prized thoroughbred is finished with his racing career, he is put out to pasture for *stud* duty, meaning the owner will use him for breeding purposes. However, the leading money-winner of all time, Kelso, with earnings of $1,977,896, was a *gelding* (castrated horse) and therefore not fit for stud duty.

A minor revolution took place in horse racing on February 7, 1969, when Diane Crump became the first woman to ride in a regular race at a major track. However, it remained for Barbara Jo Rubin to become the first girl to make it to the winner's circle at a race track. On February 22, 1969, she rode Cohesian to a neck triumph in a race run under the lights at Charles Town, West Virginia.

A number of other female riders came onto the scene in the 1970s, including Robyn Smith and Mary Bacon.

HUNTING

In no other country in the world can one enjoy better hunting than here in the United States. Africa may have a greater variety of animals and larger, more dangerous ones, but America can challenge it for the title of "hunter's paradise." Take our deer, for example—every year our hunters bag almost two million of them and still many millions remain for the following hunting season. As for rabbits, so many are taken that no one has even attempted to count them. But it has been estimated that if all the rabbits bagged by hunters in a single year were placed in one pile, they would top the Empire State Building!

The deer is the hunter's most popular big-game animal, and is found in almost every State. The white-tail deer is abundant in the East and South, and the black-tail or mule deer in the West. The white-tail has a white tail which waves like a white flag as the animal runs in graceful bounds, while the black-tail or mule deer has a white patch on its hindquarters and its tail is black-tipped, and it runs in a strange bouncing, stiff-legged manner. The colors of both range from a reddish-tan to a brownish gray. The white-tail averages 175 pounds but its size varies considerably in different areas; the black-tail is larger, averaging 250 pounds. Only the buck has antlers and he sheds them after the mating season every autumn, then regrows them during spring and summer. The size of a buck's antlers or "rack," commonly designated by its number of points, does not determine the animal's age. An old buck may be a spikehorn (one small single point on each side), while a two-year-old may have a rack like a spreading chestnut tree.

The moose is the largest member of the deer family, averaging over one thousand pounds in weight. You'll find most of these animals in the more wilderness regions, especially Canada and Alaska. Because of some magic ingredient in the Alaskan foliage on which this animal feeds, its weight sometimes reaches as much as eighteen hundred pounds—almost a ton! The color of moose varies from dark brown to brownish black. Moose are hunted only by *still-hunting*, or stalking.

The little rabbit, or cottontail, is the hunter's number one small-game animal, found from Southern Canada to South America. Enjoying almost as much hunting popularity is its cousin, the jack rabbit, which really isn't a rabbit but a hare. Another cousin well-known in Canada and the Arctic is the snowshoe rabbit, which turns white in winter and has large feet which enable it to run on soft snow. All adult rabbits and hares have large bulging eyes which enable them to see forward and backward without moving their heads. The male rabbit is called a "buck" and female a "doe."

Old "bushytail"–which is the name small-game hunters affectionately give the gray squirrel–is probably second only to the rabbit in popularity. It can be found almost everywhere throughout the United States and Canada, wherever there are heavy forests with hickory, beech, or oak trees to keep it well supplied with nuts. This little agile, gray-furred animal with a fluffed tail as long as its body is no pushover to hunt, however. It is expert in keeping a tree trunk between itself and a hunter, and in "freezing" motionless against a tree limb for hours until it seems to have become part of the tree itself.

The pheasant is classified as an "upland" game bird to distinguish it from waterfowl. The male, or "cock," is a gaudy creature. The hen is smaller and colored plain brown with a short tail.

The main difficulty in pheasant shooting is finding the bird. It can hide so skillfully in grass or brush that you can almost step on it without seeing it. And when it does decide to flee, it usually runs instead of flying—and make no mistake about it—a long-legged cockbird can run through thick brush with incredible speed. A good bird dog is the answer. It will find the pheasant by scent and make the cock so nervous it will be forced to take to air—hopefully right in front of the hunter.

Most waterfowl shooting is done from a small camouflaged boat anchored in the center of a pond or bay, or with the shooter concealed in a camouflaged *blind* built on the shore. Nearby he anchors a number of artificial cork, wood, or plastic ducks called *decoys* to attract the real ones, and also blows a duck or goose *call* to imitate their natural calls. Beginning waterfowl shooters always find it difficult to estimate when the flying birds are within range of their shotguns, which should be fifty yards at the most. Distances over water can be very deceiving. But there is a method known to the old-timers that helps. Anchor a single decoy fifty yards from your blind—then all waterfowl which fly closer than that decoy will be within range!

ICE HOCKEY

Ice hockey is a game of flashing skates, stick and puck control, lightning-fast action, and rough-and-tumble contact. Born and developed in the frozen stretches of North America, it later became the national pastime of Canada, and reached a height of popularity in the United States in the early 1970s.

As far as most historians can ascertain, Canadian youngsters fashioned pucks from frozen "horse apples" and sticks from tree branches, took to iced-over lakes and ponds—found in almost every obscure village—and learned to compete against each other. As the game's popularity mushroomed, it was moved indoors to the rinks. The earliest recorded use of the term *ice hockey* is found in a newspaper description of a game played at Victoria Skating Rink in Montreal in 1875.

The National Hockey League (NHL) was founded in 1917 with four teams participating— the Montreal Canadiens, Montreal Wanderers, Ottawa Senators, and Toronto Arenas. The first modern *Stanley Cup* championship was won by the Arenas.

In 1924, the Boston Bruins became the first United States club to join the NHL, followed in 1926 by the New York Rangers, Chicago Black Hawks, and Detroit Cougars (their nickname was changed to "Red Wings" in 1933). At the start of the 1942–43 campaign, the NHL had six operating clubs—Boston, Chicago, Detroit, New York, Montreal, and Toronto. There was no change until 1967 when six American teams were added— California, Los Angeles, Minnesota, Philadelphia, Pittsburgh, and St. Louis.

At the start of the 1976-1977 NHL season, 18 franchises were in existence. Buffalo and Vancouver were added in 1970, Atlanta and the New York Islanders in 1972 and Washington, D.C., and Kansas City in 1974. However, after suffering huge financial losses, the Kansas City and California teams changed residences in 1976. The Kansas City franchise was shifted to Denver and the California club moved to Cleveland.

Meanwhile, the World Hockey Association, created in 1972, operates eight professional teams. The formation of the WHA precipitated a money-war between the two leagues, which led to the doubling and tripling of pro hockey salaries in the NHL, and the league-jumping of former NHL stars, such as Bobby Hull, Derek Sanderson, Gordie Howe, and J. C. Tremblay.

Most professional hockey players are Canadian-born, although a recent burst of intercollegiate competition in the United States indicates that American-born players will soon join the pro ranks in increasing numbers.

The Stanley Cup—symbol of ice hockey supremacy—is the oldest professional trophy in North America. It was first won in 1893 by the Montreal Amateur Athletic Association. The NHL took over the administration of the Cup soon after it was organized, and it became the symbol of hockey supremacy.

Ice hockey is played with six men on a side—two *defensemen,* three *forwards,* and one *goalie.* Each major league team usually carries 19 players on its roster—17 skaters and two goalies.

A hockey game is divided into three periods, each lasting twenty minutes of actual playing time. Each period begins with a *face-off* at the center of the rink, whereby the puck is dropped by the referee between the sticks of two opposing players. After a goal is scored, the puck is brought back to center ice for another face-off.

The playing area is 188 to 200 feet long, and about 85 feet wide. The playing area is subdivided into three zones—defense, neutral and attacking—by two *blue lines.* A player must enter the attacking zone only in line with or behind the puck.

Players are subject to a variety of penalties leading to their dismissal from the ice for two minutes or more, thus giving the other team a one-man advantage for the duration of the penalty or until a goal is scored.

All regular season games in the NHL are restricted to three periods, and many games end in a tie. However, in Stanley Cup play, and during the regular season in the WHA, tie games are extended into overtime.

Olympic competition began in 1920; and through the years, Russia and Canada have been the dominating powers. The U.S. Olympic hockey team has won the gold medal once—in 1960.

LACROSSE

Lacrosse is an action game in its purest form. Combining the roughness of football and ice hockey with the finesse and speed of basketball, it is a fast-growing sport in the United States, especially on the college level.

However, lacrosse had its beginnings in Canada. Indians were playing it when the French began settling in the New World. A French cleric by the name of Pierre de Charlevoix gave lacrosse its name.

It happened one day in 1705, while de Charlevoix was watching the Algonquin Indians participate in their favorite sport of *baggataway.* He noticed the strange shape of the webbed stick used by the Indians, and referred to it as *lacrosse,* because it reminded him of a bishop's *crozier,* or cross. It was only a matter of time before the French invaders of Canada adopted the game. And when they did, they had a name for it.

One of the worst massacres in Canadian history occurred because an Indian tribe used the game as a medium to stage an uprising. On June 4, 1763, a band of Chippewa and Sac Indians were invited by the British to play baggataway outside Fort Mackinac. As the game reached a peak of excitement, the British opened the gates of the fort to witness the action on the field. The Indians rushed into the stockade, tomahawks flashing, and decimated the English forces inside.

In 1867, more than a century after the massacre, the National Lacrosse Association was founded in Montreal and parliament adopted the game as Canada's national sport.

Late in the nineteenth century, the United States Intercollegiate Lacrosse Association was organized, but this was at a time when football was still incubating at American universities. Now football and basketball reign supreme in college athletics, although lacrosse has remained an intercollegiate favorite at many of the top Eastern schools. The Ivy League, along with Johns Hopkins, Penn State, Maryland, Syracuse, Hofstra, Rutgers, and other universities continue to give lacrosse high-priority publicity and backing, while many schools throughout the country are beefing up their lacrosse programs to accommodate the sudden resurgence of fan interest.

Lacrosse is played on a field 110 yards long, between 53⅓ and 60 yards wide, and the goals are 80 yards apart, with 15 yards of playing area behind each goal.

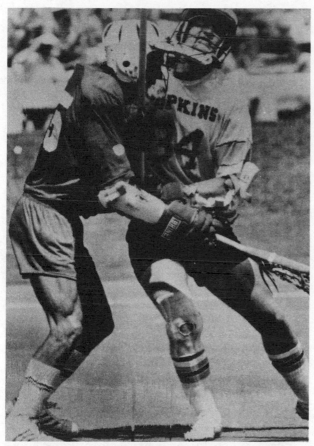

Mike Connor of Johns Hopkins (right) collides with Cornell's Bob Mathison during final round game of the 1977 NCAA University Division Tournament in Charlottesville, Va. Cornell won, 16-8.

There are 10 players on each team: defense and attack men, midfield players, and a goalkeeper. Each player must have a stick, helmet, gloves, and a uniform. The stick has a pocket which holds the ball, which is made of India-rubber sponge. The attacking player uses the stick to make passes, while the defense players use sticks with larger pockets to intercept the passes. The goalkeeper uses a stick with a larger pocket to stop the ball from going into the goal.

The object of the game is to put the ball into the goal of the opponent, and both sides utilize running, passing, and dodging tactics on offense and defense. A goal counts one point.

Lacrosse matches are 60 minutes long and, like football, are divided into four quarters of 15 minutes each. If the score is tied after regulation play, two four-minute overtime periods are played, after which sudden-death overtime periods are played if the score is still tied.

POLO

The game of polo, stripped to its barest essentials, is a stick-and-ball game played on horseback, and not unlike a soccer or hockey game in its purpose and playing area. Actually, it is a very demanding, often brutal, sport that places a premium on stick-handling, horsemanship, and team work. There are four polo players to a side, and the object of the game is to score more goals than your opponent during a match of six or eight *chukkers,* or periods.

Each chukker lasts seven minutes, with a four-minute time-out between chukkers in order to change ponies. There is also a ten-minute break at half time. The polo ball is made of willow or bamboo root and weighs about four and one-half ounces. The *mallet* (stick) is 48 to 52 inches in length. It is usually made of cane, and the head of the mallet, used to strike the ball, is set at a slight angle.

The polo field is 300 yards long and 160 yards wide. The goals, located at each end of the field, are eight yards wide. Sideboards, 10 inches high, line the sides of the field.

Polo flourished in ancient India, Tibet, Persia, China, and Japan, and reached the shores of England in the mid-nineteenth century. It was imported to the United States in 1876, when American newspaper publisher James Gordon Bennett returned from abroad with a large supply of polo mallets and balls, and a desire to introduce the sport to his socialite friends. Bennett sent for a carload of Texas cow ponies, and within a few months he and his friends began playing polo at the Jerome Park Race Track in the Bronx, New York.

The United States has produced many fine international polo players. Among them are Malcolm Stevenson, Michael Phipps, Tommy Hitchcock, Harry Payne Whitney, Louis Stoddard, Cecil Smith, Bob Skene, and the 1973 *Coronation Cup* champions, Tommy Wayman, Billy Linfoot, Bill Ylvisaker and Harold Barry.

The United States Polo Association sanctions all national and international matches for American teams and sets rules and handicaps governing play. It also acts as an information source, through its newsletter, to the many clubs that participate in polo throughout the United States.

RACQUETBALL

Racquetball is a quick-action, easy-to-learn game that utilizes simple equipment and provides the player with challenging opportunities in individual sport competition.

Racquetball was developed in the United States in the mid-1960s and was immediately criticized by handball purists, who felt the new sport was a poor facsimile of their own. They argued that racquetball players encroached upon their handball courts and that most of their rules had been stolen by these racquet-swinging upstarts. As a result, racquetball players were banned from many community centers, private clubs and the like, where almost all handball courts are located. However, the appeal of racquetball soon forced its detractors to accept the game thus allowing its widespread popularity.

The International Racquetball Association was founded in 1969, and now has close to four thousand members in the United States and Canada. Major tournaments are played throughout the year, including the International Racquetball Association Championships, the Canadian National Klondike and other regional invitational tournaments.

The game combines elements of tennis and handball. The racquet is made of aluminum, fiberglass, steel, or wood, which is meshed with nylon or gut strings. Although it resembles a tennis racquet, the handle is considerably shorter. The rubber ball used in the sport is more lively than a tennis ball or handball, and the court is a standard four-wall handball court, with all the walls, the ceiling, and floor in play.

Racquetball may be played by two (singles) or four (doubles) players. Points are scored only by the serving side when it serves an ace or wins a volley. A serve or volley is won when a side is unable to return the ball before it touches the floor twice. A game is won by the side first scoring 21 points, and a match is won by the side first winning two games.

RUGBY

Rugby originated in 1823 when William Ellis, then a student at Rugby School in England, decided to ignore the "kicking only" rule during an inter-class football match. Ellis, disgusted with his inability to kick the elusive ball, reached down, tucked it under his arm, and sprinted down the field. News of his peculiar but sensational run traveled to other English schools, and soon this unorthodox form of soccer was a common sight on the playing fields of Oxford and Cambridge. However, in honor of Ellis's movement of glory, the game was called rugby football.

Eight countries in the world—England, Scotland, Wales, Ireland, France, New Zealand, Australia and South Africa—are major centers of rugby. Both amateur (rugby union) and professional (rugby league) play attract huge crowds who support the game with an almost religious dedication. The main difference between rugby union and rugby league contests is that rugby league is somewhat rougher, and its combination of intricate ball-handling and improvisation provides a pattern more closely resembling American football than that of rugby union.

There are four rugby unions, located in England, Wales, Scotland, and Ireland, with international matches played against teams from Belgium, Italy, France, Germany, New Zealand, Australia, and Thailand. In 1973, a five-nation tournament was held by rugby union, and the European matches drew fervid partisan support from its supporters.

Rugby union teams consist of 15 players to a side, their object being to move up the field by passing a ball to one another, or kicking it until such time as they are able to score. There are six ways to score. The grounding of the ball over the opponent's goal-line is a try and counts for four points. A try can be converted to six points if the kick at goal that follows is successful. A penalty goal, dropped goal, and goal from a fair catch are each worth three points.

The field must not exceed 110 yards in length or 75 yards in width. The ball is oval-shaped, somewhat like the American football, but is fatter and rounded at the ends. Player replacements are permitted only in the event of injury. However, no more than two players may be substituted.

Rugby league teams use 13 players on a side, and two substitutes are allowed during any given match. A try is worth three points, and a conversion an additional two points. Penalty goals also earn 2 points in rugby league play, while a dropped goal counts for one point.

A major development in 1975 saw the formation of the United States of America Rugby Football Union. This governing body is composed of delegates from four territorial rugby unions—Eastern

Rugby Union of America; Midwest Rugby Football Union; Western Rugby Football Union of the United States; and the Pacific Coast Rugby Football Union.

SKIING

The skier glides majestically down the slope, kicking up powdery crystals which explode under the penetrating rays of the winter sun. Gaining momentum, he hurtles at lightning speed while freely negotiating his way toward the finish line. He is the *downhill racer,* a competitor on the loose. And, in the brief time of his race, he is a breathtaking physical marvel who charges our imagination to a peak of excitement.

The modern skier selects his snowy vistas in typical high altitude locations—the mountain areas of the United States, Europe, South America, Japan, and elsewhere. He also finds unlikely locations to indulge his ski pleasures, such as the lower latitude countries of Lebanon, India, Greece, Turkey, and Israel. When natural snow is not available, whole sections are sprayed with ammonium nitrate so that any later snowfalls harden and create a better surface for skiing. Snow machines are also on hand to produce artificial snow whenever needed.

Sweden's Ingemar Stenmark won the overall World Cup title for the second straight year in 1977. He finished 89 points ahead of the runner-up, Klaus Heidegger of Austria.

Skis were used in warfare as far back as A.D. 1200, during the Battle of Oslo, when King Sverre of Sweden equipped his troops with skis and sent them on reconnaissance missions against the Norwegian foe. One of the most inspiring war stories in history took place when Finnish ski troops held off the entire Russian Army in 1939, maneuvering brilliantly in deep snow to befuddle their less experienced ski-equipped enemy.

The Norwegians were the first to treat skiing as a sport. In 1860, the king of Norway awarded a trophy to the winner of a ski jumping contest held near Oslo, and subsequently appointed a committee to draft rules for annual tournaments. In time this tournament became the most popular sports event in the country.

The first United States ski club was founded in New Hampshire in 1872, and is still in existence. The National Ski Association was formed in 1904, with 17 charter members. By 1932, when the third Winter Olympics took place at Lake Placid, New York, thousands of new ski enthusiasts swarmed over every area that maintained a ski lodge, or had facilities for skiing. In 1964, there were about five million ski club members, and in the early 1970s the NSA estimated that more than eight hundred ski lifts were in operation in the United States.

There were three major categories of ski events: *alpine, jumping,* and *cross-country.* Alpine racing was given Olympic recognition in 1936. Performed on long vertical slopes in high terrain, it consists of downhill and slalom events. The downhill course has a vertical descent of approximately three thousand feet and a length of between one and one-half and three miles. The aim of downhill racing is to get to the bottom of the slope in the quickest time possible. The skier has the option of choosing any route he wishes in order to negotiate the course.

Jumpers are judged for distance and execution. Courage is also counted in the point total, as the explosive flight of a competitor takes as much nerve as one can find in the world of sports. Leaps of three hundred feet and more give the jumper an almost birdlike quality, even though his flight may last for only 10 seconds or less.

Slalom racing puts a premium on style and speed, requiring the racer to negotiate a snaking course with a variety of flag and gate combinations. A slalom course of five hundred to one thousand feet is used for all national championship contests.

Cross-country racing is held over natural terrain, one-third of which is uphill, one-third down-hill, and the other third on flat or rolling surface. The 15-kilometer race is the most popular of all, just long enough to completely test the strength, endurance, courage, and skill of the skier.

The sport is controlled by the International Ski Federation, with 47 member nations participating in one of the most invigorating pastimes ever conceived by man.

SOCCER

Soccer is the most popular sport in the world. The amazing growth of soccer *(association football)* began soon after World War II, and since then the sport has become a social phenomenon. The top stars make hundreds of thousands of dollars a year. More than one hundred thirty nations are members of the FIFA *(Federation Internationale de Football Associations)*, the governing body of the game, and millions of people wager in soccer pools each week, hoping to pick the games correctly and make their "retirement" money.

Soccer actually started in 1863, when the English Football Association was founded. The British developed the sport, and within a decade it was being played from continent to continent. However, almost 70 years were to elapse before English superiority was seriously challenged. Until the early 1930s, the British were masters of the game, defeating less experienced teams almost at will. Then the South American teams began to challenge the British supremacy. Yet it took another 20 years until teams from Uruguay, Argentina, Chile, and Brazil were able to reach parity. By then, other European countries like Italy, Spain, Germany, France, Belgium, Hungary, Romania, and Yugoslavia were also in the running for the World Cup.

Soccer is played in the United States at the college level, but the major thrust of American soccer is focused on professional play. The North American Soccer League (NASL) increased from 15 to 20 teams in 1975, and to 24 for the 1978 season. American professional teams have also played international matches against all-star and championship teams from Europe and South America. In 1972, as an example, the New York Cosmos of the NASL hosted the formidable Moscow Dynamos at Hofstra Stadium, on Long Island, and gave a

Steve Hunt of the Cosmos (11) was voted the most valuable player in the 1977 North American Soccer League's championship game after he scored the first goal and assisted on the other in a 2-1 victory over Seattle.

good account of themselves before losing a close, hard-fought match.

The object of a soccer match is to advance the ball toward the opponent's goal and between the goalposts by kicking, dribbling, heading, and, with the exception of the arms and hands, playing it with any part of the body. The *goalkeeper,* who guards the net, is the only one allowed to use hands, providing he stays in his own penalty area.

A soccer field is between 110 and 130 yards long, the width being from 70 to 80 yards. Players are equipped with cleated shoes and wear shin guards and other protective equipment to prevent injury. There are 11 players on each team: one *goalkeeper,* two *fullbacks,* three *halfbacks,* and five *forwards.* Goals, which count one point each, must be scored through the opponent's goal and under the crossbar. A regulation match lasts 90 minutes, with a 10-minute rest between halves.

SOFTBALL

A Minneapolis firefighter, Lewis Rober, is considered the father of softball, or kittenball as it was known when it was originated about 1895. The first softball league was formed in Minneapolis in 1900. At that time it was an indoor game.

In 1930, Leo Fischer of the *Chicago American* newspaper and M. J. Pauley, a fellow Chicagoan, decided the game should be moved outdoors where larger playing areas would insure a faster, more competitive sport.

Many credit the Great Depression with the explosive growth of softball. It was an inexpensive form of recreation. There were, by then, plenty of playgrounds and certainly many men out of work and ready for an active sport that would divert them from the grim realities of the times. The governing body for the game was the Amateur Softball Association, and the first quasi-national tournament was held in 1933 with the J. L. Gill team of Chicago the winner. From the sport's beginning, women were heavily involved and turned out teams that drew grudging praise from the men.

A survey made in the mid-1970s gave a clue to the phenomenal growth of the sport. By one count there were 95,000 teams and 1.8 million players registered with the Amateur Softball Association. In 1977, 85 percent of all softball was slow pitch, and the other 15 percent was fast pitch.

Softball is a game with as many statistics as baseball and some notable records. One record is a 42-inning game played in 1942 at Kenosha, Wisconsin and won by the Italian American Club. Its pitcher, Corky Vorraeini, went the distance in the 1–0 contest.

SURFING

Surfing remained the sport of royalty in the islands of the South Seas for hundreds of years. But a sport offering such adventure never remains the exclusive property of one people. The idea was carried northward by hardy native seamen.

Captain James Cook, the explorer who discovered Hawaii, made an important note in his log book in the year 1778. With great interest, he had watched natives riding "long, narrow boards" through the giant surf that continually pounds the shores of this tropical paradise.

With the coming of Cook to Hawaii, lives of natives changed. Civilization had arrived. More Americans and Europeans came to the islands to live. Tribal customs and rituals were slowly abandoned in favor of "western" ideas. Interest in surfing declined until it became almost nonexistent.

Then, early in the twentieth century, surfing as a sport began to grow once again and interest spread to the coastal regions of other countries, the United States in particular. No longer were the ancient grass mats used. In their place, boards of carved timber, heavy and difficult to maneuver, were challenging the waves.

Still, with such cumbersome equipment, surfing was not a truly popular sport. Only a few brave people attempted it . . . but they grew to love the struggle between themselves and the crashing surf. These same people began to devise new equipment. Hollow boards to defeat the weight problem came first. A few of these are actually still in use today.

Three of the most important innovations in surfing came one after another, very recently, and the sport opened to everybody.

The first was the use of balsa wood and fiberglass cloth, devised by Bob Simmons who was a

Reno Abellira rides a 15-foot wave to victory in the 1977 World Pro-Am competition at Sunset Beach, Hawaii. Reno received $5,000 for his first-place finish.

student at the California Institute of Technology. Balsa wood is light, and with a fiberglass coating became completely waterproof. Increasing numbers of surfers were seen along coastlines with these "Malibu boards" where the surf was up. Then, to bring the equipment to near perfection, Dave and Roger Sweet of California built a polyurethane-fiberglass surfboard, the one in popular use today. It was light, waterproof, durable, relatively inexpensive, and easy to decorate.

Only one problem remained.

The word *surf* naturally meant "seashore." But thousands of interested, potential surfers lived inland, far from the ocean. Distance alone excluded them from this new sport.

Along came surfboard manufacturer Hobie Alter with an amazing idea.

All one needs to surf, reasoned Alter, is surf alone. Nobody ever claimed that it had to be ocean surf. The wake behind a boat is surf in the real sense of the word. Perhaps it is true, as some surfers claim, that famed surfer Duke Kahanamoku of Hawaii had the same thought many years ago, and proved it could be done. Alter, in any case, is the modern father of wake riding since he proved his point so successfully. Early in 1964, he hopped on his ocean surfboard and guided it into the "feather" of the wake of the sport fishing boat *Freedom*. Although the nose of Alter's board was only three feet from the stern of the boat when in proper wake riding position, he opened a whole new field for potential surfers. For nine miles Alter rode his board, a longer ride, for sure, than any ocean surfer has a chance to enjoy with short duration waves.

Now surfing could be enjoyed anywhere, even on an inland lake. Only a boat, loaded heavy at the stern to produce enough wake, was needed. And, since the surfer is not attached to the boat by line or other means, it is true surfing.

With this, the number of people riding surfboards for fun has increased tremendously. From a small beginning in the South Seas, surfing has finally spread around the world, to every body of water. Wherever wave conditions are right, or can be made right with a boat, a surfer will sooner or later appear with a board. Then will come two surfers, then three, and a new surfing spot is named. Lately in fact, to carry things to an extreme, a few surfers have even used a board without a *skeg* (a small keel or fim) to surf on slopes of snow during the off-season.

SWIMMING AND DIVING

When Mark Spitz captured his unprecedented seven gold medals at the 1972 Munich Olympics, competitive swimming notched another proud moment in its long aquatic history.

Japan was the first country to introduce a national sports organization for swimming. An Imperial edict in A.D. 1603 ordered interschool matches as an integral part of the curriculum. Japan, however, was a closed society in those days, and it was left to the Anglo-Saxon nations to develop competitive swimming on a worldwide basis.

In 1837, England formed the National Swimming Association, marking the first time competitive races had been organized by a sports society. But it was Australian foresight that moved swimming ahead to international levels. On February 14, 1846, in Sydney, the first modern swimming championship was held, a 440-yard event won by W. Redmond, who swam the distance in 8:43.0. Twelve years later a so-called 100-yard "world championship" took place in Melbourne, won by Australian Jo Bennett over an Englishman, Charles Stedman.

England initiated a national swimming federation in 1874, the Swimming Association of Great Britain, which led to further competition in other European countries. By 1889, with the start of European championships, staged in Vienna, competitive swimming became an accepted international sport. Swimming received further credibility in 1896, when the athletic world trumpeted the return of the modern Olympic Games in Athens. Three swimming events were included on the program—with an 18-year-old Hungarian, Alfred Guttman, a double winner in the 100 meters (1:22.2) and 1,500 meters (18:22.2), and Austria's Paul Newman a victor in the 500 meters at 8:12.6.

In 1908, the Fédération Internationale de Natation Amateur (FINA) was organized as the world's governing body for swimming. Four years later, the bronzed, supple Hawaiian Duke Kahanamoku began the dominance by Americans in international events. Kahanamoku won the 100-meters title in the Stockholm Olympic Games, and remained a force in sprint competition for more than a decade. He was followed by other American champions, such as Johnny Weissmuller, Buster Crabbe (both of whom became stars of *Tarzan* motion pictures), Eleanor Holm, Esther Williams, and more recent swim champions of international fame: Don Schollander, Mark Spitz, Rick DeMont,

Debbie Meyer, and Sue Pederson. Today, the United States is a ranking power in world swimming, along with the Australians, English, Japanese, Hungarians, and Germans.

Divers are literally aquatic acrobats who specialize in intricate somersaulting and twisting dives from springboards or platforms. Anyone who witnessed the incredible diving feats of Micki King of the United States Air Force, in the 1972 Munich Games, can testify to the skill, elegance, and courage that go into world diving championships. Body control, with the emphasis on style and grace, counts heavily in the judging of contests. The most difficult dives require a high degree of understanding of body function in order to produce the multi-spinning, twisting, turning combinations that are keynotes of diving excellence. United States divers have been perennial winners in Olympic and international matches.

FINA sets all rules for swimming and diving competition. In swimming, recognized distances for the following events were drawn up for men and women by FINA in 1968: *Freestyle,* 100, 200, 400, 800, 1,500 meters, 4 X 100 meters relay, and for men the 4 X 200 meters relay; *Breaststroke,* 100 and 200 meters; *Butterfly,* 100 and 200 meters; *Backstroke,* 100 and 200 meters; and *Medley,* 200 and 400 meters individual, and 4 X 100 meters relay.

In 1957, FINA established a rule that all world records must be set only in international-size 50-meter pools. Until then, records for distances under 800 meters were also recognized in pools with a minimum size of 25 yards. In an eight-lane pool, standard for championship races, the swimmer with fastest heat time is placed in lane four, the next fastest in lane five, and then, in lesser time order, lanes three, six, two, seven, one, and eight. This is known as the *spearhead* principle. It gives the better swimmers an opportunity to see each other while they're churning through the water, and also helps the officials determine the correct order of finish.

TENNIS

It was supposed to be a typical English lawn party. But when the guests arrived, their host, Major Walter Clopton Wingfield, handed them spoon-shaped racquets with long handles and displayed his new invention—the first outdoor tennis

Virginia Wade strains in making a backhand return during the 1977 Wimbledon women's singles finals. Virginia downed Betty Stove of The Netherlands and became the first native of Britain to win the tourney since Ann Haydon-Jones in 1969.

court. Wingfield, a strikingly handsome aristocrat with a flowing mustache, long sideburns, and beard, then brought out the hollow rubber balls he had fashioned for the occasion.

Little did Wingfield realize on that December afternoon in 1873 that one century later, his brainchild, which he dubbed *sphairistike,* would be played before millions of television viewers—who groaned or squealed with delight as Billie Jean King defeated Bobby Riggs in the "Tennis Battle of the Century" at Houston's Astrodome.

Spanning the years—from Wingfield to King—tennis is a sport that has moved from the realm of the very rich to universal acceptance. Today, well over 10 million active players participate in tennis in the United States alone. Figures indicate that in 1974, 150,000 tennis courts were in use in this country and over 20 million tennis balls were sold annually. Tennis racquets costing from ten to seventy dollare are sold almost as fast as the manufacturers make them.

Tennis in the 1970s is not only big business; it is also a profession for many of the outstanding players of the game. Until 1971, the sport had been mainly amateur, with the big tournaments at Wimbledon, Forest Hills, and other sites limited to trophy prizes for the winners. It took Lamar Hunt, the successful owner of the pro football Kansas City Chiefs, and financier of basketball, baseball, and soccer teams, to devise a $1 million pro tour, which led to a mass defection of top-seeded amateurs. The pro ranks now encompass the World Championship Tennis (WCT) circuit, the Grand Prix, World Team Tennis, the Virginia Slims circuit, and others.

But amateur it was at Wingfield's famous lawn party—as it was in 1874 when Mary Ewing Outerbridge, a socially prominent sportswoman from Staten Island, New York, returned from a holiday in Bermuda with a package of tennis racquets, balls, and a net. Miss Outerbridge and her two brothers, Emilius and Eugenius, gained permission from the Staten Island Cricket and Baseball Club to lay out a tennis court on the edge of their cricket field. On a lovely spring day of that year, she and her brothers played the first game of lawn tennis in the United States. In her high-button shoes, half a dozen silk slips, and flowing dress, Mary Ewing Outerbridge thus became "the Mother of Tennis."

The first National Championships were played at Newport, Rhode Island, in 1881, and remained there until they moved to Forest Hills, New York, in 1915.

Meanwhile, in England, the game had reached a standstill until 1887, when the All-England Croquet and Lawn Tennis Club at Wimbledon held its first amateur tournament. An entrance fee of one shilling was charged, and two prizes—one gold, the other silver—were handed out to the first- and second-place winners.

Since then, a long line of brilliant tennis players have performed at Wimbledon. From Bill Tilden to Stan Smith, United States performers have engaged in dramatic contests against the best from Europe and Australia, such as England's Fred Perry and Australia's Rod Laver, Roy Emerson, and John Newcombe. United States women have also been an important part of the Wimbledon scene. Beginning in 1927, when the remarkable Helen Wills Moody captured the first of her eight Wimbledon crowns, American women have generally been in the thick of the action.

The magic of Wimbledon and the U.S. Open is just as strong today, and other tournaments, such as the 1976 World Championship of Tennis (won by Bjorn Borg of Sweden), have been created as the pro equivalent of the famed Davis Cup.

The Davis Cup was originated in 1900 by Dwight Filley Davis, who was then attending Harvard University. He conceived the idea of matching the best players of the United States against the top players from Britain. The Americans won handily, with Holcombe Ward and Davis taking the doubles, and Malcolm Whitman and Davis (again) besting their English opponents in singles matches. Ever since, the Cup has been awarded each year to the winning nation in the tournament.

Amateur tennis in America is governed by the United States Tennis Association (USTA). Founded in 1881, it set up matches (known as the Grand Slam Championships) in the United States, Australia, France, and England, and consequently brought the world's best players to its prestigious title matches. With the start of *open* tennis (wherein amateurs and pros are allowed to compete against each other), money prizes were introduced to USTA play.

Tennis is played by two (singles) or four (doubles) opponents. Play begins when the server hits the ball fairly into the opposite service court. If the first serve is hit out of the service court or into the net, this is called a *fault,* and the server serves again. If the second serve is also out of the designated service area, a *double fault* and forfeiture of the point results. Opponents alternate serves after each game.

Once the ball is in play, the opponents use a variety of strokes *(backhand, forehand, lob,* etc.) and spins to force their opponents either to miss the ball or to hit it out of bounds or into the net, in order to win the point. A player must win four points to win a game. In tennis scoring, both players begin at *love,* or zero, and advance to 15, 30, 40 and *game* with each point scored. The server's score is always called out first. If a game is tied at 40-all, or *deuce,* play continues until one opponent has achieved a two-point margin of victory. A player must win six games in order to win a *set.* Most *matches* consist of the best two out of three sets, although in many championship tournaments, a player must win three out of five sets to win the match.

A recent addition to tennis scoring is the *tie breaker*. When a set is tied at six games apiece, a predetermined number of points are played. The player who wins the most of these points wins the set.

Court boundaries are widened from 27 feet to 36 feet when *doubles* or mixed doubles (men and women) matches replace singles matches. The net is 3 feet high, the length of the court is 78 feet between the base lines, and each half of the court is divided by a service line, 21 feet from the net, while another line runs from the center of the net to divide the service area into two service courts.

Tennis matches are played on a flat surface of grass or clay, although indoor matches have also been played on carpet, wood, artificial grass, linoleum, and tarmacadam.

TRACK AND FIELD

Many of the track and field events we know today were originally skills necessary for primitive man's survival. He had to run to escape from or to pursue his enemies, and to catch animals for food and clothing. No doubt his running took the form of both the sprints and distances, as well as the hurdles when he was forced to leap over rocks or obstacles in his way.

It can be assumed that before prehistoric man had weapons he threw rocks and sticks at animals to kill them. This could have developed into our discus, shot, and javelin throws. The necessity of jumping over streams or wall-like rocks gave rise to the broad jump, pole vault, and high jump.

These were the activities of early man which came down through the ages to ancient Greece. Greece, with her love of the muscular man, began to glorify those youths who could run the fastest, throw the farthest, jump the highest and for the greatest distance.

There were scattered athletic competitions in Greece as early as 1370 B.C. But the first organized Greek games were held at Olympia in 776 B.C., and every fourth summer thereafter until A.D. 394 when they were abolished by the Roman emperor Theodosius.

All entrants in the Olympic Games had to meet certain requirements: They had to be Greeks, must never have committed a crime, must take an oath to compete fairly, must have been in training for 10 months before the Games, and must have spent the last month at Olympia.

Cuba's Alberto Juantorena (right) notices Kenya's Mike Boit right behind him as he narrowly wins the 800-meter run in 1:44.0 during the 1977 World Cup competition at Dusseldorf, West Germany. Juantorena broke his own record for the 800 meters two weeks before the World Cup with a 1:43.4 clocking. Alberto is the only man to win the 400- and 800-meter Olympic runs, having accomplished the feat in 1976 at Montreal.

The events included races, with the actual distances depending on the length of the stadium. One length of the stadium was about two hundred yards. The racers also ran twice that distance, and perhaps as far as 4,800 yards. Contestants for short runs were divided into heats of about four men each, by drawing lots. The winners of the heats ran to determine the final winner and other places. This is exactly the way our sprints are run in present-day meets. The runners of the fifth century B.C. practiced by running in deep sand.

In addition to the running events, there were competitions in jumping and throwing the javelin and the discus. The jumping events included the broad jump and the hop-step-and-jump. All competitors jumped from the same take-off into soft, loose ground; the distance was measured with a rod. In 656 B.C., Chronis of Sparta made the first long jump to be recorded: 23 feet, 1½ inches.

Throwing the javelin was one of the most popular and practical sports in Greece. The skill was necessary in war and in the hunt. The javelins used in competitions were 8 to 10 feet long, of varying weights, and had dull points. A thong was wrapped around the shaft, near the middle, with a loop for the fingers. This device trebled the distance that the javelin could be thrown and imparted a rotary motion to it.

In the original weight-throwing contests, stones and rough pieces of metal, called *hateres,* were used: later the object to be thrown took the form of the modern discus. The discus was hurled without the complete turning of the body.

In 1871, a track meet was held in New York City—the first in this country. In 1876, the ICAAAA and NCAA were formed and each initiated a track and field meet which have been annual events ever since.

The Olympic Games were revived in Greece in 1896, and, with the exception of 1916, 1940, and 1944, have been held every four years since then.

Former pro basketball star Wilt Chamberlain was named president of the International Volleyball Association in 1977. He also played for the circuit's Orange County Stars. (Photo by J. Stephen Hicks)

VOLLEYBALL

Although volleyball is a United States invention, Japan, the Soviet Union, East Germany, Belgium, Italy, Cuba, and Brazil have produced championship teams in recent years. It was called *minonette* before William Morgan, a Massachusetts YMCA instructor, began experimenting with the game in 1895. His players, who *volleyed* the ball over the net, prompted Morgan to change the direction as well as the name of the sport.

Volleyball is played by striking the ball, with either the hand, fist, or arm, over the net on serve, then hitting it with any part of the body above and including the waist. The ball cannot be hit twice in succession by a player, or more than three times by a team, before it crosses the net. If the receiving team fails to return the ball, the serving team scores a point, with 15 points determining the winner. A squad in a regulation volleyball game is limited to 12 members, with six on the court at any one time.

The first national tournament in the United States was held in 1922. From 1900 to 1925, changes were made in the rules that established the net height for men at eight feet and for women at seven feet four and one-forth inches, marked the court 30 by 60 feet, and devised other regulations which helped to make volleyball a popular sport in thousands of public schools and colleges in the United States.

The Olympics recognized volleyball in 1957, but the game did not enter competition until 1964, at which time matches in both men's and women's divisions provided exciting action for thousands.

Volleyball, as it is played today, is a game of strategy and power that requires lightning-quick reflexes on the part of the players. Generally, a team will use all three of its hits in order to set up the *spike,* a powerful downward smash into the opponents' court that, when properly placed, is all but impossible to return. In order to disguise the player who will ultimately spike the ball, many players approach the net at one instant in an attempt to confuse the opponents, and the "setter" delivers the ball to the teammate in the best position to successfully complete the attack. To offset this complicated attack, defensive plays have evolved, such as the *block,* the defensive player reaching across the net to intercept the ball at the moment it is spiked, and the *dive,* the headlong lunge at a ball by defensive players attempting to intercept the spike before it contacts the floor.

The United States Volleyball Association is the national representative for volleyball in the International Volleyball Federation and the organization delegated by the United States Olympic Committee to train and select teams participating in Pan-American and Olympic Game Competition. The USVBA is composed of organizations national in scope which also promote volleyball and conduct national championships, such as the AAU, the NCAA, and the AAHPER. The International Volleyball Association, a professional league, was organized in 1975. Wilt Chamberlain, the former basketball great, was named president of the circuit in 1977. He also played for the IVA's Orange County Stars.

WRESTLING

Professional wrestling enjoys wide popular appeal, but in recent years it has been relegated to the status of an exhibition sport, while amateur wrestling seems to be gaining momentum on the international sporting scene.

Wrestling is as old as man. The Greeks and Romans of ancient times were devotees of the sport, and in Homer's *Iliad* there is an account of a wrestling match between Ulysses and Ajax.

The Greeks founded various wrestling schools *(palaestra)* and by the seventh century B.C., wrestling was an important part of the Olympic Games. Eventually, the Romans became great wrestling enthusiasts, with many contests held in the Coliseum to compete with other sporting spectacles. Hence, the term *Greco-Roman* is now part of the wrestling litany.

Mark Churella of Michigan gets the upper hand in match against Iowa State's Joe Zuspann during NCAA University Division Championship in 1977. Churella won the match and the 150-pound class title.

The first modern Olympic Games, held in Athens in 1896, introduced Greco-Roman style wrestling, with only five athletes competing. Wrestling was removed from the 1900 Olympic program, only to return in 1904, when the United States swept the freestyle event.

In 1921, the Amateur Wrestling Federation was established in Europe, and championship matches were arranged. The AWF also opened competition to wrestlers from the United States. The United States Wrestling Federation was formed in 1969 to encourage amateur wrestling at all levels of competition. The NCAA, the National Junior College Athletic Association, and other school-oriented associations regulate the sport.

Amateur wrestling takes place on a circular mat, 24 feet in diameter for high schools, 32 feet for colleges, and nine meters for international style. A circle 10 feet in diameter is marked off in the center of the mat. A match consists of three three-minute periods in which wrestlers use a series of holds, locks, and grips in an effort to pin their opponents to the mat. A contestant is awarded a *fall* if he is able to pin both of his opponent's shoulders to the mat for a full two seconds in high school competition, one second in college, and one-half second in international matches. Points, in varying amounts according to the style of wrestling, are awarded for a *near fall,* a *takedown,* a *reversal,* and, in school-style wrestling only, an *escape.* Penalty points resulting from stalling tactics, illegal holds, and other infractions are subtracted from a contestant's point total. If a wrestler receives three *cautions* from the referee, or if an infraction is serious enough, he is eliminated. If a fall occurs at any time, the match is terminated. Otherwise, the opponent with the most points at the end of a match is declared the winner.

In freestyle wrestling, a wrestler may use his legs freely to take his opponent to the mat. In Greco-Roman events, however, it is illegal to trip or grasp an opponent below the waist, or otherwise use one's legs to take down an opponent.

Professional wrestling belongs more to the world of entertainment than to the world of sports, and more emphasis is placed on spectacular throws and dramatics than on athletic skills. However, many top amateur wrestlers and professional athletes from other sports have been drawn to professional wrestling. Antonino Rocca, a professional wrestler of the late 1950s, earned an annual six-figure salary at the peak of his career.

CHAPTER TWENTY

FOUR HUNDRED FAMOUS AMERICANS

It would be impossible to name all of the people who have played an important role in the history of the United States. But in this chapter we list some of the leading Americans from all walks of life, both living and dead, who have left their mark on American society.

You will find leading American authors described under "Authors and Their Works" (pp. 124–151). American Presidents are reviewed on pages 217–256.

AARON, HENRY L. "HANK" (1934–), baseball player. Born in Mobile, Alabama, Aaron began playing for the Indianapolis Clowns of the Negro League in 1952. He joined the Milwaukee Braves as shortstop in 1954 and soon moved to an outfield position. The next year he emerged as top batter of the National League with a .328 average. When the Braves won the World Series in 1957, Aaron was voted the league's Most Valuable Player. He moved with the Braves to Atlanta in 1966, and broke Babe Ruth's home-run record when he hit run number 715 on April 8, 1974 in Atlanta.

ABBOTT, LYMAN (1835–1922), an ordained minister of the Congregational Church; prominent journalist and exponent of the "social gospel." Abbott was associated with *Harper's Magazine* and *The Christian Union* (also known as *The Outlook).* He authored *The Life and Literature of the Ancient Hebrews* and other titles that sought to integrate religion and science. After the publication of Charles Darwin's theories of evolution, he became involved with liberal writers and thinkers. Abbott rarely opposed the theological trends of his day. He

believed that man was constantly improving, and he affirmed the essential goodness of man. Ira Brown has written an excellent biography titled *Lyman Abbott* (1953).

ABERNATHY, RALPH DAVID (1926–), civil rights leader of the Southern Christian Leadership Conference. Abernathy was closely identified with Dr. Martin Luther King and the human rights revolution of the 1960s. A deliberative preacher committed to nonviolence, he was a member of the Atlantic Ministers Union and Operation Breadbasket. This gave him a unique sensitivity to the religious applications of human needs. During the Montgomery (Alabama) bus boycott he demonstrated strength of purpose and determination that helped to change the social order. He was ordained into the Baptist ministry in 1948.

ABBOTT, BUD (1896–1974), associated in comedy with Lou Costello. A son of Harry Abbott who served with Ringling Brothers' Circus, he organized a network of burlesque houses in the generation of the Ziegfeld Follies. Abbott starred in several movies, including *One Night in the Tropics, Hold That Ghost,* and *Abbott and Costello Meet Frankenstein.* He promoted the sale of millions of war bonds in World War II and entertained troops during the war. His efforts on behalf of radio, stage, and screen performance made him a well-known entertainer in an age that placed a premium on slapstick.

ACHESON, DEAN (1893–1971), Secretary of State under President Truman; a diplomat in the early stages of the Cold War between the United

States and the Soviet Union. Acheson wrote *Power and Diplomacy,* among other titles. He was largely responsible for the establishment of the North Atlantic Treaty Organization (NATO). During the period of McCarthyism, Acheson refused to testify against his friend Alger Hiss, who had been charged with espionage. He received many honors during his lifetime, including honorary degrees from Yale University and Wesleyan University. He was affiliated with the Democratic Party.

ACUFF, ROY (1903–   ), born Nashville, Tennessee, a noted country-music singer and bandleader. Acuff organized the Smokey Mountain Boys and has been closely associated with Nashville's Grand Ole Opry. He has achieved international fame for his songs, "Wabash Cannon Ball," "That Lonely Mountain of Clay," and "The Great Judgment Morning." He produced a succession of recording classics for Columbia Records and was elected to the Country Music Hall of Fame. An automobile accident in 1965 left him severely injured, but he recovered sufficiently to record "Roy Acuff Sings Famous Opry Favorites" in 1967. He toured college campuses and received considerable recognition for his courage and determination in the face of his injuries.

ADDAMS, JANE (1860–1935), with Ellen Gates Starr organized Hull House in Chicago, Illinois, as a social and humanitarian center. Miss Addams was an early feminist and shared a Nobel Peace Prize. She authored *The Spirit of Youth* and *The City Streets.* Miss Addams was a leader of the Progressive Party and the Women's International Peace and Freedom. She sought legislation to end the corruption of political life in Chicago, and she served as an adviser to several Presidents.

ALI, MUHAMMAD (1942–   ), a significant figure in American boxing history, known for his colorful and poetic use of language. Born as Cassius M. Clay, he became associated with the Black Muslims and adopted his Muslim name. He refused to be drafted into the military in 1967 and became the center of legal controversies. He won numerous Golden Gloves awards, the Olympic Championship, and the Heavyweight Championship of the world. He has engaged in limited screen roles and frequently appears on television. Leon Spinks won the Heavyweight championship from Ali at Las Vegas, Nevada on February 15, 1978.

ALLEN, ETHAN (1737–1789), author and military figure from the Revolutionary period. During the American Revolution, Allen was captured by the British and was held as a prisoner of war. He organized a militia group in Vermont known as the Green Mountain Boys, and he asked the Continental Congress to raise similar units among the other colonies. He authored a book titled *Reason the Only Grade of Man* (1784), an apology for deism.

ALLPORT, GORDON (1897–1967), outstanding psychologist and teacher. Allport wrote *The Individual and His Religion.* He was associated with Harvard University and produced several new theories of personality and social psychology. Allport was involved in many different organizations, including the British Psychological Society and the National Research Council. He received numerous honors and recognitions, and served as editor of the *Journal for Abnormal and Social Psychology* from 1937 to 1949.

ANDERSON, MARIAN (1902–   ), black contralto recognized as an outstanding singer within concert and operatic circles. Honored in many countries for her musical excellence, she is a native of South Philadelphia. Miss Anderson authored *My Lord, What a Morning* and has travelled extensively, giving concerts in Great Britain, Scandinavia, Germany, and the Soviet Union. She has worked with Paul Robeson and others to achieve greater freedoms for black Americans. Miss Anderson has received special recognition from the National Association for the Advancement of Colored People (NAACP) and was honored by Howard University and 20 other colleges and universities with honorary doctorates.

Muhammad Ali lands a right to George Foreman during their title bout in Kinshasa, Zaire, on Oct. 29, 1976.

ANTHONY, SUSAN B. (1820–1906), an early proponent of women's rights, identified with the leadership of the American Suffrage Association and several temperance associations. Miss Anthony organized support for the enactment of the fourteenth and fifteenth amendments to the United States Constitution. She was involved in the publication of *The History of Woman's Suffrage* and worked with Ida Harper on *The Life and Work of Susan B. Anthony.*

ARBUCKLE, ROSCOE "FATTY" (1887–1933), American actor and producer born in Smith Center, Kansas. Mr. Arbuckle was identified with numerous motion picture roles in *Moonshine, The Bell Boy,* and *The Sheriff,* among others. He organized the Comique Film Corporation.

ARMSTRONG, LOUIS (1900–1971), jazz trumpeter and vocalist, also known as "Satchmo." Mr. Armstrong appeared in numerous movies, including *Pennies from Heaven, New Orleans, The Glenn Miller Story,* and *Hello Dolly.* Born in New Orleans, he revolutionized American Jazz. After touring the United States with his band, he played at the London Palladium and made numerous appearances before royalty in Sweden, Belgium, Holland, and Denmark. Mr. Armstrong's performance in *High Society* and numerous other recordings have made him an enduring part of the American scene.

ARMSTRONG, NEIL (1930–　　), veteran astronaut; the first man to set foot on the moon. Born near Wapakoneta, Ohio, he graduated from Purdue University. As a test pilot he was chosen to serve with Edwin Aldrin and Michael Collins on the historic moon flight of July 16, 1969. He also served as the command pilot for the later Gemini 8 program. Mr. Armstrong was an aviator for the United States Naval Reserve from 1949 to 1950. His name will always be associated with the famous words he spoke as he set foot on the moon: "One small step for man; one giant step for mankind."

ARNAZ, DESI (1917–　　), Latin American musician, comedian, and television producer. Born in Santiago, Cuba, he was associated in comedy with Lucille Ball during the early stages of television. Mr. Arnaz starred in several lesser-known movie musicals until he organized Desilu Productions with his wife, Lucille Ball. He co-starred with Lucille Ball in other movie productions, such as *The Long, Long, Trailer* and *Forever Darling.* He hosted *Desilu Playhouse.* After 1962, he became an independent producer and president of Desi Arnaz Productions. He served during World War II in the United States Army.

ARNOLD, BENEDICT (1741–1801), a patriot and traitor from the Revolutionary period. Arnold organized an army early in the Revolutionary War, but escaped to the British in 1781. His name is synonymous with treachery. In the winter of 1776–1777, he was accused of misconduct and of stealing property from merchants in Montreal during the Canadian campaign. In anger, he resigned his commission in 1777. He conceived the idea of turning over the command of West Point to the English for a ransom; the plot was uncovered and he was forced to seek sanctuary with the English army.

ASBURY, FRANCIS (1745–1816), an early bishop in the Methodist Episcopal Church, associated with John Wesley. Asbury came to America as a missionary and remained to become a leading spokesman for the Independent Methodist Episcopal Church of America. He preached in the Pennsylvania, Maryland, Delaware, and Virginia colonies with a vigor and effectiveness that attracted popular notice. He developed a feud with rival church leader, Thomas Rankin, and during the American Revolution, they were asked to return to England. Rankin left but Asbury remained and became a leading force in the development of religious independence. He authored *Journals and Letters,* edited by Elmer T. Clark (1958).

ASTAIRE, FRED (1899–　　), American dancer and entertainer. His more famous screen performances include *Easter Parade* (1948), *On the Beach* (1959), and *The Pleasure of His Company* (1961). Mr. Astaire authored *Steps in Time.* His dancing abilities were emphasized in most of his screen performances, such as *The Ziegfeld Follies.* He starred on numerous television specials and occasionally appeared on *The Alcoa Premier.*

ASTOR, JOHN JACOB (1763–1848), American capitalist and entrepreneur. Born in Germany, he immigrated to America and became involved in fur-trading. He organized the American

Fur Company. Mr. Astor's life was characterized by the amassing of incredible wealth. Following the Louisiana Purchase, his trading activities penetrated the Northwest Territories; his traders would collect furs and sell them in the Far East. The town of Astoria was named after the family. After 1800, he became more interested in New York City real estate.

ATTUCKS, CRISPUS (1723–1770), among the group that precipitated the Boston Massacre. Attucks was among the first to die in the struggle that led to the American Revolution. Attucks has been described as a mulatto owned by Deacon William Browne of Framingham, Massachusetts. Although little is known about his life before the Boston Massacre, he has achieved stature as a martyr and patriot. J. B. Fisher, in the *American Historical Record,* Volume I (1872), sought to analyze the deeper meaning of Crispus Attucks' life.

AUDUBON, JOHN J. (1785–1851), a popular naturalist and *ornithologist* (one who studies birds). A man of science, he was responsible for the classification of numerous bird species. Audubon authored *Birds of America,* a classic in the study of birds. His fame extended to Europe. Audubon's earliest research was completed in the wilderness of Kentucky; he travelled to Henderson, Kentucky, to study rare birds. His famous bird drawings evolve from this period. His work is judged as excellent art and science.

AUTRY, GENE (1907–   ), singer, actor, and entertainer born in Tioga, Texas. Autry made his first record in 1929, singing cowboy songs. He starred in over eighty movies and owns several radio stations in the Southwest and on the West Coast. He has written many songs, including "You're the Only Star in My Blue Heaven" and "Here Comes Santa Claus." He has also produced several television specials.

BAEZ, JOAN (1941–   ), folk singer and political activist identified with the anti-war protests of the 1960s. Her musical style reflects melancholy and sadness. Miss Baez was a student at Boston University Fine Arts School. Early in her career, she appeared in Ballard Room and Club 47, and she attracted attention at the Newport (R.I.) Folk Festival. She toured college campuses and in 1962 had a successful Carnegie Hall con-

cert. She established the Institute for the Study of Non-violence in Carmel, California.

BAILEY, F. LEE (1933–   ), defense attorney born in Waltham, Massachusetts. Bailey achieved early fame in the second murder trial of Dr. Sam Sheppard, in which he won Dr. Sheppard's acquittal. He has been described as the most significant criminal lawyer in contemporary America. After Albert DeSalvo's revelations regarding the Boston Strangler Case, he fought for DeSalvo's acquittal but lost. The DeSalvo trial has been regarded as a classic episode in American legal history.

BAILEY, PEARL (1918–   ), female singer born in Newport News, Virginia. Miss Bailey attended various public schools until she achieved early fame as a popular vocalist with stage bands in New York. She has performed in several Broadway musicals, including *The House of Flowers.* She played significant roles in several screen plays, including *Carmen Jones* and *Variety Girl.*

BALL, LUCILLE (1911–   ), actress, television personality, producer, and director. Born in Jamestown, New York, she achieved early fame with her first husband, Desi Arnaz, in the successful television comedy series, *I Love Lucy.* She organized the Desilu Production Company and achieved additional successes in several film productions, including *Forever Darling* and *Love From a Stranger.* Miss Ball has been regarded as the most significant personality from the "situation comedy" programs of American television. Her programs have been syndicated around the world.

BALL, THOMAS (1819–1911), sculptor born in Boston, Massachusetts. Ball achieved early fame at the New England Museum. He travelled to Florence, Italy, at the end of the American Civil War, and received several significant commissions. His more famous creations include *Christmas Morning, St. John the Evangelist* and *Love Memories.* He authored an autobiography titled *My Threescore Years and Ten.* He returned to America in 1897. His most famous work done in the United States is the statue of President Washington.

BARNUM, PHINEAS T. (1810–1891), showman and organizer of circus performances. In 1844, Barnum engaged the services of Tom

Thumb, a dwarf, and travelled to Europe for a series of shows. Barnum was responsible for the early and successful appearances of Jenny Lind in America. He ran for Congress and was defeated. He then organized what came to be called "The Greatest Show on Earth," launching the circus firm of Barnum and Bailey in 1881. Barnum authored the *Life of P. T. Barnum Written by Himself* in 1855.

BASIE, WILLIAM "COUNT" (1904–   ), jazz musician, band leader, and composer. Born in Red Bank, New Jersey, Basie has been featured in concerts at Carnegie Hall and Lincoln Center. He has given command performances before the Queen of England and was featured at the Kennedy Inaugural Ball. Basie has also performed on numerous television programs. His new jazz styles and themes have achieved distinction.

BEAN, ROY (1825–1903), rough-and-ready judge of the American frontier. Born in Mason County, Kentucky, Bean worked as teamster and saloonkeeper in the Southwest until he settled in San Antonio, Texas. In 1882, he moved up the Pecos River and established a saloon for workers who were building the Southern Pacific Railroad. Appointed justice of the peace, he made his saloon in Vinegaroon, Texas his courtroom. Bean was noted for his humor. He became known as "the law west of the Pecos."

BEECHER, HENRY WARD (1813–1887), clergyman and public figure born in Litchfield, Connecticut. Beecher attended Amherst College and became a minister. He sought to effect a moral change in the lives of his audience. He edited the *Western Farmer and Gardener,* based in Indianapolis. In 1847, he was called to Park Street Church as minister; he rejected the invitation and launched a public speaking campaign against slavery in the United States.

BEECHER, LYMAN (1775–1863), clergyman and father of Henry Ward Beecher. Born in New Haven, Connecticut, the elder Beecher was instrumental in organizing the American Bible Society. He served as president of Lane Theological Seminary in Cincinnati, and became embroiled in controversies of the General Assembly of the Presbyterian Church in Ohio.

BELL, ALEXANDER GRAHAM (1847–1922), prolific American inventor born in Edinburgh, Scotland. Although the telephone is his most famous invention, Bell developed many early electronic devices for the deaf. His long-time assistant was Thomas Watson. The first words transmitted by telephone on April 3, 1877 were "Mr. Watson, come here; I want you." Bell received many honors, including the Volta Prize awarded by the French Government. He wrote *Duration of Life* and *Condition Associated with Longevity* (1918).

BENNY, JACK (1894–1974), violinist, vaudeville star, radio and motion-picture personality. Born in Waukegan, Illinois, as Benjamin Kubelsky, he took the stage name of Jack Benny. He achieved significant fame through his television program, *The Jack Benny Show.* He entertained the troops during World War II, and was honored by the National Academy of Television Arts and Science in 1957 for his contributions to the world of entertainment.

BERLIN, IRVING (1888–   ), composer and musician. Born in Russia and migrated to the United States in 1893, Berlin transformed American popular music with his relaxing themes and topical lyrics. Among his famous song titles are: "All Alone," "Remember Reaching for the Moon," and "When I Lost You." His most famous composition was "God Bless America." Berlin composed the stage musicals *Annie Get Your Gun, Call Me Madam,* and *Mr. President.*

BERNSTEIN, LEONARD (1918–   ), conductor, pianist, and composer. Born in Lawrence, Massachusetts, he became a student of Fritz Reiner and Serge Koussevitsky. He was appointed musical director of the New York Philharmonic, where he achieved worldwide recognition. Among his more famous musical creations have been *West Side Story* (1957) and music for *On the Waterfront* (1954). Bernstein wrote *The Joy of Music* (1959) and *Leonard Bernstein's Young People's Concerts for Reading and Listening* (1962).

BETHUNE, MARY MCLEOD (1875–1955), black educator. Born in Mayesville, South Carolina, she studied at Moody Bible Institute of Chicago and later served as president of Bethune-Cookman College. She was appointed as special adviser for minority affairs to President

Franklin Roosevelt and was associated with the National Association for the Advancement of Colored People (NAACP). For a time, she was president of the Central Life Insurance Company and served with the United Negro College Fund. Mrs. Bethune received many honors and degrees from colleges and universities, including Howard University, Wilberforce University, Atlanta University, and the Tuskegee Institute.

BLACK HAWK (1767–1838), Indian war chief. Born in a Sauk village on the Rock River in Illinois, Black Hawk opposed a treaty negotiated by William Henry Harrison with the Sauk nation in 1804; the treaty gave the United States all Sauk country east of the Mississippi River. Black Hawk assisted the British forces in the War of 1812. During the Black Hawk War, he was taken prisoner and jailed at Fort Armstrong in 1832. In 1833, he dictated the *Autobiography of Black Hawk* to a journalist, J. B. Patterson.

BLACK, HUGO L. (1886–1971), jurist and United States Senator. Born in Harlan County, Alabama, Black attended law school at the University of Alabama. He served as prosecuting attorney for Jefferson County from 1915 to 1917, and was in general law practice from 1919 to 1927. He was elected the United States Senator from Alabama for 1927–1931. He served as an associate justice on the United States Supreme Court from 1937 until his death in 1971. Black favored a liberal interpretation of the United States Constitution. He aided the Earl Warren court rulings in the area of civil rights.

BLOCK, HERBERT "HERBLOCK" (1909–), editorial cartoonist born in Chicago, Illinois. Block has served as a cartoonist with the *Washington Post* and the *Chicago Daily News*. He received the Pulitzer Prize, 1942 and 1954. He has been associated with various civil-liberty causes. Block wrote *The Herblock Book* (1952) and *Straight Herblock* (1964), among others. He was commissioned to design the United States postage stamp to commemorate the 175th anniversary of the Bill of Rights.

BOGART, HUMPHREY (1899–1957), actor and film producer. Born in New York City, Bogart portrayed outstanding screen roles without sentimentality. Among his best-known films were *African Queen, Caine Mutiny,* and *Casablanca.* He was married to Lauren Bacall. Bogart's characterization of Captain Queeg in *Caine Mutiny* received an Academy Award.

BOONE, DANIEL (1734–1820), frontier explorer and Indian fighter. Born near Reading, Pennsylvania, Boone moved to Kentucky in 1767. There he was involved with several expeditions against the Shawnee Indians, and served as captain of the local militia when Kentucky became organized as part of Virginia. Stuart Edward White's *Daniel Boone, Wilderness Scout* (1922) is regarded as the best biography of Boone.

BOOTH, EDWIN T. (1833–1893), actor of international fame. Born near Bel Air, Maryland, Booth played minor roles in *Richard III* (1849) and *The Iron Chest* (1851). Then he travelled west to California, settled in San Francisco, and appeared in leading roles as Richard III, Macbeth, and Hamlet. He went to Australia on tour in 1854 and then to New York, where he obtained a major role in *The Fool's Revenge* in 1864. His younger brother John Wilkes Booth assassinated President Abraham Lincoln.

BOOTH, JOHN WILKES (1838–1865), actor and assassin of President Abraham Lincoln. Born in Bel Air, Maryland, Booth had considerable promise as an actor. He performed with great success at the Boston Museum in 1863. His sympathies were with the South during the Civil War, and he served as a member of the Virginia militia that arrested and executed John Brown. Booth organized the conspiracy that led to the assassination of President Lincoln on April 14, 1865.

BRADY, MATTHEW B. (1823–1896), pioneer photographer. Born in Warren County, New York, Brady began making portraits with the daguerreotype, an early photographic technique developed by S.F.B. Morse and J.W. Draper. Brady published *The Gallery of Illustrious Armericans* in 1850. With the approval of President Lincoln, he photographed many historic scenes during the Civil War. His innovations had far-reaching significance in the development of photography.

BRINKLEY, DAVID (1920–), broadcast journalist. Born in Wilmington, North Carolina, Brinkley served as a reporter with Wilmington *Star-News* and then as Washington correspondent for the National Broadcasting Company (NBC). With Chet Huntley, he established a reputation as news analyst and co-anchor for *The NBC News*. Brinkley has received the du Pont and Peabody Awards for outstanding journalism.

BROOKS, PHILLIPS (1835–1893), clergyman, author, and composer. Born in Boston, Massachusetts, Brooks became an outstanding leader in American Protestantism. He came from a family that treasured piety and learning; scholarship and eloquence in preaching were the characteristics of his ministry in Boston. Brooks was a leading voice in the Episcopal Church in America. He delivered several noted lectures on preaching before the Divinity School of Yale College in 1877. Alexander V.G. Allen's *Life and Letters of Phillips Brooks* is the most useful biography.

BROWN, JOHN (1800–1859), abolitionist leader. Brown was born in Tourington, Connecticut. He is remembered for his attack on Harpers Ferry, Virginia before the Civil War. Brown hoped to start a wider revolt among black people by seizing the arsenal and distributing arms among the blacks. But the attack failed; John Brown was indicted on three counts of treason and executed.

BRYAN, WILLIAM JENNINGS (1860–1925), lawyer, editor, orator, and political figure. Born in Salem, Illinois, Bryan ran unsuccessfully for President on three occasions. He was described as "The Great Commoner" because of his policies that favored farmers and common laborers. In 1913, he was named Secretary of State by President Woodrow Wilson. He opposed the United States' entry into World War. Later Bryan defended the anti-evolution educational laws passed by the State of Tennessee. He successfully prosecuted a teacher named Thomas Scopes for violating the anti-evolution statutes.

BUNCHE, RALPH (1904–1971), diplomat and human rights leader. Bunche was born in Detroit, Michigan. He attended the University of California and Harvard University, as well as the London School of Economics. He studied anthropology and colonial policy. Bunche participated in several study projects on race relations and international understanding. He attended the San Francisco Conference of the United Nations as a member of the United States delegation. Later he served as a member of the United Nations' Palestine Commission. He received the Nobel Prize, the Presidential Medal of Freedom, and the Spingarn Medal awarded by the National Association for the Advancement of Colored People (NAACP).

BURBANK, LUTHER (1849–1926), plant breeder and agricultural innovator. Burbank was born in Lancaster, Massachusetts. He was deeply influenced by Charles Darwin's views regarding plants and animal life. With an inheritance of 17 acres, he began a series of experiments that developed the "Burbank potato." He authored a significant publication titled *The Training of the Human Plant*. Burbank received an honorary degree from Tufts University. He was a fellow of the American Association for the Advancement of Science and the Royal Horticultural Society.

BURGER, WARREN (1907–　　), lawyer and Chief Justice of the United States. Born in St. Paul, Minnesota, Burger was appointed to the Supreme Court by President Nixon. Under his leadership, the Supreme Court has been less activist in legal sentiments than was the Earl Warren court. Burger has been involved with the Mayo Foundation. Prior to his appointment to the Supreme Court, he was a law partner in the firm Fairicy, Burger, Moore, & Costello.

BURR, AARON (1756–1836), lawyer and political figure, Vice-President under Thomas

Aaron Burr

Jefferson. Burr was born in Newark, New Jersey. After his term as Vice-President, he conspired to invade Spanish Territories in the Southwest and organize a separate nation. He killed Alexander Hamilton in a duel, which ended Burr's active involvement in politics until the conspiracy was discovered. He was tried for treason and acquitted on a legal technicality.

BURROWS, ABE (1910–   ), playwright and director born in New York City. Burrows wrote for the CBS and NBC radio networks. He was writer and star of *The Abe Burrows Show.* He co-authored *Guys and Dolls, Three Wishes for James,* and *How to Succeed in Business without Really Trying,* and he received a Pulitzer Prize for the last. Burrows' music achieved significance in recording with Decca Records.

BUSHNELL, HORACE (1802–1876), Congregational clergyman, author, and educator. Bushnell was born in Bantam, Connecticut. He rejected rigid Puritanism for liberal religious views. He authored *Christian Nurture* (1847), *God in Christ* (1848), and *Nature and the Supernatural* (1858). More conservative Christian thinkers regarded his views as heretical. He denied that religious conversion was necessary.

CAESAR, SID (1922–   ), actor and comedian born in Yonkers, New York. With the emergence of television, Sid Caesar achieved wide recognition. *Caesar's Hour* and *Sid Caesar Invites You* became popular TV programs. Mr. Caesar often appeared on *The Jackie Gleason Show* and *The Carol Burnett Show.* He starred in the motion picture, *It's a Mad, Mad, Mad, Mad World.* For his work in television, he received the Emmy Award and was named to the United States Hall of Fame.

CALDER, ALEXANDER (1898–1976), sculptor and illustrator. Born in Philadelphia, Pennsylvania, Calder studied at the Stevens Institute of Technology. He built animated wire performers called "the miniature circus" and travelled to Europe with the exhibit. As a result, he developed kinetic sculptures, or mobiles. His designs can be seen at the Lincoln Center, New York, Massachusetts Institute of Technology in Cambridge, and at the UNESCO Gardens in Paris.

CALHOUN, JOHN C. (1782–1850), American statesman and political theorist. Born in South Carolina, he served as a member of both houses of Congress and as Secretary of War in the administration of James Monroe. He served as Vice-President in 1825–1829. Calhoun authored the *South Carolina Exposition* that was a response to the so-called Tariff of Abominations. By 1830, Calhoun was promoting the theory of states' rights embraced in the Nullification Doctrine, which held that states could nullify acts of Congress. Calhoun also wrote *Disquisition on Government* and *Government of the United States,* both published posthumously.

CANTOR, EDDIE (1892–1964), comedian and humanitarian leader. Born in New York City, Mr. Cantor began his career in vaudeville and was later associated with burlesque. He toured as Sam Beverly Moon and starred in the stage productions *Broadway Brevities* (1920), *Make It Snappy* (1922), and *Whoopee* (1929). His first motion picture appearance was in 1926. Mr. Cantor was active in Jewish and Christian charities. He authored *Take My Life: The Way I See It* (1959). He received numerous recognitions for his charity work; Temple University honored him with a Doctor of Humane Letters degree.

CAPONE, ALPHONSE "AL" (1899–1947), gangster; perhaps the most notorious criminal in American history. Born in Naples, Italy, he came

Al Capone is led aboard a train to start his journey to the federal penitentiary in Atlanta, Georgia.

to the United States with his family and settled in Brooklyn, New York. In high school, he took charge of the Five Points gang. In a gang fight, he was slashed across the face with a razor blade, and carried the nickname of "Scarface Al" ever after. In 1920, gang leader Johnny Torrio summoned Capone to Chicago to supervise the sale of bootleg whiskey. Torrio retired in 1925, leaving Capone in charge of Chicago's largest crime racket. "Scarface Al" used murder, bombings, and torture to drive out his competitors. In 1927, he exerted his powers to elect "Big Bill" Thompson as mayor of the city. Capone's henchmen executed seven members of a rival gang in the infamous St. Valentine's Day Massacre of 1929. The United States Treasury Department arrested Capone in 1933 on charges of income-tax evasion. After serving 11 years in Alcatraz Prison, he retired to his Miami Beach estate.

CAPP, AL (1909–   ), newspaper cartoonist. Born in New Haven, Connecticut, Capp attended the Pennsylvania Academy of Fine Arts and the Museum of Fine Arts in Boston. He created the comic strip titled "Lil' Abner," which was widely syndicated throughout the United States. United Features Syndicate distributed "Li'l Abner." He also served as columnist for the *New York Herald Tribune*. Capp was associated with the People to People program of the United Nations.

CARNEGIE, ANDREW (1835–1919), American industrialist, businessman, and philanthropist. Carnegie was born in Scotland. He became one of the so-called "Captains of Industry" at the turn of the century. In 1848, his family settled in the Allegheny region of Pittsburg. Carnegie was a self-educated lover of books, theater, and classical music. In the 1850s, he took advantage of the rising importance of steel. With his capital, Carnegie constructed the Bessemer Steel Rail Company. Toward the close of the century, he completely dominated the United States steel industry. He authored the article entitled "Wealth," which became the core of what sociologists called the Gospel of Wealth. He believed the rich should spend their fortunes for the welfare of the community. He supported the extensive construction of libraries that bear his name.

CARROLL, JOHN (1735–1815), first bishop of the Roman Catholic Church in America. Born in Upper Marlborough, Maryland, he supported the educational and political integration of the Roman Catholic Church with early America. Carroll sought to unify the several Catholic groups in America, and he obtained religious toleration for Catholics. Regulations developed by his associates became the first canon law in America. Carroll encouraged the establishment of parochial education, secular schools, and colleges at Georgetown (1788) and Baltimore (1799).

CARSON, KIT (1809–1868), soldier, Indian agent, and hunter. Born in Madison County, Kentucky, Carson had no formal education and remained illiterate all his life. He travelled to Arizona and southern California and married an Arapaho woman. He served as John C. Fremont's guide and helped Fremont plan expeditions to Wind River Mountains, the Oregon Trail, the Dalles River, and Klamath Lake. He guided Fremont through the Sierra Nevadas to the Great Salt Lake. Carson served in the Office of Indian Affairs and died in Fort Lyon, Colorado.

CARVER, GEORGE WASHINGTON (1861–1943), black botanist, chemist, and educator. Carver was born in Kansas Territory and attended school in Minneapolis, Kansas, and San Francisco. At Booker T. Washington's invitation, he came to the Tuskegee Institute, where he established an international reputation in horticulture and farming. He became a close friend of Henry A. Wallace, who ran for the United States Presidency. He also developed enduring friendships with Thomas Edison, Luther Burbank, and Harvey Firestone.

CHAMBERLAIN, WILT (1936–   ), professional basketball player. Born in Philadelphia, Pennsylvania, Chamberlain attended Kansas State University. He then served as star center for the Los Angeles Lakers, the Philadelphia 76ers, and the Philadelphia Warriors. In 1967, he led the National Basketball Association in points scored per season. He has achieved stature as an all-time great in the National Basketball Association.

CHANCELLOR, JOHN (1927–   ), broadcast journalist. Born in Chicago, Illinois, he attended DePaul Academy and became a reporter with the *Chicago Sun-Times*. From 1950 to 1965, he was on the staff of NBC News as a newswriter and served as a correspondent in Vienna, London, and Moscow. He served briefly on the NBC *Today* program. Under President Kennedy, Chancellor served as director of the Voice of America. In recent years, he has been anchorman with David Brinkley on the *NBC Nightly News*.

CHANNING, WILLIAM ELLERY (1780–1842), Unitarian theologian and minister. Channing was born in Newport, Rhode Island. He served as minister to the Federal Street Church in Boston most of his life. He held the view that God was merciful and would save all mankind; thus Channing established the basic tenets of Unitarianism and fathered the American Unitarian Association. Through his writings, he sponsored the movement for cultural independence from England. *The Importance and Means of a National Literature* (1830) is the most significant of his writings.

CHAPMAN, JOHN "JOHNNY APPLE-SEED" (1775–1847), planter of apple orchards on the American frontier. We cannot determine his parentage and place of birth; he was simply known as "Johnny Appleseed." He enjoyed long trips for the study of birds. Chapman's orchards of apple trees became legendary, particularly around Ashland County near Mansfield, Ohio. He said he was a primitive Christian. In 1838, he travelled into Allen County, Indiana. The legend of Johnny Appleseed is closely identified with the Westward expansion.

CHAVEZ, CESAR (1927–   ), union organizer among migrant farm workers. Chavez was born near Yuma, Arizona. His early activities in the California Community Service Organization established his abilities as an activist and organizer. He became director of the Organized National Farm Workers Association, which then merged with the Agricultural Workers Organizing Committee of the AFL-CIO. Chavez' ability to organize boycotts and strikes made the growers in the Modesto and Sacramento Valleys of California hostile toward his work. Chavez served in the United States Navy Reserve during World War II.

CHISHOLM, SHIRLEY (1924–   ), black Congresswoman and outspoken political leader born in Brooklyn, New York. She attended Brooklyn College and Columbia University; she has received honorary degrees from Pratt Institute, Hampton Institute, William Patterson College, and Capital University, among others. The Congresswoman has served in numerous organizations that deal with social programs and public policy. In 1972, she made an unsuccessful bid for the United States Presidency. She has written numerous books and pamphlets, including *Unbought and Unbossed* (1970) and *The Good Fight* (1973).

CLARK, WILLIAM (1770–1838), frontier explorer and Indian fighter born in Caroline County, Virginia. Clark served with "Mad" Anthony Wayne in his campaign against the Indians. He joined Meriwether Lewis for expeditions to the Pacific Northwest. Clark was skilled in dealing with Indians and making maps. His diaries of the Lewis and Clark expeditions are essential to our early knowledge of the Northwest Territories. Clark was appointed as superintendent of Indian affairs for the Louisiana Territories. He was a highly regarded soldier and explorer.

CLAY, HENRY (1777–1852), Secretary of State and political leader for a generation (1812–1852). Born in Hanover County, Virginia, Clay fathered the "American System"— a legislative program to unite the industrial East with the farming West. Clay's plan established protective tariffs and provided federal money for public improvements. Clay ran for the Presidency in 1844 as candidate of the Whig Party and lost. He was the

Henry Clay addressing the U.S. Senate

architect of the Compromise of 1850, which delayed the controversies that erupted in Civil War a decade later.

COBB, TY (1886–1961), regarded by many as the greatest offensive player in baseball history; called "the Georgia Peach." He was born in Narros, Georgia. Cobb was a fierce competitor; he appeared in more games (3,033), batted more times (11,429), with more hits (4,191), finished with a higher lifetime average (.367) than any other major league player. Cobb achieved his reputation with the Detroit Tigers, with which he spent 22 seasons. He was elected into the Baseball Hall of Fame in 1936.

CODY, WILLIAM F. "BUFFALO BILL" (1846–1917), Indian fighter whose fame became part of literature and legend; he established a Wild West show that achieved international standing. Cody was born in Scott County, Iowa. After serving in the Civil War, he worked as a civilian scout for the United States Army. He is said to have slaughtered 4,280 buffalo in an eight-month period to provide food for the Army. His reputation in marksmanship was equalled only by his memory of terrain and geography. Cody engaged in over sixteen Indian battles; his popularity as a showman developed later in life.

COFFIN, HENRY SLOANE (1877–1954), clergyman, author and educator. Born in New York City, Coffin became a leader of liberal evangelicalism. He served as president of Union Theological Seminary and was an effective preacher. Coffin sought to apply Christianity to social problems and tried to improve theological education. He served as a fellow of the Corporation of Yale University. He was moderator of the General Assembly of the Presbyterian Church in the U.S.A. Coffin wrote numerous books, including the *Meaning of the Cross* (1931).

COLE, NAT "KING" (1919–1965), singer, entertainer, and jazz pianist. Cole was born in Montgomery, Alabama. He organized the King Cole Trio and later he achieved prominence as a singer. His musical style was relaxed. Cole's most successful recordings included "Nature Boy" and "Walking My Baby Back Home." His name and voice are associated with the song "Unforgettable." He appeared in several motion pictures without distinction.

COPELY, JOHN SINGLETON (1737–1815), American painter in the realist tradition, born in Boston, Massachusetts. Copely completed several portraits of outstanding Americans, including Paul Revere and Samuel Adams. In 1774, he travelled to Europe to avoid problems of the Revolutionary era. He was elected to the Royal Academy and painted several massive historical scenes, including *Siege of Gibraltar* (1791) and *The Death of the Earl of Chatham* (1781). Copely died in London.

COSTELLO, LOU (1906–1959), film and radio comedian associated with Bud Abbott in comedy. Born in Paterson, New Jersey, Costello worked as a common laborer at Metro-Goldwyn-Mayer Studios and then as a stunt man. After his comic talents emerged, he appeared on the *Kate Smith Hour.* Costello starred in several movies, including *Hold That Ghost, Abbott and Costello in Hollywood,* and *Abbott and Costello Meet the Mummy.* He is best known for his work in the comedy of errors.

CROCKETT, DAVID (1786–1836), political figure, Indian fighter, and celebrity of the American frontier. Born in Hawkins County, Tennessee, Crockett was involved with the so-called Creek War against Creek Indians in Alabama. He was elected to the Tennessee legislature and later won a seat in the United States House of Representatives. After three terms in Congress, he returned to Tennessee to organize an expedition to Texas, looking for new land and challenge. He died in the Battle of the Alamo.

CRONKITE, WALTER (1916–   ), broadcast journalist. Born in St. Joseph, Missouri, Cronkite began his career with the *Houston Post,* where he served as reporter. After a succession of assignments, he became a news correspondent with the American forces in World War II. He began his association with Columbia Broadcasting System (CBS) in 1950 and was assigned to develop the news department. In 1953, he began the narration of a series titled *You Are There;* in 1952, he inaugurated national television coverage of the political conventions; and in 1962, he became anchorman for the *CBS Evening News.* His name is synonymous with television news.

CROSBY, FRANCES J. "FANNY" (1820–1915), Christian composer born in New York City.

She wrote over five thousand hymns, including "Safe in the Arms of Jesus" and "There's Music in the Air." When six weeks old, she lost her eyesight. She entered an institution for the blind at age 15, and taught there from 1847 to 1858. She authored numerous publications that included *The Blind Girl and Other Poems* (1844), *A Wreath of Columbia's Flowers* (1859), and *Autobiography* (1906).

CROSBY, HARRY "BING" (1904–1977), singer, songwriter, and actor. Born in Tacoma, Washington, Crosby's easygoing manner suited the emerging style of popular music. He studied law for a period of time, then entered show business. The songs "Ghost of a Chance" and "When the Blue of the Night" became associated with his voice. He appeared in a series of filmed musical comedies with Bob Hope and Dorothy Lamour. He received an Academy Award for his performance in the film, *Going My Way* (1944). "I'm Dreaming of a White Christmas" is the song commonly associated with Crosby. His autobiography was entitled *Call Me Lucky*.

CURTIS, CYRUS H. K. (1850–1933), magazine publisher. Born in Portland, Maine, Curtis was educated in the public schools. He moved to Philadelphia, where he joined the staff of the *Tribune*. His success in publishing the *Ladies' Home Journal* achieved national recognition, and he became president of the newly organized Curtis Publishing Company. There he pursued other magazine enterprises, including *Country Gentleman* and the *Saturday Evening Post*. Under Curtis' direction, the *Post* achieved a national audience. He acquired the *New York Evening Post* in 1923 in an effort to compete with the Hearst papers and the *New York Times*.

CUSTER, GEORGE (1839–1876), soldier commonly known for his military operations against hostile Sioux and Cheyenne Indians. Custer was born in New Rumley, Ohio. In 1876, he was defeated in an epochal battle at the Little Big Horn in Wyoming. He and his entire army of 655 men were killed by a far superior force of Indians. Custer wrote an interesting commentary titled *My Life on the Plains;* his *War Memoirs* give a useful recollection of the Civil War.

DALEY, RICHARD (1902–1976), leading political figure of the Democratic Party. Born in the Bridgeport district of Chicago, Mr. Daley studied law at De Paul University. He was admitted to the bar in 1933. Through patronage and appointment power, he organized the Illinois Democratic Party with ultimate loyalty to himself. In 1955, he became mayor of Chicago and retained that post until his death, directing one of the most powerful political structures in American history. In 1960, he supported John F. Kennedy's bid for the Presidency and delivered his state for the Democratic presidential contender. In 1968, he was criticized for his treatment of anti-war protesters during the Democratic National Convention in Chicago. In spite of the criticism, political writers considered him the most effective mayor of a large metropolitan city.

DANA, CHARLES A. (1819–1897), newspaper editor and publisher. Dana was born at Hinsdale, New Hampshire. After a series of newspaper jobs, Dana used his friendship with Horace Greeley to secure the position of city editor at the *New York Tribune*. After the Civil War, he acquired the *New York Sun,* which he built into one of New York's greatest daily papers. He was described as a man of wide intellectual interests. Dana wrote *Recollections of the Civil War* (1898), *The Art of Newspaper Making* (1899), and other books.

DANIELS, JOSEPHUS (1862–1948), journalist and statesman, ambassador to Mexico, and Secretary of the Navy under President Woodrow Wilson. Daniels was born in Washington, North Carolina. He became a close friend of William Jennings Bryan and devoted his energies to the Democratic Party. Daniels used considerable restraint in his dealings with the Mexican government; he was a man of great diplomacy and political skill. Daniels authored several books, including *Tar Heel Editor, The Wilson Era: Years of War and After,* and *The Cabinet Diaries of Josephus Daniels*.

DAVIS, JEFFERSON (1808–1889), President of the Confederate States of America. Born in Todd County, Kentucky, Davis attended West Point Military Academy and graduated in 1828. He served with distinction in the Black Hawk Indian War of 1832. He then served as Secretary of War and as a Senator before the outbreak of the Civil War. After the Civil War broke the Confederacy, he lived a sad and helpless existence. Davis wrote *The Rise and Fall of the Confederate Government*.

DE FOREST, LEE (1874–1961), an inventor who pioneered in radio and broadcasting. De Forest was born at Council Bluffs, Iowa. He worked with the Western Electric Company in Chicago, where he invented the audio amplifier. This was the single most significant contribution to the advance of radio, and De Forest is often regarded as the father of radio. He held major responsibilities in the De Forest Wireless Telegraph Company and the Radio Telephone Company. He wrote *Father of Radio* (1950). William R. Maclaurin's *Invention and Innovation in the Radio Industry* explains De Forest's contributions.

DEMILLE, CECIL B. (1881–1959), motion picture producer and director who established a reputation for his spectacular portrayals of biblical themes. DeMille was born in Ashfield, Massachusetts. *The Ten Commandments, The King of Kings, The Sign of the Cross,* and *Samson and Delilah* were some of his best-known films. His screen productions cost millions, yet he was able to produce films that were highly profitable. DeMille rejected criticism that his productions were garish and unartistic by saying that public taste determines the standards of artistry. In later years, he developed movies that reflected historical themes, including *The Greatest Show on Earth, Union Pacific,* and *The Plainsman.*

DEMPSEY, JACK (1895–   ), champion heavyweight boxer. Because Dempsey was born in Manassa, Colorado, he was called the "Manassa Mauler." Initially he won the heavyweight championship from Jess Willard in 1919. The most controversial aspect of his career was the "long count" during the second fight between Dempsey and Gene Tunney. In the seventh round, Dempsey floored Tunney but failed to go to a neutral corner. The count was delayed; Tunney recovered and subsequently won the fight. After retirement, he became a restauranteur in New York City. With Bob Considine and Bill Slocum he co-authored the book, *Dempsey.*

DEWEY, JOHN (1859–1952), educator and pragmatic philosopher who advocated traditional values of education. Dewey was born in Burlington, Vermont. He believed that science was the highest manifestation of human intelligence. He established his reputation through articles in the *Journal of Speculative Philosophy.* Dewey studied at the University of Vermont, Johns Hopkins, the University of Michigan, and the University of Chicago. At Chicago, he turned to pedagogy and educational philosophy. He authored many books, including *Democracy and Education* (1916) and *Reconstruction in Philosophy* (1920).

DIMAGGIO, JOE (1914–   ), noted baseball player born in Martinez, California. DiMaggio played as an outfielder with the San Francisco Seals until 1934, when he was purchased by the New York Yankees. In his first year the Yankees recognized him as a potential star; he batted an average of .323, fielded .978, and established the longest consecutive hitting record by hitting safely in 56 consecutive games. Fans called DiMaggio the "Yankee Clipper." On December 11, 1951, he announced his retirement from baseball. His subsequent marriage to actress Marilyn Monroe drew national attention.

DEWEY, GEORGE (1837–1917), first Admiral of the Navy; hero of the Spanish-American War. Dewey served under Admiral David G. Farragut during the Civil War. In 1897, he requested sea duty in the Pacific as commodore of the new American fleet. He led his six boats into Manila Bay on May 1, 1898, and destroyed the Spanish fleet of 10

Admiral Dewey with President McKinley
and Cardinal Gibbons, 1899

ships. In August, he used the American navy to assist General Wesley Merritt's capture of Manila. He returned to a hero's welcome in the United States, where Congress named him Admiral of the Navy. Dewey published his autobiography in 1913.

DISNEY, WALTER E. "WALT" (1901–1966), filmmaker, cartoonist, and entertainment entrepreneur. A native of Chicago, Disney developed the cartoon characters Mickey Mouse and Donald Duck in the 1920s. He developed the first feature-length animated cartoons in *Snow White* (1938). Disney's later films *Pinocchio, Bambi, Fantasia,* and *Mary Poppins* achieved spectacular success. The amusement parks named Disneyland and Disney World bear his genius. *The Disney Version: The Life, Times, Art, and Commerce of Walt Disney,* by Richard Schickel (1968) is the most comprehensive study on Disney.

DIX, DOROTHEA L. (1802–1887), humanitarian associated with Dr. William Ellery Channing. Born in Hampden, Maine, Miss Dix became the tutor to Dr. Channing's children. Under Channing's influence, she initiated significant reforms in mental institutions. During the Civil War, she served as a superintendent of nurses; after the war, she continued her efforts on behalf of the mentally ill. Her reforms attracted international attention, particularly in Europe. Francis Tiffany's *The Life of Dorothea Lynde Dix* (1890) is the most definitive biography.

DOOLITTLE, JAMES H. "JIMMY" (1896–), aviator, oil company executive, and war hero. A native of Alameda, California, Doolittle became one of the most famous of American heroes during World War II. He led the first bombing of Japan and commanded thousands of planes in attacks on North Africa, Italy, and Germany. He commanded attacks upon German cities from 1944 to the end of the war in Europe. Doolittle then joined General Douglas MacArthur's command in the Far East until the end of the war in the Pacific. He became an executive of the Shell Oil Company after the war. In the 1950s, he became involved with NACA, which later became the National Aeronautics and Space Administration.

DOUGLAS, STEPHEN A. (1813–1864), United States Senator and candidate for the Presidency, identified with the Democratic Party. Born

in Brandon, Vermont, Douglas spearheaded the new Democratic Party in Chicago. He sponsored efforts to make Chicago a significant rail center. The senatorial campaign of 1858 between Douglas and Abraham Lincoln was a rehearsal for the 1860 presidential campaign, even though Lincoln lost. In the famous Lincoln-Douglas debates, Lincoln established his national reputation. Many argue that if Douglas had become President, he could have prevented a Civil War. For a review of this argument, see Gerald M. Capers, *Stephen A. Douglas, Defender of the Union,* edited by Oscar Handlin (1959).

DOUGLAS, WILLIAM O. (1898–), liberal justice of the United States Supreme Court. Douglas was born in Yakima, Washington, and attended Columbia Law School. He served briefly as a professor at the Yale Law School, worked on legal matters for the Securities and Exchange Commission. In 1939, he was appointed to the Supreme Court and became the leader of the liberal wing of the court. He challenged tradition in his opinions on obscenity, religion, desegregation, and the rights of criminals. He wrote several books, including *Points of Revolution* (1970). The best study of Douglas' career is *Douglas of the Supreme Court: A Selection of His Opinions,* edited by Vern Countryman (1959).

DOUGLASS, FREDERICK (1817–1895), abolitionist, journalist, and orator. He was born at Tuckahoe, Maryland with the name of Frederick Augustus Washington Bailey. After he escaped from slavery he changed his name to Frederick Douglass. Greatly influenced by William Lloyd Garrison's *The Liberator,* Douglass joined the Massachusetts Anti-Slavery Society. He wrote *The Narrative of the Life of Frederick Douglass, an American Slave* (1845), which some abolitionists thought was too inflammatory. Douglass disagreed with William Lloyd Garrison on proper abolitionist procedures.

DREW, CHARLES RICHARD (1904–1950), a black surgeon who developed the blood bank and new methods for training surgeons. A native of Washington, D.C., Dr. Drew implemented the blood bank in World War II as director of the American Red Cross Bank. He chaired the department of surgery at Howard University and recommended new surgical standards to the National Medical Association. Dr. Drew received the

Spingarn Medal of the National Association for the Advancement of Colored People. He was awarded numerous honorary degrees from colleges and universities.

DU BOIS, WILLIAM E. B. (1868–1963), major black scholar and leader of black protest and panafricanism. Born in Great Barrington, Massachusetts, he received the Master of Arts degree and a doctorate from Harvard University. Dr. Du Bois organized the Niagara group, an all-black protest organization of scholars and professionals. He was one of the founders of the National Association for the Advancement of Colored People (NAACP) in 1909. He edited *Crisis,* a publication of the NAACP, and regarded himself as a Socialist. Dr. Du Bois authored numerous books and pamphlets.

DULLES, JOHN FOSTER (1888–1959), foreign diplomat and Secretary of State under President Dwight D. Eisenhower. Born in the nation's capital, Dulles served at the Paris Peace Conference in 1919. He was legal adviser to the United States delegation at the San Francisco conference on the United Nations. He supported General Eisenhower during the 1952 election. As Secretary of State, Dulles developed the broader aspects of North Atlantic Treaty Organization (NATO). He dealt courageously with the Suez Crisis of 1956 by compelling President Nassar of Egypt to withdraw. Louis L. Gerson's *John Foster Dulles* (1967) is a good biography of Dulles.

DURANTE, JIMMY (1893–   ), entertainer and songwriter born in New York City. Durante began his career in the Bowery district of New York, where he organized a five-piece jazz band for Club Alamo in Harlem. At this time, he was only known as a pianist. In 1923, he opened Club Durante. Other entertainers were attracted to his comedy and musical routines. He wrote many songs after 1923, including "I'm Jimmy, That Well-Dressed Man" and "Did You Ever Have the Feeling That You Wanted to Go?" He appeared in several Broadway musicals, including *Red, Hot and Blue* with Ethel Merman, *Keep off the Grass, Stars in Your Eyes.* He was nicknamed the "Schnozzle" for the generous proportions of his nose. Durante is regarded with great affection as an entertainer.

DUROCHER, LEO (1906–   ), professional baseball manager. Born in West Springfield, Massachusetts, he played for a time as a second baseman for the New York Yankees. Then he was shortstop for the Cincinnati Reds and St. Louis Cardinals. His fame comes from his management of the Brooklyn Dodgers, who won the National League pennant in 1951 and 1954. He became a television announcer for a short time, then returned as a manager for the Chicago Cubs 1966-1972 and the Houston Astros in 1972-1973. He co-authored a book entitled, *Nice Guys Finish Last* with Ed Linn. That phrase became synonymous with his name.

DWIGHT, TIMOTHY (1752–1817), Congregationalist minister and president of Yale College. Dwight was born in Northhampton, Massachusetts, and received his education at Hopkins Grammar School in New Haven, Connecticut. Dwight served in the Massachusetts Legislature, then taught Latin and Greek. He wrote "The Conquest of Canaan," an epic poem. In 1795, he became the president of Yale College; he administered the affairs of the college, taught moral philosophy, and served the in college pulpit on Sundays. Kenneth Silverman's *Timothy Dwight* is a significant study of his life.

EARHART, AMELIA (1898–1937), aviatrix. A native of Atchison, Kansas, Miss Earhart attended Columbia University and taught extension courses for the Commonwealth of Massachusetts. She was the first woman to cross the Atlantic in an airplane. Miss Earhart became the aviation editor of *Cosmopolitan Magazine* and vice-president of National Airways. She received numerous honors and recognitions, including the Distinguished Flying Cross and the gold medal of the National Geographic Society. She wrote *20 Hours, 40 Minutes* (1928) and *The Fun of It* (1931). Miss Earhart's plane went down in the Pacific Ocean as she was completing a round-the-world flight.

EASTMAN, GEORGE (1854–1932), inventor, industrialist, and mass producer of photographic equipment. Eastman was born in Waterville, New York. He made photography available to the general public. Eastman's discoveries in chemical processing were essential to the United States war effort during World War I. He developed an innovative system of profit-sharing that allowed his employees to enjoy the Eastman Company's profits. Eastman was a lonely man who took his own life. The best single work on Eastman is Carl W. Ackerman's *George Eastman* (1930).

EDDY, MARY BAKER (1821–1910), established the Church of Christ—Scientist in an effort to apply religion to health. She was born at Bow, New Hampshire. Her nervous condition in early life brought several illnesses, which led to her study of science and health. In 1908, she established the *Christian Science Monitor.* Her book, *Science and Health,* became the basis for her religious and scientific theories. Her most significant impact remained in Boston and the East Coast. *The Life of Mary Baker Eddy* by Sibyl Wilbur is the official biography.

EDDY, NELSON (1901–1967), screen star and entertainer, a native of Providence, Rhode Island. Mr. Eddy's baritone voice was matched with the soprano voice of Jeanette MacDonald for several filmed musicals. He starred in popular stage musicals during the 1930s and 1940s, including *Naughty Marietta* (1935), *Rose Marie* (1936), *Girl of the Golden West* (1938), and *Bittersweet* (1940). After his screen career, he entered radio and nightclub entertaining. Eddy made famous the songs, "Ah, Sweet Mystery of Life" and "Indian Love Call." His rich voice singing "Stouthearted Men" was his radio trademark.

EDISON, THOMAS A. (1847-1931), inventor who made outstanding contributions in electric light and electrical devices; his greatest contribution is the incandescent lamp. Born in Melan, Ohio, Edison made significant advances in organized research. Because of deafness, he was exempt from military service. Edison made major contributions to the development of the phonograph, lighting, electric-powered plant, and the movie industry. The Edison Company produced hundreds of movies, and Edison laid the basis for "talking" movies. He also contributed to the development of synthetic rubber. Edison sponsored the early work of Charles Steinmetz and other budding inventors. The best biography of Thomas A. Edison is Matthew Josephson's *Edison: A Biography* (1959).

EDWARDS, JONATHAN (1703–1758), New England minister and missionary, commonly regarded as America's finest preacher and theologian of the eighteenth century. He was born in East Windsor, Connecticut, the son and grandson of clergymen. Edwards' *Personal Narrative* (1740) reflects a close affection for God. He is associated with the Great Awakening, an intense period of revivalism in colonial America. He wrote the influential book entitled, *The Great Christian Doctrine of Original Sin Defended* (1758). His writings and sermons changed the outlook of his entire generation. He became president of the College of New Jersey, now Princeton University.

EINSTEIN, ALBERT (1879–1955), physicist, born in Ulm, Germany, and known for his theory of relativity. Einstein's general and special theories of relativity revolutionized the world of science. He approached President Roosevelt with his theories regarding the development of atomic energy for military purposes. This resulted in the "Manhattan Project" for the development of an atomic bomb. He was expelled from Nazi Germany because of his Jewish heritage, and this had a profound impact on his life. Einstein regarded himself a pacifist and humanitarian. Carl Seelig's biography, *Albert Einstein: A Documentary Biography* (1956), is one of the best portraits of Einstein.

Albert Einstein
This photograph is considered to be the last one made of the physicist. The occasion was Professor Einstein's 76th birthday on Mar. 14, 1955.

Douglas Fairbanks, Sr. (right) and son Douglas, (ca.) 1933

FAIRBANKS, DOUGLAS SR. (1883–1939), distinguished American actor born in Denver, Colorado. His marriages attracted national attention, particularly to Mary Pickford (divorced in 1935) and Lady Ashley. He made his first stage appearance in New York City; among other plays, he appeared in *All For a Girl, The Cub,* and *Show Shop.* He also appeared in motion pictures, such as *His Majesty the American, When the Clouds Roll By, The Mark of Zorro, Robin Hood,* and *The Taming of the Shrew.* He organized his own production company and achieved national attention for his somber portrayals.

FARRAGUT, DAVID G. (1801–1870), naval officer who carried significant assignments during the American Civil War. Born at Campbells Station, Tennessee, he opposed the Southern cause and migrated north to Hastings-on-the-Hudson. His initial assignment was to open the Mississippi to Union battleships. He stationed his gunboats in the Gulf of Mexico, which gave him a more direct striking capability between 1861 to 1864. In 1864, he was assigned to strike at Confederate defenses in Mobile Bay. His success led to the command to strike defenses at Wilmington, North Carolina, which he also accomplished. Farragut was regarded as among the outstanding heroes of the Civil War. A. T. Mahan's *Admiral Farragut* (1892) is still a classic.

FIELD, MARSHALL (1835–1906), merchant and chain-store retailer. Born near Conway, Mas-

sachusetts, Field served as a travelling salesman before he was admitted to partnership in the retail firm of Farwell, Field and Company. Unlike A. T. Stewart, John Wanamaker, and other leading retailers of his day, Field was not interested in political activity nor philanthropy; but he did give money to the newly established University of Chicago and fostered the establishment of the Chicago Manual Training School. He was also associated with the establishment of the Field Museum of Natural History in Chicago, and his will provided for the construction of the building in Chicago, and that houses the Field Museum.

FIELDS, W. C. (1879–1946), comedian of the stage, motion pictures, and radio. Fields was born in Philadelphia, Pennsylvania. His first appearances were in vaudeville productions and the Ziegfeld Follies. His fame developed from his movie appearances, in films such as *So's Your Old Man, It's the Old Army Game, One in a Million, David Copperfield, Never Give a Sucker an Even Break,* and his most popular *My Little Chickadee.* He also reached a national audience through his radio broadcast, *The Chase and Sanborn Hour.* Fields was highly regarded for his wry humor.

FINNEY, CHARLES G. (1792–1875), revivalist and educator. Finney was born in Warren, Connecticut. His term as president of Oberlin College gave Presbyterianism a significant voice in educating the ministry. His preaching style contained substance and eloquence. Finney was a strong advocate of temperance; he opposed the use of tobacco, tea, and coffee. Although a Mason, he opposed masonry. Among his more significant book titles: *Sermons on Important Subjects* (1836), *Lectures to Professing Christians* (1837), and *Lectures on Systematic Theology* (1846, 1847). His revivals reached wide audiences and had significant impact on the religious patterns of nineteenth-century America.

FITZGERALD, ELLA (1918–   ), jazz vocalist with an international reputation. Born in Newport News, Virginia, at age fifteen she entered an amateur contest at the Apollo Theatre in New York City. She was hired by Chick Webb for his band. In 1938, she gained worldwide fame with her recording of "A Tisket, a Tasket." Among her more famous recordings are "Love You Madly," "Hard-Hearted Hannah," and "He's My Guy."

Miss Fitzgerald is recognized as an outstanding performer and recording artist. She has received considerable respect in the black community for her civil rights concerns.

FORD, HENRY (1863–1947), automobile manufacturer born in Dearborn Township, Michigan. Ford learned the machinist trade and was the chief engineer for the Edison Illuminating Company. In 1903, he organized the world's largest automobile corporation. In 1914, he announced plans to involve all his workers in a profit-sharing plan, distributing millions of dollars back to his workers. His plan to mass-produce the Model T and Model A made the automobile readily available to the American public at competitive prices. He constructed assembly plants at Highland Park, Michigan, and River Rouge, Michigan; the latter was regarded as the largest single factory in the world. Ford was also active in political and humanitarian efforts. He built the Henry Ford Hospital; in 1918, he ran for the Senate and lost. Ford authored *My Life and Work* (1925) among other titles.

FOSDICK, HARRY EMERSON (1878–1969), clergyman and author who established the Riverside Church in New York, which was distinctive for its interdenominational character. Fosdick was born in Buffalo, New York. His *National Vespers* radio program brought his ideas into the national arena. He was ordained as a Baptist minister, but his theological perspective is associated with a liberal interpretation. Fosdick wrote numerous books, including *The Modern Use of the Bible* (1924) and *A Faith for Tough Times* (1952). His autobiography is contained in *The Living of These Days* (1956). He also wrote numerous hymns.

FOSTER, STEPHEN C. (1826–1864), composer of musical sketches and minstrel songs. At Jefferson College, Foster's musical capacities became evident to his teachers; he continued his education under tutors; his Negro ballads, "O Susanna" and "Away Down South," achieved instant success. In 1851, he began his work with E. P. Christy, who would sing Foster's songs. Each assisted the other. Foster's more famous songs were "The Old Folks at Home," "My Old Kentucky Home," and "Massa's in the Cold, Cold Ground." He remained in Pittsburgh, Pennsylvania most of his life; but his music gave a nostalgic reflection of Negro life in the Old South.

Benjamin Franklin
Signer of the Declaration of Independence

FRANKLIN, BENJAMIN (1706–1790), author, printer, inventor, diplomat, and scientist. Born in Boston, Massachusetts, he began a writing sequence on self-improvement at an early age. These efforts are best reflected in *Poor Richard's Almanack,* which contained slogans on personal improvement, such as: "Necessity never made a good bargain" and "It is hard for an empty sack to stand upright." Franklin became interested in electricity; he initiated projects for community improvement that included the lighting of streets with natural gas. He established police forces and circulating libraries. He also established the American Philosophical Association. Franklin served in the second Continental Congress. He travelled to France in 1776 to negotiate a treaty with the French Government, and negotiated the peace treaty with Great Britain. He served as a member of the Constitutional Convention. The best biography of Franklin is Carl Van Doren's *Benjamin Franklin* (1938).

FREMONT, JOHN C. (1813–1890), soldier and politician born in Savannah, Georgia. His explorations of Minnesota and Dakotas added to his knowledge of science and topography. He travelled the Oregon Trail with Kit Carson and explored the Columbia River. Fremont was regarded as the "Great Pathfinder." He travelled to California and wintered (1845) in Oregon. He then returned to California and served a short term as United

States Senator from California. He ran as a Presidential candidate of the newly formed Republican Party. His autobiographical sketch titled, *My Life* (1887), is a useful overview of the era.

FRIEDMAN, MILTON (1912–   ), foremost economist in the United States reflecting the conservative perspective. A native of Brooklyn, New York, he served as economic adviser to President Richard Nixon. He wrote *A Monetary History of the United States, 1867–1960* (1963). Friedman advocates the competitive free-market economy, and he originated the negative tax-credit idea. He is a professor at the University of Chicago; his economic theories are commonly associated with the Chicago School. Friedman has received numerous honors and awards, including the Nobel Prize for economics.

FULBRIGHT, J. WILLIAM (1905–   ), distinguished American political figure. Born in Sumner, Missouri, he attended the University of Arkansas and won a Rhodes scholarship to Oxford University. Fulbright received his law degree from George Washington University. From 1939 to 1941, he served as president of the University of Arkansas. In 1942, he began a political career as Representative to the United States House from the Third District. He called for the creation of the United Nations during World War II. In 1944, he was elected to the United States Senate; he sponsored laws that established an educational exchange program known as the Fulbright-Hays program. Fulbright served on the Senate Banking Committee. He criticized the war in Vietnam from his position as chairman of the Senate Foreign Relations Committee.

FULLER, R. BUCKMINSTER (1895–   ), architect, designer, and inventor. Born in Milton, Massachusetts, his earliest work was the Dymaxion House, a design that blends "dynamism" and "maximum utilization." Dymaxion House, like Fuller's Dymaxion Car, had interest but little direct use in production. He is described as a "catalyst to change." By mid-century some of his more enduring creations were taking form. The United States Pavilion at the Montreal Expo in 1967 was designed by Fuller; he was responsible for the geodesic dome that was built in Dearborn, Michigan for the Ford Motor Company. Fuller's influence is discussed by Roystan Landau, *New Directions in British Architecture* (1968).

FULTON, ROBERT (1765–1815), inventor and engineer born in Lancaster County, Pennsylvania. He built the first successful steamboat. Fulton and Robert R. Livingston designed the steamboat, which came to be called the *Clermont*. In 1807, the *Clermont* made its first trip. H. W. Dickinson's *Robert Fulton: Engineer and Artist: His Life and Works* (1913) is still a classic biography.

GALLUP, GEORGE H. (1901–   ), public opinion researcher. Born in Jefferson, Iowa, Gallup established his reputation as director of the American Institute of Public Opinion. He graduated from State University of Iowa, then served as a professor of journalism at Drake University and Northwestern University. His work in public opinion surveys evolved from reader-interest surveys that Gallup developed for the Des Moines *Register & Tribune,* the Cleveland *Plain Dealer* and the St. Louis *Post-Dispatch*. He established the American Institute of Public Opinion "impartially to measure and report public opinion." His surveys have become standards for political action or popularity. He has received honorary degrees from many universities, including Northwestern University and Tufts University.

GARFUNKEL, ART (1941–   ), singer and actor, associated in his early career with Paul Simon. Simon's acoustic guitar and Garfunkel's voice became a national standard of music during the 1960s. In 1964 they cut their first album titled, *Wednesday Morning*. One song that appeared on that album achieved national attention—"The Sounds of Silence"; it eventually sold over one million copies. A succession of musical hits brought them international recognition. They composed and performed the music for the film entitled, *The Graduate*. "Bridge Over Troubled Waters" was another significant music success; in 1970, the two parted to pursue their separate careers. Garfunkel was born in Forest Hills, New York.

GARLAND, JUDY (1922–1969), actress and singer. Born in Grand Rapids, Michigan, she achieved instant success in her early portrayal of Dorothy in the film, *The Wizard of Oz*. Her singing of "Somewhere over the Rainbow" in that movie has become an American classic. She was also associated with Mickey Rooney in the Andy Hardy series of films. Her musical successes were highlighted by her performance in the film, *Easter*

Parade (with Fred Astaire); her performance in *A Star Is Born* was also widely acclaimed. In the 1960s, she made a spectacular return by appearances at the London Palladium and Carnegie Hall in New York. She received an Oscar nomination for her dramatic role in *Judgment at Nuremburg*.

GARRISON, WILLIAM L. (1805–1879), editor, reformer, and leader of abolition. In Garrison's day, the anti-slavery movement was split into two camps: those who sought gradual elimination of slavery and those who wanted immediate reform and abolition. Garrison called for the more immediate formula through his newspaper, *The Liberator*. He opposed slaveholders in his book, *Thoughts on Colonization* (1832). He criticized the New England clergy for their reluctance to condemn the broader aspects of slavery. He viewed the Civil War as a means of destroying the institution of slavery, and he wanted to disband the American Anti-Slavery Society after the Civil War. George M. Frederickson's *William Lloyd Garrison* (1969) is an excellent study of his life. Garrison was born in Newburyport, Massachusetts.

GERONIMO (1829–1909), leader of the Apache Indians. He was born with the name *Goyathlay,* and saw his family killed by Mexican troops in 1859. Taking the name *Geronimo* ("Jerome"), he led raids of revenge against white settlements in Arizona and New Mexico until he was confined to a reservation. In 1876, he led his warriors into Mexico, where he plundered white settlers for the next 10 years. He finally agreed to move to a reservation in Florida, but escaped en route. General Nelson A. Miles captured him after 18 months of pursuit. Later, Geronimo was converted to Christianity and lived peaceably with white people. He appeared in President Theodore Roosevelt's inaugural parade in 1905. *Geronimo's Story of His Life* (1906), by S. M. Barrett, gives Geronimo's own account of his experiences.

GERSHWIN, GEORGE (1898–1937), musical composer, distinguished in classical and popular fields. He was born in Brooklyn, New York. With lyricist Irving Caesar, Gershwin composed "Swanee," made famous by Al Jolson in *Sinbad*. In the 1920s he established many successes with his brother Ira: "Oh Kay," "Funny Face," "Rosalie," and "Strike Up the Band." His most distinguished efforts included *Rhapsody in Blue* (1924) for piano and jazz, and *An American in Paris* (1928). He had a fondness for jazz forms and black musical expression, and Gershwin's music reflected the current American scene. The most outstanding biography is David Ewen's *George Gershwin: His Journey to Greatness*. Gershwin's opera, *Porgy and Bess* (1935), was a stinging social commentary on racial prejudice.

Geronimo (center) and his braves shortly before surrendering.

GIBBONS, JAMES (1834–1921), Roman Catholic Cardinal born in Baltimore, Maryland. Gibbons supported the Catholic Church in a generation of change. He wrote *The Faith of Our Fathers* (1875), in which he underscored the practical applications of Catholicism. Known for his religious toleration, Gibbons supported labor organizations such as the Knights of Labor. He had considerable administrative skills, and he blended a profound affection for the church with his deep regard for America. Robert D. Cross gives a masterful summary of his contributions in *The Emergence of Liberal Catholicism in America* (1958).

GLADDEN, WASHINGTON (1836–1918), Congregationalist clergyman who sought to apply Christian principles to social problems. Gladden was born in Norwich, Connecticut. In 1866, he accepted the parish in North Adams, Massachusetts. His writings appeared in the *New York Independent* and *Scribner's Monthly,* usually on ethical themes of everyday living. He served as moderator to the National Council of Congregational Churches, where his scholarship reflected less depth and more of the conventional. He wrote several books on biblical criticism, including *Who Wrote the Bible* (1891), *How Much Is Left of the Old Doctrines* (1899), and *Social Salvation* (1902). Gladden addressed his later writings to municipal reform; he served with some distinction in interchurch associations.

GLENN, JOHN (1921–   ), aviator, astronaut, and United States Senator. Born in Cambridge, Ohio, he attended Muskingum College and trained as a naval air cadet. During World War II he flew 59 fighter bomber missions in the Pacific; he flew 90 missions in the Korean War. Glenn received the Flying Cross on five occasions and was awarded the Air Medal 19 times. He was the oldest of seven astronauts selected in April 1959 for Project Mercury program; but he was selected to make the first orbital flight in 1961. He was the first man to fly at supersonic speeds from Los Angeles to New York. In more recent years, Glenn has distinguished himself in political life as a United States Senator from Ohio.

GODDARD, ROBERT H. (1882–1945), established rocketry and the science of astronautics. Goddard's reputation was established while he was at Clark University, where the focus of his study was rocketry. He was able to perfect a system for liquid-propelled rockets. During World War II he addressed his attention to the potential of rockets in war; he concluded his life as a researcher in the employ of the Curtiss-Wright Corporation. Goddard's importance to the development of aerospace technology and interplanetary travel is great. Milton Lehman's *This High Man: The Life of Robert H. Goddard* is the only definitive biography available. *The Papers of Robert H. Goddard,* edited by Esther C. Goddard and G. Edward Pendray, is a collection of his writings.

GOLDBERG, RUBE (1883–1970), newspaper cartoonist whose funny drawings became world famous. Goldberg's political cartoons reached a wide audience through syndication. He worked for the *San Francisco Chronicle,* the *San Francisco Bulletin,* and the *New York Evening Mail.* He created the characters Lala Palooza, Mike, and Ike before he was offered the position of political cartoonist for the *New York Sun.* His reputation was established from that perspective. His cartoon, "Peace Today," was awarded a Pulitzer Prize in 1948.

GOLDWATER, BARRY M. (1909–   ), United States Senator and candidate for the Presidency in 1964. He suffered a heavy defeat in his quest for the Presidency against President Lyndon Johnson. Born in Phoenix, Arizona, Goldwater attended the University of Arizona but left to manage his family's department stores. During World War II, he served in the Army Air Forces; he helped to organize the Arizona Air National Guard. He was first elected to the Senate in 1952 and was reelected in 1958. After his defeat in 1964, he returned to Arizona for a brief period away from the Senate. The voters sent him back to the Senate in 1966. He has written numerous articles and books on his political philosophy and issues of national importance.

GOODSPEED, EDGAR J. (1871–1962), Greek scholar and Bible translator. Goodspeed studied at Denison, Ohio, Yale, and Chicago universities. In 1898, he came to the University of Chicago as a lecturer, then professor of Patristic Greek. He served as secretary to the president of the university. He devoted considerable work to developing a more readable version of the Bible. He wrote *The Conflict of Severus, The Story of the New Testament, The New Testament—an Ameri-*

can Version, The Complete Bible–an American Version. He was born in Quincy, Illinois.

GOODYEAR, CHARLES (1800–1860), inventor and noted rubber manufacturer. Goodyear was born in New Haven, Connecticut. His father was a hardware manufacturer, and Charles became associated with his father's hardware store in Philadelphia. When the store went bankrupt, he began experiments with rubber products. His fascination with inflated rubber life preservers led to his acquaintance with the American Indian Rubber Company. Goodyear wrote *Gum-Elastic and Its Varieties* and began experiments of treating rubber with sulfur and turpentine. By midcentury, the rubber industry was established in the United States and he migrated to Europe. He was honored by Napoleon III of France for his contributions to the Paris Exposition of 1855.

GOULD, CHESTER (1900–   ), cartoonist famous for his "Dick Tracy" series. Born in Pawnee, Oklahoma, Gould attended Oklahoma A & M and graduated from Northwestern University. He served as cartoonist for the Hearst Newspapers from 1924 to 1929; in 1931, he began working with the *Chicago Tribune* and created the cartoon character Dick Tracy. The character was a serious detective whose primary task was to reckon with criminal elements. "Dick Tracy" reached wide circulation through the Chicago Tribune-New York News Syndicate. The cartoon strip reached hundreds of newspapers throughout the country.

GOULD, JAY (1836–1892), builder of railroads, stock manipulator, and industrial capitalist. Born in Roxbury, New York, Gould began his career as a leather merchant. He established himself as a stock market speculator and helped the Erie Railroad compete against railroad baron Cornelius Vanderbilt. Through unscrupulous practices, he accumulated wealth at the expense of Erie Railroad and many unsuspecting investors. Later he bought an interest in the Wabash and Union Pacific Railroads. His influence extended to Manhattan's rapid transit system and the Western Union Telegraph Company. Louis M. Hacker's *The World of Andrew Carnegie* places Gould and this era into perspective.

GRAHAM, WILLIAM F. "BILLY" (1918–   ), evangelist and religious thinker. Born in Charlotte, North Carolina, he studied at Wheaton College. After a brief tenure as a pastor in Western Springs, Illinois, Graham became an evangelist. He served with Youth for Christ, then as president of Northwestern College in Minneapolis. He organized the Billy Graham Evangelistic Association for massive evangelism efforts. Through the radio program *Hour of Decision,* he is heard worldwide. He has written *My Answer, World Aflame,* and *Angels,* among many other titles. He has spoken to millions through crusades and television. John C. Pollock's *Billy Graham: The Authorized Biography* is a helpful view of Billy Graham's life.

GREELEY, HORACE (1811–1872), journalist, reformer, and editor. He was an early partner with the *New Yorker,* but the paper lacked profitability. In 1841, he began a more successful experiment known as the *New York Tribune.* Greeley urged social reform and resisted revolutionary approaches. He opposed the pro-slavery Compromise of 1850. Greeley was instrumental in the establishing of the Republican Party; after the Civil War, he became identified with the Radical Republicans. Soon frustrated with that group, he established the Liberal Republican Party. He wrote *Recollections of a Busy Life.* G.G. Van Deusen's *Horace Greeley: Voice of the People* places the man within the context of his generation.

GUGGENHEIM, MEYER (1878–1905), industrialist who established a mining empire. Born in Lengnau, Switzerland, he came to the United States in 1848. He obtained interests in silver-mining in Colorado. Guggenheim later expanded his smelting and mine acquisitions to Mexico. With the establishment of the Guggenheim Exploration Company and the American Smelting Company, his family obtained control of the broader aspects of mining and smelting in the United States. With his seven sons he was able to establish a force that dominated the American industrial scene for generations. The dated but authoritative *The Guggenheims: The Making of an American Dynasty* (1937) by Harvey O'Conner is still an outstanding overview.

HALE, GEORGE ELLERY (1822–1909), noted astronomer and astro-physicist. Born at Chicago, Illinois, Hale attended the Massachusetts Institute of Technology, the Harvard College Observatory, and the University of Berlin. He served as director of the Kenwood Astro-Physical Observatory in Chicago from 1890 to

1896. He invented the spectroheliograph, which was first used in 1892 to discover solar vortices and magnetic fields of sun spots. Hale achieved an international reputation among scientists. He wrote many books, including *The Study of Stellar Evolution, Beyond the Milky Way,* and *The New Heavens.*

HAMILTON, ALEXANDER (1757–1804), political leader and financial advisor. He was born on the island of Nevis in the British West Indies, the illegitimate son of James Hamilton and Rachel Fawcett Lavien. During the early stages of the American Revolution, Hamilton served as a close confidante of General George Washington. He became a member of the Federalist Party after the Revolution and was a co-author of the Federalist Papers. Hamilton served as Secretary of the Treasury under President Washington. He supported the concept of a central banking authority as the United States Bank and authored numerous studies on banking. Hamilton drafted the basic text of Washington's "Farewell Address." He died in a duel with Aaron Burr.

HAMMERSTEIN, OSCAR II (1895–1960), lyricist, theatrical producer, and songwriter. Born in New York City, Hammerstein was a student at Columbia University and received a law degree in 1918. His first musical success was as lyricist with "Wildflower" (1923). He then wrote "Rose Marie" (1924), "Sunny" (1925) and "Desert Song" (1926). With Jerome Kern, he achieved success with *Showboat* (1927). With Richard Rodgers his success became phenomenal. Together they wrote *Oklahoma* (1943), *Carousel* (1945), and *South Pacific* (1949), which received a Pulitzer award. Other successes included *The King and I* (1951), *Flower Drum Song* (1958), and *The Sound of Music* (1959). His more famous musical themes include "The Last Time I Saw Paris," which received an Academy Award, and "Ol' Man River."

HANCOCK, JOHN (1737–1793), first signer of the Declaration of Independence. A Colonial merchant and patriot, Hancock opposed Great Britain's efforts to restrict colonial trade. He resisted the Stamp Act by engaging in smuggling; by 1773, his name was identified with rebellion. Hancock was disappointed when the Continental Congress appointed George Washington to command the armies around Boston as the Revolution mounted. As an accountant for Harvard College, he engaged

John Hancock
Signer of the Declaration of Independence

in erratic bookkeeping that brought embarrassment to him and his family. Hancock later served as president of the States Convention where Massachusetts ratified the United States Constitution. He also served as governor of Massachusetts.

HANDY, W. C. (1873–1958), black songwriter regarded as the "Father of the Blues." Born in Florence, Alabama, Handy grew up in a home where both parents were ministers and secular music was regarded with disdain. Yet he organized tours and minstrel performances. His fame grew out of the Mahara Minstrels, a group he led. He travelled to Memphis, Tennessee, where his "Memphis Blues" became famous among musical circles. He also published the classic "St. Louis Blues." Handy was accused of plagiarism on certain musical themes, but he resisted those claims. He organized the W. C. Handy Foundation for the Blind. His book entitled, *Blues: An Anthology* contains some material about his life. He also wrote his autobiography titled *Father of the Blues,* published in 1941.

HARDY, OLIVER (1892–1957), actor and comedian. He was the senior member of a comic team with Stan Laurel. Laurel and Hardy made their first movie in 1926; in their career they were responsible for over two hundred movie features. In the 1950s, they expanded their comedy to the medium of television. The overweight Hardy and the lean Laurel developed a comedy style that reflected the anxieties of life situations. Their slapstick humor was popular in America at the time. Hardy's line, "Another fine mess that you got us into," became associated with the routine.

HATFIELD, MARK O. (1922–   ), modern political figure. Born in The Dalles, Oregon, Hatfield graduated from Stanford University. He served as instructor and dean of students at Willamette University. From 1950 to 1956, he served as the Secretary of State for Oregon, and as governor from 1959 to 1967. He won election as United States Senator in 1967. Hatfield's involvement in the anti-war movement during the 1960s generated discontent within the Republican Party; he has been identified with the liberal Republicans. Hatfield is a significant leader in evangelical Protestantism. He has written several books, including *Between a Rock and a Hard Place*.

HEARST, WILLIAM RANDOLPH (1863–1951), newspaper publisher and editor. Born in San Francisco, California, Hearst grew up in a wealthy family. He was expelled from Harvard College in 1885, and received permission from his father to work with *The Daily Examiner*. There he sensationalized and fabricated the news in irresponsible fashion. After his father's death, he moved to New York where he used the *New York Morning Journal* to compete against Joseph Pulitzer's *New York World*. In an era of "yellow journalism," Hearst's irresponsible reporting generated a newspaper boom. He established the *Chicago American* in 1900, along with other newspapers in Boston and Los Angeles. Eventually he retired on the Hearst estate at San Simeon in southern California. Ferdinand Lundberg's *Imperial Hearst: A Social Biography* (1936) is an unflattering portrait.

HENRY, CARL F. H. (1913–   ), minister and educator. Henry was born in New York City. He received the Ph.D. from Boston University and the Th.D. from Northern Baptist Theological Seminary. He established *Christianity Today,* a journal for evangelical Protestantism. Dr. Henry has held faculty positions with Gordon, Fuller, Wheaton Colleges, and numerous other colleges and universities as visiting lecturer. He has authored a number of publications in systematic theology; but his most significant views were shared through his editorials for *Christianity Today,* which he edited from 1956 to 1968.

HENRY, PATRICK (1736–1799), orator and noted political figure born in Hanover County, Virginia. As a member of the Virginia House of Burgesses, Henry spoke against the Stamp Act and opposed the power of Parliament to tax Virginians. He was described as the "Demosthenes of America." His name is synonymous with rebellion, through his impassioned cry, "I know not what course others may take; but as for me, give me liberty or give me death." After the Revolution, he served as governor of Virginia. He opposed the American Constitution because he believed it would concentrate too much power in the central government.

HOFMAN, HANS (1880–1966), cubist and abstract painter. Born in Weissenberg, Germany, Hofman suffered under the political difficulties of postwar Germany. He decided to emigrate to America and accept an appointment at the University of California. During the 1940s, he exhibited his paintings in New York, where his work received wide attention. With exhibitions at the Whitney Museum during the decade of the 1960s, his reputation as a German-American master was assured. His more famous paintings are *Fantasia* (1943), *Liberation* (1947), *The Gate* (1959), and *Agrigento* (1961).

HOGAN, BEN (1912–   ), an outstanding golfer. Born in Dublin, Texas, Hogan attended Fort Worth public schools. In his professional career as a golfer, he won the United States Open championship on four occasions; the United States Masters twice; won the British Open once. In 1946 and 1948, he won the Professional Golfers Association championship. He has received numerous awards including the Ryder Cup. Hogan was named Golfer of the Year in 1948, 1950, 1951, and 1953. He has written several books on the game of golf, including *Power Golf*.

HOMER, WINSLOW (1836–1910), a well-known American painter in the naturalist tradition. A native of Boston, Massachusetts, Homer began his career by working for *Harper's Weekly* as an illustrator. He proceeded to painting adult subjects in their natural settings; and in 1873, he began his work with watercolors in a graphic style. He moved from New York to the coast of Maine, where he sought a balance in his perspective. Late in life, he moved to the Bahamas, Bermuda, and Florida. At his death, he was regarded as the most significant American painter. *The World of Winslow Homer,* by James Thomas Flexner (1966) gives a good analysis of the man and his generation.

HOOVER, J. EDGAR (1895–1972), first director of the Federal Bureau of Investigation. Upon his initial appointment as acting director in 1924, Hoover established a fingerprint collection and national crime laboratory. The bureau was the center of Prohibition controversies and organized crime. Hoover opposed the emerging menace of Communism, particularly after World War II; he became involved in the McCarthy campaigns, writing books and articles that dealt with the themes of organized crime and Communism. *Masters of Deceit* (1958) is his most famous publication. Hoover was born in Washington, D.C.

HOPE, BOB (1903–   ), comedian and film star. Born in Eltham, England, Hope developed an instinct for comedy during his early days in vaudeville. He appeared in 1935 in the Ziegfeld Follies with Fanny Brice. He starred in the musical, *Red, Hot, and Blue* with Jimmy Durante and Ethel Merman; he developed a close partnership with Bing Crosby and Dorothy Lamour in a series of films titled *Road to . . .* During World War II, he entertained troops, particularly during the Christmas holiday season. In 1950, he appeared on the television show, *Star Spangled Revue,* and in October of 1950, he embarked on an entertainment tour for the United States Armed Forces in the Pacific. These tours were continued for over twenty-five years. His television specials draw large audiences. He authored *They've Got Me Covered* (1941), *I Never Left Home* (1944), and *So This Is Peace* (1946).

HOPKINS, JOHNS (1795–1873), merchant and philanthropist. He entered business in partnership with his brothers. In exchange for groceries, the Hopkins Brothers would receive whiskey; then they would sell the whiskey as "Hopkins Best" brand. He developed banking interests by buying up overdue notes. His primary investment was the Baltimore & Ohio Railroad; he became director of it in 1847. He advanced money to the City of Baltimore during periods of financial crisis; he established a hospital and a university that later adopted his name. His biographies have suggested that "he knew how to be generous in large matters."

HOUDINI, HARRY (1874–1926), circus entertainer and escape artist. His real name was Robert Housini. He was born soon after his parents left Budapest, Hungary for Appleton, Wisconsin. In his career as a magician, he took the name Harry Houdini; he learned his magic tricks from a variety of sources—sideshows, circuses, books. His wife Beatrice assisted him in magical routines; they worked the Orpheum circuit. After a sensational escape from Scotland Yard as a publicity stunt, he attracted great attention. Houdini toured the European continent, where he was able to extricate himself from many difficult situations. His return to America was received enthusiastically. He wrote *The Unmasking of Robert Housini* (1908) and starred in three motion pictures after World War I.

HOUSTON, SAMUEL (1793–1863), American statesman and soldier born in Rockbridge County, Virginia. Houston was a Jacksonian Democrat with great oratorical skills and military abilities. He was a lawyer with political ambitions. As a member of Congress and then governor of Tennessee, he became involved with the westward expansion. President Jackson asked Houston to negotiate treaties with various Indian tribes in the Southwest. He moved to Texas, where he advocated statehood for the territory. Houston directed military operations against Mexican president Antonio Lopez dé Santa Anna; from 1845–1859, he served as Senator from Texas. A good biography of Houston was written by Marquis James, *The Raven: A Biography of Sam Houston* (1929).

HOWARD, ROY W. (1883–1964), newspaper publisher who served as director of the Scripps-Howard newspaper chain from 1953 to 1964. Born in Gano, Ohio, his newspaper career began with the *Indianapolis News* in 1902. After he was appointed as general news manager for the United Press, he achieved a broader recognition among publishing circles. While covering World War I, he prematurely reported the signing of the Armistice. Howerd negotiated the purchase of the *New York Telegram,* the *New York World,* and the *New York Sun.*

HOWE, ELIAS (1819–1867), inventor who designed the first sewing machine, which revolutionized the garment industry. With ingenuity and persistence, Howe developed a workable sewing machine by 1845 and applied for the appropriate patents. He travelled to England to sell his machine, fell into difficult times, and sold his patents. He returned to America nearly penniless. Through legal proceedings, he was able to get the appropriate license fees on machines that had been produced from 1849 to 1854 in violation of his valid patents. With this newfound wealth, his personal life was stabilized. After the Civil War, sewing machines became major items for mass production.

HUBBLE, EDWIN P. (1889–1953), noted astronomer. Hubble was born in Marshfield, Massachusetts, and pursued a doctorate at the Yerhes Observatory near Pasadena, California. He determined the distances to several galaxies and studied their composition. He led in the development of Mount Palomar's telescope. Hubble wrote an autobiograpical sketch in *The Realm of Nebulae* and *Observational Approach to Cosmology* (both published in 1937). Harlow Shapley's *Through Rugged Ways to the Stars* places Hubble in the context of modern astronomy.

HUGHES, CHARLES EVANS (1862–1948), statesman and chief justice of the United States. After a 20-year period as a lawyer, Hughes became governor of New York State. As governor, he introduced historic reform legislation. President William Taft appointed him to the Supreme Court. In 1916, he was the Presidential candidate for the Republican Party; but he lost to Woodrow Wilson. After World War I, he supported President Wilson's proposal to join the League of Nations. He served as Secretary of State in the scandal-ridden Harding Administration, and gave excellent service. He called the Washington Conference on the limitation of Armaments and dealt with German war reparations. President Herbert Hoover appointed him as Chief Justice of the United States, where his progressive rulings foreshadowed those of the Earl Warren court.

HUGHES, HOWARD R. (1905–1976), business tycoon who achieved great renown through his efforts in aviation technology. After the death of his parents, he took control of the Hughes Tool Company. There he established his reputation and his wealth. Hughes produced motion pictures, and owned hotels, gambling casinos, an airline, television networks, and mines for precious metals. His complex personality contributed to his problems. He required privacy and developed a secretive manner. When Clifford Irving wrote a fraudulent biography on Hughes, the recluse telephoned news reporters to expose the hoax. At his death, many acquaintances of Hughes produced documents that claimed to be his will.

HULL, CORDELL (1871–1955), Congressman, Secretary of State under President Franklin D. Roosevelt. Hull generated the "Good Neighbor" policy toward Latin America. He signed the far-reaching agreement of Montevideo that made it illegal for military powers to intervene in the affairs of nations in the New World. He called for lower tariffs and opposed the expansionism of Japan that preceded World War II. He worked toward the establishment of the United Nations and earned a Nobel Peace Prize in 1945. *The Memoirs of Cordell Hull* (2 vols., 1948) provide a useful overview of the man and his era.

HUMPHREY, HUBERT H. (1911–1978), political figure, United States Senator, and Vice-President of the United States under President Lyndon Johnson. Humphrey was recognized as a spokesman for liberal political views. He was born in Wallace, South Dakota, and attended the University of Minnesota, graduating as a pharmacist from the Denver (Colorado) School of Pharmacy. His father served in the South Dakota state legislature. Hubert studied political science at the University of Minnesota while he served as pharmacist in the family drugstore. He became fascinated by the New Deal of President Franklin Roosevelt. He campaigned for mayor of Minneapolis in 1945 and won. He pursued vigorous reform of urban politics in Minneapolis, and advocated civil rights. Humphrey favored medical insurance through Social Security, the National Defense Education Act, the Peace Corps, and countless other programs of Lyndon Johnson's "Great Society."

HUNTLEY, CHET (1911–1974), television newscaster who achieved national recognition as co-anchorman with David Brinkley on the *Huntley-Brinkley Report,* featured by the National Broadcasting Company. He served as a correspondent on the West Coast for all three television networks. In 1956, he was brought to New York to co-anchor the national political conventions with Brinkley. Their partnership continued until 1970, and their news reporting received every award in broadcasting. Their famous sign-off—"Good night, Chet; Good night, David"—was immediately associated with the report. Huntley returned to Big Sky, Montana, after 1970.

IVES, BURL (1909–), singer and actor. Ives worked with the Columbia Broadcasting System as a folk song artist on radio and travelled throughout the states as a troubadour. He has appeared on numerous television programs. Ives' appearances on stage and film reflect a form of character acting. He has been featured in several films, including *East of Eden, Our Man in Havanna,* and *Cat On A Hot Tin Roof.* His television appearances on *The Bold Ones* from 1970 to 1972 developed a new character form—the lawyer. He has received numerous awards and recognitions. His autobiography is titled *Wayfaring Stranger* (1948).

IVES, CHARLES E. (1874–1954), pioneer in musical expression. Born in Danbury, Connecticut, Ives received initial musical training from his father. He graduated from Yale College in 1898 as a skilled musician and organist. He sold insurance for a time, but continued to compose music. He blended opposite musical forms, using familiar themes within his compositions. He wrote four symphonies, four separate theme works, chamber works, piano sonatas, violin sonatas, hundreds of songs, as well as piano and organ works. Peter Yates' *Twentieth Century Music* (1967) gives particular reference to Ives.

JACKSON, JESSE (1941–   ), clergyman and civic leader. Born in Greenville, North Carolina, he attended the University of Illinois and did postgraduate work at the Chicago Theological Seminary. He was ordained to the ministry of the Baptist Church and worked with Dr. Martin Luther King and the Southern Christian Leadership Conference in civil rights efforts. Jackson established Operation Breadbasket and Operation PUSH (People United to Save Humanity). He has been active in the Coalition for United Community Action, and is recognized as a fiery speaker.

JACKSON, MAHALIA (1911–1972), black singer and civil rights activist born in New Orleans, Lousiana. Miss Jackson symbolized black protest by associating with the civil rights movement. She became famous through her singing of "He's Got the Whole World in His Hands" and other popular songs. She achieved recognition in the white community after a widely acclaimed concert at Carnegie Hall in 1950. She was regularly featured in the Newport Jazz Festival after 1958.

JACKSON, THOMAS "STONEWALL" (1824–1863), Civil War general and Confederate hero. Jackson attended the United States Military Academy and served in the Mexican War. In the 1860 election, he supported John C. Breckinridge for the Presidency. After Virginia seceded from the Union he was commissioned to defend Harpers Ferry. At the First Battle of Bull Run, he earned the name "Stonewall" through his determined strategy. He was less successful in the battle to protect Richmond from Union Forces under General McClellan, but he scored a great victory for the South at the Second Battle of Bull Run. At the Battle of Fredericksburg, he was mistaken for a Union soldier and accidentally shot. This proved fatal. In strategy and audacity, Jackson remained unequalled in the Confederate ranks.

JAMES, WILLIAM (1842–1910), philosopher and psychologist. James was educated at Harvard, and his educational interests reflected a composite of the Renaissance mind. He was a determined advocate of the evolutionary theories of Charles Darwin. He wrote *Principles of Psychology* (1890), in which he underscored the human qualities of habit, emotion, consciousness of self, stream of thought, and will. His concern for individual freedom was reflected in his lectures on "The Will to Believe." His book, *Varieties of Religious Experience,* remains a classic study of the psychology of religion. Bernard P. Brennan's *William James* (1968) is a useful biography.

JAY, JOHN (1745–1829), diplomat, politician, Chief Justice of the United States. Jay served as President of the Continental Congress in 1778; after the American Revolution, he served as the new nation's Secretary for Foreign Affairs. He was a co-author of the *Federalist Papers,* which made him an advocate of the American Constitution. With James Madison and Alexander Hamilton, he called for a more centralized authority. Jay proposed the early outlines of a national judiciary. The treaty that ended the war with Great Britain bears his name; although it was written by Alexander Hamilton, it bore the diplomatic skills of John Jay.

JOLSON, AL (1888–1950), singer and star of motion pictures and radio. Born in St. Petersburg, Russia, his real name was Asa Yoelson and he was the son of a Jewish cantor. In 1909, he joined a minstrel group and entertained in the New York Garden. His role in the motion picture entitled *The Jazz Singer* (1927) is regarded as the first talking

Al Jolson in a scene from the *Jazz Singer* (ca.) 1927

picture. In 1928, he appeared in the film, *The Singing Fool.* His renditions of such songs as "Mammy" and "April Showers" became a permanent part of the American musical scene. He produced George Gershwin's *Rhapsody in Blue,* and the film entitled *The Al Jolson Story* was a phenomenal success.

JONES, E. STANLEY (1884–1973), missionary, author, and spiritual leader. Jones served as a missionary to India. His writings give a balanced, positive expression of Christian experience. He wrote several books, including *A Song of Ascents* (1968), which is his spiritual autobiography. He worked with the Ashram movement in India to communicate a religious message of love and understanding. Jones stressed the need for conversion, transformation, and the abundant life.

JONES, JOHN PAUL (1747–1792), distinguished American Revolutionary officer. His naval operations during the Revolution contributed greatly to the American victory. Historians believe the duel between Jones' ship, the *Bon Homme Richard,* and the British ship *Serapis,* was a significant episode of the war. He managed to seize the copper-bottom ship from the British. Jones received a gold medal and numerous honors for his naval successes. He served a brief period in the Russian navy, and most of his later years were spent in Paris. Alfred Thayer Mahan's book, *The Major Operations of the Navies in the American War of Independence* (1913), remains the classic on John Paul Jones and the Revolution.

JONES, RUFUS M. (1863–1948), college professor and religious leader. Born in South China, Maine, Jones attended Haverford College and the University of Heidelberg. He received his graduate degrees from Harvard and Oxford universities. In 1889, he became instructor at the Oak Grove Seminary in Maine; he taught at Haverford College from 1904 to 1934. Jones served as chairman of the American Friends Service Committee and of the European Relief in 1917–1927 and 1934–1944. He wrote numerous books, including *Autobiography of George Fox: The Story of George Fox* (1919); *The Faith and Practise of the Quakers* (1927); *Re-thinking Religious Liberalism* (1936); and *The Radiant Life* (1944).

JUDSON, ADONIRAM (1788–1850), Baptist missionary to Burma and founder of the American Board of Commissioners for Foreign Missions (1810). Judson was a Congregationalist when he travelled to India under the sponsorship of the board. There he adopted Baptist beliefs and received support from the American Baptist Missionary Union. He then went to Rangoon, Burma, to begin the translation of Scripture into Burmese. His linguistic abilities brought him into contact with broader levels of Burmese royalty. He completed an English-Burmese dictionary.

KEATON, BUSTER (1895–1966), comedian and film star. Born in Piqua, Kansas, Keaton performed in vaudeville before his appearances in Hollywood. He made comic use of pantomime, his portrayals in silent movies established his reputation as a classic performer. Keaton achieved fame in television and as a motion picture actor and director. His performances in *A Funny Thing Happened on the Way to the Forum, Around the World in 80 Days,* and *It's a Mad, Mad, Mad, Mad World* were received with acclaim. He achieved a new standard of excellence in the film, *When Comedy was King.*

KELLER, HELEN (1880–1968), author and humanitarian. Miss Keller was born in Tuscumbia, Alabama. An early illness left her blind and deaf by the age of 18 months. Her tutor Anne Sullivan helped her gain an education; and by age 16, she matriculated at Radcliffe College. She graduated *cum laude.* Her life was dedicated to the broader aspects of education and assistance to the blind and deaf. Miss Keller knew Alexander Graham Bell, whose experiments became essential to her work with the deaf and blind. She authored *Helen Keller's Journal, Out of the Dark,* and *The Story of My Life,* among other works.

KELLY, EMMETT (1898–), renowned pantomime clown. Born in Sedan, Kansas, he served as cartoonist for the Advertizing Film Company, where he created the "Wearie Willie" pen-and-ink cartoon. In 1921, he joined the circus as a clown; he worked as a trapeze artist and clown from 1924 to 1931. He appeared in several pictures, including *The Fat Man, The Greatest Show on Earth,* and others. He appeared on television with Ed Sullivan, Garry Moore, Jackie Gleason, Captain Kangaroo, and others.

KELLY, GENE (1912–), dancer, actor, and motion-picture celebrity. Born in Pittsburg, Pennsylvania, he appeared in the New York productions *Leave It To Me* (1938), *Time of Your Life* (1940), *Pal Joey* (1941), and others. Kelly directed the dancers for several movies: *Anchors Aweigh* (1944), *The Pirate* (1948), *An American in Paris* (1950), and *Brigadoon* (1954). Between 1944 and 1946, he served in the United States Naval Reserve. He authored *Take Me Out to the Ballgame* (1948).

KELLY, GRACE (1929–), actress, model, and (since 1956) princess of Monaco. Born in Philadelphia, Pennsylvania, she attended the Raven Hall Academy and Stevens School in that city. After early stage productions, she appeared in several motion pictures: *High Noon, Dial M For Murder, Rear Window, The Country Girl, To Catch A Thief,* and *High Society*. She received the Academy award for her role in *Country Girl*. Her marriage to Prince Rainier III of Monaco received considerable attention in America and Europe.

KELLY, WALT (1913–1973), newspaper cartoonist. His fame grew out of the comic strip "Pogo," with the classic line: "We have seen the enemy, and he is us." Kelly's characters reflected an innocent satire on society. Pogo was an opossum who spoke garbled language and had a community of animal friends, such as Howland Owl and the other inhabitants of Okefenokee Swamp. Kelly first worked as an animator for Walt Disney Productions. His comic strip appeared first in the *New York Star;* it reached syndication in over four hundred newspapers. Kelly was named Cartoonist of the Year in 1952.

KENNEDY, EDWARD M. (1932–), United States Senator born in Brookline, Massachusetts. Educated at Harvard and the University of Virginia Law School, he won election to the Senate in 1962 to complete the unexpired term of his brother, John F. Kennedy. In 1964, he was reelected. Mary Jo Kopechne, a campaign worker, died in an automobile accident at Chappaquiddick, Massachusetts that cast shadows on Kennedy's personal integrity. Yet he won reelection in 1970 and 1976. In the Senate, he has established a national health insurance program and favored tax reform. During the 1960s, he loudly opposed the war in Vietnam.

KENNEDY, ROBERT F. (1925–1968), United States Senator assassinated in a Los Angeles hotel after he won the 1968 California Democratic Presidential primary. Kennedy served in the United States Navy during World War II. He graduated from Harvard and received his law degree from the University of Virginia Law School in 1951. He served as assistant counsel to Senator Joseph McCarthy's Permanent Subcommittee on Investigations; and in 1957, he was chief counsel to the Senate Select Committee conducting investigations into labor racketeering. In 1960, he conducted the campaign of his brother, John F. Kennedy, for the Presidency. From 1961 to 1964, he served as Attorney General. From 1965 to his death, he was Senator from New York. Kennedy authored *The Enemy Within* (1960), *Just Friends and Brave Enemies* (1962), and *Pursuit of Justice* (1964).

KETCHAM, HANK (1920–), cartoonist. Born in Seattle, Washington, his real name is Henry King. He worked with Universal Studios and Walt Disney Productions from 1938 to 1942. He created Dennis the Menace and related cartoon characters after 1951. His "Dennis the Menace" cartoon strip was distributed through Field Newspaper Syndicate. He has received numerous awards, including the Billy de Beck Award for Outstanding Cartoonist (1952). He wrote several *Dennis the Menace* cartoon book collections, beginning in 1954, and *I Wanna Go Home* (1965).

KING, MARTIN LUTHER, JR. (1929–1968), civil rights leader who developed and practiced nonviolence as a strategy in dealing with racial prejudice and segregation. King organized a bus boycott to deal with segregation on transportation facilities. He was active in the National Association for the Advancement of Colored Peoples (NAACP); later he organized the Southern Christian Leadership Conference. King participated in the "sit-ins" to integrate lunch counters. The apex of the civil rights movement was achieved in a rally in Washington, D.C., where King delivered his speech, "Let Freedom Ring." In December of 1964, King was nominated for the Nobel Prize. He became involved in the anti-war movement shortly before he was assassinated in Memphis, Tennessee. He authored numerous publications; his most famous was, *I Have a Dream* (1968).

KISSINGER, HENRY (1914–   ), diplomat and Secretary of State. Born in Furth, Germany, he emigrated to the United States in 1938. Kissinger served during World War II. He received his doctorate from Harvard in 1954. Kissinger received national attention through publication of *Nuclear Weapons and Foreign Policy* (1957). He became a political advisor to Nelson Rockefeller in 1957. In 1968, Richard Nixon named him Presidential Assistant for National Security. Kissinger arranged the visits made by President Nixon to China and the Soviet Union. He was the architect of the treaty that ended the United States involvement in Vietnam. He also began *détente* with the Soviet Union and limited disengagement in the Middle East. Kissinger was recognized as an outstanding Secretary of State.

KOUFAX, SANDY (1935–   ), baseball pitcher and sportscaster. Born in Brooklyn, New York, he attended the University of Cincinnati. In 1955, he began his professional baseball career with the Brooklyn Dodgers (later the Los Angeles Dodgers). He appeared in World Series championships in 1959, 1963, 1965, and 1966. From 1963 to 1966, he was named to the National League All-Star Team. He was named Major League Player of the Year in 1963 and 1965. In 1963, 1965, and 1966, he received the Cy Young Award. From 1966 to 1972, he was associated with the National Broadcasting Company (NBC) as a sportscaster.

KRESGE, S. S. (1867–1966), merchandiser and businessman who established a network of "five and dime" stores throughout the country to make less expensive merchandise available to a broader market. Kresge was the founder of the S. S. Kresge stores; and from 1907 to 1925, he served as president of the company. From 1913 to 1966, he was chairman of the board; at its peak, over nine hundred thirty general merchandise stores throughout the country bore his name.

KUIPER, GERARD (1905–1973), astronomer. Born in Harencarspel, Netherlands, he analyzed early lunar photos and determined the exact sites where Apollo space craft would land. As chief scientist for the Ranger spacecraft program, he augmented United States efforts in the NASA space projects. The lunar landing of 1969 would not have been possible without his efforts.

LaFARGE, CHRISTOPHER GRANT (1862–1938), modern architect. Born in New York City, LaFarge studied at the Massachusetts Institute of Technology, 1880–1881. He obtained the Master of Fine Arts degree from Princeton University and became a partner in the firm Heins & LaFarge. LaFarge was the architect for the Cathedral of St. John the Divine in New York; St. Matthew's in Washington, D.C.; St. Patrick's in Philadelphia; as well as numerous other churches, hospitals, and governmental structures. He served as general manager of the United States Housing Corporation; also, director of the American Institute of Architects.

LaFOLLETTE, ROBERT M. (1855–1925), political reformer. LaFollette graduated from the University of Wisconsin in 1879 and was admitted to the bar one year later. He served as a member of the United States House of Representatives from

Senator Robert La Follette (left) and Senator Burton K. Wheeler, presidential and vice-presidential candidates of the League for Progressive Political Action

1885 to 1891. He campaigned against political corruption in his own state and was elected governor of Wisconsin in 1900. During his two terms there, he enacted new laws enabling voters to nominate candidates by direct primary elections, regulating government employment, and levying more reasonable taxes on business. LaFollette won election to the United States Senate in 1906 and was reelected twice thereafter. He ran for the Presidency on three occasions—the most successful being in 1924, when he and his running mate Burton K. Wheeler polled five million votes for the League for Progressive Political Action. LaFollette's ideas influenced national policy. He published his *Autobiography: A Personal Narrative of Political Experiences,* in 1913.

LANDON, ALFRED "ALF" (1887–   ), political leader and presidential candidate. Born in West Middlesex, Pennsylvania, Landon graduated from the University of Kansas in 1908. In 1912 and 1914, he worked for the Progressive Party; in 1932, he was elected governor of Kansas. He brought major governmental reform in state finance, water conservation, and utility rate regulation. In 1936 he won the Republican nomination for President, but he carried only Maine and Vermont. He opposed the United States' entry into World War II; after the war, he assumed an independent position and sought recognition of Communist China.

LAUREL, STAN (1890–1965), motion picture comedian. Born in Ulverson, England, he was part of the famous comedy team with Oliver Hardy. The Laurel and Hardy duo made slapstick comedy popular in the 1920s and 1930s. After 1926, he starred with Hardy in a succession of comedies, including *Air Raid Wardens* (1943), *Jitterbugs* (1943), *The Dancing Masters* (1943), *The Big Noise* (1944), *Nothing But Trouble,* and *The Bullfighters* (1945). He also appeared in numerous television roles after 1950; with his partner, he became an enduring part of America.

LAWRENCE, DAVID (1888–1973), editor and columnist. Born in Philadelphia, Pennsylvania, Lawrence began his career as a columnist with the *New York Evening Post* in 1916. His columns were syndicated in over three hundred daily newspapers. In 1947, he became editor of the *U.S. News and World Report.* He wrote numerous books, including *Diary of a Washington Correspondent.* He received the Presidential Medal of Freedom in 1970.

LEE, ROBERT E. (1807–1870), general of the Confederate armies and one of the greatest military strategists of history. Lee was born in

Jefferson Davis and his Cabinet with General Lee in the Council Chamber at Richmond.

Westmoreland County, Virginia, and graduated from the United States Military Academy. He fought in the Mexican War. When the Civil War began, his blood ties in Virginia affirmed his allegiance to the South. He accepted a commission as colonel in the Confederate army; within a month, he was given command of all the Southern armies. The battles of the war revealed his abilities as a strategist and diplomat—from Manassas where he achieved victory, to Fredericksburg where Stonewall Jackson fell. Gettysburg and Vicksburg were overwhelming losses for Lee. Historians of war agree that Lee had better strategic than tactical sense. *Lee's Dispatches,* revised by Grady McWhiney (1957), gives a useful perspective.

LEWIS, JERRY (1926–   ), comedian and television personality. Educated in the public schools of Irvington, New Jersey, Lewis began his career as an entertainer by appearing in the hotels and clubs of the Catskills. He formed a highly successful comedy routine with Dean Martin from 1946–1956. The Martin-Lewis comedy routine appeared on television until an embittered quarrel terminated the association. Lewis appeared in zany roles on screen, including *Sad Sack* (1957), *The Nutty Professor, Big Mouth,* and others. He has appeared on television and has developed a national relationship with the Muscular Dystrophy Association. His yearly telethons have raised millions of dollars for medical research in muscular dystrophy.

LEWIS, JOHN L. (1880–1969), labor leader who organized the Congress of Industrial Organizations (CIO) and was head of the United Mine Workers of America (UMWA). Born in Lucas, Iowa, Lewis worked as a miner in Montana and Utah. After a mine disaster in Wyoming, he dedicated his life to mine safety and defending miner's causes. He used the UMWA as a political base to launch his labor programs in Congress. During the Great Depression and Franklin Roosevelt's New Deal, he differed with the leadership of the American Federation of Labor and organized the CIO. He confronted the steel industry and the automobile industry and gained political leverage. In the 1940 election, he supported the Republican Wendell Wilkie in preference to Roosevelt. Saul Alinsky's *John L. Lewis* (1949) is a useful biography.

LEWIS, MERIWETHER (1774–1809), frontier explorer. Born in Albemarle County, Virginia, he explored the territories of the Northwest with William Clark. President Thomas Jefferson, a friend and associate, commissioned their westward expedition. With considerable difficulty, they moved westward into territories inhabited by Indians and wildlife. Lewis' skills in dealing with the Indians proved essential to avoiding war. Upon his return, he was made governor of the Upper Louisiana Territory. However, his journals about the expedition were less persuasive than were those of William Clark, and it is agreed that Clark was an essential component of the expedition. See Bernard DeVoto, *The Journals of Lewis and Clark* (1953).

LINDBERGH, CHARLES A. (1902–1974), aviator who made the first solo non-stop flight across the Atlantic Ocean. Lindbergh was competing for a $25,000 prize posted by Raymond Orteig. He assembled the necessary financial backing to construct the plane he called *Spirit of St. Louis.* On May 20, 1927, he left New York, and in 33½ hours he arrived in Paris. He received numerous awards for the feat. In 1932, he and his wife were horrified at the kidnapping of their infant son; they paid a ranson of $50,000, but the baby was found dead. Lindbergh organized the America First Organization to prevent United States' entry into World War II; after the Japanese attack on Pearl Harbor, he joined the war effort. He wrote *We* (1927) and *The Spirit of St. Louis* (1953); he received a Pulitzer Prize for the latter.

Lindbergh stands under the wing of his plane, the *Spirit of St. Louis,* before taking off on his transatlantic flight.

LINDSAY, JOHN V. (1921–   ), political leader and news commentator. Born in New York City, Lindsay graduated from Yale in 1944 and served in the Navy during World War II. He represented New York's seventeenth Congressional District in the House of Representatives from 1959 until his election as mayor of New York in 1965. He began his political career as a Republican, but later changed his party affiliation to Democrat. His years as mayor of New York saw a succession of labor difficulties and conflicts. After leaving office, he turned his attention to television and broadcast interests; he has appeared on ABC's *Good Morning, America* program as political and public affairs commentator.

LODGE, HENRY CABOT, JR. (1902–   ), Senator, government official, author, and lecturer. Lodge graduated from Harvard and Northwestern University, and was elected to the U.S. Senate from Massachusetts in 1936. He resigned the Senate for military service during World War II; he was reelected in 1946. In 1960, he ran with Richard Nixon as the Vice-Presidential candidate for the Republican Party. From 1953 to 1960, he served as the United States representative to the United Nations. He was United States Ambassador to South Vietnam from 1963 to 1964 and 1965 to 1967; there he served a significant diplomatic function. Lodge authored *The Storm Has Many Eyes;* he has received numerous honors and recognitions.

LOUIS, JOE (1914–   ), American boxer and world heavyweight champion. Louis demonstrated his boxing abilities by his successes in the Gold Gloves competition of 1933. Also called the "Brown Bomber," his successes became legendary—particularly over boxers like Billy Conn, Rocky Marciano, and "Jersey Joe" Walcott. During World War II, he boxed on behalf of Army and Navy Relief. He authored *My Life Story* (1947). Jack Olsen's *The Black Athlete: A Shameful Story* (1968) places Louis within the generation of black athletes and racial discrimination.

LUCE, HENRY R. (1898–1967), magazine publisher. Born in Tenchow, China of Presbyterian missionary parents, Luce graduated *summa cum laude* from Yale University. With Briton Hadden, he founded *Time* magazine in 1922; the success of *Time* ushered in a new form of magazine journalism. In 1930, he launched *Fortune,* designed for the business executive. His marriage to playwright Clare Boothe Brokaw was much publicized. In this same period was launched *Life,* a venture into photographic journalism. At the time of his death, the combined circulation of *Life* and *Time* was in the millions. The most definitive study on the man and his ventures is John Kobler's *Luce: His Time, Life, and Fortune* (1968).

MacARTHUR, DOUGLAS (1880–1964), American general with distinguished service in the Far East during the occupation and reconstruction of Japan after World War II. MacArthur graduated from West Point with the highest scholastic average in the history of the academy. His rise within the military was spectacular. In 1936, he was dispatched to the Philippines by President Roosevelt to devise a strategy of defense; MacArthur mistakenly thought that the Japanese

Max Schmeling hangs on the ropes as he is pummeled by Joe Louis in their championship fight on June 22, 1938.

General Douglas MacArthur strides ashore during the landing on Leyte on Oct. 20, 1944.

wouldn't engage in such an attack. During World War II, he reclaimed the Philippines. After the war, he sought to expand American military efforts in the Korean War; because this strategy disagreed with President Truman's, he was dismissed. MacArthur returned to the United States in the midst of sympathy for the military hero. He authored *Reminiscences* (1964), an autobiography.

McCORMICK, CYRUS H. (1809–1884), inventor and manufacturer. He was primarily interested in farm machinery. In 1832, he took out a patent for a horizontal plow. He built a factory in Chicago for manufacturing reapers, and by mid-century he had a national market for reapers. Throughout his life, he competed with Obed Hussey for advantage in the farm machinery market. A contest in London pitted the McCormick reaper against the Hussey, and McCormick won. He expanded his factories in the United States; he developed steam-powered, self-propelled combines. He gave large sums of money to religious causes, and he received numerous honors from governments and organizations. William T. Hutchinson's *Cyrus Hall McCormick* is the standard biography.

MacDONALD, JEANETTE (1907–1965), actress and singer. With Nelson Eddy, she starred in several outstanding musical productions, including *Naughty Marietta* (1935), *Rose Marie* (1936), *Maytime* (1937), *Sweethearts* (1938), and *New Moon* (1940). She appeared in Broadway musicals such as *Love Me Tonight* (1932) and *One Hour With You* (1932). She starred with Clark Gable in *San Francisco* (1936).

McGUFFEY, WILLIAM H. (1800–1873), author of early elementary-school readers. McGuffey served as president of Cincinnati College and sought to promote public education. In 1836, he wrote the *Eclectic Readers;* the last of the now-famous *McGuffey Readers* was completed in 1854. Each of his books contained readings, aphorisms, messages on thrift and initiative. Within the emerging public schools, the readers were popular for several generations. McGuffey became president of Ohio University, and later professor of natural and moral philosophy at the University of Virginia. Richard D. Mosier's *Making the American Mind: Social and Moral Ideas in the McGuffey Readers* (1947) describes the impact of McGuffey's books.

MACHEN, J. GRESHAM (1881–1937), theologian and Bible scholar. Born in Baltimore, Maryland, Machen studied at Johns Hopkins University, Princeton University, and Princeton Theological Seminary. He then became professor and lecturer at Princeton. Machen was ordained as a Presbyterian minister; he became a leading voice of orthodox Protestantism in the early twentieth century. His books include *The Origin of Paul's Religion* (1921), *Christianity and Liberalism* (1923), *New Testament Greek for Beginners* (1923), and *The Virgin Birth of Christ* (1930).

McNAMARA, ROBERT S. (1916–), banker, automobile executive, public servant. McNamara was born in San Francisco, California, and received his undergraduate education at the University of California. He received his graduate degree in business administration from Harvard University. McNamara served for a brief period as a professor at Harvard. He became an executive with the Ford Motor Company in 1946 and president of that firm in 1960. President John Kennedy named him as Secretary of Defense in 1961. His eight years in that office were the most difficult years of the war in Vietnam. In 1968, he became president of the World Bank. McNamara has received numerous honors and recognitions. He authored *The Essense of Security* (1968) and other titles.

MADDOX, LESTER (1915–), segregationist leader and Georgia politician. Born in Atlanta, Georgia, he engaged in various business relationships—real estate, furniture, and a restaurant. As owner of a restaurant, he was told to comply with an integration order. He refused to comply and the restaurant was closed. He subsequently ran for political office and was elected governor of Georgia from 1967 to 1971. He served as lieutenant-governor under Governor Jimmy Carter in 1971–1975.

MALCOLM X (1925–1965), black religious leader. He was born as Malcolm Little in Omaha, Nebraska. Influenced by his father and the "back to Africa" ideas of Marcus Garvey, he resolved to defend the cause of black people. As a child, he saw his father murdered. In Boston, he worked in various menial jobs and was arrested for burglary. While in prison, he was converted to the Black Muslim religion; this provided a new forum for his ideas on race. He became an assistant minister of the Detroit Mosque. After the Kennedy assassination he made certain remarks that caused his suspension from the Black Muslims. He left the Nation of Islam to join the Organization of Afro-American Unity, and was assassinated at a public rally. His experiences were included in *The Autobiography of Malcolm X* by Alexander Haley.

MANCINI, HENRY (1924–   ), popular composer. Born in Cleveland, Ohio, Mancini attended the Juilliard Institute of Music. He served as pianist and arranger for the Tex Beneke Orchestra. As staff composer for Universal Pictures, he wrote scores for *The Glenn Miller Story, The Benny Goodman Story, The Great Waldo Pepper,* and other films. His recordings have achieved national attention. Among them are "Days of Wine and Roses" and "Moon River" (with Johnny Mercer). Mancini has received over twenty Grammy awards; he received Academy Awards for his music in *Breakfast at Tiffany's, Moon River,* and *Days of Wine and Roses.*

MANN, HORACE (1796–1859), educational reformer who promoted education throughout the United States. After graduating as valedictorian from Brown University, he pursued the study of law. His legal studies were interrupted by an interest in tutoring Latin and Greek; but later he returned to his legal studies, graduated from Tapping Reeve, and was admitted to the bar in 1823. He regarded education as "the great equalizer" of society. He abandoned a political career for a position as First Secretary of the State Board of Education. His admiration for Prussian education and non-sectarian study made his views controversial. Mann served as a member of the United States House of Representatives and president of Antioch College. *The Republic and the School: The Education of Free Men* (1957) is the most comprehensive collection of his writings.

MANTLE, MICKEY (1931–   ), baseball player born in Spavinaw, Oklahoma. In 1949, he signed with the New York Yankees. He has appeared with the New York Yankees in numerous World Series and All-Star games. Mantle is regarded as an outstanding baseball player. He was inducted into the Baseball Hall of Fame in 1974.

MARSHALL, GEORGE C. (1880–1959), soldier, statesman, architect of United States foreign

policies after World War II. Marshall graduated from Virginia Military Institute and served in World War I under General John Pershing. Appointed Chief of Staff of the Army, he helped to prepare the United States for World War II. He received criticism for his failure to alert our Far East bases of the impending attack by the Japanese; but he directed military operations throughout the war and served as advisor to President Roosevelt. After the war he was named Secretary of State. The Marshall Plan set up a framework for the reconstruction of war-devastated Europe; actually, the plan combined the wisdom of George Kennan and Dean Acheson. Marshall encouraged the formation of the North Atlantic Treaty Organization (NATO). He was Secretary of Defense during the Korean War. The best work on Marshall is Forrest C. Pogue's *George C. Marshall* (2 vols., 1963, 1967).

MARSHALL, JOHN (1775–1835), the fourth Chief Justice of the United States. Marshall consolidated the principle of judicial review and strengthened the powers of the Supreme Court. Marshall was named to the court in 1801; he authored a definitive five-volume biography of George Washington. In 1803, his ruling in the celebrated case of *Marbury* vs. *Madison* established the principle of declaring acts of Congress unconstitutional. In *United States* vs. *Peters* he established the Supreme Court as the final interpreter of Federal law. In *McCulloch* vs. *Maryland* and *Gibbons* vs. *Ogden,* he upheld the principle that allowed the chartering of the Second Bank of the United States and the credit structure for interstate currency. Marshall was one of the truly outstanding Chief Justices in American history. *The Life of John Marshall,* by Albert J. Beveridge (2 vols., rev. ed. 1947) is a significant biography.

MARTIN, DEAN (1917–   ), actor, singer, and comedian. Born in Steubenville, Ohio, Martin became associated with Jerry Lewis in a successful comedy routine. The television series titled *The Martin-Lewis Comedy Hour* achieved considerable attention. His disagreement with Lewis resulted in the break-up of the comedy team. His screen roles have varied from the *Matt Helm* series to *The Bells Are Ringing* (1960), *Oceans II* (1960), *Silences* (1970), and *Airport.* His weekly television program on the National Broadcasting Company was widely received.

MARSHALL, THURGOOD (1908–   ), civil rights lawyer, Associate Justice of the United States Supreme Court. A native of Baltimore, Maryland, Marshall developed techniques for civils rights litigation during his early career as a lawyer. He served as counsel for the Baltimore chapter of the National Association for the Advancement of Colored People (NAACP). In 1938, he was admitted to practice before the United States Supreme Court. He achieved a phenomenal success ratio in his cases before the high court. For example, he argued the successful *Brown* vs. *Board of Education,* which overturned segregation in public education. In 1964, President Johnson appointed him Solicitor General; in 1967, he was named to the Supreme Court. He has received numerous honors. An excellent biography is Lewis H. Fenderson's *Thurgood Marshall* (1969).

MARTIN, MARY (1913–   ), actress and singer born in Weatherford, Texas. Miss Martin was the singer in *Leave It to Me* (1938). She then starred in numerous musical productions, including *The Great Victor Herbert, Kiss the Boys Goodbye, Birth of the Blues,* and *Night and Day.* She starred in Noel Coward's *Pacific 1860.* Her role as entertainer in tours of United States military forces received acclaim. Her roles in *Annie Get Your Gun* (1948), the stage production of *South Pacific* (1949–1952), *Peter Pan* (1954–1955), and *The Sound of Music* (1959–1961) were widely acclaimed.

MARX, JULIUS "GROUCHO" (1890–1977), comedian and entertainer. In his early days, he joined his brothers Harpo and Chico in comic routines; the vaudeville circuit became the arena for the Marx comedy. With a cigar in hand, Groucho perfected comedy of the lunatic fringe. His scandalous humor was in comedy revues such as *Monkey Business* (1929), *Horsefeathers* (1932), and *Duck Soup* (1933). After the war, he became the host of a radio quiz show, *You Bet Your Life,* which achieved remarkable television success. The last movie effort starring Harpo and Chico was *The Incredible Jewel Robbery* (1959). A useful study of Groucho and his brothers is by Allen Eyles: *The Marx Brothers: Their World of Comedy* (second edition, 1969).

MATHER, COTTON (1663–1728), a leading author from the Puritan era, associated with the Salem witchcraft trials. Mather's youth was as remarkable as his life. At twelve, he was a student at Harvard College. He studied medicine, philosophy, and science in his teens. With his father, Increase Mather, he became a guiding force in the emerging Puritan society. The Salem witchcraft mentality was generated by Cotton Mather; his ill-fated efforts to become president of Harvard College or Yale brought serious disappointments in his later life. He was honored by other means— through election to the Royal Society of London. The best biography on Cotton Mather is Barrett Wendell's *Cotton Mather: The Puritan Priest* (rev. ed., 1963).

MAULDIN, BILL (1921–   ), editorial cartoonist. Born in Mountain Park, New Mexico, he studied at the Chicago Academy of Fine Arts. Mauldin served as cartoonist for the *St. Louis Post-Dispatch* until 1962, when he joined the staff of the *Chicago Sun-Times.* During World War II, he served with the United States Army; his military service earned him The Purple Heart and Legion of Merit award. Mauldin received the Pulitzer Prize for cartoons in 1944 and 1958. He authored numerous books, including *Bill Mauldin's Army* (1951), *Bill Mauldin in Korea* (1953), and *The Brass Ring* (1972).

MAYS, WILLIE (1931–   ), professional baseball player born in Westfield, Alabama. In 1950, he joined the New York Giants, which later moved to San Francisco. From 1951 to 1972, he was characterized as a "superstar" of baseball because he held numerous records: National League home run record; National League's Most Valuable Player of 1954 and 1965; and the Sporting News Player of the Year 1954. He wrote *Willie Mays: My Life In and Out of Baseball* (1966).

MEAD, MARGARET (1901–1978), anthropologist and author. Her early studies in Samoa provided new insights into tension, social organization, and adulthood; she authored *Coming of Age in Samoa.* She served as curator of ethnology at the American Museum of National History, then returned to her anthropological studies in New Guinea and wrote *Growing up in New Guinea* (1930). In later writings, she applied her findings to issues of public policy. After World War II, she authored *The Study of Cultures at a Distance* (1953) on cultural integration and analysis. In the 1960s and 1970s, her studies concerned the need for population control.

MEANY, GEORGE (1894–   ), labor leader associated with the American Federation of Labor (AFL). In his early career, Meany was associated with the building trades unions in New York. He promoted the pro-labor legislation of the New Deal; and during World War II, he served on the War Labor Board. In 1952, he was chosen as president of the AFL; later, he became president of the combined AFL and Congress of Industrial Organizations (CIO). Meany committed the organization to social reform and civil rights. Most Presidents since Eisenhower have had to reckon with the labor movement led by George Meany.

MELLON, ANDREW W. (1855–1932), businessman and United States Secretary of the Treasury. While associated with T. Mellon & Sons, he assisted in forming the Aluminum Corporation of America and organized the Gulf Oil Corporation. He then formed the Mellon National Bank of Pittsburgh, which identified him with significant banking and investment leaders. During the 1920s, he assisted the Harding, Coolidge, and Hoover Administrations in planning their monetary policies. His tax policies contributed to the unequal distribution of income that culminated with the Great Depression. Mellon wrote *Taxation: The People's Business* (1924).

MENNINGER, KARL (1893–   ), psychiatrist and author. Born in Topeka, Kansas, Menninger attended the University of Wisconsin and Harvard, receiving his medical degree *cum laude* from Harvard University. In 1946, he established the Menninger School of Psychiatry; he has been involved in the treatment, education, and rehabilitation of mental disorders. Menninger's books include *The Vital Balance* and *Love Against Hate.*

MILLER, GLENN (1904–1944), band leader of the "swing" era. Born in Chicago, Miller attended schools in Colorado and graduated from the University of Colorado. He began his musical career as a trombone player and as arranger for various orchestras. In 1933, he organized the Glenn Miller Band. The band played on several radio programs, but regularly appeared on the *Chesterfield Radio Program.* He composed many songs that achieved national popularity, including "Moonlight Serenade." Miller died in a plane crash over Holland shortly before the end of World War II.

MONDALE, WALTER (1928–   ), Vice-President of the United States and former United States Senator. In 1948, he worked in Hubert Humphrey's campaign for the Senate. He left Minnesota to work in Washington, D.C., for the student wing of Americans for Democratic Action; then he returned to Minnesota and graduated from college in 1951. In 1956, he obtained his law degree. In 1964, while serving as attorney general for Minnesota, he was appointed to finish Humphrey's Senate term when Humphrey became Vice-President; he was reelected in 1966 and 1972. On January 20, 1977, he became the forty-second Vice-President of the United States. Mondale has projected the image of a political liberal.

MONROE, MARILYN (1926–1962), motion picture star who built her reputation on a frivolous and sexual image. She was an illegitimate child with the name of Norma Jean Mortenson. Raised by foster parents, she had an unsuccessful marriage to an aircraft worker named James Dougherty. Then she became a photographer's model. In 1954, she married baseball star Joe DiMaggio, but the marriage lasted less than a year. She married playwright Arthur Miller but again was divorced in four years. Her most famous screen roles were in *Gentlemen Prefer Blondes* (1953), *How to Marry a Millionaire* (1953), *The Seven-Year Itch* (1955), *Some Like It Hot* (1959), and *The Misfits* (1961).

MOODY, DWIGHT L. (1837–1899), revivalist and evangelist. While Moody worked as a shoe salesman in Chicago, he became interested in the Young Men's Christian Association (YMCA). He organized "Sunday Schools" for slum families, supported through the YMCA. In 1872, he teamed up with Ira D. Sankey to hold revivals throughout England and Scotland; he then returned to America where he conducted revivals in New York, Philadelphia, Chicago, and Boston. Moody established schools for ministers in Northfield, Massachusetts, and Chicago. Chicago Bible Institute (named after Moody upon his death) achieved a great reputation. James Findlay's *Dwight L. Moody; American Evangelist* (1969) is a good biography.

MORGAN, J. PIERPONT (1837–1913), banker and financier who was instrumental in the financial reorganization of the railroads. During a severe economic crisis in 1893, Morgan managed to sell government bonds for gold. He organized the House of Morgan investment and banking corporation; established United States Steel as the largest corporation of its day; and gained control of major rail routes to the West. He was an avid collector of art; through a personal interest, he provided the funds to make the Metropolitan Museum of Art in New York among the finest museums in the world. Frederick Lewis Allen's *The Great Pierpont Morgan* (1949) is the most readable biography on the man.

MORRIS, GOUVERNEUR (1752–1816), statesman and diplomat. Born in Morisania, New York, he served in the New York provisional congress during the early stages of the American Revolution. He was elected in 1778 as a delegate to the Continental Congress and served as an assistant to Robert Morris, who was Superintendent of Finance. Morris was a significant delegate to the Constitutional Convention in 1787; he helped to draft the American Constitution, which he also signed. Morris served as foreign minister to France from 1792 to 1794. He also served as Senator from New York, and was critical of Jeffersonian Democrats. The diary of Morris is contained in *A Diary of the French Revolution* (2 vols., 1939) edited by B. C. Davenport.

MORSE, SAMUEL F. B. (1781–1872), inventor and designer of the first telegraph system. Morse was born in Charlestown, Massachusetts, the son of a clergyman. He graduated from Yale College. As an artist and painter, his work attracted little attention. Then he developed an interest in electricity. He combined the existing technology of sender, receiver, and code to invent telegraphy. Congress authorized the construction and development of a telegraphic line between Washington, D.C., and Baltimore, Maryland. By 1844, he was able to send the message "What hath God wrought" over this line. Robert L. Thompson's book, *Wiring a Continent* (1947) places Morse within the broader framework of technology.

MOSES, ANNA MARY ROBERTSON "GRANDMA" (1860–1962), painter of the primitive style. Born in Greenwich, New York, she held her first show in New York City in 1940. Subsequently her paintings were exhibited in shows throughout the United States, including the Museum of Modern Art in New York, the Metropolitan Museum in New York, and the Carnegie Institute. From 1950 to 1957, her paintings were exhibited in Europe. She received the Certificate of Merit (1956), the Woman's National Press Club Award (1949), and others. She wrote *My Life's History: Autobiography of Grandma Moses* (1952).

MUHAMMAD, ELIJAH (1897–1975), leader of the black Nation of Islam. Born in Sandersville, Georgia, he became Minister to the Nation of Islam in 1934. He molded the Nation of Islam into an organization of social, economic, and religious importance. Muhammad preached a message of black nationalism and imposed a standard of strict morality. He called for separation from white America and rejected the notion of racial integration. Malcolm X and boxer Muhammad Ali were among the more influential converts to the Nation of Islam.

MURROW, EDWARD R. (1908–1965), broadcast journalist. Born near Greensboro, North Carolina, Murrow spent his early youth in Washington State. He worked in logging camps as he attended Washington State College. In 1935, joined the Columbia Broadcasting System. He travelled to London in 1937, and there he developed the dramatic "on the spot" style of radio news journalism. He won renown for his broadcasts describing the bombing raids on the city of London. After the war he developed television news journalism through the *See It Now* program; his most famous program was *Person to Person*. In 1961, he was appointed director of the United States Information Agency. Alexander Kendrick's *Prime Time* (1969) is a biography of Murrow.

NADER, RALPH (1934–   ), consumer advocate. Born in Winsted, Connecticut, Nader graduated *magna cum laude* from Princeton University. He later graduated from Harvard Law School. He was appointed as a consultant to the Department of Labor in his initial work on auto safety; served with Senator Abraham A. Ribicoff's Government Operations Subcommittee as a resource expert on safety. Nader wrote *Unsafe at Any Speed: The Designed-In-Dangers of the American Automobile* (1965) and became a bitter foe of the automobile industry. General Motors admitted spying on him, and he sued the company for $26 million in 1966. Nader organized the Center for the Study of Responsive Law in 1969. He has become identified with the consumer protection movement.

The Third-Term Panic, by Thomas Nast.
(The first use of the elephant as the symbol of the Republican Party.)

NAST, THOMAS (1840–1902), caricaturist, painter, and political cartoonist. Nast was born in Ludwig, Bavaria. As a youth he emigrated to the United States. In 1862, he began working for the *Harper's Weekly;* his initial cartoon attacks dealt with the Andrew Johnson Administration. His caricatures of Boss Tweed and the Tammany Hall political machine of New York City achieved national attention. He was offered a $200,000 bribe to stop the series, but he refused the bribe. Nast invented the symbols now associated with the Democratic and Republican parties—the donkey and elephant.

NATION, CARRY (1846–1911), temperance reformer, agitator, and an early leader in the Prohibition movement. Born in Garrard County, Kentucky, she married Dr. Charles Gloyd in 1867. He became an alcoholic and brought considerable hardship to his wife. In 1877, she married David Nation; and in 1890, she began her work with the Women's Christian Temperance Union (WCTU). Mrs. Nation and her associates organized prayer groups outside saloons and bars. In her campaign on behalf the WCTU, she carried a hatchet for breaking up saloon furniture. She displayed an aggressive character in achieving her moral ends.

NEUMANN, JOHN N. (1811–1860), religious leader; first male American saint of the Roman Catholic church. Born in Prachatice (now in Czechoslovakia), Neumann studied at the University of Prague and came to the United States as a Catholic missionary in 1836. After several years of missionary and pastoral work, he was named Bishop of Philadelphia in 1852. Neumann established about one hundred parochial schools and a Catholic seminary; he was well known for his deep personal faith in God. He was declared venerable in 1896, beatified in 1963, and canonized as a saint in 1977.

NICKLAUS, JACK (1940–   ), professional golfer born in Columbus, Ohio. Nicklaus attended Ohio State University. His career as a professional golfer included winning these major tournaments: United States Open 1962, 1967, 1972; United States Masters 1963, 1965, 1966, 1972, 1975; the British Open 196, 1970; the Professional Golfer's Association (PGA) 1963, 1971, 1973, 1974. He has won more tournament championships than any other person in the history of professional golf. Nicklaus has authored numerous publications, such as *Ways to Lower Your Golf Score* (1962) and *The Best Way to Better Golf* (1974).

NIEBUHR, H. RICHARD (1894–1962), theologian and sociologist of religion. Born in Wright City, Missouri, Niebuhr graduated from Elmhurst College (1912) and Eden Theological Seminary (1915). He received his Bachelor of Divinity degree and doctorate from Yale University. Niebuhr authored *The Social Sources of Denominationalism* (1929), in which he discusses the relationships of social groups to denominations. His *Kingdom of God in America* (1937) discusses the concept of "Kingdom" in the transformation of Puritan thought to Protestant ideas in American history. He participated in study groups that led to the major assemblies of the World Council of Churches. He was instrumental in the merger between the United Church of Christ, Congregational, and Evangelical and Reformed Churches.

NIEBUHR, REINHOLD (1892–1971), distinguished theologian within the Neo-Orthodox movement. Born in Wright City, Missouri, Niebuhr attended Elmhurst College and Eden Theological Seminary. He received his master's degree from Yale University. Niebuhr pastored a church in Detroit, Michigan, from 1915 to 1928. In 1927, he wrote *Does Civilization Need Religion?* This book criticized the capitalistic values of the American industrial order. In 1928, he joined the faculty of Union Theological Seminary in New York City. There he wrote an attack on liberal Protestantism titled *Moral Man in Immoral Society* (1932). His many books and articles underscored the social and cultural applications of theology. He opposed the expansion of United States military power in Asia during the 1960s.

OAKLEY, ANNIE (1860–1926), an outstanding figure from America's Wild West. Born in Drake County, Ohio, she teamed up with Frank E. Butler in vaudeville and later married him. In spite of her abilities in marksmanship, she was a modest woman. Her exploits inspired the modern musical, *Annie Get Your Gun.* Miss Oakley's religious views were fundamentalist. She was generous with her wealth, and many legends grew out of her reputation after she died. Annie Fern Swarthout's *Missie: An Historical Biography of Annie Oakley* (1947) is a very interesting study.

OCHS, ADOLPH S. (1858–1935), newspaper publisher and philanthropist. Born in Cincinnati, Ohio, Ochs bought and published the *Chattanooga Dispatch* and the *Chattanooga Times.* Then he moved to New York City where, in 1896, he acquired control of the *New York Times.* In an age of "yellow journalism," he sought to establish a newspaper that reflected dignity and trust. He established the *New York Times Index of Current History* (a topical journal) and funded the de-

President John F. Kennedy, Governor Connally, and Mrs. Jacqueline Kennedy stand under the wing of the presidential plane moments after arriving in Dallas, Texas, on Nov. 22, 1963.

velopment of the *Dictionary of American Biography.* Ochs tried to make editorial opinion more objective. Gay Talese's, *The Kingdom and the Power* (1969) is a massive overview of Ochs and the *New York Times.*

ONASSIS, JACQUELINE KENNEDY (1929–   ), former wife of John F. Kennedy, the thirty-fifth President of the United States. Born in Southampton, New York, she attended Vassar College and The Sorbonne in Paris, France. After the assassination of President Kennedy, she received national consolation and regard. In 1968, she married Aristotle Onassis, wealthy Greek shipbuilder; the marriage attracted considerable notice. Since Onassis' death she has served as a publishing consultant. In earlier years, she was photographer for the *Washington Times-Herald.* Mrs. Onassis is a trustee of the Whitney Museum of American Art; she has received an Emmy Award for public service.

OPPENHEIMER, J. ROBERT (1904–1967), physicist; director of the atomic energy research project at Los Alamos, New Mexico. Born in New York City, Oppenheimer attended Harvard University and Cambridge University. He joined the staff of the California Institute of Technology in Pasadena, where he established a reputation in quantum mechanics and research in the continuous spectrum. Oppenheimer served as director of the project to develop the atomic bomb. After the development of the bomb, he regretted its devastation. He became the focus of attacks by Senator Joseph McCarthy, who alleged that Oppenheimer had communist sympathies; the allegations were unfounded. In the 1960s, he received the Fermi Award and was appointed director of the Institute for Advanced Study at Princeton University.

OWENS, JESSE (1915–   ), Olympic track star. He was born in Oakville, Alabama, the son of a sharecropper. He soon became an outstanding athlete. In 1935, he competed in the National Intercollegiate Track and Field Championships, where he established new records in broad jump and track. As a member of the United States Olympic team, he won four gold medals and served to refute Adolf Hitler's concept of "Aryan superiority." After several unsuccessful enterprises, Owens was appointed national director of physical education for blacks by the Office of Civilian Defense. He served as director of personnel for Ford Motor Company in Detroit from 1942 to 1946. He has received numerous recognitions and appointments. His autobiography is entitled, *Blackthink: My Life as a Black Man and White Man* (1970).

PALEY, WILLIAM S. (1901–   ), television network executive. Born in Chicago, Illinois, he attended the University of Chicago and the University of Pennsylvania. In 1928, he joined the staff of the Columbia Broadcasting System, where he rose from president to chairman of the board. He has served on numerous federal commissions, including the White House Conference on Education, Resources for Freedom, and others. He served in the military in World War II and was decorated with the Legion of Honor and Legion of Merit.

PALMER, ARNOLD (1929–   ), professional golfer born in Youngstown, Pennsylvania. Palmer attended Wake Forest College. As a golfer, he won the Masters Tournament in 1958, 1960, 1962, and 1964; the United States Open in 1960; the British Open in 1961 and 1962; and others. His friendship with President Dwight Eisenhower (and the President's affection for golf) established Palmer as a national celebrity. He is the president of Arnold Palmer Enterprises.

PATTERSON, FLOYD (1935–   ), boxer and former heavyweight champion, born in Waco, North Carolina. In 1952, Patterson began his boxing career as an Olympic middleweight champion; later in 1952, he fought his first professional fight. In 1956, he won the World Heavyweight Championship by defeating Archie Moore (the title had been vacated by the retirement of Rocky Mar-

ciano). After several defenses of the title, he lost it to Ingemar Johansson in 1959. He regained the title from Johansson in 1960, then lost it to Sonny Liston in 1962.

PATTERSON, JOSEPH MEDILL (1879–1946), newspaper publisher. Born in Chicago, Patterson attended the Groton School and Yale University. He began a journalistic career with the *Chicago Tribune* in 1901. In 1919, he founded the *New York Daily News* and remained as editor and publisher of that newspaper from 1919 to 1946. He served during World War I and wrote several books, including *The Fourth Estate* (with J. Keeley and Harriet Ford), *By-Products,* and *Rebellion.* His *New York Daily News* emphasized sensationalism, sex, and crime. After the financial crash of 1929, he addressed the newspaper to social reform and New Deal legislation. Although he supported President Franklin Roosevelt on most items, he felt that the United States should not enter World War II.

PATTON, GEORGE S. (1885–1945), general and military strategist. Born in San Gabriel, California, Patton graduated from the United States Military Academy at West Point. He distinguished himself as a tactician and commander of mobile tank warfare. His strict discipline and colorful language earned him the nickname "Old Blood and Guts." Patton was a student of United States Civil War strategy. Between World Wars, he learned tank warfare. He established his reputation in the North African campaign and the capture of Palermo. His sweep across France with the Third Army was marked by ruthlessness and drive. Patton was strategically involved in the Battle of the Bulge. He authored *War as I Knew It.*

PAULING, LINUS (1901–   ), atomic chemist. Born in Portland, Oregon, Pauling studied at Oregon State University and California Institute of Technology. He headed the Gates and Crellin Laboratories. His studies involved hemoglobin and protein structures. He is a member of the National Academy of Sciences and numerous other associations. In 1954, he received the Nobel Prize in Chemistry and the Nobel Peace Prize in 1962. Pauling has written numerous articles; his most famous appeared in 1931 and was entitled "The Nature of the Chemical Bond." Pauling advocated military disarmament, as described in *Quest for Peace* (1966) by Mortimer Lipsky.

PEABODY, GEORGE (1795–1869), merchant, financier, and philanthropist. Peabody dealt in securities in London after 1837; he generated capital for American industries. His firm, George Peabody and Company, specialized in foreign exchange. Peabody's international banking earned him a considerable personal fortune. After the Panic of 1837, he purchased several securities that were depressed. His company brought large supplies of capital investment to the United States. His wealth was distributed in various programs of educational reconstruction and poor relief. Franklin Parker's *George Peabody: A Biography* (1971) is highly informative and readable.

PEALE, NORMAN VINCENT (1898–   ), influential Protestant clergyman. Peale obtained his undergraduate degree from Ohio Wesleyan College in 1920. He was torn between a career in journalism or the ministry; he worked for the *Morning Republican* in Findlay, Ohio, and the *Detroit Journal*. He returned to study at Boston University and was ordained into the Methodist Episcopal Church in 1921. In 1932, he became pastor of the Marble Collegiate Church in New York. He has written numerous books, including *The Art of Living* (1932), *A Guide to Confident Living* (1948), *The Art of Real Happiness* (1950), and his phenomenally successful book, *The Power of Positive Thinking* (1952). Peale also began a radio program titled *The Art of Living,* which began in 1935 on NBC. He has been criticized for his moral pragmatism.

PEALE, REMBRANDT (1778–1860), painter best known for his portraits of Revolutionary heroes. Born in Bucks County, Pennsylvania, Peale was a son of the renowned painter, Charles Willson Peale. He made several trips to France, where he met Jacques Louis David and other leading artists. Peale established the Pennsylvania Academy of Fine Arts. His portrait of George Washington (1822) achieved considerable fame. He was elected president of the American Academy of the Fine Arts in 1825. Peale wrote *Graphics: The Art of Accurate Delineation* (1835). He developed a massive series of paintings on death that reflected several allegorical figures. In an era that emphasized romanticism, Peale's realistic work achieved considerable fame, particularly in Europe.

PEARSON, DREW (1897–1969), controversial newspaper columnist. His syndicated news column "Washington Merry-Go-Round" first appeared in 1932; he shared the writing with Jack Anderson after 1959. Pearson reported President Franklin Roosevelt's plan to pack the Supreme Court; he was generally disliked among Presidents and other public officials. He sponsored humanitarian causes; for example, he organized the Friendship Train to collect food for the people of Europe. He authored several books, including *Washington Merry-Go-Round* (1931) and (with Jack Anderson) *The Case Against Congress* (1968).

PEARY, ROBERT E. (1856–1920), Arctic explorer, famous for his discovery of the North Pole. Peary was born in Cresson, Pennsylvania. After his studies in civil engineering, he served as a county surveyor and draftsman. He was commissioned in the United States Navy in 1881. His early travels to Greenland were a prelude to his subsequent discovery of the North Pole. He reached the North Pole on April 6, 1909; but controversy surrounded Frederick A. Cook's claims that he reached the North Pole in 1908. In later life, Peary became identified with the development and expansion of aviation. John Edward Weems *Race to the Pole* (1960) details the controversy between Cook and Peary.

PENN, WILLIAM (1644–1718), Quaker leader and founder of Pennsylvania. Penn was born in London, where he became associated with the development of Quakerism and the Society of Friends. At Oxford, he was influenced by Puritanism and was expelled from the university. In 1672, he became a Quaker advocate. After the Glorious Revolution of 1688, he came to establish the colony of Pennsylvania. In 1712, he sold the colony to England. His last years were filled with disappointment. Mary M. Dunn's *William Penn: Politics and Conscience* (1967) is a useful analysis of the man.

PENNEY, JAMES C. (1875–1971), business executive and philanthropist born in Hamilton, Ohio. In 1902, he established the J.C. Penney Company, which operated on the principle of the Golden Rule and Christian morality. The department stores that he opened were called Golden Rule Stores; his first store was in Kemmerer, Wyoming. By 1971, his chain of stores numbered 1,660 outlets with gross sales of $4.1 billion. Penney exhibited a deep religious perspective in his personal manner and corporate leadership.

PERRY, OLIVER H. (1785–1819), naval officer and hero of the War of 1812. Born in South Kingston, Rhode Island, Perry held the command of a flotilla at Newport, Virginia, at the outbreak of the War of 1812. Commander Robert H. Barclay challenged Perry on September 10, 1813 in a battle between Perry's *Niagra* and Barclay's *Detroit*. Barclay was defeated, and Perry sent his superiors the famous message: "We have met the enemy and they are ours." This decisive victory strengthened United States claims in the Northwest. Perry retired and received honors from Congress. He later travelled to the Mediterranean, where he died of yellow fever.

PERSHING, JOHN J. (1860–1948), distinguished American commander during World War I. After graduation from West Point in 1886, Pershing was assigned to the campaign against the Apache Indians in the Southwest United States. He was also involved in the Spanish-American War and served as military attache in Tokyo during the Russo-Japanese War (1904–1905). Pershing's most significant service came during World War I, when he called for an independent American army. The Allies questioned his strategy during the last years of the war. Congress awarded him the title General of the Armies, a title given previously to George Washington. He authored *My Experiences in the World War* (1948), which was awarded the Pulitzer Prize.

PICKFORD, MARY (1894–   ), actress and movie star born in Toronto, Canada. Her acting career began at age eight, when she appeared in various melodramas and as a child actress on Broadway. At age 13, she took the name Mary Pickford. She appeared in various roles between 1910 and 1916, when she established the Mary Pickford Film Company. She joined Douglas Fairbanks, Charlie Chaplin, and the United Artists Corporation in 1919. She starred in numerous productions on the silent screen. She aided the work of numerous philanthropic and charity organizations.

PINKERTON, ALLAN (1819–1884), founder of a famous detective agency that bears his name; prototype of the modern crime investigator. Born in Glasgow, Scotland, he migrated to Dundee, Illinois. He supported abolitionists and the Underground Railroad in the years leading up to the Civil War. In 1850, he served as the director of police in Chicago; he then organized his private agency. He worked with the United States Post Office and the Illinois Central Railroad to solve robberies. He prevented an assassination of President Lincoln during the first inaugural. He organized the framework of the most comprehensive detective agency, opposing labor unions.

POCAHONTAS (ca. 1595–1617), early symbol of the American Indians. The daughter of an Indian chief, her real name was Matoaka; *Pocahontas* means "playful one." According to tradition, she played at the fort at Jamestown. She was taken as a prisoner by Captain Samuel Argall to guarantee the safety of Englishmen who had fallen into Indian hands. She was brought to Jamestown, instructed in Christianity, and baptized. She married colonial leader John Rolfe, and the marriage brought a period of peace between the colonists and the Indians. During a trip to England, she contracted smallpox and died in 1617.

POLLOCK, JACKSON (1912–1956), painter within the abstract, expressionist tradition. Born in Cody, Wyoming, he studied with Thomas Hart Benton between 1929 and 1931. He worked with the Depression-inspired Federal Arts Project from 1938 to 1942. During World War II, his art was influenced by European developments in cubism and surrealism. His paintings attracted the attention of Peggy Guggenheim; and under the Guggenheim influence, his art was shown throughout Europe. Pollock's international reputation became established in this period. During the last years of his life, his work was seen at the Sidney Janis Gallery in New York. In 1956, he was honored by a special exhibition at the New York Museum of Modern Art.

POPE, JOHN RUSSELL (1874–1937), architect; best known for designing the National Gallery of Art in Washington, D.C. Pope was born in New York City and trained at the American Academy at Rome. He was able to duplicate historic architectural styles through his studies. Pope began his architectural career in New York. He designed the Scottish Rite Temple in Washington, D.C., and was chosen to design memorials for Theodore Roosevelt in Washington and Abraham Lincoln in Hodgenville, Kentucky.

POST, ELIZABETH L. "EMILY" (ca. 1880–1960), well-known authority on social manners.

Born in Baltimore, Maryland, she began writing short stories and novels in 1904. Her book, *Etiquette,* appeared in 1922 and went through 10 revisions and 89 printings. It served as a guide to proper behavior and manners for ordinary people. Miss Post regarded etiquette as the science of proper living. She also wrote a nationally syndicated newspaper article on etiquette and authored numerous other publications, including *The Personality of a House* (1930), *Children Are People* (1940), and the *Emily Post Cook Book* (1949).

PRESLEY, ELVIS (1935–1977), singer commonly recognized as the father of "rock and roll" music. Presley's performances were filled with emotion and intensity. His gyrating hips and suggestive stage movements became a trademark, and he was idolized by teenagers throughout the world. He signed a recording contract with RCA Victor in 1956; he then recorded success after success. His first 45 records sold over a million copies each. Presley appeared in *Love Me Tender* and a succession of movies. He grossed over $4.3 billion in his 21-year career. His more famous musical titles included "Love Me Tender," "All Shook Up," and "Are You Lonesome Tonight?" His Graceland Mansion in Memphis, Tennessee, was a mecca for his fans.

PULITZER, JOSEPH, SR. (1847–1911), newspaper publisher and editor. Born in Mako, Hungary, he grew up in Budapest and pursued an active interest in military affairs. After being rejected by the French Foreign Legion, he was recruited by the Union forces for the Civil War and obtained passage to Boston. He quickly became identified with journalism through the *Westliche Post* in 1871. He purchased the *St. Louis Post-Dispatch,* which had shaky finances until about 1881. He served as a delegate to the National Democratic Convention and was elected as a member of Congress from New York in 1885. He then purchased the *New York World,* which added strength to his emerging influence. He used the *World* to promote sensational journalism and scandal. Its fiery reports from Cuba drew the United States into the Spanish-American War.

PYLE, ERNEST T. "ERNIE" (1900–1945), outstanding newspaper correspondent of World War II. Born near Dana, Indiana, Pyle studied journalism at Indiana University. After varied assignments, he received permanent appointment with the Scripps-Howard newspaper chain. Pyle developed a column that was syndicated through two hundred daily newspapers. He received a Pulitzer Prize for his coverage of the campaigns in North Africa, Sicily, Italy, and France. Pyle was with United States forces in Iwo Jima, where he died. He authored *Ernie Pyle in England* (1941), *Here Is Your War* (1943), *Brave Men* (1944), and *Last Chapter* (1946).

RAUSCHENBUSCH, WALTER (1860–1918), clergyman associated with the "social gospel." Born in Rochester, New York, Rauschenbusch graduated from Rochester Theological Seminary and assumed a pastorate in the area of New York City known as "Hells Kitchen." His experiences in New York led him to question the capitalistic ethic, and he formulated a theology of Christian socialism. He authored several books, including *Christianity and the Social Crisis, Christianizing the Social Order,* and *A Theology of Social Gospel.*

RAYBURN, SAM (1882–1961), political leader and long-time Speaker of the House of Representatives. Born in Roane County, Texas, Rayburn graduated from Mayo Normal School (now East Texas State University). He taught in rural schools, then ran for the Texas House of Representatives. He attended law school and passed the state bar in 1908. In 1910, he won a seat in the United States House of Representatives; he was subsequently reelected for 23 terms. He served as Speaker of the House for many years. Clearly identified with the Democratic Party and its leadership, he managed the Presidential campaign of Lyndon Baines Johnson in 1960. An interesting analysis of Rayburn's impact on national politics is included in William Leuchtenburg's *Franklin D. Roosevelt and The New Deal, 1932–1940* (1963).

REAGAN, RONALD (1911–   ), Hollywood actor and political figure. Reagan appeared in over fifty movies. In 1966, he ran for governor of California against incumbent Edmund G. "Pat" Brown and was victorious. He became an important force in the Republican Party. Although he was viewed as a radical conservative because he supported Barry Goldwater for the Presidency in 1964, Reagan resisted such labeling. He opposed federally funded welfare programs and the expansion of big government. In the 1976 Presidential campaign, he unsuccessfully challenged President Gerald Ford for the Republican nomination.

Presidential candidate Ronald Reagan waves to an enthusiastic crowd on his arrival on Aug. 15, 1976, in Kansas City.

REASONER, HARRY (1923–   ), broadcast journalist. Born in Dakota City, Iowa, Reasoner began a writing career in 1946 with the *Minneapolis Times*. In 1948, he began an association with radio station WCCO in Minneapolis, a CBS radio affiliate. After a period of time with the United States Information Agency in the Far East, he returned to CBS with a television assignment in New York. He covered the racial crisis in Little Rock, Arkansas, in 1958. During the 1960s, he had numerous assignments with *CBS Reports* and narrated special documentaries on smoking, taxation, and federal aid to schools. He was seen as the weekly anchorman for *CBS Sunday News* until 1970, when he left CBS to join ABC News. He co-anchored news broadcasts at ABC with Howard K. Smith and Barbara Walters, then returned to the staff of CBS News in 1978.

REED, WALTER S. (1851–1902), military surgeon who is credited with having conquered yellow fever. Reed received two medical degrees, one from the University of Virginia and another from Bellevue Hospital Medical College. He served as a professor at the Army Medical School in Washington. He was able to determine the mode of transmission of yellow fever through many controlled experiments. He developed a way to immunize soldiers against the disease. In 1901, he resumed his teaching responsibilities at the Army Medical School. Reed received many honors, including honorary degrees from Harvard University and the University of Michigan. For more information about his life and times, read Albert E. Truby's, *Memorial of Walter Reed: The Yellow Fever Episode* (1943).

REMINGTON, FREDERIC (1861–1909), author and sculptor; painter and illustrator. Remington attended several schools, including Yale School of Fine Arts. His early work reflected his fascination with the West. He often painted horses in action. His work contained a high degree of realism. He represented the cowboy, Indian, and the Western landscape with native color. Remington wrote many significant books, including *Pony Tracks* (1895), *Stories of War and Peace* (1899), and *The Way of an Indian* (1906). A significant collection of his work can be found in the New York Public Library.

RENWICK, JAMES, JR. (1818–1895), architect most famous for St. Patrick's Cathedral in New York City. Born in the Bloomingdale section of New York, Renwick got his abilities in design from his father, James Renwick. He graduated from Columbia College. His designs for several churches brought him to national prominence—Grace Church, Church of the Puritans on Union Square, Church of the Covenant, and St. Patrick's Cathedral. Renwick also designed the New Smithsonian Institution in Washington. He taught a generation of apprentices and draftsmen and was a collector of art objects from his trips abroad.

RESTON, JAMES (1909–   ), author and journalist born in Clyde-Bank, Scotland. Reston attended the University of Illinois and began his journalistic career with the *Springfield Daily News*. In 1934, he joined the staff of the Associated Press in London. In 1939, he came back to the United States to work with the *New York Times*—first as reporter for the London bureau, then with the Washington bureau, finally as Chief Washington Correspondent (1953–1964). From 1964 to 1968, he was associate editor of the *Times*. He received the Pulitzer Prize in 1945 and 1957. Reston has received numerous other awards, recognitions, and honorary degrees.

RICKENBACKER, EDWARD "EDDIE" (1890–1973), World War I flying ace, racing driver, and executive of a major airline. Rickenbacker worked with the Frayer-Miller company as a race driver and he achieved numerous records. During World War I, he shot down more than twenty-two enemy planes, and became the most decorated pilot of the war. As general manager and later president of Eastern Airlines, he brought innovative promotions to the industry. After World War

II, he supported conservative McCarthyism and the anti-communist crusade. His autobiography is titled, *Rickenbacker—An Autobiography*.

RIDDLE, NELSON (1921–   ), composer, conductor, and arranger of popular musical themes. He was associated with numerous bands early in his career, including the Tommy Dorsey Band. He served as staff arranger for the National Broadcasting Company in Hollywood, 1947–1950; then he was musical director for Capitol Records, 1951–1962. Riddle has been guest conductor with the Hollywood Bowl and the Atlanta Symphony. He received the Emmy nomination in 1954, 1955, 1956, and 1957, and an Oscar nomination in 1960. Riddle received a Grammy award for *Come Blow Your Horn* and other musical scores. He composed theme music for the television series *Untouchables, Naked City, Route 66,* and others.

ROCKEFELLER, JOHN D., JR. (1874–1960), business entrepreneur and philanthropist. Born in Cleveland, Ohio, Rockefeller was educated at Brown University. After graduation, he became involved in the business affairs of Standard Oil Company, which his father had founded. He disliked the world of business and became involved in philanthrophy. He established the Rockefeller Institute for Medical Research and the Rockefeller Foundation. He supported the education of black people in the South. The last quarter-century of his life was devoted to conservation, the national parks system, and the restoration of Williamsburg. His modesty was in direct contrast to the image that his father projected.

ROCKEFELLER, NELSON A. (1908–1979), former governor of New York and Vice-President of the United States under President Gerald R. Ford. He was a son of John D. Rockefeller, Jr. His government service began as Assistant Secretary of State in 1944–1945. After the war, he chaired the Development Advisory Board. From 1958 to 1973, he was governor of New York, where he inaugurated a major construction program in the state capital of Albany. After President Richard Nixon's resignation, he was named by President Ford to become Vice-President. He was a trustee of the Rockefeller Brothers fund.

ROCKWELL, NORMAN (1894–1978), painter and illustrator of covers for the *Saturday Evening Post* and numerous other magazines, including the *Ladies' Home Journal, Look,* and *McCall's.* Rockwell's *Paintings of Four Freedoms* is represented in the Metropolitan Museum of Art in New York City. During World War I, he served as a first-class painter with the United States Navy. He received numerous recognitions and honorary degrees, and wrote *Norman Rockwell: My Adventures as an Illustrator* (1959), *The Norman Rockwell Album* (1961), *Norman Rockwell: Artist and Illustrator* (1970), and *Norman Rockwell's America* (1975).

RODGERS, RICHARD (1902–   ), noted composer of music. Born near Arverne, New York, Rodgers worked with Lorenze Hart and Jerome Kern in his early years. With Lorenze Hart, he produced a succession of musicals that captured national attention; among their more successful productions were: *On Your Toes* (1936), *Babes in Arms* (1937), and *Pal Joey* (1940). His more popular music with Hart included *My Funny Valentine, With a Song in My Heart, This Can't Be Love,* and *The Lady Is a Tramp.* His association with Oscar Hammerstein resulted in such musical successes as *Carousel* (1945), *South Pacific* (1949), *The King and I* (1951), and *The Sound of Music* (1959). Rodgers' most popular songs include "If I Loved You," "Hello Young Lovers," and "Climb Every Mountain."

ROGERS, WILL (1879–1935), entertainer and newspaper columnist. Rogers was born in Cologah, Oklahoma, of Indian descent; as a young man he was a cowboy—panhandling, twirling rope, and herding steers. In 1902, he joined a Wild West show in Australia. In 1912, he played in his first Broadway musical, *The Wall Street Girl,*; and in 1922, he appeared in the Ziegfeld Follies. That same year, he began writing a column that wedded political humor with wit; the column appeared daily in 1926 and was widely syndicated. He authored *Letters of a Self-Made Diplomat to His President* (1926) and *There's Not a Bathing Suit in Russia* (1927). He was an early enthusiast of air travel and was killed in a plane crash en route to Alaska.

ROONEY, MICKEY (1920–   ), actor and star of films. Born in Brooklyn, New York, he first appeared in vaudeville with his parents. Rooney starred in numerous television and film productions, including *Hold That Kiss, Babes in Arms, National Velvet, Breakfast at Tiffany's, Requiem* *for a Heavyweight,* and the entire *Andy Hardy* series. He starred in the television spectacular *Pinocchio* (1957). Rooney wrote *An Autobiography* (1965).

ROOSEVELT, ELEANOR (1884–1962), author, diplomat, and wife of President Franklin Delano Roosevelt, thirty-second President of the United States. After her husband contracted polio in 1921, she became increasingly involved with his career. She rejected her mother-in-law's notion that Franklin should surrender to his condition. During the Great Depression, she led several New Deal programs for work relief. During World War II, she became involved with several efforts on behalf of the Red Cross and war relief. After the death of her husband in 1945, she assumed international stature in connection with her work on the United Nations. She was a leading voice in the Democratic Party, particularly on behalf Adlai Stevenson's campaigns for the Presidency. Mrs. Roosevelt authored numerous books, including *On My Own* (1958).

ROOT, ELIHU (1845–1937), Secretary of War and Secretary of State; Senator from New York. Mr. Root attended Hamilton College and graduated from New York University with a law degree. He served as Secretary of War under President William McKinley during the Spanish-American War, and created the Army War College. He was highly regarded by President Theodore Roosevelt; and in 1905, he was named Secretary of State. He was awarded the Nobel Peace Prize in 1912. As Senator from New York (1909–1915), he opposed the progressive program of the Taft Administration, Root authored numerous titles. Richard Jessup's *Elihu Root* (2 vols., 1938) is the official biography.

ROSS, BETSY (1752–1836), legendary maker of the first American flag. Born in Philadelphia, Pennslyvania, she attended the Friends School in Philadelphia and demonstrated a great skill for needlework. In 1773, she eloped with John Ross, whom she married. She was a loyal member of the Society of Free Quakers. The story that George Washington commissioned her to make the first Stars and Stripes is based on tradition; but the flag was adopted as the national flag on June 14, 1777. There is considerable romance and legend associated with her making of the flag.

ROZELLE, PETE (1933–   ), football coach, flambouyant commissioner of the National Football league. Born in South Gate, California, Rozelle, was educated at the University of San Francisco. From 1948 to 1950, he served as the news director of the University of San Francisco; from 1952 to 1955, he was the public relations director for the Los Angeles Rams. Rozelle was general manager of the Los Angeles Rams from 1955 to 1957. In 1960, he was appointed commissioner of the National Football League.

RUBINSTEIN, ARTUR (1889–   ), concert pianist. Born in Lodz, Poland, he made his concert debut in Berlin at the age of twelve. He studied under I. J. Paderewski and began his concert tours with appearances in Paris, London, and the United States in 1905–1906. After World War II, Rubinstein came to live in the United States and continued a hectic pace of concert playing. He is noted for his stirring renditions of classical and patriotic themes.

RUSK, DEAN (1909–   ), Secretary of State during a turbulent era of American-Soviet relations. Appointed by President John Kennedy, he was loyal to the Kennedy-Johnson program of war in Vietnam. He personally confronted the Senate with the Administration's policies in Southeast Asia. Rusk had been president of the Rockefeller Foundation and became identified with foreign policy during the post-World War II period. However, he was unable to chart a course different from the John Foster Dulles policies of the 1950s.

RUTH, GEORGE HERMAN "BABE" (1895–1948), legendary sports figure called the

Babe Ruth hits his 60th home run.

"sultan of swat" for his ability to hit home runs. Ruth began his baseball career as a pitcher for the Boston Red Sox. Because of his reputation as a hitter, he was transferred to the outfield. He became a national celebrity and the perennial home-run king. In 1927, he hit 60 home runs, a record that remained until Roger Maris hit 61 in an extended game. His 714 lifetime home runs remained the record until Hank Aaron surpassed that mark. He is regarded as the game's greatest player. He died of cancer in 1948.

SALK, JONAS (1914–   ), developed the first vaccine to combat polio. After his study at the College of Medicine of New York, Salk interned at New York's Mount Sinai Hospital. During his stay at the University of Michigan he developed a vaccine for influenza. Working with the National Foundation for Infantile Paralysis, he developed the successful vaccine for polio. Controversies surrounded his achievements; the Sabin oral vaccine competed with his. In 1963, he established the Salk Institute for Biological Studies. For more information, see Richard Carter's *Breakthrough: The Saga of Jonas Salk* (1966).

SALOMON, HAYM (1740–1785), financier, merchant, and banker of the Revolutionary period. Salomon was born in Poland and emigrated to New York in the early 1770s. During the British occupation of New York in 1776, he was arrested as a spy. He induced Hessians to desert the British army, which established his identity among the revolutionaries. Salomon's business and commercial dealings brought him unusual successes in the area of securities. He worked with Robert Morris to maintain a flow of finance and credit during the crucial "last days" of the American Revolution. Following the war, he suffered heavy financial losses.

SARNOFF, DAVID (1891–1971), pioneer radio technician and chairman of the Radio Corporation of America. His early work with John Wanamaker's station in New York allowed him to develop his interests in radio; he was the first to receive the distress call of the S.S. *Titanic* in 1912. Sarnoff became inspector and instructor for the Marconi Institute, which was then merged with the Radio Corporation of America owned by Owen D. Young. Sarnoff supervised the manufacture of radio sets and the expansion of radio programming. RCA became a leader in radio and television broadcast and electronics manufacture. Sarnoff served as communications consultant to President Dwight Eisenhower. He received numerous honors.

SCHECHTER, SOLOMON (1847–1915), a leading voice in Judaism in the United States. Born in Focsani, Romania, his career began as a reader in rabbinics at Cambridge University. During this period, he wrote several books on rabbinic theology. In 1902, he became president of the Jewish Theological Seminary of America in New York and emerged as the leader of conservative Judaism. He became a spokesman for American Zionism. Schechter's numerous writings are contained in his *Seminary Addresses and Other Papers* (1969). He served as co-editor of the *Jewish Quarterly Review*.

SCHLESINGER, ARTHUR, JR. (1917–   ), distinguished historian and author. His father, Arthur Schlesinger, Sr. was also a historian and professor. The younger Schlesinger graduated from Harvard in 1938, and the following year his thesis was published under the title *Orestes Brownson: A Pilgrim's Progress*. During World War II, he served as a member of the Office of Strategic Services. His book entitled *The Age of Jackson* brought him into national prominence. *The Vital Center* (1949) was his third book. His study of the Roosevelt Presidency resulted in three volumes: *The Crisis of the Old Order, The Coming of the New Deal,* and *The Politics of Upheaval.* He was appointed special adviser to President John Kennedy. His study of the Kennedy Presidency, titled *A Thousand Days,* received national attention.

SCHULLER, ROBERT (1926–   ), popular clergyman, proponent of "church growth." Born in Alton, Iowa, Schuller attended Hope College and Western Theological Seminary. He established the Garden Grove (California) Community Church in 1955 and began a television and radio ministry. In 1970, he established the Robert H. Schuller Institute for Successful Church Leadership. His leadership has made a national impact. He has authored numerous titles, including *God's Way to the Good Life* (1963), *Your Future Is Your Friend* (1964), *You Can Become the Person You Want to Be* (1973), and others. Dr. Schuller's weekly television broadcast is entitled *The Hour of Power*.

SCHULZ, CHARLES (1922–   ), newspaper cartoonist, famous for his "Peanuts" series. Born in Minneapolis, Minnesota, he served as cartoonist for the *St. Paul Pioneer Press* and the *Saturday Evening Post* (1948–1949). In 1950, he created the comic strip "Peanuts," with characters Charlie Brown, Lucy, Linus, and Snoopy. Schulz has received the Outstanding Cartoonist Award from the National Cartoonist Association (1956) and an Emmy Award for the television special, *A Charlie Brown Christmas* (1966). His collected cartoons have appeared in books under numerous titles: *Peanuts; More Peanuts; Good Grief, More Peanuts; A Charlie Brown Christmas,* and others.

SCOTT, GEORGE C. (1927–   ), actor and star of motion pictures. Born in Wise, Virginia, Scott attended Redford High School in Detroit. During World War II, he enlisted in the Marines. Later he entered the School of Journalism of the University of Missouri; there he appeared in several dramatic performances. During the 1950s, he achieved very little. But during his performance in *Comes the Day* on Broadway, Otto Preminger observed Scott's abilities and offered him the lead in the film, *Anatomy of a Murder.* He received an Academy nomination for that role. *The Hustler* (1961) was his next role, followed by *Patton* (1970). Scott has made numerous television appearances in *Playhouse 90, Armstrong Theatre,* and *Hallmark Hall of Fame,* among others.

SEABURY, SAMUEL (1729–1796), the first bishop of the Episcopal Church in America. He was born in Groton, Connecticut as the son of a Congregational minister. He attended Yale College. Seabury worked diligently to maintain union with the British crown; he called for orderly change and petition. His pamphlets were answered by Alexander Hamilton and others who called for revolution. After the Revolution, Anglican officials in Great Britain consecrated him to serve the church in the now-independent colonies. Seabury's sermons and writings were published in *Discourses on Several Subjects* (1793) and *Discourses on Several Important Subjects* (1798).

SELZNICK, DAVID O. (1902–1965), motion picture producer, whose greatest work was the epic *Gone with the Wind* (1939). Selznick's name is associated with other outstanding screen productions, including *A Star is Born* (1937) and *A Farewell to Arms* (1957). He was rated Outstand-ing Producer for 22 consecutive years. Selznick received Academy Awards for the best production of the year in 1939 and 1940.

SENNETT, MACK (1884–1960), producer of silent movies. In 1912, he organized the Keystone Company; and within the first year, he produced over one hundred forty comedies under the *Keystone* label. Sennett's movies lacked logic or cohesion; they offered a succession of "slapstick" episodes instead. Gloria Swanson added a sexual delight to the Keystone series. In 1928, Sennett was awarded an honor by the Academy of Motion Picture Arts and Sciences for his "contributions to comedy techniques of the screen."

SETON, ELIZABETH B. (1774–1821), first American to be named a saint by the Roman Catholic church. The Seton family travelled to Italy in 1803 to visit the Filicchi family, prominent in banking. There Miss Seton was converted to Catholicism. Upon returning to the United States, she established a boarding school in Baltimore called Sisters of the Charity of St. Joseph. After 1814, she opened orphanages and schools under the same order in New York and Philadelphia. She was declared venerable in 1959, beatified in 1963, and canonized as a saint in 1975.

SEVAREID, ERIC (1912–   ), broadcaster, news commentator, and author. Born in Velva, North Dakota, Sevareid studied at the University of Minnesota and then travelled to France and enrolled at the Alliance Francaise. After a brief period as a reporter for the *Minneapolis Star,* he joined the staff of the *New York Herald Tribune* in Paris. In 1939, he became a European correspondent for the Columbia Broadcasting System, and broadcast the fall of France to the Nazis. After the war, he became a national correspondent for CBS News. In the 1960s, his editorial commentaries appeared on the *CBS Evening News with Walter Cronkite.* Sevareid received numerous awards, including the George Foster Peabody award in 1949, 1964, and 1968. He authored *Not So Wild a Dream* (1946) and *This Is Eric Sevareid* (1964), among others.

DeSEVERSKY, ALEXANDER P. (1894–1974), aeronautic engineer born in Tiflis (now a part of the U.S.S.R.). DeSeversky served as an aviator for Tzarist Russia and engaged in combat action during World War I. He then served as a lower-level diplomat in America. When Russia closed its Washington embassy in 1918, he decided to remain in the United States. After World War I, he became a strong advocate of strategic air power. He contributed greatly to modern aircraft technology, and developed the first automatic bombsight.

SEWARD, WILLIAM HENRY (1801–1872), Secretary of State under President Abraham Lincoln. Seward graduated from Union College and was admitted to the bar in 1822. He was elected as the Whig candidate for governor of New York; as a two-term governor, he came into conflict with governors from Southern states. Seward wrote *Argument in Defense of William Freeman,* the account of his legal defense of two Negroes. As Secretary of State, Seward was a strong defender of Lincoln. He is considered to be among the greatest Secretaries of State; his most famous action was the purchase of Alaska from Russia.

SHEPARD, ALAN B., JR. (1923–   ), the first American to travel in space. Born in East Derry, New Hampshire, Shepard graduated from the United States Naval Academy and the Naval War College. He served as a test pilot with the United States Navy Test Pilot School and joined the Project Mercury space program of NASA in 1959. He was the first American in space with a sub-orbital flight on May 5, 1961. He was selected to command the Apollo 14 Lunar Landing Mission in 1971 and became the fifth man to walk on the

Apollo 14 astronauts (left to right) Stuart Roosa, Alan Shepard, and Edgar Mitchell

moon. Shepard has received numerous honors and awards, including a Presidential Citation, the NASA Distinguished Service Award, and the Lungley Award of the Smithsonian Institution.

SHRIVER, R. SARGENT (1915–   ), lawyer and public figure, candidate for the Vice-Presidency with George McGovern in 1972. Shriver graduated from Yale College, *cum laude,* in 1938. He married Eunice Kennedy, sister of the future President John Kennedy. His work as the first director of the Peace Corps in the Kennedy Administration drew international attention. Shriver served as director of the Office of Economic Opportunity under President Johnson and was appointed Ambassador to France. Presently he practices law in Washington, D.C.; he has received numerous honors and awards. His efforts on behalf of the Peace Corps brought him into contact with world leaders in developing countries.

SIKORSKY, IGOR (1889–1972), aeronautical engineer who designed the first multi-motored airplane and the first practical helicopter (in 1939). Sikorsky served as engineering manager and consultant to the Sikorsky Aircraft Division of the United Aircraft Corporation. He designed the S-42 Clipper Ship for Pan American Airlines. United Aircraft developed Sikorsky's helicopter designs, and the V5-300 was the first helicopter to go into mass production. Although helicopters were not used in World War II, they became vital military tools in Korea and Vietnam. Frank J. Delear's *Igor Sikorsky: His Careers in Aviation* is a useful biography.

SIMON, PAUL (1940–   ), musician and composer who became famous for his compositions with Art Garfunkel. Born in Newark, New Jersey, Simon met Garfunkel in the sixth grade. They began singing together in the mid-1950s as teenagers. Simon entered Queens College to study literature and then went to law school. He and Garfunkel continued singing together, and recorded an album titled, *Wednesday Morning, 3 A.M.* The album achieved success through a song titled "The Sounds of Silence." Simon's success is evident in his musical score for *The Graduate,* for "Bridge Over Troubled Water" and other titles. In 1970, the two singers parted company. On his own, Simon has composed and performed numerous musical selections.

SINATRA, FRANK (1915–   ), singer and actor. Born in Hoboken, New Jersey, Sinatra began his career by touring with the Henry James and Tommy Dorsey Bands. He played leading roles in the movies, *Guys and Dolls, The Tender Trap, Pal Joey, Can Can,* and *Oceans II.* Sinatra received an Academy Award for best supporting role in *From Here to Eternity* (1953). He has received numerous additional awards, including the Peabody and Emmy Awards in 1965, and the Sylvania TV Award.

SIRICA, JOHN (1904–   ), judge who presided over the trials of Watergate scandal, which ousted President Richard Nixon from office. Born in Waterbury, Connecticut, he attended George Washington University Law School. Sirica found the work difficult and had to drop his studies. Later he enrolled at Georgetown University Law School. He graduated and was admitted to the bar in 1926. In 1930, he became Assistant United States Attorney for the District of Columbia; he later built a private law practice and entered Republican politics. In 1957, President Dwight Eisenhower appointed him to the United States District Court for the District of Columbia. By virtue of seniority, he became the chief judge of the District Court. He presided over the case that involved the seven Watergate defendants, including Presidential aides H. R. Haldeman and John Erlichman.

SITTING BULL (1837–1890), a Hunkpapa Sioux medicine man and Indian chief, leader of his tribe at the time of George Custer's massacre. The battle at the Little Bighorn River wiped out Custer and 265 men at the hands of Crazy Horse and his warriors. After 1879, the United States government offered amnesty to Indians who would surrender. Sitting Bull had left for Canada after the episode at Little Bighorn, so he accepted government amnesty. He was placed on a reservation in the Dakota Territory. In 1890, he was arrested on rumors that he would lead the Sioux on the warpath again; he was fatally shot in a struggle that ensued. Robert M. Utley's *The Last Days of The Sioux Nation* (1963) contains a scholarly analysis of Sitting Bull's life.

SLOAN, ALFRED P., JR. (1875–1966), business executive; first president of General Motors. Born in New Haven, Connecticut, Sloan attended public schools and the Polytechnic Institute. He

graduated from the Massachusetts Institute of Technology with a bachelor's degree in 1895. His work with the Hyatt Rolling Bearing Company provided steel roller bearings for the automobile industry. Sloane's work came to the attention of William C. Durant, the builder of General Motors. Durant made Sloan the president of United Motors Corporation, which was eventually merged with General Motors. When the control of General Motors passed to the Dupont family, Sloan assumed greater influence. At his retirement, GM controlled 52 percent of the automobile market. He endowed the Alfred P. Sloan Foundation, whose primary contributions have been to the Sloan-Kettering Cancer Research.

SMITH, JOSEPH (1805–1844), religious leader; founder of the Church of Jesus Christ of Latter Day Saints (Mormons). In 1830, he published the *Book of Mormon.* Smith stressed the need for a restored church, and he suggested that he had special revelations from God. He organized a Utopian community of followers and led them westward to Nauvoo, Illinois. Smith admonished his followers against the use of tobacco, alcohol, and hot drinks. Through the theory of the "Hamitic Curse," Smith excluded blacks from the Mormon faith. Smith was murdered on June 27, 1844, while in jail, awaiting trial.

SMITH, HOWARD K. (1914–   ), newscaster and commentator. Born in Louisiana, he attended Tulane University and travelled in Europe after graduation. There Smith accepted a Rhodes scholarship to study at Merton College, Oxford University. During World War II, he served as a reporter with United Press. In 1940, he joined the CBS editorial team. In 1942, Smith wrote *Last Train from Berlin.* After the war, he served as the chief European correspondent for CBS and worked with Edward R. Murrow on the television series, *See It Now.* In 1957, he returned to America, where he became moderator for *The Great Challenge, Face the Nation,* and other programs of public policy. Smith also moderated the first of the Kennedy-Nixon Presidential debates. In October 1961, he resigned his position with CBS over a policy dispute. He moderated ABC's *Issues and Answers* program, and later he was co-anchor with Harry Reasoner on the *ABC Evening News.*

SNEAD, SAM (1912–   ), professional golfer born in Hot Springs, Virginia. Sneed became a golfing professional in 1935. He won the Professional Golfer's Association (PGA) Championship in 1942, 1949, and 1951; the British Open in 1946; and the Master's Golf Tournament in 1949, 1952, and 1954. He was inducted into the Professional Golfer's Association Hall of Fame. Snead has written several books, including *How to Hit a Golf Ball* (1940), *How to Play Golf* (1946), and (with Al Stump) *Education of a Golfer* (1962).

SOUSA, JOHN PHILIP (1854–1932), America's foremost composer of music for marching bands. Born in Washington, D.C., he enlisted in the Marine Band. During the Centennial Exposition in Philadelphia, he played in the orchestra conducted by Jacques Offenbach. In 1880, he became the Director of the Marine Band; and in 1892, he organized what he called the New Marine Band. Sousa made several trips to Europe and was widely acclaimed. Some of his compositions achieved an international reputation: "The Stars and Stripes Forever," "The High School Cadets," "The Washington Post," and "The Gladiator." Sousa also wrote comic operas, including *The Bridge Elect*.

SPOCK, BENJAMIN (1903–   ), physician and educator, noted for his principles of child-rearing. Born in New Haven, Connecticut, Spock received his medical degree from the College of Physicians and Surgeons of Columbia University. As a pediatrician, he authored the *Common Sense Book of Baby and Child Care* (1946), which has gone through numerous printings. Spock's views on child-rearing influenced a generation of parents. In the decade of the 1960s, his opposition to the war in Vietnam brought prestige to the movement of protest and dissent. He authored other books, including *Decent and Indecent* (1970) and *A Teenagers' Guide to Life and Love* (1970). Spock has served on the faculty of the University of Pittsburg and Case Western Reserve, and on the staff of the Mayo Clinic.

STASSEN, HAROLD (1907–   ), lawyer and controversial candidate for President. A native of West St. Paul, Minnesota, Stassen attended the University of Minnesota and Hamlin University. From 1938 to 1945, he was the governor of Minnesota; and in 1948, he became president of the University of Pennsylvania. In 1953, he left the university to take assignments with the Disarmament Commission and as Special Assistant to the President. During World War II, he served in

Charles Steinmetz

the South Pacific, where he earned the Legion of Merit and the Bronze Star. He authored *Where I Stand* (1947). Stassen's liberal views made him an unsuccessful contender for the Republican Presidential nomination in 1948, 1964, and 1968. But his ideas affected Republican foreign policy.

STEINMETZ, CHARLES (1865–1923), mathematician and electrical engineer. Born in Breslau, he came to Yonkers, New York, to work with the electrical inventor Rudolph Eickemeyer in developing alternating-current devices. General Electric hired Steinmetz to do industrial research, and he gave GE a reputation for research and development. Steinmetz perfected the incandescent and arc lights. He also worked on new batteries and other electrical problems. As a consulting engineer with GE, he had freedom to explore projects and problems that were to his liking.

STEVENSON, ADLAI E. (1900–1965), diplomat, governor, and candidate for the United States Presidency. He was the grandson of Adlai E. Stevenson, who served as Vice-President in 1893–1897. He graduated from Princeton University, attended Harvard Law School, and graduated from the Northwestern Law School in 1926. During World War II, he was assistant to the Secretary of the Navy. He served as an adviser to the United States delegation at the San Francisco Conference, which chartered the United Nations. In 1948, he was elected governor of Illinois. He ran for President in 1952 and 1956 and lost. In 1960, President John Kennedy named Stevenson as United States Ambassador to the United Nations.

STOKES, CARL (1927–   ), the first black mayor of a major American city. Born in Cleveland, Ohio, he passed the bar examination in 1957 and established a law firm with his brother.

Elected to the Ohio House of Representatives in 1962, he became mayor of Cleveland in 1967. *The Cleveland Plain Dealer* lauded his election; he showed a balance in his administration. In 1969, he won reelection; but chose to enter broadcasting instead of attempting another campaign in 1971.

STONE, MELVILLE E. (1848–1929), newspaper executive. Born in Hudson, Illinois, Stone became a newspaper reporter for the *Chicago Republican* in 1867. In 1875, he organized the first penny daily in the United States, the Chicago *Daily News*. He sold out his interests in 1888 and became associated with the Globe National Bank. In 1893, he became the general manager of the Associated Press and moved the AP to New York to compete with the United Press. Stone developed a close relationship between the AP and Reuter Telegram Company of Great Britain for sharing foreign news. His autobiography is titled *Fifty Years a Journalist* (1921).

STRAUS, ISIDOR (1845–1912), merchant and chain-store president born in Otterburg, Bavaria. Educated in public schools, Straus was not able to attend West Point, due to the American Civil War. After the war, he established the enterprise of L. Straus & Son. In 1874, the basement of R. H. Macy and company became the center of Straus merchandising. Throughout Boston, Chicago, and Philadelphia, the Straus family established department stores. Isidor and brother Nathan made R. H. Macy the largest department store in the world. Through underselling, advertising and odd pricing, they controlled the merchandising market. Straus described himself as a Gold Democrat and a friend of President Grover Cleveland. He served as a United States Congressman from 1893 to 1895.

STREISAND, BARBRA (1942–), singer, actress, and film producer. A native of Brooklyn, New York, she began her career playing in summer stock theater. She appeared in numerous clubs, including Bon Soir and The Blue Angel. Miss Streisand starred in the Broadway roles of *I Can Get It For You Wholesale* (1962) and *Funny Girl* (1964–65). As a recording artist for Columbia Records, she became nationally popular. Miss Streisand has appeared in numerous screen roles, including *Funny Girl, Hello Dolly, On a Clear Day You Can See Forever, The Owl and the Pussycat, What's Up Doc? The Way We Were, A Star Is Born* (which she produced), and others. She received the Academy Award as best actress for her role in *Funny Girl* (1968).

STUART, GILBERT (1755–1828), painter and portraitist of the early Republic. During the Revolutionary period, his family moved to London, where he met fellow American exile, Benjamin West. During his London period, Stuart was regarded among the great artists, equal with Joshua Reynolds and Thomas Gainsborough. In 1792, he returned to America and achieved fame through his portraits of Washington. Although Stuart painted President Washington during the later years of his life, little of age is reflected in the portrait of the man. Stuart's portraits of other Revolutionary figures reveal a style that transcends age. He used few colors, but his mixtures reflected shadows and illusions. He set the standard for American portrait painting that prevailed in the nineteenth century.

SUNDAY, WILLIAM A. "BILLY" (1863–1935), preacher and revivalist who introduced America to the "sawdust trail." Born in Ames, Iowa, Sunday began his career as a baseball player with the Chicago White Sox in 1883. He later played with teams in Pittsburgh and Philadelphia. He embraced Christianity and left baseball in 1891 to begin working with the Young Men's Christian Organization. Sunday's preaching reflected the fundamentalist tradition. He opposed Sabbath-breaking and the use of alcohol, and he stirred religious enthusiasm. Sunday wrote several books that coincided with his athletic integration of Christianity, such as *Burning Truths from Billy's Bat* (1914).

SUSSKIND, DAVID (1920–), producer for television, motion pictures, and theatre. Susskind was born in New York City and graduated from Harvard University. He worked with the publicity department of Warner Brothers and Universal Pictures from 1946 to 1948. From 1952, he produced several Broadway plays, including *A Very Special Baby* (1956) and *Brief Lives* (1967). He produced a number of motion pictures: *Raisin in the Sun* (1960), *Requiem for a Heavyweight* (1961), *All Things Bright and Beautiful* (1976), and others. Susskind has been involved in producing several television programs, such as *The du Pont Show of the Month, Kaiser Aluminum Hour, Hallmark Hall of Fame,* and *Kraft Theatre.* He has received the Peabody Award, Academy Awards, and numerous other recognitions and honors.

SWANSON, GLORIA (1899–   ), actress and film celebrity. Born in Chicago, Illinois, she began working with Essanay Studios in Chicago. She later formed her own production company, called Gloria Swanson Productions. From 1971, she organized the Facial Fitness Clinics. Miss Swanson starred in numerous screen productions, including *Airport 1975* and *Sunset Boulevard* (1950). The first picture that recorded her speaking and singing was *The Trespasser* (1929). She appeared in the Broadway production, *Butterflies Are Free* (1970–1972). Miss Swanson is recognized for her acting abilities and business perception.

TAYLOR, ELIZABETH (1932–   ), actress and movie personality born in London, England. Miss Taylor's first major screen role was in *National Velvet* (1944). She also starred in *A Place in the Sun* (1950), *The Last Time I Saw Paris, Cat on a Hot Tin Roof, Butterfield 8, Cleopatra, The Sand Piper,* and *Who's Afraid of Virginia Wolf?* She received Academy Awards for her roles in *Butterfield 8* and *Who's Afraid of Virginia Wolf?* She has authored *Nibbles and Me* (with Richard Burton) and *World Enough and Time.* She has become notorious for her numerous marriages—to Conrad Nicholas Hilton, Jr.; to Michael Wilding; to Mike Todd; to Eddie Fisher; to Richard Burton (twice); and to John Warner.

TAYLOR, KENNETH (1917–   ), religious publishing executive. Taylor attended Wheaton (Illinois) College and began his publishing career with Moody Press. In 1963, he became president of his own company, Tyndale Press. He has served as an officer with numerous other organizations, including Living Bibles International and Coverdale Publishers. He has authored numerous titles, including *Is Christianity Credible?* (1946), *Living Letters: The Paraphrased Epistles* (1962), and *The Living Bible* (1971).

TEMPLE, SHIRLEY (1928–   ), actress, popular child star of movies in the 1930s, and politician. At the age of seven, she was Hollywood's greatest box-office attraction. She is remembered for her singing of "The Good Ship Lollipop." She portrayed a child who was capable of dealing with adult ego and hatred. Her films included *Baby Burlesks, Stand Up and Cheer, Little Miss Marker, Wee Willie Winkie,* and *The Little Princess.* In later life, she married a civic leader in San Francisco and became affiliated with the Republican Party. She ran unsuccessfully for the office of United States Representative to Congress. In 1969, President Nixon appointed her a member of the United States delegation to the United Nations General Assembly.

TESLA, NIKOLA (1857–1943), electrical engineer and inventor born in Smiljan, Croatia (now Yugoslavia). He devised an electrical transformer known as the Tesla coil. He worked briefly with Thomas Edison, designing electrical dynamos; in 1887, he established his own laboratory in New York. Tesla sided with engineers who favored alternating electrical current, rather than direct current (which Edison advocated). The alternating current system was adopted by George Westinghouse and became the basis for power generation from the Niagara Falls to Chicago's Columbian Exposition. Tesla produced motors, transformers, electrical coils, and other devices that contributed greatly to the emerging world of electrical technology.

THOMAS, LOWELL (1892–   ), radio news commentator, born in Woodington, Ohio. Thomas attended the University of Northern Indiana, University of Denver, Kent College, and Princeton University. In 1915, he made the first of a series of filmed travelogues; he toured extensively and lectured on his travels. President Woodrow Wilson appointed him to the civilian commission on World War I. In 1930, he made his debut on CBS radio; he would regularly conclude his nightly news broadcasts with the words, "So long until tomorrow." He continued producing *Lowell Thomas and the News* until 1976. He was the voice of Movietone News and served in the development of Cinerama movie features. Among his numerous publications are *Beyond the Khyber Pass* (1925), *The Untold Story of Exploration* (1936), and *With Allenby in the Holy Land* (1938).

THURMOND, STROM (1902–   ), former governor of South Carolina, Presidential candidate, and United States Senator. In 1948, Thurmond launched a Presidential campaign under the "states' rights" banner of the Dixiecrats. He attended Clemson College and was admitted to the bar in 1930. His public career has been identified with the concept of "states' rights" and racial segregation. In 1964, he broke with the Democratic Party and became a Republican. He has served in the United States Senate for over two decades. During World War II, he served in the United States Army during the invasion of Europe. He received the Bronze Star, the Purple Heart, and the Legion of Merit.

TILLICH, PAUL (1886–1965), theologian, religious scholar, and author. Born in Starzeddel, Prussia, Tillich attended the Universities of Berlin, Tübingen, and Halle. He received the Ph.D. from the University of Breslau. Ordained a minister in the Evangelican Lutheran Church, he taught at Marburg, Dresden, and Leipzig before becoming professor at the University of Frankfurt am-Main in 1929. He opposed the Nazis and was dismissed from the university, so he emigrated to the United States. Tillich taught at Union Theological Seminary (1933–1955), Harvard University (1955–1962), and the University of Chicago (1962–1965). He wrote numerous books, including a three-volume *Systematic Theology* (1951–1963).

TRUMBULL, JOHN (1756–1843), painter of historic scenes from the Revolutionary War. Trumbull was born in the Connecticut colony, where his father was governor. He took private painting lessons from John Singleton Copley and graduated from Harvard at age 17. During the Revolution, he served as aide-de-camp to General Washington. In 1780, he sailed to London, where he studied with Benjamin West. A controversy with Thomas Jefferson in 1793 damaged his later career. His art is in the tradition of Peter Paul Rubens; it deals exclusively with the American Revolution. Trumbull's works include the famous *Battle of Bunker Hill* and *Capture of the Hessians at Trenton.* He achieved fame in later life with commissions from Congress for paintings of the *Signing of the Declaration of Independence, Surrender of Cornwallis at Yorktown,* and others that decorate the rotunda of the Capitol in Washington.

TRUTH, SOJOURNER (1797–1883), abolitionist leader whose real name was Isabella Baumfree. Born in Ulster County, New York, she was the daughter of an African couple. After New York had passed an emancipation act, she asked for freedom from her master John J. Dumont. He re-

fused and she ran away with one of her five children. She worked menial jobs and came under the influence of a religious fanatic named Mathias. Eventually she left Mathias and travelled to speak on her own, with the name of Sojourner Truth. She was the first person to test the legality of segregation on Washington, D.C., street cars.

TUBMAN, HARRIET (ca. 1820–1913), black agent for the Underground Railroad. Tubman helped hundreds of slaves flee captivity. She was born a slave herself, in Dorcester County, Maryland. In 1848, she ran away with her two brothers, leaving her husband John Tubman behind. A bounty of $40,000 was placed on her. Before the Civil War, she returned to the South 20 times to help over three hundred slaves to escape. She supported John Brown's insurrection at Harpers Ferry, Virginia. Tubman spoke against slavery and in support of women's rights. During the war, she served as a scout and nurse for the Union forces.

TUNNEY, JAMES J. "GENE" (1898–1978), professional boxer; corporation director. Born in New York City, Tunney won the light heavyweight championship at Paris in 1919. In 1926, he won the heavyweight championship from Jack Dempsey. He retained that title in a return engagement at Chicago in 1927. He retired from boxing in 1928 undefeated. He has served as director to many corporations, including the Bank of Commerce of New York and the Penobscot Building in Detroit. He wrote *A Man Must Fight* (1932) and *Arms for Living* (1941). In later years, Jack Dempsey became Tunney's close personal friend.

TURNER, NAT (1800–1831), black slave leader born in Southampton County, Virginia. He was a restless young man who turned to the Bible for guidance on slavery and freedom. He believed he was appointed of God to deliver his people from slavery, and he understood a solar eclipse to be a sign from God that he was supposed to lead a rebellion. Turner and his friends killed many whites in the rebellion that bears his name. By August of 1831, the tide had turned, and blacks were executed in large numbers. After a brief escape, Turner was caught, tried, and executed. His rebellion galvanized the abolitionist movement. William Styron's *Confessions of Nat Turner* (1968) is an analysis of the man and the movement.

VALENTINO, RUDOLPH (1895–1926), actor and matinee idol of the silent-film era. Born in Castellanetz, Italy, he attended the Dante Alighieri College and the Royal Academy. He came to the United States in 1913 and began his career as a dancer. Valentino joined the Musical Comedy Company and travelled to San Francisco. He entered motion pictures during a stay in Los Angeles, and scored a remarkable triumph as Julio in *The Four Horsemen.* His other performances included *The Conquering Power, Blood and Sand, The Sainted Devil,* and others.

VALLEE, RUDY (1901–   ), orchestra leader, vocalist, and popular radio personality. In 1929 he starred in the film, *Vagabond Lover;* a succession of screen performances followed: *George White's Scandals* (1934), *Sweet Music* (1935), *Gold Diggers in Paris* (1938), and *Too Many Blondes* (1941). Vallee had a weekly radio program for Standard Brands from 1929 to 1939. He has made frequent nightclub appearances and starred in the musical comedy *How to Succeed in Business Without Really Trying* (1961). During World War I, he served in the United States Navy.

VAN BUREN, ABIGAIL (1918–   ), writer, lecturer, and newspaper columnist. Born in Sioux City, Iowa, she attended Morningside College. Miss Van Buren has engaged in volunteer activities on behalf of better mental health and the National Foundation for Infantile Paralysis. In 1956, she began writing a column for the *San Francisco Chronicle* titled "Dear Abby." Her column was syndicated through the *Chicago Tribune-New York News Syndicate.* It now appears in foreign press as well, including Brazil, Australia, Japan, Germany, and Holland. In 1963, she established a *Dear Abby* radio program on CBS. She authored *Dear Abby* (1957), *Dear Teen Ager* (1959), and *Dear Abby on Marriage* (1962).

VANDERBILT, CORNELIUS (1794–1877), wealthy builder of railroads and steamship companies. After the success of Robert Fulton and Robert Livingston with steamboats, Vanderbilt became involved with steamboat operations. In a competitive war against Daniel Drew, Vanderbilt was able to establish steamship service between New York and Peekskill. He then opened service between New York, Providence, and Boston. His primary success was achieved in connection with the expansion of railroads after the Civil War.

Commodore Vanderbilt again challenged Daniel Drew in pursuit of the Erie Railroad. Illegal maneuvers by Drew, Jay Gould, and James Fisk almost destroyed Vanderbilt in his pursuit of the Erie. He turned his attention to acquiring the Lake Shore, Illinois, and Michigan Central rail companies, which he did.

VAUGHN, SARAH (1924–   ), jazz vocalist born in Newark, New Jersey. In 1942, she joined the Earl Hines Orchestra; and in 1943, she sang with the Billy Eckstein Band. She has served as vocalist for Mercury Records. In 1942, she won the Apollo Theatre amateur contest. She received the annual Vocalist Award from *Down Beat,* 1946 to 1952; and she has appeared on numerous television programs.

WALLACE, GEORGE (1919–   ), political leader, governor, and candidate for President. Born at Clio, Alabama, Wallace studied law at the University of Alabama. As governor, he defied a Supreme Court integration order at the University of Alabama. In 1968, his challenge to the Democratic Party resulted in the formation of the American Independent Party. He captured much of the South and nationally obtained 14 percent of the popular vote in that election. In 1972, he became the object of an assassination attempt, which left him paralyzed. He was reelected governor of Alabama, but declining health made him discard plans for another term.

WARHOL, ANDY (1931–   ), pioneer in pop art and filmmaking. Warhol attended the Carnegie Institute of Technology and received a degree in pictoral design. He began work as a designer with *Glamour* magazine, then *Vogue* and *Harper's Bazaar.* He used the comic-strip characters Dick Tracy, Popeye, and Superman for colorful effects, and he painted Campbell Soup cans in endless rows to show the monotony of American society. After 1965, he concentrated on filmmaking. *The Chelsea Girls* (1966) and *Trash* (1970) received considerable public notice.

WARING, FRED (1900–   ), musical conductor and entertainer born in Tyrone, Pennsylvania. Waring attended Pennsylvania State College. He composed numerous songs and appeared in several musical shows on Broadway and in motion pictures. He organized an ensemble called "The Pennsylvanians" and began a radio program of the same title in 1933. In 1948, he organized the Fred Waring Music Workshops for Choral Directors. He conducted musical groups for *The Fred Waring Show* on television and produced numerous television programs.

WASHINGTON, BOOKER T. (1856–1915), black educator who was born a slave in Franklin County, Virginia. Booker overheard talk about a school for blacks called the Hampton Institute; the institute had been founded by a Union general and emphasized trades and manual training. In 1881, he was invited to go to Tuskegee to head up the institute, which he discovered had no buildings or program. Under his leadership, the institute became a vital force in education of black youth. In 1895, he delivered the famous "Atlanta Compromise" speech, in which he renounced protest and agitation as a means of achieving educational reform. His views were in contrast to those of Frederick Douglass, who called for racial agitation.

WAYNE, ANTHONY (1745–1796), military hero of early America. Born at Easttown, Pennslyvania, he attended local schools and learned surveying. When the Revolution began, Wayne organized a regiment of infantry and joined General George Washington at Morristown, New Jersey. He gave distinguished service in several battles; he also served with Marquis de Lafayette in Virginia until the British surrender at Yorktown. In 1792, Wayne was asked to serve as Commander-in-Chief of the Army. At Full Timbers, Ohio, he defeated Indians in the first of several battles. Indian tribes recognized his military superiority and signed the treaty of Greenville in 1795.

WAYNE, JOHN (1907–   ), actor and movie personality, noted for his character portrayals from the Old West. Born in Winterset, Iowa, his name was Marian Michael Morrison; but early in life he received the nickname "Duke." On an athletic scholarship, he studied at the University of Southern California. His career as a screen actor began as a stunt man and with bit parts in Westerns. He made two Westerns with Columbia: *Girls Demand Excitement* (1931) and *Three Girls Lost*. Over the next few years he made low-budget Westerns. During and after World War II, he emerged as an actor of some renown; his role in *True Grit* won an Academy Award nomination. During the

War in Vietnam, he projected the image of a loyalist to the Administration's expanding of the war. Mike Tomkies' *Duke* (1971) is a useful biography.

WEBSTER, DANIEL (1782–1852), celebrated lawyer and politician. Webster was born in Salisbury, New Hampshire. He graduated from Dartmouth College and then studied law. Identified as a leading spokesman for the Federalists, he was elected to the House of Representatives in 1813. In 1816, his political career temporarily ended, but he achieved prominence in arguing several significant cases before the Supreme Court. For example, Webster defended the Bank of the United States in *McCulloch* vs. *Maryland*. In 1823, he returned to the House of Representatives; and from 1825 to 1829, he supported the Federalist President John Quincy Adams. Webster's Senate record achieved historic importance. He supported President Andrew Jackson on the nullification controversy. His last debate was on behalf the unpopular Fugitive Slave Law in 1850. He served as Secretary of State in Millard Fillmore's administration.

WEBSTER, NOAH (1758–1843), lexicographer who compiled a dictionary of American usage. Webster was an active literary man; he read widely and was admitted to the bar in 1781. He authored *A Grammatical Institute of the English Language: Part I* in 1783. His grammar book sold over seventy million copies. Webster toured the United States selling his textbooks. As a Federalist, he wrote *Sketches on American Policy* (1785); he authored numerous books and pamphlets, his most famous being *The Effects of Slavery on Morals and Industry* (1793). His dictionaries became his most enduring contribution to American thought and learning.

WEISSMULLER, JOHNNY (1904–   ), Olympic swimmer and movie star as "Tarzan." Born in Windber, Pennsylvania, Weissmuller became a skilled free-style swimmer. In the 1920s, he established world records in over sixty-seven events. Weissmuller was trained as a swimmer at the Illinois Athletic Club in Chicago. In the 1924 and 1928 Olympic games, he won five gold medals; he also won a bronze medal as a member of the United States water polo team. In his acting role as "Tarzan," his abilities as a free-style swimmer made him world famous.

WELCH, RAQUEL (1942–), model, movie actress, and renowned sex symbol. She was born Raquel Tejada in Chicago, Illinois, of Castilian Spanish parents. The family moved to LaJolla, California, where her father worked for General Dynamics. After graduating from high school, she served temporarily as a weather girl for a San Diego television station while attending San Diego State College. After marriage in 1959, she had two children and became a householder. Divorced in 1964, she travelled to Texas where she modeled for Neiman-Marcus department stores. She then returned to Hollywood, where she received minor roles until she appeared in *Life* magazine (October 2, 1964). She soon obtained a contract with Twentieth Century-Fox. She then appeared in *Fantastic Voyage, Bandolero, Lady in Cement, The Magic Christian,* and *Myra Breckinridge,* among others.

WEST, BENJAMIN (1738–1820), noted painter of the Revolutionary era. Born in Springfield Township, Pennsylvania, West was among the most outstanding of America's new artists. He reflected the neo-classical tradition. He lived for a time in Italy, where he attracted numerous patrons. West received encouragement from Joshua Reynolds and won numerous portrait commissions. He became a close friend of King George III; and after the death of Reynolds, he was named president of the Royal Academy. West's more famous paintings include *Death on the Pale Horse* (1802) and *Christ Healing the Sick* (1811). West helped many young artists who visited his studio.

Orson Welles, arms raised, rehearses the
War of the Worlds broadcast.

WEST, MAE (1892–), stage and film actress; her sensuality established her stage presence in early vaudeville days. Miss West made her debut with the Keith vaudeville circuit. When she starred in a sensational Broadway play titled *Sex* (1926), she was jailed for her role and attracted national publicity. She starred in several movies, including *Diamond Lil* (1928); *The Constant Sinner* (1931) and *Night after Night* (1932). During World War II, her name was attached to the inflatable life jackets that were used by Allied soldiers. Her autobiography was titled *Goodness Had Nothing to Do With It* (1959). In 1970, she starred in the screen production of *Myra Breckinridge.*

WELK, LAWRENCE (1903–), famed orchestra leader of the "big band" era. Born in Strasburg, North Dakota, he appeared on radio station WNAX of Yankton, South Dakota in 1920. In 1927, he organized an orchestra that appeared throughout the country. Welk's orchestra appeared on television in Los Angeles from 1950 to 1955, when the American Broadcasting Company syndicated the Lawrence Welk show nationally. The program achieved considerable popularity until it was cancelled in 1971. Welk was a recording artist for Ranwood Records; he has received numerous awards and recognitions, including the Top Dance Band of America award in 1955. His program is now syndicated by the National Broadcasting Company.

WELLES, ORSON (1915–), motion picture actor, director, producer, writer, and photographer. His various theatrical roles have placed him among the outstanding actors of his generation. Born in Kenosha, Wisconsin, he studied at the Art Institute of Chicago. Welles' acting debut was made at Gate Theatre, Dublin, in the fall of 1931. He made his Broadway debut in Shakespeare's *Romeo and Juliet* (1934); he had toured with the Katherine Cornell Company in *Candida* (1933) and *The Barretts of Wimpole Street.* His radio career began with narrating the series, *The March of Time.* His simulation of a Martian invasion in 1938 created a panic among his radio listeners. He has directed numerous Shakespearean plays and has appeared on television.

WESTINGHOUSE, GEORGE (1846–1914), distinguished American inventor and manufacturer; developed the transmission of electrical power. He served with the Union Army in the Civil

War and attended Union College. His fortune came from the patents on his air-brake invention. In 1882, he formed the Union Switch and Signal Company and directed his attention to the orderly transmission of natural gas. In 1886, he formed the Westinghouse Electric Company. In the 1890s, Westinghouse received contracts to develop power from the Niagara Falls. During the 1880s, he received an average of one patent per month for his inventions; his truly significant inventions include the geared turbine and air springs.

WESTMORELAND, WILLIAM C. (1914–

), commander of American forces in Vietnam and chief military adviser to President Lyndon Johnson. Westmoreland was born in Spartanburg County, South Carolina, and graduated from West Point in 1936. He commanded the Thirty-Fourth Field Artillery Battalion of the Ninth Infantry Division in Europe during World War II. He served as an instructor at the Command and General Staff College and the Army War College. Between 1960 and 1963, he was superintendent of the U.S. Military Academy, where his effectiveness contributed to his elevation to general. He was assigned to the Military Assistance Program in Vietnam, where he advocated increased bombing and "search and destroy" missions. By 1967, he had over 500,000 men under his command. In 1968, he became Army Chief of Staff. He ran unsuccessfully for governor of South Carolina.

WHISTLER, JAMES A. McNEILL (1834–1903), lithographer and painter; emphasized "art for art's sake." Born in Lowell, Massachusetts, Whistler moved to St. Petersburg, Russia, early in his life when his father worked on a Russian rail project commissioned by Tsar Nicholas I. He returned to America in 1849 and studied at the United States Military Academy. Because he could not conform to the rules, he was dismissed in 1854. He travelled to Europe and studied for a time at the Louvre. In 1859, his first painting appeared; it was titled At the Piano. In 1871, he began certain themes titled Nocturnes in etchings, including The Artist's Mother (1872). His views on aesthetics were summarized in "Ten O'Clock," a lecture delivered at Prince's Hall.

WHITE, WILLIAM ALLEN (1868–1944), prize-winning journalist and author. Born in Emporia, Kansas, he attended Emporia College. He began his journalistic career with work on various

newspapers. He purchased the Emporia Gazette in 1895 and continued working with that paper until his death. His progressive views ran contrary to conservative political trends. He backed Teddy Roosevelt and the Bull Moose party in 1912; in the 1930s he supported the New Deal of Roosevelt. White worked enthusiastically with "The Committee to Defend America by Aiding the Allies" in generating hostility for Nazism. He received the Pulitzer Prize for The Autobiography of William Allen White.

WHITNEY, ELI (1765–1825), inventor who perfected the cotton gin. Whitney was born in Westboro, Massachusetts, and graduated from Yale college. Although a number of cotton gins were in operation in the 1790s, only Whitney's design made practical sense. He manufactured small arms for the federal government, but his delivery of these small arms was hopelessly behind schedule. He substituted machines for hand labor, made uniform parts, and accelerated production. Whitney gave substance to the concept of mass production.

WILKINS, ROY (1901–   ), important civil rights leader. Wilkins was born in St. Louis, Missouri, and attended the University of Minnesota. He served in the local chapters of the National Association for the Advancement of Colored People (NAACP) and edited Call, a militant weekly newspaper. In 1931, he joined the executive staff of the NAACP at its national headquarters. He worked on numerous internal studies for the NAACP, and in 1955, became the Executive Director of the organization. He enthusiastically supported the Kennedy Civil Rights program. His organizing abilities, articulate speech, and incisive writing made him a significant leader in the black community. He received the Medal of Freedom from President Nixon in 1969, the Spingarm Award from the NAACP, as well as many other honors and awards.

WILLARD, FRANCES E. (1839–1898), prominent temperance leader. Born in Churchville, New York, she sought independence from her parents at an early age. She attended Northwestern Female College and graduated as class valedictorian. After a brief teaching career, she authored a book titled, Nineteen Beautiful Years (1864). Miss Willard toured Europe from 1869 to 1870 and studied at the Sorbonne. She was appointed pres-

ident of Northwestern Female College in 1871. After 1874, she resigned and accepted the presidency of the Women's Christian Temperance Union (WCTU). She is best known for her work with the WCTU. Miss Willard helped establish the Prohibition Party in 1884; she became president of the World Women's Temperance Union in 1891.

WILLIAMS, ROGER (1599–1683), Puritan clergyman; spokesman for religious toleration and separation of church and state. Williams believed that sinful mankind was hopeless until Christ's return. He refused to serve the Massachusetts Church because it maintained close ties with civil authority. He was banished to Rhode Island in 1635, and there he authored a dictionary titled *A Key into the Language of America* (1643). His quest for perfection made him first a Baptist and then a Seeker. In 1643, he travelled to England and wrote *Queries of Highest Consideration* (1644). Williams opposed the Christian persecution of other Christian groups. He returned to Providence and sought to unify the colony; he disagreed with the local Quakers but granted them toleration nonetheless.

WILLIAMS, TED (1918–), baseball player born in San Diego, California. Williams was professionally associated with the Boston Red Sox of the American League; he compiled a lifetime batting average of .344. Williams' career spanned the years 1939 to 1960. He hit a total of 521 homeruns and won the triple crown of baseball (best average, most home runs, most runs batted in) twice. He was elected to the Baseball Hall of Fame in 1966. He managed the Washington Senators; in his initial year as manager he received the American League Manager of the Year Award.

WINCHELL, WALTER (1897–1972), newspaper columnist and newscaster. Winchell began his radio program with the familiar words, "Good evening, Mr. and Mrs. America and all ships at sea; let's go to press." At first he was a performer in vaudeville. His journalistic career began in 1920 with the *New York Evening Graphic;* later he was associated with the Hearst *New York Mirror.* Winchell introduced a variety of items—political and theatrical—in his column "On Broadway." His column was syndicated in over eight hundred newspapers; his radio career began in 1932. His easily recognized voice narrated the popular tele-

vision series *The Untouchables.* Later in life, he wrote for the *New York Journal Tribune.*

WINTHROP, JOHN (1588–1649), political leader and historian; a dominant figure in the early development of the Massachusetts Bay Colony. Born in Suffolk County, England, he agreed to go to America in 1629. Winthrop called for a covenant Christian community in his famous sermon, "A Model of Christian Charity." He was the political leader of the colony. New England society in the seventeenth century bore the enduring stamp of John Winthrop.

WOOD, GRANT (1892–1942), regional painter of the 1930s. A native of Anamosa, Iowa, Wood took painting lessons during the family stay at Cedar Rapids, Iowa. During World War I, he took classes in fresco painting at the Chicago Art Institute. He left for Europe in 1923 and spent time at the Academie Julian in Paris. On his return to America, he worked at a factory in Cedar Rapids while painting various subjects. In 1927, he received a commission for a stained-glass window for the Cedar Rapids City Hall. Wood was most famous for his homespun themes. His painting titled *American Gothic* (1930) attracted widespread notice; his satiric sense was evident in *Daughters of the American Revolution.* He opposed conservative political tendencies and directed several projects for the Works Project Administration (WPA).

WOOLWORTH, FRANK (1852–1919), chain-store executive; originator of the "five and dime" store concept. Born in upstate New York, Woolworth opened his first store with a modest three hundred dollars inventory. The growth of his chain stores was spectacular; he derived capital for new stores from profits. He relocated his headquarters in Brooklyn, New York, which brought him into close contact with suppliers and wholesalers. Woolworth emphasized window and counter displays. His enterprises grew rapidly between 1890 and 1910, until his gross business revenue exceeded sixty million dollars annually. In 1913, he began erecting the structure in New York that became the Woolworth Building. At his death, there were over one thousand stores nationwide.

WRIGHT, FRANK LLOYD (1869–1959), the most innovative architect of the twentieth century. Wright's work reflects his fertile imagination. He worked at the firm of Dankmar Adler and Louis Sullivan of Chicago in 1887. He was greatly influenced by Louis Sullivan; and in 1893, he opened his own office. The houses Wright built in Chicago and elsewhere gained particular attention for their innovative spirit. His international fame brought him Japanese and European projects; for example, he designed the Imperial Hotel in Tokyo. Wright blended radical and traditional concepts of architecture. His most famous creations are the Guggenheim Museum in New York, the Administration Building for the Johnson Wax Company, and the Greek Orthodox Church in Milwaukee. Wright was an authentic giant in American architecture and design.

WRIGHT BROTHERS, ORVILLE (1871–1948); WILBUR (1867–1912), aviation pioneers born in Millville, Indiana. In 1892, they opened the Wright Cycle Shop in Dayton, Ohio. The efforts of Otto Lilienthal, glider pilot, attracted the interest of the Wright Brothers. The Wrights were acquainted with the combustion engine, aerodynamics, and basic engineering. Together they developed double-winged gliders and applied motor techniques to the glider. On December 17, 1903, they made the first "heavier-than-air craft" flight (which lasted twelve seconds) at Kitty Hawk, North Carolina. On May 22, 1906, they received a patent for their machine. The federal government demonstrated an interest in the machine, and they received bids for construction and development. The brothers formed the American Wright Company to produce aircraft. The death of Wilbur Wright greatly affected Orville; in 1915, he sold his rights to the company and left manufacturing. He served as a member of the National Advisory Committee for Aeronautics (NACA), the predecessor to NASA. His efforts contributed greatly to the subsequent advances made in aerospace technology.

WYETH, ANDREW (1917–   ), the most significant American painter of his generation. His father was the book illustrator for great American classics such as *Treasure Island*. The most famous of his paintings is *Christina's World*. Wyeth used his neighbors as his subjects; he utilized high and low points of emphasis. He received numerous awards, including the Medal of Freedom. In 1970, Wyeth held a one-man exhibit at the White House. His professional technique and graphic ability have become his legacy to American art.

Flight of the Wright Brothers' first airplane.

YOUNG, BRIGHAM (1801–1877), pioneer leader of the Mormons. In 1832, he read Joseph Smith's *Book of Mormon* and was baptized into the new faith. He formed a Mormon church in Kirkland, Ohio, in 1833. In 1835, he was selected as a member of the Quorum of Twelve Apostles to assist Joseph Smith; he became the fiscal agent for the emerging church in 1841. On December 5, 1847, he was elected president of the Quorum of Twelve Apostles, a position he retained until his death. After Smith was murdered, Young led the Mormons to Utah and established Mormon communities around the Great Salt Lake. He encouraged polygamy and opposed the use of liquor, stimulants, and tobacco. Young established the University of Deseret (now the University of Utah) in 1850.

YOUNG, CHIC (1901–1973), newspaper cartoonist who created the popular feature, "Blondie." Born in Chicago, Illinois, his real name was Murat Bernard. He developed "Blondie," her husband Dagwood, and associated characters. The comic strip was syndicated nationally through King Features. At the time of his death, it was appearing in over sixteen hundred newspapers in 60 countries.

YOUNG, DENTON T. "CY" (1867–1955), baseball player from Gilmore, Ohio. Young began playing for the Cleveland team of the National League in 1890. During his career, he pitched for the St. Louis Cardinals, the Boston Red Sox, the Cleveland Indians, and the Boston Braves. He pitched 751 complete games, winning 511 of them. He also pitched baseball's first "perfect" game (in which no batters reached base) on May 5, 1904. After his death, the major baseball leagues established the Cy Young Award for the best pitcher of the year.

YOUNG, WHITNEY M. (1921–1971), civil rights leader. Born in Lincoln Ridge, Kentucky, he graduated from Kentucky State College and the University of Minnesota. Young was associated with the Urban League in St. Paul, Minnesota, and Omaha, Nebraska. He became dean of the school of Social Work at Atlanta University in 1954. After a period of study at Harvard University, he was named executive director of the Urban League; there he introduced the concept of preferential treatment of blacks in jobs and educational facilities. He tried to mediate between militant civil rights groups and those who advocated more orderly processes. President Richard Nixon awarded him the Medal of Freedom in 1969. Young authored *To Be Equal* (1964) and *Beyond Racism* (1969).

ZAHARIAS, MILDRED DIDRIKSON "BABE" (1914–1956), Olympic athlete; regarded as the greatest woman golfer of all time. She appeared in the Olympic Games at Los Angeles in 1932, where she was the top performer in the 80-meter hurdle and the javelin throw. She excelled in athletic endeavors such as baseball, basketball, swimming, and diving. But her greatest achievements were in golf. From 1935 to 1950, she won every major women's golf championship—the United States National Open in 1948, 1950, and 1954; the national amateur tournament in 1946; and the World Championship four times. In 1947, she became a professional golfer. Stricken with cancer in 1953, she waged a battle to overcome the disease. She continued her athletic successes until her death in 1956. She wrote *This Life I've Led,* her autobiography.

"Babe" Didrikson Zaharias won The AP Award six times, once for starring in track and field and the five others for golfing brilliance. Later, the award was named in her honor.

ZENGER, JOHN PETER (1697–1746), colonial newspaper publisher. Born in the Rhine Country of Germany, he became an apprentice printer to William Bradford. He moved to Chestertown, Pennslyvania, to establish his reputation. Zenger became involved in New York political controversies after he arrived there in 1732. He used his *New York Weekly Journal* to support the political faction of Lewis Morris. Zenger was arrested in 1734 and charged with printing seditious and libelous material. His lawyers with were disbarred, so Andrew Hamilton came from Philadelphia to defend Zenger. He was acquitted, and the case became a classic in constitutional law.

ZIEGFELD, FLORENZ (1869–1932), theatrical manager who made burlesque famous. Ziegfeld was born in Chicago, Illinois. In 1906, he developed "The Parisian Model," a revue that attracted popular notice. After viewing the Follies Bergere in Paris, he returned to the United States to assemble the Ziegfeld Follies. He developed several stars; Fanny Brice, Marilyn Miller, W. C. Fields, Eddie Cantor, and Will Rogers were under contract to Ziegfeld. He attempted musical comedy with such productions as *Show Boat, Rio Rita,* and *Bittersweet*. But in 1927, he abandoned the Follies because the Great Depression made it seem inappropriate.

CHAPTER TWENTY-ONE

THE BUSINESS WORLD

Whether or not you work in a business office, you're involved in business dealings every day. When you cash a paycheck, buy groceries, repair your car, or do any number of things, you must handle your money or credit in a business-like way. But how well do you run your own business affairs? This chapter will give you some basic information that should help you handle your money more wisely.

We've included a section on the duties of a secretary to help business executives and secretaries plan their work. At the end of the chapter you'll find an explanation of several common business terms.

How to Make and Use a Family Budget

The most important rule for making a family budget is: *Keep it simple.* If you try to set up a complicated system, you'll waste time with unnecessary bookkeeping. A budget is supposed to help you plan how you will spend your money, and it should help you keep track of how your plan worked. If it's so complex that you can't understand it, why bother?

Design your budget to fit your own needs. Don't try to imitate someone else's budget, because your own income and expenses are unique.

First, notice where you're spending your money now. The easiest way to do that is to study the checks you wrote last month. (The bank sends them back to you after they've been processed.) Make a stack of these, along with any bills or receipts that show how you spent your cash last month.

In another stack, collect the stubs from last month's paychecks and any other checks you received. On a slip of paper, note any cash you received and put it in this stack, too. This can be very important if you get part of your income in cash every month—for example, if you're a waitress and your customers leave you tips.

Now go through each of these stacks, making a list of your income and expenses. Under expenses, you should note how much you spent last month for:

1. Rent or house payments
2. Education
3. Insurance
4. Loan Payments
5. Food
6. Clothing
7. Transportation
8. Medical Expenses
9. Savings
10. Recreation
11. Miscellaneous Expenses

Under the income, list the different sources of your income last month:

1. Fixed Income (your paycheck, Social Security checks, or other regular income)

2. Other Income (income that varies every month, like interest from a savings account or money you get from babysitting)

Now add up the money on each list. If the total of expenses is bigger than the total list of income, it means you're trying to spend more money than you earn. Doing that over a long period of time will drive you into bankruptcy.

How much money *should* you be spending for each item? That depends on your own needs and style of life. The federal government has found that the average family of four in the United States is dividing its money something like this:

HOUSING 33%
FOOD 25%
TAXES 20%
TRANSPORTATION
   & CLOTHING 10%
MEDICAL EXPENSES 5%
OTHER PERSONAL
   EXPENSES 7%

This is only an average. Your own budget will probably call for spending more money on certain items and less on others.

Before you make a plan for spending your money, find how much you're able to spend. Work only with your *take-home pay*—your wages or salary *after* your employer has subtracted taxes and Social Security payments.

You must pay a specific amount for some items every month, such as your house rent or mortgage payment, insurance, loan payments, and so on. List these on the budget sheet first. Then look at the expenses that vary each month, such as food, clothing, and transportation. You can control the amount that you spend for these items; so if you need to spend less money, cut the amount you spend for these "variables" first.

If you're planning to make a big purchase (such as a car or a house), decide how much money you can save each month toward this expense and put it in a savings account at your bank. You may also want to put some money in a savings account to build up an emergency fund for unexpected bills.

If you're like most people, you will want to budget some money for recreation, entertainment, and impulse buying. Reduce the money you spend for these things if your budget is pinched.

After you've budgeted a sensible amount of money for every item, you may find that you've exceeded your income. If so, you need to find ways to earn more money or reduce your total spending. You may need to reduce the amount you plan to spend for several items on your budget.

Most people are learning to do some jobs for themselves instead of hiring professionals to do them. You can take care of simple car repairs, home remodeling, and yardwork by yourself. Manufacturers are offering new products to help you do these jobs at a fraction of what you'd pay someone else.

Watch for "sales" on items you know you'll need in upcoming months. Often you can plan your buying to take advantage of seasonal close-outs. For example, you can buy lawn furniture cheaply at the end of the summer and store it to use next summer.

Always try to get the best value for the dollars you spend. When you're buying a new product, compare several brand names to see which one gives you the best quality at the price you can afford to pay.

After you've worked with your budget for a while, you may want to get the advice of a money expert. Ask for help at your local bank or savings-and-loan association. If you belong to a credit union, ask their staff for the advice you need. A stock broker can give you sound advice about investments.

Whatever you do, *stick with the budget you've planned.* You will need to change it from time to time as your personal situation changes. But remember: If you spend more than you planned in one area, you'll need to spend less in other areas. Otherwise, your budget won't balance at the end of the month.

Use good common sense when you plan your budget. Your success or failure depends on you alone. It's your money and you must decide how to spend it.

How to Buy a House

Whether it's large or small, a house is probably the most expensive purchase you'll ever make. It's an important step toward financial security.

But you need to remember several things when you think about buying a house. For one thing, it will require you to spend money on other items besides the house payment. Can you afford the insurance, utilities, property taxes, and maintenance costs that come with a house? You need to know that before you buy.

Take time to compare several houses and find the one that's best for you. You'll probably live there for several years, so get a house you'll enjoy.

Of course, there are all kinds of houses to choose from. So where do you start looking? Naturally, the first big factor is *price*. There's no need to waste time looking at houses you can't afford. Here's a good rule of thumb to use for deciding how much you can spend on a house: *Multiply your annual income by two-and-a-half*. For example, if you earn $20,000, you could probably afford to buy a house that costs $40,000 to $50,000, assuming that the other house money you spend each month doesn't wreck your budget. The basic monthly expenses for your house—the total of mortgage payment, taxes, and insurance—should not be more than one-sixtieth of your annual income. In other words, if you earned $20,000 each year, you'd divide that by 60 and find your basic housing expenses shouldn't be more than $333 each month. Remember, though, that you will be paying for some variable housing expenses, such as utilities and maintenance, on top of that.

The Federal Housing Administration uses another guideline that might help you. The FHA says the total of *all* housing expenses—mortgage payments, taxes, utilities, and maintenance— should be no more than 35 percent of your take-home pay. For example, if your take-home pay is $1,000 per month, you shouldn't spend more than $350 for all of your housing expenses.

Let us say you've decided how much you can afford to pay and you've found the house you want to buy. Now you need to decide how you'll buy it. Most people can't afford to pay cash for the total price of a house, but there are several other ways you might buy it:

1. Contract. The seller may let you pay him a small down payment and sign a contract to pay him the rest in monthly installments. He does not give you the title to the house until you've paid him all of the money that the contract requires.

2. Bank Loan. You can give the seller a down payment of your own and borrow the rest of the money from a bank. The bank will loan you the money only if the house is in good condition and you've made a large enough down payment. The bank requires you to make a smaller down payment for newer houses. Under this plan, the bank holds the title to your house until you pay off the loan. If you fail to make your monthly payments, the bank can sell your house to get the rest of the money you owe. Savings-and-loan associations loan money in the same way, and sometimes they charge less interest than local banks. Mortgage companies and private loan companies can do this, too, but they often charge more interest than the banks.

3. VA Loan. If you've ever served in the United States military, you can borrow money for your house and the Veterans Administration will agree to pay off the loan if you fail to pay. Usually you don't need to put down as much of your own cash, and you pay less interest on the loan. But if you fail to make your monthly payments, the VA can sell your house to get the money you owe.

4. FHA Loan. If at least two banks refuse to loan you the money to buy a house, and if you have a fairly low income, you may get the Farmer's Home Administration to agree to pay off the loan if you fail. If the FHA agrees to do this, you'll need very little money for the down payment and you'll pay less interest than with a regular bank loan. But the FHA will want to make sure that you can afford to make the monthly payments, and the agency will check the house to see that it is a sound investment. The FHA will also require the seller to pay extra fees for setting up this kind of loan. For this reason, some people may not sell their property to you if you plan to buy it with an FHA Loan. You can buy a new house with an FHA Loan; but the house must be modest and economical to maintain. If you have an unusually low income, the FHA may give you *interest credit*, which allows you to pay much less than the normal rate of interest.

When most people buy a house, they seek the

help of a real estate broker. Home sellers usually ask brokers to offer their houses for sale, so a broker can show you several different homes in your price range. The broker will probably ask you to make a small down payment when you offer to buy a house; this is called *earnest money,* because it shows the seller that you're really interested in buying the house. If the seller accepts your offer, the earnest money will go toward buying the house; if he rejects your offer, the broker will usually give your earnest money back to you.

After you've agreed to purchase a house and you've secured the financing, you may be asked to pay certain fees for the transaction. This varies with the different types of loans, and you should ask the broker to explain these *closing costs* before you offer to buy a house.

Be sure that a lawyer examines the title papers on the property. If anything is out of order, the seller should correct it before you close the deal. Otherwise, you may discover later that other debts were standing against the house, and you may have to pay them.

To put it simply, you should know whether you can really afford to buy a house—and if so, how much you can pay—before you begin shopping for one. And you should rely on professional lawyers and real estate brokers to help you make the transaction. If you don't, you could make some costly mistakes.

How to Make a Will

A person writes a *will* to distribute his property after he dies. The will is a legal document that names the persons or institutions who will receive his belongings, and often it tells who will divide this property among the ones who receive it. A husband and wife should each have a will; their wills should work together, so that the property will be handed out properly if *both* of them die at the same time.

You should review your will and update it periodically. As your personal situation changes, you'll probably want to change your will. If you prepare a new will, you should destroy the old ones; two wills would complicate matters after you died.

It is best to consult a lawyer when you're drawing up your will. He will want a list of your property, including any real estate, money, vehicles, insurance policies, or stocks and bonds. Usually you would give all of these things to your spouse, if you are married. But be sure the will explains who will receive these things if you and your spouse die at the same time. Also be sure that the will names someone to care for your children. If you want to give part of your estate to schools, churches, or other organizations, you must name these agencies in your will and tell exactly how much you want each one to receive.

Decide who will distribute your property and carry out the other duties you mentioned in your will; you must name this person in the document. This person is called the *executor* (if male) or an *executrix* (if female).

After you have written your will and gotten a witness to sign it, put it in a secure place. Usually this would be a safety deposit box that you can rent at your local bank. Ask your lawyer to keep another copy in case yours is stolen, lost, or destroyed.

The Business Secretary

Many people dream of being secretary to an important person. The work is varied and full of interest, responsible and challenging. The compensation will match the responsibilities involved. A good secretary is held in high esteem.

Just what must you do to prepare yourself for this valued niche in the world of action?

You should have the background of a good education; your interests should be broad; your reading should be comprehensive. In addition, you should master the tools of your trade. Your stenography and typing must be perfect; you must know how to write good letters and file important papers. A secretarial course at any good business school will see to that. All this, naturally, has to be coupled with your firm determination to emerge as an expert practitioner of the required skills.

But beyond this, there is a *plus* that makes the difference between being just a routine secretary (the kind that comes by the dozen) and that topnotch, "crackerjack" secretary that every busy executive is proud to have. Such a secretary makes life in the office so much smoother for him and the rest of the organization that he is glad to turn over to his secretary much of the work of the office. An executive who has a good secretary is relieved of many of his routine responsibilities and is left free to make the big decisions that can vastly improve the performance of the firm.

PERSONALITY

Understanding, tact, judgment, memory, dependability, initiative, patience, self-control—these might head the list of qualities of the ideal secretary you are aspiring to be.

An employer expects that his secretary will be understanding and well educated, have exemplary manners, know what constitutes good business customs, and be able to practice them. The secretary should also have poise. Who would want a secretary who is shy and afraid to meet people, or one who is brash, forward, obtrusive, and loud? When it comes to personal appearance, the secretary should be neat, but not gaudy. Dress, carriage, grooming, and hair should be attractive without being in any way extreme. The secretary should have a pleasant voice; every caller is exposed to the secretary's voice. It must combine warmth and impersonality, friendliness and restraint. Surely, it is no easy task to be an excellent secretary.

ATTITUDE

Perhaps the word *loyalty* best describes the attitude the secretary should have toward job and employer. It is important to have a sincere interest, not only in the particular work being done, but in the overall welfare of the company. In every task undertaken, the good secretary puts forth the very best effort possible. Loyalty will make the job easy.

Sometimes in large organizations "the boss's secretary" gets into the habit of assuming or taking for granted privileges that others do not have. This is to be avoided. In the last analysis, you are there to do your part—and not an inconsiderable part—to guarantee this smooth functioning of the office.

DUTIES

As secretary, you keep the records; you attend to correspondence, both incoming and outgoing; you see or talk to visitors and telephone callers. In some cases you do the personal filing for your particular employer. You are ready to be called upon for what may be required in the way of business tasks.

Records

When Mr. Jones, president of the ABC Company, arrives at his office in the morning, he naturally wants to know what his day is going to bring, insofar as this is predictable. It is a good idea to let him see at a glance just what appointments and commitments he has for that day. So arrive at the office ahead of him and place on his desk, neatly typed up, a list of the day's activities. To do this, you should keep three calendars: your own, one for your employer, and a follow-up calendar (the so-called tickler file). This third file consists of a file box or drawer with 12 tab cards, one for each month of the year, and 31 tab cards, one for each day of the month. Behind the appropriate month and day (which is moved forward daily to the front of the box or file) you place notations on appointments, meetings, commitments, reminders, and so on. Each morning, you go through the material for the particular day, discarding what may have lost validity and typing up the day's schedule for Mr. Jones' desk.

Mr. Jones may also want to be reminded of significant family dates and anniversaries, holidays, pending trips, dates of payments and taxes due, and the like. If so, you should give him these reminders at the proper time. Thus, if he is planning to send a birthday check or other present to his daughter at college, remind him of this a week in advance, again three days before, and possibly on the very day (since he may want to call her long distance).

If Mr. Jones sets aside a few minutes at the start of the business day for a short conference, during which the two of you can go over the program for the day, it will make the day easier for you both. Of course, that is up to Mr. Jones. But such conferences have worked out splendidly in many offices.

Correspondence

Generally, mail addressed to a particular executive is placed unopened on his secretary's desk as soon as it arrives. It then becomes your duty to open this mail and arrange for its proper distribution. A good idea is to make a preliminary division into four categories:

1. Correspondence
2. Bills and statements
3. Newspapers and periodicals
4. Advertisements and circulars

Each of these initial piles is then further subdivided into: (a) for the employer's attention; (b) for the attention of others in the organization; (c) for the secretary's own attention; (d) possible discards. This last applies only to the fourth category above, and must depend on the very careful discretion of the secretary.

The procedure for mail marked "Personal" varies with the particular organization and the wishes of your employer. Mr. Jones may or may not want you to leave this mail unopened for him to handle himself. Perhaps he prefers to have you open *all* his mail, regardless of the notation on the envelope. He may wish to have such letters placed in a separate folder. You carry out his wishes, of course.

You may prepare letters regarding company business, personal letters, and miscellaneous courtesy letters. When you are expected to write such letters, bear in mind the newspaper reporter's essential five: Who, What, When, Where, and Why. "Short and to the point" is the rule.

For spellings, word divisions, and distinctions among synonyms, *never guess;* consult a standard dictionary. For punctuation, capitalization, and abbreviations, consult the dictionary or a good style book. As for vocabulary and grammar, follow correct usage. Much of what you will need to know will be found in the early sections of this book.

You may need to compose replies to all but the most personal letters. Or it may be Mr. Jones' custom to spend a session with you daily, going over that day's incoming mail. He may dictate all or most of his letters to you, but there are no hard and fast rules. Your employer's wishes are law; carry them out according to the letter and spirit of these wishes.

In general, toward the end of the business day, you bring all outgoing mail to Mr. Jones for his signature. Then you must check every letter to be sure that it is signed, that any enclosures are included, and that the addresses inside the letter and on the envelope conform. Only then is the outgoing mail ready for mailing. You keep copies of any of the letters that your employer wants you to file.

Callers

In seeing your employer's visitors and greeting his telephone callers, you must combine the functions of a receptionist, a diplomat, a welcoming committee, a watchdog, and even a "bouncer." When you greet the caller, you must find out the purpose of his visit and make him comfortable. On some occasions you must be able to get rid of him as quickly and expeditiously as possible. But no matter what your purpose, you must remain polite. You must not convey an air of impatience or hostility. You must not antagonize the visitor or caller; you can be firm, but you must remain friendly. A good secretary soon learns whom an employer wants to see and whom he doesn't, whether to refer the caller to someone else in the organization, or whether to deal with the caller's problem yourself. This aspect of your job calls for excellent judgment and quick decisions. It demands poise, tact, good manners, and adaptability. In making these first contacts with visitors and telephone callers, remember you are serving both your employer and the caller.

Filing

Less than twenty-four hours after the tragic death of President Kennedy, the television screen showed his private files being removed from the Presidential office. In some offices, there is a central filing system that includes all but the most personal correspondence. But in some offices the filing of an executive's private and business correspondence is his secretary's responsibility. It has been said that if you file something correctly, there is only one place where it can be found. But if you file something incorrectly, you may have to look in a thousand places and then not find it. See to it that everything you file is filed in the most logical place it belongs.

Business Terms

BUSINESS AND INVESTMENT

ASSETS—those items, property, and services that reflect the total financial value of a person, business, or estate. Assets include the value of all real property and personal property you own.

BALANCE SHEET—a statement of the financial condition of an individual or business at any given time.

BETTER BUSINESS BUREAU—a nonprofit organization that gives information about companies and corporations to the public. In many instances, it provides information you will need when purchasing or using these specific products. The bureau patrols the advertising and marketing methods used by various companies. It may also provide business speakers for different school and civic groups.

BOND—a certificate evidencing a debt of a corporation. In other words, it is the corporation's promise to repay an amount of money that it has borrowed, usually with added interest; the bond holder simply lends his money to the corporation for repayment at a later date. When a corporation issues a bond without any security behind it, the bond is called a *debenture*. When there is security, it is called a *secured bond*.

BOOK VALUE—the assets of a business as shown on its account books. As used in the stock market, the term generally refers to a company's book value for each share of common stock. This value is obtained by dividing the company's total book value by the number of outstanding shares.

BROKER'S COMMISSION—a fee paid to a person for acting as an agent in a contract of sale.

This fee is generally decided prior to the transaction and confirmed in writing.

CAPITAL—the total amount of property or assets an individual or business owns.

CAPITAL GAINS/LOSSES—In general, a *capital gain* is the excess of capital assets over the appraised value or cost of an asset. For example, if you've sold a share of stock at a higher price than what you paid for it, the excess is called a capital gain. A *capital loss* exists when an asset costs more than its appraised value, or if the asset is sold at a price less than it originally costs.

Under present tax laws, if an asset is held at least six months and then sold, the gain is considered to be a long-term capital gain and is charged at a lower tax rate.

CHARITABLE CONTRIBUTIONS—An individual or a corporation is allowed to give away a limited amount of money or property and deduct it from taxable income. Many organizations are allowed to receive these contributions. Some of them are churches, tax-exempt organizations, hospital or medical research organizations, or govenment agencies (if the money is used for public purposes).

COMMERCIAL PAPER—a piece of paper used to convey value in a business transaction. This can be exchangeable value, monetary value, or both. A good example of commercial paper would be the checks used in banking; another example would be short-term promissory notes issued by a corporation. Traditionally the charge for using commercial paper as credit is lower than the prime interest rate.

COMMON STOCK—shares of stock that receive equal dividends from a corporation. When a company issues different classes of stock, the shares without special rights are *common*. Most of the stock issued by corporations is common.

COMPOUND INTEREST—interest paid upon interest, as well as upon principal. That is, the interest earned upon the principal is added to the principal, thereby raising the amount of the return to the lender. For example, D promises to repay $100 to C at the end of the year with interest at six percent per annum, compounded quarterly. At the end of the first quarter, the interest earned would be added to the principal. At the end of the second quarter, interest would be computed on the principal plus the preceding quarter's interest. This pattern would continue for the last two quarters as well. Thus, interest would be paid upon interest, as well as upon principal.

CONSUMER PROTECTION AGENCY—an organization created by the federal government to insure a customer's rights in business transactions. This agency offers information about truth in advertising, franchises, business rights, fair debt collection, label information, credit reporting, equal credit opportunity, and truth in lending.

CONVERTIBLE BOND—a bond that may be exchanged for stock in the corporation, under the conditions stated in the bond.

CORPORATION—an association of individuals that has its own distinct legal identity. A corporation has certain legal advantages for carrying on commercial activities. Among these advantages are: (1) continuity of the business. Its work will not be stopped if a member dies or withdraws from the corporation. (2) transferability of its property interest. This is done when the corporation sells stock. In this way, the corporation shares its financial obligations with people outside the corporation. (3) centralization of business control in the hands of its board of directors. (4) little or no individual liability for the debts of the corporation.

A corporation is a separate entity in the eyes of the law. Individuals who own an interest in the corporation (evidenced by their shares or certificates of stock) are called *stockholders*. By owning a share of stock, the stockholder generally enjoys three basic rights: (1) a right to share in the profits, (2) a right to vote upon major business decisions of the corporation, and (3) a right to share in the remaining assets if the corporation is dissolved.

The shares of stock may be given away, traded, or sold. This is generally done at a stock exchange. The exchange simply acts as a place where the various shares of stock can be traded.

DEPRECIATION—the decrease in the value of an asset or property due to wear and tear, obsolescence, and so on.

EX-DIVIDEND—A corporation may declare that it will pay a dividend to everyone who owns shares of its stock at a given date, and pay the dividends at a future date. The shares traded between the given dates will be marked *Ex-Dividend,* meaning they do not entitle the buyer to the new dividend.

FAIR MARKET VALUE—the price arrived at by a buyer and seller who are ready, willing, and able to buy and sell an asset.

FIRST-IN, FIRST-OUT—a method of pricing goods, based on the assumption that a merchant sells or uses goods in the same order in which they are received.

GIFT TAX—a tax upon the transfer of property, rather than on the property itself. This tax is levied during the lifetime of the person making the gift, rather than after his death. The federal gift tax applies only to the transfer of property by individuals, and not to transfers by corporations.

The gift must be made by a taxpayer, and it may be deducted only in the year the gift was made. The Internal Revenue Service has many lengthy rules governing this type of charitable contribution, especially gifts to corporations.

GOOD WILL—an intangible asset of every successful business. A business is said to have "good will" if its customers will probably return to make additional purchases.

INTANGIBLE ASSETS—the powers of a person or business that will allow continuing business success. Intangible assets would include a variety of privileges such as good will, secret processes, patents, and copyrights.

INTEREST—payment that a lender receives for the use of his money. It is usually a fixed percentage of the amount loaned (called *principal*), and it is to be paid at an agreed time.

INVENTORY—a list of the goods or property held by an individual or business.

INVESTMENT TRUST—an organization that accepts money from subscribers and invests it for them. The organization attempts to earn profits that can be distributed to the various subscribers.

LAST-IN, FIRST-OUT—a method of pricing goods, based on the assumption that the goods last received are the goods first sold or used.

LIABILITIES—the debts and obligations of an individual, business, or state.

LISTED STOCK—a stock of a corporation that is listed on the national stock exchange, such as the New York Stock Exchange or the American Stock Exchange. A stock that is not listed on one of the national exchanges is known as *unlisted*. It is sometimes referred to as stock "sold over the counter," or *over-the-counter* stock.

LOAN SHARK—a person who lends money at an exorbitant or illegal rate of interest. This is often called a "shirt-pocket loan." Usually it is for a short time (30 days or less) and its interest rate will be very high—perhaps 40 or 50 percent. Loan sharks often use severe techniques for making loans and collecting them, sometimes resorting to violence.

MONTHLY INVESTMENT PLAN—a plan in which an investor makes monthly payments to his stock broker. With this money, the broker buys as many shares as possible of certain stocks for the investor. If stock prices are low, the investor receives more stocks; if prices are high, he receives less stock. The investor may discontinue his monthly payment at any time.

MUNICIPAL BOND—a city's promise to repay a certain amount of money at a predetermined date and at a stated rate of interest. Federal and state governments levy no income tax on the interest paid by municipal bonds, so this is a very popular source of financing. A city or a county often uses this type of bond to finance large capital improvements.

MUTUAL FUND—an investment company that sells shares to the public, usually at a price determined by supply and demand. The proceeds of the sale are invested to make a profit. As the fund earns higher profits, its shares become more valuable.

NET WORTH—what remains after liabilities or obligations are subtracted from assets. As used in stock-market trading, the term means the net worth of each outstanding share of a company. It is obtained by dividing a company's total net worth by the number of its outstanding shares (i.e., the shares owned by persons outside the corporation).

NO-LOAD MUTUAL FUND—a mutual fund that charges no commission for the shares you buy. It may be hard to purchase shares of a no-load fund; most brokers do not like to sell them because they do not make any money on the sale. Investors usually buy these shares directly from the company that manages the no-load fund.

PREFERRED STOCK—stock that is given priority in the sharing of profits (called *dividends*). The holder of preferred stock is entitled to receive dividends out of the profits of a company at a fixed

annual rate, before any profits are distributed to the common stockholders. With some preferred stocks, the fixed dividend is *cumulative*. In that case, if the fixed dividend is not paid within a given year, it must be paid the following year before any profits are distributed to common stockholders. If the preferred stock is *noncumulative*, no such accumulations take place.

PRICE-EARNINGS RATIO—the earnings of a corporation, divided by the number of shares. This ratio is a handy index to the financial condition of the corporation. Generally, as the company becomes more profitable, its price-earnings ratio increases.

PROBATE—official proof that a certain document is valid. For example, a probate court must determine whether a will is valid before the will can take legal effect. Witnesses who have signed the will are usually asked to appear; but it can be probated without their presence. After the court probates a will, it issues a certificate that declares the will legal and official.

PUTS and CALLS—A *put* is an option to sell a fixed amount of a certain stock or commodity at a specified price within a limited amount of time. A *call* is the privilege to buy a stock or commodity at a fixed price within a limited amount of time.

RECEIVABLES—the unpaid claims, bills, and notes of services or merchandise that other merchants have received from a company. These are carried on the company's books as being "due."

RULE OF 78's—the method for computing a refund of interest when a loan contract is paid before maturity. Another name for the Rule of 78's is the *Sum of the Digits*. The number *78* is the sum of the digits 1–12, which stand for the months of the year.

For example, let's say a person borrows $1,000 for 12 months. After two months, he decides to repay the loan. He should be charged only for the amount of time he used the money, so the rule of 78's says this figure would be 24/78 of the interest that would have been charged for the entire year. The borrower can get back 54/78 of the finance charge. *Note:* The rule of 78's applies only to a 12-month contract period.

SAVINGS BOND—a borrowing device that the federal government originated after World War II. The government was heavily in debt and needed a way to raise large amounts of money in a hurry. So it issued savings bonds to attract small loans from private citizens.

Today you can buy a Savings Bond for an amount smaller than its face value and turn it in for the full amount in cash at the end of a seven-year period. The savings bond earns about six percent interest during that time. Savings bonds are not as popular today as they were several years ago, because most banks and savings-and-loan companies pay a higher rate of return.

SECURITY—something given as a promise of repayment. A security may be any note, stock, treasury stock, bond, or debenture. It also includes any document that shows a person's membership or ownership in an organization that has borrowed money from him.

SHORT SALE—a contract to sell shares of stock that the seller does not own, or that are not under his control. The seller hopes that when he has to deliver the stock to the purchaser, its price will be lower than when he made the contract. If it is, he can buy the stock on the open market, deliver it, and make a profit.

SIMPLE INTEREST—interest paid only on the principal balance, and not figured on the accumulated interest. Simple interest is paid simply for the use of the money borrowed.

STOCK SPLIT—A corporation with 100,000 shares outstanding (i.e., owned by private investors) may decide to recall them and issue 200,000 shares, giving each shareholder two shares for one. This is known as a *stock split*. It does not increase or reduce the value of the shareholder's assets; his interest in the corporation remains the same. But if the price of the stock rises after a split, the value of the investor's holdings will increase more rapidly.

STRAIGHT-LINE METHOD—the most common way of figuring depreciation of an asset for tax purposes. Another name for it is *fixed percentage*. It is based on the theory that an asset will loose value at the same rate each year.

To use the straight-line method, estimate the ultimate salvage value of the item and subtract this from its original cost. Divide the result by the number of years you expect to use the item. This will give you the amount of straight-line depreciation for each year.

TREASURY BILL—an obligation of the United States Government to pay the bearer a fixed amount of money after a certain number of days. The Treasury Bill is the most important investment in today's money market. The most common Treasury Bills are the three- and six-month bills; they can be purchased at any Federal Reserve Bank. These bills raise new cash for the federal government. The biggest buyers of Treasury Bills are banks, corporations, and state and local government.

UNIFORM GIFT TO MINORS ACT—a federal law that allows an adult to make a gift to a minor without the minor's having to pay a gift tax. This gift may be in the form of money, security, proceeds from a life insurance policy, or annuities.

The gift can only be made to one minor, and only one person can act as custodian of the gift for the minor. The gift must be final, and the person who gives it must convey its legal title to the minor.

USURY—the act of lending money at an illegally high rate of interest. Usury laws vary from state to state. In some states, a violator of the usury law is required to refund the entire amount of interest paid; in other states, only the amount of excess interest is given back.

WARRANTS AND OPTIONS—A *warrant* confers the right to purchase stock in a corporation at a later date, under stated terms and conditions. A corporation may sell warrants much like it sells common stock. An *option* is similar, except that it is not necessarily sold. The corporation may give an option to a stockholder or friend of the company as a special privilege.

BANKING

BANKER'S ACCEPTANCE—a bank's agreement to accept a bill of exchange or bank draft. Since the bank becomes responsible to pay on the instrument, a person would prefer to exchange a bill or draft for an acceptance.

BILL OF EXCHANGE—a written order to pay a stated amount out of a bank account. A bill of exchange must conform to the following requirements: (1) It must be in writing and signed by the *drawer*—the person issuing the order; (2) It must contain an unconditional order to pay a certain sum in money; (3) It must be payable on demand or at a fixed time; (4) It must state that the amount is payable to a designated person or company, or to the person who holds the bill.

A bank will not honor a bill that does not conform to these requirements. If the bill does conform, it can move about quite freely in business transactions. There is an obvious risk involved in purchasing a bill of exchange that does not conform to any of these requirements, because it may not be honored by the bank that holds the drawer's account. Such a bill would be called a *non-negotiable* instrument.

Many of the common bills of exchange are checks, drafts, trade acceptances, and banker's acceptances. They involve a *drawer* (the person who draws up the bill), a *drawee* (the person who keeps the drawer's account), and a *payee* (a person to whom the bill is paid); so bills of exchange are referred to as *three-party* instruments. Promissory notes are known as *two-party* instruments, since they involve a *maker* (the person who makes the promise to pay) and a *payee* (the person to whom the note is payable).

The drawee is not responsible for the document until he accepts it. He may do this by writing the word *accepted* on the face of the document, followed by his name or initials.

CERTIFICATE OF DEPOSIT—a certificate issued by a bank to acknowledge the deposit of a specific sum of money. The bank promises to pay the depositor the face amount, along with an agreed amount of interest. Most certificates of deposit have an established expiration date; in all cases, the full payment is made only when the depositor gives the certificate back to the bank.

CERTIFIED CHECK—a bank's written promise to pay a specific amount of money on behalf of one of the bank's account holders. In effect, the bank takes funds out of the account and assumes the duty of paying the check when it is negotiated. Thus, it has been said that "a certified check is as good as cash."

CHECK—a bill of exchange drawn on a bank and payable on demand. It is the most common negotiable instrument.

When a depositor opens up a deposit account with a bank, he becomes a lender and a bank becomes his borrower. Under their contract, the bank must surrender the funds of a depositor whenever the depositor gives an order in the form of a check. The check must be presented to the bank within a reasonable time after it is issued.

A bank is not primarily responsible to pay the check; the person who wrote the check is. Therefore, a bank may refuse to honor a check. But if it refuses to pay a valid check, the bank has breached its contract with the depositor, and may be held liable for any losses the depositor incurs because the check was not honored.

COLLATERAL—a pledge of real or personal property to secure the payment of a loan or the extension of credit. Collateral can be in many forms, but it should have enough value to secure the loan. Also, it should be in a form that the lender can convert to cash, if the need arises. Many banks use only the borrower's signature as collateral for small loans. But each lending institution must decide the amount and type of collateral it will accept.

DISCOUNTING—a bank's practice of charging a fee for converting credit instruments into cash. A bank may advance money to the person who holds the instrument and charge him its usual discount rate. Then the bank holds the documents until maturity. If the person or institution that issued the document pays the bank, the transaction is closed. If not, the bank will expect the depositor to return its money.

FEDERAL RESERVE BANK—The Federal Reserve System was established in 1913 by President Woodrow Wilson when he signed the Federal Reserve Act. This act created 12 regional banks across the nation, controlled by the Federal Reserve Board of governors in Washington, D.C. These banks regulate the flow of credit and money. Any bank that wants to use money from the Federal Reserve Bank in its region must become a member of the Federal Reserve System. The Federal Reserve Bank provides many services for its member banks; it handles their reserve accounts, furnishes currency and coins, clears and collects checks, transfers funds by wire, and acts as a depository for the funds handled by government agencies.

INDEPENDENT RETIREMENT ACCOUNT—a bank account for accumulating money that a person will use during retirement. Each year the depositor can put up to fifteen percent of his earned income in the account, up to a maximum of $1,750 each year. This money is not charged Federal income taxes during the current year; it is taxed only when an individual starts withdrawing money. He can do this as early as age 59½, and he must begin withdrawing the money by age 70½. He can take out the deposit in one lump sum or in a certain amount per month.

If both husband and wife are working, each of them can have an Individual Retirement Account. They can set aside a maximum total of $3,000 for these accounts each year. The bank pays interest to these accounts while the money is on deposit; the rate of interest varies from bank to bank.

INTEREST PENALTY—an amount of interest that you forfeit to the bank if you withdraw the money in a time certificate of deposit before it matures. The federal law states that when you cash a certificate of deposit before maturity, you will earn the regular passbook savings rate *minus* 90 days' interest. This means that if you cash a time certificate of deposit early, the bank will not pay interest for 90 days of the time you had the certificate in effect. The bank would pay you the regular passbook rate for the rest of the time you had the money on deposit.

JOINT TENANTS—the partners who jointly own an asset. In banking, this term usually refers to two or more people who jointly own a bank account. If one of the partners dies, his interest or ownership is automatically transferred to the remaining owner(s). Married couples often establish bank accounts as joint tenants.

LINE OF CREDIT—the amount of money that any one person, corporation, or organization can borrow with a certain amount of collateral. Different lending institutions have different ways of arriving at this figure.

For example, let us say that a certain bank has a policy of financing only 75 percent of the value of an automobile. A certain vehicle is valued at $10,000. The bank would loan up to $7,500 for this car; that's the line of credit available.

NONTAXABLE TRUST—an account that an employer uses to provide a stock bonus, pension, or profit-sharing plan for the benefit of his employees. The money deposited in this trust account will not be taxed if it meets all the requirements imposed by federal and state governments.

PRINCIPAL—the original amount of debt, or the initial amount a person owes to another. A bank charges interest only on the principal.

PROMISSORY NOTE—a written promise to pay. A promissory note must conform to the following: (1) It must be in writing and signed by the maker; (2) It must contain an unconditional promise to pay a certain sum of money; (3) It must be payable on demand or at a fixed future time; (4) It must be payable to a designated person or to the bearer.

The payee does not need to hold the note until the maturity date. He may decide to sell it to someone else; in that case, if the instrument is *order paper* (i.e., written to pay a designated person), he endorses the instrument and gives it to the buyer. If it is *bearer paper* (i.e., written to pay the bearer), he simply gives it to the buyer.

PROXY—authorization to allow another person to vote in your absence at a business meeting.

In banking, this term usually refers to the proxies that an account holder in a savings-and-loan company may give to the officers of his company.

REDISCOUNTING—If a bank wants to convert some of its holdings into cash, it would submit its bills and notes to its local Federal Reserve Bank for rediscounting. After charging a *rediscount fee,* the Federal Reserve Bank would dispense the cash and hold the instruments until maturity. If all of the debtors pay their notes, the transaction is completed. If not, the Federal Reserve Bank will demand payment from the borrowing bank, which in turn will demand payment from the debtor(s).

SECURED LOAN—a loan that requires the borrower to make a pledge of collateral. Many institutions make only this type of loan. The greater the risk that the loan will not be repaid, the more security the lending institution will require. A good example might be an automobile loan. The bank will hold the title to the car as collateral until the debt has been paid. If the debt isn't paid, the bank may sell the car and recover the money it lended.

SIGNATURE LOAN—a loan that requires only the signature of the borrower as collateral. The lending institution relies on the integrity of the person who borrows the money. In most cases, this type of loan is for a short term and for a low amount.

TENANTS IN COMMON—ownership of an asset by two or more persons, in which each person has an individual interest. In banking, this term usually refers to the common ownership of a bank account. When one of the owners dies, his ownership passes to his heirs or to whomever he has named in his will; the surviving owners do not automatically inherit the account. Tenants in common do not necessarily have equal interests in the account. If one member wishes to dispose of his portion of the account and the others do not, he may force them to convert the account to cash so that he can receive his share.

TRADE ACCEPTANCE—a bill of exchange that arises out of a merchant's purchase of goods. The seller of goods (*drawer*) signs over the debt of the buyer (*drawee*), to a designated agent (*payee*). When the buyer accepts this document, he agrees to pay his debt to the agent.

Let us say that ABC Company has purchased a shipment of goods on credit. The company that sold the goods to ABC issues a trade acceptance. When ABC Company receives the trade acceptance, one of its officers will write the word *accepted* across the face of the document with the date and place of payment, followed by his signature. ABC Company then becomes liable to pay the bill as stated.

TRUST OFFICER—one who manages a trust for someone else. The trust officer may also be called *trustee*.

INSURANCE

ACCIDENT INSURANCE—insurance covering such risks as death, dismemberment, loss of eyesight, or loss of time as a result of accidents. An *accident* is generally defined as an unlooked-for mishap; if someone intentionally cuts off his arm or leg, it would not be an accident. Accident insurance would cover death from accidental means, but no other kind of death.

DOUBLE INDEMNITY—an insurance company's practice of giving twice the amount of insurance benefits when an insured person dies. Double indemnity is most commonly given when the insured person dies in an accident. Many insurance companies do not give double indemnity if the death occurred through suicide, service in time of war, air travel, or disease.

FIRE INSURANCE—insurance that guards against the loss of property by fire. The person who owns a fire insurance policy must have an *insurable interest* in the property involved. In other words, the insured must have a lawful, economic interest in the safety or preservation of the property from loss or destruction. (For example, the average citizen couldn't buy fire insurance on the White House.)

FLOOD INSURANCE—insurance against loss caused by cloudbursts and floods, tidal waves or overflowing streams and rivers. This type of insurance is usually available in low-lying areas and in the vicinity of rivers and dams.

HEALTH INSURANCE—insurance to cover losses caused by illness or sickness.

INCONTESTABILITY—protection against having a life insurance policy cancelled by the insurance company. Most policies state that they are incontestable after two years, unless you fail to pay your premium.

INCREASE OF HAZARD—taking unnecessary or unusual risks. Usually a fire insurance policy will state that the insurance company is not liable for loss or damage if the likelihood of fire is increased by any means within your control. For example, the company may not pay for a fire if you keep fireworks, explosives, gasoline, kerosene, or other highly flammable materials on your property.

INDUSTRIAL LIFE INSURANCE—a fairly small amount of life insurance, for which you pay premiums at weekly or other frequent intervals. Generally, this kind of life insurance policy offers the least amount of protection for the dollars you spend.

INSURABLE INTEREST—Usually a person takes out a life insurance policy on himself. However, you can take out a life insurance policy on someone else and make yourself the beneficiary, if you have an insurable interest in the life of that person. The term *insurable interest* generally means: (1) In the case of persons related by blood or law, an interest that arises from love and affection, or (2) In the case of other persons, a lawful economic interest in protecting the life of the insured person.

LIFE INSURANCE—a form of insurance that pays benefits in the event of death. An insurance company will pay an agreed sum of money to a designated person (called a *beneficiary*) when the insured person dies. The beneficiary may be the estate of the insured, a member of his family, a business associate, or even a stranger. The policy will state whether you can change the name of the beneficiary. If you can't, the beneficiary has what is called a *vested interest*—that is, his interest in the policy may not be stripped from him without his consent. Thus, you may take out a life insurance policy on a member of your family or upon the life of another person who owes you a debt. A business partnership may take out a policy on the lives of its partners. Likewise, a corporation may obtain a life insurance policy for each of its corporate officers. But if you have no insurable interest in the life of the person insured, the law considers it to be a *contract of wager*. Even if an insurance company issues a policy under these circumstances, it is illegal and unenforceable.

MARINE INSURANCE—insurance that covers losses connected with marine activities. This contract may also protect against losses on inland waters or on land, if the losses are connected with a sea voyage. The person or firm obtaining this kind of insurance must have an insurable interest in the subject of the policy (e.g., the boat or the cargo carried by the boat).

MUTUAL INSURANCE—a form of insurance in which the policyholders make up the insurance company. (The *policyholders* are those who buy insurance policies.) Mutual insurance companies only insure the lives and property of their members. When the annual premiums that members pay exceed the amount of losses covered by the company, the company often pays a *dividend* (i.e., a small refund) to the policyholders.

PAID-UP and ENDOWMENT OPTIONS—the opportunity to convert a life insurance policy to another form of insurance, so that you do not have to pay premiums. The original policy may state that when you do this you can keep the same amount of insurance in force *(paid-up option),* or that you will have a declining amount of insurance *(endowment option).* Usually these options require that: (1) The money you've invested in the policy must be earning interest equal to the amount of your premium. (2) You must ask the company to convert the policy. (3) Your request will be subject to the company's approval. (4) The company will determine how much insurance you can buy under the new plan. (5) If you've borrowed money against your present policy, your new policy will become the collateral for the loan. Not all life insurance policies carry these options.

UNOCCUPANCY—a clause that states that the insurance company will not pay for loss or damage that occurs while an insured building is vacant or unoccupied beyond a certain period of time—usually ten days.

WAIVER OF PREMIUM—a provision that allows you to stop paying premiums on a life insurance policy if you become disabled. Your policy would remain in force, and when your disability ends you resume making the payments.

REAL ESTATE

ABSTRACT OF TITLE—a legal document that shows the history of ownership for a certain piece of property. In most states, the abstract of title passes from the seller to the buyer with each sale of property, and the buyer's name is added to the permanent record. The seller must pay the expense of bringing the abstract up to date. The buyer must have an attorney check the abstract to be sure it is complete.

APPRECIATION—a property's increase in value over a length of time. It is the opposite of *depreciation.* For example, let us say that a tract of land was purchased for $500 per acre five years

ago. Today the same land would probably be worth at least $1,000 per acre.

ASSESSMENT—a government's charge against a certain parcel of real estate. This charge is usually made to cover the property owner's share of the cost of a public improvement such as a street or sewer.

BREACH OF CONTRACT—a situation in which one or both parties fail to perform a legal contract. Both parties must accept the breach. If one doesn't accept it for any reason, he may sue the other party to regain what was lost.

EARNEST MONEY—a down payment that a purchaser of real estate makes to show his good faith in the transaction. Earnest money shows the seller that the buyer really means to follow through with the agreement. Sometimes the seller refunds the money if the transaction fails to go through; sometimes he doesn't. This decision is up to the seller.

ESCROW—an account where money is held until a contract has been fulfilled. This type of arrangement is most often used in the sale of real estate. An escrow agent holds the buyer's down payment until the title search is completed and the transaction is closed. The seller receives none of the money until all the legalities are in order. Banks and lawyers are the most common escrow agents.

FEE SIMPLE—the transfer of property to someone and his heirs without limitations. An estate or inheritance that you own completely and without restrictions is called an estate in *fee simple.* You may use it in any way you choose during your life time or after your death (through your will). If you have not made any plans for the distribution of this estate, it must pass to your heirs without any future limitations.

FIRST/SECOND MORTGAGE—a lender's claim to a piece of property that the owner has used as collateral on a loan. If the property owner fails to repay his loan, the lender can force him to sell the property to repay the debt. The only difference between a first and second mortgage is the order in which the lenders file their claim on the property. A second mortgage would only be good after the first mortgage had been satisfied. A lender would prefer to have a first mortgage rather than a second mortgage, since he would be more likely to get his money back.

LIEN—a claim that a person or institution has upon the property of another. The borrower must keep the property as security for the debts. In other words, a lien puts a "hold" on a certain item until its borrower has paid the debt. A lender may hold a lien on real estate, an automobile, or any other item of personal property.

PRORATED TAXES—taxes that are split between the buyer and the seller of a piece of property. When property is sold, the taxes are usually divided according to the time the sale takes place. The buyer should only be expected to pay taxes for the time after he receives title to the property, and not for the entire year.

QUIT-CLAIM DEED—a deed that gives a buyer whatever right, title, or interest that the seller has in a piece of property. It does not indicate whether other persons have an interest in the property, too.

SURVEYOR'S REPORT—a report from a licensed surveyor, which is used to determine limits and boundaries of a piece of property. The surveyor checks legal descriptions of the tract and usually drives stakes at the corners of the property to aid anyone else determining the boundaries at a later time. A surveyor's report should include the measurements of the land in terms of acres, square miles, or square feet. It should also give definite boundaries, the corner locations, and a definite point of beginning the measurement.

The cost of this report varies upon the time required for the research. This fee is customarily paid by a person who is purchasing the property.

TITLE INSURANCE—a contract to protect the owner of real estate against loss arising from defective property titles, hidden liens, or other encumbrances.

Usually title insurance losses are very small, because title insurance companies examine all legal papers very carefully before they will insure them. The premiums paid for title insurance are quite high, because of the amount of time it takes to research the documents. The title company must examine many records of land titles involving many previous owners, deeds, mortgages, and so on. A title insurance policy remains in effect until some further change of ownership takes place, or until a claim is made against a property.

WARRANTY DEED WITH FULL COVENANTS—the most complete form of property title that a seller can give. In this type of deed, a seller guarantees: (1) that he has the right to give the purchaser the title as designated in the contract; (2) that the buyer shall enjoy the premises without having to dispute claims from others; (3) that the premises are free from encumbrances such as tax debts; (4) that the seller will provide any further necessary assurances of the title; and (5) that the seller will forever guarantee the buyer's title to the premises. This is the most valuable form of protection, from the purchaser's viewpoint.

Of course, a buyer can obtain title insurance from a title insurance company for even more protection.

CHAPTER TWENTY-TWO

COLLEGES AND UNIVERSITIES

College Entrance Examinations and Questionnaires

At the end of the nineteenth century, a group of colleges, disturbed by the great variety of subjects taught, and by the wide range of marks given, in the secondary schools of the country, set up the College Entrance Examination Board (CEEB). Through the efforts of this organization, greater uniformity of curriculum in secondary schools was obtained. To remedy existing evils, the CEEB began to administer tests of its own construction to those applying to the colleges that originally made up the group. These early tests were of the essay type—usually three-hour tests in which the candidate was asked to discuss several topics rather exhaustively. As the number of college applicants increased greatly after World War I, the CEEB found it necessary to devise simpler testing methods. At this time, the short-answer, multiple-choice question was developed and polished. Studies were conducted to learn the relative values of the various types of tests, and the reliability and validity of short-answer tests were demonstrated to the satisfaction of the colleges involved. They discovered a high degree of correlation between the marks obtained on these short-answer tests and the later success of the students in their college work. Thereupon, the number of colleges making use of these tests grew considerably.

Short-answer tests and the great reliance that some colleges place on them have been attacked, but up to now no better form has been found, and the colleges continue to rely on them.

TYPES OF TESTS

The College Entrance Examination Board of Princeton, New Jersey, through its Educational Testing Service, is today the maker of the most widely used college entrance examinations. Among these are: the Scholastic Aptitude Test (SAT), the Preliminary Scholastic Aptitude Test (PSAT), the Writing Sample Test, achievement tests in various subject-areas, and the Advanced Placement Tests.

The Scholastic Aptitude Test

This test has become a regular part of the college admission procedure for high school seniors throughout the country. The marks achieved in the two fields of verbal aptitude and of mathematical aptitude are a significant factor in most colleges' decisions concerning accepting or rejecting a candidate.

A. The Verbal Section of the SAT

The mark obtained in this section of the test reflects the student's ability to handle language concepts and to reason. Questions of four types are included.

(1) The first type of question tests knowledge of vocabulary.

Example: Each of the questions below consists of a word printed in italics, followed by five words or phrases numbered 1 to 5. Choose the numbered word or phrase which is most nearly opposite in meaning to the word in italics.

1. *acclaim*—1 discharge 2 denounce 3 applaud 4 divide 5 rationalize
2. *zenith*—1 nadir 2 compass 3 summit 4 middle 5 musical instrument
3. *superficial*—1 arrogant 2 magnanimous 3 pusillanimous 4 profound 5 young

Answers   (1)2   (2)1   (3)4

(2) The second type of question tests the student's understanding of relationships among words and ideas. The student has to analyze the relationship existing between two words and then match it with another pair that has a similar relationship.

Example: Each of the questions below consists of two words that have a certain relationship to each other, followed by five numbered pairs of words. Select the numbered pair of words that are related to each other in the same way as the original pair of words are related to each other.

1. carpenter : saw :: 1 magician : wand 2 blacksmith : anvil 3 surgeon : doctor 4 doctor : drugs 5 satirist : words
2. facile : pen :: 1 glib : tongue 2 soft : shoe 3 stubborn : mule 4 hasty : pudding 5 easy : pencil
3. admiration : love :: 1 parsimony : economy 2 jealousy : envy 3 joy : ecstasy 4 hot : tepid 5 eager : anxious

Answers   (1)5   (2)1   (3)3

(3) The third type of question tests the student's ability to complete a sentence from which one or two words have been removed.

Example: In each of the sentences below there is a blank space indicating that a word has been omitted. Beneath the sentence are five numbered words; from these five words you are to choose the one word which, when inserted in the blank space, *best* fits in with the meaning of the sentence as a whole. In some sentences, two words are omitted; in these sentences, you will be given five pairs of words. Select the pair which best completes the sentence.

1. You don't win friends by acting ____ . 1 professionally 2 nicely 3 generously 4 idealistically 5 superciliously
2. My refusal to ____ with your demands was based on the highest intelligence. 1 return 2 abscond 3 recant 4 comply 5 enter

3. Only an oaf fails to observe the ____ of life. 1 business 2 proprieties 3 ventures 4 study 5 cessation

Answers   (1)5   (2)4   (3)2

(4) The fourth type of question tests the student's ability to read with understanding.

Example: Read the following passages and answer the questions which follow each passage.

I. While the poll takers are most widely known for their political surveys, the greatest part of their work is on behalf of American business. There are three kinds of commercial surveys. One is public relations research, such as that done for banks, which finds out how the public feels about a company. Another is employee-attitude research, which learns from rank-and-file workers how they really feel about their jobs and their bosses, and which can avert strikes by getting to the bottom of grievances quickly. The third, and probably most spectacular, is marketing research, testing public receptivity to products and designs. The investment a company must make for a new product is enormous—$5,000,000 to $10,000,000, for instance, for just one product. Through the surveys a company can discover in advance what objections the public has to competing products, and whether it really wants a new one. These surveys are actually a new set of signals permitting better communication between business and the general public—letting them talk to each other. Such communication is vital in a complex society like our own. Without it, we would have not only tremendous waste but the industrial anarchy of countless new unwanted products appearing and disappearing.

1. The title below which best expresses the ideas of this passage is
   1 The poll taker
   2 Business asks questions
   3 Behind the scenes in business
   4 Our complex business world
   5 Averting industrial anarchy

2. The passage states that polls can benefit industry by
   1 reducing waste
   2 establishing fair prices
   3 strengthening people's faith in business

4 saving small businesses
5 serving as a new form of advertising

3. This paragraph is developed by means of
1 cause and effect
2 contrast
3 illustrations
4 anecdotes
5 vivid descriptions

4. Which is *not* mentioned as an area in which polls have been conducted?
1 new products
2 politics
3 public relations
4 labor-management relationships
5 family relationships

5. The passage leads the reader to believe that for business purposes surveys are
1 overrated
2 too widely used
3 often deceptive
4 necessary
5 costly
Answers   (1)2 (2)1 (3)3
           (4)5 (5)4

B. The Mathematics Section of the SAT

The mathematics section tests a student's ability to handle elementary mathematical concepts in old and new situations. The questions may be answered by those who have had a course in elementary algebra and plane geometry. Those who have had advanced courses in mathematics will, of course, be able to work more rapidly and efficiently. Some typical questions follow:

1. The dial of a meter is divided into equal sections from 0 to 60. When the needle points to 48, the meter registers 80 amperes. What is the maximum number of amperes the meter will register?

(1) 92 (2) 100 (3) 102 (4) 120
(5) 156

2. A box was made in the form of a cube. If a second cubical box has inside dimensions three times those of the first box, how many times as much does it contain?

(1) 3 (2) 9 (3) 12 (4) 27 (5) 36

3. A proper fraction is unchanged in value if both numerator and denominator are
(1) increased by the same number
(2) decreased by the same number
(3) divided by the same number
(4) raised to the second power
(5) replaced by their square roots

4. John's house is 6.3 miles due north of the community center. Dick's home is 5.5 miles due east of it. Find, to the nearest tenth of a mile, the shortest distance between their homes.

(1) 5.9m. (2) 8.3m. (3) 8.4m.
(4) 11.8m. (5) 11.9m.

5. An altitude h of a triangle is twice the base to which it is drawn. If the area of the triangle is 225 square inches, then altitude h is

(1) 15 inches (2) 20 inches (3) 25 inches (4) 30 inches (5) 35 inches

Answers (1)2 (2)4 (3)3
         (4)3 (5)4

The SAT is given several times each year during January, March, April, May, July, October, and December. Information about dates, hours, fees, centers, and so on, is contained in the College Board *Student Bulletin* which is available in most high schools or obtainable by writing to the College Entrance Examination Board, Box 592, Princeton, New Jersey, 08540, or Box 1025, Berkeley, California 94701. In general, the April or May examination should be taken by high school juniors who wish to obtain an appraisal of their general aptitude to help them in deciding which college to choose. Juniors who are interested in obtaining an early decision from a college (usually before December 1) should also take these tests. The December or January examinations should be taken by high school seniors.

It is advisable to file the application and fee at least six weeks before the examination date to insure being assigned to the center requested.

Scores obtained on these tests are forwarded to the colleges indicated by the students on the application card and to the student's high school. These scores are usually given to the students six or seven weeks after the examination date. Scores are reported on a scale which ranges from 200 to 800, to be interpreted as follows:

Between 700 and 800—Top 2% of students
Between 600 and 700—Top 16%
Between 500 and 600—Top 50%
500—50 Percentile
Between 400 and 500—Lower 50%
Between 300 and 400—Lower 16%
Between 200 and 300—Lowest 2%

Many colleges will accept students who attain scores of 450 or better, but the more selective schools, which have as many as ten times the number of applicants that they can admit, often require scores in the mid or high 600s. Most schools recognize that any student who attains a score of 450 or better is capable of doing satisfactory college work.

The Preliminary Scholastic Aptitude Test (PSAT)

Each year in October the College Board offers a test for high school juniors to help them discover how well they can do on aptitude tests. This is essentialy a shorter form of the SAT. The verbal and mathematical questions are similar in nature and difficulty to the questions described above in dealing with the Scholastic Aptitude Test. The test is shorter and costs less to take. This test is also used by a limited number of groups and colleges to determine winners of various scholarships. The college catalogs and scholarship announcements will indicate whether the test is required.

Arrangements to take this test are usually made by the principal of the high school. Students should inquire of their school advisors in September about the advisability of taking this test.

The Achievement Tests and the Writing Sample Test

Some, but not all, colleges requiring the SAT ask their applicants, in addition, to take one or more Achievement Tests. These are one-hour tests given on the afternoon of the day the SAT is offered. Tests are offered in the following fields:

American History and Social Studies, Biology, Chemistry, English Composition, European History and World Cultures (January and May only), French, German, Hebrew (January only), Latin, Advanced Mathematics, Intermediate Mathematics, Physics, Russian (January only), Spanish.

Most of these tests are of the short-answer type and usually consist of 100 to 150 questions to be answered during the hour. There may be a short essay question or a paragraph to be corrected on the English Composition Test, but this test, too, is basically a short-answer paper.

The Writing Sample Test is given at this time. This test is not marked by the College Entrance Examination Board; it is forwarded to the colleges indicated by the student at the time he takes the test. During the hour assigned to the test, the student writes his essay on an assigned topic on a special form that automatically produces four copies. The high school gets the original and all unused copies; the other copies are mailed to the indicated colleges, where they are evaluated.

Results on the Achievement Tests are reported to the colleges and the high school. The SAT scale of 200 to 800 is used.

The choice of examinations depends on the college. Some indicate the specific areas to be taken; others merely specify that two or three Achievement Tests are to be taken.

Unless a college specifically states that the Achievement Tests are to be taken in December, it is advisable to take the SAT in December and the Achievement Tests in January of the senior year.

The Educational Testing Service of the College Board also distributes several tests which are given at the student's high school in May if requested. These include Listening Comprehension Tests in French, German, Russian, and Spanish.

The Advanced Placement Tests

For high school seniors who have taken an enriched program of studies—chiefly on the college level—the College Board offers a series of tests for advanced placement in college. Such examinations are now offered in English Composition, Literature, French, German, Latin, Spanish, American History, European History, Mathematics, Biology, Chemistry, and Physics. Unlike the Achievement Tests, these examinations are of the essay type and last for three hours each. Papers are marked and forwarded to the college which has accepted the candidate. Results are reported on a scale of 1 to 5.

(1) fail (2) pass (3) creditable (4) honors
(5) highest honors

The college receiving the grade *may* permit the student to take advanced work in these subject-areas as a freshman.

The teachers of advanced high school courses in these fields will inform students about this test and make the necessary arrangements for the taking of the examination, which is usually given during the spring.

Other Tests

In addition to the Educational Testing Service of the College Entrance Examination Board, several other agencies prepare similar examinations which are used by some colleges.

A. The American College Testing Program (ACT)

The American College Testing Program tests the student's abilities in English, mathematics, social studies, and the natural sciences.

The English test covers the areas of diction, style, form, and organization.

The mathematics section covers the first three years of high school mathematics. Stress is laid on the ability to reason.

The social studies test and the natural science test emphasize the reading and interpreting of selected passages in the specific field.

Students and colleges receive five scores: one in each of the subject-areas, and a composite score.

For information and registration, students should contact their high school counselor. Additional information may be obtained by writing the American College Testing Program, Box 168, Iowa City, Iowa 52240.

This test is used by several colleges in the West and South; most colleges that require this test will accept the CEEB results.

B. The National Merit Scholarship Test

The National Merit Scholarship Corporation annually conducts the country's largest talent search. This nonprofit organization was established in 1955 thanks to grants from the Ford Foundation and the Carnegie Corporation.

Formerly a separate examination, the National Merit Scholarship Qualifying Test (NMSQT) is now the same as the Preliminary Scholastic Aptitude Test, given in October of each year to high school juniors. The students who receive the highest grades (usually in the 99th percentile) are called semifinalists and are asked to take the Scholastic Aptitude Test of the College Board in their senior year. Winners are selected on the basis of their scores on the SAT as well as an evaluation of their high school record.

Most students who take this test do not consider themselves candidates for scholarships, but are interested in learning about their relative strengths and weaknesses as revealed by the test.

C. Many other tests exist, but they have all but disappeared from the examination scene. Tests such as the American Council on Education Psychological Examination, the Ohio State Psycho-

logical Test, and the General Education Development Test resemble the tests described above. A student who prepares for the SAT or the ACT will be ready for any of these tests if he is asked to take them.

THE "COLLEGE BOARDS"

The College Entrance Examination Board, which prepares the Scholastic Aptitude Test and the various Achievement Tests, is of the opinion that very little can be done to prepare *in the weeks immediately preceding* the taking of the SAT. The College Board discourages students from spending excessive time or money on crash programs to help them prepare for the Scholastic Aptitude Test. Although the Board has slightly modified its stand in the past several years, it still maintains that such programs will do little to improve the student's score on the test. The College Board also points out that time spent on assignments will contribute just as much, if not more, to a high score on the test. The College Board also points out that time spent in this manner is a far better preparation for college than intensive cram courses which have little applicability outside their narrow purpose.

Concerning specific preparation for the tests, the College Board recommends only that the student obtain and thoroughly study the College Board Student Bulletin. This booklet contains directions on how to take the test as well as several pages of sample questions similar to those already given in the *Quick Reference Handbook of Basic Knowledge*. (See page 824 for the address of where to obtain the *Student Bulletin*.)

The idea that "you can't prepare for the College Boards" has been propounded so emphatically by the Board and by teachers and other school personnel who have repeated the statement that many students have gone into the examination without any preparation at all. It has been the experience of many high school teachers, guidance counselors, and college advisors that this statement has often proved deceptive and has actually been harmful to serious students. The disappointingly low marks that frequently resulted became a permanent part of the student's record; occasionally they resulted in a negative decision by the admissions committee of the college of the student's choice.

Intelligent preparation for the "Boards" cannot begin too early in the high school career. A wise student will concentrate on his studies from the time he enters high school. He will read widely. He will explore the world of literature beyond the limits of his work in the English classroom. He will work to develop habits of application which will result in marks that show his real level of ability.

Early in his junior year, the high school student should take the Preliminary Scholastic Aptitude Test. When he gets the results of this test (usually in December), he can evaluate his marks in comparison with his grades in school. The following table may serve as a guide in evaluating performance:

Mark in English or Mathematics	Mark on PSAT Report should be
75%	45–50
80%	50–55
85%	55–60
90%	60–65
95%	65–75

The student who gets a mark that compares favorably with his school grades (as indicated in the table) may feel satisfied with his score; the student who fails to get the indicated mark is definitely in need of help and should begin an intensive program in preparation for the SAT examinations he will take in December or January of his senior year. Preparation should include the following:

1. Obtain a copy of the College Entrance Examination Board's booklet, *The College Board Student Bulletin.* This booklet is distributed, without cost, by school guidance officers to whom you should apply. If you cannot obtain copies in your school, write to the College Entrance Examination Board, Box 592, Princeton, New Jersey, 08540 or to Box 1025, Berkeley, California, 94701.

Read the booklet carefully. Do the illustrative exercises and take the tests in verbal and mathematical ability. Be sure you understand the reasons for the correct answers given in the booklet. This will help you to uncover the areas of mathematics in which you will need to concentrate.

2. Get additional material for study and analysis. Many reference books and study outlines are available, most of them in paperback editions. A good book on building vocabulary skills should prove to be invaluable.

3. Take the College Board Scholastic Aptitude Test in March or May of your junior year, for guidance and practice. A student may reasonably expect an improvement of 40 points over the results

on the PSAT. Failure to achieve this improvement indicates the need for additional intensive study before taking the final College Board examinations in December or January of your senior year.

Despite the advice of the College Board indicated above, proper guidance and tutoring have been known to result in impressive improvement in College Board scores. Experience has shown that the best preparation lies in getting an understanding of the nature of the questions asked, and in developing the technique of answering these questions intelligently and quickly. Students who have gotten marks on the College Board examinations that were not commensurate with their scholastic ability, as shown by their school marks, are definitely advised to seek such help. To find a reliable tutoring service, your guidance counselor may be of help. Or you might turn to friends who have had successful experience along these lines.

TAKING THE "BOARDS"

Anyone who has taken the PSAT or who has looked carefully at the questions in the booklets, *A Description of the Scholastic Aptitude Test,* or *How to Prepare for College Entrance Examinations,* will realize that the SAT measures a student's ability to think and to reason. The amassing of factual information or subject matter is relatively unimportant. It is, therefore, advisable for the student to make every effort to be at the peak of mental alertness when he takes the examination. Last-minute "cramming" is valueless. The best way to reach the desired mental acuity is to taper off the studying shortly before the examination. Relaxation and rest will prove more valuable than frantic studying up to the very last moment. A good idea is to stop all studying for the examination at least two days before you take the test. A person who is well rested can analyze questions more quickly and can think more logically than can one who has worked to the point of exhaustion.

When you are taking the examination, it is well to bear in mind three factors: time, "guessing," and experimental questions.

The SAT is usually divided into five or six sections of thirty or forty-five minutes each. Students should not be unduly distressed if they find that they cannot finish the sections in the time allotted. The examination is so designed that even the best students barely have time to finish. In each section, a student can achieve a fair mark by answering correctly approximately fifty percent of the questions. The alert student will answer first those questions that are not too difficult, and then return to those that seem puzzling or confusing. It is a good idea not to spend too much time on any one question.

The College Entrance Board employs a formula to compensate for haphazard guessing, so that "wild guessing" will only result in a lower mark. However, don't be afraid to rely on intelligent analysis of questions that strike you as "tough." If you are able logically to eliminate one or more of the suggested choices, your chance of getting the right answer will be improved. So go ahead and answer such questions. Good students, although they may feel uncertain of their answers to many questions, may possess a fund of background information that will lead them to the correct answer more often than might be expected. Such students should learn to rely on their "hunches." If you feel

totally ignorant of the answer to a question, it is wisest to leave that question unanswered.

The knowledge that some questions on the SAT are experimental and do not count toward the mark the student will get, may disturb him. He begins to wonder just which part of the test is the experimental part. Actually, this phase of the examination may well serve as a source of reassurance to the student. Whenever he encounters a difficult section or an unfamiliar type of question that perplexes him, he can console himself with the thought that this may well be the "experimental" part, and that, accordingly, it will not affect his mark adversely. In general, however, students should try to answer all questions to the best of their ability.

The Achievement Tests are tests of mastery of subject matter. Before taking them, the student should review the work of the course as he would in preparing for a final examination in the subject. Most colleges asking for these tests make use of the results for guidance and placement.

U.S. Naval Academy—Michelson Hall, the new science building

Admissions Questionnaires

Each year, many thousands of applications for admission to college are filed by anxious high school juniors and seniors. The questions most frequently asked by students and suggested answers are given below.

Which colleges shall I apply to? The best advice and counsel can be obtained from the high school officials. Late in the junior year or early in the senior year, the student and his parents should confer with the school's college guidance officer or the school's principal. After a careful appraisal of the student's record, his College Board scores, his financial status, and other pertinent data, the school official shoutd be able to offer several colleges for consideration and help the student make a selection.

Having decided on the colleges to apply to, the student should write a brief note to the Director of Admissions of each school asking for a bulletin of information and an application form.

While college application forms vary in the questions asked, they fall into a general pattern. Factual questions can be answered readily. Other questions, however, calling for detailed answers of paragraph or essay length, often give high school students difficulty and cause for worry. In the remainder of this section, we shall analyze and comment on the information requested and the questions you are required to answer.

Name other colleges to which you have applied or intend to apply.

College authorities are realistic. In this day of swollen college enrollments, students are expected to apply to several colleges in order to be certain of acceptance by at least one school. In general, it is wise to apply to different kinds of schools. Thus, your answer should indicate what type of school you are considering, whether it is a large university, a small college, a noncoeducational school, a coeducational institution, or a state-supported school. Not to specify a type will make it difficult to write a convincing answer to questions below.

Who or what has influenced you to consider the college of your choice?

Don't contrive an answer; tell the truth. College advisors, alumni, friends attending the college, representatives of the college who spoke at College Night meetings at your high school may have influenced you in your choice. Mention one or more of these. You may have been influenced by the school's reputation, members of its faculty, its bulletin, the courses offered by the school in the field of your interest, its location (distance from home, etc.), its campus, its facilities (library, laboratories, dormitories), its program of accelerated studies in the field of your interest, etc.

Why do you desire a college education?

This is a more complex question. Do not limit yourself to the vocational or professional preparation aspect. While college is a prerequisite for advanced study, this should not be the sole factor that you discuss. Mention the lasting cultural values that you believe a college education can offer. If you are still undecided about your plans for the future, college may help you to find the field of interest for your life's work.

What challenges do you expect the college to offer you?

Students answering this question have mentioned the confrontation of new ideas, working with gifted teachers and classmates, making of rich and enduring friendships, and the discovery of oneself as an individual and as a member of the community.

What contribution to the life of the college do you hope to make?

The activities you have engaged in while in high school should be continued in college. It is safe to assume that, if you have been active in high school, in publications, dramatics, debating, musical activities, and athletics, you will continue in these activities while in college.

What hobbies or fields of interest do you have?

In discussing your hobby, try to show its educational value to you or to others. What did your hobby give you in addition to pleasure?

What kind of outside reading do you do?

This question appears in many forms:

Name six books you have read during the last two years and tell how the reading of one of them was of value to you.

Write a list of books, not specific course requirements, which you have read in the past year.

Reading is, obviously, an activity that is essential for college work. Your list of books should reveal your interests in many fields. You will, of course, list works of fiction. Try to include works in the fields of biography, your hobby, science, and philosophy as well. This means that during the last year or two of high school you should make ample use of your school and public library.

References

You may be asked to supply the names and addresses of two or more teachers or persons other than teachers to whom the college may refer. Before submitting any name to the college, be sure to ask the individual's permission. It is wise to select a person who can say something specific about your activity. The college knows that all of these letters of reference will be in superlatives; it is wise to have someone write in your behalf who can back up his statement about your character and personality with concrete illustrations.

The autobiographical letter

The instructions for this question range from the very simple "Write an autobiographical sketch of yourself" to the very detailed "Enclose a letter indicating so far as you can (a) your purpose in going to college, (b) the reasons for your interest in the college, (c) how you have spent the past two summers and of what value they have been to you, (d) the nature of any remunerative employment you have had, (3) any experiences—travel, employment, friendship, military service, etc.— which have had an important influence on your development and plans for the future, (f) which of the books you have read during the past two years have been most profitable and enjoyable and why, (g) which of all the things you have accomplished, either in or out of school, has given you the greatest personal satisfaction, (h) any positive or negative factors in your secondary school training which will affect your education at the college."

In writing this statement about yourself and your interests, be frank. College committees can spot the "phony" letter without much trouble. Do not try to impress the readers with long lists of books and activities which your high school record does not substantiate.

Do not begin with data about your early childhood unless the events discussed have had a definite bearing on the kind of person you are. The names and locations of elementary schools are of little importance in determining the kind of person you really are.

Concentrate on your junior and senior high school years. Begin by discussing that which is, in your opinion, the most important influence in making you the kind of person you are today. It may be a subject area which caught your interest, a person who guided your thinking along educational lines, a field of vocational endeavor which gave you an insight into your potential as a student and worker, a hobby which you have decided to follow through your life, or any experience which has colored your thinking about the future.

Describe the kind of work you have been doing in and out of school and discuss your reaction to this work. Mention honors won and positions of responsibility to which you have been appointed or elected.

If illness, or change of school, or any other factor affected your school grades adversely, this letter gives you an opportunity to explain these grades. However, it is advisable to refer to this only if the factor which caused the low marks has been removed or adjusted to.

In general, let the college know why you think you will be a credit to the school you are applying to for admission. You should try to show that you are sufficiently motivated to be eager to carry out college assignments and independent study, that you are resourceful and responsible, and that you are a person of industrious habits. A final word of caution:

Your application for admission to college represents you. Be neat, precise, and accurate. It is advisable to write all answers on another sheet of paper before making any entries on the application blank.

APPENDIX

MUSIC TERMS
SPACE TERMS*
MATHEMATICAL FORMULAS
SQUARES, SQUARE ROOTS,
CUBES, CUBE ROOTS
CHEMICAL ELEMENTS
LOGARITHMS
INDEX

*The material on space exploration was selected from **Space . . . The New Frontier** and **The Challenge of Space Exploration,** prepared by The National Aeronautics and Space Administration, Washington, D.C.

MUSIC TERMS

absolute music—"abstract" or "pure" music; instrumental music requiring for its appreciation neither words nor story nor any association beyond its basic statement.

absolute pitch—the capacity of identifying or singing any tone at proper pitch without the aid of an instrument.

a cappella—choral music sung without accompaniment.

accent—stress or pulse which emphasizes one note over others in a measure.

accidental—a natural, sharp, or flat not indicated by key-signature.

accompaniment—instrumental or choral support for soloists.

adagio—slow tempo; the name often given to a particular section of a musical work so characterized.

allegro—fast tempo; the name often given to a particular section of a musical work so characterized.

alto—a vocal range for a female voice which lies between soprano and contralto; sometimes mistakenly used for contralto; used to describe certain instruments like the viola.

andante—moderately slow tempo; the name often given to a particular section of a musical work so characterized.

antiphonal—the answering or alternation of two groups, choral or instrumental.

aria—a solo song or air in opera, oratorio, or cantata which often lends itself to a display of skill.

arpeggio—a chord, the notes of which are played successively in ascending or descending order.

art song—short song of high dramatic and formal value.

atonality—designating music in which there is no key center; a twentieth-century compositional style sometimes employing a twelve-tone scale.

augmentation—the repetition of a melody with changes provided by the use of proportionately longer notes.

ballet—an elaborate dance usually telling a story, with instrumental or full orchestral accompaniment for theatrical performance.

bar—a measure in musical notation.

baritone—male vocal register between tenor and bass.

baroque—musical style characteristic of composers from 1600 to 1750; includes works of Bach.

bass—deepest male voice.

beat—the rhythmic pulse of music marking time into relatively equal divisions in the measure.

bel canto—operatic singing technique used to produce a lyrical effect.

binary form—notable in music which uses two contrasting themes in a section.

bravura—great skill and expansiveness of style.

buffo—the character-comic in opera.

cadence—chords at the end of a tune, phrase, section, or movement, which have the effect of bringing the statement to a rest.

cadenza—an elaboration of the cadence, displaying the skill of a soloist.

canon—music, such as a round, in which two or more sections repeat the same melody, starting at different times but overlapping.

cantabile—emphasis upon a "singing" quality in the music.

cantata—an elaborate vocal and instrumental form with arias, recitatives, duets, and chorus, but not requiring dramatic or scenic implementation.

castrato—a eunuch with an adult male voice in the female range.

chamber music—music specifically intended for performance in a small hall, each part usually being taken by one instrument as contrasted with groups or sections of instruments in large orchestras.

chord—three or more tones sounded together.

chromatic—music with many half step intervals not in the diatonic scale.

classical music—the musical style of composers between 1750 and 1825, including the works of Mozart and Beethoven.

clef—sign on the left of each staff indicating sound or exact pitch.

coda—passage which rounds out a section or end of a composition.

coloratura—elaborate vocal passage demonstrating skill of both composer and soloist.

concert master—first violinist in orchestra, frequently also an assistant conductor.

concerto—composition for one or more instruments with orchestral accompaniment.

conductor—orchestra leader, chiefly responsible for musical interpretation.

contralto—lowest pitched female voice.

counterpoint—simultaneous use of two or more melodies.

crescendo—becoming gradually louder.

development—compositional exploration and restatement of thematic idea.

diatonic—opposite of chromatic; music confined to the use of notes in a given major or minor key.

discord—See dissonance.

dissonance—a combination of clashing tones requiring the addition of other tones for resolution.

divertimento—a light instrumental composition in several short movements.

dominant—fifth tone in the minor or major scale.

downbeat—first strong accent in each measure.

encore—repetition of a piece or performance of an additional one in response to applause.

enharmonic—a tone having several different forms of notation.

ensemble—combination of performers; also, overall quality of musical expression.

equal temperament—division of octave into twelve equal halftones; also characteristic method of tuning instruments.

étude—"study music" composed for practice purposes but often included in concert repertoires.

exposition—in sonata form, among others, a first section containing statement of themes to be developed.

expression—immediate personal and emotional interpretation of music by a performer.

falsetto—adult male voice used in an unnaturally high pitch.

fermata—a long pause.

finale—last section of a composition.

flat—notation indicating the lowering of a tone by a half step.

forte—loud.

fugue—a musical form similar to the canon but one in which various imitations of the melody occur in shorter phrases.

fundamental—primary note of a chord or harmonic series.

glissando—tonal effect produced by sliding finger over the strings or keys of an instrument.

grace note—an embellishing note, printed in smaller type.

Gregorian chant—early church music named for Pope Gregory I; used in Roman Catholic church services.

harmony—the simultaneous combination of tones into chords; also the study of chord functions and structure.

homophony—music composed of a melody supported by harmonic chordal accompaniment.

hymn—originally a religious song in praise of God; also used of songs with a patriotic theme.

imitation—technique of composition

which repeats theme or melody, making use of several instruments or voices as in canon, fugue, or round.

impressionism—the musical style of late nineteenth- and early twentieth-century composers, including Debussy and Ravel.

interval—the difference in pitch between two notes.

intonation—fidelity of pitch.

inversion—reversing or inverting the position of notes in chords or intervals.

-issimo—suffix meaning "very," added to many musical terms.

jazz—music of black American origin, initially called "ragtime," and characterized by syncopated rhythm.

key—scale; relating to a system of tonal relationships developed from a tonic keynote.

keynote—base or principal note from which a scale is derived.

largo—a very slow and deliberate tempo; the name often given to a particular section of a musical work so characterized.

legato—smooth transitions from note to note without breaks.

leitmotiv—thematic melody used recurrently to identify specific characters, events, places, ideas, or emotions; characteristically used by Wagner.

lento—slow tempo between andante and largo.

libretto—the entire literary text of a musical work utilizing singing and speaking.

lyrics—words set to music.

measure—a horizontally lined space between two vertical bar lines which mark off a section of a staff.

medieval music—styles of music developed during the thousand-year period beginning A.D. 500, primarily vocal; greatly influenced by church liturgy, by court and peasant life.

melodrama—scene or play in which a musical background accompanies action and dialogue.

melody—a succession of notes of varying pitch and duration having a distinct pattern.

meter—strong and weak accents in rhythmical pattern.

metronome—a clockwork pendulum invented to insure standard tempi.

mezzo—prefix meaning "half."

mezzo-soprano—female voice between soprano and alto ranges.

M.M.—letters indicating metronomic setting.

mode—general term for system(s) of arranging intervals of a scale.

moderato—moderate tempo.

modern music—styles of music de-veloped from the beginning of the twentieth century, as distinguished from earlier styles still flourishing; among the former, works of Schoenberg and Bartok.

modulation—change of key or tonality through a succession of chords.

molto—very or much more, as in molto adagio (very slowly).

monophony—unaccompanied music composed only of a melodic line.

mordent—a grace note.

motive—a musical phrase which reappears irregularly.

movement—major division of a musical composition.

natural—symbol indicating the return of a tone to its natural pitch from a previous sharping or flatting.

notation—entire system employed for writing Western music.

obbligato—an accompaniment which is an indispensable and intrinsic part of the musical statement; by misuse, in some nineteenth-century music used in the opposite sense to refer to a part which is optional.

octave—the interval covering eight successive notes in the diatonic scale, e.g., middle C to the C above it.

opera—a form of drama set to orchestral music in which most of the dialogue is sung; generally presented in an elaborate production.

opus—a composition or set of compositions; customarily accompanied by a number to indicate its place in the chronological order of a composer's work.

oratorio—a form of drama set to orchestral music and voice; differing from opera in the absence of staging, costumes, and scenery; usually on a religious subject.

overture—introductory instrumental music to an opera or play; also now an independent form.

partita—originally, variations or a set of dances; by extension, used to mean "suite."

phrase—a short distinguishable part of a melody.

piano—softly.

pitch—degree of highness or lowness of a sound.

più—more; as in più lento (more slowly).

poco—a little.

polyphony—music composed of at least two melodies played simultaneously.

polytonality—simultaneous use of two different keys.

prelude—a short composition which can be a piece of a single movement, the beginning of a longer work, or an overture.

presto—very fast tempo; the name often given to a particular section of a musicat work so characterized.

program music—descriptive music which tells a story or describes a place; frequently employs explanatory or supportive program literature; the opposite of "absolute music."

progression—advance from one tone to another or from one chord to another.

quartet—an intimate musical form for four instruments or voices.

quintet—similar to quartet but refers to five instruments or voices.

recapitulation—repetition of a thematic statement after an intervening development and contrast.

reprise—repeat of a segment of music.

rest—musical notation indicating silence.

rhapsody—a very free musical form developed during the nineteenth century.

rhythm—recurrent pattern created by the accent and duration of notes.

rondo—a musical form in which the main theme is consistently repeated throughout.

scale—a series of consecutive tones forming an octave.

scherzo—usually the third movement of a larger composition; humorous and lively.

score—written or printed piece of music in which the different instruments or voices are entered on a separate staff, one above the other.

sharp—notation raising a tone by a half step.

signature—symbol placed at the beginning of a composition specifying key and tempo.

sonata—a composition for one or more instruments.

soprano—the highest female singing voice.

staff—the five horizontal lines and intervening spaces upon which musical notation is made.

symphonic poem—a tone poem; a form of program music.

symphony—major form of orchestral work, divided into movements.

syncopation—kind of rhythm created by altering the natural accent into a weak beat.

tempo (pl: tempi)—the rate of speed at which a piece or passage of music moves.

tenor—highest normal adult male voice; also the range of some instruments.

theme—melody used as the main musical line for development and variation.

tonality—the adherence to the keynote (tonic) as the referent of all chords and harmonies used in a composition or part of a composition.

tone—a note; sound with a fixed pitch.

tone poem—*See* symphonic poem.

transpose—changing key or pitch, leaving all other musical relationships intact.

treble—the highest register of musical sound.

upbeat—weak beat preceding a heavy accent.

variation—alteration of a melody that still retains its essential qualities.

SPACE TERMS

ablation—the removal of surface material from a body by vaporization, melting, or other process; specifically the intentional removal of material from a nose cone or spacecraft during high-speed movement through a planetary atmosphere to provide thermal protection to the underlying structure.

absolute zero—the theoretical temperature at which all molecular motion ceases.

acceleration—the rate of change of velocity.

acquisition and tracking radar—a radar set that locks onto a strong signal and tracks the object reflecting the signal.

aerodynamics—the science of the motion of air and other gaseous fluids, and of the forces acting on bodies when the bodies move through such fluids, or of the movement of such fluids against or around the bodies, as "his research in aerodynamics."

aerolite—a meteorite composed principally of stony material.

aerospace—(from aeronautics and space) of or pertaining to both the earth's atmosphere and space, as in "aerospace industries."

aerothermodynamic border—an altitude at about 100 miles, above which the atmosphere is so rarefied that the motion of an object through it at high speeds generates no significant surface heat.

aerothermodynamics—the study of the aerodynamic and thermodynamic problems connected with aerodynamic heating.

airglow—a relatively steady visible emission from the upper atmosphere, as distinguished from the sporadic emission of aurorae.

albedo—the ratio of the amount of electromagnetic radiation reflected by a body to the amount falling upon it, commonly expressed as a percentage.

angel—a radar echo caused by a physical phenomenon not discernible to the eye.

annular eclipse—an eclipse in which a thin ring of the source of light appears around the obscuring body.

aphelion—the point at which a planet or other celestial object in orbit about the sun is farthest from the sun.

apogee—in an orbit about the earth, the point at which the satellite is farthest from the earth; the highest altitude reached by a sounding rocket.

areo—combining form of Ares (Mars) as in "areography."

asteroid—one of the many small celestial bodies revolving around the sun, most of the orbits being between those of Mars and Jupiter. Also called "planetoid," "minor planet."

astroballistics—the study of the phenomena arising out of the motion of a solid through a gas at speeds high enough to cause ablation; for example, the interaction of a meteoroid with the atmosphere.

attitude—the position or orientation of an aircraft, spacecraft, etc., either in motion or at rest, as determined by the relationship between its axes and some reference line or plane such as the horizon.

aurora—the sporadic visible emission from the upper atmosphere over middle and high latitudes. Also called "northern lights."

azimuth—horizontal direction or bearing.

Baker-Nunn camera—a large camera used in tracking satellites.

ballistics—the science that deals with the motion, behavior, and effects of projectiles, especially bullets, aerial bombs, rockets, or the like; the science or art of designing and hurling projectiles so as to achieve a desired performance.

balloon-type rocket—a rocket, such as Atlas, that requires the pressure of its propellants (or other gases) within it to give it structural integrity.

beam-rider—a craft following a beam, particularly one which does so automatically, the beam providing the guidance.

bipropellant—a rocket propellant consisting of two unmixed or uncombined chemicals (fuel and oxidizer) fed to the combustion chamber separately.

blip—*See* pip.

boilerplate—as in "boilerplate capsule," a metal copy of the flight model, the structure or components of which are heavier than the flight model.

boiloff—the vaporization of a cold propellant, such as liquid oxygen or liquid hydrogen, as the temperature of the propellant mass rises, as in the tank of a rocket being readied for launch.

booster engine—an engine, especially a booster rocket, that adds its thrust to the thrust of the sustainer engine.

booster rocket—1. a rocket engine, either solid or liquid fuel, that assists the normal propulsive system, or sustainer engine, of a rocket or aeronautical vehicle in some phase of its flight. 2. a rocket used to set a missile vehicle in motion before another engine takes over.

boostglide vehicle—a vehicle (half aircraft, half spacecraft) designed to fly to the limits of the sensible atmosphere, then be boosted by rockets into the space above, returning to earth by gliding under aerodynamic control.

braking ellipses—a series of ellipses, decreasing in size due to aerodynamic drag, followed by a spacecraft in entering a planetary atmosphere.

breakoff phenomenon—the feeling which sometimes occurs during high altitude flight of being totally separated and detached from the earth and human society. Also called the "breakaway phenomenon."

centrifuge—specifically, a large motor-driven apparatus with a long arm at the end of which human and animal subjects or equipment can be revolved and rotated at various speeds to simulate very closely the prolonged accelerations encountered in highperformance aircraft, rockets, and spacecraft.

checkout—a sequence of actions taken to test or examine a launch vehicle or spacecraft as to its readiness to perform its intended function.

chemosphere—the vaguely defined region of the upper atmosphere in which photochemical reactions take place.

cislunar—(Latin *cis*, "on this side") of or

pertaining to phenomena, projects, or activity in the space between the earth and moon, or between the earth and the moon's orbit.

closed ecological system—a system that provides for the maintenance of life in an isolated living chamber such as a spacecraft cabin by means of a cycle wherein exhaled carbon dioxide, urine, and other waste matter are converted chemically or by photosynthesis into oxygen, water, and food.

cold-flow test—a test of a liquid rocket without firing it to check or verify the efficiency of a propulsion subsystem, providing for the conditioning and flow of propellants (including tank pressurization, propellant loading, and propellant feeding).

companion body—a nose cone, last-stage rocket, or other body that orbits along with an earth satellite.

complex—entire area of launch site facilities. This includes blockhouse, launch pad, gantry, etc. Also referred to as a "launch complex."

composite propellant—a solid rocket propellant consisting of a fuel and an oxidizer.

conic section—a curve formed by the intersection of a plane and a right circular cone. Usually called "conic."

console—an array of controls and indicators for the monitoring and control of a particular sequence of actions, as in the checkout of a rocket, a countdown action, or a launch procedure.

control rocket—a vernier engine, retro-rocket, or other such rocket, used to guide or make small changes in the velocity of a rocket, spacecraft, or the like.

corona—the faintly luminous outer envelope of the sun. Also called "solar corona."

cosmic rays—the extremely high energy subatomic particles which bombard the atmosphere from outer space. Cosmic-ray primaries seem to be mostly protons, hydrogen nuclei, but also comprise heavier nuclei. On colliding with atmospheric particles they produce many different kinds of lower-energy secondary cosmic radiation.

cryogenic temperature—in general, a temperature range below about–50°C.; more particularly, temperatures within a few degrees of absolute zero.

deep space probes—spacecraft designed for exploring space to the vicinity of the moon and beyond. Deep space probes with specific missions may be referred to as "lunar probe," "Mars probe," "solar probe," etc.

diplexer—a device permitting an antenna system to be used simultaneously or separately by two transmitters. *Compare with* **duplexer.**

dish—a parabolic type of radio or radar antenna, roughly the shape of a soup bowl.

Doppler shift—the change in frequency with which energy reaches a receiver when the source of radiation or a reflector of the radiation and the receiver are in motion relative to each other. The Doppler shift is used in many tracking and navigation systems.

dosimeter—a device, worn by persons working around radioactive material, which indicates the amount (dose) of radiation to which they have been exposed.

Dovap—from Doppler, velocity and position, a tracking system which uses the Doppler shift caused by a target moving relative to a ground transmitter to obtain velocity and position information.

drogue parachute—a type of parachute attached to a body, used to slow it down; also called "deceleration parachute," or "drag parachute."

duplexer—a device which permits a single antenna system to be used for both transmitting and receiving.

eccentric—not having the same center; varying from a circle, as in "eccentric orbit."

ecological system—a habitable environment, either created artifically, such as in a manned space vehicle, or occurring naturally, such as the environment on the surface of the earth, in which man, animals, or other organisms can live in mutual relationship with each other.

escape velocity—the radial speed which a particle or larger body must attain in order to escape from the gravitational field of a planet or star.

extraterrestrial—from outside the earth.

film cooling—the cooling of a body or surface, such as the inner surface of a rocket combustion chamber, by maintaining a thin fluid layer over the affected area.

flashback—a reversal of flame propagation in a system, counter to the usual flow of the combustible mixture.

flux—the rate of flow of some quantity, often used in reference to the flow of some form of energy.

flying test bed—an aircraft, rocket, or other flying vehicle used to carry objects or devices being flight tested.

g or G—an acceleration equal to the acceleration of gravity, 32.2 feet per second per second at sea level; used as a unit of stress measurement for bodies undergoing acceleration.

gantry—a frame structure that spans over something, as an elevated platform that runs astride a work area, supported by wheels on each side; specifically, short for "gantry crane" or "gantry scaffold."

gas cap—the gas immediately in front of a meteoroid or reentry body as it travels through the atmosphere; the leading portion of a meteor. This gas is compressed and adiabatically heated to incandescence.

geo—a prefix meaning "earth," as in "geology," "geophysics."

geoprobe—a rocket vehicle designed to explore space near the earth at a distance of more than 4,000 miles from the earth's surface. Rocket vehicles operating lower than 4,000 miles are termed "sounding rockets."

gimbal—1. a device with two mutually perpendicular and intersecting axes of rotation, thus giving free angular movement in two directions, on which an engine or other object may be mounted. 2. in a gyro, a support which provides the spin axis with a degree of freedom.

gnotobiotics—the study of germ-free animals.

gravity—the force imparted by the earth to a mass on, or close to the earth. Since the earth is rotating, the force observed as gravity is the resultant of the force of gravitation and the centrifugal force arising from this rotation.

g-suit or G-suit—a suit that exerts pressure on the abdomen and lower parts of the body to prevent or retard the collection of blood below the chest under positive acceleration.

g-tolerance—a tolerance in a person or other animal, or in a piece of equipment, to an acceleration of a particular value.

gyro—a device which utilizes the angular momentum of a spinning rotor to sense angular motion of its base about one or two axes at right angles to the spin axis. Also called "gyroscope."

hardness—of X rays and other radiation of high energy, a measure of penetrating power. Radiation which will penetrate a 10-centimeter thickness of lead is considered "hard radiation."

hot test—a propulsion system test conducted by actually firing the propellants.

hypersonic—1. pertaining to hypersonic flow. 2. pertaining to speeds of Mach 5 or greater.

inertial guidance—guidance by means of acceleration measured and integrated within the craft.

infrared—infrared radiation; electromagnetic radiation in the wavelength interval from the red end of the visible spectrum on the lower limit to microwaves used in radar on the upper limit.

insertion—the process of putting an artificial satellite into orbit. Also the time of such action.

ionosphere—the part of the earth's outer atmosphere where ions and electrons are present in quantities sufficient to affect the propagation of radio waves.

Kepler's laws—the three empirical laws describing the motions of planets in their orbits, discovered by Johannes Kepler (1571–1630). These are: (1) The orbits of the planets are ellipses, with the sun at a common focus. (2) As a planet moves in its orbit, the line joining the planet and sun sweeps over equal areas in equal intervals of time. Also called "law of equal areas." (3) The squares of the periods of revolution of any two planets are proportional to the cubes of their mean distances from the sun.

launch ring—the metal ring on the launch pad on which a missile stands before launch.

launch vehicle—any device which propels and guides a spacecraft into orbit about the earth or into a trajectory to another celestial body. Often called "booster."

launch window—an interval of time during which a rocket can be launched to accomplish a particular purpose, as "liftoff occurred 5 minutes after the beginning of the 82-minute launch window".

lib ration—a real or apparent oscillatory motion, particularly the apparent oscillation of the moon.

Mach number—(after Ernst Mach [1838–1916], Austrian scientist) a number expressing the ratio of the speed of a body or of a point on a body with respect to the surrounding air or other fluid, or the speed of a flow, to the speed of sound in the medium; the speed represented by this number.

manometer—an instrument for measuring pressure of gases and vapors both above and below atmospheric pressure.

mass—the measure of the amount of matter in a body, thus its inertia.

mass-energy equivalence—the equivalence of a quantity of mass m and a quantity of energy E, the two quantities being related by the mass-energy relation $E = mc^2$, where c = the speed of light.

meteor—in particular, the light phenomenon which results from the entry into the earth's atmosphere of a solid particle from space; more generally, any physical object or phenomenon associated with such an event.

microwave region—commonly that region of the radio spectrum between approximately one thousand megacycles and three hundred thousand megacycles.

missile—any object thrown, dropped, fired, launched, or otherwise projected with the purpose of striking a target. Short for "ballistic missile," "guided missile."

mockup—a full-sized replica or dummy of something, such as a spacecraft, often made of some substitute material, such as wood, and sometimes incorporating functioning pieces of equipment, such as engines.

module—1. a self-contained unit of a launch vehicle or spacecraft which serves as a building block for the overall structure. The module is usually designated by its primary function as "command module," "lunar landing module," etc. 2. a one-package assembly of functionally associated electronic parts; usually a plug-in unit.

Newton's laws of motion—a set of three fundamental postulates forming the basis of the mechanics of rigid bodies, formulated by Newton in 1687.

The first law is concerned with the principle of inertia and states that if a body in motion is not acted upon by an external force, its momentum remains constant (law of conservation of momentum). The second law asserts that the rate of change of momentum of a body is proportional to the force acting upon the body and is in the direction of the applied force. A familiar statement of this is the equation

$$F = ma,$$

where F is vector sum of the applied forces, m the mass, and a the vector acceleration of the body. The third law is the principle of action and reaction, stating that for every force acting upon a body there exists a corresponding force of the same magnitude exerted by the body in the opposite direction.

normal shock wave—a shock wave perpendicular, or substantially so, to the direction of flow in a supersonic flow field. Sometimes shortened to "normal shock."

nozzle—specifically, the part of a rocket thrust chamber assembly in which the gases produced in the chamber are accelerated to high velocities.

orbital elements—a set of seven parameters defining the orbit of a satellite.

order of magnitude—a factor of 10.

paraglider—a flexible-winged, kite-like vehicle designed for use in a recovery system for launch vehicles or as a reentry vehicle.

passive—reflecting a signal without transmission, as "Echo is a passive satellite." Contrasted with "active."

perigee—that orbital point nearest the earth when the earth is the center of attraction.

photosphere—the intensely bright portion of the sun visible to the unaided eye.

pickoff—a sensing device, used in combination with a gyroscope in an automatic pilot or other automatic or robot apparatus, that responds to angular movement to create a signal or to effect some type of control.

pickup—a device that converts a sound, view, or other form of intelligence into corresponding electric signals (e.g., a microphone, a television camera, or a phonograph pickup).

pip—signal indication on the scope of an electronic instrument, produced by a short, sharply peaked pulse of voltage. Also called "blip."

pitchover—the programmed turn from the vertical that a rocket under power takes as it describes an arc and points in a direction other than vertical.

posigrade rocket—an auxiliary rocket which fires in the direction in which the vehicle is pointed, used for example in separating two stages of a vehicle.

precession—the change in the direction of the axis of rotation of a spinning body or of the plane of the orbit of an orbiting body when acted upon by an outside force.

prestage—a step in the action of igniting a large liquid rocket taken prior to the ignition of the full flow, and consisting of igniting a partial flow of propellants into the thrust chamber.

primary—1. short for "primary body." 2. short for "primary cosmic ray."

primary cosmic rays—high-energy particles originating outside the earth's atmosphere.

probe—any device inserted in an environment for the purpose of obtaining information about the environment, specifically, an instrumented vehicle moving through the upper atmosphere or space, or landing upon another celestial body in order to obtain information about the specific environment.

prominence—a filament-like protuberance from the visible portion of the sun.

proton—a positively charged subatomic particle of a positive charge equal to the negative charge of the electron but of 1,837 times the mass; a constituent of all atomic nuclei.

proving stand—a test stand for reaction engines, especially rocket engines.

purge—to rid a line or tank of residual fluid, especially of fuel or oxygen in the tanks or lines of a rocket after a test firing or simulated test firing.

radar astronomy—the study of celestial bodies within the solar system by means of radiation originating on earth but reflected from the body under observation.

radiosonde—a balloon-borne instrument for the simultaneous measurement and transmission of meteorological data.

reaction control system—a system of controlling the attitude of a craft when outside the atmosphere by using jets of gas in lieu of aerodynamic control surfaces.

readout—the action of a radio transmitter transmitting data either instantaneously with the acquisition of the data or by play of a magnetic tape upon which the data have been recorded.

real time—time in which reporting on events or recording of events is simultaneous with the events.

recombination—the process by which a positive and a negative ion join to form a neutral molecule or other neutral particle.

red shift—in astronomy, the displacement of observed spectral lines toward the longer wavelengths of the red end of the spectrum. *Compare* **space reddening.**

reentry—the event occurring when a spacecraft or other object comes back into the sensible atmosphere after being rocketed to altitudes above the sensible atmosphere; the action involved in this event.

regenerator—a device used in a thermo-dynamic process for capturing and returning to the process heat that would otherwise be lost.

relativity—a principle that postulates the equivalence of the description of the universe, in terms of physical laws, by various observers, or for various frames of reference.

rocket engine—a reaction engine that contains within itself, or carries along with itself, all the substances necessary for its operation or for the consumption or combustion of its fuel, not requiring intake of any outside substance and hence capable of operation in outer space. Also called "rocket motor."

rocketsonde—meteorological rocket.

rockoon—a high-altitude sounding system consisting of a small solid-propellant research rocket launched from a large plastic balloon.

roll—the rotational or oscillatory movement of an aircraft or similar body which takes place about a longitudinal axis through the body—called "roll" for any amount of such rotation.

rotation—turning of a body about an axis within the body, as the daily rotation of the earth.

rumble—a form of combustion instability, especially in a liquid-propellant rocket engine, characterized by a low-pitched, low-frequency rumbling noise; the noise made in this kind of combustion.

scrub—to cancel a scheduled rocket firing, either before or during countdown.

selenocentric—relating to the center of the moon; referring to the moon as a center.

selenographic—1. of or pertaining to the physical geography of the moon. 2. specifically, referring to positions on the moon measured in latitude from the moon's equator and in longitude from a reference meridian.

sensible atmosphere—that part of the atmosphere that offers resistance to a body passing through it.

sensor—the component of an instrument that converts an input signal into a quantity which is measured by another part of the instrument. Also called "sensing element."

service tower—*See* **gantry.**

shock tube—a relatively long tube or pipe in which very brief high-speed gas flows are produced by the sudden release of gas at very high pressure into a low-pressure portion of the tube; the high-speed flow moves into the region of low pressure behind a shock wave.

solar wind—a stream of protons constantly moving outward from the sun.

sounding—1. in geophysics, any penetration of the natural environment for scientific observation. 2. in meteorology, same as upper-air observation. However, a common connotation is that of a single complete radiosonde observation.

space—1. specifically, the part of the universe lying outside the limits of the earth's atmosphere. 2. more generally, the volume in which all spatial bodies, including the earth, move.

space reddening—the observed reddening, or absorption of shorter wavelengths, of the light from distant celestial bodies caused by scattering by small particles in interstellar space. *Compare* **red shift.**

specific impulse—a performance parameter of a rocket propellant, expressed in seconds, and equal to thrust (in pounds) divided by weight flow rate (in pounds per second). *See* **thrust.**

sunspot—a relatively dark area on the surface of the sun, consisting of a dark central umbra and a surrounding penumbra that is intermediate in brightness between the umbra and the surrounding photosphere.

sunspot cycle—a periodic variation in the number and area of sunspots with an average length of 11.1 years, but varying between about 7 and 17 years.

sustainer engine—an engine that maintains the velocity of a missile or rocket vehicle, once it has achieved its programmed velocity through use of a booster engine.

synchronous satellite—an equatorial west-to-east satellite orbiting the earth at an altitude of 22,300 statute miles, at which altitude it makes one revolution in 24 hours, synchronous with the earth's rotation.

synergic curve—a curve plotted for the ascent of a rocket, space-air vehicle, or space vehicle calculated to give the vehicle an optimum economy in fuel with an optimum velocity.

tektite—a small glassy body containing no crystals, probably of meteoritic origin, and bearing no antecedent relation to the geological formation in which it occurs.

telemetry—the science of measuring a quantity or quantities, transmitting the measured value to a distant station, and there interpreting, indicating, or recording the quantities measured.

thermodynamics—the study of the relationships between heat and other forms of energy.

thermonuclear—pertaining to a nuclear reaction that is triggered by particles of high thermal energy.

thrust—1. the pushing force developed by an aircraft engine or a rocket engine. 2. specifically, in rocketry, the product of propellant mass flow rate and exhaust velocity relative to the vehicle.

topside sounder—a satellite designed to measure ion concentration in the ionosphere from above the ionosphere.

transit—1. the passage of a celestial body across a celestial meridian; usually called "meridian transit." 2. the apparent passage of a celestial body across the face of another celestial body or across any point, area, or line.

translunar—of or pertaining to space outside the moon's orbit about the earth.

transponder—a combined receiver and transmitter whose function is to transmit signals automatically when triggered by an interrogating signal.

T-time—any specific time, minus or plus, as referenced to "zero," or "launch" time, during a countdown sequence that is intended to result in the firing of a rocket propulsion unit that launches a rocket vehicle or missile.

ullage—the amount that a container, such as a fuel tank, lacks of being full.

ultraviolet radiation—electromagnetic radiation shorter in wavelength than visible radiation but longer than X-rays; roughly, radiation in the wavelength interval between 10 and 4,000 angstroms.

umbilical cord—any of the servicing electrical or fluid lines between the ground or a tower and an upright rocket missile or vehicle before the launch. Often shortened to "umbilical."

Van Allen Belt, Van Allen Radiation Belt, Van Allen Radiation Region for James A. Van Allen, 1915-   ) —the zone of high-intensity radiation surrounding the earth beginning at altitudes of approximately 500 miles.

vernier engine—a rocket engine of small thrust used primarily to obtain a fine adjustment in the velocity and trajectory of a ballistic missile or space vehicle just after the thrust cutoff of the last propulsion engine, and used secondarily to add thrust to a booster or sustainer engine. Also called "vernier rocket."

weightlessness—1. a condition in which no acceleration, whether of gravity or other force, can be detected by an observer within the system in question. 2. a condition in which gravitational and other external forces acting on a body produce no stress, either internal or external, in the body.

yaw—1. the lateral rotational or oscillatory movement of an aircraft, rocket, or the like about a transverse axis. 2. the amount of this movement; i.e., the angle of yaw.

zero g—*See* **weightlessness**.

MATHEMATICAL FORMULAS

CIRCUMFERENCE

Circle .... $C = d\pi$, in which π is 3.1416 and d the diameter.

AREA

Circle .... $A = r^2\pi$, in which π is 3.1416 and r the radius.

Rectangle .... $A = ab$, in which a is the base and b the height.

Sphere .... $A = 4r^2\pi$, in which r is the radius.

Trapezoid .... $A = \dfrac{h\,(a+b)}{2}$, in which h is the height, a the longer parallel side, and b the shorter.

Triangle .... $A = \dfrac{ab}{2}$, in which a is the base and h the height.

VOLUME

Cone .... $V = \dfrac{r^2\pi h}{3}$, in which π is 3.1416, r the radius of the base, and h the height.

Cube .... $V = a^3$, in which a is one of the edges.

Cylinder .... $V = r^2\pi h$, in which π is 3.1614, r the radius of the base, and h the height.

Pyramid .... $V = \dfrac{Ah}{3}$, in which A is the area of the base and h the height.

Rectangular Prism .... $V = abc$, in which a is the length, b the width, and c the depth.

Sphere .... $V = \dfrac{4\pi r^3}{3}$, in which π is 3.1416 and r the radius.

FALLING BODIES

Speed per second acquired by falling body: $S = 32t$, in which t is the time in seconds.

Distance in feet traveled by falling body: $D = 16t$, in which t is the time in seconds.

SPEED OF SOUND

Speed of sound in feet per second through any given temperature of air: $S = \dfrac{1087\sqrt{273+t}}{16.52}$, in which t is the temperature in Centigrade.

ENERGY AND MATTER

Conversion of matter into energy (Einstein's theorem): $E = mc^2$, in which E is the energy in ergs, m the mass of the matter in grams, and c the speed of light in centimeters per second. ($c^2 = 9.10^{20}$).

FORMULAS USED IN SOLID GEOMETRY

LATERAL AREA

Cone of revolution .... $L = \pi r s$
Cylinder of revolution .... $L = 2\pi r h$
Frustum of cone of revolution .... $L = \frac{1}{2}s(c + c')$
Frustum of regular pyramid .... $L = \frac{1}{2}s(p + p')$
Prism .... $L = ep$
Regular pyramid .... $L = \frac{1}{2}sp$

TOTAL AREA

Cone of revolution .... $T = \pi r(r + s)$
Cylinder of revolution .... $T = 2\pi r(r + h)$
Sphere .... $S = 4\pi r^2$
Zone .... $S = 2\pi r h$

VOLUME

Circular cone .... $V = \frac{1}{3}\pi r^2 h$
Circular cylinder .... $V = Bh$
Cube .... $V = e^3$
Cylinder of revolution .... $V = \pi r^2 h$
Frustum of circular cone .... $V = \frac{1}{3}\pi h(r^2 + r'^2 + rr')$
Frustum of pyramid .... $V = \frac{1}{3}h(B + B' + \sqrt{BB'})$
Prism .... $V = Bh$
Prismatoid .... $V = \frac{1}{6}h(B_1 + B_2 + 4M)$
Pyramid .... $V = \frac{1}{3}Bh$
Rectangular solid .... $V = lwh$
Sphere .... $V = \frac{4}{3}\pi r^3$
Spherical sector .... $V = \frac{2}{3}rS$

PHYSICAL CONSTANTS

QUANTITY	SYMBOL	VALUE
Gravitational constant	G	$6.67 \times 10^{-11}\ n \cdot m^2/kg^2$
Acceleration of gravity at earth's surface	g	$9.81\ m/sec^2 = 32.2 ft/sec^2$
Atmospheric pressure at sea level	(none)	$14.7\ lb/in^2 = 1.01 \times 10^5\ n/m^2$
Absolute zero	$O^\circ K$	$-273^\circ C$
Boltzmann's constant	k	$1.38 \times 10^{-23}\ j/^\circ K$
Electrostatic constant	C	$9.00 \times 10^9\ n \cdot m^2/coul^2$
Electromagnetic constant	μ	$1.26 \times 10^{-6} \cdot weber/amp \cdot m$
Charge of electron	e	$1.60 \times 10^{-19}\ coul$
Electron rest mass	m_o	$9.11 \times 10^{-31}\ kg$
Proton rest mass	m_p	$1.67 \times 10^{-27}\ kg$
Neutron rest mass	m_n	$1.67 \times 10^{-27}\ kg$
Speed of light	c	$3.00 \times 10^8\ m/sec$
Planck's constant	h	$6.63 \times 10^{-34}\ j \cdot sec$

SQUARE, SQUARE ROOTS, CUBES AND
CUBE ROOTS OF NOS. 1 TO 100

No.	Sq.	Cube	Sq. Root	Cube Root	No.	Sq.	Cube	Sq. Root	Cube Root
1	1	1	1.000	1.000	51	2601	132651	7.141	3.708
2	4	8	1.414	1.260	52	2704	140608	7.211	3.732
3	9	27	1.732	1.442	53	2809	148877	7.280	3.756
4	16	64	2.000	1.587	54	2916	157464	7.348	3.779
5	25	125	2.236	1.710	55	3025	166375	7.416	3.803
6	36	216	2.449	1.817	56	3136	175616	7.483	3.825
7	49	343	2.646	1.913	57	3249	185193	7.550	3.848
8	64	512	2.828	2.000	58	3364	195112	7.616	3.870
9	81	729	3.000	2.080	59	3481	205379	7.681	3.893
10	100	1000	3.162	2.154	60	3600	216000	7.746	3.915
11	121	1331	3.317	2.224	61	3721	226981	7.810	3.936
12	144	1728	3.464	2.289	62	3844	238328	7.874	3.958
13	169	2197	3.605	2.351	63	3969	250047	7.937	3.979
14	196	2744	3.742	2.410	64	4096	262144	8 000	4.000
15	225	3375	3.873	2.466	65	4225	274625	8.062	4.020
16	256	4096	4.000	2.511	66	4356	287496	8.124	4.041
17	289	4913	4.123	2.571	67	4489	300763	8.185	4.062
18	324	5832	4.243	2.621	68	4624	314432	8.246	4.082
19	361	6859	4.359	2.668	69	4761	328509	8.307	4.102
20	400	8000	4.472	2.714	70	4900	343000	8.367	4.121
21	441	9261	4.583	2.759	71	5041	357911	8.426	4.140
22	484	10648	4.690	2.802	72	5184	373248	8.485	4.160
23	529	12167	4.796	2.844	73	5329	389017	8.544	4.179
24	576	13824	4.899	2.884	74	5476	405224	8.602	4.198
25	625	15625	5.000	2.924	75	5625	421875	8.660	4.217
26	676	17576	5.099	2.962	76	5776	438976	8.718	4.236
27	729	19683	5.196	3 000	77	5929	456533	8.775	4.254
28	784	21952	5.292	3.037	78	6084	474552	8.832	4.273
29	841	24389	5.385	3.072	79	6241	493039	8.888	4.291
30	900	27000	5.477	3.107	80	6400	512000	8.944	4.309
31	961	29791	5.568	3.141	81	6561	531441	9.000	4.327
32	1024	32768	5.657	3.175	82	6724	551368	9.055	4.344
33	1089	35937	5.745	3.208	83	6889	571787	9.110	4.362
34	1156	39304	5.831	3.240	84	7056	592704	9.165	4.371
35	1225	42875	5.916	3.271	85	7225	614125	9.220	4.397
36	1296	46656	6.000	3.302	86	7396	636056	9.274	4.414
37	1369	50653	6.083	3.332	87	7569	658503	9.327	4.431
38	1444	54872	6.164	3.362	88	7744	681472	9.381	4.448
39	1521	59319	6.245	3.391	89	7921	704969	9.434	4.465
40	1600	64000	6.325	3.420	90	8100	729000	9.487	4.481
41	1681	68921	6.403	3.448	91	8281	753571	9.539	4.498
42	1764	74088	6.481	3.476	92	8464	778688	9.592	4.514
43	1849	79507	6.557	3.503	93	8649	804357	9.644	4.531
44	1936	85184	6.633	3.530	94	8836	830584	9.695	4.547
45	2025	91125	6.708	3.557	95	9025	857375	9.747	4.563
46	2116	97336	6.782	3.583	96	9216	884736	9.798	4.579
47	2209	103823	6.856	3.609	97	9409	912673	9.849	4.595
48	2304	110592	6.928	3.634	98	9604	941192	9.899	4.610
49	2401	117649	7.000	3.659	99	9801	970299	9.950	4.626
50	2500	125000	7.071	3.684	100	10000	1000000	10.000	4.641

CHEMICAL ELEMENTS, ATOMIC WEIGHTS

Element	Symbol	Atomic number	Atomic weight	Element	Symbol	Atomic number	Atomic weight
Actinium	Ac	89	(1)	Mercury	Hg	80	200.61
Aluminum	Al	13	26.98	Molybdenum .	Mo	42	95.95
Americium ...	Am	95	(1)	Neodymium ..	Nd	60	144.27
Antimony	Sb	51	121.76	Neon	Ne	10	20.183
Argon	Ar	18	39.944	Neptunium ...	Np	93	(1)
Arsenic	As	33	74.91	Nickel	Ni	28	58.71
Astatine	At	85	(1)	Niobium	Nb	41	92.91
Barium	Ba	56	137.36	Nitrogen	N	7	14.008
Berkelium ...	Bk	97	(1)	Nobelium	No	102	(1)
Beryllium	Be	4	9.013	Osmium	Os	76	190.2
Bismuth	Bi	83	209.00	Oxygen	O	8	[2]16
Boron	B	5	10.82	Palladium ...	Pd	46	106.4
Bromine	Br	35	79.916	Phosphorus ..	P	15	30.975
Cadmium ...	Cd	48	112.41	Platinum	Pt	78	195.09
Calcium	Ca	20	40.08	Plutonium	Pu	94	(1)
Californium ...	Cf	98	(1)	Polonium	Po	84	(1)
Carbon	C	6	12.010	Potassium	K	19	39.100
Cerium	Ce	58	140.13	Praseodymium .	Pr	59	140.92
Cesium	Cs	55	132.91	Promethium ..	Pm	61	(1)
Chlorine	Cl	17	35.457	Protactinium ..	Pa	91	(1)
Chromium ...	Cr	24	52.01	Radium	Ra	88	(1)
Cobalt	Co	27	58.94	Radon	Rn	86	(1)
Copper	Cu	29	63.54	Rhenium	Re	75	186.22
Curium	Cm	96	(1)	Rhodium	Rh	45	102.91
Dysprosium ...	Dy	66	162.51	Rubidium	Rb	37	85.48
Einsteinium ..	Es	99	(1)	Ruthenium ...	Ru	44	101.1
Erbium	Er	68	167.27	Samarium	Sm	62	150.35
Europium	Eu	63	152.0	Scandium	Sc	21	44.96
Fermium	Fm	100	(1)	Selenium	Se	34	78.96
Fluorine	F	9	19.00	Silicon	Si	14	28.09
Francium	Fr	87	(1)	Silver	Ag	47	107.880
Gadolinium ..	Gd	64	157.26	Sodium	Na	11	22.991
Gallium	Ga	31	69.72	Strontium	Sr	38	87.63
Germanium ..	Ge	32	72.60	Sulfur	S	16	[3]32.066
Gold	Au	79	197.0	Tantalum	Ta	73	180.95
Hafnium	Hf	72	178.50	Technetium ..	Tc	43	(1)
Helium	He	2	4.003	Tellurium	Te	52	127.61
Holmium	Ho	67	164.94	Terbium	Tb	65	158.93
Hydrogen	H	1	1.0080	Thallium	Tl	81	204.39
Indium	In	49	114.82	Thorium	Th	90	232.05
Iodine	I	53	126.91	Thulium	Tm	69	168.94
Iridium	Ir	77	192.2	Tin	Sn	50	118.70
Iron	Fe	26	55.85	Titanium	Ti	22	47.90
Krypton	Kr	36	83.80	Tungsten	W	74	183.86
Lanthanum ..	La	57	138.92	Uranium	U	92	238.07
Lawrencium ..	Lw	103	(1)	Vanadium	V	23	50.95
Lead	Pb	82	207.21	Xenon	Xe	54	131.30
Lithium	Li	3	6.940	Ytterbium	Yb	70	173.04
Lutetium	Lu	71	174.99	Yttrium	Y	39	88.92
Magnesium ..	Mg	12	24.32	Zinc	Zn	30	65.38
Manganese ...	Mn	25	54.94	Zirconium	Zr	40	91.22
Mendelevium .	Md	101	(1)				

[1] These values are omitted because the elements do not occur in nature, and their atomic weight depends on which isotope is made.

[2] This is a defined value rather than an indicated one.

[3] Because of natural variations in the abundance ratio of the isotopes of sulfur, the atomic weight of this element has a range of ±0.003.

FOUR-PLACE LOGARITHMS

No.	0	1	2	3	4	5	6	7	8	9	No.	0	1	2	3	4	5	6	7	8	9
10	0000	0043	0086	0128	0170	0212	0253	0294	0334	0374	55	7404	7412	7419	7427	7435	7443	7451	7459	7466	7474
11	0414	0453	0492	0531	0569	0607	0645	0682	0719	0755	56	7482	7490	7497	7505	7513	7520	7528	7536	7543	7551
12	0792	0828	0864	0899	0934	0969	1004	1038	1072	1106	57	7559	7566	7574	7582	7589	7597	7604	7612	7619	7627
13	1139	1173	1206	1239	1271	1303	1335	1367	1399	1430	58	7634	7642	7649	7657	7664	7672	7679	7686	7694	7701
14	1461	1492	1523	1553	1584	1614	1644	1673	1703	1732	59	7709	7716	7723	7731	7738	7745	7752	7760	7767	7774
15	1761	1790	1818	1847	1875	1903	1931	1959	1987	2014	60	7782	7789	7796	7803	7810	7818	7825	7832	7839	7846
16	2041	2068	2095	2122	2148	2175	2201	2227	2253	2279	61	7853	7860	7868	7875	7882	7889	7896	7903	7910	7917
17	2304	2330	2355	2380	2405	2430	2455	2480	2504	2529	62	7924	7931	7938	7945	7952	7959	7966	7973	7980	7987
18	2553	2577	2601	2625	2648	2672	2695	2718	2742	2765	63	7993	8000	8007	8014	8021	8028	8035	8041	8048	8055
19	2788	2810	2833	2856	2878	2900	2923	2945	2967	2989	64	8062	8069	8075	8082	8089	8096	8102	8109	8116	8122
20	3010	3032	3054	3075	3096	3118	3139	3160	3181	3201	65	8129	8136	8142	8149	8156	8162	8169	8176	8182	8189
21	3222	3243	3263	3284	3304	3324	3345	3365	3385	3404	66	8195	8202	8209	8215	8222	8228	8235	8241	8248	8254
22	3424	3444	3464	3483	3502	3522	3541	3560	3579	3598	67	8261	8267	8274	8280	8287	8293	8299	8306	8312	8319
23	3617	3636	3655	3674	3692	3711	3729	3747	3766	3784	68	8325	8331	8338	8344	8351	8357	8363	8370	8376	8382
24	3802	3820	3838	3856	3874	3892	3909	3927	3945	3962	69	8388	8395	8401	8407	8414	8420	8426	8432	8439	8445
25	3979	3997	4014	4031	4048	4065	4082	4099	4116	4133	70	8451	8457	8463	8470	8476	8482	8488	8494	8500	8506
26	4150	4166	4183	4200	4216	4232	4249	4265	4281	4298	71	8513	8519	8525	8531	8537	8543	8549	8555	8561	8567
27	4314	4330	4346	4362	4378	4393	4409	4425	4440	4456	72	8573	8579	8585	8591	8597	8603	8609	8615	8621	8627
28	4472	4487	4502	4518	4533	4548	4564	4579	4594	4609	73	8633	8639	8645	8651	8657	8663	8669	8675	8681	8686
29	4624	4639	4654	4669	4683	4698	4713	4728	4742	4757	74	8692	8698	8704	8710	8716	8722	8727	8733	8739	8745
30	4771	4786	4800	4814	4829	4843	4857	4871	4886	4900	75	8751	8756	8762	8768	8774	8779	8785	8791	8797	8802
31	4914	4928	4942	4955	4969	4983	4997	5011	5024	5038	76	8808	8814	8820	8825	8831	8837	8842	8848	8854	8859
32	5051	5065	5079	5092	5105	5119	5132	5145	5159	5172	77	8865	8871	8876	8882	8887	8893	8899	8904	8910	8915
33	5185	5198	5211	5224	5237	5250	5263	5276	5289	5302	78	8921	8927	8932	8938	8943	8949	8954	8960	8965	8971
34	5315	5328	5340	5353	5366	5378	5391	5403	5416	5428	79	8976	8982	8987	8993	8998	9004	9009	9015	9020	9025
35	5441	5453	5465	5478	5490	5502	5514	5527	5539	5551	80	9031	9036	9042	9047	9053	9058	9063	9069	9074	9079
36	5563	5575	5587	5599	5611	5623	5635	5647	5658	5670	81	9085	9090	9096	9101	9106	9112	9117	9122	9128	9133
37	5682	5694	5705	5717	5729	5740	5752	5763	5775	5786	82	9138	9143	9149	9154	9159	9165	9170	9175	9180	9186
38	5798	5809	5821	5832	5843	5855	5866	5877	5888	5899	83	9191	9196	9201	9206	9212	9217	9222	9227	9232	9238
39	5911	5922	5933	5944	5955	5966	5977	5988	5999	6010	84	9243	9248	9253	9258	9263	9269	9274	9279	9284	9289
40	6021	6031	6042	6053	6064	6075	6085	6096	6107	6117	85	9294	9299	9304	9309	9315	9320	9325	9330	9335	9340
41	6128	6138	6149	6160	6170	6180	6191	6201	6212	6222	86	9345	9350	9355	9360	9365	9370	9375	9380	9385	9390
42	6232	6243	6253	6263	6274	6284	6294	6304	6314	6325	87	9395	9400	9405	9410	9415	9420	9425	9430	9435	9440
43	6335	6345	6355	6365	6375	6385	6395	6405	6415	6425	88	9445	9450	9455	9460	9465	9469	9474	9479	9484	9489
44	6435	6444	6454	6464	6474	6484	6493	6503	6513	6522	89	9494	9499	9504	9509	9513	9518	9523	9528	9533	9538
45	6532	6542	6551	6561	6571	6580	6590	6599	6609	6618	90	9542	9547	9552	9557	9562	9566	9571	9576	9581	9586
46	6628	6637	6646	6656	6665	6675	6684	6693	6702	6712	91	9590	9595	9600	9605	9609	9614	9619	9624	9628	9633
47	6721	6730	6739	6749	6758	6767	6776	6785	6794	6803	92	9638	9643	9647	9652	9657	9661	9666	9671	9675	9680
48	6812	6821	6830	6839	6848	6857	6866	6875	6884	6893	93	9685	9689	9694	9699	9703	9708	9713	9717	9722	9727
49	6902	6911	6920	6928	6937	6946	6955	6964	6972	6981	94	9731	9736	9741	9745	9750	9754	9759	9763	9768	9773
50	6990	6998	7007	7016	7024	7033	7042	7050	7059	7067	95	9777	9782	9786	9791	9795	9800	9805	9809	9814	9818
51	7076	7084	7093	7101	7110	7118	7126	7135	7143	7152	96	9823	9827	9832	9836	9841	9845	9850	9854	9859	9863
52	7160	7168	7177	7185	7193	7202	7210	7218	7226	7235	97	9868	9872	9877	9881	9886	9890	9894	9899	9903	9908
53	7243	7251	7259	7267	7275	7284	7292	7300	7308	7316	98	9912	9917	9921	9926	9930	9934	9939	9943	9948	9952
54	7324	7332	7340	7348	7356	7364	7372	7380	7388	7396	99	9956	9961	9965	9969	9974	9978	9983	9987	9991	9996

| No. | 0 | 1 | 2 | 3 | 4 | 5 | 6 | 7 | 8 | 9 | No. | 0 | 1 | 2 | 3 | 4 | 5 | 6 | 7 | 8 | 9 |

INDEX

New Hampshire, 232, 290, 313, 320–321, 335–336; Dartmouth College (photo), 321

New Hebrides, 395

New Jersey, 201, 240, 245, 290, 321–322, 718, 724; Morven Mansion (photo), 322

Newmann, John N., 782

Newman, Paul, 738

New math, 560–600; addition, 568–572; addition algorism, 571; associative property of addition, 569–570; commutative property of addition, 568–569; identity number of addition, 569; inverse operations in addition, 572; order of whole numbers, 570–571; other properties of addition, 570; renaming sums, 571–572; sum of more than two addends, 571; division, 582–586; division algorism, 586; one-digit divisors, 585; properties of division, 584; remainders in division, 584–585; two-digit divisors, 586; equations and problems, 587–596; multiplication property of equations, 591; solution of problems, 595–596; solution of equations, 592–594; translating English phrases into mathematical phrases, 594–595; relation symbols in equations, 587; grouping symbols in equations, 587–588; number sentences, 588; open sentences, 588–589; division property of equations, 592; addition property of equations, 590–591; multiplication, 576–577; basic multiplication facts, 579–580; associative property of multiplication, 578; commutative property of multiplication, 577; distributive property of equations, 579; estimating a product, 582; multiplying by factors of 10, 100, or 1000, 580; identity number of multiplication, 577–578; multiplication algorism, 581–582; multiplication as repeated addition, 577; sets in multiplication, 576; techniques of multiplication, 580–581; sets, 560–561; base-ten numeration, 564–565; disjoint sets, 567–568; empty sets, 561; equivalent sets, 563; exponents, 565; intersection of sets, 567; numbers, 563–564; place value, 565–566; replacement set, 589; set equality, 562; subsets, 561–562; union of sets, 566–567; subtraction, 573; properties of subtraction, 574; renaming numbers in subtraction, 575; subtraction algorism, 574–575; tests for subtraction, 575; unnamed addends, 573–574; addition and subtraction of whole numbers, 566–575; multiplication and division of whole numbers, 576–586; zero in division, 583; zero in multiplication, 578–579; zero in subtraction, 574

New Mexico, 210–211, 322–323; Acoma Mission (photo), 323

New Mexico Territory, 323. *See also* New Mexico.

New Netherlands, 201, 408. *See also* New York.

New South Wales, 349

New Testament, 691, 704–705. *See also* Bible.

Newton, Sir Isaac, 465–466, 468–470, 498, 509, 512, 682

New World, the, 201–202, 366–367, 412

New York, 201, 211, 231, 239–240, 242–243, 256, 290, 321–325, 327, 334–336, 718, 726–727, 729, 733, 735, 740; United Nations Building (photo), 324

New York Cosmos, 736

New York Giants, 779

New York Islanders, 731

New York Rangers, 731

New York Yankees, 756, 758, 778

New Zealand, 197, 349, 395–396, 400, 403, 417, 420, 723, 734; Wellington City Harbor (photo), 395

Niagara Group, the, 758

Nicaragua, 257, 364, 396

Nicholas I, Czar of Russia, 415, 802

Nicholas II, Czar of Russia, 415

Nicklaus, Jack, 727, 782

Nicolet, Jean, 338

Nicolls, Richard, 729

Niebuhr, H. Richard, 782–783

Niebuhr, Reinhold, 783

Nietzsche, Friedrich, 142

Niger, Republic of, 396

Nigeria, Colony of, 396

Nigeria, Federation of, 356, 396

Nigeria, Southern, 396

Nile, Battle of the, 181

Nineteenth-century art, 712–714

Nixon, Richard Milhous, President of the United States of America, 199, 217–218, 252, 254–255, 268–269, 273, 275, 362–363, 415, 750, 762, 773, 776, 794, 797, 802, 805, (portrait) 254; resignation of, 789; Watergate scandal, 273, 275–276, 794

Nol, Lon, Premier of Cambodia, 356

Nolde, Emil, 714

Normandy, 417

North Africa, 159, 163, 171, 188, 194–195, 251, 347, 391, 413, 702, 704

North America, 199, 201, 211, 306, 314, 357, 392, 397, 403, 408, 534, 731–732

North American Soccer League (NASL), 736

North Atlantic Treaty Organization (NATO), 196, 198, 251, 266–267, 372, 383, 397, 413, 745, 758, 778; Civilian Council, 197; Military Council, 197; Supreme Commander, 197

North Carolina, 206, 225, 229, 235, 291, 311, 325, 331–333, 336; Wright Brothers' National Memorial (photo), 323

North Dakota, 326; 332; Theodore Roosevelt National Memorial (photo), 326

Northern Ireland, 199, 416. *See also* United Kingdom.

Northern Rhodesia, 390, 402, 425

North Korea, 197, 396–397

North Vietnam, 199, 386, 420. *See also* Vietnam, Socialist Republic of.

Northwest Company. *See* Fur Trading.

Northwest Territory, 206, 209, 308–309, 316, 359, 747, 753, 775; Ordinance of 1787, 338

Norway, 182, 194, 197–198, 365, 369, 378, 397, 409, 735

Nouns, 15–17; abstract, 15; appositives, 16; case of, 16–17; collective, 15; common, 15; concrete, 15; in direct address, 17; gender, 16; as indirect objects, 16; number of, 16; as objects, 16; plurals of, 16; possessive case of, 16; predicate nominative, 16; proper, 15; singular, 16; as subject, 16

Nova Scotia, 357–358

Nubia, region of, 408

Nugent, Elliott, 149

Nullification Doctrine, 751

Numbers and Numerals, 2, 116–117; Arabic, 79–80, 84, 108; commas in, 8; period with, 2; Roman, 2, 79, 83

Numerals. *See* Numbers and Numerals.

Nuremberg Conference, 194

Nyasaland, 425

O

Oakley, Annie, 783

Objective idealism, 687

Oceania, French settlements in. *See* French Polynesia.

Oceans. *See* Geology, ocean basins.